Harper's Biochemistry

18th edition

Harper's
Review of Biochemistry

Former title: *Review of Physiological Chemistry*

DAVID W. MARTIN, JR., MD
Professor of Medicine and Biochemistry
University of California School of Medicine
San Francisco
Investigator, Howard Hughes Medical Institute

PETER A. MAYES, PhD, DSc
Reader in Biochemistry
Royal Veterinary College
University of London

VICTOR W. RODWELL, PhD
Professor of Biochemistry
Purdue University
Lafayette, Indiana

and Associate Authors

LANGE Medical Publications   **Los Altos, California 94022**

Formerly published under the title *Review of Physiological Chemistry*.

A Concise Medical Library for Practitioner and Student

Current Medical Diagnosis & Treatment 1981 (annual revision). Edited by M.A. Krupp and M.J. Chatton. 1100 pp. — 1981

Current Pediatric Diagnosis & Treatment, 6th ed. Edited by C.H. Kempe, H.K. Silver, and D. O'Brien. 1122 pp, *illus.* — 1980

Current Surgical Diagnosis & Treatment, 5th ed. Edited by J.E. Dunphy and L.W. Way. 1138 pp, *illus.* — 1981

Current Obstetric & Gynecologic Diagnosis & Treatment, 3rd ed. Edited by R.C. Benson. 1001 pp, *illus.* — 1980

Review of Medical Physiology, 10th ed. W.F. Ganong. 628 pp, *illus.* — 1981

Review of Medical Microbiology, 14th ed. E. Jawetz, J.L. Melnick, and E.A. Adelberg. 593 pp, *illus.* — 1980

Review of Medical Pharmacology, 7th ed. F.H. Meyers, E. Jawetz, and A. Goldfien. 747 pp, *illus.* — 1980

Basic & Clinical Immunology, 3rd ed. Edited by H.H. Fudenberg, D.P. Stites, J.L. Caldwell, and J.V. Wells. 782 pp, *illus.* — 1980

Basic Histology, 3rd ed. L.C. Junqueira and J. Carneiro. 504 pp, *illus.* — 1980

Clinical Cardiology, 2nd ed. M. Sokolow and M.B. McIlroy. 718 pp, *illus.* — 1979

General Urology, 10th ed. D.R. Smith. About 575 pp, *illus.* — 1981

General Ophthalmology, 9th ed. D. Vaughan and T. Asbury. 410 pp, *illus.* — 1980

Correlative Neuroanatomy & Functional Neurology, 17th ed. J.G. Chusid. 464 pp, *illus.* — 1979

Principles of Clinical Electrocardiography, 10th ed. M.J. Goldman. 415 pp, *illus.* — 1979

Handbook of Obstetrics & Gynecology, 7th ed. R.C. Benson. 808 pp, *illus.* — 1980

Physician's Handbook, 19th ed. M.A. Krupp, N.J. Sweet, E. Jawetz, E.G. Biglieri, R.L. Roe, and C.A. Camargo. 758 pp, *illus.* — 1979

Handbook of Pediatrics, 13th ed. H.K. Silver, C.H. Kempe, and H.B. Bruyn. 735 pp, *illus.* — 1980

Handbook of Poisoning: Prevention, Diagnosis, & Treatment, 10th ed. R.H. Dreisbach. 578 pp. — 1980

Table of Contents

Preface

Review of Physiological Chemistry was first published in 1939 and revised in 1944. In 1951, the third edition appeared with Harold A. Harper assuming the duties of authorship. From the outset, the *Review* was intended to serve as a concise survey of those aspects of chemistry most relevant to the study of biology and medicine. Forty-two years later, the 18th edition is impressive evidence of the success of Dr. Harper's effort. During this interval, the field has expanded at a truly remarkable rate, and its interaction with biology and medicine has become intimate.

The 18th edition of this *Review* has undergone major revision in order to achieve Professor Harper's original intentions and to keep abreast of advances in biochemistry and molecular and cellular biology. We have altered the title to include ''biochemistry,'' a contemporary name for the subject matter. As is apparent in the table of contents, the chapters have been subjected to major reorganizations including their titles, contents, and order of presentation. We have tried again to balance our desire to include all we regard as significant against the student's need for a concise review of a comprehensive body of scientific information.

To the authors, the major change in the 18th edition is the retirement of Harold Harper from active authorship of the *Review*. We hope that the example of his guidance in previous editions will enable us, in this and future editions, to provide an educational service of comparable quality for the benefit of students at many levels in multiple disciplines.

The authors and their valued contributors are most gratified by the broad base of acceptance and support this book has received all over the world. Several editions of the English language version have been reprinted in Japan, Lebanon, Taiwan, Pakistan, the Philippines, and Korea. In addition, there are now translations in Italian, Spanish, French, Portuguese, Japanese, Polish, German, Turkish, Czech, and Indonesian. Hindi, Greek, Serbo-Croatian, and Chinese translations are in preparation.

David W. Martin, Jr.
Peter A. Mayes
Victor W. Rodwell

San Francisco
July, 1981

The Authors

Gerold M. Grodsky, PhD
Professor of Biochemistry and Associate Research Director, Metabolic Unit, University of California School of Medicine, San Francisco.

David W. Martin, Jr., MD
Professor of Medicine and Biochemistry, University of California School of Medicine, San Francisco; Investigator, Howard Hughes Medical Institute.

Peter A. Mayes, PhD, DSc
Reader in Biochemistry, Royal Veterinary College, University of London.

Marion Nestle, PhD
Associate Dean and Lecturer in Medicine and Biochemistry, University of California School of Medicine, San Francisco.

Victor W. Rodwell, PhD
Professor of Biochemistry, Purdue University, Lafayette, Indiana.

Introduction | 1

Victor W. Rodwell, PhD

This chapter reviews certain aspects of organic chemistry relevant to biochemistry and provides guidelines to assist in learning and integrating the information. The early chapters of this book present basic data on the structures and chemical properties of important biochemical compounds. While some of these will be familiar, others are complex structures (eg, heterocyclic structures*) perhaps not previously encountered by the student. The biochemistry of unfamiliar molecules is largely predictable from that of structurally similar molecules (eg, molecules that possess the same functional groups†). **Each functional group in a molecule generally behaves in a predictable way with respect to its biochemical reactions.** This guideline simplifies the understanding of enzyme-catalyzed transformations in living cells. Although most biochemically important molecules contain multiple functional groups, as a rule, **only a single functional group undergoes change in a given enzyme-catalyzed reaction.** Learning is therefore enhanced by focusing attention **exclusively on that change** to the virtual exclusion of all other aspects of the molecule. The complexities of intermediary metabolism can generally be made manageable in this way.

STEREOISOMERS

Stereoisomers differ only in the way in which the constituent atoms are oriented in space. In methane (CH_4), the hydrogen atoms are at the vertices of an equilateral tetrahedron (4-sided pyramid) with the carbon atom at the center.

---

*__*Hetero atoms__ (Greek *heteros* ''other'') such as O, N, and S also form covalent bonds with carbon, eg, in ethylamine, $C_2H_5NH_2$, ethyl alcohol, C_2H_5OH, and ethyl mercaptan, C_2H_5SH. Hetero atoms have one or more pairs of electrons not involved in covalent bonding. Since these unshared electrons have a negative field, **compounds with hetero atoms** attract protons, ie, they **act as bases** (see Chapter 2). Heterocyclic structures are cyclic structures that contain hetero atoms.*

*†A **functional group** (eg, $-NH_2$, $-COOH$, $-OH$) is a specific arrangement of linked chemical elements that has well-defined chemical and physical properties.*

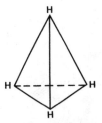

A carbon atom to which 4 different atoms or groups of atoms are attached is known as an asymmetric carbon atom. For example, in the formula for alanine, the asymmetric (alpha) carbon atom is starred (*).

$$CH_3 - \overset{\overset{\displaystyle H}{|}}{\underset{\underset{\displaystyle NH_2}{|}}{C}}{}^* - COOH$$

Alanine

Since many biochemicals contain 2 or more asymmetric C atoms, a thorough understanding of the stereochemistry of systems with more than one asymmetric center is essential.

Representation of Spatial Relationships Between Atoms

Certain spatial relationships are readily visualized using ball-and-stick atomic models. A compound having asymmetric carbon atoms exhibits **optical isomerism.** Thus, lactic acid has 2 nonequivalent optical isomers, one being the mirror image or **enantiomer** of the other (Fig 1–1).

The reader may show that these structures are indeed different by changing the positions of either enantiomer by rotation about any axis and attempting to superimpose one structure on the other.

Although enantiomers of a given compound have the same chemical properties, certain of their physical and essentially all of their physiologic properties are different. Enantiomers rotate the plane of plane-polarized light to an equal extent but in opposite directions. Since enzymes act on only one of a pair of enantiomers, only half of a **racemic mixture** (a mix-

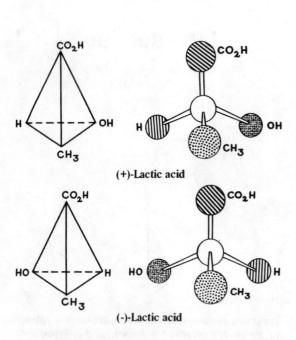

Figure 1–1. Tetrahedral and ball-and-stick model representation of lactic acid enantiomers.

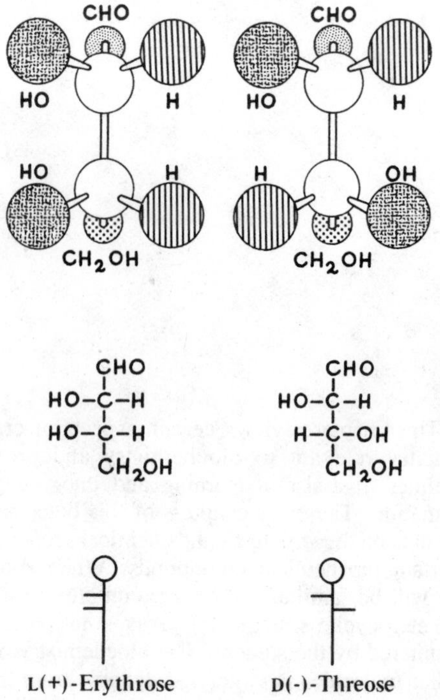

Figure 1–3. Two aldotetroses. *Top:* Ball-and-stick models. *Middle:* Fischer projection formulas. *Bottom:* Abbreviated projection formulas.

ture of equal quantities of both enantiomers) generally is physiologically active.

The number of possible different isomers is 2^n, where n = the number of different asymmetric carbon atoms. An aldotetrose, for example, contains 2 asymmetric carbon atoms; hence, there are $2^2 = 4$ optical isomers.

To represent 3-dimensional molecules in 2 dimensions, **projection formulas,** introduced by Emil Fischer, are used. The molecule is placed with the asymmetric carbon in the plane of the projection. The groups at the top and bottom project **behind** the plane of projection. Those to the right and left project equally **above** the plane of projection. The molecule is then projected in the form of a cross (Fig 1–2).

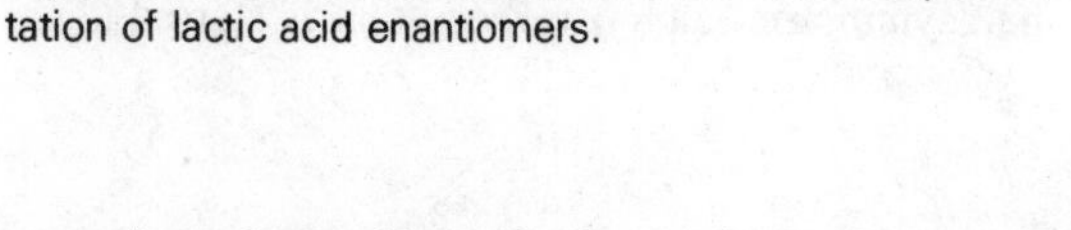

Figure 1–2. Fischer projection formula of (-)-lactic acid.

Unfortunately, the orientation of the tetrahedron differs from that of Fig 1–1. **Fischer projection formulas may never be mentally lifted from the plane of the paper and turned over.** Since the vertical bonds are really **below** the projection plane while the

horizontal bonds are **above** it, **it also is not permissible to rotate the Fischer projection formula within the plane of the paper by either a 90-degree or a 270-degree angle, although it is permissible to rotate it 180 degrees.**

The nomenclature for molecules with 2 asymmetric carbon atoms derives from the names of the 4-carbon sugars erythrose and threose. If 2 like groups (eg, two OH groups) are on the same side, the isomer is called the "**erythro**" form; if on the opposite side, the "**threo**" isomer. Fischer projection formulas inadequately represent one feature of these molecules. Look at the models from which these formulas are

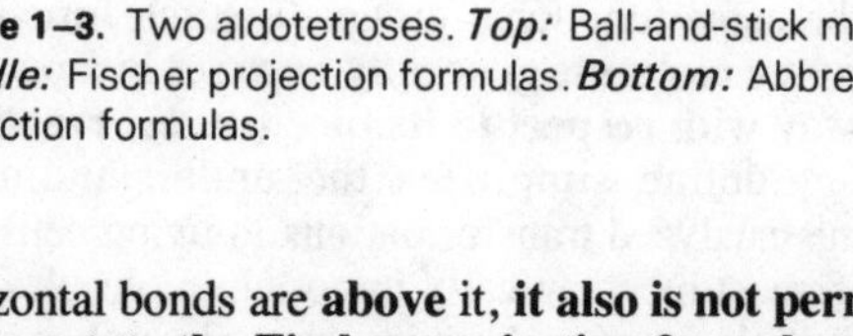

Erythro   **Threo**

Figure 1–4. Sawhorse representations of the erythro and threo enantiomers of 3-amino-2-butanol. The **erythro** and **threo** refer to the relative positions of $-OH$ and $-NH_2$ groups. Note that there are 3 ways to stagger C_2 with respect to C_3. That shown represents a structure with the bulky CH_3 groups oriented as far away from each other as possible.

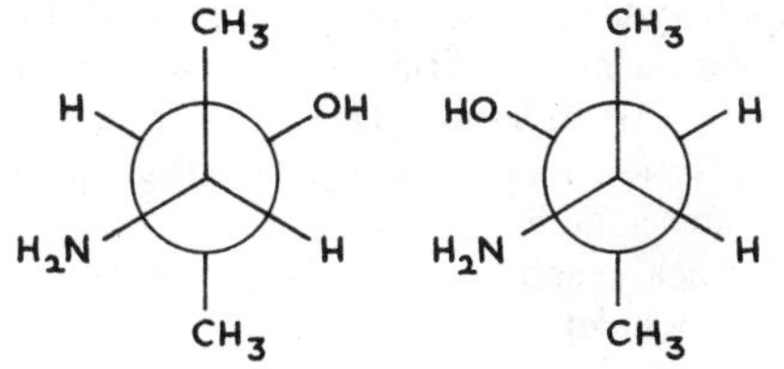

Erythro   Threo

Figure 1–5. Staggered Newman projection formulas for the erythro and threo enantiomers of 3-amino-2-butanol.

derived. The upper part of Fig 1–3 represents molecules in the **"eclipsed"** form in which the groups attached to C_2 and C_3 approach each other as closely as possible. The real shape of the molecule more closely approximates an arrangement with C_2 and C_3 rotated with respect to each other by an angle of 60 degrees, so that their substituents are **staggered** with respect to each other and are as far apart as possible. One way to represent "staggered" formulas is to use **"sawhorse"** representations (Fig 1–4). **Newman projection formulas** (Fig 1–5) view the molecule front-to-back along the bond joining the asymmetric carbon atoms. These C atoms, which eclipse each other, are represented as 2 superimposed circles (only one is shown). The bonds and groups attached to the asymmetric C atoms are projected in a vertical plane and appear as "spokes" at angles of 120 degrees for each C atom. The spokes on the rear atom are offset 60 degrees with respect to those on the front C atom. Bonds to the front carbon are drawn to the center of the circle and those for the rear carbon only to its periphery (Fig 1–5).

It is desirable to be able to convert Fischer projection formulas to sawhorse or Newman projection formulas. These most accurately illustrate the true shape of the molecule and hence are most useful in understanding its chemical and biologic properties. One way

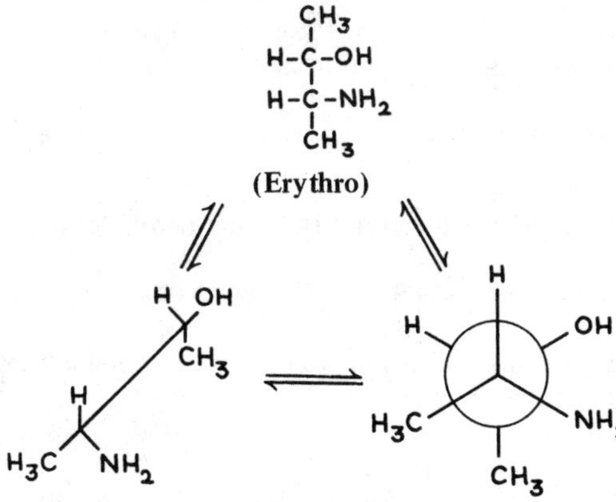

Figure 1–6. Transformation from Fischer to sawhorse or Newman formula.

is to build a model* corresponding to the Fischer projection formula, stagger the atoms, and draw the sawhorse or Newman formulas. Figure 1–6 shows how to interconvert these formulas without models. The Fischer projection formula is converted to an "eclipsed sawhorse" or Newman projection which then is rotated 180 degrees about the C_2–C_3 bond, producing a staggered sawhorse or Newman projection.

Cis-Trans Isomerism

Cis-trans isomerism (Latin *cis* "this side," *trans* "across") occurs in compounds with double bonds. Since the double bond is rigid, the atoms attached to it are not free to rotate as are those attached to a single bond. Thus the structures

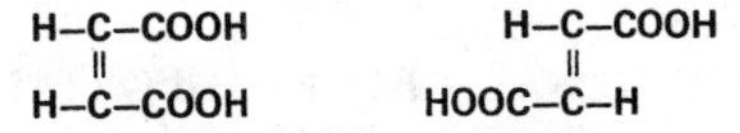

Maleic acid *(cis)*   Fumaric acid *(trans)*

are not equivalent and have **different chemical and physiologic properties.** Fumaric acid, but not maleic acid, is physiologically active. The *cis* isomer has the 2 more "bulky" groups on the same side of the double

*The student is urged to purchase an inexpensive set of models. These will prove invaluable in studying the chemistry of sugars, amino acids, and steroids in particular.

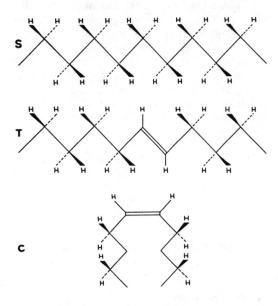

Figure 1–7. Representation of portions of the hydrocarbon backbones of a saturated fatty acid (**S**), an unsaturated fatty acid with a single *trans* double bond (**T**), and one with a single *cis* double bond (**C**). Bonds drawn as solid lines are in the plane of the paper. Bonds drawn as dotted lines project behind, and those drawn ◢ project in front of the plane of the paper.

bond. If they are on opposite sides of the double bond, the *trans* isomer is produced.

Introduction of *trans* double bonds in an otherwise saturated hydrocarbon chain deforms the shape of the molecule relatively little. A *cis* double bond, by contrast, entirely changes its shape. It can thus be appreciated why *cis* and *trans* isomers of a compound are not interchangeable in cells. Membranes composed of *trans* and *cis* isomers would have entirely different shapes. Enzymes acting on one isomer might be expected to be entirely inert with the other.

Again, the usual formulas fail to represent the actual shape of the molecules. Portions of the hydrocarbon backbone of a saturated fatty acid and of the *cis* and *trans* isomers of an 18-carbon unsaturated fatty acid are represented in Fig 1–7.

FUNCTIONAL GROUPS IMPORTANT IN BIOCHEMISTRY

A **functional group** is a specific arrangement of elements (generally C, H, O, N, P, or S) that has well-defined chemical and physical properties. The properties of biochemical molecules are best understood in terms of the chemical and physical properties of the functional groups these molecules contain.

Alcohols

Many biochemical compounds (eg, sugars, certain lipids, and amino acids) are **alcohols.** These have both **polar** (hydroxy, OH) and **nonpolar** (alkyl) character. They are thus best regarded both as **hydroxylated hydrocarbons** and as **alkyl derivatives of water.** Although alcohols with up to 3 carbon atoms are infinitely soluble in water, water solubility decreases with increasing length of the carbon chain, ie, with increasing nonpolar character. Primary, secondary, and tertiary alcohols have respectively one, 2, and 3 alkyl groups attached to the carbon atom bearing the –OH group.

$$CH_3\,CH_2\,CH_2\,CH_2-OH$$

**Primary butyl alcohol
(1-butanol)**

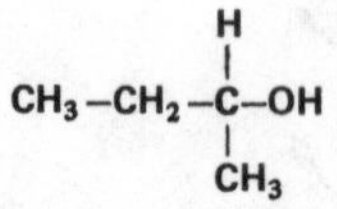

$$CH_3-CH_2-\overset{\overset{\displaystyle H}{|}}{\underset{\underset{\displaystyle CH_3}{|}}{C}}-OH \qquad CH_3-\overset{\overset{\displaystyle CH_3}{|}}{\underset{\underset{\displaystyle CH_3}{|}}{C}}-OH$$

**Secondary butyl alcohol   Tertiary butyl alcohol
 (1-methylpropanol)   (1,1-dimethylethanol)**

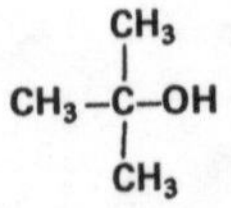

Both monohydric (one –OH group) and polyhydric (more than one –OH group) alcohols are of physiologic significance. Sugars are derivatives of polyhydric alcohols, as are cyclic or ring-containing alcohols such as **inositol.** Their highly polar character

makes polyhydric alcohols far more water-soluble than corresponding monohydric alcohols with equivalent numbers of carbon atoms. Thus, even polyhydric alcohols with 6 or more carbon atoms (eg, sugars) are highly water-soluble.

Chemical reactions of alcohols with biochemical analogies include:

A. Oxidation: Primary alcohols are oxidized by strong oxidizing agents to aldehydes and acids, whereas secondary alcohols are oxidized to ketones.

Primary:

$$R-CH_2OH \xrightarrow{\ [O]\ } RCHO + RCOOH$$

Secondary:

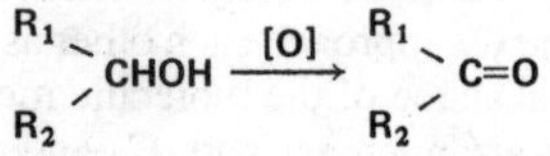

$$\begin{matrix} R_1 \\ \\ R_2 \end{matrix}\!\!\!\diagdown\!\!\!\diagup CHOH \xrightarrow{\ [O]\ } \begin{matrix} R_1 \\ \\ R_2 \end{matrix}\!\!\!\diagdown\!\!\!\diagup C{=}O$$

Tertiary alcohols cannot be oxidized (dehydrogenated) without rupture of a C–C bond.

B. Esterification: An ester is formed when water is split out between an alcohol and an acid.

$$R-\overset{\overset{\displaystyle O}{\|}}{C}-OH + HO-R' \longrightarrow R-\overset{\overset{\displaystyle O}{\|}}{C}-O-R' + H_2O$$

The acid may be organic or inorganic. Esters of H_3PO_4 (see phosphorylated sugars and phospholipids) and H_2SO_4 are of great significance in biochemistry. Many lipids contain carboxylic ester linkages.

C. Ether Formation: Ethers are derivatives of alcohols in which the hydrogen of the –OH group is replaced by an alkyl group (R–O–R'). The ether linkage is comparatively uncommon in living tissues.

Sulfur, which is in the same group of the periodic table as oxygen, forms similar compounds. Thioalcohols (thiols, mercaptans), thioesters, and thioethers all occur in nature.

$$R-CH_2-SH \qquad\qquad R-\overset{\overset{\displaystyle O}{\|}}{C}-S-R' \qquad\qquad R-S-R'$$

Thioalcohol   Thioester   Thioether

In addition, the disulfides (left) and peroxides (right)

$$R-S-S-R' \qquad\qquad R-O-O-R'$$

play an important role in protein structure and in prostaglandin biosynthesis, respectively.

Aldehydes & Ketones

Aldehydes and ketones possess the strongly reducing carbonyl group $>C{=}O$. Aldehydes have one and ketones 2 alkyl groups attached to the carbon bearing the carbonyl group:

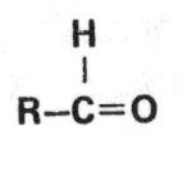

$$R-C=O \quad \overset{R}{\underset{R'}{\diagdown}}C=O$$
with H above the aldehyde carbon

Aldehyde 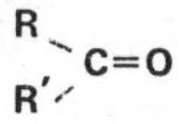   **Ketone**

The sugars, in addition to being polyhydric alcohols, are also either aldehydes or ketones.

Reactions of aldehydes and ketones of biochemical interest include the following:

A. Oxidation: Oxidation of an aldehyde to the corresponding carboxylic acid. Ketones are not readily oxidized, since, like tertiary alcohols, they cannot lose hydrogen without rupture of a C–C bond.

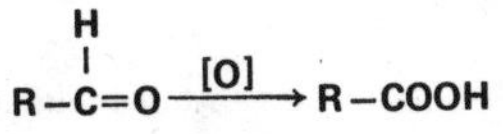

$$R-\overset{\overset{H}{|}}{C}=O \xrightarrow{[O]} R-COOH$$

B. Reduction: Reduction of an aldehyde yields the corresponding primary alcohol, and reduction of a ketone yields the corresponding secondary alcohol.

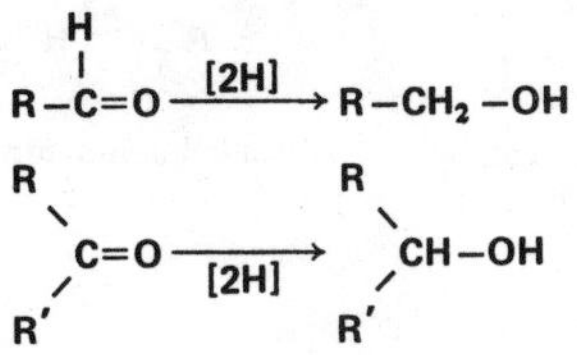

$$R-\overset{\overset{H}{|}}{C}=O \xrightarrow{[2H]} R-CH_2-OH$$

$$\overset{R}{\underset{R'}{\diagdown}}C=O \xrightarrow{[2H]} \overset{R}{\underset{R'}{\diagdown}}CH-OH$$

C. Hemiacetal and Acetal Formation: Under acidic conditions, aldehydes can combine with one or 2 of the hydroxyl groups of an alcohol, forming, respectively, a hemiacetal or an acetal:

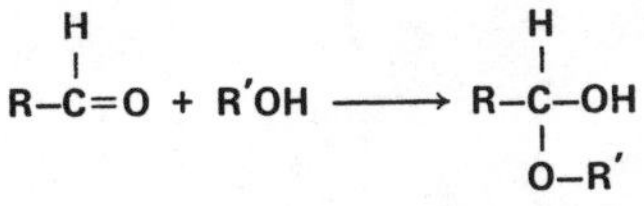

$$R-\overset{\overset{H}{|}}{C}=O + R'OH \longrightarrow R-\overset{\overset{H}{|}}{\underset{\underset{O-R'}{|}}{C}}-OH$$

A hemiacetal

$$R-\overset{\overset{H}{|}}{C}=O + 2\,R'OH \xrightarrow{H_2O} R-\overset{\overset{H}{|}}{\underset{\underset{OR'}{|}}{C}}-OR'$$

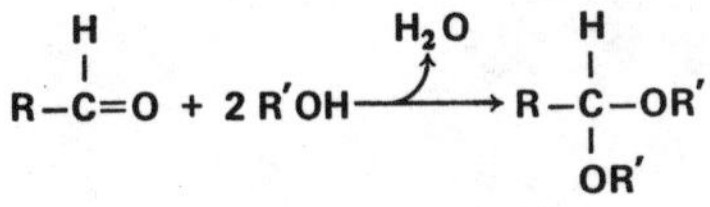

An acetal

The carbonyl and alcohol functions may be part of the same molecule. For example, the aldose (aldehyde) sugars exist in solution primarily as internal hemiacetals. Analogous structures (hemiketals and ketals) are formed from alcohols and ketones.

Aldehydes may also form **thiohemiacetals** and **thioacetals** with thioalcohols. Thiohemiacetals function as enzyme-bound intermediates in the enzymic oxidation of aldehydes to acids.

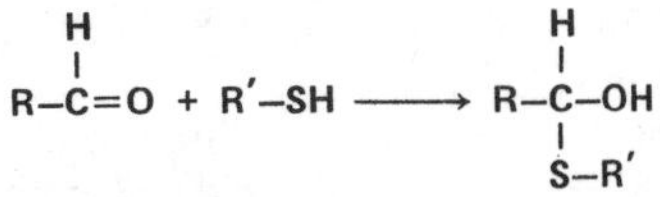

$$R-\overset{\overset{H}{|}}{C}=O + R'-SH \longrightarrow R-\overset{\overset{H}{|}}{\underset{\underset{S-R'}{|}}{C}}-OH$$

A thiohemiacetal

D. Aldol Condensation: In alkali, aldehydes and, to a lesser extent, ketones undergo condensation between their carbonyl and their α-carbon atoms to form aldols or β-hydroxy aldehydes or ketones. The β-hydroxy acids derived from these are important in fatty acid metabolism.

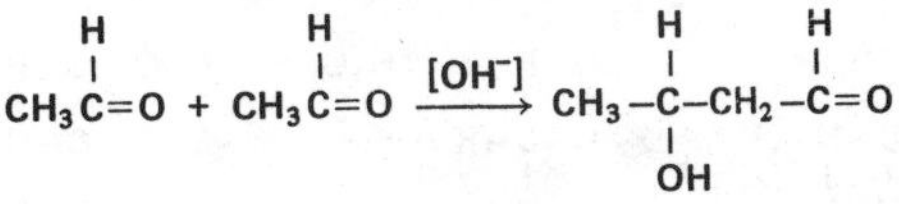

$$CH_3\overset{\overset{H}{|}}{C}=O + CH_3\overset{\overset{H}{|}}{C}=O \xrightarrow{[OH^-]} CH_3-\overset{\overset{H}{|}}{\underset{\underset{OH}{|}}{C}}-CH_2-\overset{\overset{H}{|}}{C}=O$$

Carboxylic Acids

Carboxylic acids have both a carbonyl ($>C=O$) and a hydroxyl group on the same carbon atom. They are typical **weak acids** and only partially dissociate in water to form a hydrogen ion (H^+) and a **carboxylate anion** ($R-COO^-$) with the negative charge shared equally by the 2 oxygen atoms. Some reactions of carboxylic acids of biochemical interest include the following:

A. Reduction: Complete **reduction** yields the corresponding **primary alcohol.**

$$R-COOH \xrightarrow{[4H]} R-CH_2OH + H_2O$$

B. Ester and Thioester Formation: See alcohols.

C. Acid Anhydride Formation: A molecule of water is split out between the carboxyl groups of 2 acid molecules.

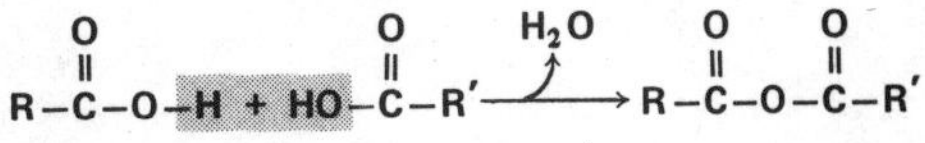

$$R-\overset{\overset{O}{\|}}{C}-O-H + HO-\overset{\overset{O}{\|}}{C}-R' \xrightarrow{H_2O} R-\overset{\overset{O}{\|}}{C}-O-\overset{\overset{O}{\|}}{C}-R'$$

When both acid molecules are the same, a **symmetric anhydride** is produced. Molecules of different acids yield **mixed anhydrides.** Anhydrides found in nature include those of phosphoric acid (in ATP) and the **mixed anhydrides** formed from phosphoric acid and a carboxylic acid, eg:

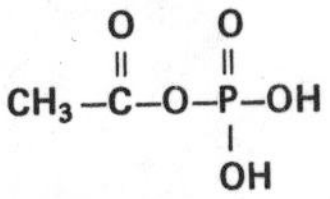

$$CH_3-\overset{\overset{O}{\|}}{C}-O-\overset{\overset{O}{\|}}{\underset{\underset{OH}{|}}{P}}-OH$$

Acetyl phosphate

D. Salt Formation: Carboxylic acids react stoichiometrically (equivalent for equivalent) with bases to form salts. Na^+ and K^+ salts are 100% dissociated in solution.

E. Amide Formation: Splitting out a molecule of water between a carboxylic acid and ammonia or an amine forms an amide. Particularly important amides are **peptides,** formed from the amino group of one amino acid and the carboxyl group of another.

$$CH_3-\overset{\overset{O}{\|}}{C}-OH + H-NH_2 \xrightarrow{\quad H_2O \quad} CH_3-\overset{\overset{O}{\|}}{C}-NH_2$$

Acetic acid   Acetamide

$$R-\overset{\overset{COOH}{|}}{\underset{H}{C}}-\overset{H}{\underset{H}{N}}-H + HO-\overset{\overset{O}{\|}}{C}-\overset{H}{\underset{NH_2}{C}}-R' \xrightarrow{\quad H_2O \quad} R-\overset{\overset{COOH}{|}}{\underset{H}{C}}-\overset{H}{\underset{H}{N}}-\overset{\overset{O}{\|}}{C}-\overset{H}{\underset{NH_2}{C}}-R'$$

Peptide bond

Amines

Amines, alkyl derivatives of ammonia, are usually gases or volatile liquids with odors resembling ammonia but more "fishlike." Primary, secondary, and tertiary amines are formed by replacement of one, 2, or 3 of the hydrogens of ammonia, respectively.

$$\overset{H}{\underset{H}{N}}-H \qquad R-NH_2 \qquad \overset{R}{\underset{R'}{}}NH \qquad \overset{R}{\underset{R''}{R'-N}}$$

Ammonia   Primary   Secondary   Tertiary
                   amine   amine   amine

Ammonia in solution exists in both charged and uncharged forms:

$$NH_3 + H^+ \rightleftharpoons NH_4^+$$

Ammonia   Ammonium ion

Amines behave in an entirely analogous way:

$$\overset{R}{\underset{R'}{}}NH + H^+ \rightleftharpoons \overset{R}{\underset{R'}{}}\overset{\oplus}{N}\overset{H}{\underset{H}{}}$$

An amine   An alkylammonium ion

Water | 2

Victor W. Rodwell, PhD

INTRODUCTION

Biochemistry is concerned, for the most part, with the properties and reactions of organic compounds. For this reason, it may be forgotten that **in living cells most biochemicals exist and most reactions occur in an aqueous environment. Water is an active participant in many biochemical reactions and is an important determinant of the properties of macromolecules such as proteins.** It is therefore appropriate to consider those properties of water that enable it to play such a key role in biochemistry.

MOLECULAR STRUCTURE OF WATER

The water molecule is an irregular tetrahedron with oxygen at its center (Fig 2–1). The 2 bonds with hydrogen are directed toward 2 corners of the tetrahedron, while the unshared electrons on the 2 sp^3-hybridized orbitals occupy the 2 remaining corners. The angle between the 2 hydrogen atoms (105 degrees) is slightly less than the tetrahedral angle (109.5 degrees), forming a slightly skewed tetrahedron. In contrast to methane, electrical charge is not uniformly distributed about the water molecule. The side of the oxygen opposite to the 2 hydrogens is relatively rich in electrons, while on the other side the relatively unshielded hydrogen nuclei form a region of local positive charge. The term **dipole** refers to molecules such as water that have electrical charge (electrons) un-

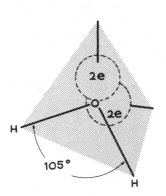

Figure 2–1. Water.

equally distributed about their structure. Ammonia is a dipole and, like water, has a tetrahedral structure (Fig 2–2). In ammonia, the bond angles between the hydrogens (107 degrees) approach the tetrahedral angle even more closely than in water. Many biochemicals are dipoles. Examples include alcohols, phospholipids, amino acids, and nucleic acids.

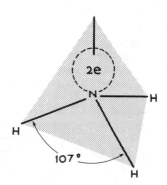

Figure 2–2. Ammonia.

MACROMOLECULAR STRUCTURE OF WATER

Water molecules can assume ordered arrangements (recall a snowflake). Molecular ordering of water molecules is not, however, restricted to ice. Liquid water exhibits macromolecular structure that parallels the geometric disposition of water molecules in ice. The ability of water molecules to associate with one another in both solid and liquid states arises from the dipolar character of water. It remains a liquid rather than a solid because of the transient nature of these macromolecular complexes (the half-life for association-dissociation of water molecules is about 1 microsecond). In the solid state, each water molecule is associated with 4 other water molecules. In the liquid state, the number is somewhat less (about 3.5). With the exception of the transient nature of intermolecular interactions in liquid water, it thus resembles ice in its macromolecular structure more closely than might at first be imagined.

HYDROGEN BONDS

The dipolar character of water molecules favors their mutual association in ordered arrays with a precise geometry dictated by the internal geometry of the water molecule (Fig 2–3).

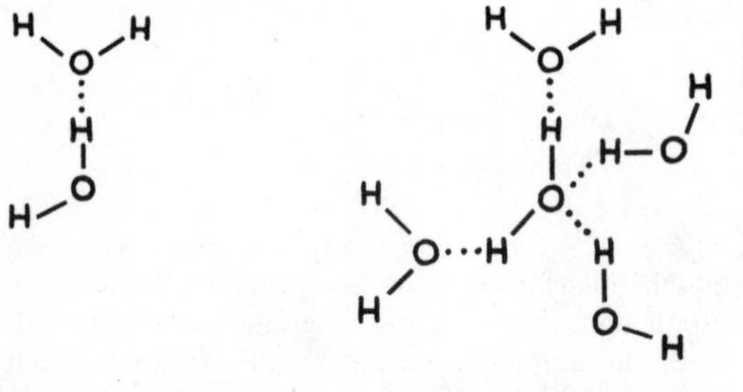

Figure 2–3. *Left:* Association of 2 dipolar water molecules. The dotted line represents a hydrogen bond. *Right:* Association of a central water molecule with 4 other water molecules by hydrogen bonding. This structure is typical of ice and, to a lesser extent, of liquid water.

The electrostatic interaction between the hydrogen nucleus of one water molecule and the unshared electron pair of another is termed a hydrogen bond. Compared to covalent bonds, hydrogen bonds are quite weak. To break a hydrogen bond in liquid water requires about 4.5 kcal of energy per mole—about 4% of the energy required to rupture the O–H bond in water (110 kcal/mol). While individually weak, hydrogen bonds play significant roles in biochemistry because they can be formed in large numbers. Multiple hydrogen bonds confer significant structure not only upon water but also upon other dipolar molecules as diverse as alcohols, DNA, and proteins. Fig 2–4 illustrates hydrogen bonds formed between representative biochemicals.

Note that hydrogen bonds are not restricted to water molecules, and in particular that the hydrogens of nitrogen atoms can also participate in hydrogen bonding. This topic will again be considered in connection with the 3-dimensional structure of proteins and with base pairing in DNA.

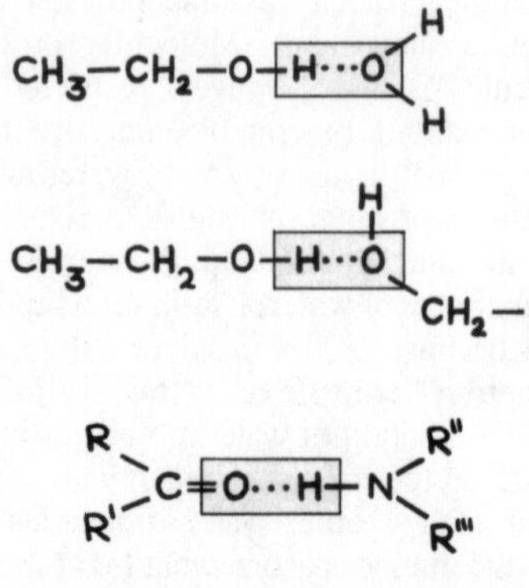

DISSOCIATION OF WATER

Water molecules have a limited tendency to dissociate (ionize) into H^+ and OH^- ions:

$$H_2O \rightleftharpoons H^+ + OH^-$$

Since ions are continuously recombining to form water molecules and vice versa, it cannot be stated whether an individual hydrogen or oxygen is present as an ion or as part of a water molecule. At one instant it is an ion; an instant later, part of a molecule. Fortunately, individual ions or molecules need not be considered. Since 1 gram of water contains 3.46×10^{22} molecules, the ionization of water is described statistically. It is sufficient to know the **probability** that a hydrogen will be present as an ion or as part of a water molecule.

To state that the probability that a hydrogen exists as an ion is 0.01, means that a hydrogen atom has one chance in 100 of being an ion and 99 chances out of 100 of being in a water molecule. The actual probability of a hydrogen atom in pure water existing as a hydrogen ion is approximately 0.0000000018, or 1.8×10^{-9}. Consequently, the probability of its being part of a molecule is almost unity. Stated another way, for every hydrogen ion and hydroxyl ion in pure water, there are 1.8 billion or 1.8×10^9 water molecules. Hydrogen and hydroxyl ions nevertheless contribute significantly to the properties of water.

The tendency of water to dissociate is expressed as follows:

$$K = \frac{[H^+] \, [OH^-]}{[H_2O]}$$

where the bracketed terms represent the molar concentrations of hydrogen ions, hydroxyl ions, and undissociated water molecules,* and K is termed the **dissociation constant.** To calculate the dissociation constant for water, recall that 1 mol of water weighs 18 g. One liter (L) (1000 g) of water therefore contains $1000 \div 18 = 55.56$ mol. Pure water is thus 55.56 molar. Since the probability that a hydrogen in pure water will exist as an H^+ ion is 1.8×10^{-9}, the molar concentration of H^+ ions (or of OH^- ions) in pure water is calculated by multiplying the probability, 1.8×10^{-9}, by the molar concentration of water, 55.56 molar. This result is 1.0×10^{-7} molar.

Figure 2–4. Formation of hydrogen bonds between an alcohol and water, between 2 molecules of ethanol, and between the peptide carbonyl oxygen and the hydrogen on the peptide nitrogen of an adjacent peptide.

*Strictly speaking, the bracketed terms represent molar activity rather than molar concentration.

We can now calculate K for water:

$$K = \frac{[H^+]\,[OH^-]}{[H_2O]} = \frac{[10^{-7}]\,[10^{-7}]}{[55.56]}$$

$$= 0.018 \times 10^{-14} = 1.8 \times 10^{-16} \text{ molar}$$

The high concentration of molecular water (55.56 M) is not significantly affected by dissociation. It is therefore convenient to consider it as essentially constant. This constant may then be incorporated into the dissociation constant, K, to provide a new constant, K_W, termed the **ion product** for water. The relationship between K_W and K is shown below:

$$K = \frac{[H^+]\,[OH^-]}{[H_2O]} = 1.8 \times 10^{-16} \text{ molar}$$

$$K_W = (K)\,[H_2O] = [H^+]\,[OH^-]$$

$$= (1.8 \times 10^{-16} \text{ molar})\,(55.56 \text{ molar})$$

$$= 1.00 \times 10^{-14} \text{ molar}^2$$

Note that the dimensions of K are moles per liter and of K_W moles^2 per liter^2. As its name suggests, the ion product, K_W, is numerically equal to the product of the molar concentrations of H^+ and OH^-:

$$K_W = [H^+]\,[OH^-]$$

At 24 C, $K_W = (10^{-7})^2 = 10^{-14}$ molar^2. At temperatures below 25 C, K_W is less than 10^{-14}, and, at the temperatures above 25 C, greater than 10^{-14}. For example, at the temperature of the human body (37 C), the concentration of H^+ in pure water is slightly more than 10^{-7} molar. Within the stated limitations of the effect of temperature, $K_W = 10^{-14}$ **molar^2 for all aqueous solutions**—even those that contain acids or bases. We shall use this constant in the calculation of pH values for acidic and basic solutions.

THE CONCEPT OF pH

The term **pH** was introduced in 1909 by Sorensen, who defined pH as **the negative log of the hydrogen ion concentration:**

$$pH = -\log[H^+]$$

This definition, while not rigorous,* is adequate for most biochemical purposes. To calculate the pH of a solution:

(1) Calculate hydrogen ion concentration, $[H^+]$.
(2) Calculate the base 10 logarithm of $[H^+]$.
(3) pH is the negative of the value found in step 2.

*pH = $-\log$ (H^+ activity).

For example, for pure water at 25 C:

$$pH = -\log[H^+] = -\log 10^{-7} = -(-7) = 7.0$$

Low pH (acidic) values (below 7.0) correspond to high concentrations of H^+, and high pH (basic) values (above 7.0) to low concentrations of H^+.

Acids are **proton donors** and bases are **proton acceptors.** A distinction is made, however, between strong acids (eg, HCl, H_2SO_4), which completely dissociate even in strongly acidic solutions (low pH); and **weak acids,** which dissociate only partially in acidic solution. A similar distinction is made between **strong bases** (eg, KOH, NaOH) and **weak bases** (eg, Ca[OH]$_2$). Only strong bases are dissociated at high pH. Many biochemicals are **weak acids.** Exceptions include phosphorylated intermediates, which also possess the strongly acidic primary phosphoric acid group.

The following examples illustrate how to calculate the pH of acidic and basic solutions.

Example: What is the pH of a solution whose hydrogen ion concentration is 3.2×10^{-4} molar?

$$pH = -\log[H^+]$$
$$= -\log(3.2 \times 10^{-4})$$
$$= -\log(3.2) - \log(10^{-4})$$
$$= -0.5 + 4.0$$
$$= 3.5$$

Example: What is the pH of a solution whose hydroxide ion concentration is 4.0×10^{-4} molar?

To approach this problem, we define a quantity **pOH** that is equal to $-\log[OH^-]$ and that may be derived from the definition of K_W:

$$K_W = [H^+]\,[OH^-] = 10^{-14}$$

therefore: $\log[H^+] + \log[OH^-] = \log 10^{-14}$

or: $pH + pOH = 14$

To solve the problem by this approach:

$$[OH^-] = 4.0 \times 10^{-4}$$
$$pOH = -\log[OH^-]$$
$$= -\log(4.0 \times 10^{-4})$$
$$= -\log(4.0) - \log(10^{-4})$$
$$= -0.60 + 4.0$$
$$= 3.4$$

Now: $pH = 14 - pOH = 14 - 3.40$
$$= 10.6$$

Example: What is the pH of (a) 2.0×10^{-2}M KOH, (b) 2.0×10^{-6}M KOH? The OH^- arises from 2 sources: KOH and water. Since pH is determined by the **total** $[H^+]$ (and pOH by the **total** $[OH^-]$), both sources must be considered. In the first case, the contribution of water to the total $[OH^-]$ is negligible. The same cannot be said for the second case:

	(a)	(b)
Molarity of KOH	2.0×10^{-2}	2.0×10^{-6}
$[OH^-]$ from KOH	2.0×10^{-2}M	2.0×10^{-6}M
$[OH^-]$ from water	1.0×10^{-7}M	1.0×10^{-7}M
Total $[OH^-]$	2.00001×10^{-2}M	2.1×10^{-6}M

Once a decision has been reached about the significance of the contribution by water, pH may be calculated as above.

In the above examples, it was assumed that the strong base KOH was completely dissociated in solution and that the molar concentration of OH^- ions was thus equal to the molar concentration of KOH. This assumption is valid for relatively dilute solutions of **strong** bases or acids but **not for solutions of weak bases or acids.** Since these weak electrolytes dissociate only slightly in solution, we must calculate the concentration of H^+ (or $[OH^-]$) produced by a given molarity of the acid (or base) using the **dissociation constant** before calculating total $[H^+]$ (or total $[OH^-]$), and subsequently calculating the pH.

PROTONIC EQUILIBRIA OF FUNCTIONAL GROUPS THAT ARE WEAK ACIDS OR BASES

Dissociation Behavior & Acid Strength

Many biochemicals possess functional groups that are weak acids or bases. One or more of these functional groups—frequently carboxyl groups, amino groups, or the secondary phosphate dissociation of phosphate esters—are present in all proteins and nucleic acids, most coenzymes, and most intermediary metabolites. The dissociation behavior (protonic equilibria) of weakly acidic and weakly basic functional groups is therefore fundamental to an understanding of the influence of intracellular pH on the structure and biochemical activity of these compounds. Their separation and identification in research and clinical laboratories is also facilitated by knowledge of the dissociation behavior of their functional groups.

We term the protonated form of an acid (eg, HA or RNH_3^+) the **acid** and the unprotonated form (eg, A^- or RNH_2) its **conjugate base** (Table 2–1). Similarly, we may refer to a **base** (eg, A^- or RNH_2) and its **conjugate acid** (eg, HA or RNH_3^+) (Latin *coniungere* "to join together").

The relative strengths of weak acids and of weak bases are expressed quantitatively as their **dissociation constants,** which express their tendency to ionize. Shown below are the expressions for the dissociation

Table 2–1. Selected examples of weak acids and their conjugate bases.

Acid	Conjugate Base
CH_3COOH	CH_3COO^-
$CH_3NH_3^+$	CH_3NH_2

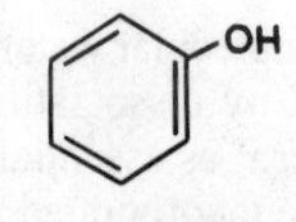

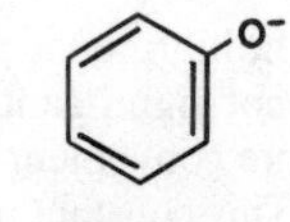

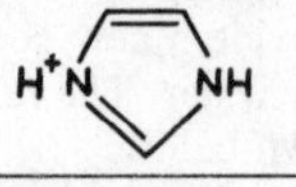

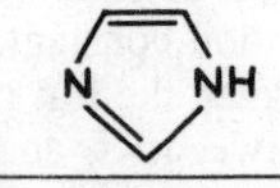

constant (K) for 2 representative weak acids, R–COOH and $R–NH_3^+$.

$$R–COOH \rightleftharpoons R–COO^- + H^+$$

$$K = \frac{[R–COO^-][H^+]}{[R–COOH]}$$

$$R–NH_3^+ \rightleftharpoons R–NH_2 + H^+$$

$$K = \frac{[R–NH_2][H^+]}{[R–NH_3^+]}$$

Since the numerical values of K for weak acids are negative exponential numbers, it is convenient to express K as pK, where

$$pK = -\log K$$

Note that pK is related to K as pH is to H^+ concentration. Table 2–2 lists illustrative K and pK values for a monocarboxylic, a dicarboxylic, and a tricarboxylic acid. Observe that the **stronger acid groups have lower pK values.**

Table 2–2. Dissociation constants and pK values for representative carboxylic acids.

Acid		K	pK
Acetic		1.76×10^{-5}	4.75
Glutaric	(1st)	4.58×10^{-5}	4.34
	(2nd)	3.89×10^{-6}	5.41
Citric	(1st)	8.40×10^{-4}	3.08
	(2nd)	1.80×10^{-5}	4.74
	(3rd)	4.00×10^{-6}	5.40

From the above equations that relate K to $[H^+]$ and to the concentrations of undissociated acid and its conjugate base, note that when

$$[R–COO^-] = [R–COOH]$$

or when

$$[R-NH_2] = [R-NH_3^+]$$

then

$$K = [H^+]$$

In words, **when the associated (protonated) and dissociated (conjugate base) species are present in equal concentration, the prevailing hydrogen ion concentration [H$^+$] is numerically equal to the dissociation constant, K.** If the logarithms of both sides of the above equation are taken and both sides are multiplied by −1, the expressions would be as follows:

$$K = [H^+]$$

$$-\log K = -\log [H^+]$$

−log K is defined as pK, and −log [H$^+$] is the definition of pH. Consequently, the equation may be rewritten as

$$pK = pH$$

ie, **the pK of an acid group is that pH at which the protonated and unprotonated species are present at equal concentrations.** The pK for an acid may be determined experimentally by adding 0.5 equivalent of alkali per equivalent of acid. The resulting pH will be equal to the pK of the acid.

Inductive Effects of Neighboring Groups on Acid Strength

The electrons of covalent bonds between dissimilar atoms tend to associate with the more electronegative (electron-attracting) atom, forming a **dipole:**

$$\boxed{Cl \longleftarrow CH_2-CH_3}$$
$$\quad - \qquad\qquad +$$

The arrow —◄— represents the direction of electron "drift." Factors that increase the electron density on the carboxyl group from which the positively charged proton must dissociate hinder its leaving and have an **acid-weakening effect.** Conversely, anything that decreases the electron density on the carbonyl group will assist dissociation of the proton and have an **acid-strengthening effect.** The closer an electronegative atom is to the carboxyl group, the more pronounced the acid-strengthening effect. These effects are readily seen with the strongly electronegative atom chlorine:

	pK
$CH_3 CH_2 COOH$	4.9
$\underset{\underset{Cl}{\mid}}{CH_2}-CH_2-COOH$	4.1
$CH_3 \underset{\underset{Cl}{\mid}}{CH}-COOH$	2.8

Alkyl groups supply electrons, but in a less dramatic manner:

	pK
$CH_3 COOH$	4.7
$CH_3-CH_2 COOH$	4.9
$(CH_3)_3 C-COOH$	5.0

Charged groups may either supply or withdraw electrons:

		pK For carboxyl
Acetic acid	CH_3-COOH	4.7
Glycine	$\underset{\underset{NH_3^+}{\mid}}{CH_2}-COOH$	2.3
Glutamic acid ($a-$COOH)	$HOOC-{^a}CH_2-CH_2-\underset{\underset{NH_3^+}{\mid}}{CH_2} \quad \underset{\underset{COOH}{\mid}}{} $	2.2

The second (γ) carboxyl dissociation of glutamic acid (pK = 4.2) is intermediate in acid strength between that of glycine and acetic acid since the molecule has both + and − charged groups.

The carbonyl group and hydroxyl groups also exert inductive effects and are acid strengthening:

		pK
Propionic acid	$CH_3 CH_2 COOH$	4.9
Lactic acid	$CH_3-\underset{\underset{OH}{\mid}}{CH}-COOH$	2.9
Pyruvic acid	$CH_3 \underset{\underset{O}{\parallel}}{C}-COOH$	2.7

The aromatic amines such as aniline and the nitrogen atoms of cyclic amines such as pyridine or purines and pyrimidines are, by contrast, moderately strong acids. **Aromatic amines, therefore, exist for the most part in the dissociated or uncharged form at pH 7.4.** Their acidity is attributable to their aromatic

Table 2–3. Acid dissociation constants of the conjugate acids of selected amines.[*]

	Acid Form	pK
Ammonia	NH_4^+	9.26
Methylamine	$CH_3 NH_3^+$	10.64
Dimethylamine	$(CH_3)_2 NH_2^+$	10.72
Trimethylamine	$(CH_3)_3 NH^+$	9.74
Aniline	$C_6 H_5 NH_3^+$	4.58
Pyridine	$C_5 H_5 NH^+$	5.23

[*]From Weast RC (editor): *Handbook of Chemistry & Physics,* 46th ed. Chemical Rubber Publishing Co., 1965–1966.

"electron sink" which reduces the negative charge on the nitrogen and facilitates dissociation of a proton.

Many drugs and other pharmacologically active compounds are amines. The uncharged forms are bases, ie, proton acceptors, whereas the charged forms are acids, ie, proton donors. The relative strengths of various amines may be expressed by the pK_a values for the dissociation:

$$R \overset{R}{\underset{R^1}{\overset{|}{\underset{|}{N^{\oplus}}}}} \overset{H}{\underset{H}{}} \rightleftharpoons H^+ + \overset{R}{\underset{R^1}{\overset{|}{N}}}-H$$

Some prefer to use pK_b values for amines. Conversion of pK_b to pK_a, is accomplished thus:

$$pK_a = 14 - pK_b$$

The pK_a values show that the aliphatic amines are weaker acids (stronger bases) than ammonia and that **at pH 7.4 essentially all of an aliphatic amine is in the charged form.** In body fluids, therefore, these amines are associated with an anion such as Cl^-.

HENDERSON–HASSELBALCH EQUATION

The pH of a solution containing a weak acid is related to its acid dissociation constant, as shown above for the weak acid water. The relationship can be stated in the convenient form of the **Henderson-Hasselbalch** equation, derived below.

A weak acid, HA, ionizes as follows:

$$HA \rightleftharpoons H^+ + A^-$$

The equilibrium constant for this dissociation is written:

$$K = \frac{[H^+][A^-]}{[HA]}$$

cross-multiply,

$$[H^+][A^-] = K[HA]$$

divide both sides by $[A^-]$,

$$[H^+] = K\frac{[HA]}{[A^-]}$$

take the log of both sides,

$$\log[H^+] = \log\left(K\frac{[HA]}{[A^-]}\right) = \log K + \log\frac{[HA]}{[A^-]}$$

multiply through by -1,

$$-\log[H^+] = -\log K - \log\frac{[HA]}{[A^-]}$$

substitute pH and pK for $-\log[H^+]$ and $-\log K$, respectively; then

$$pH = pK - \log\frac{[HA]}{[A^-]}$$

Then, to remove the minus sign, invert the last term.

$$\boxed{pH = pK + \log\frac{[A^-]}{[HA]}}$$

The Henderson-Hasselbalch equation has proved to be an expression of great predictive value in protonic equilibria.

(1) When an acid is exactly half neutralized, $[A^-] = [HA]$. Under these conditions,

$$pH = pK + \log\frac{[A^-]}{[HA]} = pK + \log\frac{1}{1} = pK + 0$$

Therefore, at half neutralization, pH = pK.

(2) When the ratio $[A^-]/[HA] = 100$ to 1,

$$pH = pK + \log\frac{[A^-]}{[HA]}$$

$$pH = pK + \log 100/1 = pK + 2$$

(3) When the ratio $[HA]/[A^-] = 10$ to 1,

$$pH = pK + \log 1/10 = pK + (-1)$$

If the equation is evaluated at several ratios of $[A^-]/[HA]$ between the limits 10^3 and 10^{-3}, and the calculated pH values plotted, the result obtained describes the titration curve for a weak acid (Fig 2–5).

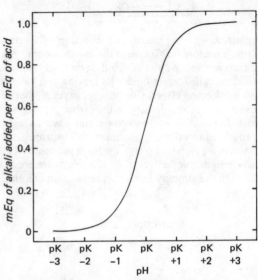

Figure 2–5. General form of a titration curve calculated from the Henderson-Hasselbalch equation.

BUFFERS & BUFFERING

Solutions of weak acids and their conjugate bases (or of weak bases and their conjugate acids) exhibit the phenomenon of **buffering—the tendency of a solution to resist a change in pH following addition of a strong acid or base more effectively than an equal volume of water.** The phenomenon of buffering is best illustrated by titrating a weak acid or base using a pH meter. Alternatively, we may calculate the pH shift that accompanies addition of acid or base to a buffered solution. In the example, the buffered solution (a mixture of a weak acid, pK = 5.0, and its conjugate base) is present initially at one of 4 pH values. We will calculate the pH shift that results when 0.1 mEq of KOH is added to 1 mEq of each of these solutions:

Initial pH	5.00	5.37	5.60	5.86
$[A^-]_{initial}$	0.50	0.70	0.80	0.88
$[HA]_{initial}$	0.50	0.30	0.20	0.12
$([A^-]/[HA])_{initial}$	1.00	2.33	4.00	7.33

Addition of 0.1 mEq of KOH produces

$[A^-]_{final}$	0.60	0.80	0.90	0.98
$[HA]_{final}$	0.40	0.20	0.10	0.02
$([A^-]/[HA])_{final}$	1.50	4.00	9.00	49.0
$\log([A^-]/[HA])_{final}$	0.176	0.602	0.95	1.69
Final pH	5.18	5.60	5.95	6.69
Δ pH	0.18	0.60	0.95	1.69

Observe that the pH change per milliequivalent of OH^- added varies greatly depending on the pH. At pH values close to pK, the solution resists changes in pH most effectively, and it is said to exert a **buffering effect. Solutions of weak acids and their conjugate bases buffer most effectively in the pH range pK ±**

2.0 pH units. This means that if it is desired to buffer a solution at pH X, a weak acid or base whose pK is no more than 2.0 pH units removed from pH X should be used.

Shown in Fig 2–6 is the net charge on one molecule of the acid as a function of pH. A fractional charge of −0.5 does not mean that an individual molecule bears a fractional charge but that the statistical probability that a given molecule has a unit negative charge is 0.5. Consideration of the net charge on macromolecules as a function of pH provides the basis for many separatory technics, including the electrophoretic separation of amino acids, plasma proteins, and abnormal hemoglobins (see Chapters 3 and 4).

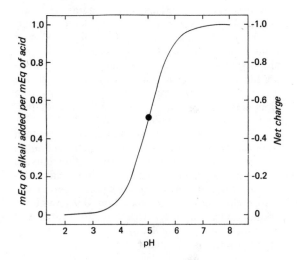

Figure 2–6. Titration curve for an acid of the type HA having pK = 5.0 (●).

● ● ●

Reference

Segel IM: *Biochemical Calculations*. Wiley, 1968.

3 | Amino Acids & Peptides

Victor W. Rodwell, PhD

INTRODUCTION

Living cells produce an impressive variety of **macromolecules (proteins, nucleic acids, polysaccharides)** that serve as structural components, biocatalysts, hormones, receptors, or repositories of genetic information. These macromolecules are **biopolymers** constructed of **monomer units** or **building blocks.** For nucleic acids, the monomer units are **nucleotides;** for complex polysaccharides, the monomer units are **sugar derivatives;** and for proteins, the monomer units are **amino acids.**

While proteins may have substances other than amino acids attached to them, the 3-dimensional structure and many of the biologic properties of proteins are determined largely by the **kinds of amino acids present,** the **order in which they are linked together** in a polypeptide chain, and the **spatial relationship of one amino acid to another.** Therefore, to comprehend protein chemistry, some knowledge of the chemistry of amino acids is essential.

AMINO ACIDS

Alpha-amino acids have both an amino and a carboxylic acid moiety attached to the same (α) carbon atom.

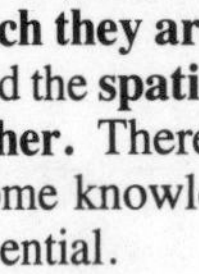

$$\begin{array}{c} H \\ | a \\ R-C-NH_2 \\ | \\ COOH \end{array}$$

Figure 3–1. An α-amino acid.

Although about 300 amino acids occur in nature, less than one-tenth of these occur in proteins. Complete acid-, base-, or enzyme-catalyzed hydrolysis* of proteins produces the 20 L-α-amino acids listed in Table 3–2. Proteins from all forms of life—plant, animal, or microbial—contain the same 20 amino

*Hydrolysis = rupture of a covalent bond with addition of the elements of water.

acids. The reason for this becomes apparent when the universality of the genetic code is discussed (see Chapter 29). While utilization of only 20 amino acids restricts the possible number of proteins, this fact lacks practical significance. For proteins containing 100 amino acids, 20^{100} distinct proteins are possible, although many would differ with respect to the position of only a small number of amino acids.

PROTONIC EQUILIBRIA OF AMINO ACIDS

Amino acids bear at least 2 ionizable weak acid groups, a –COOH and an –NH$_3^+$. In solution, 2 forms of these groups, one charged and one uncharged, exist in protonic equilibrium:

$$R-COOH \rightleftharpoons R-COO^- + H^+$$

$$R-NH_3^+ \rightleftharpoons H^+ + R-NH_2$$

R–COOH and R–NH$_3^+$ represent the **protonated** or **acid** partners in these equilibria. R–COO$^-$ and R–NH$_2$ are the **conjugate bases** (ie, proton acceptors) of the corresponding acids. Although both R–COOH and R–NH$_3^+$ are weak acids, R–COOH is a several thousand times stronger acid than is R–NH$_3^+$. At the pH of blood plasma or the intracellular space (7.4 and 7.1, respectively), carboxyl groups exist almost entirely as **carboxylate ion,** R–COO$^-$. At these pH values, most amino groups are predominantly in the associated (protonated) form, R–NH$_3^+$. In terms of the prevalent ionic species present in blood and most tissues, amino acid structures should be represented as shown in Fig 3–2(A). Structure B (Fig 3–2) cannot

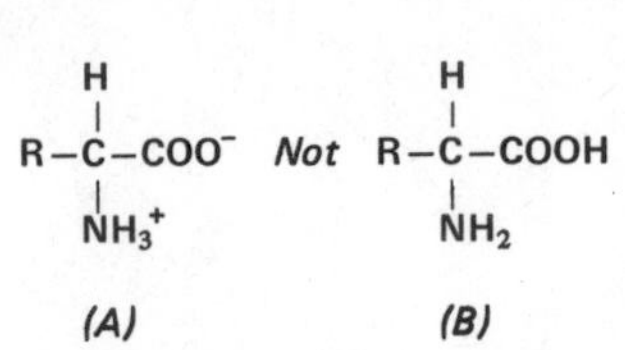

$$\begin{array}{ccc} H & & H \\ | & & | \\ R-C-COO^- & Not & R-C-COOH \\ | & & | \\ NH_3^+ & & NH_2 \\ & & \\ (A) & & (B) \end{array}$$

Figure 3–2. Ionically correct structure for an amino acid at or near physiologic pH *(A)*. The structure shown as *(B)* cannot exist at any pH but is frequently used as a convenience when discussing the chemistry of amino acids.

Table 3–1. Weak acid groups of amino acids.

	Conjugate Acid	Conjugate Base	Approximate pK
α-Carboxyl (all)	$R-COOH$	$R-COO^-$	2.1 ± 0.5
Non-α-carboxyl (aspartate, glutamate)	$R-COOH$	$R-COO^-$	4.0 ± 0.3
Imidazolinium (histidine)		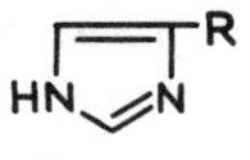	6.0
α-Amino (all)	$R-NH_3^+$	$R-NH_2$	9.8 ± 1.0
ϵ-Amino (lysine)	$R-NH_3^+$	$R-NH_2$	10.5
Phenolic OH (tyrosine)	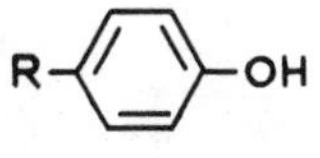 $R-\langle\bigcirc\rangle-OH$	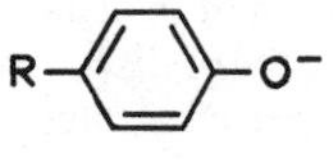 $R-\langle\bigcirc\rangle-O^-$	10.1
Guanidinium (arginine)			12.5
Sulfhydryl (cysteine)	$R-SH$	$R-S^-$	8.3

exist at *any* pH. At a pH sufficiently low to repress ionization of the carboxyl group, the more weakly acidic amino group would be protonated. If the pH is raised, the proton from the carboxyl will be lost long before that from the $R-NH_3^+$. At any pH sufficiently high for $R-NH_2$ to be the predominant species, the carboxylate ion ($R-COO^-$) must also be present. Convenience dictates, however, that the B representation be used for many equations involving reactions other than protonic equilibria.

As discussed in Chapter 2, the relative acid strengths of weak acids may be expressed in terms of their dissociation constants or of their pK, the negative log of the dissociation constant, ie:

$$pK = -\log K$$

pK values for α-amino groups of free amino acids average about 9.8. Thus, they are much weaker acids than are carboxyl groups. The weak acid groups of amino acids are shown in Table 3–1.

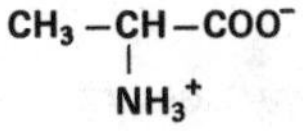

$$CH_3-CH-COO^-$$
$$\underset{NH_3^+}{|}$$

Figure 3–3. Isoionic or "zwitterionic" structure of alanine. Although charged, the zwitterion bears no *net* charge.

The **isoelectric pH (pI)** of an amino acid is **that pH at which it bears no net charge** and hence does not move in an electrical field. For an aliphatic amino acid such as alanine, the isoionic species is the form shown in Fig 3–3.

Since pK_1 (RCOOH) = 2.35 and pK_2 (RNH_3^+) = 9.69, the isoelectric pH (pI) of alanine is:

$$pI = \frac{pK_1 + pK_2}{2} = \frac{2.35 + 9.69}{2} = 6.02$$

Fig 3–4 illustrates ionic forms of an amino acid that has ionizable groups in addition to those attached to the α-carbon atom.

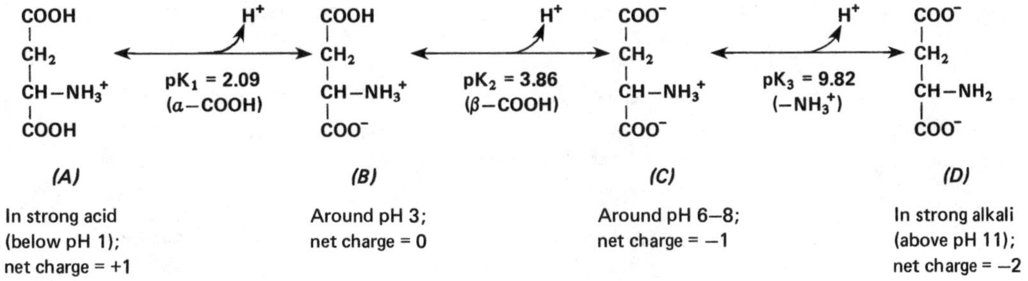

(A)	(B)	(C)	(D)
COOH CH$_2$ CH–NH$_3^+$ COOH	COOH CH$_2$ CH–NH$_3^+$ COO$^-$	COO$^-$ CH$_2$ CH–NH$_3^+$ COO$^-$	COO$^-$ CH$_2$ CH–NH$_2$ COO$^-$
pK$_1$ = 2.09 (α–COOH)	pK$_2$ = 3.86 (β–COOH)	pK$_3$ = 9.82 (–NH$_3^+$)	
In strong acid (below pH 1); net charge = +1	Around pH 3; net charge = 0	Around pH 6–8; net charge = –1	In strong alkali (above pH 11); net charge = –2

Figure 3–4. Protonic equilibria of aspartic acid.

From consideration of Fig 3–4, what would be the isoelectric pH (pI) for aspartic acid? To answer such a query, write out all possible ionic structures for a compound in the order in which they occur as one proceeds from strongly acidic to basic solution (eg, as for aspartic acid in Fig 3–4). Next, identify the isoionic, zwitterionic, or neutral representation (as in Fig 3–4, structure [B]). pI is the pH at the midpoint between the pK values on either side of the isoionic species. In this example,

$$pI = \frac{2.09 + 3.86}{2} = 2.98$$

This approach works equally well for amino acids with additional dissociating groups, eg, lysine or histidine. It is also applicable to calculation of the charge on a molecule with any specified number of dissociating groups at any pH. The ability to perform calculations of this type is of value in the clinical laboratory to predict the mobility of compounds in electrical fields and to select appropriate buffers for separations. After writing the formulas for all possible charged species of the basic amino acids lysine and arginine, observe that

$$pI = \frac{pK_2 + pK_3}{2}$$

For lysine, pI is 9.7; for arginine, pI is 10.8. The student should determine the pI for histidine.

STRUCTURES OF AMINO ACIDS

The amino acids present in proteins may be divided into 2 broad groups on the basis of the **polarities** of the R groups attached to the α-carbon atom (Table 3–2).

For many purposes, it is convenient to subdivide the amino acids in proteins into 7 classes as in Table 3–3. At present, **2 systems of chemical nomenclature are used for amino acids.** The older of these designates the carbon atom bearing the carboxyl and amino groups as the α-carbon. The adjacent carbon is termed β, the next γ, etc. While this system is slowly being supplanted by the familiar system of numbering the carbon atoms, it cannot be completely dispensed with at present. For example, reference is not made to a "2-amino acid" but to an "α-amino acid."

Table 3–3 gives, in addition, the 3-letter and

Table 3–2. Classification of the L-α-amino acids present in proteins on the basis of the relative polarities of their R groups. A nonpolar group is one which has little or no charge difference from one region to another, whereas a polar group has a relatively large charge difference in different regions.

Nonpolar	Polar
Alanine	Arginine
Isoleucine	Aspartic acid
Leucine	Asparagine
Methionine	Cysteine
Phenylalanine	Glutamic acid
Proline	Glutamine
Tryptophan	Glycine*
Valine	Histidine
	Lysine
	Serine
	Threonine
	Tyrosine

*Glycine is a special case since the R is hydrogen, which ineffectively shields the polar groups on the α-carbon atom.

single-letter abbreviations in common use among protein chemists. In this book, the 3-letter abbreviations will frequently be used. The shorter symbols are useful primarily when very long structures must be represented. Tables 3–4 and 3–5 list selected examples of important amino acids that occur in various natural products but not in proteins.

OPTICAL ISOMERS OF AMINO ACIDS

With the exception of glycine, each amino acid has at least one **asymmetric carbon atom** and hence is **optically active** (rotates the plane of plane-polarized light). Although some amino acids found in proteins are dextrorotatory and some levorotatory at pH 7.0, all have the **absolute configurations** of L-glyceraldehyde and hence are **L-α-amino acids.** Although D-amino acids occur in cells and even in polypeptides (eg, in polypeptide antibiotics), they are not present in proteins.

Threonine, isoleucine, 4-hydroxyproline, and hydroxylysine have 2 asymmetric carbon atoms and therefore exist in 4 isomeric forms. Of these, 2 are forms of allothreonine or of alloisoleucine, etc (Fig 3–5). Although a sheep liver enzyme (allothreonine aldolase) acts on allothreonine, neither allothreonine nor alloisoleucine appears to occur in nature.

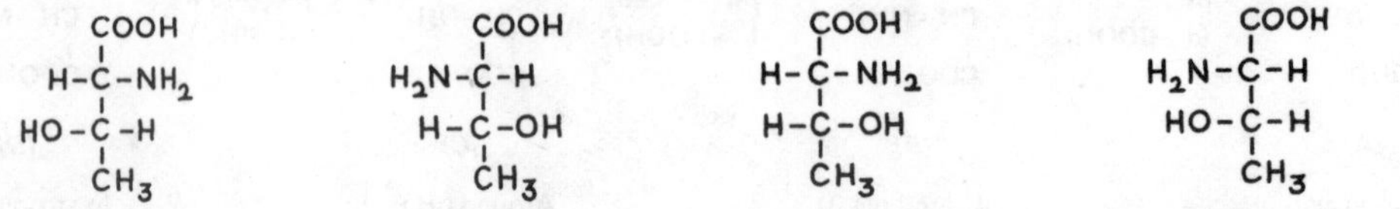

Figure 3–5. Isomers of threonine.

Table 3–3. L-a-Amino acids found in proteins.*

Group	Trivial Name	Symbol	Structural Formula
	With Aliphatic Side Chains		
I	Glycine†	Gly [G]	$H-CH-COOH$ $\quad\quad NH_2$
	Alanine	Ala [A]	$CH_3-CH-COOH$ $\quad\quad\quad NH_2$
	Valine	Val [V]	H_3C $\quad\ CH-CH-COOH$ $H_3C \quad\quad NH_2$
	Leucine	Leu [L]	H_3C $\quad\ CH-CH_2-CH-COOH$ $H_3C \quad\quad\quad\quad NH_2$
	Isoleucine	Ile [I]	CH_3 CH_2 $CH-CH-COOH$ $CH_3 \quad NH_2$
	With Side Chains Containing Hydroxylic (OH) Groups		
II	Serine	Ser [S]	$CH_2-CH-COOH$ $OH \quad NH_2$
	Threonine	Thr [T]	$CH_3-CH-CH-COOH$ $\quad\quad OH \quad NH_2$
	With Side Chains Containing Sulfur Atoms		
III	Cysteine‡	Cys [C]	$CH_2-CH-COOH$ $SH \quad NH_2$
	Methionine	Met [M]	$CH_2-CH_2-CH-COOH$ $S-CH_3 \quad NH_2$
	With Side Chains Containing Acidic Groups or Their Amides		
IV	Aspartic acid	Asp [D]	$HOOC-CH_2-CH-COOH$ $\quad\quad\quad\quad NH_2$
	Asparagine	Asn [N]	$H_2N-C-CH_2-CH-COOH$ $\quad\quad O \quad\quad\quad NH_2$

*Except for hydroxylysine and hydroxyproline, which are incorporated into polypeptide linkages as lysine and proline and subsequently hydroxylated (see Chapter 20), specific transfer RNA molecules exist for all the amino acids listed in Table 3–3. Their incorporation into proteins is thus under direct genetic control.

†Since glycine has no asymmetric carbon atom, there can be no D or L form.

‡The amino acid cystine consists of 2 cysteine residues linked by a disulfide bond:

$$NH_2$$
$$HOOC-CH-CH_2-S-S-CH_2-CH-COOH$$
$$NH_2$$

Table 3–3 (cont'd). L-α-Amino acids found in proteins.*

Group	Trivial Name	Symbol	Structural Formula
IV	Glutamic acid	Glu [E]	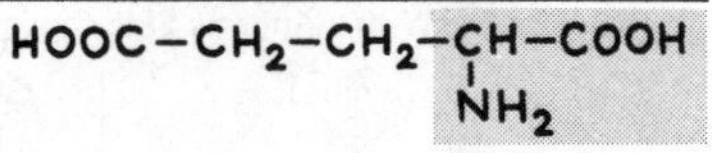 $HOOC-CH_2-CH_2-\underset{\underset{NH_2}{\mid}}{CH}-COOH$
	Glutamine	Gln [Q]	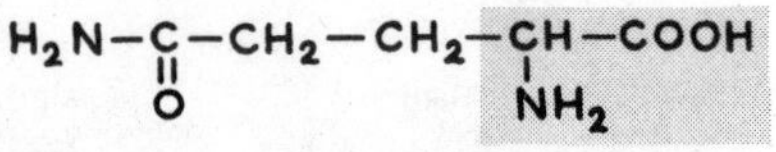 $H_2N-\underset{\underset{O}{\parallel}}{C}-CH_2-CH_2-\underset{\underset{NH_2}{\mid}}{CH}-COOH$

With Side Chains Containing Basic Groups

Group	Trivial Name	Symbol	Structural Formula
V	Arginine	Arg [R]	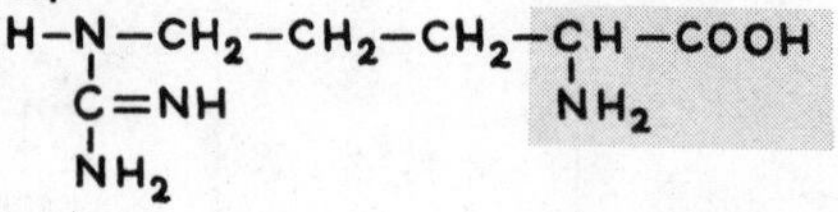 $H-\underset{\underset{\underset{NH_2}{\mid}}{\underset{\parallel}{C=NH}}}{N}-CH_2-CH_2-CH_2-\underset{\underset{NH_2}{\mid}}{CH}-COOH$
	Lysine	Lys [K]	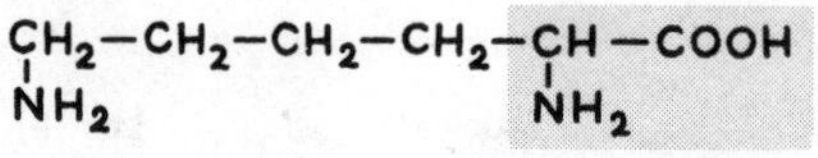 $\underset{\underset{NH_2}{\mid}}{CH_2}-CH_2-CH_2-CH_2-\underset{\underset{NH_2}{\mid}}{CH}-COOH$
	Hydroxylysine*	Hyl	$\underset{\underset{NH_2}{\mid}}{CH_2}-\underset{\underset{OH}{\mid}}{CH}-CH_2-CH_2-\underset{\underset{NH_2}{\mid}}{CH}-COOH$
	Histidine	His [H]	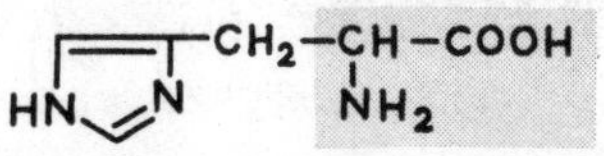 $CH_2-\underset{\underset{NH_2}{\mid}}{CH}-COOH$ (imidazole ring)

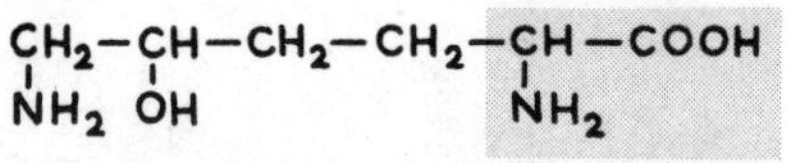

Containing Aromatic Rings

Group	Trivial Name	Symbol	Structural Formula
VI	Histidine (see above)		
	Phenylalanine	Phe [F]	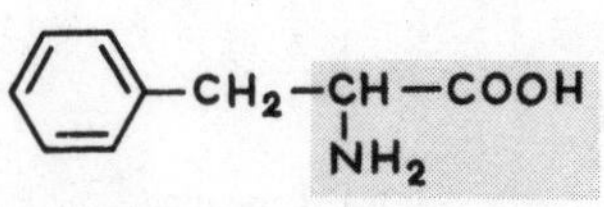 (benzene ring)$-CH_2-\underset{\underset{NH_2}{\mid}}{CH}-COOH$
	Tyrosine	Tyr [Y]	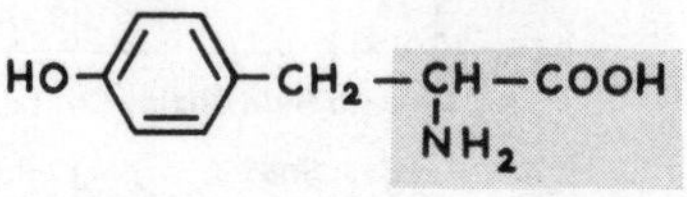 $HO-$(benzene ring)$-CH_2-\underset{\underset{NH_2}{\mid}}{CH}-COOH$
	Tryptophan	Trp [W]	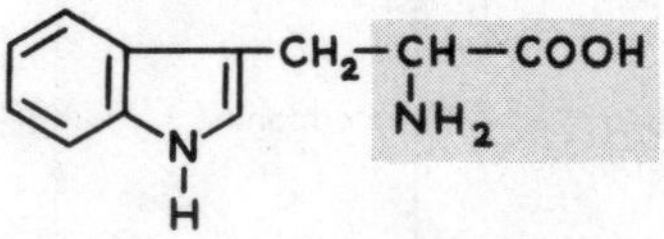 (indole ring)$-CH_2-\underset{\underset{NH_2}{\mid}}{CH}-COOH$

Imino Acids

Group	Trivial Name	Symbol	Structural Formula
VII	Proline	Pro [P]	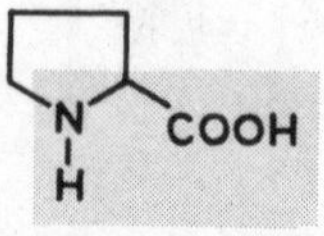 (pyrrolidine ring)$-COOH$
	4-Hydroxyproline	Hyp	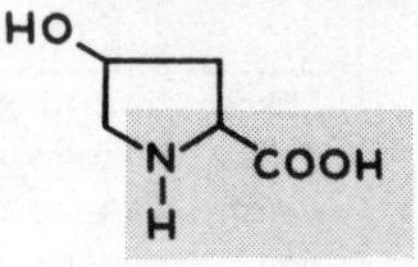 $HO-$(pyrrolidine ring)$-COOH$

*Thus far, found only in collagen and in gelatin.

Table 3–4. Selected examples of α-amino acids that do not occur in proteins but perform essential functions in mammalian metabolism.

Common and Systematic Names	Formula	Significance
Homocysteine (2-amino-4-mercapto-butanoic acid)	$CH_2-CH_2-CH-COOH$ $\quad\lvert\qquad\qquad\lvert$ $\;SH\qquad\quad NH_2$	An intermediate in methionine biosynthesis (see Chapter 20).
Cysteinesulfinic acid (2-amino-3-sulfinopropanoic acid)	$CH_2-CH-COOH$ $\quad\lvert\qquad\lvert$ $SO_2H\;\;NH_2$	An intermediate in cysteine catabolism (see Chapter 22).
Homoserine (2-amino-4-hydroxy-butanoic acid)	$CH_2-CH_2-CH-COOH$ $\quad\lvert\qquad\qquad\lvert$ $\;OH\qquad\quad NH_2$	An intermediate in threonine, aspartate, and methionine metabolism (see Chapter 22).
Ornithine (2,5-bisaminopentanoic acid)	$CH_2-CH_2-CH_2-CH-COOH$ $\quad\lvert\qquad\qquad\qquad\lvert$ $\;NH_2\qquad\qquad NH_2$	An intermediate in the biosynthesis of urea (see Chapter 21).
Citrulline (2-amino-5-ureidopentanoic acid)	$CH_2-CH_2-CH_2-CH-COOH$ $\quad\lvert\qquad\qquad\qquad\;\lvert$ $\;NH\qquad\qquad\;\; NH_2$ $\quad\lvert$ $\;C=O$ $\quad\lvert$ $\;NH_2$	Intermediate in the biosynthesis of urea (see Chapter 21).
Argininosuccinic acid	$\qquad\qquad CH_2-CH_2-CH_2-CH-COOH$ $\qquad\; NH\;\lvert\qquad\qquad\qquad\quad\lvert$ $\qquad\qquad\;\|\qquad\qquad\qquad\qquad\; NH_2$ $HN-\;C-NH$ $\;\lvert$ $HOOC-CH_2-C-COOH$	Intermediate in the biosynthesis of urea (see Chapter 21).
Dopa (3,4-dihydroxyphenyl-alanine)	HO—⟨ring⟩—$CH_2-CH-COOH$ with HO substituent, $\lvert\;NH_2$	Precursor of melanin (see Chapter 23).
3-Monoiodotyrosine	HO—⟨ring with I⟩—$CH_2-CH-COOH$, $\lvert\;NH_2$	Precursor of thyroid hormones.
3,5-Diiodotyrosine	HO—⟨ring with I, I⟩—$CH_2-CH-COOH$, $\lvert\;NH_2$	Precursor of thyroid hormones.
3,5,3′-Triiodothyronine (T_3)	HO—⟨ring with I⟩—O—⟨ring with I, I⟩—$CH_2-CH-COOH$, $\lvert\;NH_2$	Precursor of thyroid hormones.
Thyroxine (3,5,3′,5′-tetraiodothyronine) (T_4)	HO—⟨ring with I, I⟩—O—⟨ring with I, I⟩—$CH_2-CH-COOH$, $\lvert\;NH_2$	Precursor of thyroid hormones.

Table 3—5. Selected examples of non-α-amino acids that perform important functions in mammalian metabolism.

Common and Systematic Names	Formula	Significance
β-Alanine (3-aminopropanoic acid)	CH_2-CH_2-COOH $\vert$ NH_2	Part of coenzyme A and of the vitamin pantetheine (see Chapter 10).
Taurine (2-aminoethylsulfonic acid)	$CH_2-CH_2-SO_3H$ $\vert$ NH_2	Occurs in bile combined with bile acids (see Chapter 38).
γ-Aminobutyric acid (GABA) (4-aminobutanoic acid)	$CH_2-CH_2-CH_2-COOH$ $\vert$ NH_2	Neurotransmitter formed from glutamate in brain tissue (see Chapter 23).
β-Aminoisobutyric acid (2-methyl-3-aminopropanoic acid)	$H_2N-CH_2-CH-COOH$ $\vert$ CH_3	End product of pyrimidine catabolism in urine of some persons (see Chapter 26).

Table 3—6. Color reactions for specific amino acids.

Amino Acid Detected	Name	Reagents	Color
Arginine	Sakaguchi reaction	α-Naphthol and sodium hypochlorite	Red
Cysteine	Nitroprusside reaction	Sodium nitroprusside in dilute NH_4OH	Red
Cysteine	Sullivan reaction	Sodium 1,2-naphthoquinone-4-sulfonate and sodium hydrosulfite	Red
Histidine, tyrosine	Pauly reaction	Diazotized sulfanilic acid in alkaline solution	Red
Tryptophan	Glyoxylic acid reaction (Hopkins-Cole reaction)	Glyoxylic acid in $36N\ H_2SO_4$	Purple
Tryptophan	Ehrlich reaction	p-Dimethylaminobenzaldehyde in 12N HCl	Blue
Tyrosine	Millon reaction	$HgNO_3$ in HNO_2; heat	Red
Tyrosine	Folin-Ciocalteu reaction	Phosphomolybdotungstic acid	Red
Tyrosine, tryptophan, phenylalanine	Xanthoproteic reaction	Boiling concentrated HNO_3	Yellow

Figure 3—6. 4-Hydroxy-L-proline.

Note in Fig 3–5 that I–II and III–IV form **enantiomeric pairs** and hence have similar chemical properties. I–III and II–IV are **diastereoisomeric pairs** with different chemical properties.

The configuration of the 4-hydroxy-L-proline found in proteins is as shown in Fig 3–6.

Various other amino acids (see Tables 3–4, 3–5, and 3–6) in free or combined states fulfill important roles in metabolic processes other than as constituents of proteins. Many additional amino acids occur in plants or in antibiotics. Over 20 D-amino acids occur naturally. These include the D-alanine and D-glutamic acid of certain bacterial cell walls and a variety of D-amino acids in antibiotics.

PHYSICAL PROPERTIES OF AMINO ACIDS

Solubility

Most amino acids are readily solvated by and hence soluble in polar solvents such as water and ethanol but insoluble in nonpolar solvents such as benzene, hexane, or ether. Their high melting points (above 200 C) reflect the presence of charged groups—ie, the high energy needed to disrupt the ionic forces maintaining the crystal lattice.

Ultraviolet Absorption Spectrum

The aromatic amino acids tryptophan, tyrosine, histidine, and phenylalanine absorb ultraviolet light. As shown in Fig 3–7, above 240 nm, **most of the ultraviolet absorption of proteins is due to their tryptophan content.**

CHEMICAL REACTIONS OF AMINO ACIDS

The carboxyl and amino groups of amino acids exhibit all the expected reactions of these functions, eg, salt formation, esterification, and acylation.

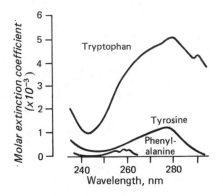

Figure 3–7. The ultraviolet absorption spectra of tryptophan, tyrosine, and phenylalanine.

Color Reactions

Ninhydrin oxidatively decarboxylates α-amino acids to CO_2, NH_3, and an aldehyde with one less carbon atom than the parent amino acid. The reduced ninhydrin then reacts with the liberated ammonia, forming a blue complex which maximally absorbs light of wavelength 570 nm. This blue color forms the basis of a **quantitative test for α-amino acids.** Amines other than α-amino acids also react with ninhydrin, forming a blue color but without evolving CO_2. The evolution of CO_2 is thus indicative of an α-amino acid. NH_3 and peptides also react but more slowly than α-amino acids. Proline and 4-hydroxyproline produce a yellow color with ninhydrin.

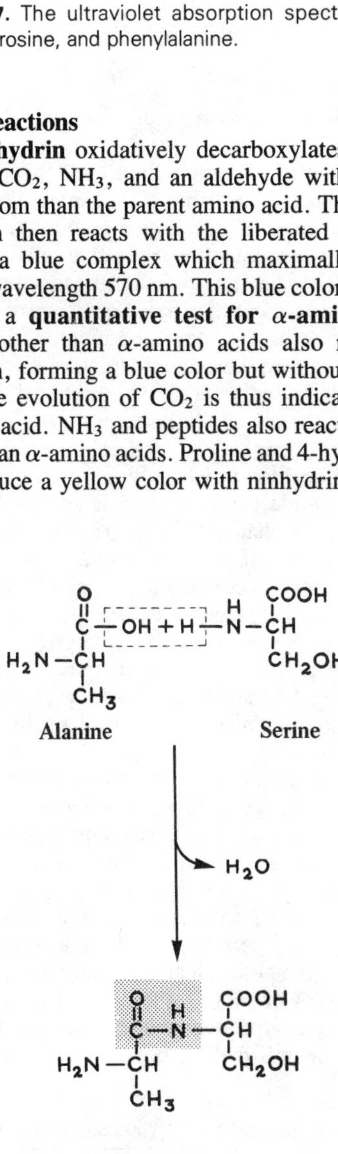

Alanyl-serine (Ala-Ser);
a dipeptide

Figure 3–8. Amino acids united by a peptide bond (shaded portion).

Various color reactions specific for particular functional groups in amino acids are useful in qualitative and quantitative identification of particular amino acids. In many cases, these color reactions may be used for amino acids combined in peptides or proteins (Table 3–6.)

Formation of Peptide Bonds

The most important reaction of amino acids is the formation of the **peptide bond.** In principle, peptide bond formation involves removal of 1 mole of water between the α-amino group of one amino acid and the α-carboxyl group of a second amino acid (Fig 3–8).

This reaction does not, however, proceed as written since the equilibrium constant strongly favors peptide bond hydrolysis. To actually synthesize peptide bonds between 2 amino acids, the carboxyl group must first be **activated.** Chemically, this may involve prior conversion to an acid chloride. **Biologically, activation involves initial condensation with ATP** (see Chapter 29).

PEPTIDES

Definitions

When the amino and carboxyl groups of amino acids combine to form peptide bonds, the constituent amino acids are termed amino acid residues. **A peptide consists of 2 or more amino acid residues linked by peptide bonds.** Peptides of more than 10 amino acid residues are termed **polypeptides.**

Representation of Polypeptide Structures

Figure 3–9 shows a tripeptide made up of the amino acid residues alanine, cysteine, and valine. Note that a tripeptide is one with 3 residues, not 3 peptide bonds. Dotted lines delineate the 3 amino acid residues. By convention, peptide structures are written with the **N-terminal residue** (the residue with a free α-amino group) **at the left** and with the **C-terminal residue** (the residue with a free α-carboxyl group) **at the right.** This peptide has a **single** free α-amino group and a **single** free α-carboxyl group (circled). This is true for all polypeptides comprised solely of amino

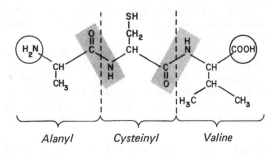

Alanyl   *Cysteinyl*   *Valine*

Figure 3–9. Structural formula for a tripeptide. Peptide bonds shaded for emphasis.

acid residues linked by peptide bonds formed between α-amino and α-carboxyl groups. In some peptides, the terminal amino or carboxyl groups may be derivatized and thus not free.

Writing Structural Formulas of Polypeptides

First draw its "backbone" of linked α-NH$_2$, α-COOH, and α-carbon atoms. These alternate along the backbone. Now insert the appropriate side chains on the α-carbon atoms. This is illustrated below.

(1) Write a zig-zag with the N-terminal amino group:

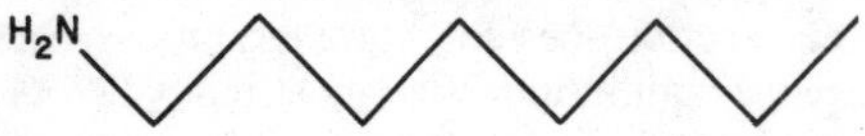

(2) Add the α-carbon, α-carboxyl, and α-amino groups:

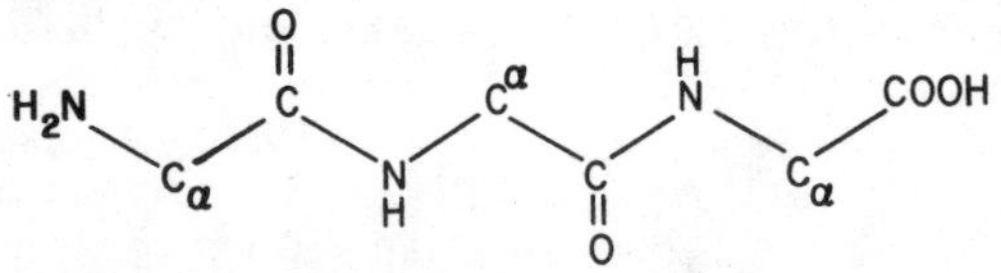

(3) Add the appropriate R groups (shaded) and α-hydrogens to the α-carbon atoms:

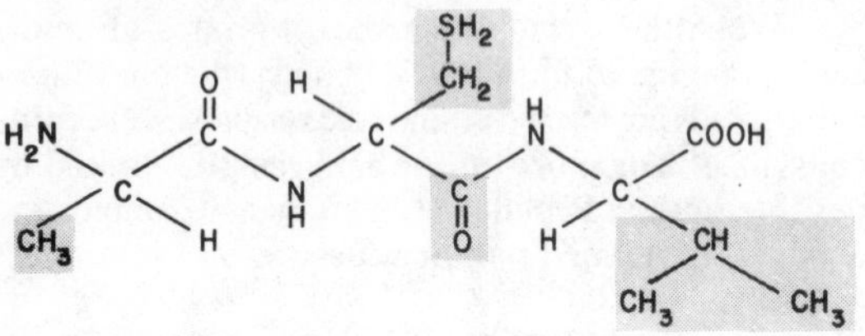

Primary Structure of Peptides

The linear sequence of amino acid residues in a polypeptide constitutes its **primary structure.** When the **number, chemical structure,** and **order** of all of the amino acid residues in a polypeptide are known, its primary structure has been determined.

Since polypeptides (proteins) may contain 100 or more residues, it is often inconvenient to use conventional structural formulas to represent primary structure. The "chemical shorthand" used is the 3-letter or one-letter abbreviation for the amino acids in column 3 of Table 3–3* (Fig 3–10). Note that **peptides are named as derivatives of the C-terminal amino acid residue.**

Three-letter abbreviations for amino acid residues linked by straight lines represent the primary structure that is known and unambiguous. These lines are omitted for single-letter abbreviations. Where there is uncertainty about the precise **order** of the amino acid residues of a portion of a polypeptide, the questionable

*Additional abbreviations are used in specific instances. For example, Cys–S–S–Cys for 2 cysteine residues linked by a disulfide bond.

Glu-Ala-Lys-Gly-Tyr-Ala

E A K G Y A

Figure 3–10. Use of 3-letter and one-letter abbreviations for amino acid residues to represent the primary structure of a hexapeptide with glutamate (Glu, E) at the N-terminal and alanine (Ala, A) at the C-terminal.

Glu-Lys-(Ala,Gly,Tyr)-His-Ala

Figure 3–11. A heptapeptide with a region of uncertain primary structure.

residues are enclosed in brackets and separated by commas (Fig 3–11).

Physiologic Consequences of Changes in Primary Structure

Substitution of a single amino acid for another in a linear sequence of possibly 100 or more amino acids may reduce or abolish biologic activity with potentially serious consequences (eg, sickle cell disease; see Chapter 14). Indeed, many inherited metabolic errors may involve no more than a subtle change of this type. The introduction of new chemical and physical methods to determine protein structure has markedly increased knowledge of the biochemical bases for many inherited metabolic diseases.

Protonic Equilibria of Peptides

The peptide (amide) bond is neither basic nor acidic and is uncharged at any pH of physiologic interest. Formation of peptides from amino acids at pH 7.4 is therefore accompanied by a net loss of one positive and one negative charge per peptide bond formed. Peptides are, however, charged molecules at physiologic pH owing to the charges on the C- and N-terminal groups and on functional groups present in polar amino acid residues attached to the α-carbon atoms.

Polypeptides, like amino acids and other charged molecules, may be isolated by technics (eg, electrophoresis, ion exchange chromatography) that separate on the basis of charge. The pK value for the C-terminal carboxyl group of a polypeptide is higher than that of the carboxyl group in the corresponding amino acid (the peptide COOH is a weaker acid). Conversely, the N-terminal amino group is a stronger acid (has a lower pK) (Table 3–7). These pK shifts result chiefly from conversion of the charged α-amino group to a neutral peptide bond.

Table 3–7. pK values for glycine and glycine peptides.

	pK (COOH)	pK (NH$_3^+$)
Gly	2.34	9.60
Gly-Gly	3.12	8.17
Gly-Gly-Gly	3.26	7.91

Conformation of Peptides in Solution

From examination of molecular models, it is apparent that a large number of conformations (spatial arrangements) are possible for a polypeptide. The available evidence suggests, however, that peptides in solution may be more rigid than might be supposed and that one or a narrow range of conformations tends to predominate. These favored conformations result from the action of factors such as steric hindrance, coulombic interactions, H-bonding, and hydrophobic interactions (see Chapter 4). As is the case for proteins, there is evidence that specific conformations are required for physiologic activity of polypeptides such as angiotensin and vasopressin (see Chapter 36). Association or aggregation of several identical polypeptide chains may also be a significant factor in their biologic activity. This appears to be the case for the tyrocidins.

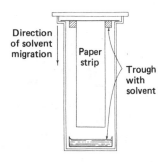

Figure 3–12. Apparatus for descending paper chromatography.

SEPARATORY TECHNICS FOR AMINO ACIDS & PEPTIDES

Chromatography

In all chromatographic separations, molecules are **partitioned between a stationary and a mobile phase** (Table 3–8). **Separation depends on the relative tendencies of molecules in a mixture to associate more strongly with one or the other phase.**

Table 3–8. Phase relationships for chromatographic systems important in biochemistry.

Form of Chromatography	Stationary Phase	Mobile Phase
Partition chromatography on paper sheets, thin layers of cellulose powder, or columns of inert supports coated with thin layers of liquid; gel filtration.	Liquid	Liquid
Ion exchange; adsorption on thin layers or particles in columns.	Solid	Liquid
Partition chromatography between thin layer of liquid on support and mobile gas.	Liquid	Gas

While these separatory technics are discussed principally with respect to amino acids and peptides, their use is by no means restricted to these molecules.

Paper Chromatography

While to a large extent supplanted by more sophisticated technics, paper chromatography still is widely used in amino acid separations. Samples are applied at a marked point about 5 cm from the end of a filter paper strip and suspended in a sealed vessel that contains the chromatographic solvent (Fig 3–12).

For amino acid separations, solvents are polar binary, ternary, or more complex mixtures of water, alcohols, and acids or bases. The more polar components of the solvent associate with the cellulose and form the stationary phase. The less polar components constitute the mobile phase. This is **normal partition chromatography.** For **reversed phase partition chromatography,** the polarities of the mobile and stationary phases are reversed (eg, by first dipping the paper in a solution of a silicone). Reversed phase partition chromatography is used to separate nonpolar peptides or lipids, not amino acids. The solvent may migrate up or down the paper. When it has migrated almost to the end, the strip is dried and treated to allow visualization of the molecules of interest (eg, for amino acids, with 0.5% ninhydrin in acetone followed by heating at 90–110 C for a few minutes). Amino acids with large nonpolar side chains (Leu, Ile, Phe, Trp, Val, Met, Tyr) migrate farther than those with shorter nonpolar side chains (Pro, Ala, Gly) or with polar side chains (Thr, Glu, Ser, Arg, Asp, His, Lys, Cys). This reflects the greater relative solubility of polar molecules in the hydrophilic stationary phase and of nonpolar molecules in organic solvents. Note that, for a nonpolar series (Gly, Ala, Val, Leu), increasing length of the nonpolar side chain results in increased mobility.

The ratio of the distance traveled by an amino acid to that traveled by the solvent front, both measured from the marked point of application of the amino acid mixture, is called the **R_f value** for that amino acid. R_f values for a given amino acid vary with experimental conditions, eg, the solvent used. Although it is possible to tentatively identify an amino acid by its R_f value alone, it is preferable to chromatograph known amino acid standards simultaneously with the unknown mixture (Fig 3–13).

Quantitation of amino acids may be accomplished by cutting out each spot, eluting with a suitable solvent, and performing a quantitative colorimetric (ninhydrin) analysis. Alternatively, the paper may be sprayed with ninhydrin and the color densities of the spots measured with a recording transmittance or reflectance photometer.

For **2-dimensional paper chromatography,** sample is applied to one corner of a square sheet of paper or other suitable medium and chromatographed in one solvent mixture. The sheet is then removed,

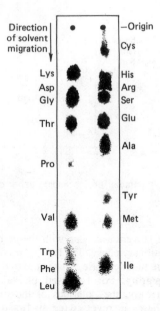

Figure 3–13. Identification of amino acids present in proteins. After descending paper chromatography in butanol-acetic acid, spots were visualized with ninhydrin.

dried, turned through 90 degrees, and chromatographed in a second solvent (Fig 3–14). Formerly used extensively for peptide mapping, 2-dimensional chromatography is rapidly being supplanted by more sophisticated technics such as reversed phase high-pressure liquid chromatography (see below).

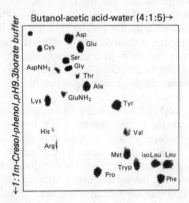

Figure 3–14. Two-dimensional chromatogram of protein amino acids. (Redrawn, slightly modified, from Levy & Chung: *Anal Chem* 1953;**25**:396. Copyright © 1953 by American Chemical Society; reproduced with permission.)

Thin Layer Chromatography

There are 2 distinct classes of thin layer chromatography (TLC). Partition TLC (PTLC) closely resembles partition chromatography on paper. Adsorption TLC (ATLC) bears no similarity to paper chromatography except that both are conducted on thin sheets. For PTLC on powdered cellulose or other relatively inert supports, the solvent systems and detection reagents used for paper chromatography are fully ap-

plicable. Reversed phase PTLC also is possible. For ATLC, chromatography depends on the ability of the solvent (which need not be binary or more complex) to elute sample components from adsorption sites on an activated sorbent such as heated silica gel. ATLC is applicable to nonpolar materials such as lipids and hence not to amino acids or most peptides.

Automated Ion Exchange Chromatography

While amino acids may be separated by various technics, analysis of amino acid residues after hydrolysis of a polypeptide generally involves **automated ion exchange chromatography.** Complete separation, identification, and quantitation require less than 3 hours. The procedure of Moore and Stein uses a short and long column containing the Na^+ form of a sulfonated polystyrene resin. When acid hydrolysate at pH 2 is applied to the columns, the amino acids bind via cation exchange with Na^2. The columns are then eluted with sodium citrate under preprogrammed conditions of pH and temperature. The short column requires a single elution buffer; the long column, two. Eluted material is reacted with ninhydrin reagent, and color densities are monitored in a flow-through colorimeter. Data are displayed on a strip chart recorder that may incorporate computer-linked integration of peak areas (Fig 3–15).

Gas-Liquid Chromatography

In gas-liquid chromatography (GLC), sample components are partitioned between a thin film of a relatively nonpolar, nonvolatile liquid (eg, a silicone) coated on a finely divided inert support (firebrick, diatomaceous earth). The mobile gas phase is generally argon or nitrogen. GLC is applicable only to materials that have some tendency to vaporize at temperatures below their decomposition points. Highly polar materials such as amino acids and peptides must therefore first be derivatized to make them volatile. Highly successful for resolution of complex lipid mixtures, GLC has not found wide favor for chromatography of amino acids or peptides owing to difficulties in achieving quantitative derivatization and to thermal decomposition on the column. In addition, the detection technics generally used for GLC destroy all or some of the sample. For amino acid separations, ion exchange methods are preferred; for high-molecular-weight peptides, either gel filtration or reversed phase high-pressure liquid chromatography is preferred.

Gel Filtration

Automated sequencing utilizes small numbers of large (30- to 100-residue) peptides. However, many denatured, high-molecular-weight polypeptides are insoluble owing to exposure during denaturation of previously buried hydrophobic residues. While insolubility can be overcome by urea, alcohols, organic acids, or bases, these restrict the subsequent use of ion exchange technics for peptide purification. Gel filtration of large hydrophobic peptides may, however, be performed in 1–4M formic or acetic acid (Fig 3–16).

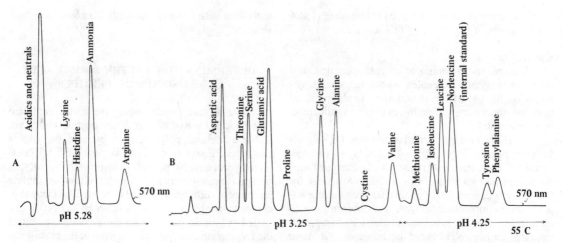

Figure 3–15. Automated analysis of an acid hydrolysate of corn endosperm on Moore-Stein Dowex 50 columns (at 55 C). *A:* A short (5.0 × 0.9 cm) column used to resolve basic amino acids by elution at pH 5.28. Time required = 60 minutes. *B:* A longer (55 × 0.9 cm) column used to resolve neutral and acidic amino acids by elution first with pH 3.25 and then with pH 4.25 buffer. An internal standard of norleucine is included for reference. Basic amino acids remain bound to the column. Time required = 180 minutes. Emerging samples are automatically reacted with ninhydrin and the optical density of samples recorded at 570 nm and 440 nm. The latter wavelength is used solely to detect proline and hydroxyproline (absent from corn endosperm). Ordinate = optical density plotted on a log scale. Abscissa = time in minutes. (Courtesy of Professor ET Mertz, Purdue University.)

Reversed Phase High-Pressure Liquid Chromatography (RPHPLC)

A technic that may supplant gel filtration for purification of high-molecular-weight nonpolar peptides is high-pressure liquid chromatography on nonpolar materials with elution by polar solvents (RPHPLC). Figure 3–17 illustrates resolution of the

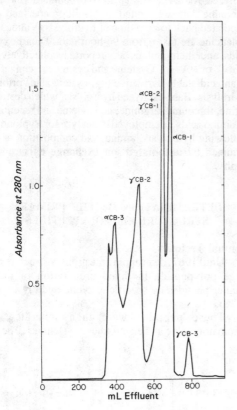

Figure 3–16. Gel filtration chromatography of cyanogen bromide (CB) fragments of human fetal globin. Chromatography was on G-50 Sephadex equilibrated and eluted with 1% HCOOH. Designations refer to arbitrarily numbered fragments from the α- or γ-chains. (Courtesy of Pearson JD & others, Department of Biochemistry, Purdue University.)

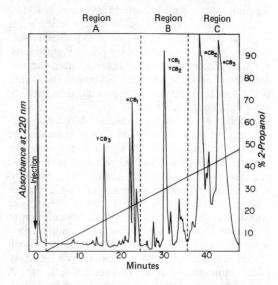

Figure 3–17. RPHPLC elution profile for cyanogen bromide (CB) fragments of human fetal globin. Designations are for arbitrarily numbered fragments from the α- and γ-chains. (Courtesy of Pearson JD & others, Department of Biochemistry, Purdue University.)

same cyanogen bromide fragments of human fetal globin as shown in Fig 3–16 by this technic.

Electrophoresis

Separations of amino acids, polypeptides, and other ampholytes (molecules whose net charge depends on the pH of the surrounding medium) in an imposed direct current field has extensive applications in biochemistry.

A. High-Voltage Electrophoresis (HVE) on Inert Supports: Paper sheets or thin layers of powdered cellulose are most frequently used as inert supports. Separations in a 2000- to 5000-volt field for 0.5–2 hours depend upon the net charge on the ampholyte and its molecular weight. For molecules with identical charge, the lower-molecular-weight material migrates farther. Net charge is, however, the more important factor in determining separation. Applications include amino acids, low-molecular-weight polypeptides, certain proteins, nucleotides, and phosphosugars. Samples are applied to the support, which is then moistened with buffer of an appropriate pH and connected to buffer reservoirs by paper wicks. The paper may be covered by a glass plate or immersed in a hydrocarbon coolant. When current is applied, molecules with a net negative charge at the selected pH migrate toward the anode and those with a net positive charge toward the cathode. For visualization, the dried **electropherogram** is treated with ninhydrin (amino acids, peptides) or exposed to ultraviolet light (nucleotides), etc.

The choice of pH is dictated by the pK values of the dissociating groups on the molecules in the mixture. At pH 6.4, glutamate and aspartate bear a net charge of -1, move toward the anode, and are readily separated on the basis of their difference in molecular weight. Lysine, arginine, and histidine move in the opposite direction, whereas all of the other protein amino acids remain at or near the point of application. For separation of the peptides resulting from enzymic digestion of a protein, a pH of 3.5 is better. The technic is also used for separation of oligonucleotides (pH 2.5) or of nucleotides (pH 4.5).

B. HVE on Molecular Sieves: Molecular sieving may be superimposed on charge separation to facilitate separation. While starch and agarose are used, most commonly the support is a cross-linked polymer of acrylamide ($CH_2 = CH.CONH_2$). For **polyacrylamide gel electrophoresis (PAGE),** protein solutions are applied to buffered tubes or blocks of polyacrylamide cross-linked 2–10% by inclusion of methylene bisacrylamide (''bis'') or similar cross-linking reagents. Direct current is then applied. Visualization is by staining with Coomassie blue (polypeptides), ethidium bromide (polynucleotides), etc. A popular variant is PAGE under denaturing conditions. Proteins are boiled in urea or sodium dodecyl sulfate (SDS) before separation to produce conditions that favor separation based strictly on molecular size. SDS-PAGE is widely used to establish subunit molecular weights of proteins by comparison of

mobilities with those of standards of known molecular weight.

DETERMINATION OF THE AMINO ACID COMPOSITION OF PEPTIDES

The peptide bonds linking the amino acids are first broken by hydrolysis. Since peptide bonds are stable at neutral pH, catalysis by acid or base is employed. Enzymic catalysis is unsuitable for complete hydrolysis. No procedure completely hydrolyzes proteins to constituent amino acids without incomplete recovery of certain amino acid residues. The method of choice generally is hydrolysis in 6N HCl at 110 C in a sealed evacuated tube. Under these conditions, all of the tryptophan and cysteine and most of the cystine are destroyed. If metals are present, methionine and tyrosine are partially lost. Glutamine and asparagine are quantitatively deamidated to glutamate and aspartate. Recovery of serine and threonine is incomplete and decreases with increasing time of hydrolysis. Finally, certain bonds between neutral residues (Val-Val, Ile-Ile, Val-Ile, Ile-Val) are only 50% hydrolyzed after 20 hours. Typically, replicate samples are hydrolyzed for 24, 48, 72, and 96 hours. Serine and threonine data are plotted on semilog paper and extrapolated back to zero time of hydrolysis. Valine and isoleucine are taken from 96-hour data. Dicarboxylic acids and their amides are reported collectively as ''Glx'' or ''Asx.'' Cysteine and cystine are converted to an acid-stable derivative (eg, cysteic acid) prior to hydrolysis. Base-catalyzed hydrolysis, which destroys serine, threonine, arginine, and cyteine and racemizes all amino acids, is employed to analyze for tryptophan. Following hydrolysis, amino acid composition is determined by **automated ion exchange chromatography.**

DETERMINATION OF THE PRIMARY STRUCTURE OF POLYPEPTIDES

Manual Technics

Until 1967, determining the primary structure of a large polypeptide involved preparation of many smaller peptides by specific enzymic hydrolysis (Fig 3–18).

These peptides were then separated by chromatographic and electrophoretic technics. The se-

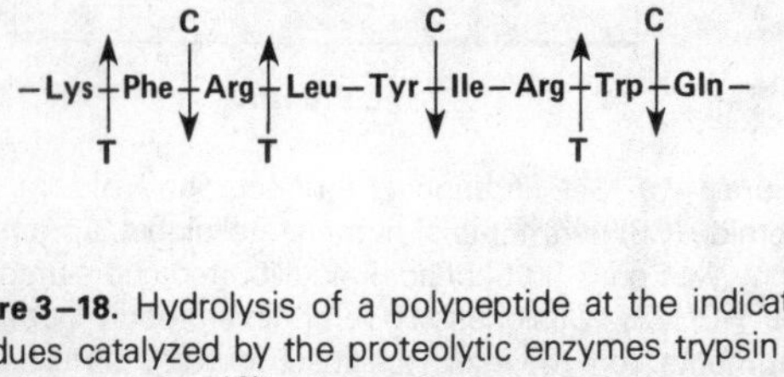

Figure 3–18. Hydrolysis of a polypeptide at the indicated residues catalyzed by the proteolytic enzymes trypsin (T) and chymotrypsin (C).

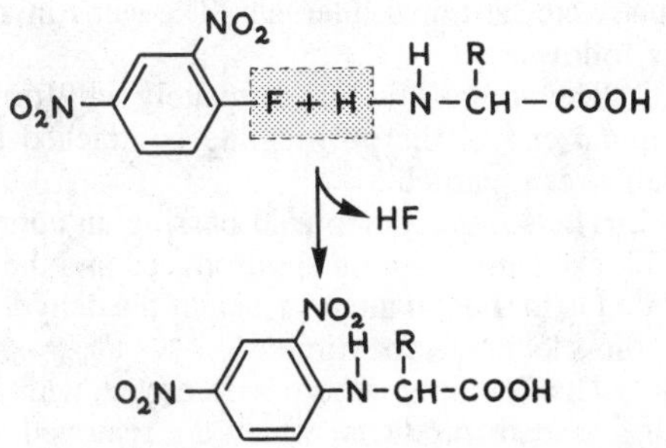

Figure 3–19. Reaction of an amino acid with 1-fluoro-2,4-dinitrobenzene (Sanger's reagent). The reagent is named for the Nobel laureate (1958) biochemist Frederick Sanger, who used it to determine the primary structure of insulin.

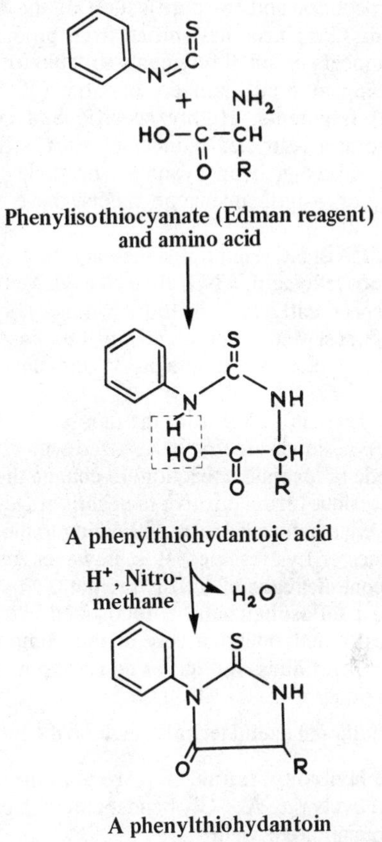

Phenylisothiocyanate (Edman reagent)
and amino acid

A phenylthiohydantoic acid

A phenylthiohydantoin

Figure 3–20. Conversion of an amino acid (or of the N-terminal residue of a polypeptide) to a phenylthiohydantoin. The principal use of this reaction, which identifies the N-terminal residues of a peptide, is in automated sequencing of polypeptides.

quence of many was then determined by wet chemical methods such as the following:

A. Hydrazinolysis: Peptides are treated with hydrazine, converting all peptide and amide bonds to acid hydrazides. The C-terminal carboxyl group does not react. The unchanged amino acid is thus that originally at the C-terminal end.

B. 1-Fluoro-2,4-dinitrobenzene (Sanger's Reagent): This quantitatively arylates all free amino groups, producing intensely yellow 2,4-dinitrophenyl amino acids (Fig 3–19). These derivatives are readily quantitated by spectrophotometry. In addition to the N-terminal residue, the ϵ-amino groups of lysine, the imidazole of histidine, the OH of tyrosine, and the SH of cysteine also react with fluorodinitrobenzene. Since the dinitrophenyl group is resistant to removal by acid hydrolysis, it was used to determine the N-terminal amino acid of polypeptides.

C. Phenylisothiocyanate (Edman Reagent): Phenylisothiocyanate reacts with the amino groups of amino acids and peptides, yielding phenylthiohydantoic acids. On treatment with acid in nonhydroxylic solvents, these cyclize to phenylthiohydantoins (Fig 3–20).

D. Aminopeptidases or Carboxypeptidases: These enzymes catalyze successive removal of N- or C-terminal residues, respectively. The order of appearance of residues in the nonprotein fraction tells much of their order in a polypeptide.

The final task involved fitting together all the peptides with overlapping regions to give an unambiguous structure for the original polypeptide. Apart from the colossal effort involved, a serious shortcoming was that regions of uncertainty tended to remain unless exactly the right peptides were sequenced.

Automated Technics

The determination of the primary structure of polypeptides—and thus also of proteins (see Chapter 4)—was revolutionized by Edman in 1967 by introduction of an automated system of analysis. The heart of the instrument is a spinning cup reaction chamber in which reactions occur in a thin film of solution on the cup wall. This facilitates extractions and subsequent removal of solvents. Several companies now market fully automated apparatus for the determination of polypeptide sequences of up to 30–40 residues (or, in exceptional cases, up to 60 or even 80 residues) in one continuous operation. The apparatus is programmed to perform sequential Edman degradations on the N-terminal residue of a polypeptide. After the initial N-terminal amino acid has been removed, separated, and identified, an Edman derivative (Fig 3–20) of the next one in the sequence is formed, etc. The apparatus lengthens the sequence that can be determined by manual technics 4- to 5-fold and is incomparably faster.

Cleavage of Polypeptides Into Fragments Suitable for Automated Sequencing

Automated sequencing instruments (sequenators) most efficiently operate on polypeptides 20–60 residues long. Automated technics have therefore greatly influenced selection of the technics for initial cleavage of polypeptides and for purification of the resulting fragments. Emphasis has shifted from production of large numbers of small fragments suitable for manual sequencing to small numbers of large (30- to 100-residue) fragments. Highly specific and complete cleavage at a restricted number of sites is therefore desired. Cleavage with cyanogen bromide (CNBr), trypsin, or o-iodosobenzene meets these requirements.

A. CNBr: Cysteine residues are first modified with iodoacetic acid. CNBr then cleaves Met-peptide bonds specifically and, in most instances, quantitatively. Since Met is comparatively rare in polypeptides, this generates fragments in the desired size range.

B. Trypsin: To restrict the number of cleavage sites, Lys residues are first derivatized with citraconic anhydride (a reversible reaction) to change the charge on Lys residues from positive to negative. Derivatization of Arg residues is less useful owing to the relative abundance of Lys residues. It is, however, useful for subsequent cleavage of CNBr fragments.

C. o-Iodosobenzene: o-Iodosobenzene cleaves specifically and quantitatively at the comparatively rare Trp-X residues. It requires no prior protection of other residues.

Additional useful technics include the following:

D. Hydroxylamine: Hydroxylamine cleaves comparatively rare Asn-Gly bonds, although generally not in quantitative yield.

E. Protease: *Staphylococcus aureus* protease V8 cleaves Glu-X-peptide residues with a preference for situations where X is hydrophobic. Glu-Lys resists cleavage. This reaction is useful for subsequent degradation of CNBr fragments.

Two or 3 digests of the original polypeptide, normally at Met, Trp, Arg, and Asn-Gly, combined with appropriate subdigests of the resulting fragments, usually will give the entire primary structure of the polypeptide. Barring unusual difficulties in purification of fragments, this can—with care—be accomplished with a few micromoles of polypeptide.

Fragment purification is achieved chiefly by gel filtration in acetic or formic acid (Fig 3–16), by RPHPLC (Fig 3–17), or by ion exchange chromatography on phosphocellulose in solutions of phosphoric acid.

SYNTHESIS BY AUTOMATED TECHNICS

While classic chemical technics were adequate for synthesis of the octapeptides vasopressin and oxytocin, and later of bradykinin (see below), the yields of final product are too low to permit synthesis of long polypeptides or proteins. This has been achieved by the automated, solid-phase synthesis technic developed by R. B. Merrifield. In this process, an automated synthesis is carried out in a single vessel by a machine programmed to add reagents, remove

products, etc, at timed intervals. The steps involved are as follows:

(1) The amino acid that ultimately will form the C-terminal end of the polypeptide is attached to an insoluble resin particle.

(2) The second amino acid bearing an appropriately blocked amino group is introduced and the peptide bond is formed in the presence of the dehydrating agent dicyclohexylcarbodiimide.

(3) The blocking group is removed with acid, forming gaseous products, which are removed.

(4) Steps 2 and 3 are repeated with the next amino acid in sequence, then the next, until the entire polypeptide attached to the resin particle has been synthesized.

(5) The polypeptide is cleaved from the resin particle.

The process proceeds rapidly and with excellent yields. About 3 hours are required per peptide bond synthesized. By this technic, the A chain of insulin (21 residues) was synthesized in 8 days and the B chain (30 residues) in 11 days. The crowning achievement to date has been the total synthesis of pancreatic ribonuclease (124 residues; see Fig 4–11) in 18% overall yield, the first total synthesis of an enzyme. It foreshadows a new era not only in confirmation of protein structures but in related areas such as immunology and perhaps in the treatment of inborn errors of metabolism. A variety of physiologically important peptides, prepared synthetically from L-amino acids by routes which involve no racemization, have full physiologic activity. These include the octapeptides oxytocin and vasopressin, ACTH, and melanocyte-stimulating hormone (see Chapter 36).

PHYSIOLOGICALLY ACTIVE PEPTIDES

Animal, plant, and bacterial cells contain a wide variety of low-molecular-weight polypeptides (3–100 amino acid residues) having profound physiologic activity. Some, including most mammalian polypeptide hormones, contain only peptide bonds formed between α-amino and α-carboxyl groups of the 20 L-α-amino acids present in proteins. However, additional amino acids or derivatives of the protein amino acids may also be present in polypeptides (though not in proteins). Shown below are a few selected examples.

The short polypeptides bradykinin and kallidin are smooth muscle hypotensive agents liberated from specific plasma proteins exposed to snake venom or trypsin. Since they are derived from proteins, these peptides contain only protein amino acids.

Arg-Pro-Pro-Gly-Phe-Ser-Pro-Phe-Arg

Bradykinin

Lys-Arg-Pro-Pro-Gly-Phe-Ser-Pro-Phe-Arg

Kallidin

Glutathione (Fig 3–21), an atypical tripeptide in which the N-terminal glutamate is linked to cysteine via a non-α-peptidyl bond, is present in all forms of life. In humans and other animals, glutathione is required for the action of several enzymes and of insulin. It is believed that glutathione and the enzyme glutathione reductase function either in insulin degradation or in formation of the correct disulfide bonds in insulin (see Chapter 4).

Polypeptide antibiotics elaborated by fungi frequently contain D- as well as L-amino acids, and amino acids not present in proteins. Examples include tyrocidin and gramicidin S, cyclic polypeptides that contain D-phenylalanine, and the nonprotein amino acid ornithine (Orn). These polypeptides are not synthesized on ribosomes.

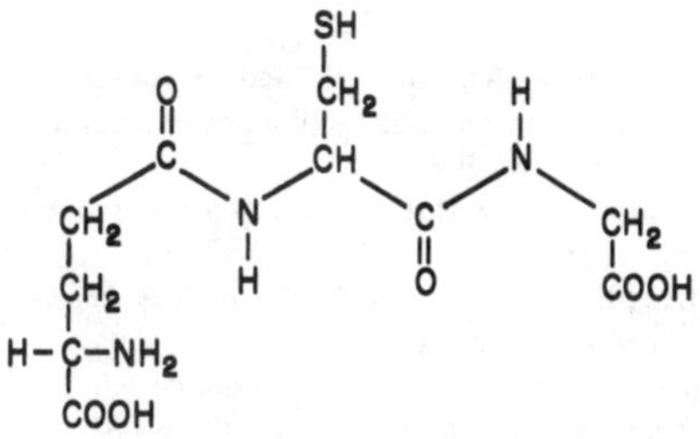

Figure 3–21. Glutathione (γ-glutamyl-cysteinyl-glycine).

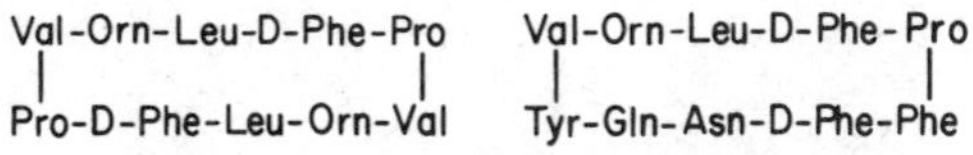

```
Val-Orn-Leu-D-Phe-Pro        Val-Orn-Leu-D-Phe-Pro
 |                   |         |                   |
Pro-D-Phe-Leu-Orn-Val        Tyr-Gln-Asn-D-Phe-Phe

     Gramicidin S                   Tyrocidin
```

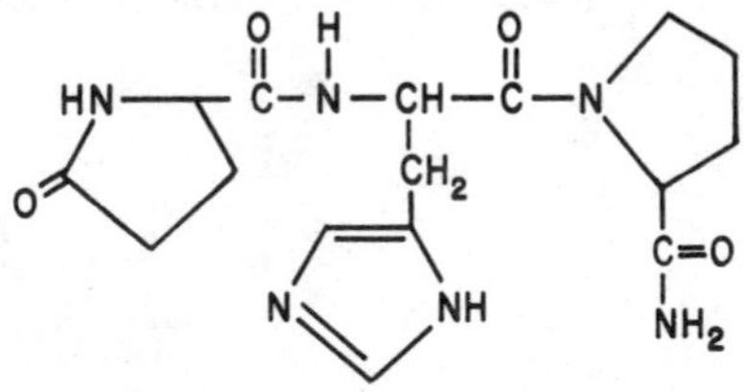

Figure 3–22. TRH (pyroglutamylhistidylprolinamide).

Thyrotropic regulatory hormone (TRH) (Fig 3–22) illustrates yet another variant. The N-terminal glutamate is cyclized to pyroglutamic acid, and the C-terminal prolyl carboxyl is present as amidated.

A mammalian polypeptide may contain more than one physiologically potent polypeptide. Within the primary structure of β-lipotropin—a hypophyseal hormone that stimulates the release of fatty acids from adipose tissue—are sequences of amino acids that are common to several other polypeptide hormones with diverse physiologic activities (Fig 3–23). It is therefore probable that the large polypeptide is a precursor of the smaller peptides.

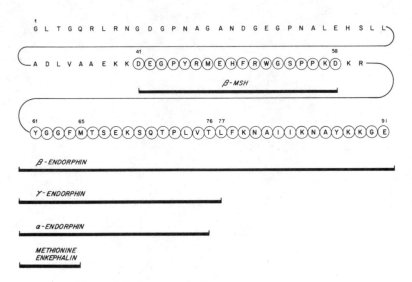

Figure 3–23. Primary structure of β-lipotropin. Residues 41–58 are melanocyte-stimulating hormone (β-MSH). Residues 61–91 contain the primary structures of the indicated endorphins.

• • •

References

Craig LC, Cowburn D, Bleich H: Methods for the study of small polypeptide hormones and antibiotics in solution. *Annu Rev Biochem* 1975;**44**:509.

Greenstein JP, Winitz M: *Chemistry of the Amino Acids.* 3 vols. Wiley, 1961.

Hash JH (editor): Antibiotics. In: *Methods in Enzymology.* Vol 43. Academic Press, 1975.

Heftman E: *Chromatography: A Laboratory Handbook of Chromatographic and Electrophoretic Methods,* 3rd ed. Van Nostrand, 1975.

Klee WA: Peptides of the central nervous system. *Adv Protein Chem* 1979;**33**:243.

Marglin A, Merrifield RB: Chemical synthesis of peptides and proteins. *Annu Rev Biochem* 1970;**39**:841.

Meister A: *Biochemistry of the Amino Acids,* 2nd ed. Academic Press, 1965.

Snyder SH, Innes RB: Peptide neurotransmitters. *Annu Rev Biochem* 1979;**48**:755.

Stewart JM, Young JD: *Solid Phase Peptide Synthesis.* Freeman, 1969.

Storm DR, Rosenthal KS, Swanson PE: Polymyxin antibiotics. *Annu Rev Biochem* 1977;**46**:723.

Touchstone JC: *Practice of Thin Layer Chromatography.* Wiley-Interscience, 1978.

Zweig G, Sherma J: *Handbook of Chromatography.* 2 Vols. CRC Press, 1972.

Proteins | 4

Victor W. Rodwell, PhD

Proteins are **high-molecular-weight polypeptides and their derivatives.** While all proteins are polypeptides, many contain additional non-amino acid substances. Proteins that consist solely of amino acids are termed **simple proteins;** those that contain additional materials, **complex proteins.** For simple proteins, the dividing line between a large polypeptide and a small protein generally is drawn at MW 8000–10,000.

CLASSIFICATION OF PROTEINS

No single system of classifying proteins is altogether satisfactory. Useful systems include those based on solubility, overall shape, function, and 3-dimensional structure.

Solubility

A classification system based on solubility that was developed in 1907–1908 is still in use today, particularly in clinical biochemistry (Table 4–1). The lines of demarcation between the classes are not rigid. For example, a clear distinction between albumins cannot be made solely on the basis of their solubility in water or salt solutions. Globulins were therefore subdivided into pseudoglobulins, which are freely water-soluble, and euglobulins, which are insoluble in salt-free water.

Overall Shape

Two broad classes of proteins may be dis-

Table 4–1. Classification of proteins based on their solubilities.

Albumins	Soluble in water and salt solutions. No distinctive amino acids.
Globulins	Sparingly soluble in water but soluble in salt solutions. No distinctive amino acids.
Prolamines	Soluble in 70–80% ethanol but insoluble in water and absolute ethanol. Arginine-rich.
Histones	Soluble in salt solutions. Lysine-rich.
Glutelins	Insoluble in all the above solvents but soluble in acid or base.
Scleroproteins	Insoluble in water or salt solutions. Rich in Gly, Ala, Pro.

tinguished on the basis of their **axial ratios** (ratios of length to breadth). **Globular proteins** have axial ratios less than 10 and generally not over 3–4 and are characterized by compactly folded and coiled polypeptide chains. Examples include insulin, plasma albumins and globulins, and many enzymes. **Fibrous proteins** have axial ratios greater than 10 and are characterized by polypeptide chains or groups of chains coiled in a spiral or helix and cross-linked by disulfide and hydrogen bonds. Examples include keratin (the major protein of hair, wool, and skin) and myosin (the major contractile protein of muscle).

Function

Proteins may be classified according to their biologic functions—for example, as structural, catalytic, or transport proteins. Catalytic proteins (enzymes), which comprise the majority of proteins, are themselves classified by the type of reaction they catalyze, which correlates well with biologic function (see Chapter 6).

For certain proteins of great medical interest, there are specialized systems of classification that distinguish between closely related proteins. This is illustrated for the plasma lipoproteins, which function in transport of dietary and endogenously formed lipids. Two systems of nomenclature are in wide use, and a third is under consideration. The 2 commonly used systems distinguish classes of lipoproteins based on their behavior in electrical or gravitational fields. Thus, we distinguish "origin," α_1-, α_2-, β-, and γ-lipoproteins, on the basis of whether they remain at the origin or migrate to the positions of the corresponding globulins on electrophoresis at pH 8.6. Alternatively, lipoproteins often are classified on the basis of their hydrated densities as chylomicrons [density = 0.94 g/mL], VLDL (very low density lipoproteins) [D = 0.94–1.006], LDL (low-density lipoproteins) [D = 1.006–1.063], HDL (high-density lipoproteins) [D = 1.063–1.21], and VHDL (very high density lipoproteins) [D = > 1.21].

Progress in determination of the primary structures of the various apoproteins of plasma lipoproteins suggests yet another way in which they might be classified, ie, on the basis of the primary structure of the apoproteins present. Six broad classes of plasma lipoproteins might therefore be differentiated, based on whether apoprotein A, B, C, D, E, or F is present in the lipoprotein molecule. Since these apoproteins are antigenic, they may be differentiated by immunologic criteria.

Recent evidence suggests that the amount of cholesterol in HDL as compared to that within other density classes of lipoproteins may be a highly significant finding that is related to the incidence of coronary artery disease. For this reason, the classification, structure, and metabolic roles of plasma lipoproteins have considerable medical interest (see Chapter 18).

Three-Dimensional Structure

One may distinguish 2 broad classes of proteins on the basis of whether or not they possess quaternary structure (see below). In addition, similarities in fine structure, revealed primarily by x-ray crystallography, provide a potentially valuable basis for protein classification. For instance, all proteins that bind nucleotides share a common "nucleotide-binding domain" of tertiary structure, and there is evidence that all of these proteins may be evolutionarily related. As more information becomes available, classification of proteins based on fine structural similarities may gradually supplant other systems, because this should correlate well with biologic function and be of high predictive value.

BONDS RESPONSIBLE FOR PROTEIN STRUCTURE

Protein structures are stabilized by 2 classes of strong bonds (peptide and disulfide) and 3 classes of weak bonds (hydrogen, hydrophobic, and electrostatic or salt).

Peptide Bonds

The primary structure of proteins derives from linkage of L-α-amino acids by α-peptide bonds. The principal evidence is summarized below.

(1) Proteins have few titratable carboxyl or amino groups.

(2) Proteins and synthetic polypeptides react with **biuret reagent** (an alkaline $CuSO_4$ solution), giving a purple color, a reaction specific for 2 or more peptide bonds.

(3) The infrared spectra of proteins suggest many peptide bonds.

(4) Proteases hydrolyze both known polypeptides and proteins.

(5) The peptide bond has been conclusively identified in proteins by x-ray diffraction at the 0.2-nm level.

(6) Insulin and ribonuclease have been synthesized solely by linking amino acids by peptide bonds.

The term **conformation** refers to the relative positions in space of each of the constituent atoms of a molecule. For a simple molecule like ethane (C_2H_6), 2 conformations are possible—"staggered" and "eclipsed" (Fig 4–1). Since the carbon atoms can

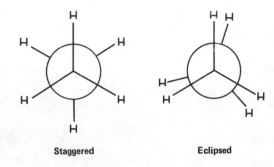

Staggered   **Eclipsed**

Figure 4–1. Staggered and eclipsed forms of ethane.

rotate freely about the single bond connecting them, the conformational forms of ethane are interconvertible. The staggered form is, however, favored thermodynamically over the sterically hindered eclipsed form. Free rotation about the bond connecting the carbon atoms would not be possible if it were a double bond.

The peptide bond itself is planar and has some double bond character; thus, free rotation about this bond does not occur. This semirigidity (Fig 4–2) has important consequences for orders of protein structure above the primary level.

Disulfide Bonds

The disulfide bond interconnects 2 portions of

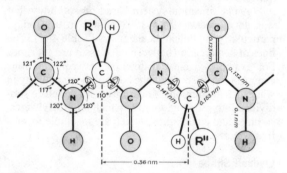

Figure 4–2. Dimensions of a fully extended polypeptide chain. The groups of 4 shaded atoms are **coplanar**, ie, they lie in the same plane. These same 4 atoms comprise the polypeptide bond. The unshaded atoms are the α-carbon atom, the α-hydrogen atom, and the α-R group of the particular amino acid. Free rotation can occur about the bonds connecting the α-carbon with the α-nitrogen and α-carbonyl functions (white arrows). The extended polypeptide chain is thus a semirigid structure with two-thirds of the atoms of the backbone held in a fixed planar relationship one to another. The distance between adjacent α-carbon atoms is 0.36 nm. The interatomic distances and bond angles, which are not equivalent, are also shown. (Redrawn and reproduced, with permission, from Corey LP, Branson HR: *Proc Natl Acad Sci USA* 1951;**37**:205.)

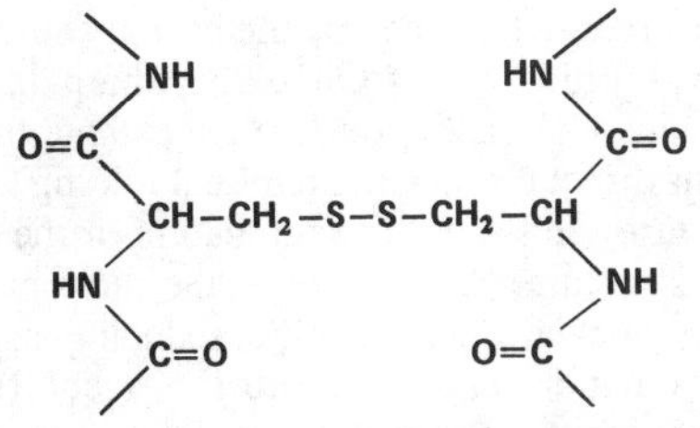

$$O=C \quad CH-CH_2-S-S-CH_2-CH \quad C=O$$

Figure 4–3. Peptide chains united by a disulfide bond.

polypeptide chains through cysteine residues (Fig 4–3). This relatively stable cystine bond is resistant to usual conditions for protein denaturation. Performic acid, which oxidizes S–S bonds, or β-mercaptoethanol, which reduces the S–S bonds regenerating 2 cysteine residues, can be used to separate polypeptide chains without affecting primary structure.

Hydrogen Bonds (See Chapter 1.)

Hydrogen bonds result from sharing of hydrogen atoms between the nitrogen and the carbonyl oxygen of different peptide bonds in the same or different polypeptide chains (Fig 4–4). Each hydrogen bond is by itself quite weak. Their importance in protein structure arises from their extremely large number.

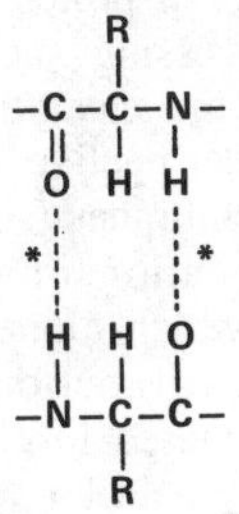

$$-C-C-N-$$
$$O \quad H \quad H$$
$$* \quad \vdots \quad *$$
$$H \quad H \quad O$$
$$-N-C-C-$$
$$R$$

Figure 4–4. *Hydrogen bonds.

Hydrophobic Bonds

The nonpolar side chains of neutral amino acids tend to associate in proteins. The relationship is nonstoichiometric; hence no true bond may be said to exist. Nonetheless, these interactions play a significant role in maintaining protein structure.

Electrostatic Bonds

These are salt bonds formed between oppositely charged groups in the side chains of amino acids. The epsilon-amino group of lysine bears a net charge of +1 at physiologic pH and the non-α-carboxyl of aspartate and glutamate a net charge of −1. These may therefore interact electrostatically.

Bond Stabilities

During denaturation of proteins, hydrogen, hydrophobic, and electrostatic bonds—but not peptide or disulfide bonds—are broken.

ORDERS OF PROTEIN STRUCTURE

Primary

Protein structure must be considered at several levels of organization. Primary structure, familiar from the study of peptide sequences (see Chapter 3), refers to the **order of the individual amino acids** in the polypeptide chain or chains of the protein (Fig 4–5).

–Ala–Gly–Gly–His–Leu–
–Ala–Gly–His–Gly–Leu–

Figure 4–5. Portions of polypeptide chains that contain the same amino acids. Since their order (sequence) differs, they have different primary structures.

Secondary

The folding of the polypeptide chains into coiled or pleated structures held together by hydrogen bonds—or folding stabilized by disulfide bonds—is referred to as the secondary structure of the protein.

Figure 4–6. Representation of secondary and tertiary structure of a protein (whale muscle myoglobin, drawn from x-ray analysis data of Kendrew). The large dots represent α-carbon atoms of amino acids. The sequence of dots therefore denotes the primary structure of the molecule. This consists of a single polypeptide chain with a COOH end at the upper left and an α-amino end at the lower left. The spiral portions drawn in perspective represent regions where the polypeptide chain is coiled in an α-helix. The entire polypeptide chain is wound about itself, conferring tertiary structure. Since the myoglobin molecule contains but a single subunit, no quaternary structure is possible. Note also (in the upper right corner) the heme group attached by 2 histidine molecules to 2 different regions of the polypeptide chain. (Courtesy of RE Dickerson.)

Tertiary

The overall arrangement and interrelationship of the various regions and individual amino acid residues of a single polypeptide chain is called the tertiary structure of the protein. Tertiary structure is maintained by weak interatomic forces such as hydrogen bonds or Van der Waals forces. For example, the protein of tobacco mosaic virus has a tertiary structure resembling a kernel of corn. These "kernels" line up along the "cob" of nucleic acid to produce the elongated nucleoprotein rods visible under the electron microscope. Figure 4–6 illustrates the secondary and tertiary structure of the hemoprotein myoglobin.

Quaternary

Proteins are said to possess quaternary structure if they consist of 2 or more polypeptide chains **united by forces other than covalent bonds** (ie, not peptide or disulfide bonds). The forces that stabilize these aggregates are hydrogen bonds and electrostatic or salt bonds formed between residues on the surfaces of the polypeptide chains. Such proteins are termed **oligomers,** and the individual polypeptide chains of which they are composed are variously termed **protomers, monomers,** or **subunits.**

The most commonly encountered oligomeric proteins contain 2 or 4 protomers and are termed dimers or tetramers, respectively. Oligomers containing more than 4 protomers are also common, however, particularly among regulated enzymes (eg, aspartate transcarbamoylase). Ferritin (Fig 4–7) is example of an oligomeric protein with many protomers. Oligomeric proteins play special roles in intracellular regulation because the protomers can assume different spatial orientations relative to each other with resulting changes in the properties of the oligomer. The best-studied example is hemoglobin (see Chapter 5), in which a variety of conformations exist depending on the degree of oxygenation.

Protein Folding

The secondary and tertiary structures of a protein are themselves determined by the primary structure of the polypeptide chain. Once the chain has been formed, the chemical groups that extend from the α-carbons direct the specific regional folding (secondary structure) and specific aggregation of the regions (tertiary structure). Treatment of the monomeric enzyme ribonuclease with a mild reducing agent (β-mercaptoethanol) and a denaturing agent (urea or guanidine) inactivates it as it assumes a random coil "conformation" (shape). Slow removal of the denaturing agent and gentle reoxidation to reform the S–S bonds leads to almost complete reactivation of the enzyme. Thus, the primary structure specifies the secondary, tertiary, and (when present) quaternary structure (ie, conformation) of a protein. This native conformation of a protein such as ribonuclease appears to be that which is thermodynamically most stable for a given environment, eg, a hydrophilic versus hydrophobic one. Assuming low energy conformations to be biologically active forms, computer programs predict low-energy structures from the primary sequence and a limited amount of other data. These structures may then be projected on an oscilloscope screen and viewed from any angle. The aim is to predict correct, enzymically active conformations from primary structure data alone. At present, it is not necessary to postulate independent genetic control of orders of protein structure above the primary level.

The structure of a protein may change during posttranslational processing, such as the conversion of a preproenzyme to the catalytically active form or removal of the "leader peptide" that directs exported proteins through membranes (see Chapter 31).

Finally, aggregation of different functional proteins—each of which alone has all 4 orders of structure—into multifunctional macromolecular complexes is encountered in electron transport (see Chapter 12), in fatty acid biosynthesis (see Chapter 17), and in pyruvate metabolism (see Chapter 15).

DENATURATION OF PROTEINS

The comparatively weak forces responsible for maintaining secondary, tertiary, and quaternary structure of proteins are readily disrupted by a variety of manipulations with a resulting loss of biologic activity. This disruption of native structure is termed **denaturation.** Physically, denaturation may be viewed as randomizing the conformation of a polypeptide chain without affecting its primary structure. For a protomer, the process may be represented as shown in Fig 4–8.

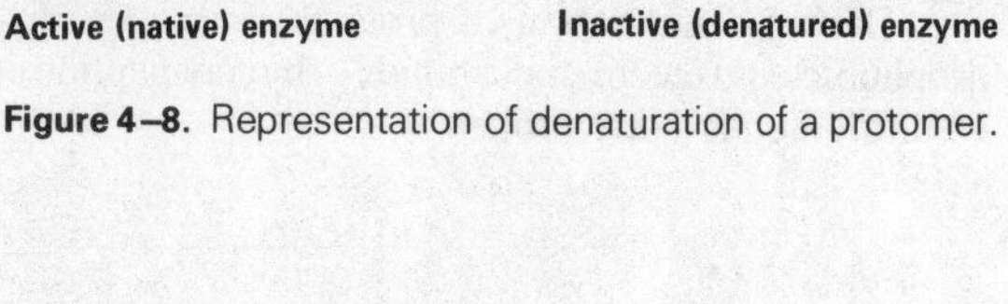

Figure 4–7. Representation of quaternary structure of a protein. "Ping-pong ball" model of the apoferritin molecule. This consists of 20 subunits, each with a molecular weight of about 20,000. The subunits are arranged to form a hollow sphere which may become packed with iron salts forming the iron storage protein ferritin. (Courtesy of RA Fineberg.)

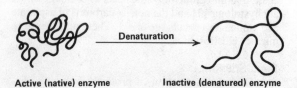

Active (native) enzyme   **Inactive (denatured) enzyme**

Figure 4–8. Representation of denaturation of a protomer.

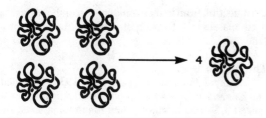

Figure 4–9. Representation of denaturation of an oligomeric protein under conditions not sufficiently severe to alter protomer conformation.

For an oligomeric protein, denaturation may involve dissociation of the protomers with or without accompanying changes in protomer conformation (Fig 4–9).

The biologic activity of most proteins is destroyed by exposure to strong mineral acids or bases, heat, ionic detergents (amphipaths), chaotropic agents (urea, guanidine), heavy metals (Ag, Pb, Hg), or organic solvents at or above room temperature. Denatured proteins generally are less soluble in water, and they often precipitate from aqueous solution. This property is used to advantage in the clinical laboratory. Blood or serum samples to be analyzed for small molecules (eg, glucose, uric acid, drugs) generally are first treated with acids such as trichloroacetic, phosphotungstic, or phosphomolybdic acid to precipitate most of the protein present. This is removed by centrifugation, and the protein-free supernatant liquid is then analyzed.

The heat, acid, and protease lability of most enzymes provides a simple test to decide whether a reaction is enzyme-catalyzed. If a cell extract having catalytic activity loses this activity when boiled, acidified and reneutralized, or treated with a protease, the catalyst probably was an enzyme.

Frequently, enzymes are either more or less readily denatured if their substrate is present. Either effect is attributed to a conformational change in the enzyme structure occurring when substrate is bound. The new conformation may be either more or less stable than before.

DETERMINATION OF PRIMARY STRUCTURE

Methods

Complex proteins are first treated to remove prosthetic groups (eg, heme). Disulfide bonds are oxidized to yield linear polypeptides. The methods used to sequence these polypeptides are discussed in Chapter 3. While most proteins contain only the amino acids listed in Table 3–3, derivatives of these amino acids also occur in certain proteins (Tables 4–2 and 4–3).

Primary Structures of Specific Proteins

A. Insulin: This protein (or large polypeptide) consists of 2 polypeptide chains linked covalently by

Table 4–2. Representative modifications of α-COOH and α-NH₂ groups in proteins.*

Group modified			
α-COOH	α-NH₂		
Type of modification			
Amide	N-Formyl	N-Acetyl	N-Methyl
Amino acid residues subject to modification			
		Ala	Ala
Asp		Asp	Asp
Glu			
Gly	Gly	Gly	Gly
His			
Met	Met	Met	Met
Phe			
Pro			
		Ser	Ser
		Thr	Thr
Tyr			
Val		Val	

*Modified and reproduced, with permission, from Vy R, Wold F: *Science* 1977;**198**:890. Copyright 1977 by the American Association for the Advancement of Science.

Table 4–3. Representative modifications of non-α-functional groups in proteins.*

Group modified			
—OH	Non-α-N		
Type of modification			
PO₃H₂	N-Methyl	N-Dimethyl	N-Trimethyl
Amino acid residues subject to modification			
	Arg	Arg	
	His		
	Lys	Lys	Lys
Ser			
Thr			
Tyr			

*Modified and reproduced, with permission, from Vy R, Wold F: *Science* 1977;**198**:890. Copyright 1977 by the American Association for the Advancement of Science.

disulfide bonds (Fig 4–10). The A chain has an N-terminal Gly and a C-terminal Asn; the B chain has Phe and Ala as the N- and C-terminal residues, respectively. When insulin is oxidized with performic acid, the disulfide bonds linking the A and B chains are ruptured.

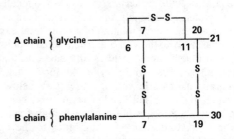

Figure 4–10. Relationship of the A and B chains of insulin.

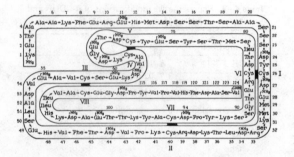

Figure 4–11. Structure of bovine ribonuclease. Two-dimensional schematic diagram showing the arrangement of the disulfide bonds and the sequence of the amino acid residues. Arrows indicate the direction of the peptide chain starting from the amino end. (Reproduced, with permission, from Smyth, Stein, & Moore: The sequence of amino acid residues in bovine pancreatic ribonuclease: Revisions and confirmations. *J Biol Chem* 1963;**238**:227.)

Both chains are biosynthesized as a single polypeptide chain, **proinsulin,** which undergoes proteolytic posttranslation processing, forming insulin (see Chapter 35).

B. Ribonuclease: The primary structure of performic acid–oxidized ribonuclease, established in 1960 by Hirs, Moore, and Stein, consists of a single chain of 124 residues with Lys N-terminal and Val C-terminal. Eight cysteine residues are joined by disulfide bonds, forming 4 cross-linkages in the protein (Fig 4–11).

DETERMINATION OF SECONDARY & TERTIARY STRUCTURE

X-Ray Diffraction

Single crystals of a protein or protein fibers deflect x-rays. The resultant image on a photographic plate yields information on the crystal or the fiber structure. X-ray crystallographic analysis has provided detailed 3-dimensional structures of many proteins.

Optical Rotatory Dispersion

The ability of solutions of proteins to rotate the plane of circulatory polarized light is examined at various wavelengths. Since proteins are composed of L-α-amino acids which are themselves optically active, proteins are highly optically active. In certain instances, the optical rotation of a protein far exceeds that due solely to the sum of the individual rotations of its constituent amino acids. This suggests that the protein possesses asymmetry in addition to that of the α-carbon atoms. Helical structures (see below) can exist in right- or left-handed forms and hence are optically active. The presence of a high fraction of helical structure therefore contributes to the optical rotation. Other asymmetric structures can also contribute. The change in optical rotation accompanying

the transition from helix to random coil or the reverse is used to assess the fraction of α-helix structure in proteins.

The α-Helix

X-ray data obtained in the early 1930s indicated that hair and wool α-keratins possessed repeating units spaced 0.5–0.55 nm along their longitudinal axis. As shown in Fig 4–2, no dimension of the extended polypeptide chain appears to measure 0.5–0.55 nm. This apparent anomaly was resolved by Pauling and Corey, who proposed that the polypeptide chain of α-keratin is arranged as an α-helix (Fig 4–12). In this structure, The R-groups on the α-carbon atoms protrude outward from the center of the helix. There are 3.6 amino acid residues per turn of the helix, and the distance traveled per turn is 0.54 nm—a reasonable approximation of the 0.5–0.55 nm spacing observed by x-ray diffraction. The spacing per amino acid residue is 0.15 nm, which also corresponds with x-ray data. The main features of the α-helix are as follows:

(1) The α-helix is stabilized by inter-residue hydrogen bonds formed between the H atom attached to a peptide N and the carbonyl O of the residue fourth in line behind in the primary structure.

(2) Each peptide bond participates in the H-bonding. This confers maximum stability.

(3) All of the main chain peptide N and carbonyl O residues are hydrogen bonded, thus greatly reducing the hydrophilic (increasing the hydrophobic) nature of the α-helical region.

(4) An α-helix forms spontaneously as it is the lowest energy, most stable conformation for a polypeptide chain.

(5) When the residues are L-amino acids, the right-handed helix that occurs in proteins is significantly more stable than the left-handed helix.

Certain amino acids tend to disrupt the α-helix. Among these are proline (the N-atom is part of a rigid ring and no rotation of the N–C bond can occur) and amino acids with charged or bulky R-groups which either electrostatically or physically interfere with helix formation (Table 4–4).

Table 4–4. Effect of various amino acid residues on helix formation.

Promote α-Helix	Destabilize α-Helix	Terminate α-Helix
Ala	Arg	Pro
Asn	Asp	Hyp
Cys	Glu	
Gln	Gly	
His	Lys	
Leu	Ile	
Met	Ser	
Phe	Thr	
Trp		
Tyr		
Val		

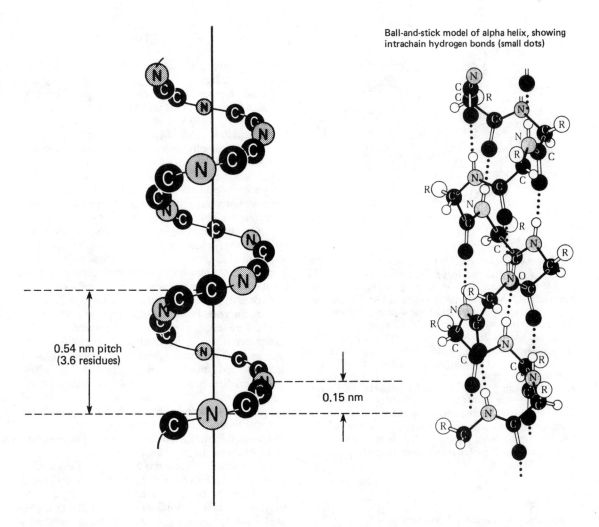

Ball-and-stick model of alpha helix, showing intrachain hydrogen bonds (small dots)

0.54 nm pitch
(3.6 residues)

0.15 nm

Figure 4–12. Alpha helix structure of a protein. The figure on the left shows the α-carbons, α-nitrogens, and carboxyl carbons that form the right-handed helical backbone. The structure on the right shows, in addition, the R substituents on the α-carbons and the H and O atoms involved in the hydrogen bonds (dots) that hold the protein in the α-helical conformation. (Reprinted [right], with permission, from Haggis GH & others: *Introduction to Molecular Biology.* Wiley, 1964.)

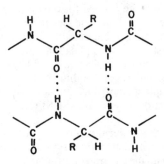

Figure 4–13. Diagrammatic representation of formation of a region of antiparallel pleated sheet structure by formation of hydrogen bonds (. . .) between 2 regions of polypeptide chain. The bond angles are such that, when viewed on end, the polypeptide chains assume a conformation resembling a pleated sheet of paper.

Pleated Sheet

When extended sections of different peptide chains are parallel to one another and close enough so that hydrogen bonds are formed between them, the protein is said to possess regions of pleated sheet structure (Fig 4–13).

If the 2 regions of polypeptide chain run in the same direction (ie, N-terminal to C-terminal), the sheet is said to be parallel. This form tends to be more common than the alternate antiparallel sheet arrangement. Regions of pleated sheet structure in a specific protein are shown shaded in Fig 4–14. Extensive pleated sheets exist in silk fibroin and in the proteins deposited as amyloid in human diseases.

Random Coil

Regions of proteins that are not organized as α-helix or as pleated sheets are termed random coil.

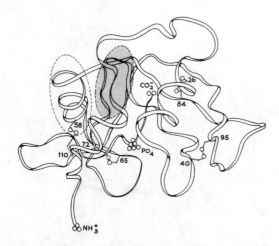

Figure 4–14. Schematic diagram of the main chain folding of bovine pancreatic ribonuclease. This protein is a single chain of 124 amino acid residues starting at the amino end (marked NH_3^+) and ending at the carboxy terminal (marked CO_2^-). The chain is cross-linked at 4 places by disulfide bridges from half cystine residues. The disulfide pairings for these bridges are 26–84, 40–95, 58–110, and 65–72 in the sequence. A region of α-helix is indicated by the dotted oval, and a region of pleated sheet is shaded. Other portions of the molecule are predominantly random coil. The region of the active site (see Chapter 8) is indicated by the binding of the phosphate ion (PO_4^{3-}) in the cleft of the molecule. This model was obtained by x-ray diffraction studies of crystalline bovine pancreatic ribonuclease at 0.2 nm resolution. (Adapted from Kartha, Bello, & Harker: *Nature* 1967;**213**:862.) The protein has been chemically synthesized in its entirety.

Secondary & Tertiary Structures
of Specific Proteins

A. Ribonuclease: X-ray diffraction studies of bovine ribonuclease indicate molecular dimensions of about $3.2 \times 2.8 \times 2.2$ nm. The limited α-helix content is restricted to 2 turns at residues 5–12 and 2 turns near residues 28–35 (Fig 4–14). In contrast to myoglobin (Fig 4–6), ribonuclease has much more of its structure exposed. No portion is shielded by more than one layer of the main chain. A phosphate ion is present at the catalytic site near His residues 119 and 112. Lys 7 and 41 and His 48 also are implicated as being at the catalytic site. The enzyme subtilisin splits ribonuclease into a short S-peptide and a longer S-protein, with loss of enzymic activity. These may be noncovalently reassociated, with restoration of catalytic activity.

B. Lactate Dehydrogenase: This was the first oligomeric protein to have its secondary-tertiary structure determined by x-ray crystallography. The protomer contains regions of α-helix and pleated sheet and is relatively compact except for the N-terminal portion of the polypeptide, which projects out and is thought to interact with other protomers. The protomer contains a deep nucleotide binding cleft that binds the coenzyme NAD^+ close to the essential thiol at the catalytic site.

DETERMINATION OF QUATERNARY
STRUCTURE

Determining the quaternary structure of oligomeric proteins encompasses determining the number and kind of protomers present, their mutual orientation, and the nature of the interactions that unite them.

Determination of the Molecular Weight

As long as oligomers are not first denatured and do not undergo denaturation during the procedure used to determine their molecular weight, many methods can yield molecular weight data for oligomers. These same technics may be used to determine protomer molecular weight if the oligomer is first denatured.

A. Ultracentrifugation: The method developed by Svedberg, which depends upon measurement of sedimentation rate in an ultracentrifugal field of around $10^5 \times g$ remains the primary reference method, but it has tended in recent years to be replaced by the less complex technics described below.

B. Sucrose Density Gradient Centrifugation: Unlike the Svedberg technic, which requires an analytic ultracentrifuge, a preparative ultracentrifuge available in most research laboratories is used. Protein standards and unknowns are layered over a 5–20% sucrose gradient in a plastic tube and centrifuged overnight at around $10^5 \times g$. A small hole is then punched in the bottom of the tube, the contents collected in a set of small tubes, the tube location (and thus relative position in the gradient) of the protein determined, and the mobility of the proteins computed.

C. Filtration Through Molecular Sieves: Columns of Sephadex or similar materials are calibrated using proteins of known molecular weight. The molecular weight of an unknown protein is then calculated from its mobility relative to these standards. Large errors may result if the protein is highly asymmetric or interacts strongly with the materials from which the molecular sieve was manufactured.

D. Polyacrylamide Gel Electrophoresis (PAGE): Protein standards are separated by electrophoresis in 2–8% cross-linked gels of varying porosity. Gels are stained for protein, generally with Coomassie blue stain, and the molecular weight is estimated relative to the mobility of the standards. By far the most common application of this technic is to determine protomer molecular weight by first denaturing the oligomer (eg, by boiling in urea in the presence of β-mercaptoethanol) and separating on gels that contain sodium dodecylsulfate (SDS) (SDS-PAGE).

Electron Photomicrography

An actual picture of very small objects can be obtained with the electron microscope. Magnifications as high as 100,000 diameters can be obtained with this instrument. This permits the visualization of proteins of high molecular weight, such as virus particles.

Table 4–5 lists examples of the numbers and molecular weights of protomers contributing to the quaternary structures of selected enzymes.

Table 4–5. Quaternary structures of selected enzymes.*

Enzyme (Oligomer)	Number of Protomers	Molecular Weight of Protomer
Chicken or rabbit muscle creatine kinase (ATP:creatine phosphotransferase, E.C. 2.7.3.2)	2	40,000
Chicken heart aspartate transaminase (L-aspartate:2-oxoglutarate aminotransferase, E.C. 2.6.1.1)	2	50,000
Rabbit liver fructose diphosphatase (D-fructose-1,6-diphosphate 1-phosphohydrolase,	2†	29,000
E.C. 3.1.3.11)	2†	37,000
Rat liver ornithine transaminase (L-ornithine:2-oxoacid aminotransferase, E.C. 2.6.1.13)	4	33,000
Beef heart, liver, or muscle LDH (L-lactate:NAD oxidoreductase, E.C. 1.1.1.27)	4†	35,000
Rabbit muscle glyceraldehyde-3-phosphate dehydrogenase (D-glyceraldehyde-3-phosphate:NAD oxidoreductase [phosphorylating], E.C. 1.2.1.12)	4†	37,000
Rabbit muscle aldolase (ketose-1-phosphate aldehyde-lyase, E.C. 4.1.2.7)	4	40,000
Beef liver catalase (H_2O_2:H_2O_2 oxidoreductase, E.C. 1.11.1.6)	4	57,500
Beef heart mitochondrial ATPase (ATP phosphohydrolase, E.C. 3.6.1.3)	10	26,000
Pigeon liver fatty acid synthetase	2	230,000
E coli glutamine synthetase (L-glutamate:NH_3 ligase [ADP], E.C. 6.3.1.2)	12	48,500
Pig heart propionyl-CoA carboxylase (propionyl-CoA:CO_2 ligase [ADP], E.C. 6.4.1.2)	4	175,000
Chicken liver acetyl-CoA carboxylase (acetyl-CoA:CO_2 ligase [ADP], E.C. 6.4.1.2)	2†	4,100,000
	10†	409,000

*Adapted from Klotz IM, Langerman NR, Darnall DW: Quaternary structure of enzymes. *Annu Rev Biochem* 1970;**39**:25.
†Nonidentical subunits.

•   •   •

References

Advances in Protein Chemistry. Academic Press, 1944–1980. [Annual publication.].

Aisen P, Listowsky I: Iron transport and storage proteins. *Annu Rev Biochem* 1980;**49**:357.

Amsel M, Poljak RJ: Three-dimensional structure of immunoglobulins. *Annu Rev Biochem* 1979;**48**:961.

Baldwin RL: Intermediates in protein folding. *Annu Rev Biochem* 1975;**44**:453.

Bradbury JH: The structure and chemistry of keratin fibers. *Adv Protein Chem* 1973;**27**:111.

Chou PY, Fassman GD: Empirical predictions of protein structure. *Annu Rev Biochem* 1978;**47**:251.

Croft LR: *Handbook of Amino Acid Sequences of Proteins.* Joynson-Bruvvers Ltd (Oxford, England), 1973.

Dayhoff MO (editor): *Atlas of Protein Structure.* Vol 5. National Biomedical Research Foundation, 1972.

Gurd FN, Rothgeb TM: Motions in proteins. *Adv Protein Chem* 1979;**33**:74.

Haschemeyer RH, deHarven E: Electron microscopy of enzymes. *Annu Rev Biochem* 1974;**43**:279.

Isenberg I: Histones. *Annu Rev Biochem* 1979;**48**:159.

Klotz IM, Langerman NR, Darnall DW: Quaternary structure of enzymes. *Annu Rev Biochem* 1970;**39**:25.

Kuntz ID Jr, Kauzmann W: Hydration of proteins and polypeptides. *Adv Protein Chem* 1974;**28**:239.

Lennarz WJ (editor): *The Biochemistry of Glycoproteins and Proteoglycans.* Plenum Press, 1980.

Lijas A, Rossmann MG: X-ray studies of protein interactions. *Annu Rev Biochem* 1974;**43**:475.

Neurath H, Hill RL (editors): *The Proteins,* 3rd ed. Academic Press, 1975.

Niederwieser A, Pataki G (editors): *New Techniques in Amino Acid, Peptide and Protein Analysis.* Ann Arbor, 1971.

Osborne JC Jr, Brewer HB Jr: The plasma lipoproteins. *Adv Protein Chem* 1977;**31**:253.

Privalov PL: Stability of proteins. *Adv Protein Chem* 1979;**33**:167.

Smith LC, Pownall HJ, Gotto AM Jr: The plasma lipoproteins: Structure and metabolism. *Annu Rev Biochem* 1978;**47**:751.

Wu TT, Fitch WM, Margdiash E: The information content of protein amino acid sequences. *Annu Rev Biochem* 1974;**43**:539.

5 | Structure & Function of a Protein—Hemoglobin

David W. Martin, Jr., MD

Hemoglobin is a readily available major protein in the human body and carries out a well-known function, the **transport of oxygen** from the lungs to the peripheral tissues and CO_2 from the peripheral tissues back to the lungs. Thus, hemoglobin has been an attractive model protein for the study of the structure/function relationships of a macromolecule. However, equally interesting is the observation that when a hemoglobin molecule malfunctions in a human as a result of an inherited defect, it usually induces an illness that may then come to the attention of an astute and inquisitive physician. Subsequently, careful molecular analysis of the abnormal hemoglobin may lead to important deductions concerning the structure/function relationship of both the abnormal and the normal hemoglobin molecule. At present, the structure/function relationship of the hemoglobin molecule is probably better understood than that of any other protein. Accordingly, in this chapter the structure/function relationship of the normal and, when indicated, abnormal molecules will be reviewed as a general model of how protein molecules carry out their important biologic functions.

HEME-OXYGEN INTERACTION

The transport of oxygen is based on a chemical interaction between molecular O_2 and **heme,** a tetrapyrrole porphyrin ring containing ferrous (Fe^{2+}) iron. The porphyrin ring is synthesized in most cells, including plant cells, where it exists as chlorophyll. (Chlorophyll contains magnesium rather than iron.) The four N atoms oriented toward the center of the prophyrin ring help to neutralize the charges on their ferrous ion and thereby hold it in place (Fig 5–1). In solution, heme will bind to oxygen very tightly; in fact, the binding is so tight that it is essentially irreversible. This tight binding is due to the fact that molecular oxygen oxidizes Fe^{2+} to Fe^{3+}, generating superoxide ion.

The **oxidation** of Fe^{2+} to Fe^{3+} in heme involves an intermediate of **one oxygen molecule with 2 heme molecules.** Thus, if heme is to function effectively as a carrier of oxygen molecules, the **hemes must be separated** from one another so as to avoid the oxidation of Fe^{2+} to Fe^{3+}. Furthermore, the ferrous-oxygen bond

must be weakened so as to provide **reversible association** of oxygen with the heme moiety.

There are 2 major heme-containing proteins, **myoglobin** and **hemoglobin,** concerned with the transport of oxygen. Both are **red** proteins because of their heme content. Myoglobin and hemoglobin both hold their heme moieties in separated **pockets** and thus avoid the above-described oxidation. In both myoglobin and hemoglobin, the ferrous ion of heme is also attached to the nitrogen atom of a particular **proximal histidine residue,** which by donating electrons **weakens the ferrous-oxygen bond and thereby confers reversibility.** When oxygen is present in the myoglobin and hemoglobin molecules, the O_2 is bound reversibly and noncovalently to the Fe^{2+} of heme and to a **distal histidine residue** on the side of the molecule opposite the histidine residue to which the Fe^{2+} itself is attached (Fig 5–2). Thus, by attaching the heme moiety to a specific protein molecule and by **separating each of the hemes in different pockets, nature has made the heme-oxygen interaction weaker and reversible.**

MYOGLOBIN

The secondary and tertiary structure of myoglobin was solved by Kendrew using x-ray crystallog-

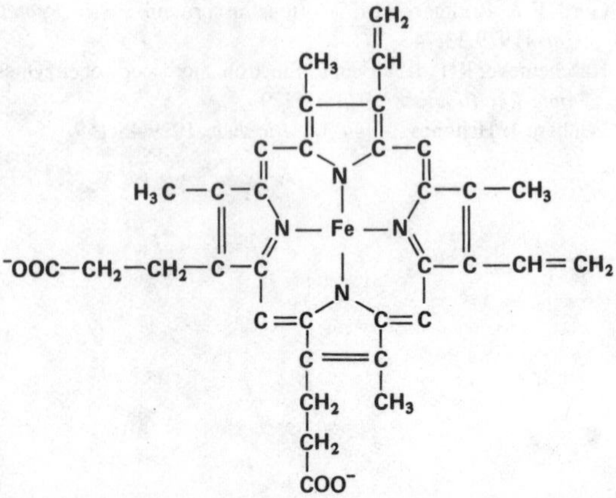

Figure 5–1. The structure of heme.

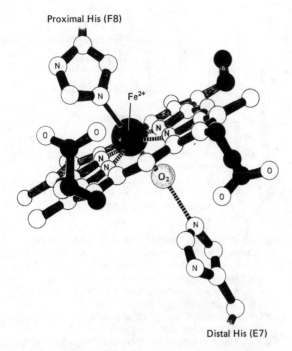

Proximal His (F8)

Fe^{2+}

O_2

Distal His (E7)

Figure 5–2. Addition of oxygen to heme iron in oxygenation. Shown also are the imidazole side chains of the 2 important histidine residues of globin that attach to the heme iron. (Reproduced, with permission, from Harper HA & others: *Physiologische Chemie.* Springer-Verlag, 1975.)

raphy. This 17,000-MW protein contains **8 α-helical regions** varying from 7 to 20 amino acid residues in length, each separated by interhelical regions (Fig 5–3). Each helical region is given a letter designation A through H, starting with the amino-terminal end of the molecule. The interhelical junctional regions are given the 2 letters denoting the helices between which they reside in the primary structure. The amino-terminal region is referred to as NA and the carboxy-terminal region as HC, since they separate the N terminal from the A helix and the H helix from the carboxy terminal, respectively. The amino acid residues are given designations according to their position within or between helical regions (Fig 5–4). The tenth amino acid of myoglobin, valine, is the eighth residue in the A helix and is designated Val A8 (10). The residue at position 120, proline, is designated Pro GH2 (120).

The heme in myoglobin resides in the pocket **between helix E and helix F** and is attached to the nitrogen atom of **His F8** (the proximal His). The heme moiety is also in contact with the side chains of 15 other amino acid residues from 7 helices.

| H_2 - | Val - | Leu - | Ser - | Glu - | Gly - | Glu - | Trp - | Gln - | Leu - | Val - | Leu - |
| NA1 | NA2 | A1 | A2 | A3 | A4 | A5 | A6 | A7 | A8 | A9 | |

| His - | Val - | Trp - | Ala - | Lys - | Val - | Glu - | Ala - | Asp - | Val - | Ala - |
| A10 | A11 | A12 | A13 | A14 | A15 | A16 | AB1 | B1 | B2 | B3 |

| Gly - | His - | Gly - | Gln - | Asp - | Ile - | Leu - | Ile - | Arg - | Leu - | Phe - |
| B4 | B5 | B6 | B7 | B8 | B9 | B10 | B11 | B12 | B13 | B14 |

| Lys - | Ser - | His - | Pro - | Glu - | Thr - | Leu - | Glu - | Lys - | Phe - | Asp - |
| B15 | B16 | C1 | C2 | C3 | C4 | C5 | C6 | C7 | CD1 | CD2 |

| Arg - | Phe - | Lys - | His - | Leu - | Lys - | Thr - | Glu - | Ala - | Glu - | Met - |
| CD3 | CD4 | CD5 | CD6 | CD7 | CD8 | D1 | D2 | D3 | D4 | D5 |

| Lys - | Ala - | Ser - | Glu - | Asp - | Leu - | Lys - | Lys - | His - | Gly - | Val - |
| D6 | D7 | E1 | E2 | E3 | E4 | E5 | E6 | E7 | E8 | E9 |

| Thr - | Val - | Leu - | Thr - | Ala - | Leu - | Gly - | Ala - | Ile - | Leu - | Lys - |
| E10 | E11 | E12 | E13 | E14 | E15 | E16 | E17 | E18 | E19 | E20 |

| Lys - | Lys - | Gly - | His - | His - | Glu - | Ala - | Glu - | Leu - | Lys - | Pro - |
| EF1 | EF2 | EF3 | EF4 | EF5 | EF6 | EF7 | EF8 | F1 | F2 | F3 |

| Leu - | Ala - | Gln - | Ser - | His - | Ala - | Thr - | Lys - | His - | Lys - | Ile - |
| F4 | F5 | F6 | F7 | F8 | F9 | FG1 | FG2 | FG3 | FG4 | FG5 |

| Pro - | Ile - | Lys - | Tyr - | Leu - | Glu - | Phe - | Ile - | Ser - | Glu - | Ala - |
| G1 | G2 | G3 | G4 | G5 | G6 | G7 | G8 | G9 | G10 | G11 |

| Ile - | Ile - | His - | Val - | Leu - | His - | Ser - | Arg - | His - | Pro - | Gly - |
| G12 | G13 | G14 | G15 | G16 | G17 | G18 | G19 | GH1 | GH2 | GH3 |

| Asn - | Phe - | Gly - | Ala - | Asp - | Ala - | Gln - | Gly - | Ala - | Met - | Asn - |
| GH4 | GH5 | GH6 | H1 | H2 | H3 | H4 | H5 | H6 | H7 | H8 |

| Lys - | Ala - | Leu - | Glu - | Leu - | Phe - | Arg - | Lys - | Asp - | Ile - | Ala - |
| H9 | H10 | H11 | H12 | H13 | H14 | H15 | H16 | H17 | H18 | H19 |

| Ala - | Lys - | Tyr - | Lys - | Glu - | Leu - | Gly - | Tyr - | Gln - | Gly - | COOH |
| H20 | H21 | H22 | H23 | H24 | HC1 | HC2 | HC3 | HC4 | HC5 | |

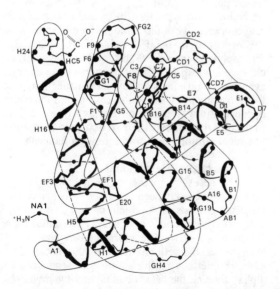

Figure 5–3. A model of myoglobin at high resolution. Only the α-carbon atoms are shown. (Based on Dickerson RE in: *The Proteins,* 2nd ed. Vol 2. Neurath H [editor]. Academic Press, 1964. Reproduced with permission.)

Figure 5–4. Amino acid sequence of sperm whale myoglobin. The labels below each residue in the sequence refer to its position in an α-helical region or a nonhelical region. (Based on Edmundson AE in: *Nature* 1965;**205**:883; and Watson HC in: *Progr Stereochem*1969;4:299.)

The binding of oxygen to the heme moiety of myoglobin increases as the concentration of oxygen in the environment of the molecule increases and decreases as the oxygen concentration decreases. This relationship can be represented graphically as an **oxygen dissociation curve,** in which the fractional O_2 saturation of the myoglobin molecule is compared with the O_2 concentration in its environment, represented by the partial pressure of oxygen (P_{O_2} in millimeters of mercury). The oxygen dissociation curve for myoglobin is hyperbolic, as shown in Fig 5–5. The P_{O_2} in the lung is 100 mm Hg; in venous blood, 40 mm Hg; and in the capillaries of active muscle, 20 mm Hg. Thus, the difference between the P_{O_2} of blood in lungs and that of blood in the capillaries of active muscle tissue would not be sufficient to release more than about 12% of the oxygen being carried by myoglobin (Fig 5–5). Because of the relatively high affinity of myoglobin for oxygen and the hyperbolic shape of the curve, the available oxygen would be released to the peripheral tissues only when the P_{O_2} there dropped below 5 mm Hg.

Myoglobin functions in red muscle to pass oxygen absorbed from the blood on to mitochondria, where the P_{O_2} is quite low. Thus, myoglobin working where the P_{O_2} is in the range of 4–5 mm Hg can effectively discharge most of its O_2 content to mitochondria.

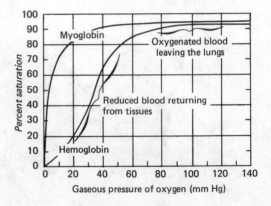

Figure 5–5. Oxygen equilibrium curves of hemoglobin and myoglobin. Arterial oxygen tension is about 100 mm Hg; mixed venous oxygen tension is about 40 mm Hg; capillary (active muscle) oxygen tension is about 20 mm Hg; and the minimum oxygen tension required for the cytochrome enzymes is about 5 mm Hg. The figure illustrates that association of chains into a tetrameric structure (hemoglobin) results in much greater oxygen delivery than would be possible with single chains. (Myoglobin and hemoglobin chains have about the same oxygen affinity.) (Modified, with permission, from Stanbury JB, Wyngaarden JB, Fredrickson DS [editors]: *The Metabolic Basis of Inherited Disease,* 4th ed. McGraw-Hill, 1978.)

THE HEMOGLOBIN MOLECULE

The oxygen carrier molecule in pulmonary venous (lung) blood must be saturated with O_2 at a P_{O_2} of 100 mm Hg but yet discharge a significant quantity, if not most, of this O_2 when it reaches the peripheral tissues, where the capillary P_{O_2} will be no lower than 20 mm Hg. Furthermore, the oxygen carrier molecule of blood must regain maximal O_2 with a limited increase in P_{O_2} (ie, to 100 mm Hg) as it returns to the lung. Such requirements clearly cannot be satisfied by a hyperbolic oxygen dissociation curve but require a **sigmoid oxygen dissociation curve** (Fig 5–5).

A sigmoid oxygen dissociation curve requires an interaction between the heme moieties of a protein. Thus, the oxygen-carrying protein molecule in blood must consist of multiple interacting subunits, each with its own heme moiety. Hemoglobin is such a molecule, containing **4 interacting subunits** that generate a **"cooperative" effect.** The cooperative effect of the tetrameric hemoglobin can be described as follows: **If a hemoglobin molecule takes up one oxygen, it tends to go on and acquire 4 oxygen molecules; and if a hemoglobin molecule saturated with oxygen loses one oxygen, 2 or 3 more oxygens are usually cast off.** Thus, over the range of P_{O_2} values between pulmonary venous blood and peripheral tissue capillary blood, the hemoglobin molecule discharges 35–45% of the oxygen it carries (Fig 5–5). It should be clear that myoglobin is incapable of generating such a cooperative effect, since there is only one heme moiety per myoglobin molecule, precluding any indirect heme-heme interaction as occurs in the tetrameric hemoglobin molecule.

The greater the sigmoid character of the oxygen dissociation curve, the greater will be the oxygen released per unit drop in P_{O_2}. This effect can be described quantitatively by Hill's number (Chapter 8). The cooperativity of the hemoglobin molecule within the erythrocyte is affected by pH, CO_2, 2,3-diphosphoglycerate (DPG, bisphosphoglycerate), and chloride ion (Fig 37–5); but of course these chemical agents have no effect on myoglobin function, since that molecule does not exhibit any subunit interaction or cooperativity. Hemoglobin is a prototype of **protein molecules that change their structure in response to chemical stimuli,** such as the oxygen molecule.

The Structure of Hemoglobin

The necessity for hemoglobin having multiple subunits has already been described. The hemoglobin molecule consists of 4 protein chains or subunits, 2 designated alpha and 2 designated beta, and is represented as $(\alpha)_2(\beta)_2$. The **alpha chains** contain 141 amino acids; the **beta chains,** 146 amino acids. Each has a distinct but similar amino acid sequence. The alpha subunits, the beta subunits, and the myoglobin molecule are remarkably similar in their tertiary structures. The myoglobin molecule and the beta subunit contain 8 alpha helices; the alpha subunit contains only 7. The hemoglobin molecule and its subunits contain mostly **hydrophobic amino acids internally** and hy-

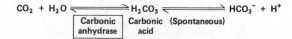

$$CO_2 + H_2O \xrightleftharpoons[\substack{\text{Carbonic} \\ \text{anhydrase}}]{} H_2CO_3 \xrightleftharpoons[\substack{\text{Carbonic} \\ \text{acid}}]{\text{(Spontaneous)}} HCO_3^- + H^+$$

Figure 5–6. The formation of carbonic acid by erythrocyte carbonic anhydrase and the dissociation of carbonic acid to bicarbonate ion and proton.

drophilic amino acids on their surfaces. Thus, the hemoglobin molecule is waxy inside and soapy outside, making it **soluble in water but impermeable to water.** Each subunit contains one **heme moiety hidden within a waxy pocket.**

In addition to transporting oxygen from the lungs to peripheral tissues, hemoglobin facilitates the **transport of CO_2** from tissues to the lungs for exhalation. Hemoglobin can bind CO_2 directly when oxygen is released, and about 15% of the CO_2 carried in blood is carried directly on the hemoglobin molecule. However, as CO_2 is absorbed in blood, the carbonic anhydrase in erythrocytes catalyzes the formation of carbonic acid (Fig 5–6). Carbonic acid rapidly dissociates into bicarbonate and proton; the equilibrium is toward the dissociation. To avoid the extreme danger of increasing the acidity of blood, there must exist a buffering system to absorb this excess proton. **Hemoglobin binds 2 protons for every 4 oxygen molecules lost** and thus provides a major buffering capacity of blood (Fig 5–7). In the lungs, the process is reversed—ie, **as oxygen binds to the deoxygenated hemoglobin, protons are released** and bind with the bicarbonate to drive the bicarbonate toward carbonic acid. With the aid of the very efficient carbonic anhydrase, the carbonic acid forms CO_2, which is exhaled. Thus, the **binding of oxygen forces the exhalation of CO_2.** This reversible phenomenon is called the **Bohr effect.** The Bohr effect is a property of the tetrameric hemoglobin and is dependent upon its heme-heme interaction or cooperative effects. Myoglobin does not exhibit any Bohr effect.

Cooperativity Between Hemoglobin Subunits

The 4 subunits of hemoglobin can be pictured as occupying the apices of a tetrahedron; thus, there are 6 edges of contact. There is a 2-fold symmetry to the hemoglobin molecule, leaving 4 interfaces for subunit interactions. For purposes of discussion, the 2 alpha subunits can be labelled α_1 and α_2, and the 2 beta subunits β_1 and β_2. The α_1/β_1 interaction and the α_2/β_2 interaction each are held together by 17–19 hydrogen bonds and thus are **very rigid;** therefore, these subunit interactions—α_1/β_1 and α_2/β_2—are not affected by the binding of oxygen to heme moieties and there is no **no cooperativity** between them. The α_1/β_2 and α_2/β_1 contacts are less extensive and are therefore weaker. In addition, the contacts between α_1/β_2 and between α_2/β_1 are very **different in oxygenated versus deoxygenated hemoglobin.** These specific contacts act as a "**snap action switch**" between these 2 states of hemoglobin, ie, the oxygenated and the deoxygenated forms of hemoglobin.

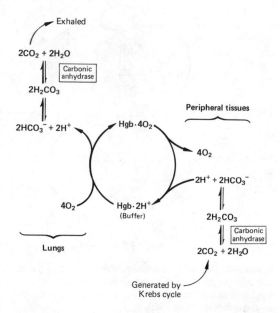

Figure 5–7. The Bohr effect. The carbon dioxide generated in peripheral tissues combines with water to form carbonic acid which dissociates into proton and bicarbonate ions. The deoxygenated hemoglobin acts as a buffer by binding protons and delivering them to the lungs. In the lungs the binding of oxygen by hemoglobin forces the protons off of the hemoglobin. The protons combine with bicarbonate ion generating carbonic acid which, with the aid of carbonic anhydrase, becomes carbon dioxide. The carbon dioxide is exhaled in the lungs.

The Two States of Hemoglobin

Based on the allosteric theory of Monod and Changeaux, the 2 states of hemoglobin are designated relaxed (R, oxygenated) and taut (T, deoxygenated). These 2 forms, R and T, are interconvertible, and each form has its own equilibrium constant (K_R and K_T) for the binding of oxygen:

$$R \rightleftharpoons T$$
$$R + O_2 \rightleftharpoons RO_2 \quad ; \quad K_R = \frac{(RO_2)}{(R)(O_2)}$$
$$T + O_2 \rightleftharpoons TO_2 \quad ; \quad K_T = \frac{(TO_2)}{(T)(O_2)}$$

The binding of oxygen to the R form is several hundred times more favored than the binding of oxygen to the T structure ($K_R >> K_T$,), and the **oxygen affinity of R is thus much greater than the oxygen affinity of T.**

L is defined as the ratio of T to R (L = T/R) and is an index of which form, T or R, is predominant in any solution of hemoglobin. Chemicals such as DPG, protons, chloride, and CO_2, which do not interact directly with the heme moiety of the hemoglobin subunits, all **lower the oxygen affinity by favoring the T structure,** ie, by **increasing L without changing the equilibrium constants for the association of oxygen with R (K_R) or with T (K_T).**

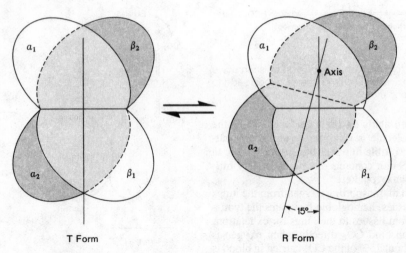

T Form

R Form

Figure 5–8. During the transition of the T form to the R form of hemoglobin, there occurs a rotation of one pair of rigid subunits (α_2-β_2) through 15 degrees relative to the other rigid pair of subunits (α_1-β_1). The axis of rotation is eccentric, and the α_2-β_2 pair also shifts toward the axis somewhat. In the diagram, the α_1-β_1 pair is unshaded and held fixed, while the shaded α_2-β_2 pair rotates and shifts.

Since the α_1/β_1 dimer and the α_2/β_2 dimer are themselves rigid structures, the transition from R to T and vice versa must involve movement of the α_1/β_1 dimer relative to the α_2/β_2 dimer. By x-ray crystallography, it is apparent that if the α_1/β_1 dimer is fixed, the other dimer, α_2/β_2, rotates 15 degrees about an eccentric axis and shifts a bit along that axis (Fig 5–8). Thus, the hemoglobin molecule can snap back and forth between its 2 structures, R and T. Subtle changes of internal subunit structure that accompany the bind-ing and dissociation of oxygen are responsible for the switches between the R and T forms.

Salt bridges, defined as ionic bonds between positively charged nitrogen atoms and negatively charged oxygen atoms, play major roles in the switch mechanism. The **T form of the hemoglobin is stabilized by salt bridges,** and **agents that promote oxygen dissociation thus strengthen or add salt bridges** to the T form (increasing the value of L) (Fig 5–9).

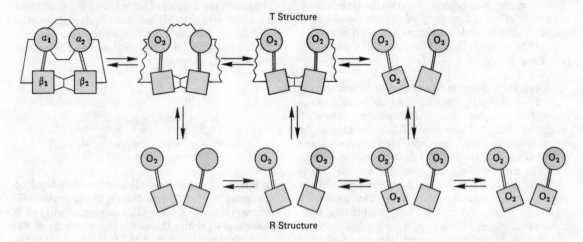

T Structure

R Structure

Figure 5–9. Transition from the T structure to the R structure increases in likelihood as each of the 4 heme groups is oxygenated. In this more realistic model, salt bridges linking the subunits in the T structure break progressively as oxygen is added, and even those salt bridges that have not yet ruptured are progressively weakened. The transition from T to R does not take place after a fixed number of oxygen molecules have been bound, but it becomes more probable with each successive oxygen bound. The transition between the 2 structures is influenced by several factors, including protons, carbon dioxide, chloride, and DPG. The higher their concentration, the more oxygen must be bound to trigger the transition. Fully saturated molecules in the T structure and fully deoxygenated molecules in the R structure are not shown, because they are too unstable to exist in significant numbers. (Modified and redrawn, with permission, from Perutz MF: Hemoglobin structure and respiratory transport. *Sci Am* [Dec] 1978;**239**:92.)

Changes Accompanying Binding of Oxygen to T form of Hemoglobin

The heme pockets in the alpha subunits of hemoglobin are of a size just adequate for the entry of an oxygen molecule, but the entry of oxygen into the heme pockets of the beta subunits is **blocked by a valine residue.**

In the deoxygenated state, or T form, the Fe^{2+} bound to His F8 (87), commonly referred to as proximal His, is **not in the plane of the porphyrin ring.** Instead, as shown in Fig 5–10, the Fe^{2+} is approximately 0.07 nm out of the plane of the porphyrin ring in the direction of the F helix. When oxygen enters the pocket and binds to heme, the Fe^{2+} moves **back into the plane of the porphyrin ring, pulling with it the F8 His** and, of course, the F helix itself (Fig 5–10). This movement of the F helix toward the porphyrin ring is transmitted to the other subunits by a forced breaking of salt bridges. **In the T form, the penultimate tyrosine (HC2) is wedged into a pocket between the H and F helices,** where it is hydrogen-bonded to valine FG5. The C-terminal residue, Arg HC3 in the alpha chain and His HC3 in the beta chain, is constrained by its participation in specific salt bridges, as indicated in Fig 5–11.

The movement of the F helix toward the porphyrin ring upon occupancy of the alpha pocket by oxygen narrows the space between H and F helices, thereby excluding the tyrosyl residues. This rotation of the tyrosyl residues out of the space between the H and F helices forces a loosening of the salt bridges between

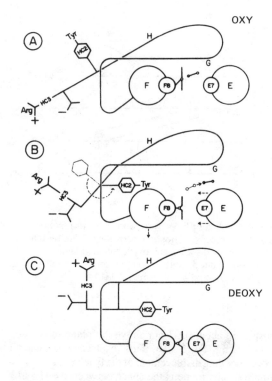

Figure 5–11. The changes in teriary structure produced by transition from oxy- to deoxyhemoglobin. In oxyhemoglobin *(A)*, iron is in the plane of the heme, pulling His F8 upward. Arg HC3 rotates freely. When oxygen moves out *(B)*, the E helix moves in and the F helix moves down, forming a pocket between it and the H helix. The phenolic group of Tyr HC2 can occupy this pocket *(C)*, and its entry pulls Arg HC3 into position so that it can form the salt bridges indicated in the text. (Reproduced, with permission, from Stanbury JB, Wyngaarden JB, Fredrickson DS [editors]: *The Metabolic Basis of Inherited Disease,* 4th ed. McGraw-Hill, 1978.)

the HC3 residues of α_1 and the α_2 Val NA1 and Asp H9. It is these salt bridges that restrain hemoglobin in its T structure (Fig 5–12). Therefore, **when a sufficient number of salt bridges is broken between and within the subunits, the T structure will snap or click to the R structure.** The R structure has an affinity for oxygen many hundred–fold greater than does the T structure. **Thus, upon the binding of oxygen by the heme moieties in one or 2 subunits of hemoglobin, enough salt bridges are broken to change the structure of the hemoglobin to a form that exhibits a much greater oxygen affinity.** This is the basis of the **cooperative effect.** In the R form, there is no Val residue blocking the heme pocket. The binding of one or 2 oxygen molecules to the alpha subunits of the hemoglobin molecule by favoring the R form makes the binding of subsequent oxygen molecules to the other unoccupied heme moieties much more likely.

Upon removal of an oxygen molecule from oxygenated hemoglobin, the electron being shared by Fe^{3+} and the superoxide oxygen is returned to the Fe^{3+} to reestablish its Fe^{2+} state, and the Fe^{2+} is then again

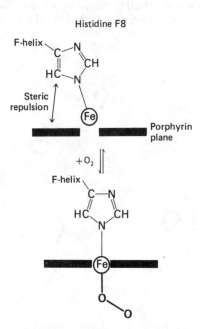

Figure 5–10. The iron atom moves 0.075 nm into the plane of the heme on oxygenation because its diameter becomes smaller. Histidine F8 is pulled along with the iron atom. (Slightly modified and reproduced, with permission, from Stryer L: *Biochemistry,* 2nd ed. Freeman, 1981.)

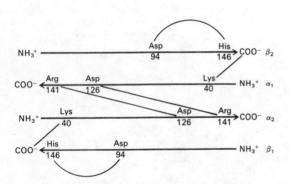

Figure 5–12. Salt-links between different subunits in deoxyhemoglobin. These noncovalent, electrostatic interactions are disrupted on oxygenation. (Slightly modified and reproduced, with permission, from Stryer L: *Biochemistry,* 2nd ed. Freeman, 1981.)

displaced about 0.07 nm above the plane of the porphyrin ring (Fig 5–10). This displacement causes a corresponding displacement of the F helix via the proximal His and reopens the space between the H and F helices for occupancy by the tyrosyl HC2 residue. The reentry of the tyrosyl residue into that space between the H and F helices favors the re-formation of the salt bridges by the C-terminal residues. **When a sufficient number of the salt bridges are re-formed, the hemoglobin molecule will snap or click back into the T state from its R state.** This snapping into the T state will pull the heme ferrous ions of the other subunits out of the plane of the porphyrin ring, **stretching the Fe^{2+}-oxygen bond until it breaks, thus releasing the oxygen.** Again, this **allosteric change** induced by the release of one or two O_2 molecules from the hemoglobin molecule forces oxygen away from the other heme moieties, causing a cooperative release of oxygen—ie, once one or two O_2 molecules have been lost from the oxygenated hemoglobin molecules, the others are effectively pushed out.

Perhaps it is more reasonable to consider the hemoglobin molecule a molecular lung rather than an oxygen tank, since **it changes its structure upon the binding and releasing of oxygen.**

The Bohr Effect at the Submolecular Level

The protons responsible for the Bohr effect are generated by the breaking of salt bridges during the binding of oxygen to the T structure. When oxygen binds to the T structure, salt bridges are broken, and the protons are released from the N atoms of beta chain His residues HC3 (146). These released protons drive the equilibrium with bicarbonate toward carbonic acid, which is then released as CO_2 in alveolar blood (Fig 5–7).

Conversely, upon the release of oxygen, the T structure and its salt bridges are re-formed, requiring

protons to bind to the beta chain HC3 residues. Thus, the presence of protons from peripheral tissues favors the formation of salt bridges by protonating the terminal His residue of the beta subunits. Re-formation of the salt bridges, of course, forces the release of oxygen from oxygenated (R form) hemoglobin. Overall, **an increase in protons causes oxygen release,** while **an increase in oxygen causes proton release.** The former can be represented in an oxygen dissociation curve by a rightward shift in the dissociation curve upon increasing hydrogen ions (protons) (Fig 37–5).

Diphosphoglycerate (DPG, Bisphosphoglycerate) Binding

In peripheral tissues, an oxygen shortage causes an increased accumulation of diphosphoglycerate (DPG). One molecule of DPG is bound per hemoglobin tetramer in a central cavity formed by residues of all 4 subunits. The central cavity is of sufficient size for the entry of DPG only when the hemoglobin molecule is in the **T form,** ie, when the space between the H helices of the beta chains is wide enough. The DPG is bound by salt bridges between its oxygen atoms and both beta chains via their N-terminal amino groups (Val NA1), Lys EF6, and **His H21** residues, Fig 5–13. Thus, **DPG stabilizes the T or deoxygenated form of hemoglobin by cross-linking the beta chains** and contributing additional salt bridges that must be broken for the T form to click into the R form of hemoglobin.

DPG binds more weakly to **fetal hemoglobin** than adult hemoglobin because the **H21** residue of the gamma chain of fetal hemoglobin is **Ser rather than His** and cannot contribute to the salt bridges that hold

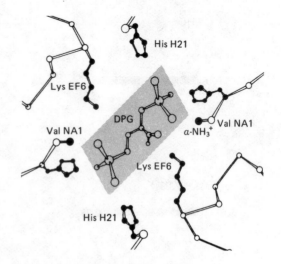

Figure 5–13. Mode of binding of diphosphoglycerate to human deoxyhemoglobin. DPG interacts with 3 positively charged groups on each β chain. (Based on Arnone A: X-ray diffraction study of binding of 2,3-diphosphoglycerate to human deoxyhemoglobin. *Nature* 1972;**237**:146. Reproduced with permission.)

the DPG in the central cavity. Therefore, **DPG has a less profound effect on the stabilization of the T form of fetal hemoglobin** and is responsible for fetal hemoglobin appearing to have a **higher affinity** for oxygen than adult hemoglobin.

The **trigger** for the transition between the R and T forms of hemoglobin is the **movement of the iron in and out of the plane of the porphyrin ring.** Both steric and electronic factors mediate this trigger with a free energy of about 3000 calories per mole. Thus, a minimal change in the position of Fe^{2+} relative to the porphyrin ring induces very significant switching of the conformations of hemoglobin and crucially affects its biologic function in response to an environmental signal.

INSIGHTS FROM MUTANT HEMOGLOBINS

Because of the intricate relationship between hemoglobin structure and function described above, one might expect that alterations in the primary structure of a hemoglobin subunit would have the potential for greatly affecting its biologic function. An enormous number of abnormal hemoglobins with mutations in the alpha and beta subunits have been described in humans. A few of these will be summarized as illustrative examples.

Hemoglobin M

The **methemoglobinemias** associated with abnormal hemoglobin structure result from the heme iron remaining in the **ferric state.** Hemoglobin with Fe^{3+} in its heme will **not bind oxygen** even though it may be in the R form. Because deoxygenated hemoglobin is less red than oxygenated hemoglobin, clinical cyanosis can result from methemoglobinemia. When oxygen binds to the Fe^{2+} of heme (as described above), the iron donates an electron to oxygen, thus forming Fe^{3+} and superoxide anion (O_2^-) in the heme pockets (Fig 5–14). Upon the removal of oxygen, the superoxide anion returns the electron to the Fe^{3+} to regenerate Fe^{2+} and molecular oxygen. However, the superoxide will return the electron to the Fe^{3+} only so long as **no other electron acceptor is available within the heme pocket.** Of course, **water** is an effective electron acceptor and does occasionally gain access to the heme pocket. This results in the formation of hydrogen

peroxide, Fe^{3+}, and oxygen. However, the erythrocyte contains an enzymatic reducing system with a limited capacity for the reduction of methemoglobin (Fe^{3+}) to hemoglobin (Fe^{2+}).

In the event that the structure of hemoglobin is altered so as to stabilize the Fe^{3+}, increased quantities of methemoglobin are generated and exceed erythrocyte-reducing capacity. Five types of hemoglobin M have been described, and 4 involve the substitution of Tyr for His residues. These latter substitutions involve replacement of the proximal or distal histidines in either alpha or beta units. The Tyr residue, by virtue of its **phenolate ion, forms a very tight complex with the ferric cation,** thereby conferring great stability on ferric hemoglobin and strongly favoring its formation. These new bonds formed between the substituted tyrosines and heme iron are strong enough so that molecular instability is not a component of the M hemoglobinopathies.

The 2 **alpha chain variants,** hemoglobin M Boston and hemoglobin M Iwait, have low oxygen affinity and do not exhibit the Bohr effect. In **hemoglobin M Boston,** the Tyr E7 forms a stronger bond with the iron than does the normal distal His E7. This strong bond allows the F helix to rotate away from the heme, opening the space between the F and H helices sufficiently for the entire HC2 to remain in that space. As described above, this promotes the formation of interchain salt bridges and prevents the abnormal alpha chains from undergoing the switching required for the conversion of the T form to the R form. Thus, the hemoglobin M Boston molecules are **locked in the T conformation with its lower oxygen affinity.** The Bohr effect and the cooperativity of oxygen binding, both of which are dependent upon this switching, accordingly cannot exist.

In **hemoglobin M Iwait,** the alpha chain Tyr F8 binds to the ferric ion and also prevents the T–R transition, thereby conveying the diminished oxygen affinity, absent Bohr effect, and lack of cooperativity.

Hemoglobin M Hyde Park and hemoglobin M Saskatoon, both of which contain tyrosine substitutions for His residues in the **beta chains,** do appear to be capable of undergoing R and T interconversion or switching, even though the affected beta subunits contain a stabilized Fe^{3+} in the heme moiety. Accordingly, both hemoglobin M Hyde Park and hemoglobin M Saskatoon exhibit a Bohr effect and relatively normal oxygen affinity by those subunits still containing ferrous heme.

The fifth M hemoglobinopathy, **hemoglobin M Milwaukee-1,** has a substitution of Glu for the normal Val residue at E11 (67) of the beta chain. The carboxyl group of the Glu coordinates with Fe^{3+} and causes the quaternary structure to favor the T form. Accordingly, low oxygen affinity results, but the ferric beta subunits of M Milwaukee-1 can undergo the T–R switch upon oxygenation of the alpha chains. Thus, a Bohr effect does exist, but cooperativity is reduced since only 2 of the oxygen-binding sites are available per abnormal hemoglobin tetramer. In summary, for the **alpha**

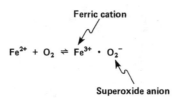

Ferric cation

$$Fe^{2+} + O_2 \rightleftharpoons Fe^{3+} \cdot O_2^-$$

Superoxide anion

Figure 5–14. When oxygen binds to the ferrous cation of heme, the iron donates an electron to oxygen forming a ferric cation and a superoxide anion in the heme pocket.

chain-substituted hemoglobins M, the R–T equilibrium is greatly in favor of T, so that oxygen affinity is reduced and no Bohr effect is observed. The **beta chain**-substituted hemoglobins M exhibit R–T switching, and a Bohr effect is therefore present.

Hemoglobins With Increased Oxygen Affinities

Hemoglobins that exhibit increased oxygen affinity do not release as much oxygen to the peripheral tissues as does normal hemoglobin. The tissue hypoxia leads to **polycythemia,** an increased number of red cells per unit volume of blood, in order to meet its O_2 needs. Any mutation favoring the R form of hemoglobin will promote an early switch from the T form to the R form and will result in a hemoglobin with high oxygen affinity. **Hemoglobin Chesapeake** has a substitution of Arg for Leu at G4 (92) of the alpha chain. This change stabilizes the R conformation, and hemoglobin Chesapeake thus has a high oxygen affinity and loss of cooperativity, functionally resembling those of myoglobin.

The α_1/β_2 interface is made up of many nonpolar bonds and one H bond (Fig 5–15). In the T form, the H bond exists between Asp G1 (99) β_2 and Tyr C7 (42) α_1; the one H bond in the R form crosses the α_1/β_2 interface between Asn G4 (102) β_2 and Asp G1 (94) α_1. In several mutant hemoglobins, such as Yakima and Upsilanti, Asp G1 (99) β is replaced with a residue that cannot participate in H bonding to stabilize the T structure. Thus, the equilibrium is shifted toward R, greatly increasing oxygen affinity and decreasing cooperativity.

As described above, the penultimate Tyr HC2 is extremely important in the R–T switching. When the Tyr HC2 is absent (hemoglobin McKees Rocks) or replaced by another residue (hemoglobin Bethesda, hemoglobin Osler), the T confirmation is destabilized, generating a hemoglobin with a high oxygen affinity

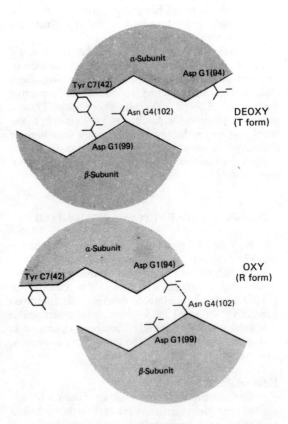

Figure 5–15. Changes at the $\alpha_1\beta_2$ contact on oxygenation. The contact "clicks" from one dovetailing area to another, involving a switch from one hydrogen bond to a second. The other bonds are nonpolar. (Reproduced, with permission, from Perutz MF: Molecular pathology of human hemoglobin: Stereochemical interpretation of abnormal oxygen affinities. *Nature* 1971;232:408.)

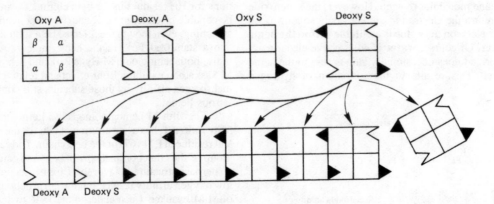

Figure 5–16. Diagrammatic representation of the sticky patch (▲) on hemoglobin S and the sticky patch "receptor" (Δ) present on deoxyhemoglobin A and deoxyhemoglobin S. The complementary surfaces allow deoxyhemoglobin A to polymerize into a fibrous structure, but the presence of deoxyhemoglobin A will terminate the polymerization by failing to provide sticky patches. (Modified and reproduced, with permission, from Stryer L: *Biochemistry,* 2nd ed. Freeman, 1981.)

and lower cooperativity. The C-terminal (HC) portion of the beta chains is also important in the binding of DPG and in generating the Bohr effect; all of these hemoglobins have a reduced Bohr effect, and many of them exhibit reduced binding of DPG.

Sickle Hemoglobin

Hemoglobin S is a substitution of Glu A2 (6) β by a Val residue and was described in 1949 by Linus Pauling and his colleagues. This was the first description of a molecular disease. The A2 residue, whether it be Glu or Val, can be seen to be on the surface of the hemoglobin molecule, exposed to water. The substitution in hemoglobin S replaces the polar glutamate residue with a nonpolar one and thereby generates a **"sticky patch"** on the outside of the beta chain. The sticky patch is present on oxygenated and deoxygenated hemoglobin S but, of course, not on hemoglobin A. On the surface of **deoxygenated hemoglobin,** there exists a **complement to the sticky patch** formed by the Val A2 (6), but in oxygenated hemoglobin the complementary site is masked (Fig 5–16). When hemoglobin S is deoxygenated, the sticky patch of hemoglobin S can bind to the complementary patch on another deoxygenated hemoglobin molecule. This binding causes a **polymerization of deoxyhemoglobin S, forming long fibrous precipitates** that mechanically distort (sickle) the red cell, causing lysis and multiple secondary clinical effects. Thus, if hemoglobin S can be maintained in an oxygenated state or at least if the concentration of deoxygenated hemoglobin S can be kept at a minimum, formation of these

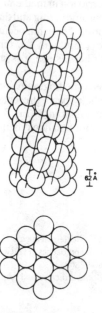

Figure 5–17. Proposed helical structure of a fiber of aggregated deoxyhemoglobin S. (Reproduced, with permission, from Maugh T II: A new understanding of sickle cell emerges. *Science* 1981;**211**:265. Copyright 1981 by the American Association for the Advancement of Science.)

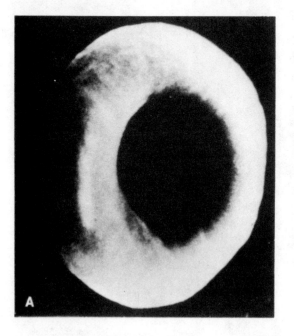

Figure 5–18. Scanning electron micrograph of normal and sickle red cells. *A.* A normal red cell, × 20,000. *B.* A deoxygenated sickle cell, × 15,000. (Reproduced, with permission, from Stanbury JB, Wyngaarden JB, Fredrickson DS [editors]: *The Metabolic Basis of Inherited Disease,* 4th ed. McGraw-Hill, 1978.)

polymers of deoxygenated hemoglobin S will not occur and "sickling" can be prevented. Clearly, it is the **T form of hemoglobin S that is subject to polymerization.** It is interesting but of no practical use to note that the ferric ion in methemoglobin remains in the plane of the porphyrin ring and thus stabilizes the R form of hemoglobin. The same occurs in sickle hemoglobin; ie, hemoglobin S in the ferric state will not polymerize into fibers, since it is stabilized in the R form.

Although deoxyhemoglobin A contains the receptor sites for the sticky patch present on oxygenated or deoxygenated hemoglobin S (Fig 5–14), the binding of sticky hemoglobin S to deoxyhemoglobin A cannot extend the polymer, since the latter does not itself have a sticky patch to promote binding to still another hemoglobin molecule. Therefore, the **binding of deoxyhemoglobin A to either the R or the T form of hemoglobin S will terminate the polymerization.**

The polymerization of deoxyhemoglobin S forms a helical fibrous structure, each hemoglobin molecule making contact with 4 neighbors in a tubular helix (Fig 5–17). The formation of these tubular fibers is responsible for the mechanical distortion of the erythrocyte containing them, so that they take on the shape of a sickle (Fig 5–18) and are vulnerable to lysis as they penetrate the interstices of the splenic sinusoids.

●   ●   ●

References

Dean J, Schechter AN: Sickle-cell anemia: Molecular and cellular basis of therapeutic approaches. (Three parts.) *N Engl J Med* 1978;**299**:752, 804, 863.

Perutz MF: Hemoglobin structure and respiratory transport. *Sci Am* 1978;**239**:92.

Perutz MF: The regulation of oxygen-affinity of hemoglobin: Influence of structure of globin on heme iron. *Annu Rev Biochem* 1979;**48**:327.

Stamatoyannopoulos G: The molecular basis of hemoglobin disease. *Annu Rev Genet* 1972;**6**:47.

General Properties of Enzymes | 6

Victor W. Rodwell, PhD

CATALYSIS

Catalysts accelerate chemical reactions. Catalysts participate in and undergo physical change during a reaction but revert to their original state when the reaction is complete. **Enzymes** are **protein catalysts** for chemical reactions in biologic systems. Most chemical reactions of living cells would occur very slowly were it not for catalysis by enzymes. In contrast to nonprotein catalysts (H^+, OH^-, metal ions), each enzyme catalyzes a small number of reactions, frequently only one. Enzymes are thus **reaction-specific** catalysts. **Essentially all biochemical reactions are enzyme-catalyzed.** For almost every organic compound in nature—and for many inorganic compounds—there is an enzyme in some organism capable of reacting with it and catalyzing a chemical change.

Although enzyme activity was formerly thought to be expressed only in intact cells (hence the term *en-zyme* "in yeast"), enzymes may be extracted from cells without loss of their biologic (catalytic) activity. Enzyme-containing extracts are used in studies of metabolic reactions and their regulation, the structure and mechanism of action of enzymes, and as catalysts for industrial synthesis of hormones and drugs. Since the enzyme content of human serum changes significantly in certain pathologic conditions, serum enzyme levels provide an important diagnostic tool.

COENZYMES

Many enzymes catalyze reactions of their substrates only in the presence of a specific heat-stable, small, nonprotein organic molecule, the coenzyme. Where coenzymes are required, the complete system or **holoenzyme** consists of the protein part or **apoenzyme** plus bound **coenzyme**. A particular coenzyme may bind covalently or noncovalently to the apoenzyme. The term "prosthetic group" was formerly employed to denote covalently bonded coenzymes. Reactions that require coenzymes include oxidoreductions, group transfer and isomerization reactions, and reactions that form covalent bonds (classes 1, 2, 5, and 6; see below). Lytic reactions, including hydrolytic reactions such as those catalyzed by digestive en-

zymes, do not require coenzymes (classes 3 and 4; see below).

B vitamins form part of the structure of many coenzymes. For example, many enzymes of amino acid metabolism require vitamin B_6. The B vitamins **nicotinamide, thiamin, riboflavin,** and **pantothenic acid** are important constituents of coenzymes for biologic oxidations and reductions, and **folic acid** and **cobamide** coenzymes function in one-carbon metabolism.

It is often helpful to regard the coenzyme as a second substrate or **cosubstrate.** This is so for 2 reasons. First, **the chemical changes in the coenzyme exactly counterbalance those taking place in the substrate.** For example, in oxidoreduction (dehydrogenase) reactions (E.C. class 1.1), one molecule of substrate is oxidized (dehydrogenated) and one molecule of coenzyme is reduced (hydrogenated) (Fig 6–1).

Similarly, in transamination reactions (class 2.6), pyridoxal phosphate acts as a second substrate in 2 concerted reactions and as carrier for transfer of an amino group between different α-keto acids. For every molecule of alanine converted to pyruvate, one molecule of the aldehyde form of pyridoxal phosphate is aminated. The amino form of the coenzyme does not appear as a reaction product since the aldehyde form is regenerated by transfer of the amino group to α-ketoglutarate, forming glutamate (Fig 6–2).

A second reason to give equal emphasis to the reactions of the coenzyme is that this aspect of the reaction may actually be of greater fundamental physiologic significance. For example, the importance of the ability of muscle working anaerobically to convert pyruvate to lactate resides not in pyruvate or lactate themselves. The reaction serves merely to con-

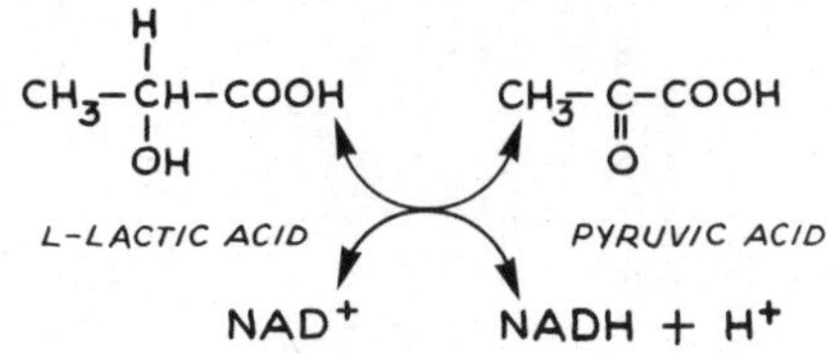

Figure 6–1. NAD^+ acting as cosubstrate in an oxidoreduction reaction.

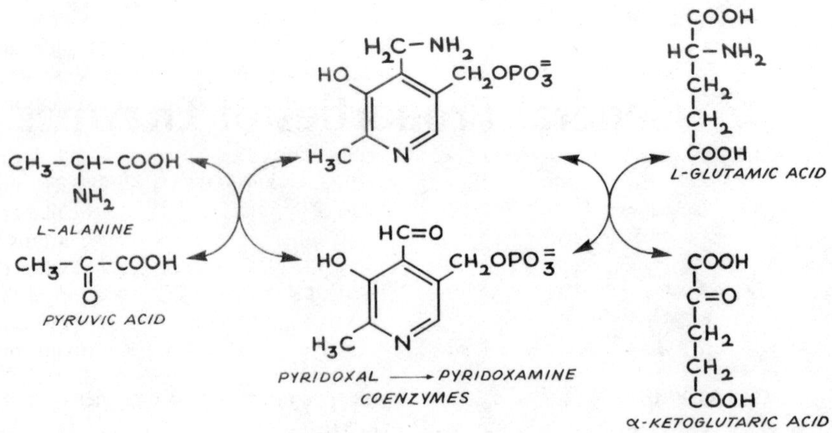

Figure 6–2. Participation of pyridoxal phosphate as cosubstrate in transamination reactions.

vert NADH to NAD^+. Without NAD^+, glycolysis cannot continue and anaerobic ATP synthesis (and hence muscular work) ceases. Under anaerobic conditions, reduction of pyruvate to lactate reoxidizes NADH and permits synthesis of ATP. Other reactions can serve this function equally well. In bacteria or yeast growing anaerobically, substances derived from pyruvate serve as oxidants for NADH and are themselves reduced (Table 6–1).

Table 6–1. Mechanisms for anaerobic regeneration of NAD^+.

Oxidant	Reduced Product	Life Form
Pyruvate	Lactate	Muscle, homolactic bacteria
Acetaldehyde	Ethanol	Yeast
Dihydroxyacetone phosphate	α-Glycerophosphate	E coli
Fructose	Mannitol	Heterolactic bacteria

Classification of Coenzymes Based on Functional Characteristics

All coenzymes function in group transfer reactions.

  A. For transfer of groups other than H.
      Sugar phosphates.
      CoA.
      Thiamin pyrophosphate.
      B_6 phosphate.
      Folate coenzymes.
      Biotin.
      Cobamide (B_{12}) coenzymes.
      Lipoic acid.
  B. For transfer of H.
      NAD^+, $NADP^+$.
      FMN, FAD.
      Lipoic acid.
      Coenzyme Q.

Classification of Coenzymes Based on Structure

Particularly striking is the frequent occurrence in coenzymes of the adenine ring joined to D-ribose and phosphate. Many coenzymes may therefore be regarded as derivatives of adenosine monophosphate (AMP) (Table 6–2).

Table 6–2. Coenzymes and related compounds that are derivatives of adenosine monophosphate.

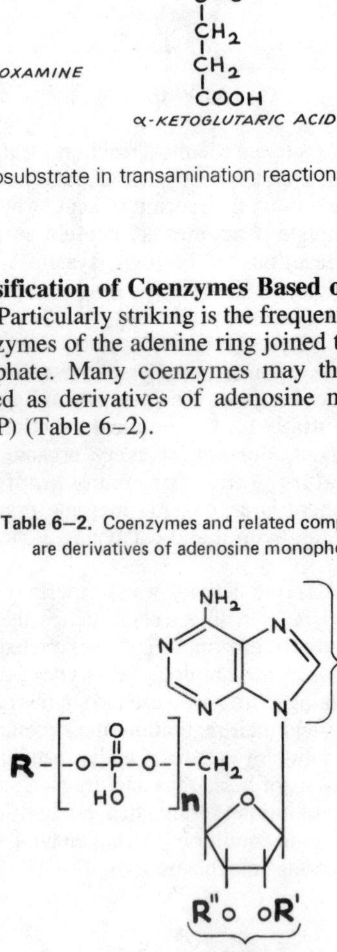

Coenzyme	R	R'	R''	n
Active methionine	Methionine*	H	H	0
Amino acid adenylates	Amino acid	H	H	1
Active sulfate	SO_3H_2	H	PO_3H	1
3',5'-Cyclic AMP	H	H	PO_3H	
NAD^+	†	H	H	2
$NADP^+$	†	PO_3H	H	2
FAD	†	H	H	2
CoA	†	H	PO_3H	2

*Replaces phosphate group.
†See Chapters 10 and 12.

ENZYME SPECIFICITY

Nonprotein catalysts typically accelerate many chemical reactions. By contrast, a given enzyme catalyzes very few reactions (frequently only one). The ability of an enzyme to catalyze one specific reaction and essentially no others is perhaps its most significant property. The rates of metabolic processes may thus be minutely regulated by changes in the catalytic efficiency of enzymes (see Chapter 9). However, most enzymes catalyze the same type of reaction (phosphate transfer, oxidation-reduction, etc) with a few structurally related substrates. Reactions with alternate substrates take place if these are present in high concentration. Whether all of the possible reactions will occur in living organisms depends on the relative concentration of alternate substrates in the cell and their relative affinities for an enzyme. Some general aspects of enzyme specificity are those given below.

Optical Specificity

With the exception of epimerases (racemases), which interconvert optical isomers, **enzymes generally show absolute optical specificity for at least a portion of a substrate molecule.** Thus, maltase catalyzes the hydrolysis of α- but not β-glycosides, while enzymes of the glycolytic and direct oxidative pathways catalyze the interconversion of D- but not L-phosphosugars. With a few exceptions, such as the D-amino acid oxidase of kidney, the vast majority of mammalian enzymes act on the L-isomers of amino acids. Other life forms may have enzymes with equal specificity for D-amino acids.

Optical specificity may extend to a portion of the substrate molecule or to its entirety. Glycosidases illustrate both extremes. They catalyze hydrolysis of glycosidic bonds between sugars and alcohols, are highly specific for the sugar portion and for the linkage (α or β), but are relatively nonspecific for the alcohol portion or aglycone.

Many substrates apparently form 3 bonds with enzymes. This "3-point attachment" can thus confer asymmetry on an otherwise symmetric molecule. A substrate molecule, represented as a carbon atom having 3 different groups (Fig 6–3), is shown about to attach at 3 points to a planar enzyme site. If the site can be approached only from one side and only complementary atoms and sites can interact, the molecule can bind in only one way. The reaction itself may be confined to the atoms bound at sites 1 and 2 even though atoms 1 and 3 are identical. By mentally turning the substrate molecule in space, note that it can attach at 3 points to one side of the planar site with only one orientation. Consequently, atoms 1 and 3, although identical, become distinct when the substrate is attached to the enzyme. Extension of this line of reasoning can explain why the enzyme-catalyzed reduction of the optically inactive pyruvate molecule results in formation of L- and not D,L-lactate.

Group Specificity

Lytic enzymes act on particular chemical groupings, eg, glycosidases on glycosides, pepsin and trypsin on peptide bonds, and esterases on esters. A large number of substrates may be attacked, thus, for example, lessening the number of digestive enzymes that might otherwise be required.

Certain lytic enzymes exhibit higher group specificity. Chymotrypsin preferentially hydrolyzes peptide bonds in which the carboxyl group is contributed by the aromatic amino acids phenylalanine, tyrosine, or tryptophan. Carboxypeptidases and aminopeptidases split off amino acids one at a time from the carboxyl- or amino-terminal end of polypeptide chains, respectively.

Although some oxidoreductases utilizes either NAD^+ or $NADP^+$ as electron acceptor, most use one or the other. As a broad generalization, **oxidoreductases functional in biosynthetic processes in mammalian systems (eg, fatty acid synthesis) tend to use NADPH as reductant, while those functional in degradative processes tend to use NAD^+ as oxidant.** Occasionally, a tissue may possess 2 oxidoreductases that differ only in their coenzyme specificity (eg, the NAD^+- and $NADP^+$-specific isocitrate dehydrogenases of rat mitochondria, Table 6–3). In liver, about 90% of the $NADP^+$-specific enzyme occurs extramitochondrially. This may be concerned with biosynthetic processes, as the NAD^+-specific enzyme of mitochondria is specifically activated by ADP. Since ADP

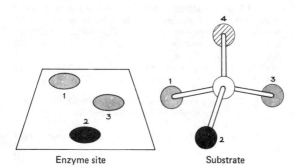

Figure 6–3. Representation of 3-point attachment of a substrate to a planar active site of an enzyme.

Enzyme site   Substrate

Table 6–3. Distribution of NAD^+- and $NADP^+$-specific isocitrate dehydrogenases in mitochondria of rat tissue.*

Organ	Specific Activity (μmol/min/mg) of	
	NAD^+-Specific Enzyme	$NADP^+$-Specific Enzyme
Skeletal muscle	0.84	0.78
Heart	0.57	2.22
Kidney	0.28	1.20
Brain	0.25	0.054
Liver	0.16	0.33

*From Lowenstein JM: The tricarboxylic acid cycle. Page 168 in: *Metabolic Pathways.* Vol 1. Greenberg DM (editor). Academic Press, 1967.

levels rise during depletion of ATP stores, this suggests a degradative role for the NAD^+-specific isocitrate dehydrogenase of mitochondria. High ADP (low ATP) levels would promote carbon flow through the citric acid cycle by activating the NAD^+-specific mitochondrial enzyme.

ENZYME CLASSIFICATION & NOMENCLATURE

Early attempts at enzyme nomenclature produced ambiguous and uninformative names such as emulsin, ptyalin, and zymase. Enzymes were later named for the substrates on which they acted by adding the suffix **-ase**. Thus enzymes that split starch (amylon) were termed amylases; those that split fat (lipos), lipases; and those that acted on proteins, proteases. Groups of enzymes were designated as oxidases, glycosidases, dehydrogenases, decarboxylases, etc.

The mechanism of organic and of enzyme-catalyzed reactions provides a more rational classification of enzymes based on reaction type and reaction mechanism. The International Union of Biochemistry (IUB) System, while complex, is precise, descriptive, and informative. The major features of the **IUB system for classification of enzymes** are as follows:

A. Reactions and the enzymes that catalyze them are divided into 6 classes, each with 4–13 subclasses.

B. The enzyme name has 2 parts. The first names the substrate or substrates. The second, ending in **-ase,** indicates the **type of reaction catalyzed.**

C. Additional information, if needed to clarify the reaction, may follow in parentheses. For example, the enzyme catalyzing L-malate + NAD^+ = pyruvate + CO_2 + NADH + H^+ is designated 1.1.1.37 L-malate:NAD oxidoreductase (decarboxylating).

D. Each enzyme has a systematic code number (E.C.). This number characterizes the reaction type as to class (first digit), subclass (second digit), and sub-subclass (third digit). The fourth digit is for the specific enzyme. Thus, E.C. 2.7.1.1 denotes class 2 (a transferase), subclass 7 (transfer of phosphate), subsubclass 1 (an alcohol functions as the phosphate acceptor). The final digit denotes the enzyme, hexokinase, or ATP:D-hexose-6-phosphotransferase, an enzyme catalyzing phosphate transfer from ATP to the hydroxyl group on carbon 6 of glucose.

The 6 classes of enzymes with some illustrative examples are given below. The name in brackets is the trivial name.

1. Oxidoreductases. Enzymes catalyzing oxidoreductions between 2 substrates, S and S′.

$$S_{reduced} + S'_{oxidized} = S_{oxidized} + S'_{reduced}$$

Enzymes catalyzing oxidoreductions of CH–OH, CH–CH, C=O, CH–NH_2, and CH=NH groups. Representative subclasses:

1.1 Enzymes acting on the CH–OH group as electron donor. For example:

1.1.1.1 Alcohol:NAD oxidoreductase [alcohol dehydrogenase].

$$Alcohol + NAD^+ = Aldehyde\ or\ ketone + NADH + H^+$$

1.4 Enzymes acting on the CH–NH_2 group as electron donor. For example:

1.4.1.3 L-Glutamate:NAD(P) oxidoreductase (deaminating) [glutamic dehydrogenase of animal liver]. NAD(P) means that either NAD^+ or $NADP^+$ acts as the electron acceptor.

$$L\text{-Glutamate} + H_2O + NAD(P)^+ =$$
$$\alpha\text{-Ketoglutarate} + NH_4^+ + NAD(P)H + H^+$$

1.11 Enzymes acting on H_2O_2 as electron acceptor. For example:

1.11.1.6 H_2O_2:H_2O_2 oxidoreductase [catalase].

$$H_2O_2 + H_2O_2 = O_2 + 2H_2O$$

2. Transferases. Enzymes catalyzing a transfer of a group, G (other than hydrogen), between a pair of substrates S and S′.

$$S\text{-}G + S' = S'\text{-}G + S$$

Enzymes catalyzing the transfer of one-carbon groups, aldehyde or ketone residues, and acyl, alkyl, glycosyl, phosphorus, or sulfur containing groups. Representative subclasses:

2.3 Acyltransferases. For example:

2.3.1.6 Acetyl-CoA: choline O-acetyltransferase [choline acyltransferase].

$$Acetyl\text{-}CoA + Choline = CoA + O\text{-}Acetylcholine$$

2.7 Enzymes catalyzing transfer of phosphorus containing groups. For example:

2.7.1.1 ATP:D-hexose-6-phosphotransferase [hexokinase].

$$ATP + D\text{-}Hexose = ADP + D\text{-}Hexose\ 6\text{-}phosphate$$

3. Hydrolases. Enzymes catalyzing hydrolysis of ester, ether, peptide, glycosyl, acid-anhydride, C–C, C-halide, or P–N bonds. For example:

3.1 Enzymes acting on ester bonds. For example:

3.1.1.8 Acylcholine acyl-hydrolase [pseudocholinesterase].

$$An\ acylcholine + H_2O = Choline + An\ acid$$

3.2 Enzymes acting on glycosyl compounds. For example:

3.2.1.23 β-D-Galactoside galactohydrolase [β-galactosidase].

$$A\ \beta\text{-D-Galactoside} + H_2O = An\ alcohol + D\text{-}Galactose$$

3.4 Enzymes acting on peptide bonds. Classification (11 subclasses) distinguishes peptidases from proteases, whether dipeptides or longer peptides are substrates, whether one or more amino acids are removed, and whether attack is from the C- or the N-terminal end. Proteinases are further distinguished by their catalytic mechanism as serine, –SH, or metalloenzyme proteinases.

3.4.21 Serine proteinases. For example: Chymotrypsin, trypsin, plasmin, coagulation factors IXa and XIa.

3.4.23 Carboxyl (acid) proteinases. For example: Pepsin A, B, and C.

4. Lyases. Enzymes that catalyze removal of groups from substrates by mechanisms other than hydrolysis, leaving double bonds.

$$X \quad Y$$
$$| \quad |$$
$$C{-}C = X{-}Y + C{=}C$$

Enzymes acting on C–C, C–O, C–N, C–S, and C-halide bonds. Representative subgroups:

4.1.2 Aldehyde-lyases. *For example:*
4.1.2.7 Ketose-1-phosphate aldehyde-lyase [aldolase].

A ketose-1-phosphate = Dihydroxyacetone phosphate
+ An aldehyde

4.2 Carbon-oxygen lyases. *For example:*
4.2.1.2 L-Malate hydro-lyase [fumarase].

L-Malate = Fumarate + H_2O

5. Isomerases. Includes all enzymes catalyzing interconversion of optical, geometric, or positional isomers. Two subclasses:

5.2 Cis-trans isomerases. *For example:*
5.2.1.3 All-*trans*-retinene 11-*cis-trans* isomerase [retinene isomerase].

All *trans*-retinene = 11-*cis*-retinene

5.3 Enzymes catalyzing interconversion of aldoses and ketoses. *For example:*
5.3.1.1 D-Glyceraldehyde-3-phosphate ketolisomerase [triosephosphate isomerase].

D-Glyceraldehyde-3-phosphate =
Dihydroxyacetone phosphate

6. Ligases. (*Ligare* = ''to bind.'') Enzymes catalyzing the linking together of 2 compounds coupled to the breaking of a pyrophosphate bond in ATP or a similar compound. Included are enzymes catalyzing reactions forming C–O, C–S, C–N, and C–C bonds. Representative subclasses are:

6.2 Enzymes catalyzing formation of C–S bonds.
6.3 Enzymes catalyzing formation of C–N bonds. *For example:*
6.3.1.2 L-Glutamate:ammonia ligase (ADP) [glutamine synthetase].

ATP + L-Glutamate + NH_4^+ =
ADP + Orthophosphate + L-Glutamine

6.4 Enzymes catalyzing formation of C–C bonds. *For example:*
6.4.1.2 Acetyl-CoA:CO_2 ligase (ADP) [acetyl-CoA carboxylase].

ATP + Acetyl-CoA + CO_2 = ADP + P_i + Malonyl-CoA

QUANTITATIVE MEASUREMENT OF ENZYME ACTIVITY

The extremely small quantities present introduce problems in determining the amount of an enzyme in tissue extracts or fluids quite different from those of determining the concentration of more usual organic or inorganic substances. Fortunately, **the catalytic activity of an enzyme provides a sensitive and specific device for its own measurement.** To measure the amount of an enzyme in a sample of tissue extract or other biologic fluid, the **rate of the reaction** catalyzed

by the enzyme in the sample is measured. Under appropriate conditions, **the measured rate is proportionate to the quantity of enzyme present.** Where possible, this rate is compared with the rate catalyzed by a known quantity of the highly purified enzyme. Provided that both are assayed under conditions where the enzyme concentration is rate-limiting (high substrate and low product concentration, favorable pH and temperature), the quantity of enzyme in the extract may be calculated. However, it is not easy to determine the number of molecules or mass of enzyme present. Results are therefore expressed in **enzyme units.** Relative amounts of enzyme in different extracts may then be compared. Enzyme units are best expressed in micromoles (μmol; 10^{-6} mol), nanomoles (nmol; 10^{-9} mol), or picomoles (pmol; 10^{-12} mol) of substrate reacting or product produced per minute. The corresponding International Enzyme Units are μU, nU, and pU.

In reactions involving NAD^+ (dehydrogenases), advantage is taken of the property of NADH or NADPH (but not NAD^+ or $NADP^+$) to absorb light at a wavelength of 340 nm (Fig 6–4).

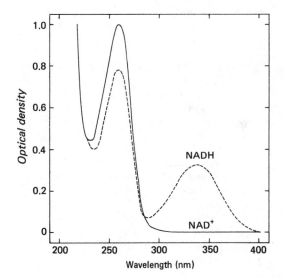

Figure 6–4. Absorption profiles of NAD^+ and NADH. Densities are for a 44 mg/L solution in a cell of 1 cm light path. $NADP^+$ and NADPH have similar profiles.

When NADH is oxidized to NAD^+ (or vice versa), the optical density (OD) at 340 nm changes. Under specified conditions, the rate of change in OD depends directly on the enzyme activity(Fig 6–5).

A calibration curve (Fig 6–6) is prepared by plotting the slopes of the lines in Fig 6–5 versus the quantity of standard enzyme preparation added. The quantity of enzyme present in an unknown solution may then be referred to this standard.

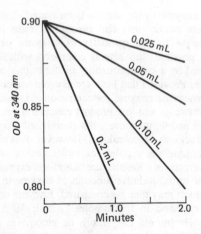

Figure 6–5. Assay of an NADH- or NADPH-dependent dehydrogenase. The rate of change in OD at 340 nm due to conversion of reduced to oxidized coenzyme is observed. Oxidized substrate (S) and reduced coenzyme (NADH) plus buffer are added to a cuvette and light of 340 nm wavelength is passed through it. Initially, the OD is high since NADH (or NADPH) absorbs at 340 mm. On addition of 0.025–0.2 mL of a standard enzyme solution, the OD decreases.

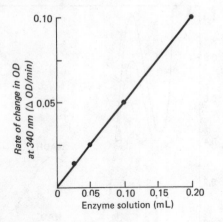

Figure 6–6. Calibration curve for enzymic analysis. Data of Fig 6–5.

Coupled Enzymic Analyses

In the above example, the rate of formation of a product (NADH) was measured to determine enzyme activity. The activity of enzymes other than dehydrogenases is also determined by measuring the rate of appearance of a product (or, less commonly, the rate of disappearance of a substrate). The chemical and physical properties of the product/substrate determine the specific method selected for quantitation. Since these may be cumbersome, it often is convenient to "couple" the product of a reaction to a dehydrogenase for which this product is a substrate. When the dehydrogenase is present in excess, the rate of appearance or disappearance of NAD(P)H may then be used to

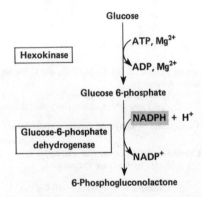

Figure 6–7. Coupled assay for hexokinase activity. The reaction is coupled to that catalyzed by glucose-6-phosphate dehydrogenase. Glucose-6-phosphate dehydrogenase, glucose, ATP, Mg^{2+}, and NADPH all are added in excess. The quantity of hexokinase present then determines the rate of the overall coupled reaction and therefore the rate of oxidation of NADPH.

quantify an enzyme that itself does not use NAD(P)H as a substrate (Fig 6–7).

ISOLATION OF ENZYMES

Much knowledge about the pathways of metabolism and of regulatory mechanisms operating at the level of catalysis have come from studies of isolated, purified enzymes. Indeed, those areas of metabolism where the enzymes involved have not been purified are exactly those where information is fragmentary and controversial. Reliable information concerning the kinetics, cofactors, active sites, structure, and mechanism of action also requires highly purified enzymes.

Enzyme purification involves the isolation of a specific enzyme protein from a crude extract of whole cells containing many other components. Small molecules may be removed by dialysis, nucleic acids by adsorption on charcoal, etc. The problem is to separate the desired enzyme from a mixture of hundreds of chemically and physically similar proteins. Useful methods include precipitation with varying salt concentrations (generally ammonium or sodium sulfate) or solvents (acetone or ethanol), differential heat or pH denaturation, differential centrifugation, gel filtration, and electrophoresis. Selective adsorption and elution of proteins from the cellulose anion exchanger diethylaminoethylcellulose and the cation exchanger carboxymethylcellulose have also been extremely successful for extensive and rapid purification. Separation of proteins on molecular sieves such as Sephadex that segregate proteins on the basis of their size is also widely used. Recently, **affinity column chromatography** has been used with great success. A small molecule—eg, a substrate analog—is bonded chemically to an inert support. Proteins that interact strongly with this material (eg, an enzyme whose active site

Table 6–4. Summary of a typical enzyme purification scheme.

Enzyme Fraction	Total Activity (pU)	Total Protein (mg)	Specific Activity (pU/mg)	Overall Recovery (%)
Crude liver homogenate	100,000	10,000	10	(100)
100,000 X g supernatant liquid	98,000	8,000	12.2	98
40–50% $(NH_4)_2SO_4$ precipitate	90,000	1,500	60	90
20–35% acetone precipitate	60,000	250	240	60
DEAE column fractions 80–110	58,000	29	2,000	58
43–48% $(NH_4)_2SO_4$ precipitate	52,000	20	2,600	52
First crystals	50,000	12	4,160	50
Recrystallization	49,000	10	4,900	49

"recognizes" the analog) may then be separated from other proteins. Ultimately, crystallization of the enzyme may be achieved, generally from an ammonium sulfate solution. Crystallinity does not, however, assure homogeneity. Exhaustive physical, chemical, and biologic tests must still be applied as criteria of purity.

The progress of a typical enzyme purification for a liver enzyme with good recovery and 490-fold overall purification is shown in Table 6–4. Note how specific activity and recovery of initial activity are calculated. The aim is to achieve the maximum specific activity (enzyme units per mg protein) with the best possible recovery of initial activity.

INTRACELLULAR DISTRIBUTION OF ENZYMES

Structure & Functions of Intracellular Components

In multicellular organisms, diverse kinds of cells serve specialized functions. Certain features are, however, common to all eukaryotic cells. All possess a cell membrane, a nucleus, and a cytoplasm containing cellular organelles and soluble proteins essential to the biochemical and physiologic functions of that cell. Although no "typical" cell exists, Fig 6–8 represents intracellular structures in general. In the electron micrograph of a section of an actual cell (rat pituitary gland), the cell membrane, mitochondria, and endoplasmic reticulum with associated ribosomes may be seen (Fig 6–9). Note also, the secretion granules, in this instance responsible for production of mammotropic (lactogenic) hormone.

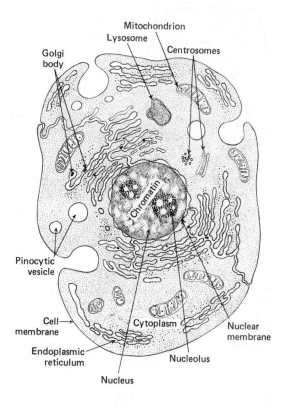

Figure 6–8. Structural components of an idealized "typical cell."

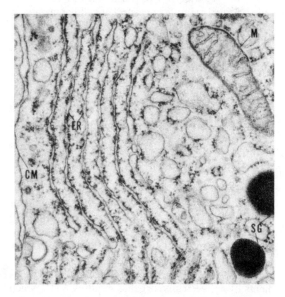

Figure 6–9. Portion of a mammotropic hormone-producing cell of rat anterior pituitary gland. (Reduced 30% from × 50,000.) Shown are several rows of endoplasmic reticulum with associated ribosomes (ER), mitochondria (M), secretion granules (SG), and a portion of cell membrane (CM). (Courtesy of RE Smith and MG Farquhar.)

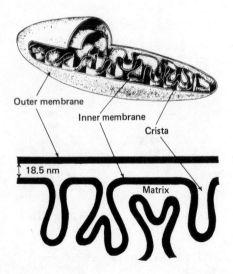

Figure 6–10. Representation of the structure of a mitochondrion.

Under a light microscope, the **cell membrane** appears only as a limiting boundary, since it is less than 10 nm thick. In electron micrographs, the membranes of many cells are seen to possess definite structures that often can be related to the specific functions of the tissue from which the cell is derived. That the membrane should possess such structures is not surprising, for it must maintain selective permeability in order to preserve within the cell the precise chemical environment necessary to the cell's function. Indeed, the mechanism of transport of metabolites in and out of cells is a highly significant aspect of cellular metabolic activity, and substances that affect transport across membranes thereby exert control over intracellular biochemical activities. Substances that affect transport include hormones such as insulin and growth hormone.

Solutes of low molecular weight present in extracellular fluid at a higher concentration than in the cell tend to diffuse into the cell. The converse also holds true, for solutes tend to diffuse from a region of high to a region of low concentration. **Passive transport** of solutes across cellular or intracellular membranes results from just such random molecular motion. Water, for example, is passively transported across membranes. Certain solutes, however, migrate across membranes in a direction opposite to that predicted from their concentrations on either side of the membrane (eg, K^+ in cells, Na^+ in extracellular fluid). This establishes a **solute gradient** that can only be maintained by expending energy. Maintaining these gradients by **active transport** thus requires ATP, which must be supplied by the cell. Many small molecules appear to be actively transported across membranes.

In many cells, large molecules and other macromaterials enter by **pinocytosis** ("cell drinking"). An inpocketing of the cell membrane forms a vesicle which surrounds and ultimately completely envelops the material to be ingested in a vacuole that enters the cytoplasm as a free-floating structure.

Among the largest cytoplasmic structures are the **mitochondria** (3–4 μm in length). These "power plants" of the cell trap the energy released by oxidative processes with simultaneous formation of adenosine triphosphate (ATP) (Fig 6–10). Mitochondria have membranes. The inner membrane forms **cristae** that extend into the matrix. The components of the respiratory chain (see Chapter 12) associated with oxidative phosphorylation are present in the inner mitochondrial membrane. Enzymes of the citric acid cycle (see Chapter 14) are located in the fluid matrix.

Lysosomes, subcellular organelles approximately the same size as mitochondria, lack internal structure. Lysosomes contain digestive enzymes that break down macromolecules into smaller molecules capable of being further metabolized. As long as the lipoprotein membrane of the lysosome remains intact, the enzymes within the lysosome are unable to act on substrates in the cytoplasm. Once the membrane is ruptured, release of lysosomal enzymes is quickly followed by dissolution (lysis) of the cell (Fig 6–11).

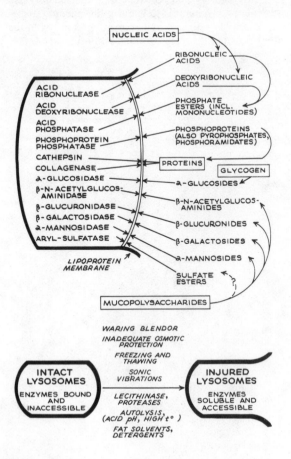

Figure 6–11. The lysosome. (Redrawn and reproduced, with permission, from De Duve C: The Lysosome Concept. Ciba Foundation Symposium: *Lysosomes.* Little, Brown, 1963.)

The **endoplasmic reticulum** is a system of internal membranes continuous with the external cell membrane. The **Golgi bodies** may serve as a means of producing and maintaining this internal membrane. Associated with the inner surface of the endoplasmic reticulum are numerous granules rich in ribonucleic acid (RNA) termed **ribosomes.** The ribosomes are the sites of protein synthesis within the cell. The reticular system and the ribosomes are most highly developed in cells (such as those of the liver and pancreas) actively engaged in the production of proteins.

Other cytoplasmic structures include the **centrosomes** or centrioles, which are apparent only when a cell is preparing to divide. At that time, the centrosomes form the poles of the spindle apparatus involved in chromosomal replication during mitosis.

The **nucleus** is characterized by its high content of chromatin, which contains most of the cellular DNA. When the cell is not in the process of dividing, the chromatin is distributed throughout the nucleus. Immediately before cell division, it assumes the organized structure of the chromosomes that will eventually be distributed equally to each daughter cell. The **nucleolus,** a discrete body within the nucleus, contains much RNA in granules resembling ribosomes.

Intracellular Distribution of Enzymes

The concept of the cell as a "sack of enzymes" has yielded to recognition of the cardinal significance of spatial arrangement and compartmentalization of enzymes, substrates, and cofactors within the cell. In rat liver cells, for example, the enzymes of glycolysis are located in the cytoplasm, whereas enzymes of the citric acid cycle are in the mitochondrion.

The metabolic functions of cellular organelles may be studied following their separation by differential centrifugation. After rupture of the cell membrane, centrifugation in fields of 600–100,000 × g separates cell components into microscopically identifiable fractions: intact cells, cell debris and nuclei (600 × g for 5 min), mitochondria (10,000 × g for 30 min), microsomes (100,000 × g for 60 min), and the remaining soluble or nonsedimentable fraction. The enzyme content of each fraction is then examined.

Localization of a particular enzyme in a tissue or cell in a relatively unaltered state may frequently be accomplished by histochemical procedures ("histoenzymology"). Thin (2–10 μm) frozen sections of tissue, prepared with a low-temperature microtome, are treated with a substrate for a particular enzyme. In regions where the enzyme is present, the product of the enzyme-catalyzed reaction is formed. If the product is colored and insoluble, it remains at the site of formation and serves as a marker for the localization of the enzyme. Histoenzymology provides a graphic and relatively physiologic picture of patterns of enzyme distribution. Histochemical technics are available for acid and alkaline phosphatases, monoamine oxidase, and many dehydrogenases.

ISOZYMES

Oligomeric enzymes with dissimilar protomers can exist in several forms. Frequently, one tissue produces one protomer predominantly and another tissue a different protomer. If these can combine in various ways to construct an active enzyme (eg, a tetramer), **isozymes** of that enzymic activity are said to be formed.

Isozymes are physically distinct forms of the same catalytic activity. They thus catalyze the same reaction. Isozymes are analogous to dimes from several different mints, eg, Philadelphia, Denver, and San Francisco. The monetary value (reaction catalyzed) is identical, and each coin (isozyme) is physically similar. But, just like "mint marks" on a coin, subtle physical, chemical, and immunologic differences between isozymes are apparent on careful examination.

Medical interest in isozymes was stimulated by the discovery in 1957 that **human sera contained several lactate dehydrogenase isozymes and that their relative proportions changed significantly in certain pathologic conditions.** Isozymes are common in sera and tissues of all vertebrates, insects, plants, and unicellular organisms. Both the kind and the number of enzymes involved are equally diverse. Isozymes of numerous dehydrogenases, oxidases, transaminases, phosphatases, transphosphorylases, and proteolytic enzymes have been reported.

Serum lactate dehydrogenase isozymes may be visualized by subjecting a serum sample to electrophoresis, usually at pH 8.6, on a starch, agar, or polyacrylamide gel support. The isozymes have different charges at this pH and migrate to 5 regions of the electropherogram. Isozymes are then localized by means of their ability to catalyze reduction of a colorless dye to a colored form.

A typical dehydrogenase assay reagent contains the following:

(1) Reduced substrate (eg, lactate).

(2) Coenzyme (NAD^+).

(3) Oxidized dye (eg, nitroblue tetrazolium salt [NBT]).

(4) An intermediate electron carrier to transport electrons between NADH and the dye (eg, phenazine methosulfate [PMS]).

(5) Buffer; activating ions if required.

Lactate dehydrogenase catalyzes transfer of 2 electrons and one H^+ from lactate to NAD^+ (Fig 6–12). The reaction proceeds at a measurable rate only in the presence of lactate dehydrogenase. When the

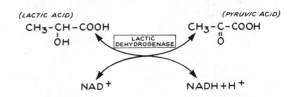

Figure 6–12. The L-lactate dehydrogenase reaction.

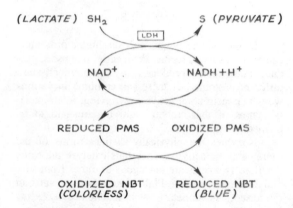

Figure 6–13. Coupled reactions in detection of lactate dehydrogenase activity on an electropherogram.

assay mixture is spread on the electropherogram and incubated at 37 C, concerted electron transfer reactions take place only in those regions where lactate dehydrogenase is present (Fig 6–13). The bands are visible to the naked eye, and their relative intensities may be quantitated by a suitable scanning photometer (Fig 6–14). The most negative isoenzyme, as detected in an electropherogram, is I_1.

Lactate dehydrogenase isozymes differ at the level of quaternary structure. The active lactate dehydrogenase molecule (MW 130,000) consists of 4 protomers of 2 types, H and M (MW about 34,000). Only the tetrameric molecule possesses catalytic activity. If

order is unimportant, these protomers might be combined in the following 5 ways:

HHHH
HHHM
HHMM
HMMM
MMMM

C. L. Markert used conditions known to disrupt and reform quaternary structure to clarify the relationships between the lactate dehydrogenase isozymes. Splitting and reconstitution of lactate dehydrogenase-I_1 or lactate dehydrogenase-I_5 produces no new isozymes. These therefore consist of a single type of protomer. When a mixture of lactate dehydrogenase-I_1 and lactate dehydrogenase-I_5 is subjected to the same treatment, lactate dehydrogenase-I_2, -I_3, and -I_4 are generated. The proportions of the isozymes found are those that would result if the relationship were:

Lactate Dehydrogenase Isozyme	Subunits
I_1	HHHH
I_2	HHHM
I_3	HHMM
I_4	HMMM
I_5	MMMM

Syntheses of H and M subunits are controlled by distinct genetic loci.

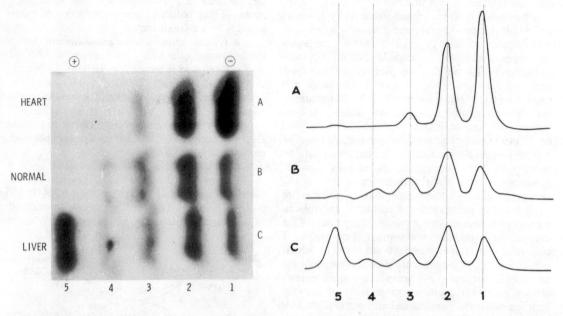

Figure 6–14. Normal and pathologic patterns of lactate dehydrogenase isozymes in human serum. LDH isozymes of serum were separated on cellulose acetate at pH 8.6 and stained for enzyme. The photometer scan shows the relative proportion of the isozymes. Pattern A is serum from a patient with a myocardial infarct, B is normal serum, and C is serum from a patient with liver disease. (Courtesy of Dr Melvin Black & Mr Hugh Miller, St Luke's Hospital, San Francisco.)

ENZYMES IN CLINICAL DIAGNOSIS

Distinction Between Functional & Nonfunctional Plasma Enzymes

Certain enzymes and proenzymes are present at all times in the circulation of normal individuals. Their substrates also are present in the circulation either continuously or intermittently, and they perform a physiologic function in blood. Examples of **functional plasma enzymes** include lipoprotein lipase, pseudocholinesterase, and the proenzymes of blood coagulation and of blood clot dissolution. They generally are synthesized in the liver but are present in blood in equivalent or higher concentrations than in tissues.

As the name implies, **nonfunctional plasma enzymes** perform no known physiologic function in blood. Their substrates frequently are absent from plasma, and the enzymes themselves are present in the blood of normal individuals at levels up to a millionfold lower than in tissues. Their presence in plasma at levels elevated above normal values suggests an increased rate of tissue destruction. Measurement of these nonfunctional plasma enzyme levels can thus provide the physician with valuable diagnostic and prognostic clinical evidence.

Nonfunctional plasma enzymes include those present in exocrine secretions and true intracellular enzymes. Exocrine enzymes—pancreatic amylase, lipase, bile alkaline phosphatase, and prostatic acid phosphatase—diffuse passively into the plasma. The true intracellular enzymes are normally absent from the circulation.

Origin of Nonfunctional Plasma Enzymes

Low levels of nonfunctional enzymes found ordinarily in plasma arise apparently from the routine, normal destruction of erythrocytes, leukocytes, and other cells. With accelerated cell death, soluble enzymes enter the circulation. Although elevated plasma enzyme levels are generally interpreted as evidence of cellular necrosis, vigorous exercise also results in release of small quantities of muscle enzymes.

Diagnostic Value of Specific Enzymes

The determination by the clinical laboratory analyst of the activity of the following enzymes can provide the physician with valuable confirmatory or suggestive diagnostic evidence.

A. Lipase: The plasma lipase level may be low in liver disease, vitamin A deficiency, some malignancies, and diabetes mellitus. It may be elevated in acute pancreatitis and pancreatic carcinoma.

B. Amylase: The plasma amylase level may be low in liver disease and increased in high intestinal obstruction, parotitis, acute pancreatitis, and diabetes.

C. Trypsin: Elevated levels of trypsin in plasma occur during acute pancreatic disease with resultant changes in the coagulability of the blood reported as antithrombin titer. Direct measurement of plasma trypsin is also possible. Elevation of plasma trypsin is probably a more sensitive and reliable indicator of pancreatic disease than plasma amylase or lipase.

D. Cholinesterase: In general, low levels are found in patients ill with liver disease, malnutrition, chronic debilitating and acute infectious diseases, and anemias. High levels occur in nephrotic syndrome. Many drugs produce a temporary decrease in cholinesterase activity, but the alkyl fluorophosphates irreversibly inhibit the enzyme. Some insecticides depress cholinesterase activity, and tests for the activity of this enzyme in the plasma may be useful in detecting overexposure to these agents.

Since the content of cholinesterase in young red blood cells is considerably higher than in the adult red blood cells, the cholinesterase titer of erythrocytes in peripheral blood gives an indication of hematopoietic activity.

E. Alkaline Phosphatase: The level of enzymes capable of catalyzing the hydrolysis of various phosphate esters at alkaline pH (alkaline phosphatase activity) may be increased in rickets, hyperparathyroidism, Paget's disease, osteoblastic sarcoma, obstructive jaundice, and metastatic carcinoma.

Isozymes of alkaline phosphatase are present in body fluids. These include specific isozymes originating from bone, liver, placenta, and intestine. Measurement of specific alkaline phosphatase isozymes may therefore improve the diagnostic value of this test. Serum alkaline phosphatase levels may increase in congestive heart failure as a result of injury to the liver. Of great value is the use of alkaline phosphatase isozyme measurements to distinguish liver lesions from bone lesions in cases of metastatic carcinoma.

F. Acid Phosphatase: The level of enzymes capable of catalyzing the hydrolysis of various phosphate esters at acidic pH (acid phosphatase activity) may be elevated in metastatic prostatic carcinoma.

G. Transaminases: Two transaminases are of clinical interest. **Glutamic oxaloacetic transaminase (GOT)** catalyzes the transfer of the amino group of aspartic acid to α-ketoglutaric acid, forming glutamic and oxaloacetic acids; **glutamic pyruvic transaminase (GPT)** transfers the amino group of alanine to α-ketoglutaric acid, forming glutamic and pyruvic acids. Serum transaminase levels in normal subjects are low, but after extensive tissue destruction these enzymes are liberated into the serum. An example is heart muscle, which is rich in transaminases. Consequently, myocardial infarcts are followed by rapid and striking increases in serum transaminase levels. Values decrease toward normal within a few days. Estimation of glutamic oxaloacetic transaminase is widely used to confirm a diagnosis of myocardial infarction.

Liver tissue, rich in both transaminases, contains more GPT than GOT. While both transaminases are elevated in sera of patients with acute hepatic disease, GPT, which is only slightly elevated by cardiac necrosis, is a more specific indicator of liver damage.

Extensive skeletal muscle damage, as in severe trauma, also elevates serum transaminase levels.

H. Lactate Dehydrogenase: In myocardial infarction, the concentration of serum lactate dehydrogenase rises within 24 hours after the infarct and returns to the normal range within 5–6 days. High levels of LD also occur in patients with acute and chronic leukemia in relapse, with generalized carcinomatosis, and, occasionally, with acute hepatitis during its clinical peak, but not in patients with jaundice due to other causes. Serum LD is normal in patients with acute febrile and chronic infectious diseases as well as those with anemia, pulmonary infarction, localized neoplastic disease, and chronic disease processes.

I. LD Isozymes: Cardiac muscle contains a preponderance of LD-I_1. Measurement of the plasma isozyme pattern (Fig 6–14) following myocardial infarction is a more sensitive and lasting indication of myocardial necrosis than is simple measurement of the total serum or plasma lactate dehydrogenase activity.

J. Isocitrate Dehydrogenase: Measurement of serum **isocitrate dehydrogenase** activity (ICD) is useful in diagnosis of liver disease. The KD level of cerebrospinal fluid is also elevated in patients with cerebral tumors or meningitis of various types. With tumors, the values are about 10 times normal. With meningitis, the values may be as much as 50 times normal, but gradually decrease to normal as the patient recovers.

K. Creatine Phosphokinase: Measurement of serum creatine phosphokinase (CK or CPK) activity is of value in the diagnosis of disorders affecting skeletal and cardiac muscle as well as in studies of families affected with pseudohypertrophic muscular dystrophy. Nonmuscular tissues other than brain do not contain high levels of creatine phosphokinase, so determinations of activity of this enzyme should be more specific to particular tissues than the transaminases or dehydrogenases that are more widely distributed. In human tissue, creatine phosphokinase exists as 3 different dimeric isozymes composed of M (for muscle) and B (for brain) protomers. These are designated CK_1 (BB), CK_2 (MB), and CK_3 (MM). While measurement of creatine phosphokinase levels is relatively routine in confirming a diagnosis of myocardial infarction, determination of differential levels of creatine phosphokinase isozymes—as with LD—provides valuable additional information. In addition to electrophoretic separation (see Fig 6–14), creatine phosphokinase isozymes may be separated by ion exchange chromatographic technics.

In normal individuals, the MB isozyme accounts for over 2% of the total creatine phosphokinase of plasma. By contrast, MB accounts for 4.5–20% of the total creatine phosphokinase in plasma of patients with a recent myocardial infarct, and the total MB isozyme level is elevated up to 20-fold above normal.

L. Ceruloplasmin: This copper-containing serum globulin shows oxidase activity **in vitro** toward several amines, including epinephrine, 5-hydroxytryptamine, and dihydroxyphenylalanine. Plasma ceruloplasmin levels, determined as oxidase activity, are elevated in several circumstances (cirrhosis, hepatitis, bacterial infections, pregnancy, etc). Decreased levels, however, provide a useful confirmatory test for Wilson's disease (hepatolenticular degeneration).

•   •   •

References

General Enzymology

Boyer PD, Lardy H, Myrbäck K (editors): *The Enzymes,* 3rd ed. 7 vols. Academic Press, 1970–1973.

Nord FF (editor): *Advances in Enzymology.* Interscience. Issued annually.

Enzyme Structure

Hirs CHW, Timascheff SN (editors): Enzyme structure. Parts A–H in: *Methods in Enzymology.* Vol 11, 1967; Vols 25 and 26, 1972; Vol 27, 1973; Vol 47, 1977; Vols 48 and 49, 1978; Vol 49, 1979. Academic Press.

Coenzymes

McCormick DB, Wright LD (editors): Vitamins and coenzymes. Parts A–F in: *Methods in Enzymology.* Vol 18A, 1970; Vols 18B and 18C, 1971; Vol 62, 1979; Vols 66 and 67, 1980. Academic Press.

Nomenclature

Enzyme Nomenclature 1978. Recommendations of the Nomenclature Committee of the International Union of Biochemistry on the Nomenclature and Classification of Enzymes. Academic Press, 1979.

Assay & Purification of Enzymes

Bergmeyer H-U (editor): *Methods of Enzymatic Analysis,* 2nd English ed. 4 vols. Academic Press, 1974.

Boyer PD, Lardy H, Myrbäck K (editors): *The Enzymes,* 3rd ed. 7 vols. Academic Press, 1970–1973.

Colowick SP, Kaplan NO (editors): *Methods in Enzymology.* 69 vols. Academic Press, 1955–1980.

Hoffmann-Ostenhoff O & others: *Affinity Chromatography.* Pergamon Press, 1978.

Jacoby WB (editor): Enzyme purification and related techniques. In: *Methods in Enzymology.* Vol 22. Academic Press, 1971.

Jacoby WB, Wilchek M (editors): Affinity techniques. In: *Methods in Enzymology.* Vol 34, 1974; Vol 46, 1977. Academic Press.

Mosbach K (editor): Immobilized enzymes. In: *Methods in Enzymology.* Vol 44. Academic Press, 1976.

Intracellular Distribution of Enzymes

DePierre JW, Ernster L: Enzyme topology of intracellular membranes. *Annu Rev Biochem* 1977;**46**:201.

Clinical Enzymology

Bergmeyer HU: Aspartate aminotransferase. *Test of the Month 6* 1980; No. 2.

Bergström K: Determination of serum alkaline phosphatase activity. *Test of the Month 1* 1974; No. 22.

Fishinger AF: Creatine phosphokinase and its isoenzymes. *Test of the Month 2* 1976; No. 6.

McNair RD: Lactate dehydrogenase. *Test of the Month 2* 1976; No. 3.

Wilkinson JH: Clinical applications of isozymes. *Clin Chem* 1970;**16**:733.

Wilkinson JH: Clinical significance of enzyme activity measurements. *Clin Chem* 1970;**16**:733.

7 | Bioenergetics

Peter A. Mayes, PhD, DSc

INTRODUCTION

Bioenergetics or **biochemical thermodynamics** is the study of the energy changes accompanying biochemical reactions. These reactions are accompanied by liberation of energy as the reacting system moves from a higher to a lower energy level. Most frequently, the energy is liberated in the form of heat. In nonbiologic systems, heat energy may be transformed into mechanical or electrical energy. Since biologic systems are essentially isothermic, no direct use can be made of heat liberated in biologic reactions to drive the vital processes that require energy. These processes—eg, synthetic reactions, muscular contraction, nerve conduction, and active transport—obtain energy by chemical linkage or **coupling** to oxidative reactions. In its simplest form, this type of coupling may be represented as shown in Fig 7–1.

The conversion of metabolite A to metabolite B occurs with release of energy. It is coupled to another reaction, in which energy is required to convert metabolite C to metabolite D. As some of the energy liberated in the degradative reaction is transferred to the synthetic reaction in a form other than heat, the normal chemical terms exothermic and endothermic cannot be applied to these reactions. Rather, the terms

exergonic and endergonic are used to indicate that a process is accompanied by loss or gain, respectively, of free energy, regardless of the form of energy involved. In practice, an endergonic process cannot exist independently but must be a component of a coupled exergonic/endergonic system where the overall net change is exergonic.

The Concept of Free Energy

Change in free energy (ΔG)* is that portion of the total energy change in a system which is available for doing work, ie, it is the useful energy.

If the reaction shown in Fig 7–1 is to go from left to right, then the overall process must be accompanied by loss of free energy as heat. One possible mechanism of coupling could be envisaged if a common obligatory intermediate (I) took part in both reactions, ie,

$$A + C \longrightarrow I \longrightarrow B + D$$

Some exergonic and endergonic reactions in biologic systems are coupled in this way. It should be appreciated that this type of system has a built-in mechanism for biologic control of the rate at which oxidative processes are allowed to occur since the existence of a common obligatory intermediate for both the exergonic and endergonic reactions allows the rate of utilization of the product of the synthetic path (D) to determine by mass action the rate at which A is oxidized. Indeed, these relationships supply a basis for the concept of **respiratory control,** the process that prevents an organism from burning out of control. An extension of the coupling concept is provided by dehydrogenation reactions, which are coupled to hydrogenations by an intermediate carrier (Fig 7–2).

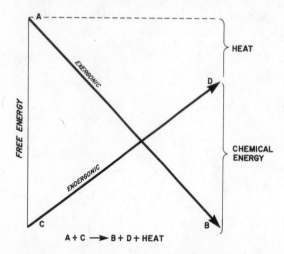

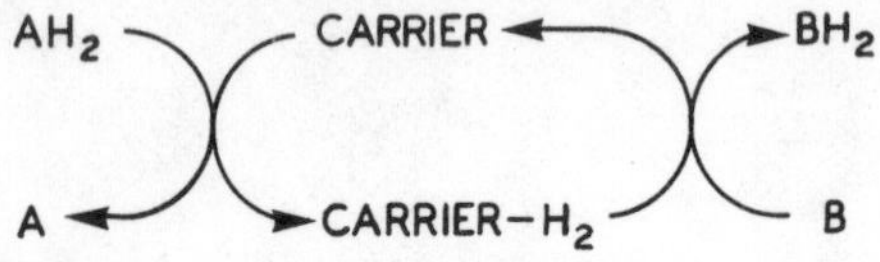

Figure 7–1. Coupling of an exergonic to an endergonic reaction.

Figure 7–2. Coupling of dehydrogenation and hydrogenation reactions by an intermediate carrier.

*ΔG is the same as ΔF, which is used in some texts.

An alternative method of coupling an exergonic to an endergonic process is to synthesize a compound of high-energy potential in the exergonic reaction and to incorporate this new compound into the endergonic reaction, thus effecting a transference of free energy from the exergonic to the endergonic pathway (Fig 7–3).

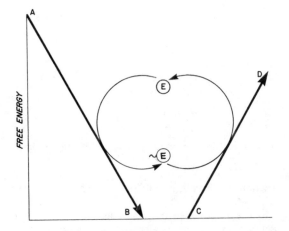

Figure 7–3. Transference of free energy from an exergonic to an endergonic reaction through the formation of a high-energy intermediate compound.

In Fig 7–3, ~Ⓔ is a compound of high potential energy and Ⓔ is the corresponding compound of low potential energy. The biologic advantage of this mechanism is that Ⓔ, unlike I in the previous system, need not be structurally related to A, B, C, or D. This would allow Ⓔ to serve as a transducer of energy from a wide range of exergonic reactions to an equally wide range of endergonic reactions or processes, as shown in Fig 7–4.

In the living cell, the principal high-energy intermediate or carrier compound (designated ~Ⓔ) is **adenosine triphosphate** or **ATP.**

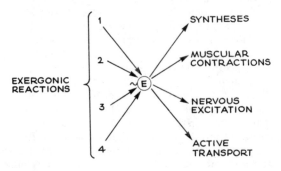

Figure 7–4. Transduction of energy through a common high-energy compound to energy-requiring (endergonic) biologic processes.

The Laws of Thermodynamics as Applied to Biochemical Systems

The first law of thermodynamics states that "the total energy of a system, plus its surroundings, remains constant." This is also the law of conservation of energy. It implies that within the total system, energy is neither lost nor gained during any change. However, within that total system, energy may be transferred from one part to another or may be transformed into another form of energy. For example, chemical energy may be transformed into heat, electrical energy, radiant energy, or mechanical energy.

The second law of thermodynamics states that "the total entropy of a system must increase if a process is to occur spontaneously." Entropy represents the extent of disorder or randomness of the system and becomes maximum in a system as it approaches true equilibrium. Under conditions of constant temperature and pressure, the relationship between the free energy change (ΔG) of a reacting system and the change in entropy (ΔS) is given by the following equation which combines the 2 laws of thermodynamics:

$$\Delta G = \Delta H - T\Delta S$$

where ΔH is the change in **enthalpy** and T is the absolute temperature.

Under the conditions of biochemical reactions, because ΔH is approximately equal to ΔE, the total change in internal energy of the reaction, the above relationship may be expressed in the following way:

$$\Delta G = \Delta E - T\Delta S$$

If ΔG is negative in sign, the reaction proceeds spontaneously with loss of free energy, ie, it is **exergonic.** If, in addition, ΔG is of great magnitude, the reaction goes virtually to completion and is essentially irreversible. On the other hand, if ΔG is positive, the reaction proceeds only if free energy can be gained, ie, it is **endergonic.** If, in addition, the magnitude of ΔG is great, the system is stable with little or no tendency for a reaction to occur. If **ΔG is zero,** the system is at **equilibrium** and no net change takes place.

Relationship Between Equilibrium Constant & Standard Free Energy Change

In a model reaction

$$A + B \rightleftharpoons C + D$$

$$\Delta G = \Delta G^0 + RT\ln \frac{[C]\,[D]}{[A]\,[B]}$$

where R is the gas constant and T is the absolute temperature. When the reactants [A], [B], [C], and [D] are present in concentrations of 1.0M, ΔG⁰ is known as the **standard free energy change.**

At equilibrium, ΔG = 0, ie,

$$0 = \Delta G^0 + RT\ln \frac{[C]\,[D]}{[A]\,[B]}$$

and therefore at equilibrium

$$\Delta G^0 = -RT\ln \frac{[C]\ [D]}{[A]\ [B]}$$

For biochemical reactions, a standard state is defined as having a pH of 7. The standard free energy change at this standard state is denoted by $\Delta G^{0'}$. Since the equilibrium constant under standard conditions is

$$K'_{eq} = \frac{[C]\ [D]}{[A]\ [B]}$$

substitution gives

$$\Delta G^{0'} = -RT\ln K'_{eq}$$

or

$$\Delta G^{0'} = -2.303\ RT \log K'_{eq}$$

Thus, the standard free energy change can be calculated from the equilibrium constant K'_{eq}. It is important to note that ΔG may be larger or smaller than $\Delta G^{0'}$ depending on the concentrations of the various reactants.

ROLE OF HIGH–ENERGY PHOSPHATES IN BIOENERGETICS & ENERGY CAPTURE

In order to maintain living processes, all organisms must obtain supplies of free energy from their environment. In the case of autotrophic organisms, this is achieved by coupling their metabolism to some simple exergonic process in their surroundings, eg, green plants utilize the energy of sunlight. On the other hand, heterotrophic organisms obtain free energy by coupling their metabolism to the breakdown of complex organic molecules in their environment. In all of these processes, ATP plays a central role in the transference of free energy from the exergonic to the endergonic processes (Figs 7–3 and 7–4). As can be seen from Fig 7–5, ATP is a specialized nucleotide containing adenine, ribose, and 3 phosphate groups. In its

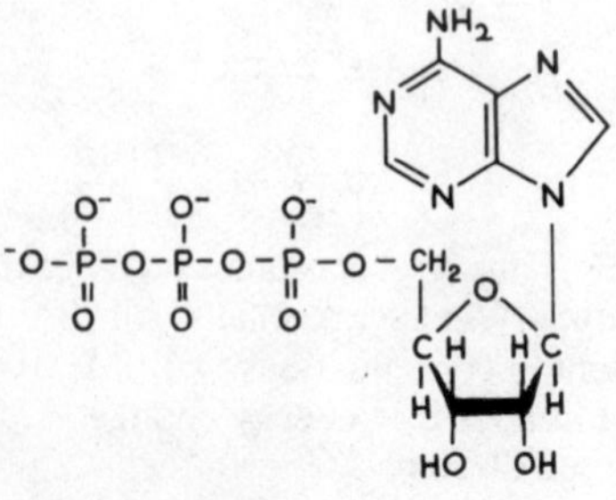

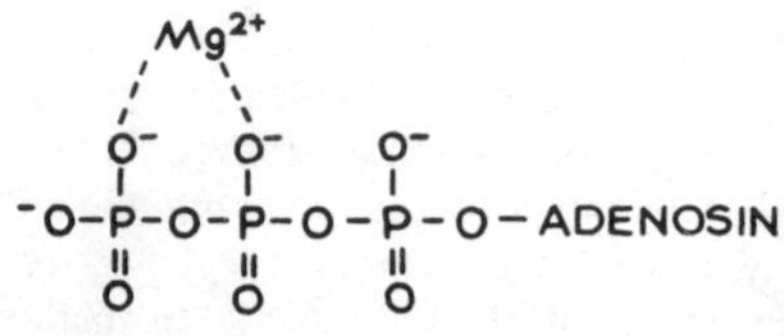

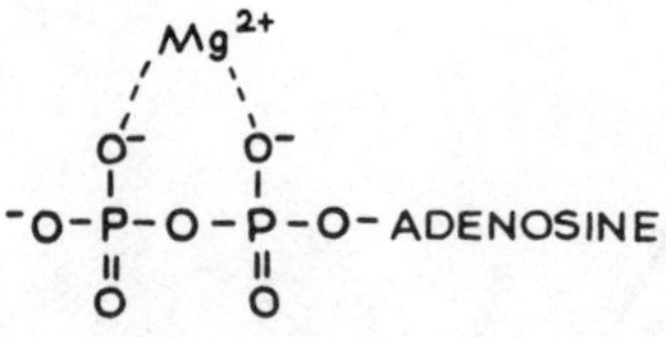

Figure 7–6. The magnesium complexes of ATP and ADP.

reactions in the cell, it functions as the Mg^{2+} complex (Fig 7–6).

The importance of phosphates in intermediary metabolism became evident in the period between 1930 and 1940 with the discovery of the chemical details of glycolysis and of the role of ATP, ADP, and inorganic phosphate (P_i) in this process. ATP was considered to be a means of transferring phosphate radicals in the process of phosphorylation. The role of ATP in biochemical energetics was indicated in experiments demonstrating that ATP and creatine phosphate were broken down during muscular contraction and that their resynthesis depended on supplying energy from oxidative processes in the muscle. It was not until 1941, when Lipmann introduced the concept of "high-energy phosphates" and the "high-energy phosphate bond," that the role of these compounds in bioenergetics was clearly appreciated.

The Free Energy of Hydrolysis of ATP & Other Organophosphates

The standard free energy of hydrolysis of a number of biochemically important phosphates is shown in Table 7–1. An estimate of the comparative tendency of each of the phosphate groups to transfer to a suitable acceptor may be obtained from the $\Delta G^{0'}$ of hydrolysis. It may be seen from the table that the value for the hydrolysis of the terminal phosphate of ATP of -8.8 kcal (-36.8 kJ) per mol (as it is also for the terminal phosphate of ADP) divides the list into 2 groups. One group of "low-energy phosphates," exemplified by the ester phosphates found in the intermediates of glycolysis, has $\Delta G^{0'}$ values which are smaller than that of ATP, while in the other group, designated "high-energy phosphates," the value is higher than that of ATP. The components of this latter group are usually anhydrides (eg, ATP, ADP, the 1-phosphate of 1,3-bisphosphoglycerate), enolphosphates (eg, phosphoenolpyruvate), and phos-

Figure 7–5. Adenosine triphosphate (ATP).

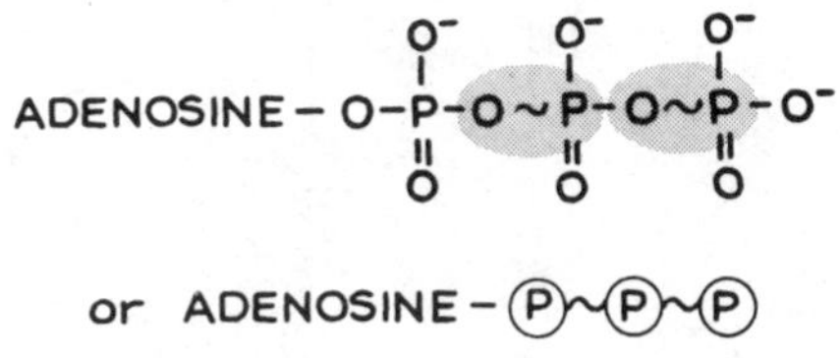

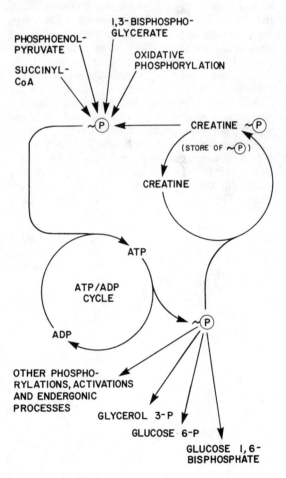

ADENOSINE – O–P–O~P–O~P–O⁻

or ADENOSINE – Ⓟ~Ⓟ~Ⓟ

Adenosine triphosphate (ATP)

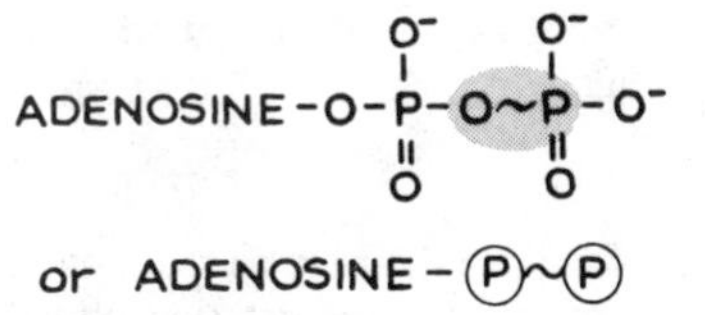

ADENOSINE–O–P–O~P–O⁻

or ADENOSINE – Ⓟ~Ⓟ

Adenosine diphosphate (ADP)

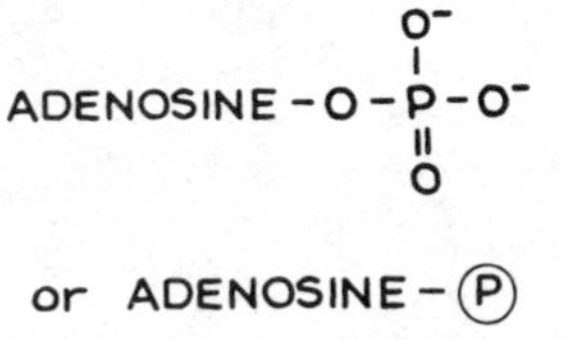

ADENOSINE – O–P–O⁻

or ADENOSINE – Ⓟ

Adenosine monophosphate (AMP)

Figure 7–7. Structure of ATP, ADP, and AMP showing the position and the number of high-energy bonds (~).

Table 7–1. Standard free energy of hydrolysis of some organophosphates of biochemical importance.

Compound	$\Delta G^{0\prime}$	
	kJ/mol	kcal/mol
Phosphoenolpyruvate	−61.9	−14.8
Carbamoyl phosphate	−51.4	−12.3
1,3-Bisphosphoglycerate (to 3-phosphoglycerate)	−49.3	−11.8
Creatine phosphate	−43.1	−10.3
ATP → ADP + P_i	36.8	−8.8
Glucose 1-phosphate	−20.9	−5.0
Fructose 6-phosphate	−15.9	−3.8
Glucose 6-phosphate	−13.8	−3.3
Glycerol 3-phosphate	−9.2	−2.2

P_i, inorganic orthophosphate

ADP can accept high-energy phosphate to form ATP from those compounds above ATP in the table. In effect, an **ATP/ADP cycle** connects these processes which **generate** ~Ⓟ to those processes that **utilize** ~Ⓟ (Fig 7–8).

phoguanidines (eg, creatine phosphate, arginine phosphate). Other biologically important compounds that are classed as "high-energy compounds" are thiol esters involving coenzyme A (eg, acetyl-CoA), acyl carrier protein, amino acid esters involved in protein synthesis, S-adenosylmethionine (active methionine), and UDPG (uridine diphosphate glucose).

High-Energy Phosphates

To indicate the presence of the high-energy phosphate group, Lipmann introduced the symbol ~Ⓟ, indicating **high-energy phosphate bond.** The symbol indicates that the group attached to the bond, on transfer to an appropriate acceptor, results in transfer of the larger quantity of free energy. For this reason, the term **group transfer potential** is preferred by some to "high-energy bond." Thus, ATP contains 2 high-energy phosphate groups and ADP contains one, whereas the phosphate bond in AMP (adenosine monophosphate) is of the low-energy type since it is a normal ester link (Fig 7–7).

Role of High-Energy Phosphates as the "Energy Currency" of the Cell

As a result of its position midway down the list of standard free energies of hydrolysis (Table 7–1), ATP is able to act as a donor of high-energy phosphate to those compounds below it in the table. Likewise, provided the necessary enzymic machinery is available,

Figure 7–8. Role of ATP/ADP cycle in transfer of high-energy phosphate. Note that ~Ⓟ does not exist in a free state but is transferred in the reactions shown.

The processes that feed ~ⓅⓇ into this cycle can be divided into 4 main groups. The greatest quantitative source of ~Ⓟ in aerobic organisms is from reactions catalyzed by ATP synthetase, which effectively reverses the hydrolysis of ATP. The free energy to drive this process is derived from respiratory chain oxidation within the mitochondria (see p 130). This process, **oxidative phosphorylation,** is part of the mechanism within the cell that operates to achieve **energy conservation** or **energy capture.** Energy capture also results from the catabolism of glucose to lactic acid in the series of reactions known as the Embden-Meyerhof pathway of glycolysis (Fig 15–3), wherein—per mole of glucose catabolized—there is net formation of 2 high-energy phosphate groups, resulting in the formation from ADP of 2 mol of ATP. The chemical processes resulting in this net formation of ATP involve the incorporation of P_i into 3-phosphoglyceraldehyde, which, after dehydrogenation, forms 1,3-bisphosphoglycerate. This compound contains a high-energy phosphate that in turn reacts with ADP to form ATP. As a result of further molecular changes, another intermediate, phosphoenolpyruvate, is formed that contains a high-energy phosphate which again is transferred to ADP to form ATP (Fig 7–9). Further energy capture occurs at the succinyl thiokinase step of the citric acid cycle (see p 155), where additional high-energy phosphate is liberated.

Another group of compounds represented in Table 7–1 acts as storage forms of high-energy phosphate. These include creatine phosphate (phosphagen), occurring in vertebrate muscle and brain, and arginine phosphate, in invertebrate muscle.

Under physiologic conditions, this reaction permits ATP concentrations to be maintained in muscle while ATP is rapidly being utilized as a source of energy for muscular contraction. On the other hand, when ATP is plentiful, its concentration can build up

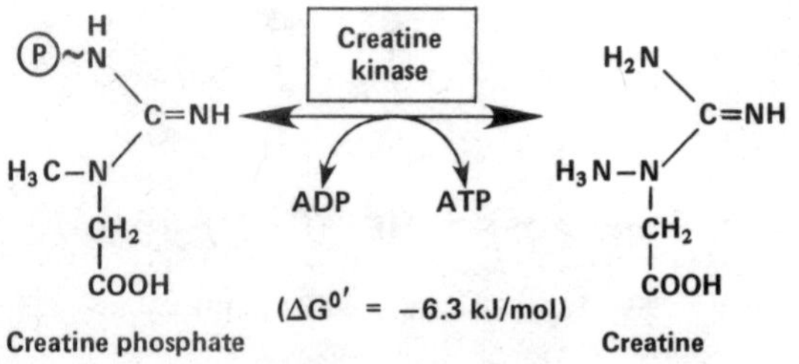

Figure 7–10. Transfer of high-energy phosphate between ATP and creatine.

sufficiently to cause the reverse reaction to occur and allow the concentration of creatine phosphate to increase substantially so as to act as a store of high-energy phosphate. When ATP acts as a phosphate donor to form those compounds of lower free energy of hydrolysis (Table 7–1), the phosphate group is invariably converted to one of low energy, eg,

Bioenergetics of Coupled Reactions

We can now consider in more detail the energetics of coupled reactions, as depicted in Fig 7–1 or 7–3. Such a reaction is the first in the glycolysis pathway (see p 160), the phosphorylation of glucose to glucose 6-phosphate, which is highly endergonic and would not proceed as such under physiologic conditions.

(1) Glucose + P_i ⟶ Glucose 6-P + H_2O

$$(\Delta G^{0'} = +13.8 \text{ kJ/mol})$$

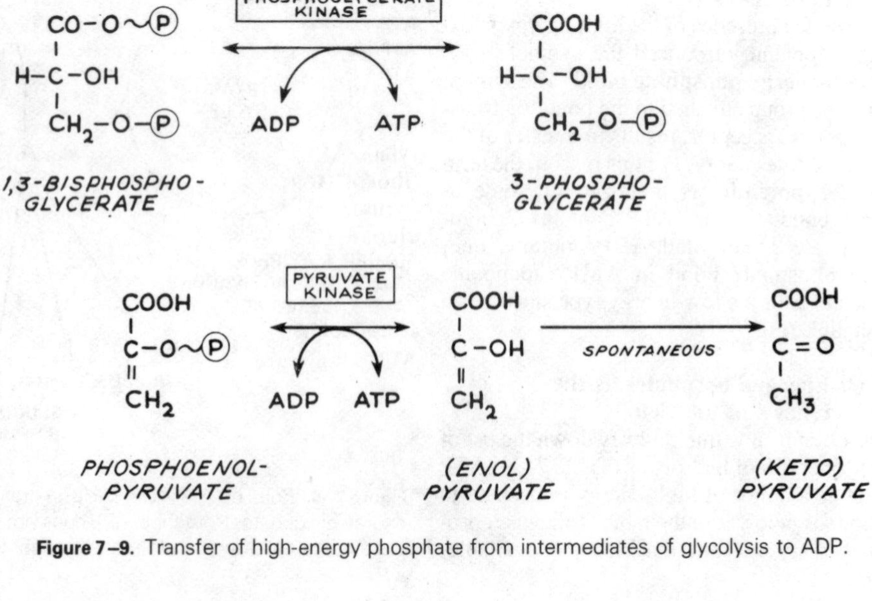

Figure 7–9. Transfer of high-energy phosphate from intermediates of glycolysis to ADP.

To take place, the reaction must be coupled with another reaction that is more exergonic than the phosphorylation of glucose is endergonic. Such a reaction is the hydrolysis of the terminal phosphate of ATP.

$$(2)\ ATP \longrightarrow ADP + P_i\ (\Delta G^{0'} = -36.8\ kJ/mol)$$

When (1) and (2) are coupled in a reaction catalyzed by hexokinase, phosphorylation of glucose readily proceeds in a highly exergonic reaction that under physiologic conditions is far from equilibrium and thus irreversible for practical purposes.

$$Glucose + ATP \xrightarrow{\text{Hexokinase}} Glucose\ 6\text{-}P + ADP$$

$$(\Delta G^{0'} = -23.0\ kJ/mol)$$

Many "activation" reactions follow this pattern.

Interconversion of Adenine Nucleotides

The enzyme **adenylate kinase** (myokinase) is present in most cells. It catalyzes the interconversion of ATP and AMP on the one hand and ADP on the other:

$$Adenosine - \textcircled{P} \sim \textcircled{P} \sim \textcircled{P} + Adenosine - \textcircled{P}$$
$$(ATP) \qquad\qquad (AMP)$$
$$\xrightarrow[\text{kinase}]{\text{Adenylate}}$$
$$\longleftrightarrow 2\ Adenosine - \textcircled{P} \sim \textcircled{P}$$
$$(2\ ADP)$$

This reaction has several functions. It allows the high-energy phosphate in ADP to be used in the formation of ATP, and it is also a means whereby AMP, formed as a consequence of several activating reactions involving ATP, can be rephosphorylated to form ADP. Finally, it allows AMP, which increases in concentration when ATP becomes depleted, to act as a metabolic (allosteric) signal to increase the rate of catabolic reactions, which in turn leads to the generation of more ATP (see p 247).

When ATP reacts to form AMP, inorganic pyrophosphate (PP_i) is formed, as occurs, for example, in the activation of long-chain fatty acids:

$$ATP + CoA \cdot SH + R \cdot COOH \xrightarrow{\text{Thiokinase}}$$
$$AMP + PP_i + R \cdot CO \sim SCoA$$

This reaction is accompanied by loss of free energy as heat, which ensures that the activation reaction will go to the right; this is further aided by the hydrolytic splitting of PP_i, catalyzed by **inorganic pyrophosphatase,** a reaction that itself has a large $\Delta G^{0'}$ of -4.6 kcal/mol. Note that activations via the pyrophosphate pathway result in the loss of 2 $\sim\textcircled{P}$

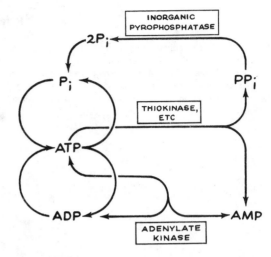

Figure 7–11. Phosphate cycles and interchange of adenine nucleotides.

rather than one $\sim\textcircled{P}$, as occurs when ADP and P_i are formed.

$$PP_i + H_2O \xrightarrow{\text{Inorganic pyrophosphatase}} 2\ P_i$$

A combination of the above reactions makes it possible for phosphate to be recycled and the adenine nucleotides to interchange (Fig 7–11).

Nucleoside Phosphates Related to ATP & ADP

By means of the enzyme **nucleoside diphosphate kinase,** nucleoside triphosphates similar to ATP but containing a different base from adenine, can be synthesized from their diphosphates, eg:

$$ATP + UDP \xleftrightarrow{\text{Nucleoside diphosphate kinase}} ADP + UTP\ \text{(uridine triphosphate)}$$
$$ATP + GDP \longleftrightarrow ADP + GTP\ \text{(guanosine triphosphate)}$$
$$ATP + CDP \longleftrightarrow ADP + CTP\ \text{(cytidine triphosphate)}$$

All of these triphosphates take part in phosphorylations in the cell. Similarly, **nucleoside monophosphate kinases,** specific for each purine or pyrimidine nucleoside, catalyze the formation of nucleoside diphosphates from the corresponding monophosphates

$$ATP + Nucleoside - \textcircled{P} \xleftrightarrow{\text{Specific nucleoside diphosphate kinase}}$$
$$ADP + Nucleoside - \textcircled{P} \sim \textcircled{P}$$

Thus, adenylate kinase is a specialized diphosphate kinase.

References

Florkin M, Stotz EH (editors): *Bioenergetics*. In: *Comprehensive Biochemistry*. Vol 22. Elsevier, 1967.

Kaplan NO, Kennedy EP (editors): *Current Aspects of Biochemical Energetics*. Academic Press, 1966.

Klotz IM: *Energy Changes in Biochemical Reactions*. Academic Press, 1967.

Krebs HA, Kornberg HL: *Energy Transformations in Living Matter*. Springer, 1957.

Lehninger AL: *Biochemistry*, 2nd ed. Worth, 1975.

Lehninger AL: *Bioenergetics: The Molecular Basis of Biological Energy Transformations*, 2nd ed. Benjamin, 1971.

Kinetic Properties of Enzymes | 8

Victor W. Rodwell, PhD

To understand how enzymes control the rates of individual reactions and of overall metabolic processes, we must review briefly how certain factors affect the rates of chemical reactions in general.

KINETIC THEORY OF REACTION

The **kinetic** or **collision theory** states that for molecules to react they must collide (ie, come within bond-forming distance) and must also possess sufficient energy to overcome the **energy barrier for reaction.** If the molecules have sufficient kinetic energy to react, anything that increases the frequency of collision between molecules will increase their rate of reaction. Factors that decrease either collision frequency or kinetic energy will decrease the rate of reaction.

If some molecules have insufficient energy to react, increased temperature, which increases kinetic energy, will increase the rate of the reaction. These concepts are illustrated diagrammatically in Fig 8–1. In A none, in B a portion, and in C all of the molecules have sufficient kinetic energy to overcome the energy barrier for reaction.

Molecules are in motion at all temperatures above absolute zero (−273 C), the temperature at which all molecular motion ceases. Concrete evidence of molecular motion is provided by the phenomenon of diffusion. This may be seen by use of a colored solute or gas that will in time become uniformly distributed throughout a solvent or container. With increasing temperature, the rate of diffusion (a result of increased molecular motion due to increased kinetic energy) increases. The pressure of a gas results from gas molecules colliding with the container walls. As the temperature of the gas increases, molecular motion, and hence the number of collisions with the vessel walls, increases. In a rigid container this causes increased pressure; in a flexible container it causes expansion. Lowering the temperature decreases the frequency of collisions with the container walls, causing a drop in pressure or a contraction in volume.

In the absence of enzymic catalysis, many chemical reactions proceed exceedingly slowly at the temperature of living cells. However, even at this temperature molecules are in motion and undergo collisions. **They fail to react rapidly because most possess insufficient kinetic energy to overcome the energy barrier for reaction.** At a considerably higher temperature (and higher kinetic energy), the reaction will occur more rapidly. That the reaction takes place at all shows that it is spontaneous (ΔG = negative). At the lower temperature, it is spontaneous but slow; at the higher temperature, spontaneous and fast. **Enzymes make spontaneous reactions proceed rapidly under the conditions prevailing in living cells.**

The mechanism by which enzymes accelerate reactions may be illustrated by a mechanical analogy. Consider a boulder at rest on a hillside (Fig 8–2).

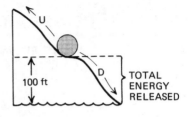

Figure 8–2.

Although the boulder might move up or down the hill, neither reaction is highly probable. It is necessary to supply a small amount of energy to send the boulder rolling downhill. This energy represents the **energy barrier** for reaction D. Similarly, the energy required to move the boulder uphill corresponds to the energy barrier for reaction U.

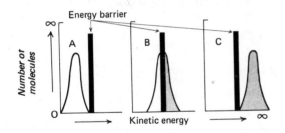

Figure 8–1. The energy barrier for chemical reactions.

Consider now the same boulder on a different hill, but the same height above ground level (Fig 8–3).

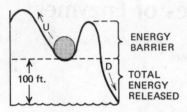

Figure 8–3.

The energy barrier for reaction D is now far greater. Note, however, that since the energy supplied in moving the boulder up from the initial position to the hump is released in its fall to ground level, the net energy potential is the same as in Fig 8–2. This illustrates the concept that **overall energy changes in chemical reactions are independent of the path or reaction mechanism.** The reaction mechanism determines the height of the hump or energy barrier only. In thermodynamic terms, ΔG for the overall downhill reaction is exactly the same in both Figs 8–2 and 8–3. **Thermodynamics, which deals exclusively with overall energy changes, can therefore tell us nothing of the path a reaction follows (ie, its mechanism).** This, as will be shown below, is the task of kinetics.

If we now construct a tunnel through the energy barrier (Fig 8–4), reaction D' becomes more probable. Although ΔG remains the same, the activation energy requirement is reduced. The tunnel lowers the energy barrier for the reaction. Enzymes may be considered to lower energy barriers for chemical reactions in roughly this way—**by providing an alternate path with the same overall change in energy,** ie, by "tunneling through" the energy barrier.

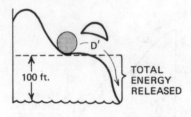

Figure 8–4.

Note also that since the initial and final states remain the same with or without enzymic catalysis, **the presence or absence of catalysts does not affect ΔG.** This is determined solely by the chemical potentials of the initial and final states.

EFFECT OF REACTANT CONCENTRATION

General Principles

At high reactant concentrations, both the number of molecules with sufficient energy to react and their frequency of collision are high. This is true whether all or only a fraction of the molecules have sufficient energy to react. For reactions involving 2 different molecules, A and B,

$$A + B \rightarrow AB$$

doubling the concentration either of A or of B will double the reaction rate. Doubling the concentration of both A and B will increase the probability of collision 4-fold. The reaction rate therefore increases 4-fold. **The reaction rate is proportionate to the concentrations of the reacting molecules.** Square brackets ([]) are used to denote molar concentrations;* $\propto$ means "proportionate to." The rate expression is:

$$Rate \propto [reacting\ molecules]$$

or

$$Rate \propto [A]\ [B]$$

For the situation represented by

$$A + 2B \rightarrow AB_2$$

the rate expression is given by

$$Rate \propto [A]\ [B]\ [B]$$

or

$$Rate \propto [A]\ [B]^2$$

For the general case where n molecules of A react with m molecules of B

$$nA + mB \rightarrow A_nB_m$$

the rate expression is

$$Rate \propto [A]^n[B]^m$$

Since all chemical reactions are reversible, for the reverse reaction:

$$A_nB_m \rightarrow nA + mB$$

the appropriate rate expression is

$$Rate \propto [A_nB_m]$$

*Strictly speaking, molar activities rather than concentrations should be used.

We represent reversibility by double arrows:

$$nA + mB \rightleftharpoons A_nB_m$$

which reads: "n molecules of A and m molecules of B are in equilibrium with A_nB_m." We may replace the "proportionate to" symbol ($\propto$) with an equality sign by inserting a proportionality constant, k, characteristic of the reaction under study. For the general case

$$nA + mB \rightleftharpoons A_nB_m$$

expressions for the rates of the forward reaction (Rate$_1$) and back reaction (Rate$_{-1}$) are:

$$Rate_1 = k_1 [A]^n [B]^m$$

and

$$Rate_{-1} = k_{-1} [A_nB_m]$$

When the rates of the forward and back reactions are equal, the system is said to be **at equilibrium**, ie,

$$Rate_1 = Rate_{-1}$$

Then

$$k_1 [A]^n [B]^m = k_{-1} [A_nB_m]$$

and

$$\frac{k_1}{k_{-1}} = \frac{[A_nB_m]}{[A]^n [B]^m} = K_{eq}$$

The ratio of k_1 to k_{-1} is termed the **equilibrium constant, K_{eq}**. The following important properties of a system at equilibrium should be kept in mind.

1. The equilibrium constant is the ratio of the reaction rate constants k_1/k_{-1}.

2. At equilibrium the reaction rates (not the reaction rate constants) **of the forward and back reactions are equal.**

3. Equilibrium is a dynamic state. Although no **net** change in concentration of reactant or product molecules occurs at equilibrium, A and B are continually being converted to A_nB_m and vice versa.

4. The equilibrium constant may be given a numerical value if we know the concentrations of A, B, and A_nB_m at equilibrium. The equilibrium constant is related to ΔG^0 as follows:

$$\Delta G^0 = -RT \ln K_{eq}$$

R is the gas constant and T the absolute temperature. Since these are known, **knowledge of the numerical value of K_{eq} permits one to calculate a value for ΔG^0.** If the equilibrium constant is greater than 1, the reaction is spontaneous, ie, the reaction as written (from left to right) is favored. If it is less than 1, the opposite is true, ie, the reaction is more likely to proceed from right to left. In terms of the mechanical analogy, **if the equilibrium constant is greater than 1, the reaction from left to right is "downhill" and the reverse reaction "uphill."** Note, however, that

although the equilibrium constant for a reaction indicates the **direction** in which a reaction is spontaneous, it does not indicate whether it will take place **rapidly**. That is, it does not tell us anything about the **magnitude of the energy barrier** for reaction. This follows because K_{eq} determines ΔG^0, previously shown to concern only initial and final states. **Reaction rates depend on the magnitude of the energy barrier, not that of ΔG^0.**

Most factors affecting the velocity of enzyme-catalyzed reactions do so by **changing reactant concentration.**

Enzyme Concentration

In many situations, both clinical and scientific, it is useful to know not only whether a given enzyme is present but also *how much* is present. Under appropriate conditions, the velocity of an enzyme-catalyzed reaction will be directly proportionate to the amount of the enzyme present. (See Figs 6–5 and 6–6.) That the rate is not always proportionate to enzyme concentration may be seen by considering the situation at equilibrium. Although the reaction is proceeding, the rate of the reverse reaction equals it. Accordingly, it would appear that the reaction velocity is zero—ie, the *net* reaction velocity is zero, a requirement of the equilibrium condition. However, when the enzyme-catalyzed reaction initiates the conversion of one or more substrates to product (P), there is no P for the reverse reaction to occur. Furthermore, at the initiation of the (forward) reaction, the concentration of S will not have been depleted at all. Therefore, at the initiation of the reaction, the velocity, ie, the **initial velocity (v)**, will be **directly proportionate to the enzyme concentration** [Enz] (see Fig 6–6).

The enzyme is a reactant that combines with substrate to form an **enzyme-substrate complex, EnzS**, which decomposes to form a product, P, and free enzyme:

$$Enz + S \underset{k_{-1}}{\overset{k_1}{\rightleftharpoons}} EnzS \underset{k_{-2}}{\overset{k_2}{\rightleftharpoons}} Enz + P$$

Note that although the rate expressions for the forward, back, and **overall** reactions include the term [Enz],

$$Enz + S \underset{k_{-2}}{\overset{k_1}{\rightleftharpoons}} Enz + P$$

$$Rate_1 = k_1 [Enz] [S]$$

$$Rate_{-2} = k_{-2} [Enz] [P]$$

in the expression for the overall equilibrium constant, [Enz] cancels out.

$$K_{eq} = \frac{k_1}{k_{-2}} = \frac{[Enz] [P]}{[Enz] [S]} = \frac{[P]}{[S]}$$

The enzyme concentration thus has no effect on the equilibrium constant. Stated another way, since enzymes affect rates, not rate constants, they cannot affect K_{eq}, which is a ratio of rate constants. **The K_{eq} of a reaction is the same regardless of whether equilibrium is approached with or without enzymatic catalysis** (recall ΔG^0). In terms of the mechanical analogy, enzymes "dig tunnels" and change the reaction path but do not affect the initial and final positions of the boulder that determine K_{eq} and ΔG^0.

Substrate Concentration

If the concentration of the substrate [S] is increased while all other conditions are kept constant, the **measured initial velocity, v** (the velocity measured when very little substrate has reacted), increases to a maximum value, V, and no further (Fig 8–5).

The velocity increases as the substrate concentration is increased up to a point where the enzyme is said to be "saturated" with substrate. The measured initial velocity reaches a maximal value and is unaffected by further increases in substrate concentration because even at low substrate concentrations, substrate still is present in large molar excess of the enzyme. For example, if an enzyme with a molecular weight of 100,000 acts on a substrate with a molecular weight of 100 and both are present at a concentration of 1 mg/mL, there are 1000 mol of substrate for every mole of enzyme. More realistic figures might be

$$[Enz] = 0.1\ \mu g/mL = 10^{-9}\ molar$$
$$[S] = 0.1\ mg/mL = 10^{-3}\ molar$$

giving a 10^6 molar excess of substrate over enzyme. Even if [S] is decreased 100-fold, substrate is present in 10,000-fold molar excess over enzyme.

The situation at points A, B, and C in Fig 8–5 is illustrated in Fig 8–6. At points A and B not all the enzyme present is combined with substrate, even though there are many more molecules of substrate than of enzyme. This is because the equilibrium constant for the reaction Enz + S $\rightleftharpoons$ EnzS is not infinitely large. **At point A or B, increasing or decreasing [S] will therefore increase or decrease the amount of Enz associated with S as EnzS, and v will thus depend on [S].** At C, essentially all the enzyme is

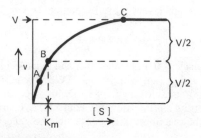

Figure 8–5. Effect of substrate concentration on the velocity of an enzyme-catalyzed reaction.

combined with substrate, so that a further increase in [S], although it increases the frequency of collision between Enz and S, cannot result in increased rates of reaction since no free enzyme is available to react.

Case B depicts a situation where exactly half the enzyme molecules are "saturated with" substrate. The velocity is accordingly **half the maximal velocity** attainable at that particular enzyme concentration. **The substrate concentration that produces half-maximal velocity, termed the K_m value or Michaelis constant,** may be determined experimentally by graphing v as a function of [S] (Fig 8–5).

When [S] is approximately equal to the K_m value, **v** is very responsive to changes in [S], and the enzyme is working at half maximal efficiency. In fact, it seems that "by design" most enzymes possess K_m values that are approximately equal to the physiologic concentration of their substrate.

The Michaelis-Menten expression

$$v = \frac{V[S]}{K_m + [S]}$$

describes the behavior of many enzymes as substrate concentration is varied. The dependence of the initial velocity of an enzyme-catalyzed reaction on [S] and on K_m may be illustrated by evaluating the Michaelis-Menten equation as follows:

1. When [S] is very much less than K_m (point A in Figs 8–5 and 8–6). Adding [S] to K_m now changes

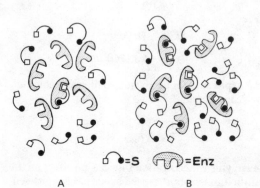

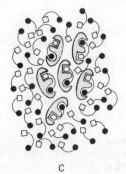

Figure 8–6. Representation of an enzyme at low *(A)*, at high *(C)*, and at the K_m concentration of substrate *(B)*. Points A, B, and C correspond to those of Fig 8–5.

its value very little, so the [S] term is dropped from the denominator. Since V and K_m are both constants, we can replace their ratio by a new constant, K. [$\approx$ means "approximately equal to."]

$$v = \frac{V[S]}{K_m + [S]} \ , \ v \approx \frac{V[S]}{K_m} \approx \frac{V}{K_m}[S] \approx K[S]$$

In other words, **when the substrate concentration is considerably below that required to produce half-maximal velocity (the K_m value), the initial velocity, v, depends upon the substrate concentration [S].**

2. When [S] is very much greater than K_m (point C, Figs 8–5 and 8–6). Now adding K_m to [S] changes the value of [S] very little, so the term K_m is dropped from the denominator.

$$v = \frac{V[S]}{K_m + [S]} \ , \ v \approx \frac{V[S]}{[S]} \approx V$$

This states that **when the substrate concentration [S] far exceeds the K_m value, the initial velocity, v, is maximal, V.**

3. When [S] = K_m (point B, Figs 8–5 and 8–6),

$$v = \frac{V[S]}{K_m + [S]} \ , \ v = \frac{V[S]}{[S] + [S]} = \frac{V[S]}{2[S]} = \frac{V}{2}$$

This states that **when the substrate concentration is equal to the K_m value, the initial velocity, v, is half-maximal.** It also tells how **to evaluate K_m,** namely, to **find the substrate concentration where the initial velocity is half-maximal.**

Since few enzymes give saturation curves that readily permit evaluation of V (and hence of K_m) when v is plotted versus [S], it is convenient to rearrange the Michaelis-Menten expression to simplify evaluation of K_m and V. The Michaelis-Menten equation may be inverted and factored as follows:

$$v = \frac{V[S]}{K_m + [S]}$$

Invert:
$$\frac{1}{v} = \frac{K_m + [S]}{V[S]}$$

Factor:
$$\frac{1}{v} = \frac{K_m}{V} \times \frac{1}{[S]} + \frac{[S]}{V[S]}$$

$$\frac{1}{v} = \frac{K_m}{V} \times \frac{1}{[S]} + \frac{1}{V}$$

This is the equation for a **straight line**

$$y = ax + b$$

where if y, or $1/v$, is plotted as a function of x, or $1/[S]$, the y intercept, b, is $1/V$, and the slope, a, is K_m/V. The negative x intercept may be evaluated by setting y = 0. Then

$$x = -\frac{b}{a} = -\frac{1}{K_m}$$

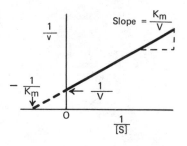

Figure 8–7. Double-reciprocal or Lineweaver-Burk plot of $\frac{1}{v}$ versus $\frac{1}{[S]}$ used for graphic evaluation of K_m and V.

From the **double-reciprocal or Lineweaver-Burk plot,** K_m may be estimated (Fig 8–7) either from the slope and y intercept or from the negative x intercept. Since [S] is expressed in molarity, **the dimensions of K_m are molarity or moles per liter.** Velocity, v, may be expressed in any units, since **K_m is independent of [Enz].** The double-reciprocal treatment requires relatively few points to define K_m and is the method most often used to determine K_m. Apart from their usefulness in interpretation of the mechanisms of enzyme-catalyzed reactions, K_m values are of considerable practical value. At a substrate concentration of 100 times K_m, the enzyme will act at essentially maximum rate, and therefore the **maximal velocity (V) will reflect the amount of active enzyme present.** This is generally desirable in the assay of enzymes. The **K_m value tells how much substrate to use in order to measure V. The double-reciprocal treatment also finds extensive application in the evaluation of inhibitors.**

Enzyme-Substrate Affinity

The **affinity** of an enzyme for its substrate is equal to the **inverse of the dissociation constant, k_d, for ES.**

$$k_d = \frac{k_{-1}}{k_1} \ \text{ when } E + S \underset{k_{-1}}{\overset{k_1}{\rightleftharpoons}} ES$$

The K_m value of an enzyme for its substrate may also serve as a measure of its k_d. However, in order for this to be true, an assumption included in the derivation of the Michaelis-Menten expression must be valid. In the derivation, it was assumed that the first step of the enzyme-catalyzed reaction

$$E + S \rightleftharpoons ES$$

is fast and always at equilibrium. In other words, the rate of dissociation of ES to E + S must be much faster than its dissociation

$$ES \underset{k_{-2}}{\overset{k_2}{\rightleftharpoons}} E + P$$

In the Michaelis-Menten expression, the [S] that gives $v = V/2$ is

$$[S] = \frac{k_2 + k_{-1}}{k_1} = K_m$$

But when $\quad\quad k_{-1} \gg k_2$

then $\quad\quad k_2 + k_{-1} \approx k_{-1}$

and $\quad\quad [S] = \frac{k_{-1}}{k_1} \equiv k_d$

Under these conditions, $1/K_m = 1/k_d =$ **affinity.** If $k_2 + k_{-1} \not\approx k_{-1}$, then $1/K_m$ underestimates the affinity, $1/k_d$.

Sigmoidal Saturation Kinetics

Certain enzymes and other ligand-binding proteins, such as hemoglobin (see Chapters 5 and 9), do not exhibit classic Michaelis-Menten saturation kinetics. When [S] is plotted versus v, the saturation curve is sigmoid (Fig 8–8). This generally indicates cooperative binding of substrate to multiple sites. Binding at one site affects binding at the others as described in Chapter 5 for hemoglobin.

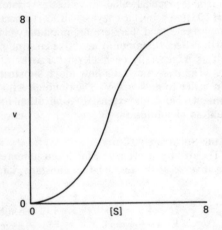

Figure 8–8. Sigmoid saturation kinetics.

For sigmoid substrate saturation kinetics, the methods of graphic evaluation of the substrate concentration that produces half-maximal velocity discussed above are invalid (straight lines are not produced). To evaluate sigmoid saturation kinetics, we employ a graphic representation of the Hill equation, an equation originally derived to describe the cooperative binding of O_2 to hemoglobin (see Chapter 5). Written in the form of a straight line, the Hill equation is

$$\log \frac{v}{V - v} = n\log [S] - \log k'$$

where k' is a complex constant. The equation states that, when [S] is low compared to k', the reaction velocity increases as the nth power of [S]. Figure 8–9

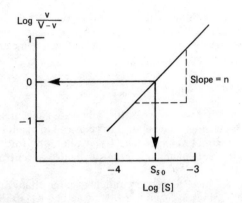

Figure 8–9. Graphic evaluation of the Hill equation to determine the substrate concentration that produces half-maximal velocity when substrate saturation kinetics are sigmoid.

illustrates a Hill plot of kinetic data for an enzyme with cooperative binding kinetics. Log $v/V - v$ plotted versus log [S] yields a straight line with slope $= n$, where n is an empirical parameter whose value depends on the number of substrate binding sites and the number and type of interactions between binding sites. When $n = 1$, the binding sites act independently of one another. If $n > 1$, the sites are cooperative; and the greater the value of n, the stronger is the cooperativity and thus the more "sigmoid" are the saturation kinetics.

At half-maximal velocity ($v = V/2$), $V/V - v = 1$, and hence log $v/V - v = 0$. Hence, to determine S_{50} (the concentration of substrate that produces half-maximal velocity), drop a perpendicular line to the X-axis from the point where log $v/V - v = 0$.

Enzymic Reactions With 2 or More Substrates

Most enzymes catalyze a reaction between 2 or more substrates yielding one or more products. For some enzymes, all substrates must be present simultaneously for the reaction to occur. For others, the enzyme first alters one substrate, then catalyzes its reaction with a second substrate. The order in which an enzyme binds its substrates may be **random** or **ordered** (Fig 8–10).

Many reactions that require coenzymes proceed by "ping-pong" mechanisms (so termed because the enzyme alternates between forms E and E') (Figs 8–11 and 8–12).

Coenzyme Concentration

As stated earlier (see Figs 6–1 and 6–2), the coenzyme may frequently be regarded as a second substrate. In this instance, the comments of the previous section apply equally to substrates and to coenzymes. However, certain coenzymes (eg, pyridoxal phosphate) are covalently bonded to the enzyme or bound noncovalently so tightly that dissociation rarely occurs (eg, thiamin pyrophosphate). In these cases, we regard the enzyme-coenzyme complex as the enzyme.

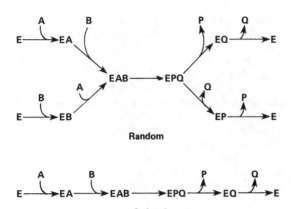

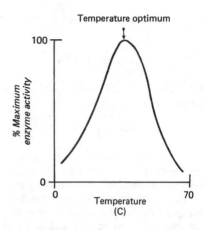

Figure 8–10. Random (top) and ordered addition of substrates A and B and dissociation of products P and Q from an enzyme, E.

Figure 8–13. Effect of temperature on the velocity of a hypothetical enzyme-catalyzed reaction.

A $\xrightarrow{}$ EA $\xrightarrow{}$ E'P $\xrightarrow{}$ E' $\xrightarrow{}$ E'B $\xrightarrow{}$ EQ $\xrightarrow{}$ E

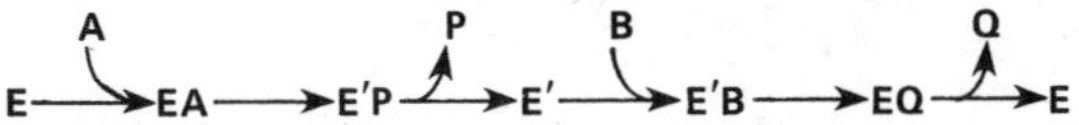

Figure 8–11. Generalized "ping-pong" mechanism for enzymic catalysis.

Temperature

Over a limited range of temperatures, the velocity of enzyme-catalyzed reactions increases as temperature rises. The exact ratio by which the velocity changes for a 10 C temperature rise is the Q_{10}, **or temperature coefficient.** The velocity of many biologic reactions roughly doubles with a 10 C rise in temperature ($Q_{10} = 2$), and is halved if the temperature is decreased by 10 C. Many physiologic processes—eg, the rate of contraction of an excised heart—consequently exhibit a Q_{10} of about 2.

For rates of enzyme-catalyzed reactions measured at several temperatures, Fig 8–13 is typical. There is an optimal temperature at which the reaction is most rapid. Above this, the reaction rate decreases sharply, mainly due to denaturation of the enzyme by heat.

For most enzymes, optimal temperatures are at or above those of the cells in which they occur. Enzymes from microorganisms adapted to growth in natural hot springs may exhibit optimal temperatures close to the boiling point of water.

The increase in rate below optimal temperature

results from the increased kinetic energy of the reacting molecules. As the temperature is raised still further, however, the kinetic energy of the enzyme molecule becomes so great that it exceeds the energy barrier for breaking the secondary bonds that hold the enzyme in its native or catalytically active state. There is consequently a loss of secondary and tertiary structure and a parallel loss of catalytic activity.

pH

Moderate pH changes affect the **ionic state of the enzyme** and frequently that of the substrate also. When enzyme activity is measured at several pH values, optimal activity is generally observed between pH values of 5.0 and 9.0. However, a few enzymes, eg, pepsin, are active at pH values well outside this range.

The shape of pH-activity curves is determined by the following factors:

1. Enzyme denaturation at extremely high or low pH.

2. Effects on the charged state of the substrate or enzyme. For the enzyme, charge changes may affect activity either by changing structure or by changing the charge on a residue functional in substrate-binding or catalysis. To illustrate, consider a negatively charged enzyme (Enz⁻) reacting with a positively charged substrate (SH⁺)

$$\text{Enz}^- + \text{SH}^+ \rightarrow \text{EnzSH}$$

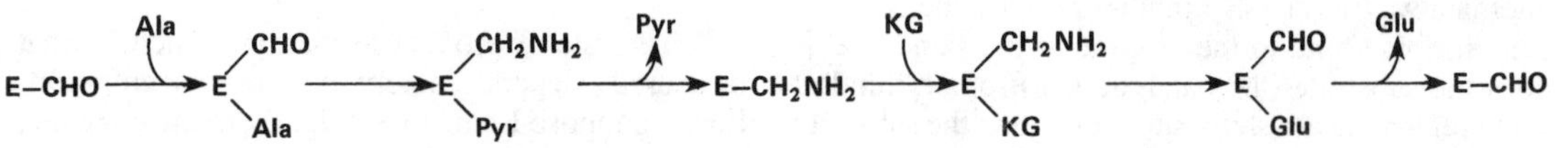

Figure 8–12. "Ping-pong" mechanism for transamination (compare with Fig 6–2). E–CHO and E–CH₂NH₂ represent the enzyme-pyridoxal phosphate and enzyme-pyridoxamine phosphate complexes, respectively. Ala = alanine, Pyr = pyruvate, KG = α-ketoglutarate, and Glu = glutamate.

At low pH, Enz$^-$ protonates and loses its negative charge:

$$Enz^- + H^+ \rightarrow Enz\text{-}H$$

Similarly, at high pH, SH$^+$ ionizes and loses its positive charge:

$$SH^+ \rightarrow S + H^+$$

Since the only forms that will interact are SH$^+$ and Enz$^-$, extreme pH values will lower the effective concentration of Enz$^-$ and SH$^+$, thus lowering the reaction velocity (Fig 8–14). Only in the cross-hatched area are both Enz and S in the appropriate ionic state, and the maximal concentrations of Enz and S are correctly charged at X.

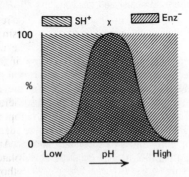

Figure 8–14. Effect of pH on enzyme activity.

Another important factor is a change in conformation of the enzyme when the pH is varied. A charged group distal to the region where the substrate is bound may be necessary to maintain an active tertiary or quaternary structure, as described for hemoglobin (see Chapter 5). As the charge on this group is changed, the protein may unravel, become more compact, or dissociate into protomers—all with resulting loss of activity.

INHIBITION OF ENZYME ACTIVITY

We distinguish 2 broad classes of inhibitors of enzyme activity—competitive and noncompetitive—depending on whether the inhibition is (competitive) or is not (noncompetitive) relieved by increasing substrate concentration. In practice, many inhibitors do not exhibit the idealized properties of pure competitive or noncompetitive inhibition discussed below. An alternate way to classify inhibitors is by their site of action. Some bind to the enzyme at the same site as does the substrate (the catalytic site); others bind at some region (an allosteric site) other than the substrate site.

Competitive or Substrate Analog Inhibition

Classic competitive inhibition occurs at the substrate-binding or catalytic site. The chemical structure of a substrate analog inhibitor (I) generally resembles that of the substrate (S). It may therefore combine reversibly with the enzyme, forming an enzyme inhibitor (EnzI) complex rather than an EnzS complex. When both the substrate and this type of inhibitor are present, they compete for the same binding sites on the enzyme surface. A much studied case of competitive inhibition is that of malonate (I) with succinate (S) for succinate dehydrogenase.

Succinate dehydrogenase catalyzes formation of fumarate by removal of one hydrogen atom from each α-carbon atom of succinate (Fig 8–15).

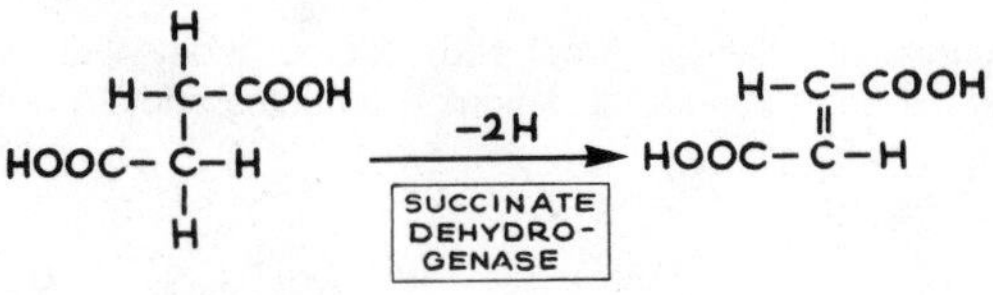

$$
\begin{array}{ccc}
H & & H \\
| & & | \\
H-C-COOH & & H-C-COOH \\
| & \xrightarrow[\substack{\text{SUCCINATE} \\ \text{DEHYDRO-} \\ \text{GENASE}}]{-2H} & \| \\
HOOC-C-H & & HOOC-C-H \\
| & & \\
H & &
\end{array}
$$

Succinic acid   Fumaric acid

Figure 8–15. The succinate dehydrogenase reaction.

Malonate (I) (HOOC–CH$_2$–COOH) can combine with the dehydrogenase, forming an EnzI complex. This cannot be dehydrogenated since there is no way to remove even one H atom from the single α-carbon atom of malonate without forming a pentavalent carbon atom. The only reaction the EnzI complex can undergo is decomposition back to free enzyme plus inhibitor. For the reversible reaction,

$$
EnzI \underset{k_{-1}}{\overset{k_1}{\rightleftharpoons}} Enz + I
$$

the equilibrium constant, K_i, is

$$
K_i = \frac{[Enz][I]}{[EnzI]} = \frac{k_1}{k_{-1}}
$$

The action of competitive inhibitors may be understood in terms of the following reactions:

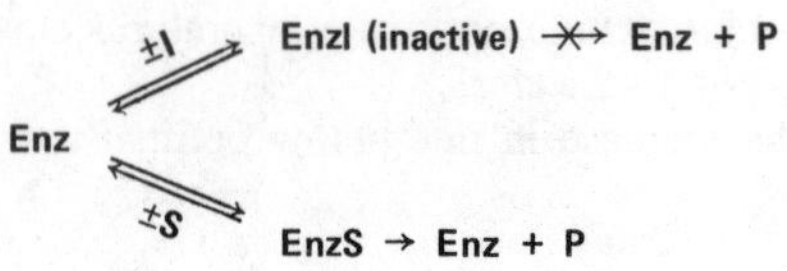

$$
Enz \quad
\begin{array}{l}
\overset{+I}{\rightleftharpoons} \quad EnzI \text{ (inactive)} \xrightarrow{\quad} Enz + P \\
\overset{+S}{\rightleftharpoons} \quad EnzS \rightarrow Enz + P
\end{array}
$$

The rate of product formation, which is what is measured, depends solely on the concentration of EnzS. Suppose I binds very tightly to the enzyme (K_i = a small number). There now is little free enzyme (Enz) available to combine with S to form EnzS and to decompose to Enz + P. The reaction rate (formation of P) will thus be slow. For analogous reasons, an equal concentration of a less tightly bound inhibitor (K_i = a larger number) will not decrease the rate of the catalyzed reaction so markedly. Suppose that, at a fixed concentration of I, more S is added. This increases the probability that Enz will combine with S rather than with I. The ratio of EnzS/EnzI and the reaction rate also rise. At a sufficiently high concentration of S, the concentration of EnzI should be vanishingly small. If so, the rate of the catalyzed reaction will be the same as in the absence of I (Fig 8–16).

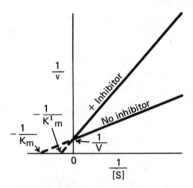

Figure 8–16. Lineweaver-Burk plot of classic competitive inhibition. Note the complete relief of inhibition at high [S] (low 1/[S]).

The reaction velocity (v) at a fixed concentration of inhibitor was measured at various concentrations of S. The lines drawn through the experimental points coincide at the y-axis. Since the y-intercept is 1/V, this states that **at an infinitely high concentration of S (1/S = O), v is the same as in the absence of inhibitor.** However, the intercept on the x-axis (which is related to K_m) varies with inhibitor concentration and becomes a larger number ($-1/K'_m$ is smaller than $-1/K_m$) in the presence of I. Thus, **a competitive inhibitor raises the apparent K_m (K'_m) for the substrate.** Since K_m is the substrate concentration where the concentration of free enzyme is equal to the concentration of enzyme as EnzS, substantial free enzyme is available to combine with inhibitor. For simple competitive inhibition, the intercept on the x-axis is

$$ y = \frac{1}{K_m \left(1 + \frac{[I]}{K_i} \right)} $$

K_m may be evaluated in the absence of I, and K_i evaluated using the above equation. If the number of moles of I added is much greater than the number of moles of enzyme present, [I] may generally be taken as the added (known) concentration of inhibitor. The K_i values for a series of substrate analog (competitive) inhibitors indicate which are most effective. **At a low concentration, those with the lowest K_i values will cause the greatest degree of inhibition.**

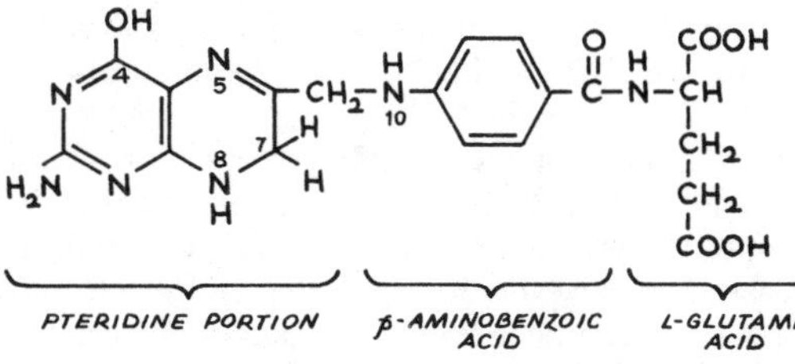

Figure 8–17. 7,8-Dihydrofolic acid.

Competitive inhibitors that block enzyme reactions in a parasite are potent **chemotherapeutic agents.** For example, many microorganisms require p-aminobenzoic acid to form folic acid (Fig 8–17), a human B vitamin.

Sulfanilamide, a structural analog of p-aminobenzoate, will block folic acid synthesis. The resulting folate deficiency is fatal to the microorganism. Since humans lack the enzymes necessary to synthesize folic acid, this compound is required as a vitamin in the diet. It follows that sulfonamides do not act as competitive inhibitors of folic acid synthesis in man.

Folic acid analogs used as chemotherapeutic agents against human tumors include aminopterin (4-aminofolic acid) and amethopterin (Fig 8–18), which inhibit growth of Ehrlich ascites tumor cells. Amethopterin is a competitive inhibitor for dihydrofolate in the dihydrofolate reductase reaction. An amethopterin-resistant strain of Ehrlich cells has been shown to have as much as 100 times more dihydrofolate reductase than the sensitive strain, although levels of other folate-utilizing enzymes are unchanged. This illustrates one mechanism of drug resistance, ie, hyperproduction of the drug-sensitive enzyme.

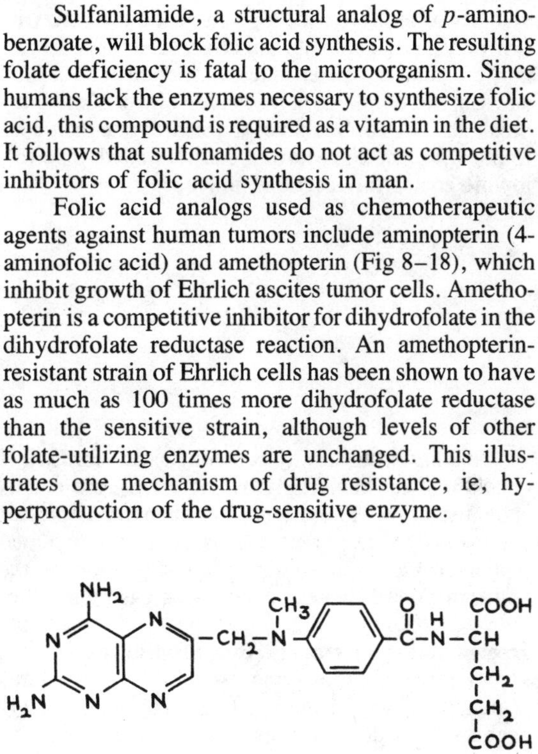

Figure 8–18. Amethopterin (methotrexate, 4-amino-N[10]-methylfolic acid).

Other **antagonists to B vitamins** include pyrithiamine and oxythiamine (antagonists to thiamin), pyridine-3-sulfonic acid (to nicotinamide), pantoyl taurine and ω-methylpantothenic acid (to pantothenic acid), deoxypyridoxine (to pyridoxine), desthiobiotin (to biotin), and dicumarol (to vitamin K).

Many other drugs that inhibit enzyme action operate in a similar manner. D-Histidine competitively inhibits the action of histidase on L-histidine. **Physostigmine** competitively inhibits the hydrolysis of acetylcholine by cholinesterase, probably because it is structurally similar to acetylcholine. Even ATP and

ADP are competitive inhibitors for many oxidoreductases where NAD^+ and $NADP^+$ are required as coenzymes. Recall that both the coenzymes and the inhibitors are derivatives of AMP (see Table 6–2).

The sulfonamide derivative **acetazolamide** (Diamox), a potent inhibitor of carbonic anhydrase, intensifies renal excretion of water and electrolytes because of the importance of carbonic anhydrase in renal tubular reabsorption of electrolytes and thus of water.

Reversible Noncompetitive Inhibition

As the name implies, in this case no competition occurs between S and I. I usually bears little or no structural resemblance to S and may be assumed to bind to a different region on the enzyme. **Reversible noncompetitive inhibitors lower the maximum velocity attainable with a given amount of enzyme (lower V) but usually do not affect K_m.** Since I and S may combine at different sites, formation of both EnzI and EnzIS complexes is possible. Since EnzIS may break down to form product at a slower rate than does EnzS, the reaction is slowed but not halted. The following competing reactions may occur:

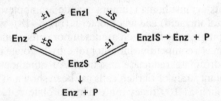

If S has equal affinity both for Enz and for EnzI (I does not affect the affinity of Enz for S), the results shown in Fig 8–19 are obtained when 1/v is plotted against 1/[S] in the presence of inhibitor. (It is assumed that there has been no significant alteration of the conformation of the active site when I is bound.)

Irreversible Noncompetitive Inhibition

A variety of enzyme "poisons," eg: iodoacetamide, heavy metal ions (Ag^+, Hg^{2+}), oxidizing agents, etc, reduce enzyme activity. Since these inhibitors bear no structural resemblance to the substrate, an increase in substrate concentration generally does not relieve this inhibition. Kinetic analysis of the type discussed above may not distinguish between enzyme poisons and true reversible noncompetitive inhibitors. Reversible noncompetitive inhibition is, in any case, rare. Unfortunately this is not always appreciated since both reversible and irreversible noncompetitive inhibition exhibit similar kinetics.

Extracts of the intestinal parasite *Ascaris* contain pepsin and trypsin inhibitors. The parasitic worm thus escapes digestion in the intestine. These protein inhibitors occur also in pancreas, lung, serum, soybeans, and raw egg white. Animals may also produce antibodies that irreversibly inactivate enzymes in response to the parenteral injection of the enzyme as antigen. This seriously limits the use of enzymes as chemotherapeutic agents.

THE CATALYTIC SITE

General Principles

The large size of proteins relative to substrates led biochemists at the turn of the century to postulate that a restricted region of the enzyme was concerned with catalysis. This region was termed the active site. Today, we refer to the **catalytic site,** since we now know that other sites are "active" (eg, allosteric sites). Initially, it was extremely puzzling to biochemists why enzymes were so large, when only a portion of their structure appeared to be required for substrate binding and catalysis. Today, we recognize from 3-dimensional models of enzymes that a far greater portion of the protein interacts with the substrate than was formerly supposed. When the need for allosteric sites of equal size also arises (see Chapters 5 and 9), the wonder is that proteins are as small as they are.

Rigid Model of the Catalytic Site

The original model of a catalytic site, proposed by Emil Fischer, visualized interaction between substrate and enzyme in terms of a "lock and key" analogy. This lock and key, or rigid template model (Fig 8–20), is still useful for understanding certain properties of enzymes—for example, the ordered binding of 2 or more substrates (Fig 8–21) or the kinetics of a simple substrate saturation curve (Fig 8–5).

Flexible Model of the Catalytic Site

An unfortunate feature of the Fischer model is the

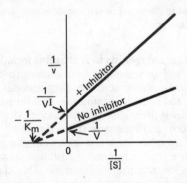

Figure 8–19. Lineweaver-Burk plot for reversible noncompetitive inhibition.

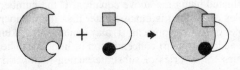

Figure 8–20. Representation of formation of an EnzS complex according to the Fischer template hypothesis.

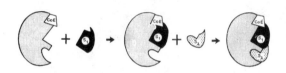

Figure 8–21. Representation of sequential adsorption of a coenzyme (CoE) and of 2 substrates (S_1 and S_2) to an enzyme in terms of the template hypothesis. The coenzyme is assumed to bear a group essential for binding the first substrate (S_1), which in turn facilitates binding of S_2.

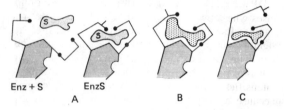

Figure 8–23. Representation of conformational changes in an enzyme protein when binding substrate *(A)* or inactive substrate analogs *(B, C).* (After Koshland.)

implied rigidity of the catalytic site. A more useful model is the **"induced fit" model** of Koshland. Originally little more than an attractive hypothesis, this model now has considerable experimental support.

An essential feature is the flexibility of the catalytic site. In the Fischer model, the catalytic site is presumed to be preshaped to fit the substrate. In the induced fit model, the substrate induces a conformational change in the enzyme. This aligns amino acid residues or other groups on the enzyme in the correct spatial orientation for substrate binding, catalysis, or both. At the same time, other amino acid residues may become buried in the interior of the enzyme.

In the example (Fig 8–22), hydrophobic groups (hatched) and charged groups (dots) both are involved in substrate binding. A phosphoserine (–P) and the –SH of a cysteine residue are involved in catalysis. Other residues involved in neither process are represented by Lys and Met residues. In the absence of substrate, the catalytic and the substrate-binding groups are several bond distances removed from one another. Approach of the substrate induces a conformational change in the enzyme protein, aligning the groups correctly for substrate binding and for catalysis. At the same time, the spatial orientations of other regions are also altered—the Lys and Met are now closer together (Fig 8–22). An alternative representation is shown in Fig 8–23.

Substrate analogs may cause some, but not all, of the correct conformational changes. On attachment of the true substrate (A), all groups (shown as closed circles) are brought into correct alignment. Attachment of a substrate analog that is too "bulky" (Fig

8–23B) or too "slim" (Fig 8–23C) induces incorrect alignment. One final feature is the site shown as a small notch on the right. One may visualize a regulatory molecule attaching at this point and "holding down" one of the polypeptide arms bearing a catalytic group. Substrate binding, but not catalysis, might then occur.

Experimental evidence for the induced fit model includes demonstration of conformational changes during substrate binding and catalysis with creatine kinase, phosphoglucomutase, and several other enzymes. With phosphoglucomutase, substrate analogs (eg, inorganic phosphate or glycerol phosphate) produce less extensive conformational changes. With carboxypeptidase, substrate binding induces an appreciable change in the location of 2 residues which may also be involved in catalysis.

The exact sequence of events in a substrate-induced conformational change remains to be established. Several possibilities exist (Fig 8–24).

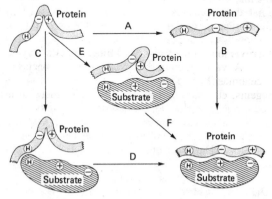

Figure 8–24. Representation of alternative reaction paths for a substrate-induced conformational change. The enzyme may first undergo a conformational change *(A),* then bind substrate *(B).* Alternatively, substrate may first be bound *(C),* whereupon a conformational change occurs *(D).* Finally, both processes may occur in a concerted manner *(E)* with further isomerization to the final conformation *(F).* (Adapted from Koshland & Neet: *Annu Rev Biochem* 1968;**37**:387.)

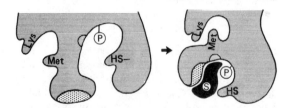

Figure 8–22. Representation of an induced fit by a conformational change in the protein structure. (After Koshland.)

Even when the complete primary structure of an enzyme is known, it may still be difficult to decide exactly which residues constitute the catalytic site. As illustrated by the induced fit model, these may be distant one from another in the primary structure but spatially close in the 3-dimensional (tertiary) structure.

In the representation of a catalytic site, several regions of a polypeptide chain each contribute residues to the site. Furthermore, these residues generally are not all sequential within a polypeptide chain, as described for hemoglobin in Chapter 5.

Modifiers of Enzyme Activity

The flow of carbon and energy in metabolism is profoundly influenced both by enzyme synthesis and by activation of proenzymes. However, these processes are irreversible. Like all mammalian proteins, enzymes are degraded to amino acids (protein turnover). In bacteria, the activity is diluted out among daughter cells on successive divisions.* Although both mechanisms effectively reduce enzyme concentration and hence catalytic activity, they are slow, wasteful of carbon and energy, and rather like turning out a light by smashing the bulb, then inserting a new one when light is needed. An "on-off" switch for enzymes clearly would be advantageous. It thus is not surprising that the **catalytic activity** of certain key enzymes can be reversibly decreased or increased by low-molecular-weight intermediary metabolites (see Chapter 5). Small molecule **modifiers** that decrease catalytic activity are termed **negative modifiers;** those which increase activity are called **positive modifiers.**

Examples of Catalytic Sites of Specific Enzymes

A. Lysozyme: Lysozyme, present in tears, nasal mucus, sputum, tissues, gastric secretions, milk, and egg white, catalyzes the hydrolysis of β-1,4- linkages of N-acetylneuraminic acid (see Chapter 13) in mucopolysaccharides or mucopeptides. It performs the function, in tears and nasal mucus, of destroying the cell walls of many airborne gram-positive bacteria. Lysozyme (MW about 15,000) consists of a single polypeptide chain of 129 residues. Since there is no coenzyme or metal ion, catalysis, specificity, and 3-dimensional structure are determined solely by these residues. There are small regions of pleated sheet, little α-helix, and large regions of random coil. For a model of lysozyme and its substrate, photographed in 3-dimensional color, see *J Biol Chem* 1968;**243**:1633. The molecule bears a deep central cleft which harbors a catalytic site with 6 subsites (Fig 8–25) that bind various substrates or inhibitors. The residues responsible for bond cleavage are thought to lie between sites D and E close to the carboxyl groups of Asp 52 and Glu 35. Glu 35 apparently protonates the acetal bond of the substrate while the negatively charged Asp 52 stabilizes the resulting carbonium ion from the back side.

*However, protein turnover also occurs in bacteria.

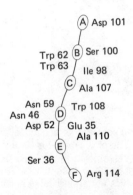

Figure 8–25. Schematic representation of the catalytic site in the cleft region of lysozyme. A to F represent the glycosyl moieties of a hexasaccharide. Some residues in the cleft region are shown with their numbers in the lysozyme sequence. (Adapted from Koshland & Neet: *Annu Rev Biochem* 1968;**37**:364.)

B. Ribonuclease: Unlike lysozyme, considerable information about the catalytic site of ribonuclease was available prior to solution of the 3-dimensional structure. The conclusions based on chemical investigations were largely confirmed by crystallography. The structure contains a cleft similar to that of lysozyme across which lie 2 residues, His 12 and His 119. These previously were implicated by chemical evidence as being at the catalytic site. Both residues are near the binding site for uridylic acid (Fig 8–26).

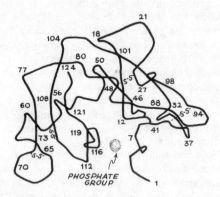

Figure 8–26. Structure of ribonuclease as determined by x-ray diffraction. Numbers refer to specific residues. See also Fig 4–14.

Amino Acid Sequences at Catalytic Sites

Partial decoding of the primary structures of active sites has revealed many similarities between hydrolytic enzymes (Table 8–1). This implies that the number of bond-breaking mechanisms operating in biologic systems is relatively small. In view of these similarities, it is perhaps not surprising that the amino acid sequences near the catalytic sites of the same

Table 8–1. Amino acid sequences in the neighborhood of the catalytic sites of several bovine proteases. Regions shown are those on either side of the catalytic site seryl (S) and histidyl (H) residues. For explanation of single letter abbreviations for amino acids, see Chapter 3. (Reproduced, with permission, from Dayhoff MO [editor]: *Atlas of Protein Sequence and Structure.* Vol 5. National Biomedical Research Foundation, 1972.)

Bovine Enzyme	Sequence Around Serine Ⓢ
Trypsin	D S C Q D G Ⓢ G G P V V C S G K
Chymotrypsin A	S S C M G D Ⓢ G G P L V C K K N
Chymotrypsin B	S S C M G D Ⓢ G G P L V C Q K N
Thrombin	D A C E G D Ⓢ G G P F V M K S P

Bovine Enzyme	Sequence Around Histidine Ⓗ
Trypsin	V V S A A Ⓗ C Y K S G I Q
Chymotrypsin A	V V T A A Ⓗ G G V T T S D
Chymotrypsin B	V V T A A Ⓗ C G V T T S D
Thrombin	V L T A A Ⓗ C L L Y P

enzyme from different species bear even greater similarity.

MECHANISM OF ENZYME ACTION

General Principles

Detailed discussion of the mechanisms whereby enzymes accelerate rates of reactions lies beyond the scope of this book.

General Acid-Base Catalysis

Reactions whose rates vary in response to changes in H^+ or H_3O^+ concentration but are independent of the concentrations of other acids or bases present in the solution are said to be subject to **specific acid** or **specific base catalysis.** Reactions whose rates are responsive to all the acids (proton donors) or bases (proton acceptors) present in solution are said to be subject to **general acid** or to **general base catalysis.** Mutarotation of glucose (see Chapter 13) is one reaction subject to general acid-base catalysis.

Role of Metal Ions

Metal ions perform essential **catalytic** and **structural** roles in proteins. Over 25% of all enzymes contain tightly-bound metal ions or require them for activity. The functions of these metal ions are studied by x-ray crystallography, nuclear magnetic resonance (NMR), and electron spin resonance (ESR). Coupled with knowledge of the formation and decay of metal complexes and of reactions within the coordination spheres of metal ions, this provides insight into the roles of metal ions in enzymic catalysis.

A. Metalloenzymes and Metal-Activated Enzymes: **Metalloenzymes** contain a definite quantity of functional metal ion that is retained throughout purification. **Metal-activated enzymes** bind metals less tightly but require added metals. The distinction between metalloenzymes and metal-activated enzymes thus rests on the affinity of a particular enzyme for its metal ion. The mechanisms whereby metal ions perform their functions appear to be similar both in metalloenzymes and metal-activated enzymes.

B. Ternary Enzyme-Metal-Substrate Complexes: For ternary (3-component) complexes of the catalytic site (Enz), a metal ion (M), and substrate (S) which exhibit 1:1:1 stoichiometry, 4 schemes are possible:

Enz–S–M
Substrate-bridge complex

M–Enz–S
Enzyme-bridge complex

Enz–M–S
Simple metal-bridge complex

$$Enz \diagdown \begin{matrix} M \\ | \\ S \end{matrix}$$
Cyclic metal-bridge complex

All 4 are possible for metal-activated enzymes. Metalloenzymes cannot form the Enz-S-M complex because they retain the metal throughout purification (ie, are already as Enz–M). Three generalizations can be stated:

1. Most but not all kinases (ATP:phosphotransferases) form substrate-bridge complexes of the type Enz–nucleotide–M.

2. Phosphotransferases using pyruvate or phosphoenolpyruvate as substrate, enzymes catalyzing other reactions of phosphoenolpyruvate, and carboxylases form metal-bridge complexes.

3. A given enzyme may form one type of bridge complex with one substrate and a different type with the other.

C. Enzyme-Bridge Complexes (M–Enz–S):

The metals in enzyme-bridge complexes are presumed to perform structural roles maintaining an active conformation (eg, glutamine synthetase) or to form a metal bridge to a substrate (eg, pyruvate kinase). In addition to its structural role, the metal ion in pyruvate kinase appears to hold one substrate (ATP) in place and to activate it.

$$\text{Pyruvate kinase} - \text{ATP} \overset{\displaystyle M}{\underset{\displaystyle \text{Creatine}}{\diagup\!\!|}}$$

D. Substrate-Bridge Complexes (Enz–S–M):

The formation of ternary substrate-bridge complexes of nucleoside triphosphates with enzyme, metal, and substrate appears attributable to displacement of H_2O from the coordination sphere of the metal by ATP:

$$ATP^{4-} + M(H_2O)_6{}^{2+} \rightleftharpoons ATP-M(H_2O)_3{}^{2-} + 3H_2O$$

Substrate then binds, forming the ternary complex:

$$ATP-M(H_2O)_3{}^{2-} + Enz \rightleftharpoons Enz-ATP-M(H_2O)_3{}^{2-}$$

In phosphotransferase reactions, metal ions are thought to activate the phosphorus atoms and form a rigid, polyphosphate-adenine complex of appropriate conformation in the active, quaternary complex.

E. Metal-Bridge Complexes:

$$Enz-M-S \text{ or } Enz\overset{\displaystyle M}{\underset{\displaystyle S}{\diagdown\!\!|}}$$

Crystallographic and sequencing data have established that a His residue is concerned with metal binding at the active site of many proteins (eg, carboxypeptidase A, cytochrome c, rubredoxin, metmyoglobin, and methemoglobin; see Chapter 5). For binary (2-component) Enz-M complexes, the rate-limiting step is in many cases the departure of water from the coordination sphere of the metal ion. For many peptidases, activation by metal ions is a slow process requiring many hours. The slow reaction probably is conformational rearrangement of the binary Enz-M complex to an active conformation, eg:

Metal binding:

$$Enz + M(H_2O)_6 \xrightarrow{\text{Rapid}} Enz-M(H_2O)_{6-n} + nH_2O$$

Rearrangement to active conformation (Enz*):

$$Enz-M(H_2O)_{6-n} \xrightarrow{\text{Slow}} Enz^*-M(H_2O)_{6-n}$$

For metalloenzymes, however, the ternary

metal-bridge complex must be formed by combination of the substrate (S) with the binary Enz-M complex:

$$Enz-M + S \rightleftharpoons Enz-M-S \text{ or } Enz\overset{\displaystyle M}{\underset{\displaystyle S}{\diagdown\!\!|}}$$

Role of Metal Ions in Catalysis

Metal ions may participate in each of the 4 mechanisms by which enzymes are known to accelerate the rates of chemical reactions: (1) general acid-base catalysis, (2) covalent catalysis, (3) approximation of reactants, and (4) induction of strain in the enzyme or substrate.

Metal ions, like protons, are Lewis acids (electrophiles) and can share an electron pair forming a sigma bond. Metal ions may also be considered "super acids" since they exist in neutral solution, frequently have a positive charge of > 1, and may form pi bonds. In addition (and unlike protons), metals can serve as 3-dimensional templates for orientation of basic groups on the enzyme or substrate.

Metal ions can also accept electrons via sigma or pi bonds to activate electrophiles or nucleophiles (general acid-base catalysis). By donating electrons, metals can activate nucleophiles or act as nucleophiles themselves. The coordination sphere of a metal may bring together enzyme and substrate (approximation) or form chelate-producing distortion in either the enzyme or substrate (strain). A metal ion may also "mask" a nucleophile and thus prevent an otherwise likely side-reaction. Finally, stereochemical control of the course of an enzyme-catalyzed reaction may be achieved by the ability of the metal coordination sphere to act as a 3-dimensional template to hold reactive groups in a specific steric orientation (Table 8–2).

The mechanisms of catalyses mediated by the coenzyme functions of some of the B vitamins are discussed in Chapter 10.

Table 8–2. Selected examples of the roles of metal ions in the mechanism of action of enzymes.[*]

Enzyme	Role of Metal Ion
Histidine deaminase	Masking a nucleophile
Kinases, lyases, pyruvate decarboxylase	Activation of an electrophile
Carbonic anhydrase	Activation of a nucleophile
Cobamide enzymes	Metal acts as a nucleophile
Pyruvate carboxylase, carboxypeptidase, alcohol dehydrogenase	π-Electron withdrawal
Nonheme iron proteins	π-Electron donation
Pyruvate kinase, pyruvate carboxylase, adenylate kinase	Metal ion gathers and orients ligands
Phosphotransferase, D-xylose isomerase, hemoproteins	Strain effects

[*]Adapted from Mildvan AS: Metals in enzyme catalysis. Vol 2, p 456, in: *The Enzymes*. Boyer PD, Lardy H, Myrbäck K (editors). Academic Press, 1970.

References

Kinetics

Christensen HN: *Dissociation, Enzyme Kinetics, Bioenergetics*. Saunders, 1975.

Engle PC: *Enzyme Kinetics*. Wiley, 1977.

Piszkiwicz D: *Kinetics of Chemical and Enzyme-Catalyzed Reactions*. Oxford Univ Press, 1977.

Purich DL (editor): Enzyme kinetics and mechanisms. Parts A and B in: *Methods in Enzymology*. Vol 63, 1979; Vol 64, 1980. Academic Press.

Segel IH: *Enzyme Kinetics*. Wiley, 1975.

Van Tamlen EE (editor): *Bioorganic Chemistry*. Vol 1, *Enzyme Action*, 1977. Vol 2, *Macro- and Multimolecular Systems*, 1977. Vol 3, *Substrate Behavior*, 1978. Academic Press.

The Active Site

Sigman DS, Mooser G: Chemical studies of enzyme active sites. *Annu Rev Biochem* 1975;**44**:889.

Mechanism of Enzyme Action

Crane F: Hydroquinone dehydrogenases. *Annu Rev Biochem* 1977;**46**:439.

Kraut J: Serine proteases: Structure and mechanism of catalysis. *Annu Rev Biochem* 1977;**46**:331.

Mildvan AS: Mechanism of enzyme action. *Annu Rev Biochem* 1974;**43**:357.

Wimmer MJ, Rose IA: Mechanisms of enzyme-catalyzed group transfer reactions. *Annu Rev Biochem* 1978;**47**:1031.

Wood HG, Barden RE: Biotin enzymes. *Annu Rev Biochem* 1977;**46**:385.

9 | Regulation of Enzyme Activity

Victor W. Rodwell, PhD

METABOLIC REGULATION

Homeostasis

The concept of homeostatic regulation of the internal milieu advanced by Claude Bernard in the late 19th century stressed the ability of animals to maintain the constancy of their intracellular environments. This implies that all the necessary enzyme-catalyzed reactions proceed at rates responsive to changes in the internal and external environment. A cell or organism might be defined as diseased when it responds inadequately or incorrectly to an internal or external stress. Knowledge of factors affecting the rates of enzyme-catalyzed reactions is essential both to understand homeostasis in normal cells and to comprehend the molecular basis of disease.

All chemical reactions, including enzyme-catalyzed reactions, are to some extent reversible.* Within living cells, however, reversibility may not obtain because reaction products are promptly removed by additional enzyme-catalyzed reactions. Metabolite flow in living cells is analogous to the flow of water in a pipe. Although the pipe can transfer water in either direction, in practice the flow is unidirectional. Metabolite flow in living cells also is largely unidirectional. True equilibrium, far from being characteristic of life, is approached only when cells die. The living cell is a steady-state system maintained by a unidirectional flow of metabolites (Fig 9–1). In mature cells, the mean concentrations of metabolites remain relatively constant over considerable periods of time.† The flexibility of the steady-state system is well illustrated in the delicate shifts and balances by which organisms maintain the constancy of the internal environment despite wide variations in food, water, and mineral intake, work output, or external temperature.

Scope of Metabolic Regulation

For life to proceed in orderly fashion, metabolite

---

*A readily reversible reaction has a small numerical value of ΔG. One with a large negative value for ΔG ($\Delta G < -5000$ cal) might be termed "effectively irreversible" in most biochemical situations.

†Short-term oscillations of metabolite concentrations and of enzyme levels do occur, however, and are of profound physiologic importance.

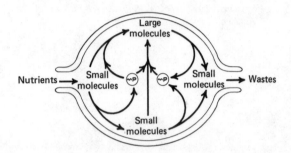

Figure 9–1. An idealized cell in steady state.

flow through anabolic and catabolic pathways must be regulated. All requisite chemical events must proceed at rates consistent with the requirements of the intact organism in relation to its environment. ATP production, synthesis of macromolecular precursors, transport, secretion, and tubular reabsorption all must respond to subtle changes in the environment of the cell, organ, or intact animal. These processes must be coordinated and must respond to short-term changes in the external environment (eg, addition or removal of a nutrient) as well as to periodic intracellular events (eg, DNA replication). The mechanisms by which cells and intact organisms regulate and coordinate overall metabolism are of concern to biochemists with as seemingly diverse research interests as cancer, heart disease, aging, microbial physiology, differentiation and metamorphosis, or the mechanism of hormone action. At present, the molecular details of regulation are best understood in bacteria, which lack the complexities of rapid protein turnover or of hormonal or nervous control and in which genetic studies can readily be conducted to analyze molecular events.

While knowledge of cellular regulatory processes in humans is central to an understanding and therapy of metabolic diseases, the molecular events in regulation of most metabolic processes in mammals are poorly understood. It is clear that metabolic regulation in mammals differs significantly from superficially similar phenomena in bacteria. In the sections that follow, the regulation of metabolic processes in bacteria will be discussed because metabolic regulation in bacteria has given rise to a conceptual framework for considering regulation in humans. In this chapter, mechanisms by which metabolic processes are regulated via enzymes are illustrated by selected examples. The intent is to characterize overall patterns of regulation. Throughout this book, reference is made to many other specific examples to illustrate these diverse features of metabolic regulation.

Available Options for Regulation of Enzymes

Net flow of carbon through any enzyme-catalyzed reaction might be influenced (1) by changing the absolute quantity of enzyme present, (2) by altering the pool size of reactants other than enzyme, and (3) by altering the catalytic efficiency of the enzyme. All 3 options are exploited in most forms of life.

REGULATION OF ENZYME QUANTITY

General Principles

The absolute quantity of an enzyme present is determined by its rate of synthesis (k_s) and rate of degradation (k_{deg}) (Fig 9–2). The quantity of an enzyme in a cell may be raised either by an increase in its rate of synthesis (increase in k_s), by a decrease in its rate of degradation (decrease in k_{deg}), or by both. Similarly, a lower quantity of enzyme can result from a decrease in k_s, an increase in k_{deg}, or both. In all forms of life, enzyme (protein) synthesis from amino acids and enzyme (protein) degradation to amino acids are distinct processes catalyzed by entirely different sets of enzymes. Independent regulation of enzyme synthesis and enzyme degradation is thus readily achieved.

Enzyme

k_s k_{deg}

Amino acids

Figure 9–2. Enzyme quantity is determined by the net balance between enzyme synthesis and enzyme degradation.

Basis for Regulation of Gene Expression

The primary structure of an enzyme, like that of all proteins, is dictated by the trinucleotide (triplet) code of its messenger RNA (mRNA). The sequence of nucleotide bases of the mRNA is in turn dictated by a complementary base sequence in a DNA template or gene (see Chapters 28 and 29). Information for protein synthesis, stored in DNA, thus determines a cell's ability to synthesize a particular enzyme.

Genetic **mutations** alter the DNA code and result in synthesis of proteins with modified primary structures. This may alter structure at higher levels of organization if the new amino acid is significantly different from the old. Mutations may cause partial or complete loss of catalytic activity, or rarely, enhanced catalytic activity. Since mutations at various genetic loci can produce an enzyme with impaired activity, a large number of molecular diseases can result.

Induction

Enzyme induction is illustrated by the following experiment: *Escherichia coli* grown on glucose will not ferment lactose due to the absence of a transport system or of the enzyme β-galactosidase, which hydrolyzes lactose. If lactose or certain other β-galactosides are added to the growth medium, synthesis of the β-galactosidase is induced and the culture can now ferment lactose.

The inducer (lactose) is a substrate for the induced protein (β-galactosidase). Although many inducers are substrates for the enzymes they induce, compounds structurally similar to the substrate may be inducers but not substrates. These are termed **gratuitous inducers.** Conversely, a compound may be a substrate but not an inducer. Frequently, a compound induces several enzymes of a catabolic pathway (eg, β-galactoside permease and β-galactosidase are both induced by lactose).

Enzymes whose concentration in a cell is independent of added inducer are termed **constitutive.** A particular enzyme may be constitutive in one strain, inducible in another, and neither constitutive nor inducible (ie, absent) in a third. Cells capable of being induced for a particular enzyme always contain a small measurable **basal level** of that enzyme even when grown in the absence of added inducer. The extent to which a particular organism responds to an inducer is genetically determined (see Chapter 30). Increases in enzyme content from 2- to 1000-fold may be observed on induction in different strains. The genetic heritage of the cell thus determines both the nature and magnitude of the response to an inducer. The terms "constitutive" and "inducible" are therefore relative terms, like "hot" and "cold," which represent the extremes of a spectrum of responses.

Bacteria exhibit complex patterns of enzyme induction of catabolic enzymes. While the inducer frequently is either a substrate or the product of the inducible enzyme, this is not always the case. Induction may be by the substrate, the product, or by further products of catabolism. Where the inducer is something other than the substrate (eg, a product), formation of the inducer is thought to occur via the activity of low, basal levels of the inducible enzyme or enzymes required. Where the structural genes that specify a group of catabolic enzymes comprise an operon, all enzymes of that operon are induced by a single inducer **(coordinate induction).** The ability to avoid synthesis of the enzyme in the absence of the nutrient permits the bacterium to use its available nutrients to maximum advantage, ie, it does not synthesize "unnecessary enzymes."

Examples of inducible enzymes in animals are tryptophan pyrrolase, threonine dehydrase, tyrosine-α-ketoglutaric transaminase, invertase, enzymes of the urea cycle, and HMG-CoA reductase. An important example in bacteria is the inducible penicillinase that provides *Bacillus cereus* with a defense against penicillin.

Repression & Derepression

In bacteria capable of synthesizing a biosynthetic metabolite, its presence in the medium curtails new synthesis of that metabolite via **repression.** A small molecule such as a purine or amino acid, acting as a **corepressor,** can ultimately block synthesis of the enzymes involved in its own biosynthesis. For example, in *Salmonella typhimurium,* addition of His represses synthesis of all the enzymes of His biosynthesis, and addition of Leu represses synthesis of the first 3 enzymes unique to Leu biosynthesis. In both cases, these biosynthetic enzymes comprise **operons; coordinate repression** occurs following addition of the end products His or Leu. Coordinate repression is not general for all biosynthetic pathways. Following removal or exhaustion of an essential biosynthetic intermediate from the medium, enzyme biosynthesis again occurs. This constitutes **derepression.** Derepression may be coordinate or noncoordinate.

The above examples illustrate **product feedback repression** characteristic of biosynthetic pathways in bacteria. **Catabolite repression,** a related phenomenon, refers to the ability of an intermediate in a sequence of **catabolic** enzyme-catalyzed reactions to repress synthesis of catabolic enzymes. This effect was first noted in cultures of *E coli* growing on a carbon source (X) other than glucose. Addition of glucose repressed synthesis of the enzymes concerned with catabolism of X. This phenomenon was initially termed the "glucose effect." With the recognition that many oxidizable nutrients other than glucose produced similar effects, the term **catabolite repression** was adopted. Catabolite repression is mediated by cAMP.

The molecular mechanisms of induction, repression, and derepression are discussed in Chapter 30.

In multiple-branched biosynthetic pathways such as those generating the branched chain amino acids or the aspartate family of amino acids, early enzymes function in the biosynthesis of several amino acids (Fig 9–3).

Following addition of Lys to the medium of growing bacteria, synthesis of the enzymes unique to Lys biosynthesis (Enz$_L$) are repressed. Repression of the enzymes unique to Thr biosynthesis (Enz$_T$) follows addition of Thr to the medium. These effects illustrate simple product feedback repression. Enzymes Enz$_1$ and Enz$_2$, however, function both in Lys and Thr biosynthesis. Product feedback repression of their synthesis by Lys or Thr alone would starve the bacterium of the other amino acid. If, however, both Lys and Thr are added to the medium, Enz$_1$ and Enz$_2$ become redundant, and repression of synthesis of Enz$_1$ and Enz$_2$ could be advantageous to survival, since it would permit more efficient use of available nutrients.

In the presence of all necessary end products of a branched or multiple-branched biosynthetic pathway, **multivalent repression** may occur. This occurs when, and only when, all end products of a particular set of biosynthetic enzymes are present in ample supply. Complete repression of aspartokinase (Enz$_1$) should therefore require Met and Ile in addition to Lys and Thr.

Enzyme Turnover

In rapidly growing bacteria, the overall rate of protein degradation is about 2% per hour, and control of enzyme levels is achieved primarily by increases or decreases in k_S. This is not true for starving bacteria or for bacteria transferred to fresh medium providing a poorer source of carbon for growth ("stepdown culture"). Under these conditions, bacteria degrade protein at 7–10% per hour.

The combined processes of enzyme synthesis and degradation constitute **enzyme turnover.** While turnover occurs both in bacteria and mammals, the importance of enzyme degradation as a device by which enzyme levels are regulated in bacteria has received little emphasis. Turnover of protein was recognized as a characteristic property of all mammalian cells long before it was shown also to occur in bacteria. The existence of protein (enzyme) turnover in humans was deduced from dietary experiments well over a century ago. It was, however, Schoenheimer's classic work, just prior to and during World War II, that conclusively established that turnover of cellular protein occurred throughout life. By measuring the rates of incorporation of ^{15}N-labeled amino acids into protein and the rates of loss of ^{15}N from protein, Schoenheimer deduced that body proteins are in a state of "dynamic equilibrium," a concept since extended to other body constituents, including lipids and nucleic acids.

In mammals, control of intracellular enzyme levels involves regulation both of enzyme synthesis and degradation. While the major events in protein synthesis are well understood, those in enzyme degradation are not. Enzyme degradation involves hydrolysis by proteolytic enzymes, but little is known of the processes by which proteolytic activity is regulated

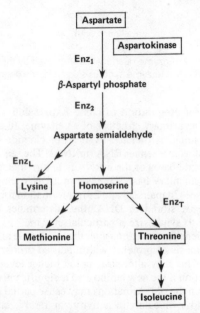

Figure 9–3. The aspartate family of amino acids. Enz$_L$ and Enz$_T$ denote groups of enzymes involved in lysine and threonine biosynthesis, respectively.

other than that it requires ATP. The susceptibility of an enzyme to proteolytic degradation depends upon its conformation. The presence or absence of substrates, coenzymes, or metal ions, which can alter protein conformation, alter proteolytic susceptibility. The concentrations of substrates, coenzymes, and possibly ions in cells may thus determine the rates at which specific enzymes are degraded. Arginase and tryptophan oxygenase (tryptophan pyrrolase), illustrate these concepts. Regulation of liver arginase levels can involve a change either in k_s or in k_{deg}. Following ingestion of a protein-rich diet, liver arginase levels rise due to an increased rate of arginase synthesis. Liver arginase levels also rise in starved animals. Here, however, it is arginase degradation that is decreased, while k_s remains unchanged. In a second example, injection of glucocorticoids and ingestion of Try both elevate levels of tryptophan oxygenase in mammals. The hormone raises the rate of oxygenase synthesis (raises k_s). Try, however, has no effect on k_s but lowers k_{deg} by stabilizing the oxygenase toward proteolytic digestion. Contrast these 2 examples with enzyme induction in bacteria. For arginase, the increased intake of nitrogen on a high-protein diet may elevate liver arginase levels (see Chapter 21). The increased rate of arginase synthesis thus superficially resembles that of substrate induction in bacteria. For tryptophan pyrrolase, however, even though Try may act as an inducer in bacteria (affects k_s), its effect in mammals is solely on the enzyme degradative process (lowers k_{deg}).

Enzyme levels in mammalian tissues may be altered by a wide range of physiologic, hormonal, or dietary manipulations. Examples are known for a variety of tissues and metabolic pathways (Table 9–1), but our knowledge of the molecular details that account for these changes is fragmentary.

Glucocorticoids increase the concentration of tyrosine transaminase by stimulating k_s. This was the first clear case of a hormone regulating the synthesis of a mammalian enzyme. Insulin and glucagon—despite their mutually antagonistic physiologic effects—both independently increase k_s 4- to 5-fold. The effect of glucagon probably is mediated via cAMP, which mimics the effect of the hormone in organ cultures of rat liver.

Proenzymes

One method for regulation of enzyme activity is synthesis in a catalytically inactive or proenzyme form. To become catalytically active, the proenzyme must undergo limited proteolysis, a process accompanied by conformational changes that either reveal or "create" the catalytic site. Synthesis as a catalytically inactive proenzyme is characteristic of digestive enzymes and enzymes of blood coagulation and of blood clot dissolution. This phenomenon is not restricted to proteolytic enzymes. Proinsulin, a hormonally inactive insulin precursor, undergoes limited proteolysis to produce active insulin (see Chapter 35).

Conversion of proenzymes to active enzymes is catalyzed by proteolytic enzymes or by H^+ (Fig 9–4).

Table 9–1. Selected examples of rat liver enzymes that adapt to an environmental stimulus by changes in activity.*

Enzyme	t½ (hours)	Stimulus	Fold Change
Amino acid metabolism			
Arginase	100–120	Starvation or glucocorticoids.	+2
		Change from high- to low-protein diet.	−2
Serine dehydratase	20	Glucagon or dietary amino acids.	+100
Histidase	60	Change from low- to high-protein diet.	+20
Carbohydrate metabolism			
Glucose-6-P dehydrogenase	15	Thyroid hormone or fasted rats re-fed a high-carbohydrate diet.	+10
a-Glycerophosphate dehydrogenase	100	Thyroid hormone.	+10
Fructose-1,6-phosphatase		Glucose.	+10
Lipid metabolism			
Citrate cleavage enzyme		Starved rats re-fed a high-carbohydrate, low-fat diet.	+30
Fatty acid synthetase		Starvation.	−10
		Starved animals re-fed a fat-free diet.	+30
HMG-CoA reductase	2–3	Fasting or 5% cholesterol diet.	−10
		Twenty-four-hour diurnal variation.	±5
		Insulin or thyroid hormone.	+2 to 10
Purine or pyrimidine metabolism			
Xanthine oxidase		Change to high-protein diet.	−10
Aspartate transcarbamoylase	60	One percent orotic acid diet.	+2
Dihydroorotase	12	One percent orotic acid diet.	+3

*Data, with the exception of those for HMG-CoA reductase, from Schimke RT, Doyle D: *Annu Rev Biochem* 1970;39:929.

Pepsinogen $\xrightarrow{\text{H}^+ \text{ or pepsin}}$ Pepsin

Trypsinogen $\xrightarrow{\text{Trypsin or enterokinase}}$ Trypsin

Chymotrypsinogen $\xrightarrow{\text{Trypsin}}$ Chymotrypsin

Procarboxypeptidase $\xrightarrow{\text{Trypsin}}$ Carboxypeptidase

Figure 9–4. Conversion of digestive proenzymes to active proteases. Since proenzyme activation is catalyzed by the enzyme, activation of pepsinogen and of trypsinogen is autocatalytic and proceeds with ever-increasing velocity.

Frequently, large portions of the proenzyme are removed. Conversion of pepsinogen (MW 42,500) to pepsin (MW 34,500) involves the loss of almost 20% of the molecule. Similarly, conversion of procarboxypeptidase to carboxypeptidase is accompanied by a drop in molecular weight from 96,000 to 34,300, a decrease of two-thirds. Conversion of trypsinogen to trypsin, however, involves the removal of only 6 amino acids.

Conversion of fibrinogen to fibrin involves limited proteolysis catalyzed by thrombin. Activation of the inactive precursor, prothrombin, requires a complex sequence or cascade of activation reactions, many of which involve proteolysis. Limited proteolysis is thus one key regulatory factor in blood coagulation (see Chapter 39).

Viewed as a physiologic control mechanism, synthesis of inactive enzyme precursors provides for rapidly increasing the level of an enzyme in response to physiologic demand. It would be a disadvantage, for example, if the enzymes of blood coagulation had first to be provided by the slower process of protein synthesis.

Proteolysis of several regulated enzymes can mimic other forms of regulation. For example, activation of phosphorylase b kinase or conversion of the glucose 6-phosphate-dependent form of glycogen synthetase to the independent form may be achieved by limited proteolysis.

REGULATION OF THE CATALYTIC EFFICIENCY OF ENZYMES

Definition of Terms

If a physiologic manipulation alters the level of enzyme activity, we have no way of knowing whether the quantity of enzyme has changed or whether the enzyme is a more or less efficient catalyst. **We shall refer to all changes in enzyme activity that occur without change in the quantity of enzyme present as "effects on catalytic efficiency."**

Availability of Reactants

A. General Principles: The kinetic and regulatory properties of enzymes provide insights into physiologic processes in intact cells, tissues, and organisms. However, most information was obtained by studying enzymes free in solution under conditions that differ substantially from those in living cells. Application of this knowledge to the in vivo situation therefore requires considerable caution. For instance, the concentrations of substrates studied in vitro differ significantly from those in vivo.

B. Enzyme Compartmentation: The importance of compartmentation of metabolic processes in eukaryotic cells, including those of mammals, cannot be overemphasized. Localization of specific metabolic processes in the cytosol or in cellular organelles facilitates regulation of these processes independent of processes proceeding elsewhere. The extensive compartmentalization of metabolic processes characteristic of higher forms of life thus confers the potential for finely tuned regulation of metabolism. At the same time, it poses problems with respect to translocation of metabolites across compartmental barriers. This is achieved via "shuttle mechanisms" that convert the metabolite to a form permeable to the compartmental barrier. This is followed by transport and conversion back to the original form on the other side of the barrier. Consequently, these interconversions require, for example, cytosolic and mitochondrial forms of the same catalytic activity. Since these 2 forms of the enzyme are physically separated, their independent regulation is facilitated. The role of shuttle mechanisms in achieving equilibration of metabolic pools of reducing equivalents, of citric acid cycle, and of other amphibolic intermediates is discussed in Chapter 14.

C. Macromolecular Complexes: Organization of a set of enzymes that catalyze a protracted sequence of metabolic reactions as a macromolecular complex coordinates the enzymes and channels intermediates along a metabolic path. Appropriate alignment of the enzymes can facilitate transfer of product between enzymes without prior equilibration with metabolic pools. This permits a finer level of metabolic control than is possible with the isolated components of the complex. In addition, conformational changes in one component of the complex may be transmitted by protein-protein interactions to other enzymes of the complex. Amplification of regulatory effects thus is possible.

D. Effective Concentrations of Substrates, Coenzymes, & Cations: The **mean** intracellular concentration of a substrate, coenzyme, or metal ion may have little meaning for the in vivo behavior of an enzyme. Information on the concentrations of essential metabolites **in the immediate neighborhood of the enzyme in question** is needed. However, even measuring metabolite concentrations in different cellular compartments does not account for local discontinuities in metabolite concentrations within compartments brought about by factors such as proximity to the site of entry or production of a metabolite. Finally, little consideration generally is given to the discrepancy between total and free metabolite concentrations. For example, while the total concentration of

2,3-bisphosphoglycerate in erythrocytes is extremely high, the concentration of free bisphosphoglycerate is comparable to that of other tissues. Erythrocytes contain approximately 5 mmol of hemoglobin, which binds 1 mol of bisphosphoglycerate per mol of deoxygenated tetramer. A **total** concentration of 4 mmol of bisphosphoglycerate would therefore result in a minuscule concentration of **free** bisphosphoglycerate in venous erythrocytes. Similar considerations apply to other metabolites in the presence of proteins that bind them effectively and reduce their concentrations in the free state.

An assumption of the Michaelis kinetic approach was that the concentration of total substrate was essentially equal to the concentration of free substrate. As noted above, this assumption may well be invalid in vivo. In addition, in vivo concentrations of free substrates often are of the same order of magnitude as those of the enzyme concentration. A modified kinetic approach for in vivo situations employs an equation of the Michaelis-Menten form, but assumes steady-state kinetics:

$$v = \frac{kE_t S_f}{K_m + S_f}$$

where S_f, the concentration of free substrate, is substituted for S. However, application of this equation is hampered by the absence of exact values for S_f in the neighborhood of enzymes. Also, it applies only to an unconstrained solution of enzyme, a situation invalid for macromolecular complexes.

Metal ions, which perform catalytic and structural roles in over one-fourth of all known enzymes, may also fulfill regulatory roles, particularly for reactions where ATP is a substrate. Where the ATP-metal ion complex is the substrate for the reaction, maximal activity typically is observed at molar ratio of ATP to metal of about unity. Excess metal or excess ATP is inhibitory. Since nucleoside di- and triphosphates form stable complexes with divalent cations, intracellular concentrations of the nucleotides can influence intracellular concentrations of free metal ions and hence the activity of certain enzymes. For example, in the absence of metal ions, *E coli* glutamine synthetase assumes a "relaxed" configuration that is catalytically inactive. Mg^{2+} or Mn^{2+} converts the synthetase to the active, "tightened" form. In addition, adenylylation of the synthetase changes the divalent cation specificity from Mg^{2+} to Mn^{2+}. The activity of the adenylylated enzyme is, furthermore, sensitive to the ATP:Mg^{2+} ratio, whereas that of the unadenylylated form is not.

Feedback Inhibition

General principles: The catalytic activity of certain **regulatory enzymes** is modulated by low molecular weight **allosteric effectors** which generally have little or no structural similarity to the substrates or coenzymes for the regulatory enzyme. **Feedback inhibition** refers to the inhibition of the activity of an enzyme early in a biosynthetic pathway by an end product of that pathway. For biosynthesis of D from A, catalyzed by enzymes Enz_1 through Enz_3,

$$A \xrightarrow{Enz_1} B \xrightarrow{Enz_2} C \xrightarrow{Enz_3} D$$

a high concentration of D typically inhibits conversion of A to B. This involves not simple "backing up" of intermediates but the ability of D to bind to and inhibit Enz_1. D thus acts as a **negative allosteric effector** or **feedback inhibitor** of Enz_1. **Feedback inhibition** of Enz_1 by D therefore regulates the synthesis of D. Typically, D binds to the sensitive enzyme at an **allosteric site** remote from the catalytic site.

The kinetics of feedback inhibition may be competitive, noncompetitive, partially competitive, uncoupled, or mixed. Feedback inhibition is commonest in biosynthetic pathways. **Frequently the feedback inhibitor is the last small molecule before a macromolecule** (eg, amino acids before proteins, nucleotides before nucleic acids). **Feedback regulation generally occurs at the earliest functionally irreversible* step unique to a particular biosynthetic sequence.**

Examples of feedback inhibition in microorganisms include inhibition by His of phosphoribosyl:ATP pyrophosphorylase, by Try of anthranilate synthetase, and by CTP of aspartate transcarbamoylase. In each case the regulated enzyme is involved in biosynthesis of a single end product—His, Try, or CTP.

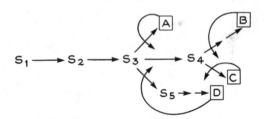

Figure 9–5. Sites of feedback inhibition in a branched biosynthetic pathway. S_1–S_5 are intermediates in the biosynthesis of end products A–D. Straight arrows represent enzymes catalyzing the indicated conversions. Curved arrows represent feedback loops and indicate probable sites of feedback inhibition by specific end products.

Frequently a biosynthetic pathway may be branched, with the initial portion serving for synthesis of 2 or more essential metabolites. Fig 9–5 shows probable sites of simple feedback inhibition in a branched biosynthetic pathway (eg, for amino acids, purines or pyrimidines). S_1, S_2, and S_3 are precursors of all 4 end products (A, B, C, and D), S_4 is a precursor

---

*One strongly favored (in thermodynamic terms) in a single direction, ie, one with a large negative ΔG.

of B and C, and S_5 a precursor solely of D. The
sequences:

$$S_3 \longrightarrow A$$
$$S_4 \longrightarrow B$$
$$S_4 \longrightarrow C$$
$$S_3 \longrightarrow S_5 \longrightarrow D$$

thus constitute linear reaction sequences that might be
expected to be feedback-inhibited by their end products.

Multiple feedback loops (Fig 9–6) provide additional fine control. For example, if B is present in
excess, the requirement for S_2 decreases. The ability of
B to decrease production of S_2 thus confers a biologic
advantage. However, if excess B inhibits not only the
portion of the pathway unique to its own synthesis but
also portions common to that for synthesis of A, C, or
D, excess B should curtail synthesis of all 4 end products. Clearly, this is undesirable. Mechanisms have,
however, evolved to circumvent this difficulty.

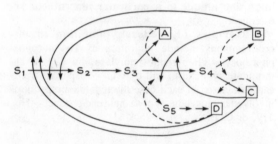

Figure 9–6. Multiple feedback inhibition in a branched
biosynthetic pathway. Superimposed on simple feedback
loops (dashed, curved arrows) are multiple feedback loops
(solid, curved arrows) that regulate enzymes common to
biosynthesis of several end products.

In **cumulative feedback inhibition** the inhibitory
effect of 2 or more end products on a single regulatory
enzyme is strictly additive.

In **concerted** or **multivalent feedback inhibition,** complete inhibition occurs only when 2 or more
end products both are present in excess.

In **cooperative feedback inhibition,** a single end
product present in excess inhibits the regulatory enzyme, but **the inhibition when 2 or more end products are present far exceeds the additive effects of
cumulative feedback inhibition.**

The aspartate family provides yet another
variant—**multiple enzymes** each with distinct regulatory characteristics. *E coli* produces 3 aspartokinases. One (AK_L) is specifically and completely
inhibited by Lys, a second (AK_T) by Thr, and the third
(AK_H) by homoserine, a precursor of Met, Thr, and Ile
(Fig 9–7). In the presence of excess Lys, AK_L is
inhibited and β-aspartyl phosphate production decreases. This alone would not suffice to channel
metabolites toward synthesis of homoserine and its

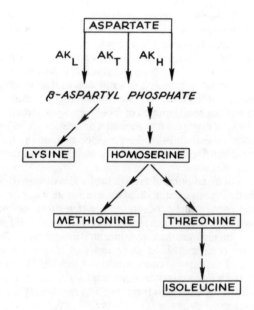

Figure 9–7. Regulation of aspartokinase (AK) activity in *E
coli.* Multiple enzymes are subject to end product inhibition
by lysine (AK_L), threonine (AK_T), or homoserine (AK_H).

products. Channeling is achieved by feedback inhibition at secondary sites further along the pathway. Lys
also inhibits the first enzyme in the sequence leading
from β-aspartyl phosphate to Lys. This facilitates unrestricted synthesis of homoserine, and hence of Thr
and Ile. Additional control points exist at the branch
point where homoserine leads both to Met and to Thr
and Ile.

That all these variations can regulate metabolism
is suggested by the persistence in different bacteria of
distinctive patterns of feedback inhibition of a single
biosynthetic pathway (Table 9–2).

The most extensively studied allosteric enzyme,
aspartate transcarbamoylase, catalyzes the first
reaction unique to pyrimidine biosynthesis (Fig
9–8).

Aspartate transcarbamoylase (ATCase) is
feedback-inhibited by cytidine triphosphate (CTP).
Following treatment with mercurials, ATCase loses its
sensitivity to inhibition by CTP but retains its full
activity for carbamoyl aspartate synthesis. This
suggests that CTP is bound at a different (allosteric)

Table 9–2. Patterns of allosteric regulation of aspartokinase.

Organism	Feedback Inhibitor	Repressor
E coli (kinase I)	Homoser	...
E coli (kinase II)	Lys	Lys
E coli (kinase III)	Thr	...
R rubrium	Thr	...
B subtilis	Thr + Lys	...

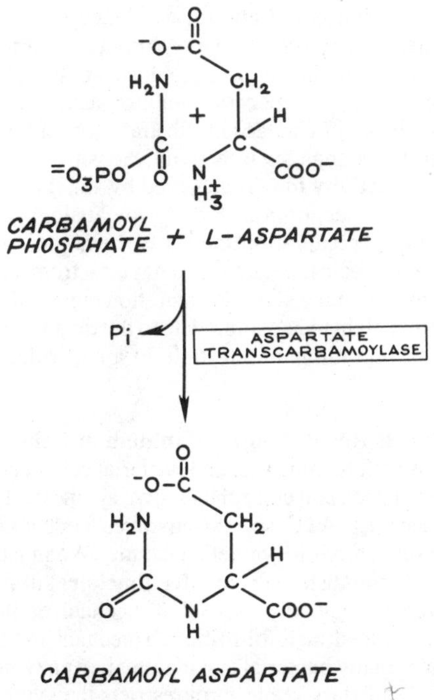

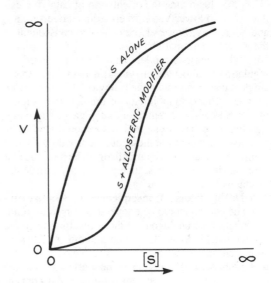

Figure 9–8. The aspartate transcarbamoylase (ATCase) reaction.

site from either substrate. ATCase consists of 2 catalytic and 3 or 4 regulatory protomers. Each catalytic protomer contains 4 aspartate (substrate) sites and each regulatory protomer at least 2 CTP (regulatory) sites. Each type of protomer is subject to independent genetic control, as shown by the production of mutants lacking normal feedback control of CTP and, from these, of revertants with essentially normal regulatory properties.

A. Evidence for Allosteric Sites on Regulated Enzymes: About 1963, Monod noted the lack of structural similarity between a feedback inhibitor and the substrate for the enzyme whose activity it regulated. Since the effectors are not isosteric with a substrate but **allosteric** (''occupy another space''), he proposed that enzymes whose activity is regulated by **allosteric effectors** (eg, feedback inhibitors) bind the effector at an **allosteric site** that is physically distinct from the catalytic site. **Allosteric enzymes** thus are enzymes whose activity at the catalytic site may be modulated by the presence of allosteric effectors at an allosteric site. Lines of evidence that support the existence of physically distinct allosteric sites on regulated enzymes include the following:

(1) Regulated enzymes modified by chemical or physical technics frequently become insensitive to their allosteric effectors without alteration of their catalytic activity. Selective denaturation of allosteric sites has been achieved by treatment with mercurials, urea, x-rays, proteolytic enzymes, extremes of ionic strength or pH, aging at 0–5 C, by freezing, or by heating.

(2) Allosteric effectors frequently protect the **catalytic** site from denaturation under conditions where the substrates themselves do not protect. Since it seems unlikely that an effector bound at the catalytic site would protect when substrates do not, this suggests a second, allosteric site elsewhere on the enzyme molecule.

(3) In certain bacterial and mammalian cell mutants, the regulated enzymes have altered regulatory properties. The catalytic properties are, however, identical to those of the wild-type from which the mutant derived. The structure of the allosteric and catalytic sites thus are genetically distinct.

(4) Binding studies of substrates and of allosteric effectors to regulated enzymes show that each may bind independently of the other.

(5) In certain cases (eg, ATCase), the allosteric site is present on a different protomer from the catalytic site.

B. Kinetics: Figure 9–9 illustrates the rate of a reaction catalyzed by a typical allosteric enzyme measured at several concentrations of substrate in the presence and absence of an allosteric inhibitor. In the absence of the allosteric inhibitor, hyperbolic saturation kinetics are observed. However, in the presence of an allosteric inhibitor, the substrate saturation curve is distorted from a hyperbola into a sigmoid, which at high substrate concentrations may merge with the hyperbola. Note the analogy to the relationship between myoglobin and hemoglobin (see Chapter 5).

Kinetic analysis of feedback inhibition may appear to be competitive, noncompetitive, partially competitive, or of other types. If, at high concentrations of S, comparable activity is observed in the presence or absence of the allosteric inhibitor, the kinetics superficially resemble those of competitive inhibition. However, since the substrate saturation curve is sigmoid rather than hyperbolic, it is not possi-

Figure 9–9. Sigmoid saturation curve for substrate in the presence of an allosteric inhibitor.

ble to obtain meaningful results by graphing data for the allosteric inhibition by the double-reciprocal technic. This method of analysis was developed for substrate competitive inhibition **at the catalytic site.** Since allosteric inhibitors act at a different (allosteric) site, the kinetic model is invalid.

The sigmoid character of the V versus S curve in the presence of an allosteric inhibitor reflects the phenomenon of **cooperativity.** At low concentrations of S, the activity in the presence of the inhibitor is low relative to that in its absence. However, as S is increased, the extent of inhibition becomes relatively less severe. The kinetics are consistent with the presence of 2 or more interacting substrate-binding sites, where the presence of a substrate molecule at one catalytic site facilitates binding of a second substrate molecule at a second site. Cooperativity of substrate binding has been described in Chapter 5 for hemoglobin. The sigmoid O_2 saturation curve results from cooperative interactions between 4 O_2 binding sites located on different protomers.

C. Models: Reference to the kinetics of allosteric inhibition as "competitive" or "noncompetitive" with substrate carries mechanistic implications which are misleading. We refer instead to 2 classes of regulated enzymes, K-series and V-series enzymes. For K-series allosteric enzymes, the substrate saturation kinetics are competitive in the sense that K_m is raised (decreased affinity for substrate) without effect on V_{max}. For V-series allosteric enzymes, the allosteric inhibitor lowers V_{max} (lowered catalytic efficiency) without affecting the apparent K_m. Alterations in K_m or V_{max} probably result from conformational changes at the catalytic site induced by binding of the allosteric effector at the allosteric site. For a K-series allosteric enzyme, this conformational change may weaken the bonds between substrate and substrate-binding residues. For a V-series allosteric enzyme, the primary effect may be to alter the orientation of catalytic residues so as to lower V_{max}. Intermediate effects on K_m and V_{max} may, however, be observed consequent to these conformational changes.

While various models have been proposed for regulation of allosteric enzymes, it is unlikely that a single model can explain the behavior of all regulatory enzymes. Since sigmoidicity of the substrate saturation curve confers a regulatory advantage, any mutation that gives rise to sigmoidicity should tend to be retained. To expect that these mutations would involve similar mechanisms is unrealistic. The presence of sigmoid kinetics does not, therefore, imply a particular mechanism of inhibition.

D. Physiologic Consequences of Cooperativity: The consequences of cooperative substrate binding kinetics are analogous to those resulting from the cooperative binding of O_2 to hemoglobin. At low substrate concentrations, the allosteric effector is an effective inhibitor. It thus regulates most effectively at the time of greatest need, ie, when intracellular concentrations of substrates are low. As more substrate becomes available, stringent regulation is less necessary.

As substrate concentration rises, the degree of inhibition therefore lessens, and more product is formed. As with hemoglobin, the sigmoid substrate saturation curve in the presence of inhibitor also means that relatively small changes in substrate concentration result in large changes in activity. Sensitive control of catalytic activity thus is achieved by small changes in substrate concentration. Finally, by analogy with the differing O_2 saturation curves of hemoglobins from different species, regulatory enzymes from different sources may have sigmoid saturation curves shifted to the left or right to accommodate to the range of prevailing concentrations of substrate in a particular cell or organism.

Feedback Regulation in Mammalian Cells

In both mammalian and bacterial cells, end products feed back and control their own synthesis. In some instances (eg, ATCase), this involves feedback inhibition of an early biosynthetic enzyme. We must, however, distinguish between **feedback regulation,** a phenomenologic term devoid of mechanistic implications, and **feedback inhibition,** a mechanism for regulation of many bacterial and mammalian enzymes. For example, dietary cholesterol restricts the synthesis of cholesterol from acetate in mammalian tissues. This feedback regulation does not, however, appear to involve feedback inhibition of an early enzyme of cholesterol biosynthesis. An early enzyme (HMG-CoA reductase) is affected, but the mechanism involves curtailment by cholesterol or a cholesterol metabolite of the expression of the genes that code for the formation of reductase. Cholesterol added directly to HMG-CoA reductase has no effect on its catalytic activity.

Covalent Modification

A. General Principles: Reversible modulation of the catalytic activity of enzymes can occur by covalent attachment of a phosphate group (predominates in mammals) or a nucleotide (predominates in bacteria). Enzymes that undergo covalent modification with attendant modulation of their activity are termed "interconvertible enzymes" (Fig 9–10).

Interconvertible enzymes exist in 2 activity states, one of high and the other of low catalytic efficiency. Depending on the enzyme concerned, the

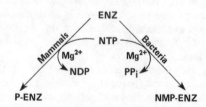

Figure 9–10. Regulation of enzyme activity by covalent modification. *Left:* phosphorylation. *Right:* nucleotidylation. For both processes the nucleoside triphosphate (NTP) generally is ATP.

Table 9–3. Examples of mammalian enzymes whose catalytic activity is altered by covalent phosphorylation-dephosphorylation. E = dephosphoenzyme; EP = phosphoenzyme.

Enzyme	Activity State	
	Low	High
Acetyl-CoA carboxylase	EP	E
Glycogen synthetase	EP	E
Pyruvate dehydrogenase	EP	E
HMG-CoA reductase	EP	E
Glycogen phosphorylase	E	EP
Pyruvate dehydrogenase	E	EP
Phosphorylase b kinase	E	EP
HMG-CoA reductase kinase	E	EP

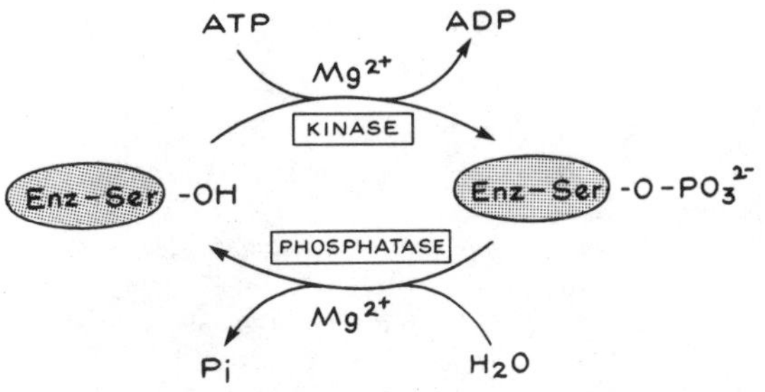

Figure 9–11. Covalent modification of a regulated enzyme by phosphorylation-dephosphorylation of a Ser residue.

phospho- or the dephosphoenzyme may be the more active catalyst (Table 9–3).

B. Phosphorylation Site: A specific Ser residue is phosphorylated, forming O-phosphoseryl residue. While an interconvertible enzyme may contain many Ser residues, phosphorylation is highly selective and occurs at only a small number (1–3) of possible sites (Table 9–4). These sites probably do not form part of the catalytic site, at least in a primary structural sense, and thus constitute another example of an allosteric site.

C. Converter Proteins: Phosphorylation and dephosphorylation are catalyzed by protein kinases and protein phosphatases (converter proteins), respectively (Fig 9–11). In specific instances, the converter proteins themselves may be interconvertible enzymes (Table 9–3). Thus there are protein kinase kinases and protein kinase phosphatases that catalyze the interconversion of these converter proteins. Evidence that pro-

tein phosphatases are also interconvertible proteins is less convincing, although their activity is regulated. The activity of both protein kinases and protein phosphatases is under hormonal and neural control, although the precise details by which these agents act are in most instances far from clear.

D. Energetics: The reactions of Fig 9–11 resemble those for interconversion of glucose and glucose 6-phosphate or of fructose 6-phosphate and fructose 1,6-bisphosphate (see Chapter 15). The net result of phosphorylating and then dephosphorylating 1 mole of substrate (enzyme or sugar) is the hydrolysis of 1 mole of ATP.

1. $$\text{Glucose} + \text{ATP} \longrightarrow \text{ADP} + \text{Glucose 6-}P$$

2. $$H_2O + \text{Glucose 6-}P \longrightarrow P_i + \text{Glucose}$$

Net: $$H_2O + \text{ATP} \longrightarrow \text{ADP} + P_i$$

3. $$\text{Enz–Ser–OH} + \text{ATP} \longrightarrow \text{ADP} + \text{Enz–Ser–O–}P$$

4. $$H_2O + \text{Enz–Ser–O–}P \longrightarrow P_i + \text{Enz–Ser–OH}$$

Net: $$H_2O + \text{ATP} \longrightarrow \text{ADP} + P_i$$

The activity of the kinases (catalyzing reactions 1 and 3) and of the phosphatases (catalyzing reactions 2 and 4) should themselves be regulated, for if not, they would act together to catalyze uncontrolled hydrolysis of ATP.

E. Analogies to Feedback Inhibition: Regulation of enzyme activity by phosphorylation-dephosphorylation has analogies to regulation by feedback inhibition. Both provide for short-term regulation of metabolite flow in response to specific physiologic signals; both act without altering gene expression, both act at early enzymes of a protracted (often biosynthetic) metabolic sequence; and both act at allosteric rather than catalytic sites. Feedback inhibition, however, involves a single protein and lacks hormonal and neural features. By contrast, regulation of mammalian enzymes by phosphorylation-dephosphorylation involves several proteins and is under direct neural and hormonal control.

Table 9–4. Primary structure in the neighborhood of the seryl residue of proteins phosphorylated by protein kinases.

Phosphorylase kinase (α-subunit)	S G ⓢ V Y E P L K
Phosphorylase kinase (β-subunit)	L ⓢ I S T E S Z P
Glycogen synthetase (site 1)	S N ⓢ V D T S S L S
Glycogen synthetase (site 2)	A ⓢ
Glycogen synthetase (site 3)	Z I ⓢ V R
Pyruvate kinase (pig liver)	A ⓢ L G
Pyruvate kinase (rat liver)	A S ⓢ V A Z L
Phosphorylase (rat, rabbit muscle)	Q I S ⓢ V R
Phosphorylase (human muscle)	E I S ⓢ V R
Phosphorylase (pig, rabbit, liver)	Q I S ⓢ V R
Fructose-1,6-bisphosphatase	P ⓢ L P L P

•   •   •

References

Gumaa KA, McLean P, Greenbaum AL: Compartmentation in relation to metabolic control in liver. *Essays Biochem* 1971;**7**:39.

Kun E, Grisolia S: *Biochemical Regulatory Mechanisms in Eukaryotic Cells.* Wiley, 1972.

Newsholme EA, Stuart C: *Regulation in Metabolism.* Wiley, 1973.

Schimke RT, Doyle D: Control of enzyme levels in animal tissues. *Annu Rev Biochem* 1970;**39**:929.

Sols A, Marco R: Concentrations of metabolites and binding sites: Implications in metabolic regulation. *Curr Top Cell Regul* 1970;**2**:227.

Stanbury JB, Wyngaarden JB, Fredrickson DS (editors): *The Metabolic Basis of Inherited Disease,* 4th ed. McGraw-Hill, 1978.

Umbarger HE: Amino acid biosynthesis and its regulation. *Annu Rev Biochem* 1978;**47**:533.

Weber G (editor): *Advances in Enzyme Regulation.* Vols 1–6. Pergamon Press, 1963–1979.

Water-Soluble Vitamins | 10

David W. Martin, Jr., MD

The water-soluble vitamins have chemical structures that are remarkably diverse, but they do share the property of being polar molecules and therefore are soluble in water.

Of the water-soluble vitamins, all but one— **cobalamin** (vitamin B_{12})—can be synthesized by plants and are therefore provided by legumes, whole grains, leafy green vegetables, and yeast, as well as meat and milk. Because of their water-solubility, the B complex vitamins and vitamin C have no stable storage form and must be **provided continuously** in the diet. Vitamin B_{12} is an exception in that the normal human liver can store several years' supply of cobalamin. All of the water-soluble vitamins except vitamin C serve as **coenzymes or cofactors in enzymatic reactions.**

THE VITAMINS OF THE B COMPLEX

The recognized B vitamins important for human nutrition are as follows:

(1) Thiamin (vitamin B_1)
(2) Riboflavin (vitamin B_2)
(3) Pantothenic acid (vitamin B_5)
(4) Niacin (nicotinic acid)
(5) Pyridoxine (vitamin B_6)
(6) Biotin
(7) Cobalamin (vitamin B_{12})
(8) Folic acid (pteroylglutamic acid)

Because of their water-solubility, these vitamins can be excreted in urine and thus rarely accumulate in toxic concentrations. Deficiencies of the water-soluble vitamins are not uncommon and frequently occur in the setting of a multiple vitamin deficiency state.

THIAMIN*

Thiamin consists of a substituted pyrimidine joined by a methylene bridge to a substituted thiazole (Fig 10–1).

*The word thiamin is derived from thi(o + vit)amin; more commonly but inappropriately spelled thiamine.

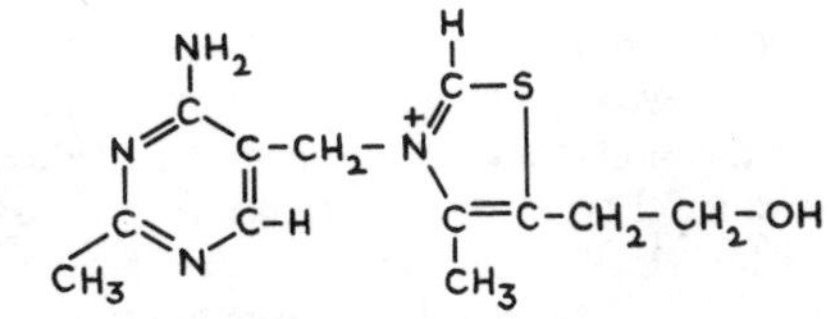

2,5,Dimethyl-   4-Methyl-5-hydroxy-
6-aminopyrimidine   ethylthiazole

Figure 10–1. Thiamin.

Sources

Thiamin is present in almost all plant and animal tissues commonly used as food, but the content is usually small. Among the more abundant sources are unrefined cereal grains and meat. Enrichment of flour, bread, corn, and macaroni products with thiamin has increased the availability of this vitamin in the diet. Deficiencies of thiamin are likely to occur not only in persons with poor dietary habits or in the indigent but also in many patients suffering from organic disease, particularly alcoholism. In addition, certain raw fish contain a heat-labile enzyme (thiaminase) that destroys thiamin. Attention was drawn to this "thiaminase" by the appearance of "Chastek paralysis" in foxes fed a diet containing 10% or more of uncooked fish. The disease is characterized by anorexia, weakness, progressive ataxia, spastic paraplegia, and hyperesthesia. The similarity between the focal lesions of the nervous system in this paralysis in the fox and the lesions seen in Wernicke's syndrome in humans have lent support to the concept that the latter is in part attributable to thiamin deficiency.

Thiamin is readily absorbed from the intestines but cannot be stored in the body to a significant degree. Any excess of thiamin is promptly excreted in the urine, and there is no evidence for thiamin toxicity.

Metabolism

An ATP-dependent thiamin pyrophosphotransferase (thiamin pyrophosphokinase) present in at least the brain and liver is responsible for the conversion of thiamin to its active form, **thiamin pyrophosphate** (Fig 10–2). Phosphatases in food sources, the gastrointestinal tract, and other human tissues are ca-

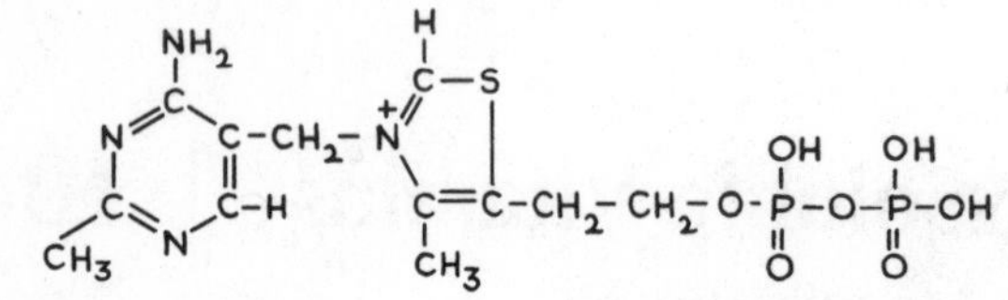

Figure 10–2. Thiamin pyrophosphate (thiamin diphosphate).

pable of removing the pyrophosphate from thiamin pyrophosphate.

Biochemical Function

Thiamin pyrophosphate serves as a coenzyme in enzymatic reactions transferring an activated aldehyde unit. There are 2 types of such reactions—an **oxidative decarboxylation** of α-keto acids (α-ketoglutarate and pyruvate) and **transketolase** reactions, in which aldehyde groups are removed from a molecule. In each case, the thiamin pyrophosphate provides a reactive carbon on the thiazole that forms a carbanion,

stabilized by the positively charged ring nitrogen of thiamin pyrophosphate (Fig 10–3). This carbanion is then free to add to the carbonyl group of—for instance—pyruvate (Fig 10–3). The addition compound then decarboxylates, eliminating CO_2 and generating the 2 resonance forms of ionized hydroxyethyl thiamin pyrophosphate (Fig 10–4). This reaction occurs in a multi-enzyme complex known as the **pyruvate dehydrogenase complex** (see Chapter 15). The hydroxyethyl thiamin pyrophosphate, as an integral part of the enzyme complex, transfers the acetaldehyde moiety to lipoamide (Fig 10–5). This

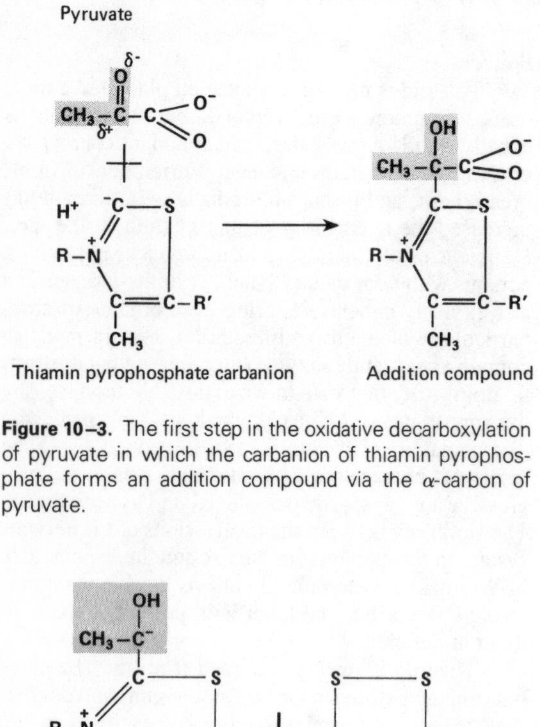

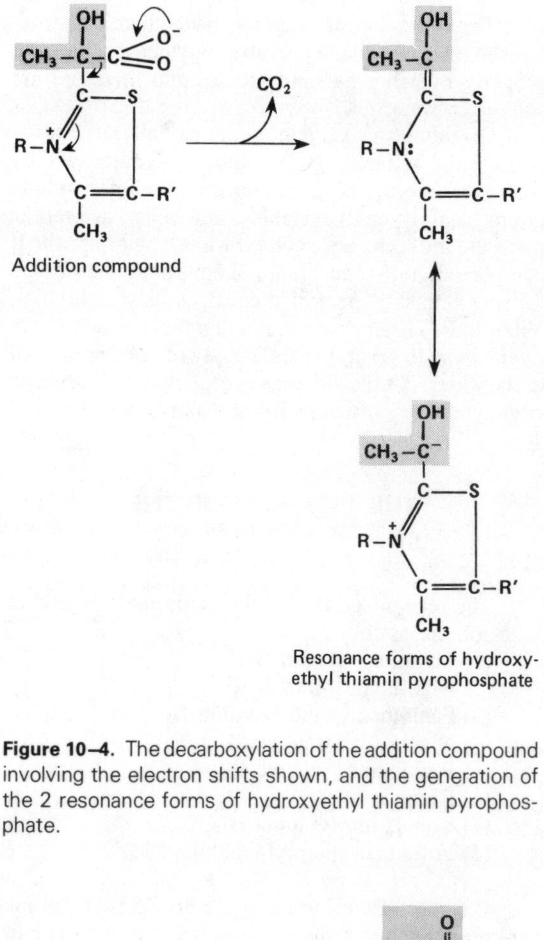

Figure 10–4. The decarboxylation of the addition compound involving the electron shifts shown, and the generation of the 2 resonance forms of hydroxyethyl thiamin pyrophosphate.

Figure 10–3. The first step in the oxidative decarboxylation of pyruvate in which the carbanion of thiamin pyrophosphate forms an addition compound via the α-carbon of pyruvate.

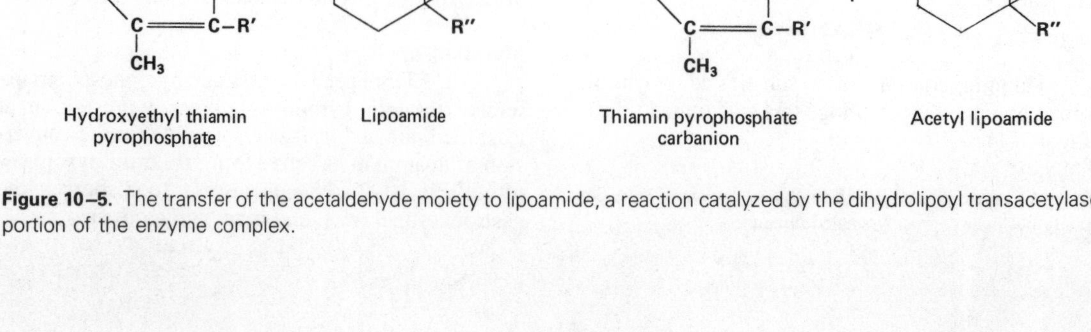

Figure 10–5. The transfer of the acetaldehyde moiety to lipoamide, a reaction catalyzed by the dihydrolipoyl transacetylase portion of the enzyme complex.

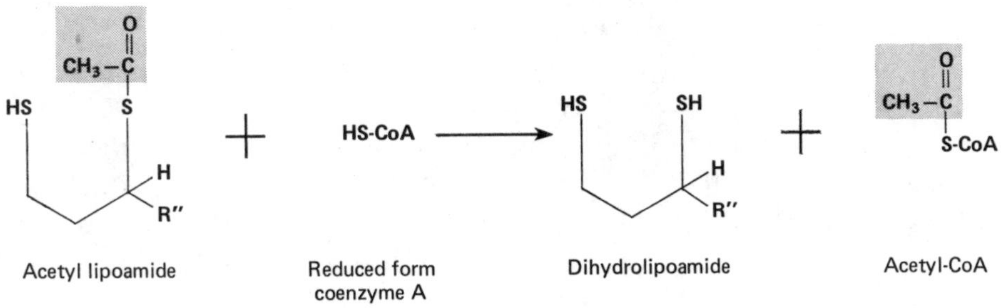

Figure 10–6. The acetyl group of acetyl lipoamide is transferred to the reduced form of coenzyme A to form acetyl-CoA.

phase of the reaction is catalyzed by the dihydrolipoyl transacetylase portion of the complex, yielding acetyl lipoamide. The dihydrolipoyl transacetylase also catalyzes the transfer of the acetyl group from acetyl lipoamide to CoA (Fig 10–6).

The oxidized form of lipoamide is regenerated by a dihydrolipoyl dehydrogenase of which flavin adenine dinucleotide is a prosthetic group.

The role of thiamin pyrophosphate as a coenzyme in the transketolase reactions is very similar to that described above for the oxidative decarboxylations. However, the hydroxyethyl moiety of hydroxyethyl thiamin pyrophosphate is transferred to a ribose diphosphate to form sedoheptulose 7-phosphate (see Chapter 15) rather than to lipoamide, as in the pyruvate dehydrogenase reaction above.

The oxidative decarboxylation of α-ketoglutarate to succinyl-CoA and CO_2 (see Chapter 14) is catalyzed by an enzyme complex structurally very similar to the pyruvate dehydrogenase complex. Again, the thiamin pyrophosphate provides a stable carbanion to react with the alpha carbon of α-ketoglutarate. A similar oxidative decarboxylation of the α-ketocarboxylic acid derivatives of the branched chain amino acids (Chapter 22) utilizes thiamin pyrophosphate.

Accordingly, in the thiamin-deficient human, these thiamin pyrophosphate–dependent reactions are prevented or severely limited, leading to accumulation of the substrates of the reactions, eg, pyruvate, pentosugars, and the α-ketocarboxylate derivatives of the branched chain amino acids leucine, isoleucine, and valine.

RIBOFLAVIN

Riboflavin consists of a heterotricyclic structure to which is attached ribitol (Fig 10–7). The ring structure is conjugated; thus, riboflavin is a colored and fluorescent pigment. It is relatively heat-stable but sensitive to irreversible decomposition upon exposure to visible light. Riboflavin is synthesized by all plants and many microorganisms but not by higher animals. The absorption of riboflavin in the intestine occurs concomitantly with its phosphorylation by the intestinal mucosa to form riboflavin phosphate or riboflavin mononucleotide (Fig 10–8). The enzyme flavokinase,

Figure 10–7. Riboflavin.

which phosphorylates riboflavin, is competitively inhibited by chlorpromazine, a widely used phenothiazine drug. Riboflavin is excreted in urine, particularly when ingested in excess; thus, there is no known toxicity of riboflavin.

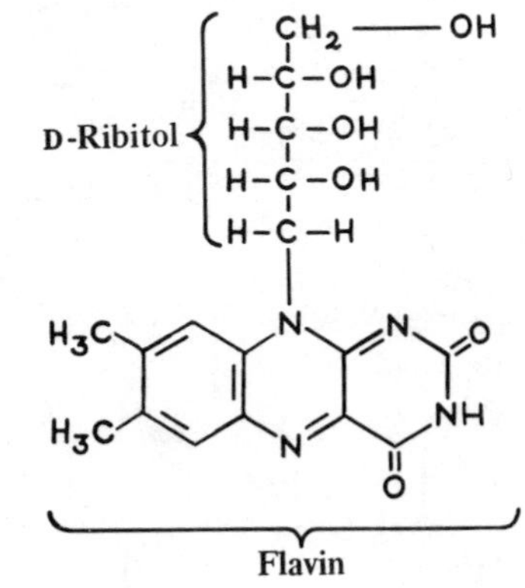

Riboflavin is a component of the flavin nucleotides. **Flavin mononucleotide (FMN)** is formed by the ATP-dependent phosphorylation of riboflavin. **Flavin adenine dinucleotide (FAD)** is formed by the

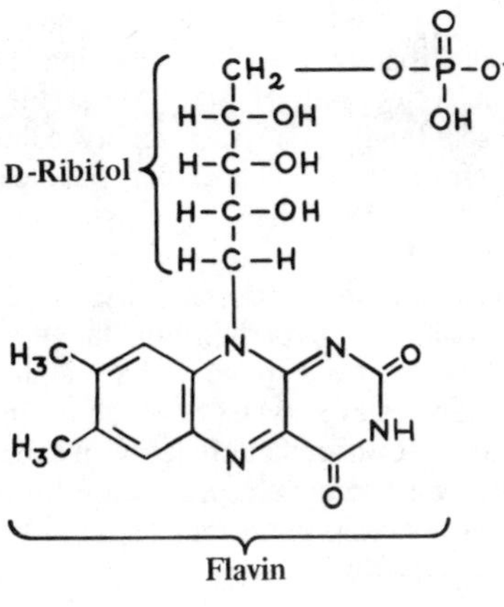

Figure 10–8. Riboflavin phosphate (flavin mononucleotide, FMN).

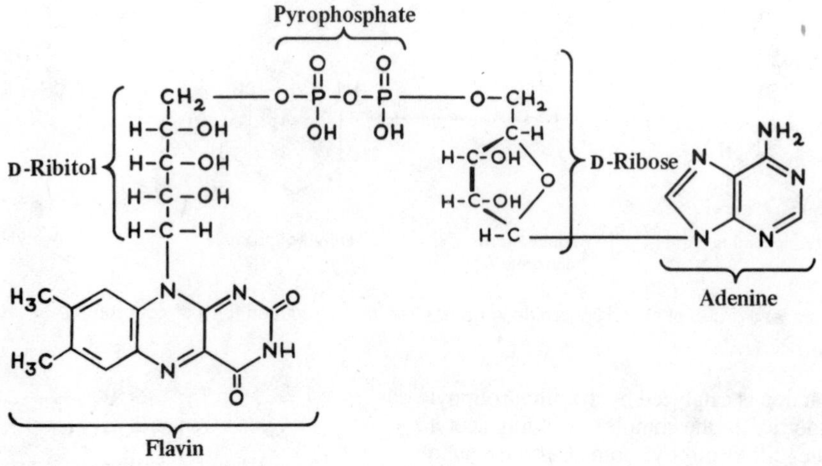

Figure 10–9. Flavin adenine dinucleotide (FAD).

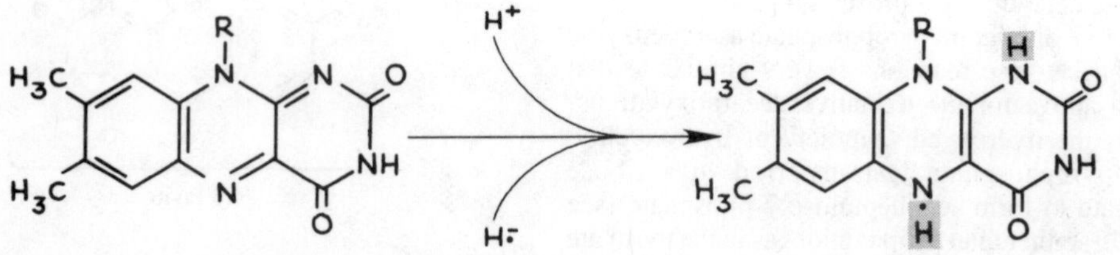

Figure 10–10. Reduction of isoalloxazine ring in flavin nucleotides.

transfer of an AMP moiety from another ATP molecule to the FMN (Fig 10–9). These reactions seem to occur in most tissues. The FMN and FAD serve as prosthetic groups of oxidation-reduction enzymes, known as **flavoenzymes** or **flavoproteins.** They are usually tightly but not covalently bound to the protein. Many flavoproteins contain one or more metals as additional cofactors and are referred to as the **metalloflavoproteins.**

In the catalytic cycle of the flavoproteins, the flavin moiety of the flavin nucleotides undergoes reversible reduction of the isoalloxazine ring to yield the reduced nucleotides $FMNH_2$ and $FADH_2$ (Fig 10–10). The oxidized flavoproteins are highly colored as a result of their flavonucleotide content but bleach when the conjugation through the 3 rings is disrupted upon reduction (Fig 10–10).

Because of the light-sensitivity of riboflavin, newborn infants with hyperbilirubinemia treated with phototherapy have been shown to have signs of riboflavin deficiencies even when riboflavin supplements were provided. **Riboflavin deficiency** in experimental animals may be teratogenic, ie, induce birth defects when it occurs during pregnancy.

NIACIN & NIACINAMIDE

Niacin, or nicotinic acid, is a **pyridine derivative** that is a nontoxic component of the toxic alkaloid nicotine of tobacco. Plants and most animals can synthesize nicotinic acid from the amino acid **tryptophan** by the rearrangement shown in Fig 10–11. Note that this pathway to nicotinic acid requires **pyridoxal phosphate,** the active coenzyme form of vitamin B_6, or pyridoxine. Thus, the major sources of niacin are tryptophan-containing proteins such as meat and those foodstuffs containing nicotinic acid per se (unrefined grains and cereals, yeasts, milk, leafy vegetables, etc). Of note is the fact that **corn is very poor in tryptophan and niacin.** Thus, diets in which corn is a major source of protein can result in a niacin deficiency syndrome called **pellagra.** For every 60 mg of tryptophan, only 1 mg of nicotinic acid can be generated in the presence of an active pathway. Thus, pellagra is usually associated with a deficiency of not only niacin but also tryptophan and pyridoxine. Rarely, in specific diseases of tryptophan metabolism such as carcinoid syndrome and Hartnup's disease, pellagra can occur as an isolated entity.

Nicotinic acid is absorbed in the intestines as nicotinate but is not excreted unmodified in the urine. The largest portion of niacin is excreted as the N-methyl derivative N-methylnicotinamide.

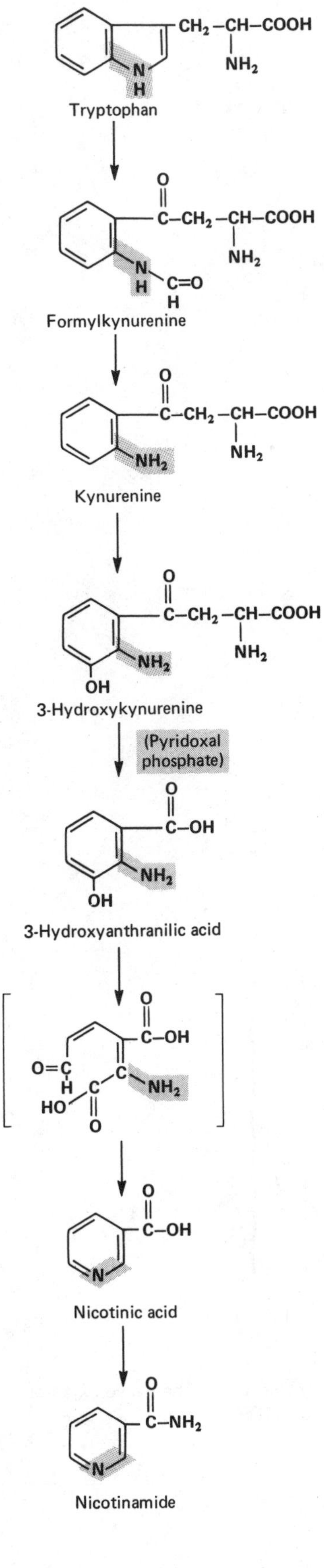

Tryptophan

Formylkynurenine

Kynurenine

3-Hydroxykynurenine

(Pyridoxal phosphate)

3-Hydroxyanthranilic acid

Nicotinic acid

Nicotinamide

Figure 10–11 (at left). The synthesis of nicotinic acid and nicotinamide from tryptophan.

In the cellular cytosol, nicotinate is phosphoribosylated by PPriboseP to form **nicotinate mononucleotide** (NMN). The latter compound is then adenylylated by ATP to form desamidonicotinamide dinucleotide (desamido-NAD$^+$) (Fig 10–12). The amido group of glutamine then contributes its amide to form the coenzyme **nicotinamide dinucleotide,** or **NAD$^+$.** A phosphorylated derivative of NAD, **nicotinamide dinucleotide phosphate, NADP$^+$** also acts as an important coenzyme.

The niacin nucleotides, NAD$^+$ and NADP$^+$, serve as coenzymes in a large number of reversible oxidation-reduction reactions, as shown in Fig 10–13. The property of these pyridine nucleotides that is responsible for their effectiveness as coenzymes for the oxidation-reduction reactions is the ability of the pyridine ring to serve as an **electron sink**—ie, the hydride or reduced form can exist in multiple resonant forms and therefore is relatively stable.

Some oxidation-reduction enzymes utilize exclusively NAD$^+$ *or* NADP$^+$, ie, one but not the other; others may use *either* pyridine nucleotide coenzyme.

Nicotinic acid (but not nicotinamide) in high doses can induce skin flushing, pruritus, and gastrointestinal distress and also has demonstrated efficacy for lowering serum cholesterol levels by mechanisms that are not understood.

In the deficiency of niacin, the dermatitis, diarrhea, dementia, etc, of pellagra respond rapidly to niacin, frequently within 1 day. The metabolic abnormalities associated with pellagra are difficult to define, because, as mentioned above, a deficiency of niacin is usually accompanied by the deficiencies of multiple vitamins and by other specific diseases.

PYRIDOXINE

Vitamin B$_6$ consists of 3 closely related naturally occurring pyridine derivatives: **pyridoxine, pyridoxal,** and **pyridoxamine** (Fig 10–14). All 3 appear to be equally active as precursors for the coenzyme pyridoxal phosphate. Seeds, grains, liver, and to some extent milk, eggs, and leafy green vegetables are good sources of vitamin B$_6$.

Pyridoxine and its analogs are readily absorbed in the intestines. In the cellular cytoplasm, all 3 serve as substrate for the enzyme pyridoxal kinase, which utilizes ATP to phosphorylate all 3 derivatives to their respective **phosphate esters** (Fig 10–15). Only pyridoxal phosphate and pyridoxamine phosphate are active as coenzymes. The major metabolite of vitamin B$_6$ excreted in urine is 4-pyridoxic acid (Fig 10–16), which can be measured by a fluorometric method.

The coenzyme pyridoxal phosphate binds to its apoenzyme via a **Schiff base** between its 4-aldehyde group and an ϵ-amino group of a lysine residue in the enzyme and via an ionic bond (salt bridge) between its

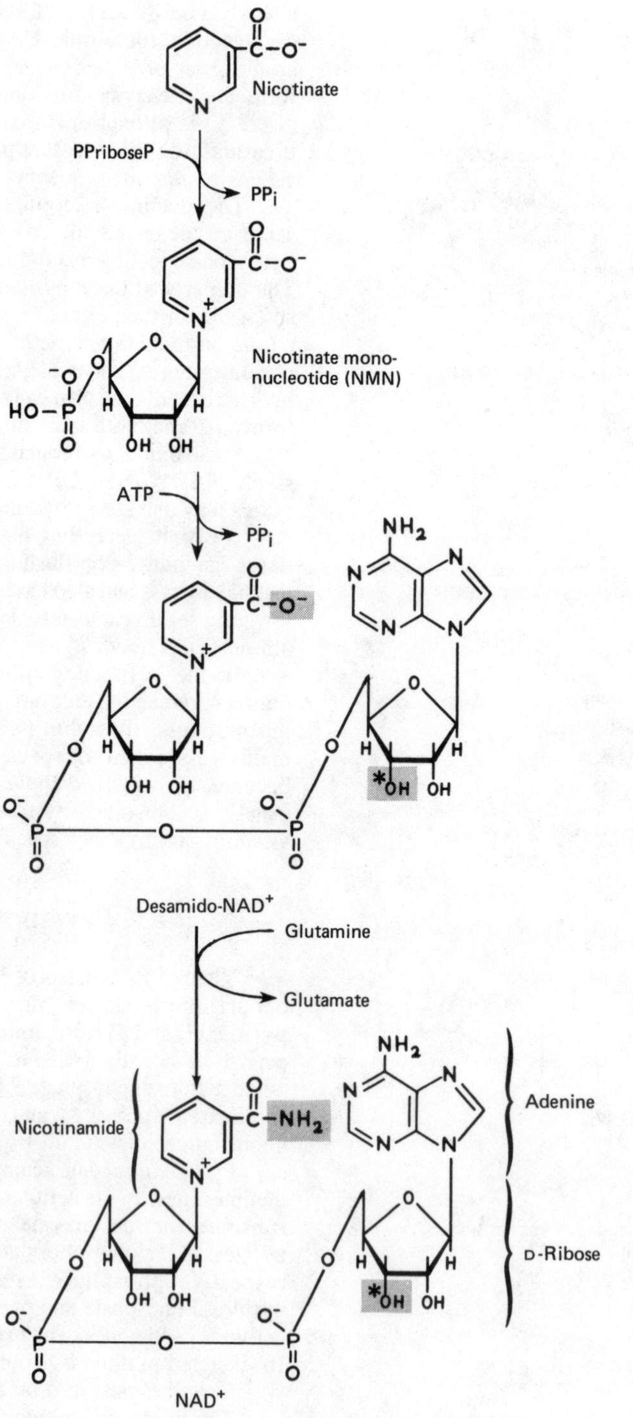

Figure 10–12. The synthesis of nicotinamide adenine dinucleotide (NAD⁺) from nicotinate. The 3′-hydroxyl group (*) of the adenosine moiety is phosphorylated in nicotinamide dinucleotide phosphate (NADP⁺).

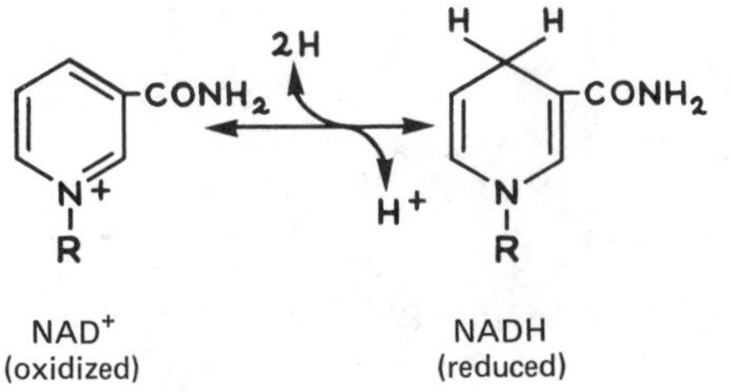

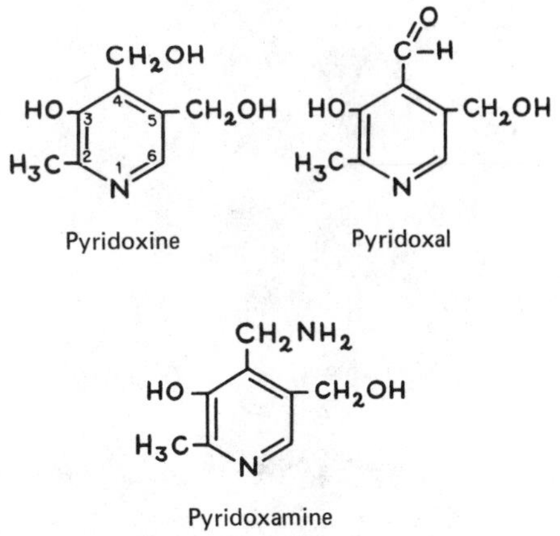

Figure 10–14. Naturally occurring forms of vitamin B$_6$.

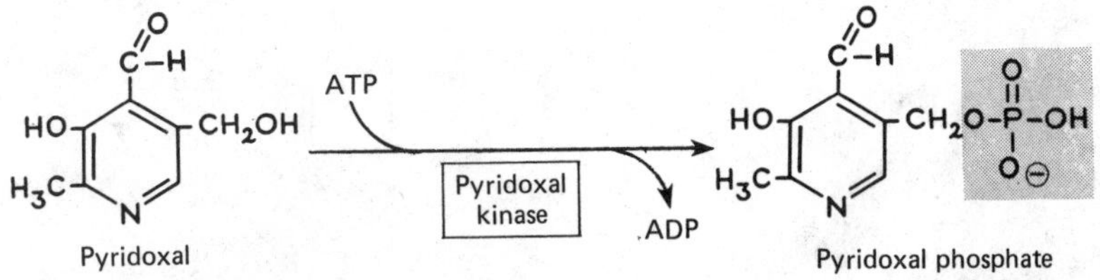

Figure 10–13. Reduction of NAD$^+$.

Figure 10–15. The phosphorylation of pyridoxal by pyridoxal kinase to form pyridoxal phosphate.

phosphate and the enzyme (Fig 10–16). The ability of pyridoxal phosphate to form the Schiff base with an amine is of utmost importance for its function as a coenzyme in **transamination** and **decarboxylation reactions.** In the absence of substrate, the 4-aldehyde group of pyridoxal phosphate remains in the Schiff base linkage with the lysyl residue of the enzyme-active site. Upon the entry of an α-amino group of a substrate, such as an amino acid, the α-amino group displaces the ε-amino group of the lysyl residue, forming a new Schiff base; but the coenzyme remains bound to the enzyme by the salt bridge (Fig 10–16). By a series of electron shifts and rearrangements, the pyridoxal phosphate becomes **pyridoxamine phosphate** as the substrate is oxidatively deaminated (Fig 10–17) to form the corresponding α-keto acid. Subsequently, the aldehyde substrate of the transamination reaction forms a Schiff base with the pyridoxamine phosphate (Fig 10–18), and the α-amino group removed from the amino acid is transferred to the α-keto acid, completing the transamination cycle.

Pyridoxal phosphate serves also as a coenzyme in decarboxylation reactions of amino acids, again with the formation of the intermediate Schiff base and the

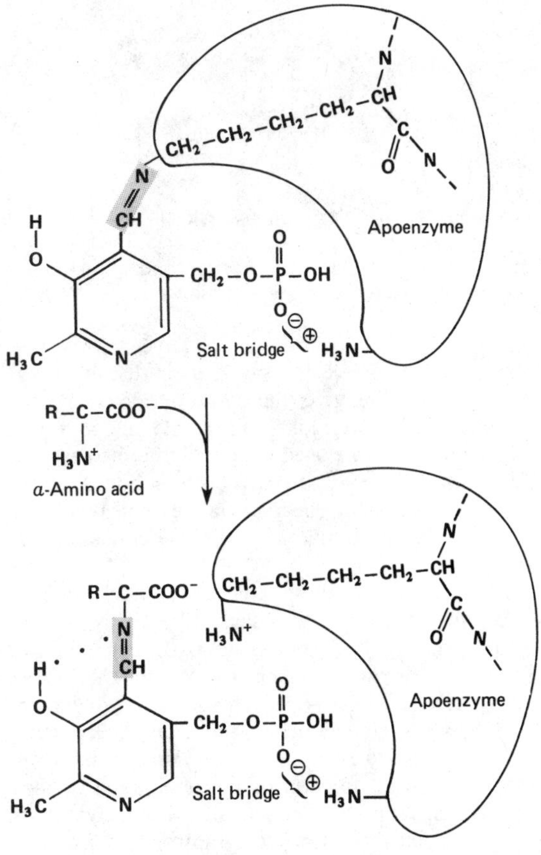

Figure 10–16 (at right). The binding of pyridoxal phosphate to its apoenzyme. When an α-amino acid enters, it displaces the ε-amino group of the apoenzyme lysyl residue and forms its own Schiff base with the 4-aldehyde of pyridoxal phosphate.

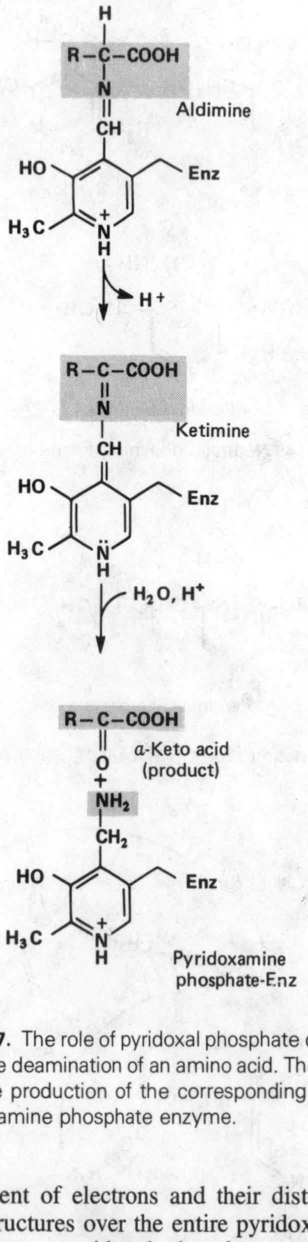

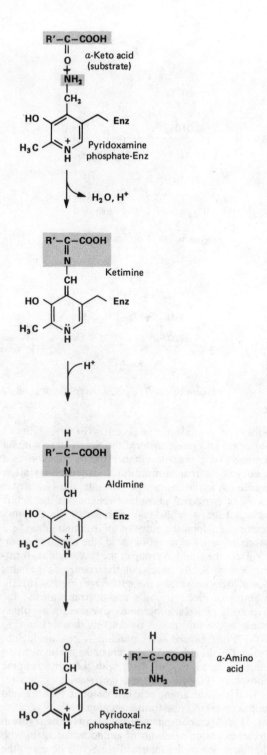

Figure 10–17. The role of pyridoxal phosphate coenzyme in the oxidative deamination of an amino acid. The first phase involves the production of the corresponding α-keto acid and pyridoxamine phosphate enzyme.

rearrangement of electrons and their distribution in resonant structures over the entire pyridoxal moiety. As coenzymes, pyridoxal phosphate and pyridoxamine phosphate are used widely in intermediary metabolism. Figure 10–19 depicts the bonds of the α-amino acid that can be made labile by its binding to different specific pyridoxal phosphate-containing enzymes.

Deficiency of pyridoxine alone rarely occurs. However, a widely used antituberculosis drug, isonicotinic acid hydrazide (**isoniazid**), can induce an isolated pyridoxine deficiency by forming a hydrazone with pyridoxal (Fig 10–20). The pyridoxal-hydrazone is rapidly excreted in urine, and vitamin deficiency ensues. Isoniazid is normally acetylated in the liver, but a significant fraction of the population of most racial groups consists of genetically slow acetylators of isoniazid. Only in **slow acetylators** does isoniazid

Figure 10–18. The role of pyridoxamine phosphate coenzyme in the second phase of oxidative deamination of an α-amino acid. The α-keto acid substrate (frequently α-ketoglutarate) receives the amino group from pyridoxamine phosphate to generate the corresponding α-amino acid (glutamate) and pyridoxal phosphate, completing the transamination cycle.

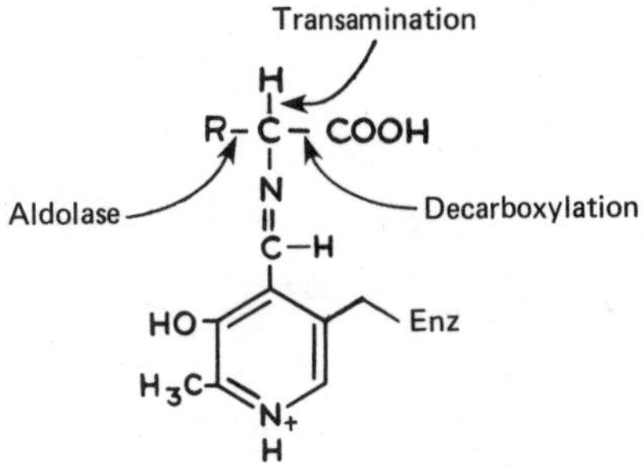

Figure 10–19 (at right). The covalent bonds of an α-amino acid that can be labilized by its binding to specific pyridoxal phosphate–containing enzymes.

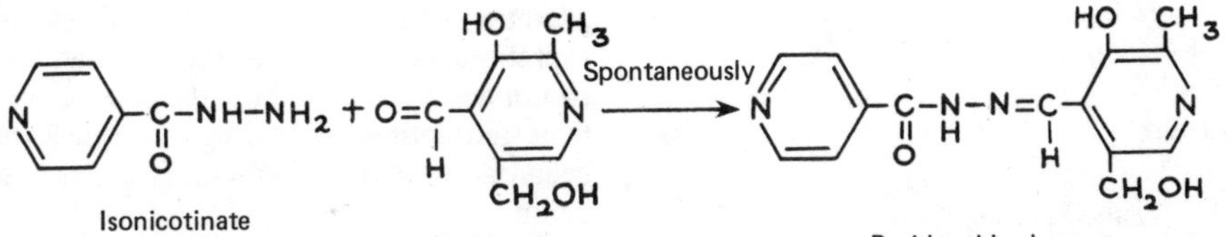

Isonicotinate hydrazide   Pyridoxal   Pyridoxal-hydrazone

Figure 10–20. The formation of the rapidly excreted pyridoxal-hydrazone from pyridoxal and isonicotinate hydrazine (isoniazid).

have the opportunity to form the hydrazone of pyridoxal. There is some evidence that in renal failure, pyridoxal kinase is inhibited and there ensues a deficiency of the coenzyme pyridoxal phosphate in spite of adequate intake of vitamin B_6.

As mentioned above in the discussion of niacin, the generation of nicotinic acid from tryptophan is dependent upon pyridoxal phosphate as coenzyme. Hence, **pellagra is a frequent accompaniment of pyridoxine deficiency.**

Pyridoxine is also necessary in the transulfuration reactions that convert methionine to cysteine (Chapter 22). Homocystinuria and cystathioninuria are metabolic indicators of pyridoxine deficiency.

A number of genetic diseases in humans result from the inability of specific apoenzymes to bind pyridoxal phosphate with adequate avidity. Some of those diseases will respond to pharmacologic doses of vitamin B_6 (see Chapter 41).

There is no known toxicity of vitamin B_6.

PANTOTHENIC ACID

Pantothenic acid is an amide of pantoic acid and β-alanine (Fig 10–21). It is widely distributed in foods, being particularly abundant in animal tissues, whole grain cereals, and legumes. A specific pantothenate deficiency syndrome in humans has been recognized only experimentally after the administration of specific antagonists. Deficiency of pantothenate is usually associated with deficiencies of other B complex vitamins. There is no known toxicity of pantothenic acid.

Pantothenic acid is absorbed readily in the intestines and subsequently phosphorylated by ATP to form

$4'$-phosphopantothenic acid (Fig 10–22). On the path to conversion to the active coenzyme, **coenzyme A,** cysteine is added to the phosphopantothenic acid, and the carboxyl group of cysteine is subsequently removed, resulting in the net addition of thioethanolamine to phosphopantothenic acid, generating $4'$-phosphopantetheine. Like the active coenzymes of so many other water-soluble vitamins, the active coenzyme of pantothenate contains an adenine nucleotide. Thus, $4'$-phosphopantetheine is adenylylated by ATP to form dephospho-coenzyme A. The final phosphorylation occurs with ATP adding phosphate to the $3'$-hydroxyl group of the ribose moiety to generate coenzyme A (Fig 10–22). Coenzyme A contains adenine at one pole and a thiol at the opposite pole of the molecule. This latter **thiol group acts as a carrier of acyl groups** in reactions involving fatty acid oxidation and synthesis, acetylation reactions, and (as discussed above) oxidative decarboxylations in which thiamin pyrophosphate also participates. The acyl-sulfur bond formed from coenzyme A and a transferred acyl moiety is a **high-energy bond,** equivalent to the high-energy bond of ATP. Formation of these high-energy bonds therefore requires a source of energy, either from a coupled exergonic reaction or from the transfer of energy from a high-energy phosphate or a

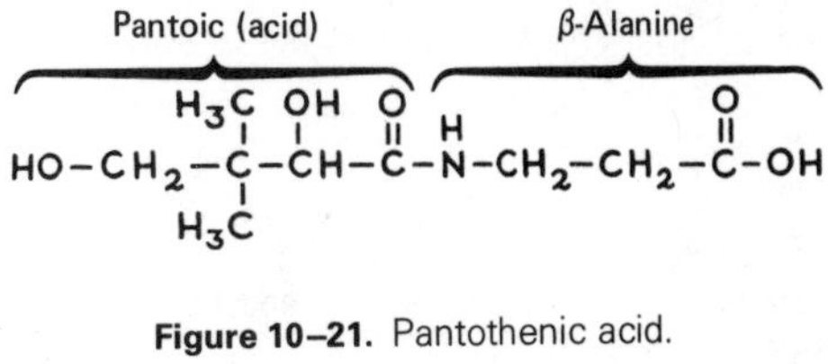

Pantoic (acid)   β-Alanine

Figure 10–21. Pantothenic acid.

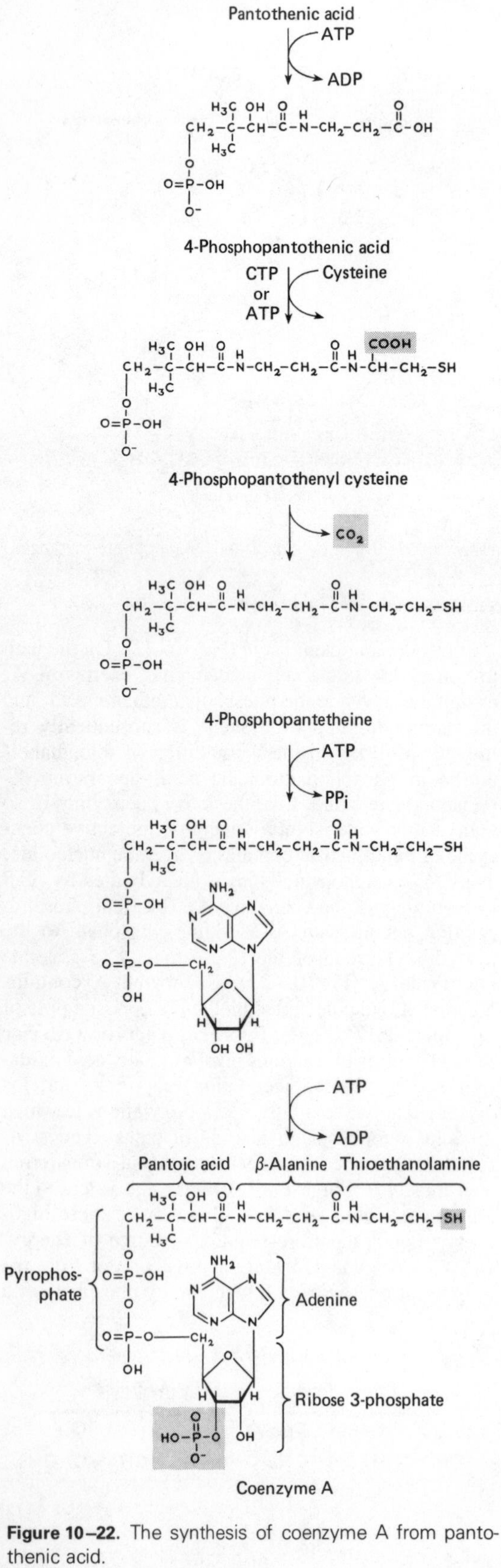

Pantothenic acid

4-Phosphopantothenic acid

4-Phosphopantothenyl cysteine

4-Phosphopantetheine

Pantoic acid   β-Alanine   Thioethanolamine

Pyrophosphate

Adenine

Ribose 3-phosphate

Coenzyme A

Figure 10–22. The synthesis of coenzyme A from pantothenic acid.

high-energy sulfur bond. It is customary to abbreviate the structure of the free (ie, reduced) coenzyme A as CoA·SH, in which the reactive SH group of the coenzyme is designated.

BIOTIN

Biotin is an imidazole derivative widely distributed in natural foods (Fig 10–23). A large portion of the human biotin requirement is probably **supplied from the intestinal bacteria.** Careful balance studies in humans have shown that in many instances urinary excretion of biotin exceeded dietary intake and fecal excretion was 3–6 times greater than dietary intake. Biotin deficiency can be induced more readily in animals fed antibacterial drugs to reduce the intestinal bacterial flora to a minimum. Biotin is absorbed in the ileum.

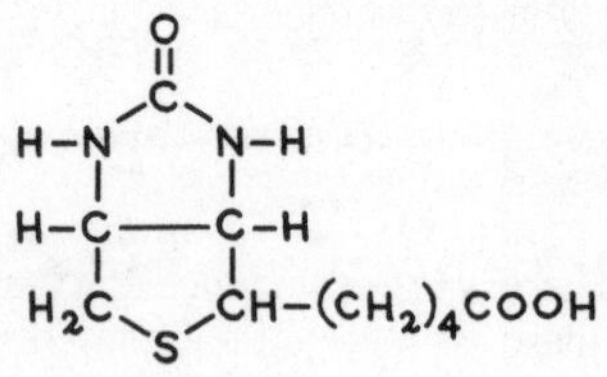

Figure 10–23. Biotin.

The bioavailability of biotin differs widely in various foodstuffs. For example, while the biotin of corn and soy meals is completely available, that of wheat is almost unavailable. Egg yolk, animal tissues, tomatoes, and yeast are excellent sources of biotin. Egg white contains heat-labile protein, **avidin,** which combines very tightly with biotin, thereby preventing its absorption from the intestine and inducing an isolated biotin deficiency.

Biotin functions as a component of specific multisubunit enzymes (Table 10–1) that catalyze carboxylation reactions. It is attached to the apoenzyme by an amide linkage to the ϵ-amino group of a lysyl residue.

Table 10–1. Biotin-dependent enzymes in animals.

Enzyme	Role
Pyruvate carboxylase	First reaction in pathway that converts 3-carbon precursors to glucose (gluconeogenesis)
	Replenishes oxaloacetate for citric acid cycle
Acetyl-CoA carboxylase	Commits acetate units to fatty acid synthesis by forming malonyl-CoA
Propionyl-CoA carboxylase	Converts proprionate to succinate, which can then enter citric acid cycle
β-Methylcrotonyl-CoA carboxylase	Catabolism of leucine and certain isoprenoid compounds

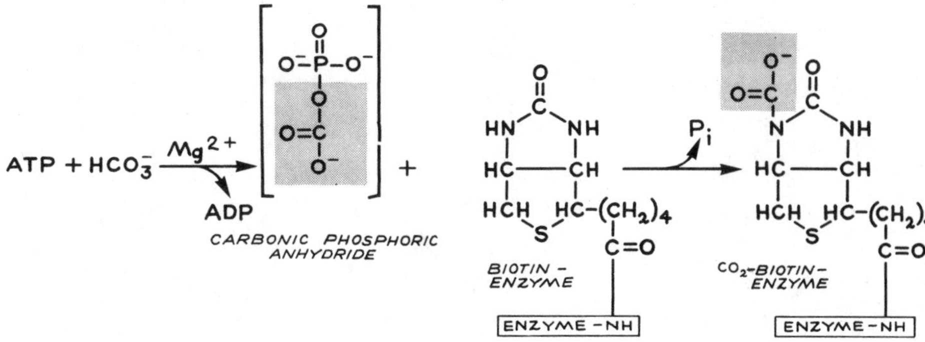

Figure 10–24. Formation of the CO_2-biotin enzyme complex.

In the first step of the reaction of pyruvate carboxylase, a carboxylate ion is attached to the N^1 of the biotin, generating an activated intermediate, **carboxybiotin-enzyme** (Fig 10–24). This step requires HCO_3^-, ATP, Mg^{2+}, and acyl-CoA (as an allosteric effector). The activated carboxyl group is then transferred from the carboxybiotin enzyme intermediate to pyruvate to form oxaloacetate and the biotin-holoenzyme. The long flexible arm between the biotin and the enzyme probably enables this prosthetic group (biotin) to move from one active site of the multisubunit enzyme (eg, the phosphocarbonate-forming component) to the other site (eg, that possessing the pyruvate).

There appears to be a single enzyme responsible for attaching biotin to the proper lysyl residue of all the carboxylase apoenzymes. This enzyme is called holocarboxylase synthetase. In the absence of holocarboxylase synthetase activity, substrates of the biotin-dependent carboxylase enzymes accumulate and can be detected in urine. These metabolites include lactate, β-methylcrotonate, β-hydroxyisovalerate, and β-hydroxypropionate. Children with this enzyme deficiency exhibit dermatitis, retarded growth, alopecia, loss of muscular control, and, in some cases, immune deficiency diseases.

There is no known toxicity of biotin.

VITAMIN B_{12}

Vitamin B_{12}, or cobalamin, consists of a corrin ring similar to the porphyrins that includes a **cobalt ion** at its center (Fig 10–25). A cyano group is usually attached to the cobalt as an artifact of isolation and must be removed in the body before cobalamin can be converted to its active form. Cobalamin is **synthesized exclusively by bacteria** but is present in normal animal liver, where it exists as methylcobalamin, adenosylcobalamin, and hydroxocobalamin. The cyanocobalamin is the most stable form and therefore that form in which the vitamin is commercially produced from bacterial fermentation. It is water-soluble and heat-stable.

The intestinal absorption of vitamin B_{12} is mediated by receptor sites in the ileum that require cobalamin to be bound by the highly specific glycoprotein **intrinsic factor,** secreted by gastric mucosal cells. Other cobalamin-binding proteins, known collectively as R proteins, exist in food and saliva but do not aid in the intestinal absorption of cobalamin. The latter proteins are normally degraded by pancreatic proteases, but in pancreatic insufficiency cobalamin molecules are not released from the R proteins in order to bind to intrinsic factor for normal absorption.

As the cobalamin–intrinsic factor complex crosses the ileal mucosa, intrinsic factor is released and the vitamin is transferred to a plasma transport protein, **transcobalamin II.** Other cobalamin-binding proteins, such as transcobalamin I, exist in the liver and provide an effective storage form of cobalamin, a unique situation for water-soluble vitamins. Cobalamin is secreted in bile and participates in enterohepatic circulation; thus, there is an enhanced requirement for exogenous cobalamin whenever the enterohepatic circulatory system is disturbed. Once the cobalamin is bound to transcobalamin II in the portal blood, it disappears from the plasma in a few hours. The major circulating vitamin is **methylcobalamin,** with a trace of hydroxocobalamin detectable. However, in the liver, **adenosylcobalamin** accounts for 70% of the total cobalamins, whereas methylcobalamin contributes only 3%.

The transcobalamin II complex binds to specific cell surface receptors and enters the cell by way of an endocytotic process, ultimately releasing free cobalamin as **hydroxocobalamin in the cytosol.** There it is either converted to methylcobalamin or enters the **mitochondria,** where the cobalt is **reduced** and **5'-deoxyadenosylcobalamin** subsequently formed (Fig 10–26).

There are in humans only 2 enzymatic reactions for which cobalamin serves as a coenzyme. **Methylation of homocysteine to methionine** occurs in the cytoplasm and utilizes methylcobalamin as coenzyme and N^5-methyltetrahydrofolate as methyl source (Fig 10–27). The methyltransferase apoenzyme binds cobalamin, and the N^5-**methyltetrahydrofolate** trans-

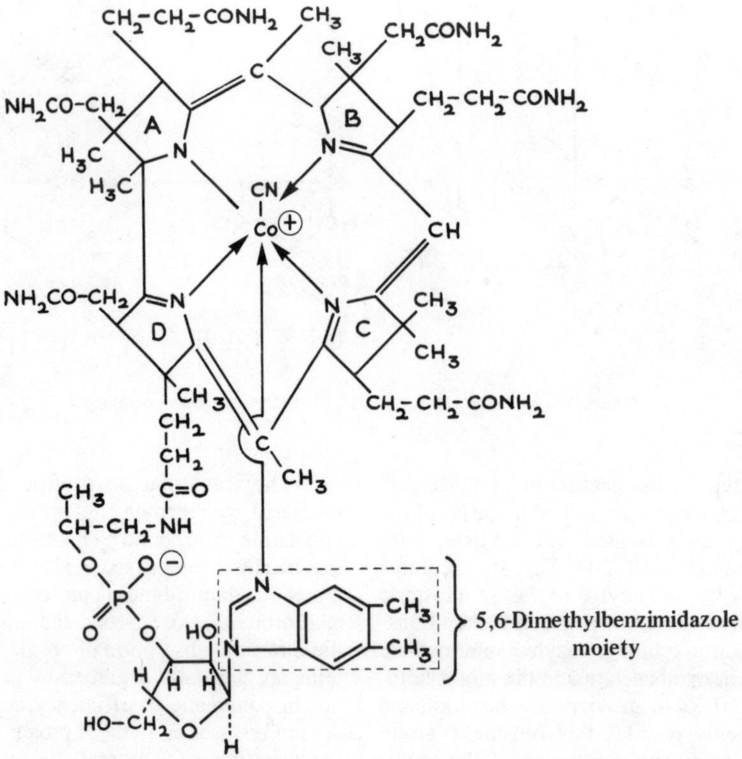

Figure 10-25. Cyanocobalamin; vitamin B_{12} ($C_{63}H_{88}O_{14}N_{14}PCo$).

fers its methyl group to the cobalamin prosthetic group. The methyl group bound to the cobalamin is then transferred to homocysteine, generating methionine. As will be discussed below, absence of cobalamin effects a block in this reaction and an accumulation of N^5-methyltetrahydrofolate. Thus, a deficiency of cobalamin generates a **trap for tetrahydrofolate,** an important cofactor discussed below.

The second enzymatic reaction that utilizes cobalamin is isomerization of L-methylmalonyl-CoA to succinyl-CoA by the enzyme **L-methylmalonyl-CoA mutase** and the coenzyme **5'-deoxyadenosylcobalamin** (Fig 10-27). As described above, the deoxyadenosyl-cobalamin is formed from ATP and reduced cobalamin in mitochondria, and the isomerization likewise occurs in the **mitochondria** (Fig 10-26).

In the cobalamin-deficient states, whether they be

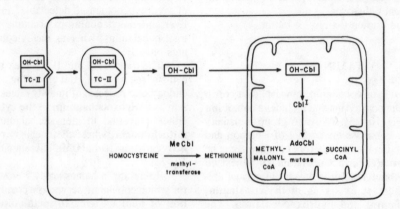

Figure 10-26. Pathway of cellular uptake and subcellular compartmentation of cobalamin and cobalamin coenzymes. (OH-Cbl, hydroxocobalamin; TC II, transcobalamin II; MeCbl, methylcobalamin; AdoCbl, 5'deoxyadenosylcobalamin.) (Reproduced, with permission, from Stanbury JB, Wyngaarden JB, Fredrickson DS: *The Metabolic Basis of Inherited Disease,* 4th ed. McGraw-Hill, 1978.)

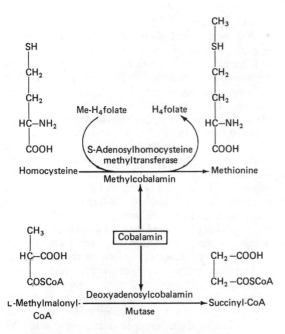

Figure 10–27. Reactions catalyzed by cobalamin coenzymes in mammalian tissues. Note the specificity of deoxyadenosylcobalamin for the isomerization of methylmalonyl-CoA and of methylcobalamin for the methylation of homocysteine. (Me-H$_4$folate = N^5-methyltetrahydrofolate; H$_4$folate = tetrahydrofolate.) (Redrawn, with permission, from Stanbury JB, Wyngaarden JB, Fredrickson DS: *The Metabolic Basis of Inherited Disease,* 4th ed. McGraw-Hill, 1978.)

FOLATE OR FOLACIN

The term folic is derived from Latin *folium* "leaf." Chemically, folic acid or folate consists of the heterobicyclic pteridine, para-aminobenzoic acid (PABA), and glutamic acid (Fig 10–28). Animal cells are not capable of synthesizing PABA or of attaching the first glutamate to pteroic acid. Thus, unlike bacteria and plants, they require folic acid in their diets. The major source of folic acid is, of course, leafy vegetables. **Folate deficiency is probably the most common vitamin deficiency in the USA.**

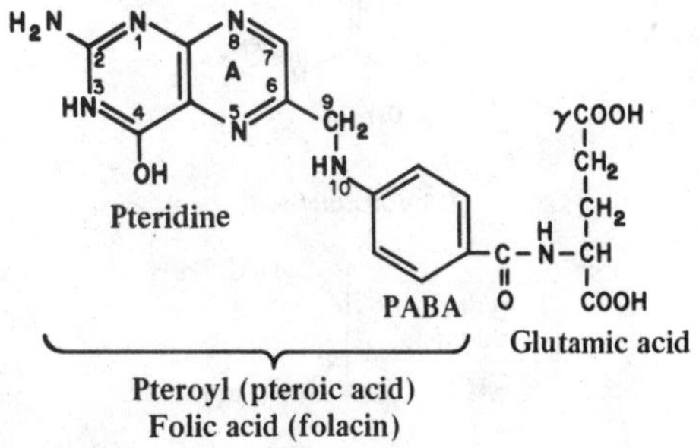

Figure 10–28. The structure and numbering of atoms of folic acid.

due to malabsorption of vitamin B$_{12}$ or to defective delivery of cobalamin to the peripheral tissues, homocystinuria and methylmalonic aciduria occur.

Although in some bacteria vitamin B$_{12}$ derivatives are necessary for the reduction of ribonucleotides to the 2'-deoxyribonucleotide substrates of DNA synthesis, there is no evidence for direct involvement of cobalamin coenzymes in the formation of the substrates for DNA synthesis in humans. As discussed below with folates, the megaloblastic anemia characteristic of vitamin B$_{12}$ deficiency is probably due to a secondary deficiency of reduced folate, a consequence of the accumulation of excessive N^5-methyltetrahydrofolate (see above).

In some inherited diseases discussed in Chapter 41, massive quantities of vitamin B$_{12}$—1000 times the normal requirement—are administered to effect a functional cure of an inherited metabolic disease.

Four inherited disorders of cobalamin metabolism have been described in humans. Two affect the synthesis of deoxyadenosyl cobalamin only; in the other 2, patients are unable to synthesize either deoxyadenosylcobalamin or methylcobalamin.

In plants, folic acid exists as a polyglutamate conjugate with an unusual gamma-linked polypeptide chain of 7 glutamic acids. In the liver, the major folate is a pentaglutamyl conjugate. These unusual gamma-linked glutamyl peptide chains are resistant to hydrolysis by the usual proteolytic enzymes present in the intestine. However, they are cleaved by a specific group of intestinal enzymes, folyl polyglutamate hydrolases.

The hydrolysis of pteroylheptaglutamate to pteroylmonoglutamate by intestinal enzymes is rapid and not rate-limiting for the absorption of the folates into the mesenteric circulation. Only the monoglutamyl form is absorbed, and a major portion of that is reduced to tetrahydrofolate (H$_4$folate) and methylated to N^5-methyl-H$_4$folate within the intestinal cell as an integral part of the absorption process. After the oral administration of folic acid to normal humans, there is a transitory rise in the plasma concentration of N^5-methyltetrahydrofolate regardless of the form in which folates are administered. Folate absorption is impaired in idiopathic steatorrhea and tropical sprue and in various other disorders of the small intestine.

In the blood plasma, approximately two-thirds of the folate is bound to a protein. Of the folates filtered by the kidney glomerulus, only a negligible fraction is reabsorbed by the tubules when the plasma folate concentration exceeds 10 μg/L. Some folate cleavage products may be excreted in bile.

This rather complex molecule folic acid, after being **reduced to tetrahydrofolate** (H$_4$folate), serves

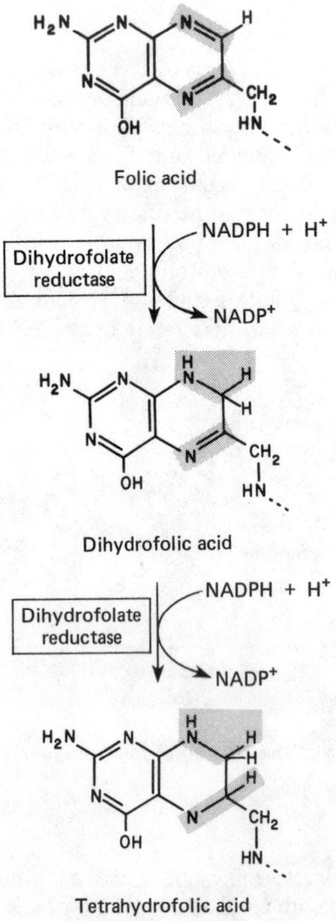

Folic acid

Dihydrofolate reductase

NADPH + H$^+$

NADP$^+$

Dihydrofolic acid

Dihydrofolate reductase

NADPH + H$^+$

NADP$^+$

Tetrahydrofolic acid

Figure 10–29. The reduction of folic acid to dihydrofolic acid and dihydrofolic acid to tetrahydrofolic acid by the enzyme dihydrofolate reductase.

as a carrier molecule for single-carbon moieties of different redox states. In order to serve as carrier, the folate is reduced by the enzyme **(dihydro)folate reductase,** which uses NADPH as hydride donor (Fig 10–29). **Trimethoprim** is a selective inhibitor of dihydrofolate reductase from gram-negative bacteria and has little efficacy as inhibitor of the mammalian enzyme. However, the inhibitor methotrexate (amethopterin) binds more strongly to dihydrofolate reductase from both bacteria and mammalian sources than do the naturally occurring substrates. These folate antagonists are important tools for treatment of infections and cancers.

The one-carbon moiety carried on H$_4$folate may be a **methyl, methylene, methenyl, formyl,** or **formimino moiety.** All are metabolically interconvertible.

Folate metabolism is complex, because of the interconversions, the number of one-carbon moieties carried by tetrahydrofolate, and the many reactions in which they participate.

Serine is the major source of the one-carbon moiety for the H$_4$folates. Serine transfers its hydroxy-

methylene group to H$_4$folate, generating glycine and N^5,N^{10}-methylene-H$_4$folate (Fig 10–30, reaction 1). The N^5,N^{10}-methylene-H$_4$folate plays a central role in the metabolism of H$_4$folates. It can be reduced to N^5-methyl-H$_4$folate (Fig 10–30, reaction 2), the folate derivative mentioned above, which plays an important role in the function of cobalamin. The N^5,N^{10}-methylene-H$_4$folate can be dehydrogenated to N^5,N^{10}-methenyl-H$_4$folate (Fig 10–30, reaction 3). The N^5,N$_{10}$-methenyl-H$_4$folate, without changing its redox state, can be isomerized to N^{10}-formyl-H$_4$folate (Fig 10–30, reaction 4) or to N^5-formyl-H$_4$folate (Fig 10–30, reaction 5). The latter, also referred to as **folinic acid,** is a stable form of H$_4$folate that can be administered orally or parenterally to provide reduced folate; ie, folinic acid does not need to be acted upon by folate reductase in order to function as a carrier for the one-carbon moiety. However, before its absorption, the N^5-formyl moiety is mostly removed and replaced by a methyl moiety in the intestinal mucosal cell.

Formiminoglutamate can transfer its formimino group to H$_4$folate to form formimino-H$_4$folate, which in turn can be deaminated to form folinic acid (Fig 10–30, reaction 6). Formiminoglutamic acid (Figlu) is a catabolite of histidine, an α-amino acid. In folate deficiency, Figlu will accumulate when oral histidine is administered.

The N^5,N^{10}-methylene-H$_4$folate provides the methyl group to deoxyuridylate to form thymidylate, a necessary precursor of DNA synthesis (Fig 10–31). Note that the redox state of the methylene changes as the methyl group is added to deoxyuridylate. Thus, concomitant with the reduction of the methylene to the methyl moiety is oxidation of tetrahydrofolate to dihydrofolate.

N^5-Methyl-H$_4$folate acts as methyl donor to homocysteine, discussed above under cobalamin metabolism. The N^5,N^{10}-methenyl-H$_4$folate provides the carbon at position 8 of purines (see Chapter 26), whereas the N^{10}-formyl-H$_4$folate provides the carbon at position 2 of the purine ring.

As depicted in Fig 10–30, N^5,N^{10}-methylene-H$_4$folate can also provide a hydroxymethylene group to glycine, forming serine, a reversal of the serine hydroxymethyl transferase reaction (Fig 10–30, reaction 1).

Because of the close interrelationship between folic acid and cobalamin metabolism and the presence of a megaloblastic anemia when either one of these vitamins is deficient, the clinical distinction between the 2 deficiency states is sometimes difficult. However, in a truly folic acid–deficient patient, the administration of 300–500 μg of folate per day will produce a positive hematologic response. This small dose will achieve no response in a patient with pernicious anemia, ie, vitamin B$_{12}$ deficiency. The use of this conservative but adequate dose of folate can serve as a means of differentiating between the deficiency of vitamin B$_{12}$ and that of folate.

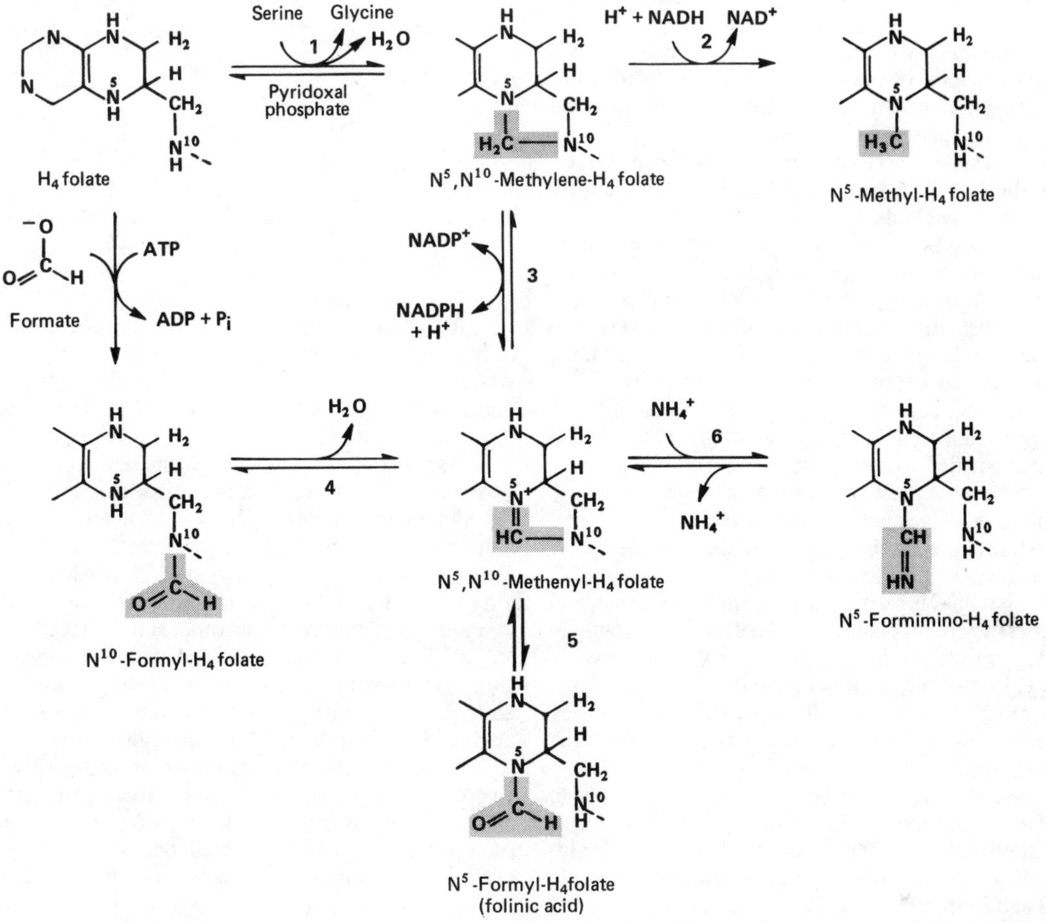

Figure 10-30. The interconversions of one carbon moieties attached to tetrahydrofolate.

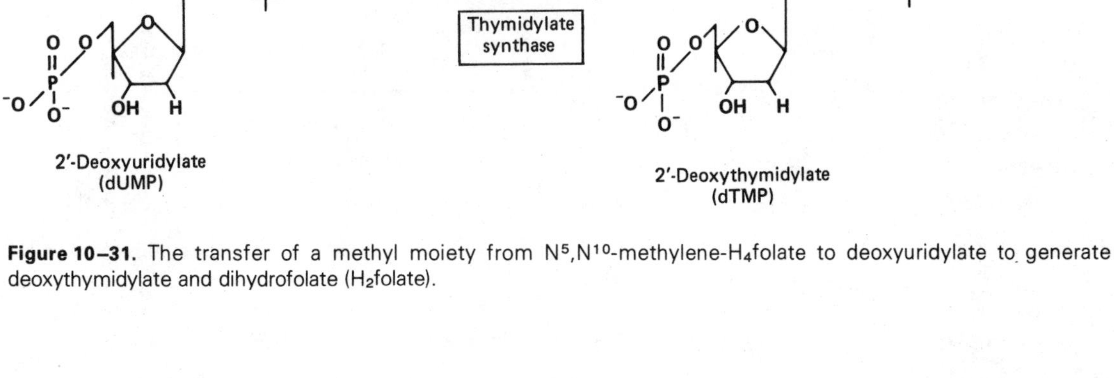

Figure 10-31. The transfer of a methyl moiety from N^5,N^{10}-methylene-H_4folate to deoxyuridylate to generate deoxythymidylate and dihydrofolate (H_2folate).

VITAMIN C (ASCORBIC ACID)

The structure of ascorbic acid resembles that of a monosaccharide but contains an enediol group from which the removal of a hydrogen occurs to produce dehydroascorbate (Fig 10–32). Dehydroascorbate is generated spontaneously from vitamin C by oxidation in air, but both forms are physiologically active and are found in body fluids.

The best sources of vitamin C are citrus fruits, berries, melons, tomatoes, green peppers, raw cabbage, and leafy green vegetables. Vitamin C is probably the **least stable** of the water-soluble vitamins. It is particularly labile to **heating** in the presence of trace metals such as copper. It is stable to freezing.

Ascorbic acid is widely required in metabolism. It can be synthesized in a variety of plants and in all animals studied except primates and the guinea pig. Animals such as humans that are unable to synthesize ascorbic acid lack the enzyme necessary to convert L-gulonic acid to ascorbic acid and thus require ascorbic acid in their diet (Fig 10–32).

Vitamin C is readily absorbed in the intestine, and a deficiency of this nutrient is therefore attributable to inadequate dietary intake. The normal stores of vitamin C in the body cannot be rapidly depleted. Thus, 3–4 months are required for a vitamin C deficiency state, **scurvy,** to develop in a human placed on a diet free of vitamin C.

Ascorbic acid can be converted in humans to oxalate, which appears in the urine. The calcium salt of oxalate is quite insoluble and capable of forming kidney stones. A study of the urinary excretion of ascorbic acid and its metabolites following daily oral ingestion of 3 g of ascorbic acid for 2 weeks revealed that 90% was excreted as unchanged ascorbic acid and 6% as dehydroascorbic acid. In addition, 31 mg of oxalic acid was excreted daily. Even after the administration of 9 g of ascorbic acid daily for 3 consecutive days, only 40–45 mg of oxalic acid was excreted daily in urine, the normal value being approximately 20 mg/d. Thus, the major excretory products of ascorbic acid are ascorbic acid itself and dehydroascorbate. However, doubling of the excretion of oxalic acid after 9 g of oral ascorbic acid is not an insignificant change.

Table 10–2. Compounds that can be reduced by ascorbic acid.

$\frac{1}{2}O_2$
NO_3^-
Cytochrome a Fe^{3+}
Cytochrome c Fe^{3+}
Crotonyl-CoA
Methemoglobin

In animal and plant tissues, large concentrations of vitamin C are present in comparison with other water-soluble vitamins. For example, human blood plasma contains about 1 mg of ascorbic acid per deciliter.

Ascorbic acid is a reducing agent with a hydrogen potential of +0.08 V, making it capable of reducing the compounds shown in Table 10–2 but not capable of reducing NAD^+ to NADH, pyruvate to lactate, or acetoacetate to β-hydroxybutyrate. The oxidation of p-hydroxy-phenylpyruvate to homogentisate requires vitamin C and copper for maximal activity (see Chapter 22). The subsequent step in the oxidative **degradation of tyrosine** is catalyzed by homogentisate dioxygenase, a ferrous iron-containing enzyme that also requires ascorbic acid for maximal activity.

The hydroxylation of proline in collagen (see Chapter 33) requires ascorbic acid. Ascorbic acid may also function in other oxidation-reduction systems such as that coupled with glutathione, cytochrome c, pyridine nucleotides, or flavin nucleotides. The adrenal cortex contains large amounts of vitamin C, and this is rapidly depleted when the gland is stimulated by adrenocorticotropic hormone. The function of ascorbate in the adrenal cortex is not known.

There are no known toxic effects of vitamin C. Potential complications of chronic massive overdosage include calcium oxalate stones and detrimental effects of ascorbate on the biotransformation or absorption of other vitamins (eg, vitamin B_{12}) and drugs present simultaneously in the gastrointestinal tract. Ascorbic acid is capable of acidifying urine, at times a useful and at other times a detrimental effect.

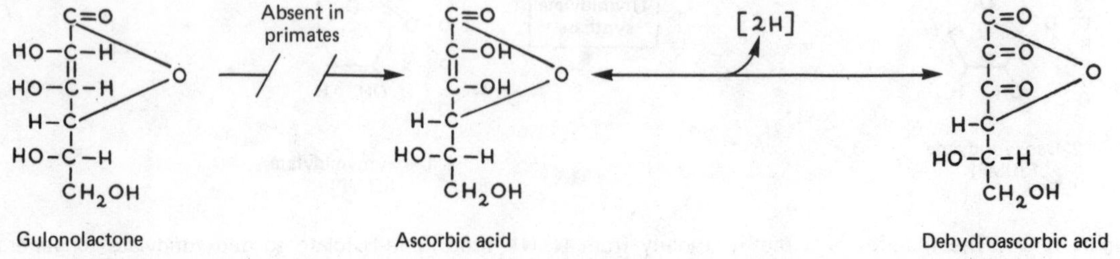

Gulonolactone   Ascorbic acid   Dehydroascorbic acid

Figure 10–32. Ascorbic acid, its source in nonprimates, and its oxidation to dehydroascorbic acid.

•   •   •

References

Benkovic SJ: On the mechanism of action of folate and biopterin-requiring enzymes. *Annu Rev Biochem* 1980;**49:**227.

Erbe R: Inborn errors of folate metabolism. *N Engl J Med* 1975;**293:**753.

Katz M, Lee SK, Cooper BA: Vitamin B_{12} malabsorption due to a biologically inert intrinsic factor. *N Engl J Med* 1972; **287:**425.

Rivlin RS: Hormones, drugs and riboflavin. *Nutr Rev* 1979; **37:**241.

Rosenberg IH: Folate absorption and malabsorption. *N Engl J Med* 1975;**293:**1303.

Rosenberg L: Disorders of propionate, methylmalonate, and cobalamin metabolism. Pages 411–429 in: *The Metabolic Basis of Inherited Disease,* 4th ed. Stanbury JB, Wyngaarden JB, Fredrickson DS (editors). McGraw-Hill, 1978.

Rubin RH, Swartz MN: Trimethroprim-sulfamethoxazole. *N Engl J Med* 1980;**303:**426.

Saunders M & others: Biotin-responsive organicaciduria. *J Clin Invest* 1979;**64:**1695.

Wood HG, Barden RE: Biotin enzymes. *Annu Rev Biochem* 1977;**46:**385.

11 | Fat-Soluble Vitamins

David W. Martin, Jr., MD

FAT-SOLUBLE VITAMINS

As is apparent from the name, the fat- or lipid-soluble vitamins are **apolar hydrophobic** molecules all of which are **isoprene derivatives** (Fig 11–1). All

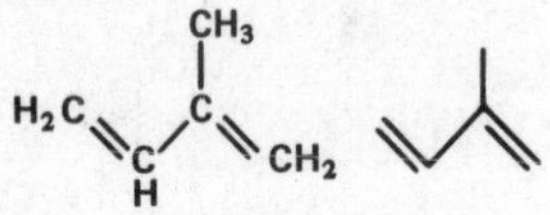

Figure 11–1. Two representations of the isoprene unit.

are handled by the gastrointestinal system in the same manner as dietary fat. In general, the lipid-soluble vitamins require **normal fat absorption** to be absorbed themselves. Therefore, steatorrhea and biliary system disorders can result in malabsorption of the fat-soluble vitamins. Once absorbed, the lipid-soluble vitamins are transported to the liver in chylomicrons and stored either in the liver (vitamins A, D, K) or in adipose tissue (vitamin E) for varying periods of time. These vitamins are transported in blood by **lipoproteins** or **specific binding proteins,** since they are not directly soluble in plasma water, as are the water-soluble vitamins. Accordingly, lipid-soluble vitamins are not excreted in urine but are more likely to appear in bile and are thus excreted in feces. Because of the body's ability to store excess fat-soluble vitamins, toxicity occurs at least from vitamin A and D overdosage.

Although once thought to be a vitamin in the true sense, **vitamin D (cholecalciferol) is a hormone** intimately involved in regulation of calcium and phosphate metabolism.

VITAMIN A
(RETINOIDS)

Vitamin A, or retinol, is a polyisoprenoid compound containing a cyclohexenyl ring (Fig 11–2). Vitamin A is a generic term referring to all compounds other than the carotenoids that exhibit the biologic activity of retinol. In recent years, the term retinoids has been used to describe both the natural forms and the synthetic analogs of retinol. Vitamin A is necessary in higher animals to support growth and health and is particularly necessary for **vision, reproduction, mucus secretion,** and the maintenance of differentiated **epithelia.**

Although the retinoids are required for normal function of many tissues in humans and experimental animals, the **loss of night vision** is an early sign of vitamin A deficiency. The full syndrome of vitamin A deficiency includes xeroderma, xerophthalmia, keratomalacia, severe growth retardation (including that of the nervous system), glandular degeneration, and sterility. Because vitamin A can be stored in the liver, both acute and chronic toxicity may result from excessive intake. The excessive intake of the provitamin β-carotene from plants results only in a benign yellow discoloration of the skin. Because it must be metabolized to generate vitamin A, one molecule of β-carotene is only one-sixth as effective a source of vitamin A as oral retinol.

In animal products, dietary vitamin A exists as long chain fatty acid **esters of retinol.** In vegetables, dietary vitamin A exists as a provitamin in the form of β-**carotenes,** which are yellow pigments (Fig 11–3). The retinol esters are hydrolyzed within the intestinal lumen and absorbed directly in the intestines. The ingested β-carotenes are oxidatively cleaved by β-carotene dioxygenase. This cleavage utilizes molecular oxygen and requires bile salts (and lecithin in vitro) to generate 2 molecules of **retinaldehyde (retinal).** Also in the **intestinal mucosa,** the retinaldehyde is reduced by a specific reductase utilizing NADPH to form retinol (Fig 11–3). A small fraction of the retinal generated from the β-carotene is oxidized to **retinoic acid** in the intestines. The retinoic acid is

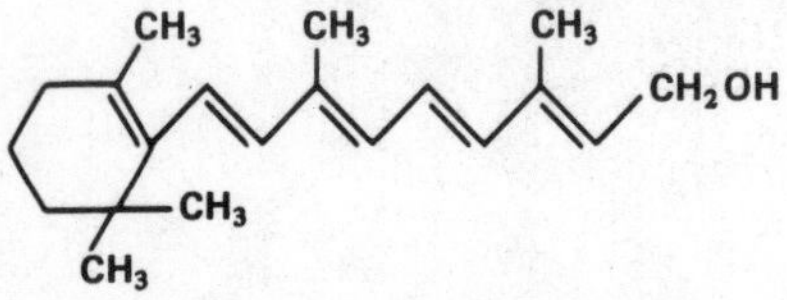

Figure 11–2. Retinol (vitamin A).

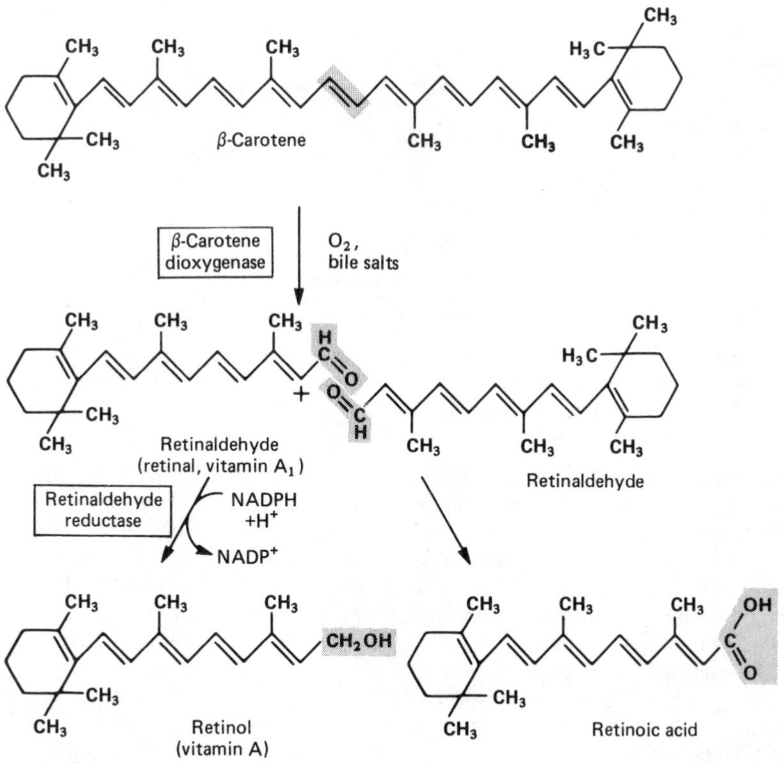

Figure 11–3. β-Carotene and its cleavage to retinaldehyde. The reduction of retinaldehyde to retinol and the oxidation of retinaldehyde to retinoic acid are also shown.

absorbed through the portal system and does not generally accumulate in the liver or other tissues. Retinoic acid can be metabolized to more polar compounds and excreted in urine and bile.

The absorbed retinol is reesterified with long chain saturated fatty acids, incorporated into lymph chylomicrons, and then enters the bloodstream. The retinyl esters are eventually removed from the circulation, almost exclusively by the **liver.** In hepatocytes, the retinyl esters are hydrolyzed and subsequently reesterified as retinyl palmitate to be stored in hepatic lipid droplets.

Stored retinol is mobilized from the liver by hydrolysis of its ester and by binding of retinol to **aporetinol-binding protein,** which is synthesized in the hepatocyte. The retinol-binding protein complex, called **holoretinol-binding protein,** then enters the circulation and delivers retinol to the target tissues.

Aporetinol-binding protein is also capable of binding retinal and retinoic acid, even though the majority of retinoic acid in the circulation is transported bound to serum albumin. The holoretinol-binding protein has a high affinity for **prealbumin** in a strong protein-protein interaction that is dependent upon the presence of retinol. The prealbumin complex also carries thyroxine at an independent site. Leaving the aporetinol-binding protein behind, the retinol enters its target cell.

It appears that **vitamin A toxicity** occurs in vivo only after the capacity of the retinol-binding protein has been exceeded and the cells exposed to unbound retinol. Thus, the nonspecific and unregulated delivery of free vitamin A to tissues may lead to vitamin A toxicity.

Most target cells for vitamin A are capable of metabolizing the retinol to retinal and retinoic acid. However, within the cellular environment, retinoic acid cannot be reduced back to retinal or to retinol. Retinol can satisfy all of the requirements for vitamin A, but retinoic acid has only selective vitamin A–like biologic activity. Experimental animals provided with retinoic acid as the only source of retinoids will become blind and sterile but otherwise remain in good general health. Thus, **retinoic acid can support the normal rate of growth and differentiation but cannot replace retinal as a visual pigment precursor or support normal function of the reproductive system in males or females.**

Each of the 3 major retinoids—retinol, retinal, and retinoic acid—appears to have its own unique biologic function, as discussed below. Retinol, in the lowest oxidation state, probably serves as a **hormone.** Retinal is a necessary precursor of the visual pigment **rhodopsin.** Retinoic acid serves as a **carrier** for oligosaccharides in the synthesis of glycoproteins.

When retinol enters its target cell, it is promptly

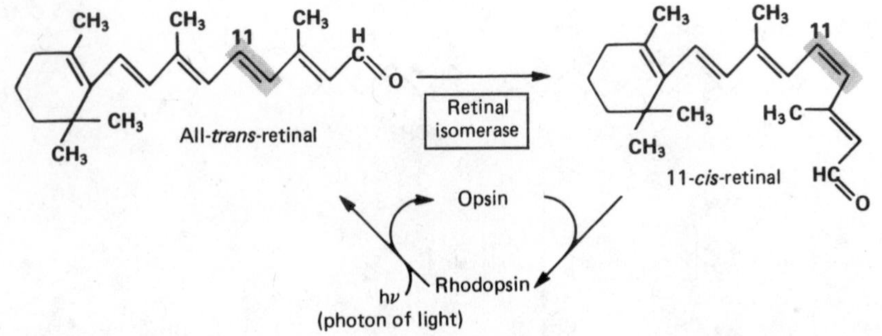

Figure 11–4. 11-*cis*-Retinal, formed from all-*trans*-retinal, combines with opsin to form rhodopsin in the rod cell of the eye. The absorption of a photon of light by rhodopsin causes it to bleach, generating opsin and all-*trans*-retinal. The all-*trans*-retinal is incompletely isomerized back to 11-*cis*-retinal.

bound to a **cellular retinol-binding protein (CRBP)** distinct from the retinol-binding protein present in serum. The CRBP transports the retinol within the cell, where it appears to bind specifically to **nuclear proteins,** perhaps with a function analogous to that of the intracellular steroid hormone receptor molecules (see Chapter 34). Of the 2 biologic functions that retinoic acid cannot support, one, the visual pigment precursor, can be provided by retinal. Thus, it seems that the reproductive function of the retinoids depends upon **retinol acting as a sterol hormone.**

The next oxidation state of the retinoids is retinal. It is clearly required for its role as a component of the **visual pigment, rhodopsin,** of the rod cells in the retina. In rod cells, **11-*cis* retinal,** an isomer of all-*trans*-retinal, is **specifically bound to the visual protein, opsin** (Fig 11–4). When rhodopsin is exposed to light, it dissociates as it bleaches and forms **all-*trans*-retinal** and **opsin.** This reaction is accompanied by a conformational change that induces a **calcium ion channel** in the membrane of the rod cell. The rapid influx of the calcium ions triggers a nerve impulse, allowing light to be perceived by the brain. The all-*trans*-retinal, generated from rhodopsin by the absorption of photons of light, is incompletely converted back to the 11-*cis*-retinal (Fig 11–4). Hence, in order to regenerate rhodopsin for vision, a **constant supply** of all-*trans*-retinal is required from the diet.

The third distinct biochemical function of the retinoids involves the participation of a phosphorylated retinoic acid as a polyisoprenoid carrier of specific oligosaccharide residues in the **synthesis of glycoproteins** (see Chapter 32). Oligosaccharide retinyl phosphate is a minor product of the microsomal systems that use mostly the polyisoprenoid derivative dolichol phosphate as carrier. It has been proposed that the retinyl phosphate functions as a carrier of the oligosaccharides across the lipid bilayer of the cell by way of an enzymatic *trans-cis* isomerization analogous to that described above in the *trans-cis* isomerization of rhodopsin generation. The evidence that retinoic acid is involved in glycoprotein synthesis is compelling. A deficiency of vitamin A can cause an 80% reduction in the amount of mannose bound to liver glycoproteins in experimental animals.

Many tissues contain an intracellular protein that binds retinoic acid. This **cellular retinoic acid-binding protein (CRABP)** shows no affinity for retinol or retinal. The tissue distribution of CRABP is different from that of CRBP, even though the proteins are similar in structure. The retinoic acid–CRABP complex does not have an affinity for the cell nucleus, as does the retinol-CRBP complex.

Retinoic acid elicits many biologic and biochemical responses from cells in vitro, including increasing the number of epidermal growth factor receptors on surfaces of cultured cells, stimulation of differentiation of embryonal carcinoma cells, prevention of the expression of the Epstein-Barr virus in virus-infected cells, and the reversible inhibition of growth of human breast cancer cell lines in long-term tissue culture. Whether all of the listed biologic effects are mediated by the involvement of retinyl phosphate in glycoprotein synthesis is at present unclear; other physiologic effects of the retinoids may yet be discovered.

VITAMIN D

Only in humans **not exposed to sunlight** is vitamin D a necessary organic nutrient, thereby satisfying the classic criteria for vitamin status. Vitamin D is a legitimate prohormone of a sterol type. Thus, the D vitamins are a group of sterol compounds that occur in nature chiefly in animals but also in plants and yeasts.

The D vitamins are generated from the provitamins **ergosterol** and **7-dehydrocholesterol** in plants and animals, respectively. Ergosterol and 7-dehydrocholesterol differ chemically only in the side chains at position 21 (Fig 11–5). Ultraviolet irradiation spontaneously cleaves the B ring of ergosterol or of 7-dehydrocholesterol. In plants, the irradiation of ergosterol leads to the production of ergocalciferol (vitamin D_2). In animals, the 7-dehydrocholesterol is converted to cholecalciferol (vitamin D_3) by irradiation of skin (Fig 11–5). Ergocalciferol and cholecalciferol are of equal biologic potency as D vitamins, and the rest of this discussion will deal only with cholecalciferol.

Humans have 2 main sources of vitamin D: inges-

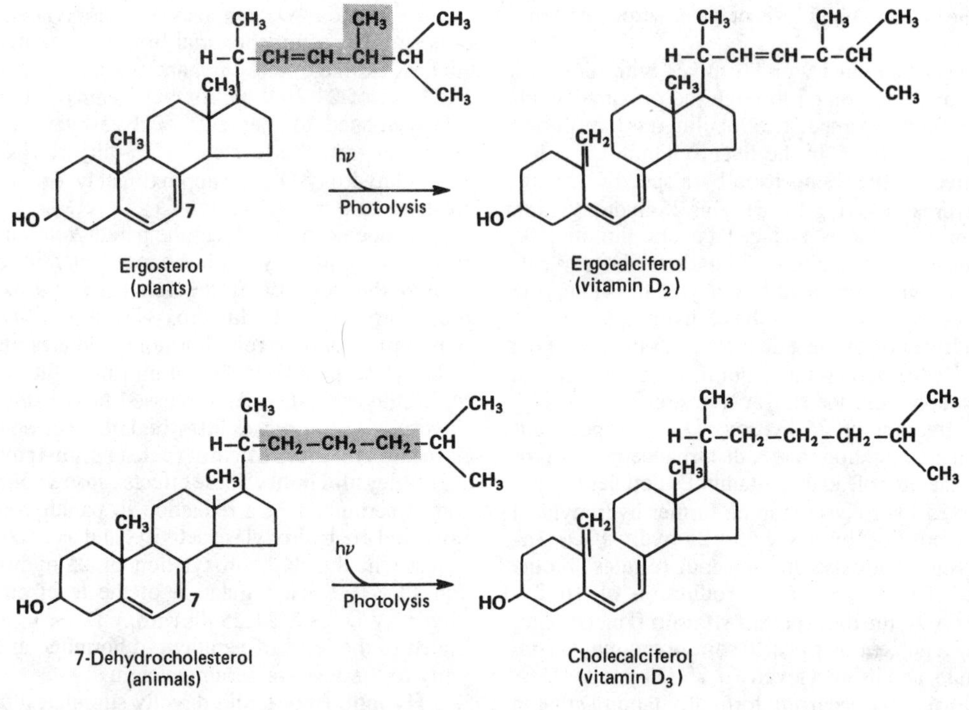

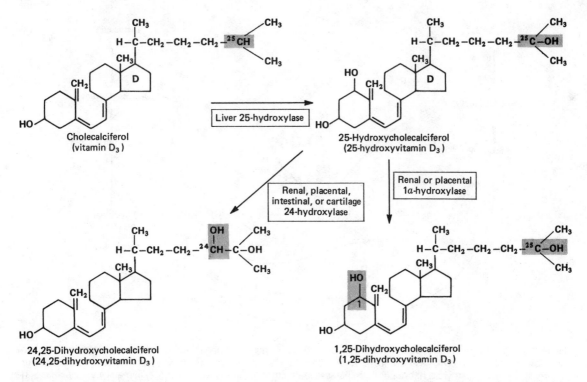

Figure 11–5. Ergosterol and 7-dehydrocholesterol and their conversion by photolysis to ergocalciferol and cholecalciferol, respectively.

Figure 11–6. Cholecalciferol can be hydroxylated at the C_{25} position by a liver enzyme. The 25-hydroxycholecalciferol is further metabolized to 1α,25-dihydroxycholecalciferol or to 24,25-dihydroxycholecalciferol. The levels of 24,25-dihydroxycholecalciferol and 1,25-dihydroxycholecalciferol are regulated in a reciprocal manner.

tion in the diet and photolysis of 7-dehydrocholesterol in skin.

Dietary vitamin D_2 or D_3 mixes with intestinal micelles and is absorbed through the proximal small intestine. Bound to a specific globulin, it is transported in blood to the liver. In the **liver**, vitamin D_3 is **hydroxylated on the 25 position** by a specific vitamin D_3 25-hydroxylase (Fig 11–6). This 25-hydroxylation occurs in microsomes and can be rate-limiting. At physiologic concentrations, 25-hydroxy-D_3 (or calcifediol) has no direct action in any of the vitamin D target tissues. Regulation of the 25-hydroxylation step is dependent upon the hepatic level of 25-hydroxy-D_3.

25-Hydroxy-D_3 is the major form of vitamin D in the circulation and the **major storage form.** A significant fraction of 25-hydroxy-D_3 undergoes enterohepatic circulation, and a disturbance in that process can therefore lead to a vitamin D–deficient state.

The 25-hydroxy-D_3 can be further hydroxylated on the 1 position by a specific 25-hydroxy-D_3 **1α-hydroxylase** that exists in the **renal tubules** and the placenta (Fig 11–6). The production of 1α,25-dihydroxy-D_3, the **most potent vitamin D** metabolite, is tightly regulated by **parathyroid hormone, serum phosphate,** and **its own level.** 1α,25-Dihydroxy-D_3 is the only naturally occurring form of vitamin D that in physiologic amounts can maintain normal serum calcium in animals without kidneys or without parathyroid glands. 25-Hydroxy-D_3 1α-hydroxylase is a **mitochondrial** enzyme.

25-Hydroxy-D_3 can also be hydroxylated at the 24 position by a mitochondrial enzyme present in renal tubules, cartilage, intestine, and placenta (Fig 11–6). The level of 24,25-dihydroxy-D_3 seems to be reciprocally related to the level of 1,25-hydroxy-D_3 in serum. In fact, the levels of 1,25-dihydroxy-D_3 and 24,25-dihydroxy-D_3 are approximately equal in the presence of a normal serum Ca^{2+} level.

Hypocalcemia induces the parathyroid glands to excrete more parathyroid hormone, which in turn increases the activity of the renal 1α-hydroxylase, generating more 1,25-dihydroxy-D_3 (Fig 11–7). Concomitantly, parathyroid hormone reduces the 24-hydroxylase pathway, thus diminishing the level of 24,25-dihydroxy-D_3. As discussed below, the 1,25-dihydroxy-D_3 **increases intestinal absorption of calcium and enhances calcium reabsorption from both the kidney and bone.** These effects cause a normalization of serum Ca^{2+}, a reduction in parathyroid hormone and 1α-hydroxylase activity, and a concomitant increase in the 24-hydroxylation of 25-hydroxy-D_3 (Fig 11–7). Thus, regulation of the level on 1,25-dihydroxy-D_3 and 24,25-dihydroxy-D_3 is intimately related to the level of parathyroid hormone and indirectly to the level of serum calcium.

Hypophosphatemia directly stimulates the synthesis of 1,25-dihydroxy-D_3. 1,25-Dihydroxy-D_3 also increases the absorption of **phosphate** by the intestine and, in the absence of parathyroid hormone, enhances the **reabsorption of phosphate** by the kidney tubules.

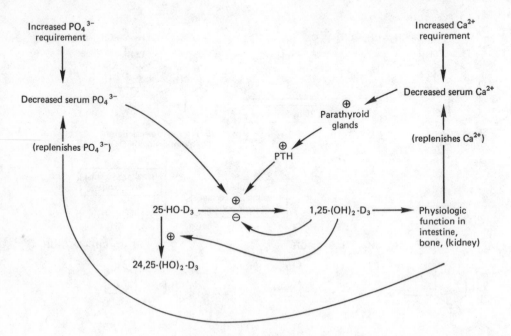

Figure 11–7. Summary of regulation of vitamin D_3 hydroxylation. Increased phosphate or calcium requirement will cause diminished concentrations of these ions in the serum. Decreased serum phosphate (directly) and decreased serum calcium (indirectly through parathyroid hormone) both increase the activity of the renal 1α-hydroxylase activity to increase the formation of 1,25-dihydroxy-D_3. The 1,25-dihydroxy-D_3 has 3 effects: it inhibits its own production, it stimulates the 24-hydroxylase to generate 24,25-dihydroxy-D_3 and it has physiologic functions in the intestine, bone, and kidney. All of the physiologic functions of 1,25-dihydroxy-D_3 operate in the direction of replenishing serum phosphate and serum calcium.

Thus, plasma phosphate levels also regulate the level of 1,25-dihydroxy-D₃ (Fig 11–7).

Accordingly, in the presence of a high plasma phosphate (hyperphosphatemia) or in a disorder such as uremia, the production of 1,25-dihydroxy-D₃ will be inhibited and calcium absorption from the intestine will thus be minimal. Once the serum phosphate is lowered, such as by chelating phosphate in the intestine, the 1,25-dihydroxy-D₃ will increase and calcium absorption will follow.

The mechanism of action of 1,25-dihydroxy-D₃ resembles that of the steroid hormones. The target tissues include the **intestine, bone, and kidney.** In the intestine, 1,25-dihydroxy-D₃ enters the cell and is bound to a specific **cytoplasmic receptor molecule.** The 1,25-dihydroxy-cholecalciferol-receptor complex is then translocated to the nucleus, where, by poorly defined mechanisms, it effects an increase in the synthesis of the intestinal **calcium-binding protein** necessary for intestinal absorption of calcium.

In the intestine 1,25-dihydroxy-D₃ also increases intestinal phosphate absorption by mechanisms that have not been defined. In the kidney, 1,25-dihydroxy-D₃ enhances the reabsorption of filtered tubular phosphate, but **this effect of the active vitamin D metabolite is usually masked by the inhibition of phosphate reabsorption by parathyroid hormone.** 1,25-Dihydroxy-D₃ seems to affect the cross-linking of bone collagen and thereby influences the **mineralization** of bone tissues. The active metabolite of vitamin D₃ also seems to prevent a **myopathy** that occurs in the vitamin D–deficient states, but the mechanism is unknown.

24,25-Dihydroxycholecalciferol also has an effect of increasing intestinal calcium absorption but decreases the serum concentrations of both calcium and phosphorus. 24,25-Dihydroxy-D₃ **promotes normal bone mineralization** and the synthesis of hydroxyapatite, the major form of calcium in mineralized bone and cartilage.

The 26-hydroxylation of 1,25-dihydroxy-D₃ appears to be on the pathway of vitamin D oxidative degradation.

25-Hydroxy-D₃ is degraded by hepatic microsomes, and these enzymes can be induced by numerous pharmacologic agents, including phenytoin and phenobarbital. Glucocorticosteroids in large pharmacologic doses result in a decrease in 25-hydroxy-D₃ levels.

The major biochemical abnormalities of vitamin D deficiency are **hypocalcemia and hypophosphatemia.** Vitamin D–deficient states were common during the industrial revolution in England, when air pollution and the urban environment prevented adequate exposure of children to sunlight, and vitamin D supplementation of foodstuffs was nonexistent. The vitamin D–deficient clinical states are beyond the scope of this chapter.

VITAMIN E
(α-Tocopherol)

α-Tocopherol is an oil present in plants, particularly wheat germ, rice, and cotton seeds. Although fish liver oils are rich in vitamins A and D, they are devoid of vitamin E. Vitamin E is required in higher animals such as poultry and cattle for **fertility.** (The word tocopherol is derived from Greek *tokos,* ''childbirth,'' and *pherein,* ''to bear.'') There are 7 naturally occurring tocopherols (Table 11–1). All are isoprenoid substituted 6-hydroxychromanes or tocols (Fig 11–8). **α-Tocopherol** has the widest natural distribution and the greatest biologic activity as a vitamin. Although there is no reliable evidence that vitamin E is necessary for fertility in humans, it is clear that a vitamin E-deficient state exists in humans with severely **impaired intestinal fat absorption.** The signs of vitamin E deficiency in humans are muscular weakness, creatinuria, and fragile erythrocytes. All disappear after the administration of α-tocopherol. α-Tocopherol is readily absorbed through the small intestine, transported to the liver probably in chylomicrons, and delivered in lipoproteins to peripheral tissues. The phospholipids of mitochondria, endoplasmic reticulum, and plasma membranes possess specific affinities for α-tocopherol, and the vitamin

Table 11–1. The naturally occurring tocopherols.

Tocopherol	Substituents
Alpha	5,7,8-Trimethyl tocol
Beta	5,8-Dimethyl tocol
Gamma	7,8-Dimethyl tocol
Delta	8-Methyl tocol
Eta	7-Methyl tocol
Zeta	5,7-Dimethyl tocol

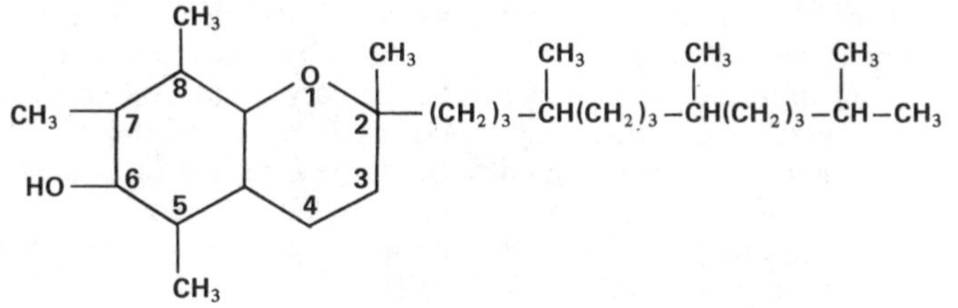

Figure 11–8. α-Tocopherol.

appears to concentrate at these sites.

Vitamin E has at least 2 metabolic roles: It acts as nature's most potent fat-soluble **antioxidant,** and it plays a specific but incompletely understood role in **selenium metabolism.** The level of vitamin E in plasma lipoproteins and organelle phospholipids depends on 4 factors: (1) the amount of α-tocopherol being consumed, (2) the level of pro-oxidants and antioxidants in the diet, (3) the adequacy of dietary selenium, and (4) the dietary intake of sulfur-containing amino acids.

Vitamin E appears to be the first line of defense against peroxidation of cellular and subcellular membrane phospholipids. However, even in the presence of adequate vitamin E, some peroxides are formed. **Glutathione peroxidase,** of which selenium is an integral component, provides a second line of defense to destroy the peroxides before they cause damage to the membranes. Thus, the biochemical actions of vitamin E and selenium seem to be prevention of peroxidative damage to cellular and subcellular elements and thereby preserve the organelles necessary to cope with disease, physical and chemical environmental insults, and other stresses. α-Tocopherol does not readily engage in reversible oxidation; in humans, the chromane ring and the side chain of α-tocopherol are oxidized to produce the product shown in Fig 11–9. This oxidation product is conjugated with glucuronic acid via the 2 hydroxyl groups and excreted in bile.

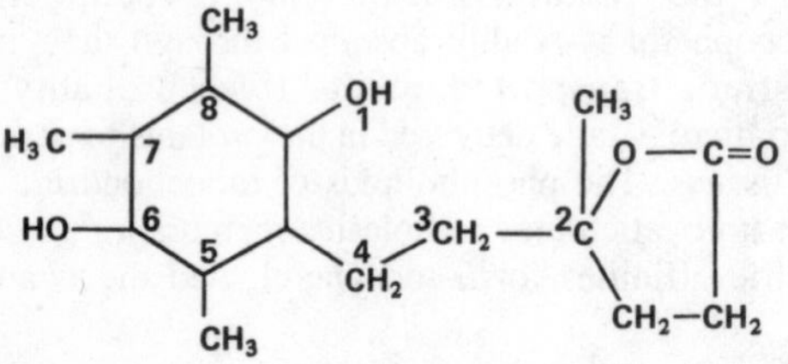

Figure 11–9. The oxidation product of α-tocopherol. The numbers allow one to relate the atoms to those in the parent compound.

Selenium spares vitamin E or reduces the vitamin E requirements in at least 3 ways: (1) Selenium is required for normal pancreatic function and thus the digestion and absorption of lipids, including vitamin E. (2) As a component of glutathione peroxidase, selenium helps destroy peroxides and thereby reduces the peroxidation of polyunsaturated acids of lipid membranes. This diminished peroxidation greatly reduces the vitamin E requirement for the maintenance of membrane integrity. (3) In some unknown way, selenium aids in the retention of vitamin E in the blood plasma lipoproteins.

Conversely, vitamin E appears to reduce the selenium requirement, at least in experimental animals, by preventing loss of selenium from the body or maintaining it in an active form. By preventing autox-

idation of membrane lipids from within, vitamin E reduces the amount of glutathione peroxidase needed to destroy peroxides formed in the cell.

There is reliable experimental evidence for the need of supplemental vitamin E in the diets of pregnant and lactating women and for newborn infants, particularly premature infants. Other evidence suggests that vitamin E is efficacious for older persons suffering from circulatory disturbances, particularly intermittent claudication. In experimental animals, a reversible muscular dystrophy is associated with vitamin E deficiency.

VITAMIN K

The K vitamins (Danish *Koagulation*) are polyisoprenoid substituted naphthoquinones (Fig 11–10). They were the last of the 4 fat-soluble vita-

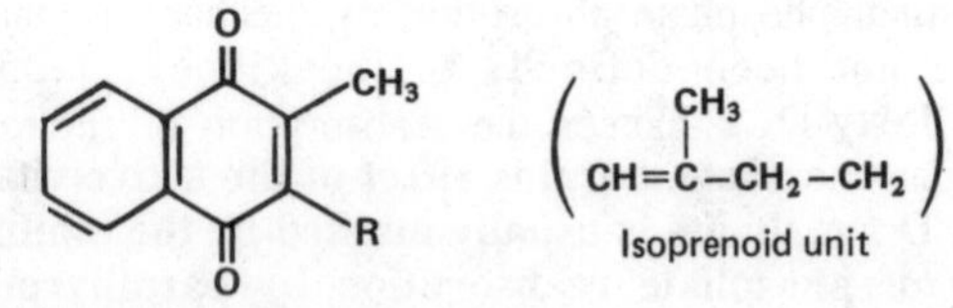

2-Methyl-1,4-naphthoquinone

Figure 11–10. Substituted naphthoquinone and the isoprenoid unit. In the vitamins K, the R substitutions are polyisoprenoids.

mins to be discovered and characterized. However, the metabolic role of vitamin K can be described in more molecular detail than is the case with any other fat-soluble vitamin. **Menadione,** the parent compound of the vitamin K series, exhibits biologic activity in vivo after it has been alkylated to one of the menaquinones by animal tissues (Fig 11–11). Phylloquinone (vitamin K_1) is the major form of vitamin K found in plants. Menaquinone-7 is one of the series of polyprenoid unsaturated forms of vitamin K found in animal tissues and bacteria. Vitamin K_1 is abundant in vegetable oils, leafy green vegetables, and wheat bran. Menaquinones (vitamin K_2) are synthesized by the intestinal bacterial flora, and vitamin K is therefore not required in the diet.

Absorption of vitamin K from the intestines requires normal fat absorption. Thus, the most common causes of vitamin K deficiency are the **fat malabsorption syndromes** associated with pancreatic dysfunction, biliary disease, intestinal mucosal atrophy, or any other cause of steatorrhea. In addition, **sterilization of the large intestine** by eliminating the bacterial flora removes the most reliable source of vitamin K and can result in a deficiency state when dietary intake is limited.

The **menaquinones** are absorbed only in the presence of bile salts and via the lymphatics.

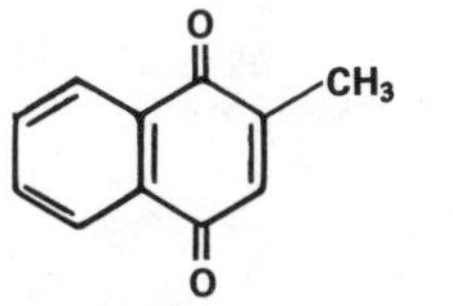

Menadione (Vitamin K_3)

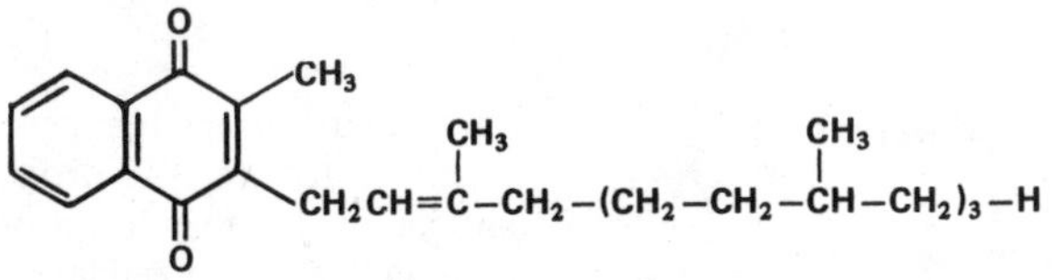

Phylloquinone (Vitamin K_1, phytonadione, Mephyton)

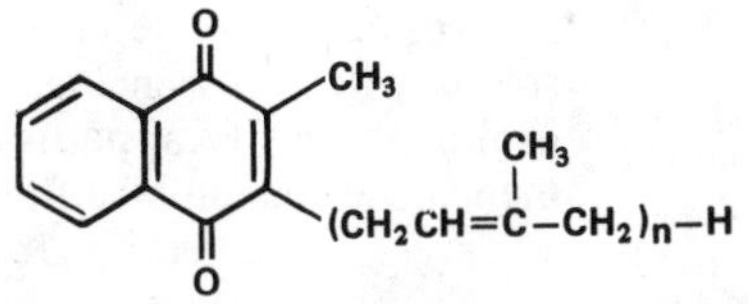

Menaquinone-n (vitamin K_2; n = 6, 7, or 9)

Figure 11–11. The naturally occurring vitamins K.

Menadione and its water-soluble derivatives are absorbed even in the absence of bile salts and go directly into the bloodstream.

Although vitamin K accumulates initially in the liver, its hepatic concentration declines rapidly. Little vitamin K accumulates in peripheral tissues. A deficiency state, indicated by hypoprothrombinemia, can occur within several weeks when acute biliary disease halts its absorption.

Vitamin K has been known to be required for the maintenance of normal levels of blood clotting factors II, VII, IX, and X, all of which are synthesized in the liver (see Chapter 39). It has recently been discovered that each of these specific clotting factor proteins is synthesized by the liver in an **inactive precursor** form that is dependent upon vitamin K for conversion to the biologically active clotting factors. Generation of these mature clotting factors involves the vitamin K-dependent **posttranslational modification** of glutamic acid (Glu) residues to **γ-carboxyglutamic acid** (Gla), a previously unrecognized amino acid (Fig 11–12). The Gla residues, of which prothrombin contains 10, allow these proteins to **chelate calcium** in a

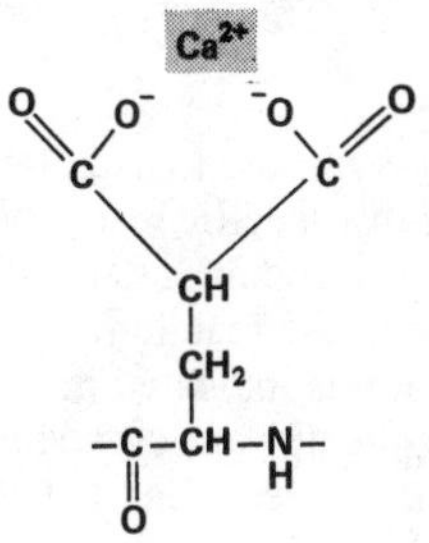

Figure 11–13. The chelation of calcium ion by the γ-carboxyglutamyl residue in clotting factor proteins.

specific protein-calcium-phospholipid interaction that is essential to their biologic role (Fig 11–13).

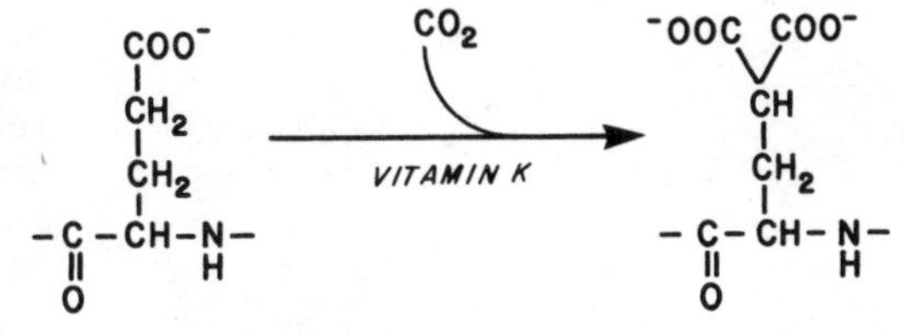

Initially, only these clotting factors (II, VII, IX, X) were thought to contain vitamin K-dependent Gla residues, but now it has been recognized that other proteins in bones ("osteocalcin"), kidney, placenta, lung, and spleen contain them. These modifications have also been described in both bacterial and mammalian ribosomal proteins. However, physiologic roles for the Gla residues have not been defined for any of the nonclotting factor, vitamin K-dependent proteins.

The major—if not the only—function of vitamin K is to serve as an essential cofactor for the carboxylase enzyme that forms the Gla residues from the Glu residues in the specific protein molecules. The vitamin K-dependent carboxylase reaction occurs in **microsomes** and requires molecular oxygen, carbon dioxide, and the **hydroquinone form of vitamin K.** In liver microsomes, there exists a **vitamin K cycle** (Fig 11–14), in which the hydroquinone form can be con-

Figure 11–12. Carboxylation of a glutamic acid residue catalyzed by vitamin K.

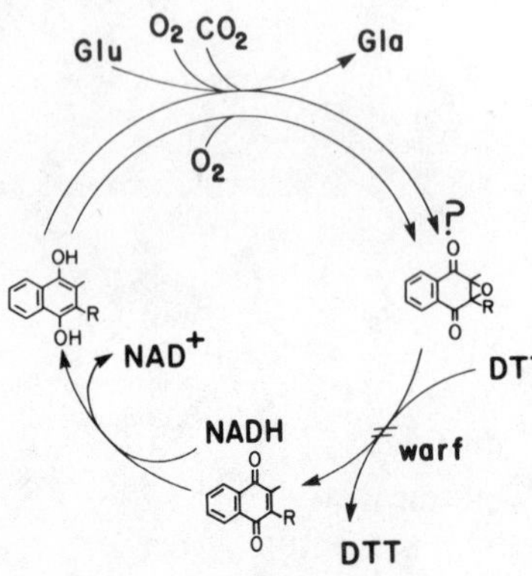

Figure 11–14. Vitamin K-related metabolic activities in liver microsomes. The pathway crossed and indicated warf is sensitive to the action of the coumarin anticoagulants. The (?) in the figure indicates that the product of the involvement of vitamin K hydroquinone in the carboxylation reaction is not known. The figure indicates that the epoxide is reduced by a warfarin-sensitive pathway that used dithiothreitol (DTT) as a reducing agent, and that the quinone form of the vitamin can be reduced to the hydroquinone by a pyridine nucleotide-linked dehydrogenase. (Modified and reproduced, with permission, from Suttie JW: The metabolic role of vitamin K. *Fed Proc* 1980;**39**:2730.)

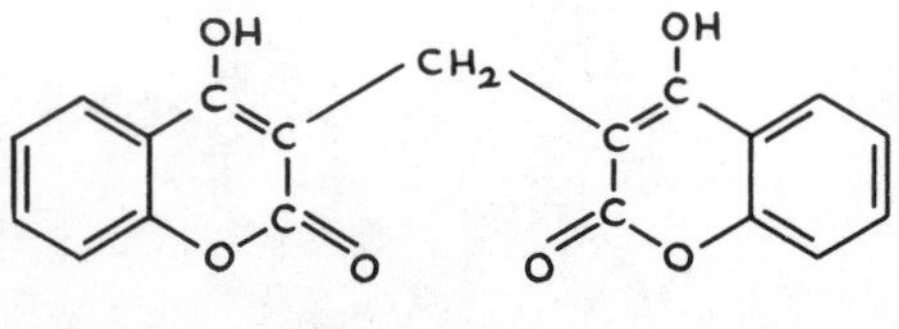

Figure 11–15. Dicumarol (bishydroxycoumarin; 3,3'-methylene-bishydroxycoumarin).

An important therapeutic use of vitamin K is as an antidote to the 4-hydroxycoumarin anticoagulant drugs. The quinone forms of vitamin K will bypass the inhibited epoxide reductase and provide a potential source of the active hydroquinone form of vitamin K. For these purposes, large oral doses of vitamin K_1 will suffice, but there are also available synthetic water-soluble vitamin K analogs such as menadiol sodium diphosphate (Kappadione, Synkayvite) and menadione sodium bisulfite (Hykinone) (Fig 11–16).

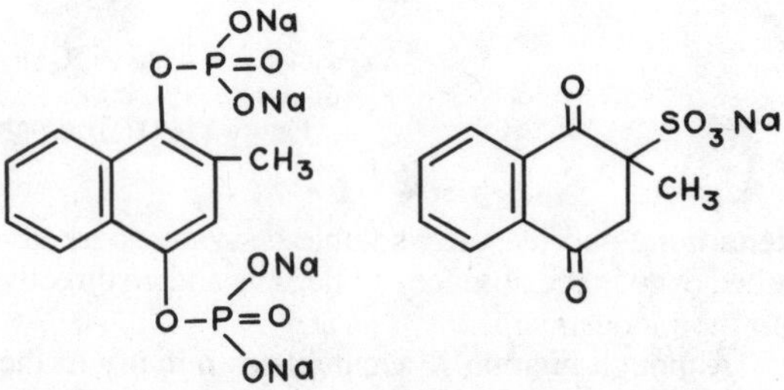

Figure 11–16. Menadiol diphosphate (Kappadione,Synkay-vite) (left) and menadione sodium bisulfite (Hykinone) (right), 2 forms of vitamin K for clinical use.

verted by a monooxygenase to its 2,3-epoxide. It is not yet clear whether this specific reaction is an obligatory one in which the hydroquinone of vitamin K participates in the carboxylase reaction, but it appears to be so. This uncertainty is indicated in Fig 11–14 by the question mark of the upward curved arrow representing that carboxylation reaction. The 2,3-epoxide is a substrate for another microsomal enzyme, an epoxide reductase, that utilizes a still unidentified sulfhydryl reducing compound to form the quinone. This **epoxide reductase** is sensitive to **inhibition by the 4-hydroxydicoumarin** compounds (Fig 11–15) and thus is the target for the pharmacologic action of these **anticoagulants.** Subsequent reduction of the quinone form to the hydroquinone form by NADH completes the vitamin K cycle by regenerating the active form of vitamin K.

These water-soluble vitamin K analogs may be administered parenterally. Given that liver function is adequate to manufacture active prothrombin, the prothrombin time (a laboratory index of the presence of mature prothrombin; see Chapter 39) will usually return to normal 12–36 hours after the administration of vitamin K.

There is the potential of toxicity of large doses of vitamin K; menadione in particular can cause hemolysis in infants and aggravate hyperbilirubinemia.

• • •

References

Vitamin D

DeLuca HF: Regulation of vitamin D metabolism. *Life Sci* 1976;**17**:1351.

DeLuca HF, Schnoes HK: Metabolism and mechanism of action of vitamin D. *Annu Rev Biochem* 1976;**45**:631.

Favus M: Vitamin D physiology and some clinical aspects of the vitamin D endocrine system. *Med Clin North Am* 1978;**62**:1291.

Feldman D, Colston K: Nuclear translocation of the 1,25-dihydroxy cholicalciferol receptor in mouse kidney. *J Biol Chem* 1980;**255**:7510.

Jacobs MD: Vitamin D deficient states. *West J Med* 1979;**131**:305.

Vitamin A

Goodman DS: Vitamin A metabolism. *Fed Proc* 1980;**39**:2716.

Goodman DS & others: Vitamin A and retinoids: Recent advances. *Fed Proc* 1979;**38**:2501.

Jetten AM: Retinoids specifically enhance the number of epidermal growth factor receptors. *Nature* 1980;**284**:626.

LaCroix A, Lippman ME: Binding of retinoids to human breast cancer cell lines and their effects on cell growth. *J Clin Invest* 1980;**65**:586.

Vitamin E

Corash L & others: Reduced chronic hemolysis during high dose vitamin E administration in Mediterranean-type glucose 6-phosphate dehydrogenase deficiency. *N Engl J Med* 1980;**303**:416.

Scott ML: Advances in our understanding of vitamin E. *Fed Proc* 1980;**39**:2736.

Vitamin K

Jackson CM, Nemerson Y: Blood coagulation. *Annu Rev Biochem*1980;**49**:767.

Suttie JW: The metabolic role of vitamin K. *Fed Proc* 1980;**39**:2730.

Suttie JW, Jackson CM: Prothrombin structure, activation, and biosynthesis. *Physiol Rev* 1977;**57**:1.

Whitlon DS & others: Mechanism of coumarin action: Significance of vitamin K epoxide reductase inhibition. *Biochem* 1978;**17**:1371.

Wolf IL, Babior BM: Vitamin K and warfarin. Metabolism, function and interaction. *Am J Med* 1972;**53**:261.

12 | Biologic Oxidation

Peter A. Mayes, PhD, DSc

Historical Review

Chemically, **oxidation is defined as the removal of electrons** and **reduction as the gain of electrons,** as illustrated by the oxidation of ferrous to ferric ion.

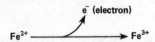

It follows that oxidation is always accompanied by reduction of an electron acceptor. The above definition covers a much wider range of reactions than did the older restricted definition, which covered only the addition of oxygen or removal of hydrogen.

Modern concepts of oxidation in biologic systems may be traced back to Lavoisier, who demonstrated that animals utilize oxygen from the air and replace it with carbon dioxide and water. He showed that respiration was similar in this respect to the burning of a candle. However, Pasteur, in his studies of the fermentation of glucose by yeast, firmly established that living organisms could respire in the absence of oxygen, ie, under anaerobic conditions. In the period around 1930, two diametrically opposed concepts of biologic oxidation prevailed. Warburg advocated the view that a widely distributed enzyme (**Atmungsferment**) catalyzed the activation of oxygen and its combination with substrate molecules. Opposed to this concept was the thesis of Wieland, that substrate molecules were activated and oxidized by removal of hydrogen in reactions catalyzed by specific enzymes called **dehydrogenases.** With the discovery by Keilin of a group of respiratory catalysts designated the **cytochrome system,** the 2 concepts were reconciled, as it became clear that most substrates were in fact oxidized by a combination of both processes. Dehydrogenation initiated oxidation, and the reducing equivalents were transported via the cytochrome system to react ultimately with molecular oxygen in the presence of Warburg's enzyme, the last member of the cytochrome system, now renamed **cytochrome oxidase.** The sequence of enzymes and carriers responsible for the transport of reducing equivalents from substrates to molecular oxygen is known as the **respiratory chain.** Further elucidation by Warburg and others of the role of **nicotinamide nucleotides** and **flavoproteins** made it possible by 1940 to construct the following sequence of components of the respiratory chain. The arrows indicate the direction of flow of reducing equivalents (H or electrons).

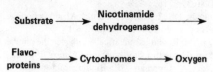

The respiratory chain is localized within mitochondria.

Oxidation-Reduction Equilibria; Redox Potential

In reactions involving oxidation and reduction, the free energy exchange is proportionate to the tendency of reactants to donate or accept electrons. Thus, in addition to expressing free energy change in terms of $\Delta G^{0'}$ (see p 66), it is possible, in an analogous manner, to express it numerically as an **oxidation-reduction** or **redox potential** (E_0'). It is usual to compare the redox potential of a system (E_0) against the potential of the hydrogen electrode, which at pH 0 is designated as 0.0 volts. However, for biologic systems it is normal to express the redox potential (E_0') at pH 7.0, at which pH the electrode potential of the hydrogen electrode is -0.42 volts. The redox potentials of some redox systems of special interest in mammalian physiology are shown in Table 12–1. The list of

Table 12–1. Some redox potentials of special interest in mammalian oxidation systems.

System	E_0' volts
Oxygen/water	+0.82
Cytochrome a; Fe^{3+}/Fe^{2+}	+0.29
Cytochrome c; Fe^{3+}/Fe^{2+}	+0.22
Ubiquinone; ox/red	+0.10
Cytochrome b; Fe^{3+}/Fe^{2+}	+0.08
Fumarate/succinate	+0.03
Flavoprotein-old yellow enzyme; ox/red	−0.12
Oxaloacetate/malate	−0.17
Pyruvate/lactate	−0.19
Acetoacetate/β-hydroxybutyrate	−0.27
Lipoate; ox/red	−0.29
$NAD^+/NADH$	−0.32
H^+/H_2	−0.42
Succinate/α-ketoglutarate	−0.67

redox potentials shown in the table allows prediction of the direction of flow of electrons from one redox couple to another. The reduced member of a redox couple can potentially reduce the oxidized member of a redox couple **above** (ie, with a larger E_0') it in Table 12–1.

ENZYMES & COENZYMES INVOLVED IN OXIDATION & REDUCTION

All enzymes concerned in oxidative processes are designated oxidoreductases. In the following account, they are classified into 5 groups.

(1) Oxidases: Enzymes that catalyze the removal of hydrogen from a substrate but use only oxygen as a hydrogen acceptor.* They invariably contain **copper** and form water as a reaction product (with the exception of uricase and monoamine oxidase, which form H_2O_2) (Fig 12–1).

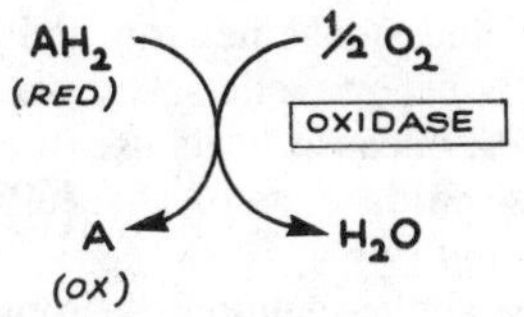

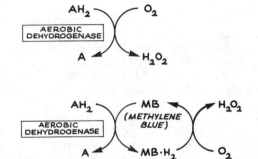

Figure 12–1. Oxidation of a metabolite catalyzed by an oxidase.

(2) Aerobic dehydrogenases: Enzymes catalyzing the removal of hydrogen from a substrate but which, as distinct from oxidases, can use either oxygen or artificial substances such as methylene blue as hydrogen acceptor. Characteristically, these dehydrogenases are **flavoproteins.** Hydrogen peroxide rather than water is formed as a product (Fig 12–2).

(3) Anaerobic dehydrogenases: Enzymes catalyzing the removal of hydrogen from a substrate but not able to use oxygen as hydrogen acceptor. There are a large number of enzymes in this class. They perform 2 main functions:

(a) Transfer of hydrogen from one substrate to another in a coupled oxidation-reduction reaction not

*Sometimes the term "oxidase" is used collectively to denote all enzymes that catalyze reactions involving molecular oxygen.

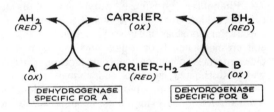

Figure 12–2. Oxidation of a metabolite catalyzed by an aerobic dehydrogenase.

involving a respiratory chain (Fig 12–3). These dehydrogenases are specific for their substrates but often utilize the same coenzyme or hydrogen carrier as other dehydrogenases. As the reactions are reversible, these properties enable reducing equivalents to be freely transferred within the cell. This type of reaction, which enables a substrate to be oxidized at the expense of another, is particularly useful in enabling oxidative processes to occur in the absence of oxygen.

Figure 12–3. Oxidation of a metabolite catalyzed by anaerobic dehydrogenases, not involving a respiratory chain.

(b) As components in a respiratory chain of electron transport from substrate to oxygen (Fig 12–4).

(4) Hydroperoxidases: Enzymes utilizing hydrogen peroxide as a substrate. Two enzymes fall into this category: **peroxidase,** found in milk, plants, leukocytes, and erythrocytes; and **catalase,** found in animals and plants.

(5) Oxygenases: Enzymes that catalyze the direct transfer and incorporation of oxygen into a substrate molecule.

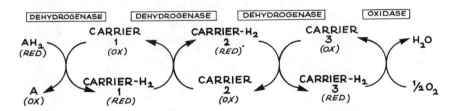

Figure 12–4. Oxidation of a metabolite by anaerobic dehydrogenases and finally by a true oxidase in a respiratory chain.

Oxidases

True oxidases are conjugated proteins that contain copper.

Cytochrome oxidase is a hemoprotein widely distributed in many plant and animal tissues. It is the terminal component of the chain of respiratory carriers found in mitochondria and is therefore responsible for the reaction whereby electrons resulting from the oxidation of substrate molecules by dehydrogenases are transferred to their final acceptor, oxygen. The enzyme is poisoned by carbon monoxide (only in the dark), cyanide, and hydrogen sulfide. It is considered to be identical with Warburg's respiratory enzyme and with what has also been termed cytochrome a_3. It was formerly assumed that cytochrome a and cytochrome oxidase were separate compounds since each has a distinct spectrum and different properties with respect to the effects of carbon monoxide and cyanide. More recent studies show that the 2 cytochromes are combined with the same protein, and the complex is known as **cytochrome aa₃.** It contains 2 molecules of heme, each having one Fe atom that oscillates between Fe^{3+} and Fe^{2+} during oxidation and reduction. Also, 2 atoms of Cu are present and are associated with the cytochrome oxidase activity for the reaction of electrons with molecular oxygen.

Phenolase (tyrosinase, polyphenol oxidase, catechol oxidase) is a copper-containing enzyme that is specific for more than one type of reaction. It is able to convert monophenols or o-diphenols to o-quinones. Other enzymes containing copper are **laccase,** which is widely distributed in plants and animals (converts p-hydroquinones to p-quinones), and **ascorbic acid oxidase,** found only in plants. Copper has been claimed to be present in a number of other enzymes such as **uricase,** which catalyzes the oxidation of uric acid to allantoin, and **monoamine oxidase,** an enzyme that oxidizes epinephrine and tyramine in mitochondria.

Aerobic Dehydrogenases

Aerobic dehydrogenases are flavoprotein enzymes containing **flavin mononucleotide (FMN)** or **flavin adenine dinucleotide (FAD)** (see Fig 10–4 for structure). The flavin groups vary in their affinity for their respective apoenzyme protein, some being detached easily and others not detached without destroying the enzyme. Many of these flavoprotein enzymes contain, in addition, a metal that is essential for the functioning of the enzyme; these are known as **metalloflavoproteins.**

Enzymes belonging to this group of aerobic dehydrogenases include **D-amino acid dehydrogenase** (D-amino acid oxidase), an FAD-linked enzyme, found particularly in liver and kidney, that catalyzes the oxidative deamination of the unnatural (D-) forms of amino acids. Other substrates include glycine, D-lactate, and L-proline, demonstrating that the enzyme is not completely specific for D-amino acids. **L-Amino acid dehydrogenase** (L-amino acid oxidase) is an FMN-linked enzyme found in kidney with general specificity for the oxidative deamination of the naturally occurring L-amino acids. **Xanthine dehydrogenase** (xanthine oxidase) has a wide distribution, occurring in milk, small intestine, kidney, and liver. It contains molybdenum and plays an important role in the conversion of purine bases to uric acid. It is of particular significance in the liver and kidneys of birds, which excrete uric acid as the main nitrogenous end product not only of purine metabolism but also of protein and amino acid catabolism.

Aldehyde dehydrogenase (aldehyde oxidase) is an FAD-linked enzyme present in pig and other mammalian livers. It is a metalloflavoprotein containing molybdenum and nonheme iron and acts upon aldehydes and N-heterocyclic substrates.

Of interest because of its use in estimating glucose is **glucose oxidase,** an FAD-specific enzyme prepared from fungi.

All of the above-mentioned aerobic dehydrogenases contain 2 molecules of the flavin nucleotide per mole. The metalloflavoproteins also have a fixed stoichiometry with regard to the number of atoms of metal per molecule, usually Mo:Fe as 2:8. The mechanisms of oxidation and reduction of these enzymes are complex. There seem to be different detailed mechanisms for each enzyme with the possible involvement of free radicals. However, evidence points to reduction of the isoalloxazine ring taking place in 2 steps via a semiquinone (free radical) intermediate (Fig 12–5).

Anaerobic Dehydrogenases

A. Dehydrogenases Dependent on Nicotinamide Coenzymes: A large number of dehydrogenase enzymes fall into this category. They are linked as coenzymes either to **nicotinamide adenine dinucleotide (NAD)** or to **nicotinamide adenine dinucleotide phosphate (NADP).** The coenzymes are reduced by the specific substrate of the dehydrogenase and reoxidized by a suitable electron acceptor. They may freely and reversibly dissociate from their respective apoenzymes. The nicotinamide nucleotides are syn-

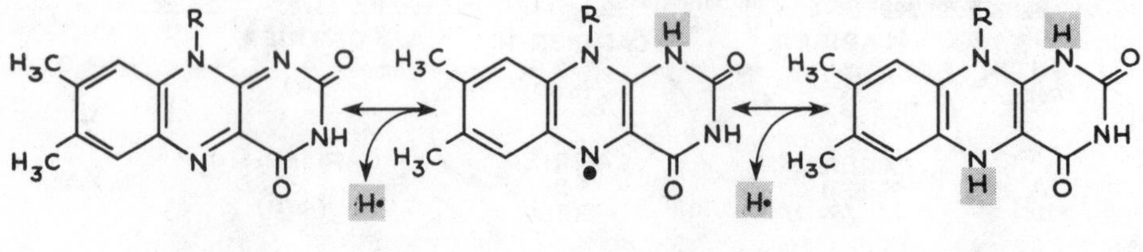

Figure 12–5. Reduction of isoalloxazine ring in flavin nucleotides.

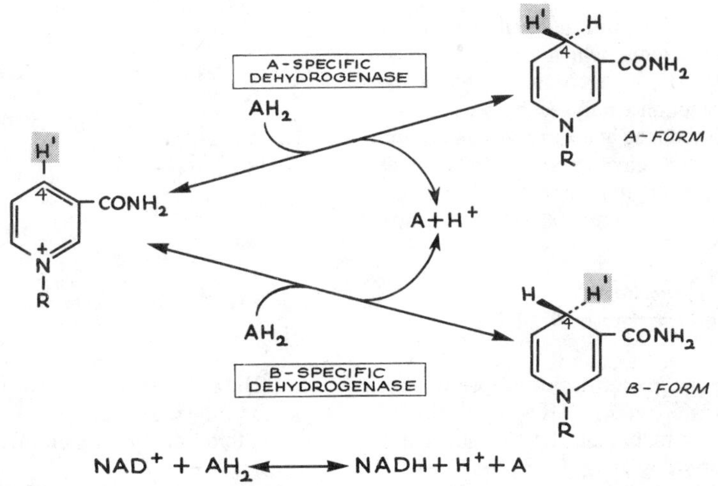

Figure 12–6. Mechanism of oxidation of nicotinamide coenzymes.

thesized from the vitamin niacin (see Chapter 10). The mechanism of oxidation of the coenzymes is as shown in Fig 12–6.

There is stereospecificity about position 4 of nicotinamide when it is reduced by a substrate AH_2. One of the hydrogen atoms is removed from the substrate as a hydrogen nucleus with 2 electrons (hydride ion, H^-) and is transferred to the 4 position where it may be attached in either the A- or B- position according to the specificity determined by the particular dehydrogenase catalyzing the reaction. The remaining hydrogen of the hydrogen pair removed from the substrate remains free as a hydrogen ion. Deuterium-labeled substrates have been used in elucidating these mechanisms.

Generally, **NAD-linked dehydrogenases** catalyze oxidoreduction reactions in the **oxidative pathways** of metabolism, particularly in glycolysis, in the citric acid cycle, and in the respiratory chain of mitochondria. **NADP-linked dehydrogenases** are found characteristically in **reductive syntheses,** as in the extramitochondrial pathway of fatty acid synthesis and steroid synthesis. They are also to be found as coenzymes to the dehydrogenases of the hexose monophosphate shunt. Some nicotinamide coenzyme-dependent dehydrogenases have been found to contain zinc, notably alcohol dehydrogenase from liver and glyceraldehyde-3-phosphate dehydrogenase from skeletal muscle. The zinc ions are not considered to take part in the oxidation and reduction.

B. Dehydrogenases Dependent on Riboflavin: The flavin groups associated with these dehydrogenases are similar to those of the aerobic dehydrogenase group, namely FMN and FAD. They are in the main more tightly bound to their apoenzymes than the nicotinamide coenzymes. Most of the riboflavin-linked anaerobic dehydrogenases are concerned with electron transport in (or to) the respiratory chain. **NADH dehydrogenase** is a member of the respiratory chain acting as a carrier of electrons between NADH

and the more electropositive components. Other dehydrogenases such as **succinate dehydrogenase, acyl-CoA dehydrogenase,** and **mitochondrial glycerol-3-phosphate dehydrogenase** transfer reducing equivalents directly from the substrate to the respiratory chain. Another role of the flavin-dependent dehydrogenases is in the dehydrogenation (by dihydrolipoyl dehydrogenase) of reduced lipoate, an intermediate in the oxidative decarboxylation of pyruvate and α-ketoglutarate (Fig 14–5). In this particular instance, due to the low redox potential, the flavoprotein (FAD) acts as a hydrogen carrier from reduced lipoate to NAD^+. The **electron-transferring flavoprotein** is an intermediary carrier of electrons between acyl-CoA dehydrogenase and the respiratory chain.

C. The Cytochromes: Except for cytochrome oxidase (previously described), the cytochromes are classified as anaerobic dehydrogenases. Their identification and study are facilitated by the presence in the reduced state of characteristic absorption bands that disappear on oxidation. In the respiratory chain they are involved as **carriers of electrons from flavoproteins on the one hand to cytochrome oxidase** on the other. The cytochromes are iron-containing hemoproteins in which the iron atom oscillates between Fe^{3+} and Fe^{2+} during oxidation and reduction. Several identifiable cytochromes occur in the respiratory chain, viz, cytochromes b, c_1, c, a, and a_3 (cytochrome oxidase). Of these, only cytochrome c is soluble. Study of its structure has revealed that the iron porphyrin group is attached to the apoprotein by 2 thioether bridges derived from condensation of cysteine residues of the protein with vinyl groups of the heme. Besides the respiratory chain, cytochromes are found in other locations, eg, the endoplasmic reticulum (cytochromes P-450 and b_5), plant cells. bacteria, and yeasts.

Hydroperoxidases

A. Peroxidase: Although typically a plant enzyme, peroxidase is found in milk and leukocytes. The prosthetic group is protoheme, which, unlike the situation in most hemoproteins, is only loosely bound to the apoprotein. In the reaction catalyzed by peroxidase, hydrogen peroxide is reduced at the expense of several substances that will act as electron acceptors, such as ascorbate, quinones, and cytochrome c. The reaction catalyzed by peroxidase is complex, but the overall reaction is as follows:

$$H_2O_2 + AH_2 \xrightarrow{\boxed{\text{Peroxidase}}} 2H_2O + A$$

In erythrocytes, the enzyme **glutathione peroxidase** catalyzes the destruction of H_2O_2 by reduced glutathione, protecting membrane lipids and hemoglobin against oxidation by H_2O_2 (see p 562).

B. Catalase: Catalase is a hemoprotein containing 4 heme groups. In addition to possessing peroxidase activity, it is able to use one molecule of H_2O_2 as a substrate electron donor and another molecule of H_2O_2 as oxidant or electron acceptor. Under most conditions in vivo, the peroxidase activity of catalase seems to be favored.

$$2H_2O_2 \xrightarrow{\boxed{\text{Catalase}}} 2H_2O + O_2$$

Catalase is found in blood, bone marrow, mucous membranes, kidney, and liver. Its function is assumed to be the **destruction of hydrogen peroxide** formed by the action of aerobic dehydrogenases. Microbodies or **peroxisomes** are found in liver. These are rich in aerobic dehydrogenases and in catalase, which suggests that there may be a biologic advantage in grouping the enzymes which produce H_2O_2 with the enzyme that destroys it (Fig 12–7). In addition to the peroxisomal enzymes, mitochondrial and microsomal electron transport systems must be considered as sources of H_2O_2.

Oxygenases

Enzymes in this group catalyze the incorporation of oxygen into a substrate molecule. This takes place in 2 steps: (1) oxygen binding to the enzyme at the active site, and (2) the reaction in which the bound oxygen is reduced or transferred to the substrate. Oxygenases may be divided into 2 subgroups:

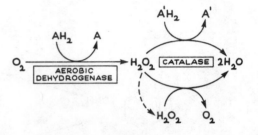

Figure 12–7. Role of catalase in oxidative reactions.

A. Dioxygenases (Oxygen Transferases, True Oxygenases): These enzymes catalyze the incorporation of both atoms of oxygen into the substrate:

$$A + O_2 \longrightarrow AO_2$$

Examples of this type include enzymes that contain iron such as **homogentisate dioxygenase** and **3-hydroxyanthranilate dioxygenase** from the supernatant fraction of the liver, and enzymes utilizing heme such as **L-tryptophan dioxygenase** (tryptophan pyrrolase) from the liver.

B. Mono-oxygenases (Mixed Function Oxidases, Hydroxylases): These enzymes catalyze the incorporation of only one atom of the oxygen molecule into a substrate. The other oxygen atom is reduced to water, an additional electron donor or cosubstrate being necessary for this purpose.

Example:

$$A-H + O_2 + ZH_2 \longrightarrow A-OH + H_2O + Z$$

Hayaishi has subdivided the mono-oxygenases into subgroups according to the nature of the cosubstrate electron donor involved. For example, many of the enzymes involved in steroid syntheses or transformations are mono-oxygenases utilizing NADPH as a cosubstrate. These are found mainly in the endoplasmic reticulum (microsomes) of the liver and in both the mitochondria and the endoplasmic reticulum of the adrenal glands.

The enzymes involved in the metabolism of many drugs by hydroxylation belong to this group. They are found in the microsomes of the liver together with cytochrome P-450 and cytochrome b_5. Both NADH and NADPH donate reducing equivalents for the reduction of these cytochromes (Fig 12–8), which in

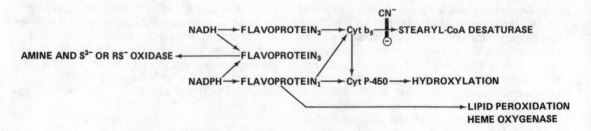

Figure 12–8. Electron transport chain in microsomes. Cyanide (CN^-) inhibits the indicated step.

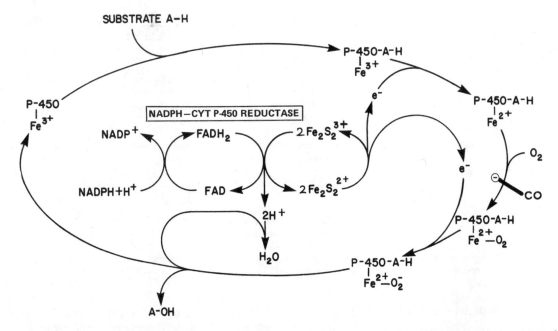

Figure 12–9. Cytochrome P-450 hydroxylase cycle in microsomes. The system shown is typical of steroid hydroxylases of the adrenal cortex. Liver microsomal cytochrome P-450 hydroxylase does not require the iron-sulfur protein Fe_2S_2. Carbon monoxide (CO) inhibits the indicated step.

turn are oxidized by substrates in a series of enzymic reactions collectively known as hydroxylase (Fig 12–9).

Example: See below.

DRUG–H + O_2 + 2 Fe^{2+} + 2 H^+ $\xrightarrow{\boxed{\text{Hydroxylase}}}$
(P-450)
DRUG–OH + H_2O + 2 Fe^{3+}
(P-450)

Among the drugs metabolized by this system are benzpyrene, aminopyrine, aniline, morphine, and benzphetamine. Many drugs such as phenobarbital have the ability to induce the formation of microsomal enzymes and of cytochrome P-450.

Oxygenases do not take part in reactions that have as their purpose the provision of energy to the cell; rather, they are concerned with the synthesis or degradation of many different types of metabolites.

Superoxide Metabolism

Oxygen is a potentially toxic substance, the toxicity of which has hitherto been attributed to the formation of H_2O_2. Recently, however, the ease with which oxygen can be reduced in tissues to the superoxide anion (O_2^-) and the occurrence of **superoxide dismutase** in aerobic organisms (although not in obligate anaerobes) has suggested that the toxicity of oxygen is due to its conversion to superoxide (Friedovich, 1975).

Superoxide is formed when reduced flavins, eg, xanthine dehydrogenase, are reoxidized univalently by molecular oxygen. It is also formed during univalent oxidations with molecular oxygen in the respiratory chain.

$$EnzH_2 + O_2 \longrightarrow EnzH + O_2^- + H^+$$

Superoxide can reduce oxidized cytochrome c

$$O_2^- + Cyt\ c \cdot Fe^{3+} \longrightarrow O_2 + Cyt\ c \cdot Fe^{2+}$$

or be removed by the presence of the specific enzyme superoxide dismutase.

$$O_2^- + O_2^- + 2H^+ \xrightarrow{\boxed{\begin{array}{c}\text{Superoxide}\\\text{dismutase}\end{array}}} H_2O_2 + O_2$$

It has been proposed that O_2^- bound to cytochrome P-450 is an intermediate in the activation of oxygen in hydroxylation reactions (Fig 12–9).

The function of superoxide dismutase seems to be that of protecting aerobic organisms against the deleterious effects of superoxide. The cytosolic enzyme is composed of 2 similar subunits, each one containing one equivalent of Cu^{2+} and Zn^{2+}, whereas the mitochondrial enzyme contains Mn^{2+}, being similar to the enzyme found in bacteria. This finding supports the hypothesis that mitochondria have evolved from a prokaryote that entered into symbiosis with a protoeukaryote. The distribution of the dismutase is widespread, being present in all major aerobic tissues. Exposure of animals to an atmosphere of 100% oxygen causes an adaptive increase of the enzyme, particularly in the lungs.

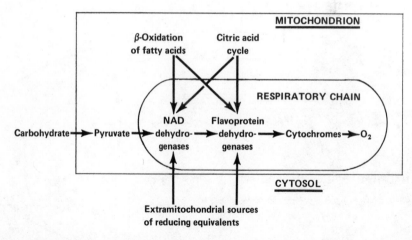

Figure 12–10. The major sources of reducing equivalents and their relationship to the mitochondrial respiratory chain. The main extramitochondrial source is NADH formed in glycolysis.

THE RESPIRATORY CHAIN

The mitochondrion has appropriately been termed the "powerhouse" of the cell since it is within the mitochondria that most of the useful energy derived from oxidation within the tissues is captured in the form of the high-energy intermediate ATP. All the useful energy liberated during the oxidation of fatty acids and amino acids and nearly all of that from the oxidation of carbohydrate is made available within the mitochondria as reducing equivalents (–H or electrons). To accomplish this, the mitochondria contain the series of catalysts known as the respiratory chain, which is concerned with the transport of reducing equivalents, their final reaction with oxygen to form water, together with the machinery for trapping the liberated free energy as high-energy phosphate. Mitochondria also contain the enzyme systems responsible for producing most of the reducing equivalents in the first place, ie, the enzymes of β-oxidation and of the citric acid cycle. The latter is the final common metabolic pathway for the oxidation of all the major foodstuffs. These relationships are shown in Fig 12–10.

Organization of the Respiratory Chain in Mitochondria

The major components of the respiratory chain (Fig 12–11) are arranged sequentially in order of increasing redox potential (Table 12–1). Electrons or

hydrogen flow through the chain in a stepwise manner **from the more electronegative components to the more electropositive oxygen.** Thus, the redox potential of a component of the respiratory chain contributes to the information necessary to assign it a tentative position in the chain. Several other approaches have been used to identify components and their relative positions. Chance and his associates have developed sophisticated technics for following the absorption spectra of the individual components in intact mitochondria. Other investigators, including Green, have broken the chain down into separate components or complexes and attempted to reconstruct it from the separate parts. Slater and others have used inhibitors that block specific reactions in the chain; these are frequently employed with artificial electron acceptors and donors. Chance and Williams introduced the concept of "crossover" to locate the site of action of inhibitors. The concept is based upon the assumption that when an inhibitor is introduced into an active series of redox components of the respiratory chain in the steady state, those components on the electronegative side of the block become more reduced while those on the electropositive side become more oxidized.

The main respiratory chain in mitochondria proceeds from the NAD-linked dehydrogenase systems on the one hand, through flavoproteins and cytochromes, to molecular oxygen on the other. Not all substrates are linked to the respiratory chain through NAD-specific dehydrogenases; some, because their redox potentials

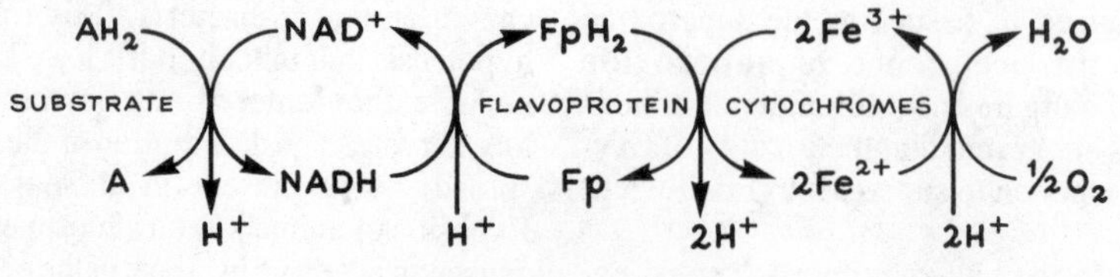

$$AH_2 \quad NAD^+ \quad FpH_2 \quad 2Fe^{3+} \quad H_2O$$

SUBSTRATE   FLAVOPROTEIN CYTOCHROMES

$$A \quad NADH \quad Fp \quad 2Fe^{2+} \quad \tfrac{1}{2}O_2$$
$$H^+ \qquad H^+ \qquad 2H^+ \qquad 2H^+$$

Figure 12–11. Transport of reducing equivalents through the respiratory chain.

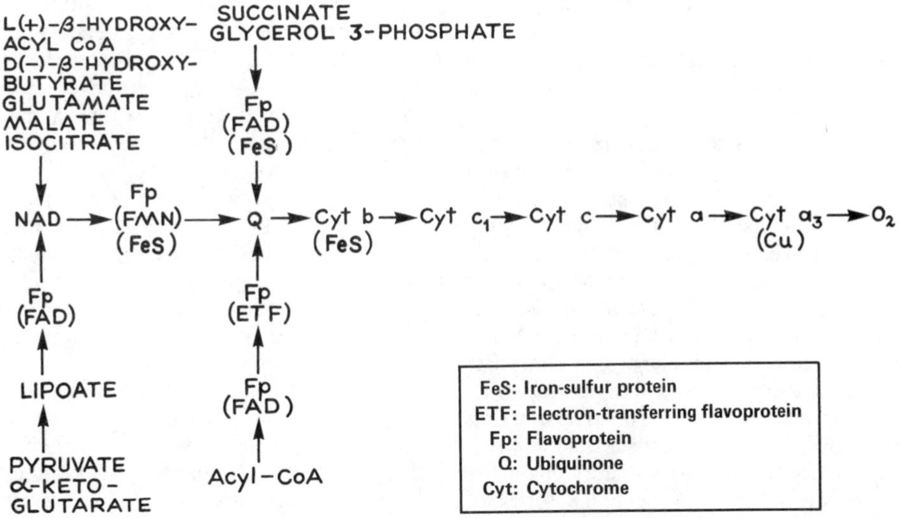

Figure 12–12. Components of the respiratory chain in mitochondria.

are more positive (eg, fumarate/succinate, Table 12–1), are linked directly to flavoprotein dehydrogenases, which in turn are linked to the cytochromes of the respiratory chain (Fig 12–12).

In recent years it has become clear that an additional carrier is present in the respiratory chain linking the flavoproteins to cytochrome b, the member of the cytochrome chain of lowest redox potential. This substance, which has been named **ubiquinone** or **Q** (**coenzyme Q;** see Fig 12–13), exists in mitochondria in the oxidized quinone form under aerobic conditions and in the reduced quinol form under anaerobic conditions. Q is a constituent of the mitochondrial lipids, the other lipids being predominantly phospholipids that constitute part of the mitochondrial membrane. Its structure is very similar to those of vitamin K and vitamin E (see Chapter 11). It is also similar to plastoquinone, found in chloroplasts. All of these substances are characterized by the possession of a polyisoprenoid side chain. In mitochondria there is a large stoichiometric excess of Q compared to other members of the respiratory chain.

An additional component found in respiratory chain preparations is the **iron-sulfur protein (FeS;** nonheme iron). It is associated with the flavoproteins (metalloflavoproteins) and with cytochrome b. The iron-sulfur-protein complex is similar to the ferredoxins of bacteria and to iron proteins present in plants. On denaturation with acid or heat, H_2S is liberated in an amount stoichiometrically related to the iron present. Some iron-sulfur proteins contain 2 iron atoms and 2 sulfur atoms (Fe_2S_2) while others contain 4 iron atoms and 4 sulfur atoms (Fe_4S_4), both structures connected by 4 cysteine residues to the protein. The sulfur and iron are thought to take part in the oxidoreduction mechanisms.

A current view of the principal components of the respiratory chain is shown in Fig 12–12. At the electronegative end of the chain, dehydrogenase enzymes catalyze the transfer of electrons from substrates to NAD of the chain. Several differences exist in the manner in which this is carried out. The α-keto acids pyruvate and ketoglutarate have complex dehydrogenase systems involving lipoate and FAD prior to the passage of electrons to NAD of the respiratory chain. Electron transfers from other dehydrogenases such as L(+)-β-hydroxyacyl-CoA, D(−)-β-hydroxybutyrate, glutamate, malate, and isocitrate dehydrogenases ap-

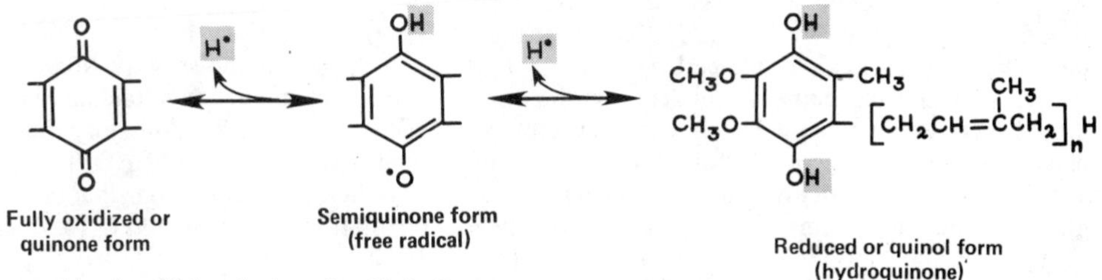

n = number of isoprenoid units, which varies from 6 to 10, ie, Q_{6-10}

Figure 12–13. Structure of ubiquinone (Q).

pear to couple directly with NAD of the respiratory chain.

The reduced NADH of the respiratory chain is in turn oxidized by a metalloflavoprotein enzyme — **NADH dehydrogenase.** This enzyme contains FeS and FMN and is tightly bound to the respiratory chain. Q is the collecting point in the respiratory chain for reducing equivalents derived from other substrates that are linked directly to the respiratory chain through flavoprotein dehydrogenases. These substrates include succinate, glycerol 3-phosphate, and acyl-CoA (Fig 12–12). The flavin moiety of all these dehydrogenases appears to be FAD, and those catalyzing the dehydrogenation of succinate and glycerol 3-phosphate contain FeS. In the dehydrogenation of acyl-CoA, an additional flavoprotein, the **electron-transporting flavoprotein (ETF,** Fig 12–12), is necessary to effect transference of electrons to the respiratory chain.

Electrons flow from Q, through the series of cytochromes shown in Fig 12–12, to molecular oxygen. The cytochromes are arranged in order of increasing redox potential. The terminal cytochrome a₃ (cytochrome oxidase) is responsible for the final combination of reducing equivalents with molecular oxygen. It has been noted that this enzyme system contains copper, an essential component of true oxidase enzymes. Cytochrome oxidase has a very high affinity for oxygen, which allows the respiratory chain to function at the maximum rate until the tissue has become virtually anoxic (depleted of O_2).

The structural organization of the respiratory chain has been the subject of considerable speculation. Of significance is the finding of nearly constant molar proportions between the components. The cytochromes are present in the approximate molar proportions, one with another, of 1:1. These findings, together with the fact that many of the components appear to be structurally integrated with the mitochondrial membranes, have suggested that these components have a definite spatial orientation in the membranes.

THE ROLE OF THE RESPIRATORY CHAIN IN ENERGY CAPTURE

ADP is envisaged as a molecule that captures, in the form of **high-energy phosphate,** some of the free energy resulting from catabolic processes and which as **ATP** passes on this free energy to drive those processes requiring energy. Thus, ATP has been called the **energy "currency"** of the cell.

As indicated in Chapter 15, under anaerobic conditions there is a net capture of 2 high-energy phosphate groups in the glycolytic reactions equivalent to approximately 74 kJ/mol of glucose. Since 1 mol of glucose yields approximately 2870 kJ on complete combustion, the energy captured by phosphorylation in glycolysis is small. The reactions of the citric acid cycle, the final pathway for the complete oxidation of glucose, include only one phosphorylation step, the

conversion of succinyl-CoA to succinate, which allows the capture of 2 more high-energy phosphates per mole of glucose. All of the phosphorylations described so far occur **at the substrate level.** Examination of intact respiring mitochondria reveals that when substrates are oxidized via an NAD-linked dehydrogenase, 3 mol of inorganic phosphate are incorporated into 3 mol of ADP to form 3 mol of ATP per ½ mol of O_2 consumed, ie, the P:O ratio = 3. On the other hand, when a substrate is oxidized via a flavoprotein-linked dehydrogenase, only 2 mol of ATP are formed, ie, P:O = 2. These reactions are known as **oxidative phosphorylation at the respiratory chain level.** Taking into account dehydrogenations in the pathway of catabolism of glucose in both glycolysis and the citric acid cycle, plus phosphorylations at the substrate level, it is now possible to account for at least 46% of the free energy resulting from the combustion of glucose, captured in the form of high-energy phosphate.

If phosphorylation is coupled directly to certain reactions in the respiratory chain in a manner analogous to phosphorylation in the glycolytic sequence of reactions, it is pertinent to inquire at what sites this could occur. There must be a redox potential of approximately 0.2 volts or a free energy change of approximately 37 kJ between components of the respiratory chain if that particular site is to support the coupled formation of 1 mol of ATP. Location of the phosphorylation sites has been elucidated by experiments in which the P:O ratio is measured in the presence of inhibitors of known reactions in the chain and in the presence of artificial electron acceptors.

The rate of respiration of mitochondria can be controlled by the concentration of ADP. This is because **oxidation and phosphorylation are tightly coupled** and ADP is an essential component of the phosphorylation process. When ADP is deficient in the presence of excess substrate, 3 crossover points can be identified, since the component at the substrate side of the crossover point becomes more reduced and that on the oxygen side becomes more oxidized. These crossover points coincide with 3 of the possible sites previously identified on thermodynamic grounds. The 3 sites of phosphorylation have been designated as sites I, II, and III, respectively (Fig 12–14). The above findings explain why oxidation of succinate via the respiratory chain produces a P:O ratio of only 2, as site I would be bypassed by the flavoprotein-linked succinate dehydrogenase (Fig 12–12).

Respiratory Control

As stated above, oxidation and phosphorylation are tightly coupled in mitochondria. Thus, respiration cannot occur via the respiratory chain without concomitant phosphorylation of ADP. Chance and Williams have defined 5 conditions that can control the rate of respiration in mitochondria. These are listed in Table 12–2.

Generally most cells in the resting state seem to be in state 4, respiration being controlled by the availability of ADP. When work is performed, ATP is

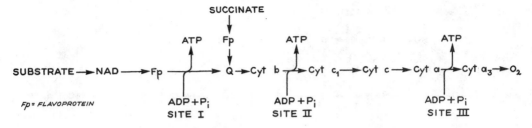

Figure 12–14. Sites of phosphorylation in the respiratory chain.

Table 12–2. States of respiratory control.

	Conditions Limiting the Rate of Respiration
State 1	Availability of ADP and substrate
State 2	Availability of substrate only
State 3	The capacity of the respiratory chain itself, when all substrates and components are present in saturating amounts
State 4	Availability of ADP only
State 5	Availability of oxygen only

converted to ADP, allowing more respiration to occur, which in turn replenishes the store of ATP (Fig 12–15). It would appear that under certain conditions the concentration of inorganic phosphate and ATP could also affect the rate of functioning of the respiratory chain.

Thus, the manner in which biologic oxidative processes allow the free energy resulting from the oxidation of foodstuffs to become available and to be captured is stepwise, efficient (40–50%), and controlled—rather than explosive, inefficient, and uncontrolled. The remaining free energy that is not captured is liberated as **heat.** This need not be considered as "wasted," since in the warm-blooded animal it contributes to maintenance of body temperature.

Inhibitors of the Respiratory Chain & of Oxidative Phosphorylation

Much information about the respiratory chain has been obtained by the use of inhibitors, and their proposed loci of action are shown in Fig 12–16. For descriptive purposes, they may be divided into inhibitors of the respiratory chain proper, inhibitors of oxidative phosphorylation, and uncouplers of oxidative phosphorylation.

Inhibitors that arrest respiration by blocking the respiratory chain appear to act at 3 loci that may be identical to the energy transfer sites I, II, and III. Site I is inhibited by **barbiturates** such as **amobarbital,** by the antibiotic **piericidin A,** and by the fish poison **rotenone.** Some steroids and mercurials also affect this site. These inhibitors prevent the oxidation of substrates that communicate directly with the respiratory chain via an NAD-linked dehydrogenase, eg, β-hydroxybutyrate.

Dimercaprol and **antimycin A** inhibit the respiratory chain at or around site II, between cytochrome b and cytochrome c; and the inhibitors of cytochrome oxidase, **H₂S, carbon monoxide,** and **cyanide,** that have been known for many years are considered to act at or near site III.

The antibiotic **oligomycin** completely blocks oxidation and phosphorylation in intact mitochondria. However, in the presence of oligomycin and the uncoupler **dinitrophenol,** oxidation proceeds without phosphorylation, indicating that oligomycin does not act directly on the respiratory chain but subsequently on a step in phosphorylation.

Atractyloside inhibits oxidative phosphorylation, which is dependent on the transport of adenine

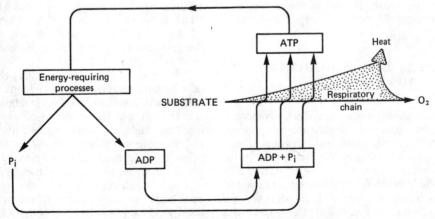

Figure 12–15. The role of ADP in respiratory control.

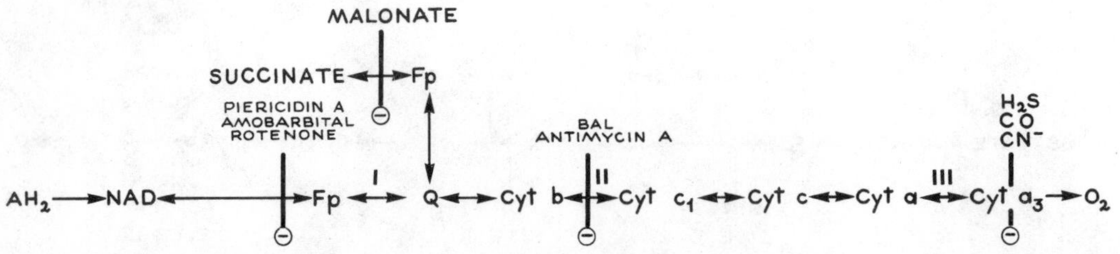

Figure 12–16. Proposed sites of inhibition ($\ominus$) of respiratory chain by specific drugs, chemicals, and antibiotics. The energy transfer sites (I, II, and III) are indicated. BAL = dimercaprol.

nucleotides across the inner mitochondrial membrane. It is considered to inhibit a "transporter" of ADP into the mitochondrion and of ATP out of the mitochondrion. Thus, it acts only on intact mitochondria but does not inhibit phosphorylation in particles that have no intact membrane.

The action of **uncouplers** is to dissociate oxidation in the respiratory chain from phosphorylation (see Chapter 31). This results in respiration becoming uncontrolled, the concentration of ADP or P_i no longer limiting the rate of respiration. The uncoupler that has been used most frequently is 2,4-dinitrophenol, but other compounds act in a similar manner, including dinitrocresol, pentachlorophenol, and CCCP (*m*-chlorocarbonyl cyanide phenylhydrazone). The latter, compared with dinitrophenol, is about 100 times as active.

Reversal of Electron Transport

Mitochondria catalyze the energy-dependent reversal of electron transport through the respiratory chain. The energy is provided either by ATP, where the effect is mediated by a complete reversal of oxidative phosphorylation, or by some other intermediate. Although these experiments demonstrate the reversibility of electron transport, the physiologic significance of the process is unknown.

Energy-Linked Transhydrogenase

There is evidence for an energy-linked transhydrogenase that can catalyze the transfer of hydrogen from NADH to NADP. It appears that a nonphosphorylated intermediate supplies energy for the transfer.

MECHANISMS OF OXIDATIVE PHOSPHORYLATION

Two principal hypotheses have been advanced to account for the coupling of oxidation and phosphorylation. The **chemical hypothesis** postulates direct chemical coupling at all stages of the process, as in the reactions that generate ATP in glycolysis. The **chemosmotic hypothesis** postulates that oxidation of components in the respiratory chain generates hydrogen ions, which are ejected to the outside of a coupling membrane in the mitochondrion. The elec-

trochemical potential difference resulting from the asymmetric distribution of the hydrogen ions (protons, H^+) is used to drive the mechanism responsible for the formation of ATP.

Other hypotheses have been advanced in which it is envisaged that energy from oxidation is conserved in conformational changes of molecules which in turn lead to the generation of high-energy phosphate bonds.

The chemical hypothesis postulated the existence of an energy-rich intermediate ($I \sim X$) linking oxidation with phosphorylation. Because this has never been isolated, the hypothesis has become somewhat discredited and will no longer be described in detail in this text. For an account of the chemical hypothesis, see Harper and others (1979).

THE CHEMOSMOTIC HYPOTHESIS

According to Mitchell, the primary event in oxidative phosphorylation is the translocation of protons (H^+) to the exterior of a coupling membrane (ie, the mitochondrial inner membrane) driven by oxidation in the respiratory chain. It is also postulated that the membrane is impermeable to ions in general but particularly to protons which accumulate outside the membrane, creating an **electrochemical potential difference across the membrane.** This consists of a chemical potential (difference in pH) and an electrical potential. The electrochemical potential difference is used to drive a **membrane-located ATP synthetase** (or the reversal of a membrane-located ATP hydrolase) which in the presence of P_i + ADP forms ATP (Fig 12–17). Thus, there is no high-energy intermediate that is common to both oxidation and phosphorylation as in the chemical hypothesis.

It is proposed that the respiratory chain is folded into 3 oxidation/reduction (**o/r**) loops in the membrane, each loop corresponding functionally to site I, site II, and site III of the respiratory chain. An idealized single loop consisting of a hydrogen carrier and an electron carrier is shown in Fig 12–18. A possible configuration of the respiratory chain folded into 3 functional o/r loops is shown in Fig 12–19.

In this scheme, each electron pair transferred from NADH to oxygen causes 6 protons to be translocated from the inside to the outside of the mitochondrial membrane. NADH first donates one proton and 2

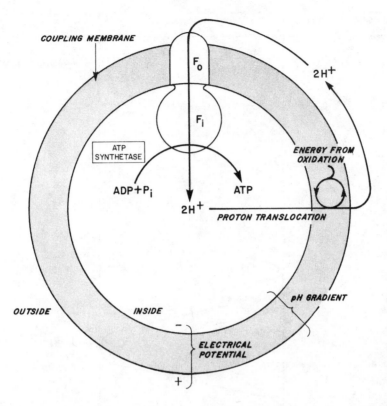

Figure 12–17. Principles of the chemosmotic hypothesis of oxidative phosphorylation. F_i, F_o, protein subunits responsible for phosphorylation.

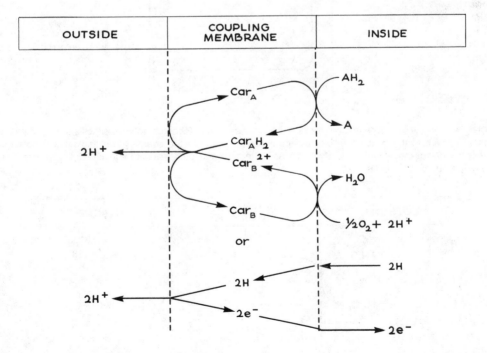

Figure 12–18. Proton-translocating oxidation/reduction (o/r) loop (chemosmotic hypothesis).

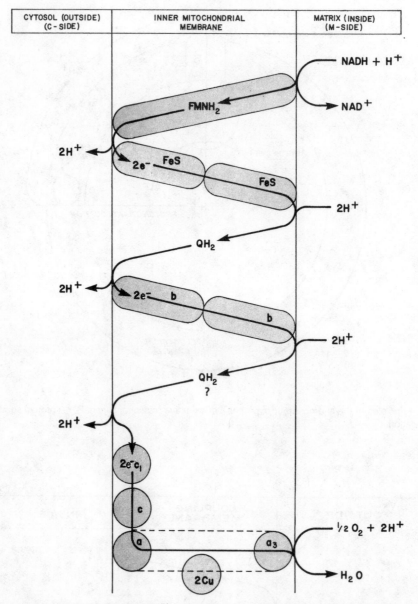

Figure 12–19. Possible configuration of o/r loops in the respiratory chain (chemosmotic hypothesis). Much of this scheme is still tentative, particularly around the Q/cytochrome b region, where the exact nature and relative positions of the intermediates are not known with certainty. It is possible that the semiquinone (QH') is involved. Cytochromes are shown respectively as b, c_1, c, a, and a_3.

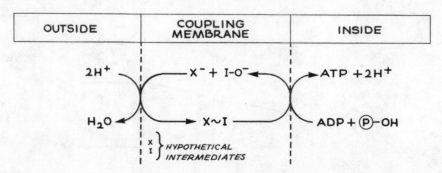

Figure 12–20. Proton-translocating reversible ATP synthetase of the chemosmotic hypothesis.

electrons, which, together with another proton from the internal medium, reduce FMN to $FMNH_2$. FMN is part of a large protein complex which is considered to extend the full width of the membrane, enabling it to release 2 protons to the outside of the membrane and then to return 2 electrons to the inside surface via FeS proteins, which become reduced. Each reduced FeS complex donates one electron to an ubiquinone (Q) molecule which, upon taking up a proton from inside the membrane, forms QH_2. Being lipid-soluble and a small molecule, QH_2 is free to move to the outside of the membrane, where it discharges a proton pair into the cytosol and donates 2 electrons to 2 molecules of the next carrier in the respiratory chain, cytochrome b. This electron carrier is thought to span the mitochondrial membrane, enabling the electrons to join another molecule of ubiquinone together with 2 more protons from the internal medium. The resulting QH_2 shuttles to the outer surface, where 2 protons are liberated and 2 electrons passed to 2 molecules of cytochrome c. These electrons then pass through the remainder of the cytochrome chain, traversing the membrane to cytochrome a_3, which lies on the inside of the membrane. At this site, 2 electrons combine with two H^+ from the internal medium and an oxygen atom to form water.

The mechanism of coupling of proton translocation to the anisotropic (vectorial) ATP synthetase system is the most conjectural aspect of the hypothesis. Mitchell has postulated an anhydride intermediate $X \sim I$ in a system depicted in Fig 12–20.

The existence of a membrane potential required to synthesize ATP would cause ions of a charge opposite to the internal phase to leak in through the coupling membrane. To prevent swelling and lysis, the ion leakage would have to be balanced by extrusion of ions against the electric gradient. It was therefore necessary to postulate that the coupling membrane contains exchange diffusion systems for exchange of anions against OH^- ions and of cations against H^+ ions. Such systems would be necessary for uptake of ionized metabolites through the membrane.

The chemosmotic hypothesis can account for the phenomenon of respiratory control. The electrochemical potential difference across the membrane, once built up as a result of proton translocation, would inhibit further transport of reducing equivalents through the o/r loops unless it was discharged by back-translocation of protons across the membrane through the vectorial ATP synthetase system. This in turn depends on the availability of ADP and P_i.

Several corollaries arise from the chemosmotic hypothesis that have experimental support. These are as follows:

(1) Mitochondria are generally impermeable to protons and other ions. There is, however, evidence for the existence of specific transport systems that enable ions to penetrate the inner mitochondrial membrane.

(2) Uncouplers such as dinitrophenol increase the permeability of mitochondria to protons, thus reducing the electrochemical potential and short-circuiting the

anisotropic ATP synthetase system for the generation of ATP.

(3) Addition of acid to the external medium, establishing a proton gradient, leads to the generation of ATP.

(4) The P/H^+ (transported out) quotient of the ATP synthetase is 1/2 and the H^+ (transported out)/O quotients for succinate and β-hydroxybutyrate oxidation are 4 and 6, respectively, conforming with the expected P/O ratios of 2 and 3, respectively. These ratios are compatible with the postulated existence of 3 o/r loops in the respiratory chain.

(5) Oxidative phosphorylation does not occur in soluble systems, where there is no possibility of a vectorial ATP synthetase. Some structural element involving a closed membrane must be present in the system in order to obtain oxidative phosphorylation.

The respiratory chain contains components organized in a sided manner (transverse asymmetry) as required by the chemosmotic hypothesis (Fig 12–19).

Anatomy & Function of the Mitochondrial Membranes

An account of the general structure of mitochondria is to be found in Chapter 6. Mitochondria have an outer membrane which is permeable to most metabolites, an inner membrane which is selectively permeable and which is thrown into folds or cristae, and a matrix within the inner membrane. The outer membrane may be removed by treatment with digitonin and is characterized by the presence of monoamine oxidase and a few other enzymes (eg, acyl-CoA synthetase, glycerophosphate acyltransferase, monoacyl glycerophosphate acyltransferase, phospholipase A_2). Adenylate kinase is found in the intermembrane space. Cardiolipin is concentrated in the inner membrane where most of the lipid is phospholipid. The exact relationship of the lipid to the protein of the membranes is not understood. Delipidation of the inner membrane does not lead to its disruption.

The inner membrane contains the enzyme proteins of the respiratory chain arranged in a sided manner as indicated in Fig 12–19. Scattered over the surface of the inner membrane are the phosphorylating subunits responsible for the production of ATP (Fig 12–21). These consist of several proteins, collectively known as an F_1 subunit, which project into the matrix and which contain the ATP synthetase (Fig 12–17). These subunits are attached, possibly by a stalk, to a membrane protein subunit known as F_0 which probably extends through the membrane (Fig 12–17). For every proton pair passing through the F_0-F_1 complex, one ATP molecule is formed from ADP and P_i. It is of interest that similar phosphorylating units are found inside the plasma membrane of bacteria but outside the membrane of chloroplasts. It is significant that the proton gradient is from outside to inside in mitochondria and bacteria but in the reverse direction in chloroplasts.

Sonication of the inner mitochondrial membrane leads to the formation of vesicles (submitochondrial

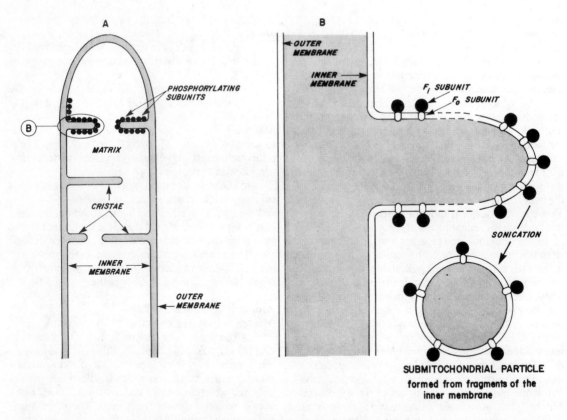

Figure 12–21. Structure of the mitochondrial membranes.

particles) that are "inside-out," as it were, so that the phosphorylating units are located on the outside rather than on the inside of the membrane (Fig 12–21). Studies on submitochondrial particles have been useful in determining the properties of the inner surface of the inner mitochondrial membrane.

The soluble enzymes of the citric acid cycle and the enzymes of β-oxidation of fatty acids are found in the matrix, necessitating mechanisms for transporting ions and fatty and other organic acids, as well as nucleotides, across the inner membrane. Succinate dehydrogenase is found on the inner surface of the inner mitochondrial membrane, where it transports reducing equivalents into the respiratory chain at ubiquinone, bypassing the first o/r loop. β-Hydroxybutyrate dehydrogenase is also bound to the matrix side of the inner mitochondrial membrane.

TRANSPORT OF SUBSTANCES INTO & OUT OF MITOCHONDRIA

Oxidation of Extramitochondrial NADH

Although NADH cannot penetrate the mitochondrial membrane, it is produced continuously in the cytosol by 3-phosphoglyceraldehyde dehydrogenase, an enzyme in the Embden-Meyerhof glycolysis sequence (p 162). However, under aerobic conditions, extramitochondrial NADH does not accumulate and is presumed to be oxidized by the respiratory chain in mitochondria. Several possible mechanisms have been considered to permit this process. These involve transfer of reducing equivalents through the mitochondrial membrane via substrate pairs, linked by suitable dehydrogenases. Substrate pairs that have been considered include acetoacetate/β-hydroxybutyrate, lactate/pyruvate, dihydroxyacetone phosphate/glycerol 3-phosphate, and malate/oxaloacetate. It is necessary that the specific dehydrogenase be present on both sides of the mitochondrial membrane. However, β-hydroxybutyrate dehydrogenase is found only in mitochondria and lactate dehydrogenase only in the cytosol, ruling out these substrate pairs. Glycerol-3-phosphate dehydrogenase is NAD-linked in the cytosol, whereas the enzyme found in the mitochondria is a flavoprotein enzyme. In some species, the activity of the latter enzyme decreases after thyroidectomy and increases after administration of thyroxine. The mechanism of transfer using this system is shown in Fig 12–22. It is to be noted that since the mitochondrial enzyme is linked to the respiratory chain via a flavoprotein rather than NAD, only 2 rather than 3 mol of ATP are formed per atom of oxygen consumed. Thus, if more reducing equivalents are passed through the **glycerophosphate shuttle,** oxygen consumption must increase to maintain ATP production. This mechanism may account for at least part of the extra oxygen consumption of hyperthyroid ani-

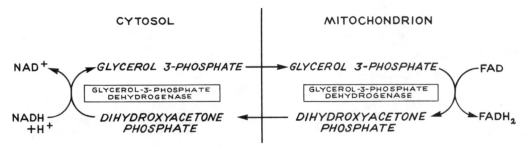

Figure 12–22. Glycerophosphate shuttle for transfer of reducing equivalents from the cytosol into the mitochondrion.

mals. Although this shuttle is present in insect flight muscle and might be important in liver, in other tissues (eg, heart muscle) the mitochondrial glycerol-3-phosphate dehydrogenase is deficient. It is therefore believed that a transport system involving malate and malate dehydrogenase is of more universal utility. Rapid oxidation of NADH occurs only when aspartate-α-ketoglutarate transaminase and malate dehydrogenase, together with glutamate, aspartate, and malate, are added to mitochondria. The malate "shuttle" system is shown in Fig 12–23. The complexity of this system is due to the impermeability of the mitochondrial membrane to oxaloacetate. However, even the other anions are not freely permeable, requiring specific transport systems for passage across the membrane.

Energy-Linked Ion Transport in Mitochondria

Actively respiring mitochondria in which oxidative phosphorylation is taking place maintain or accumulate cations such as K^+, Na^+, Ca^{2+}, and Mg^{2+} and P_i. Uncoupling with dinitrophenol leads to loss of ions from the mitochondria, but the ion uptake is not inhibited by oligomycin, suggesting that the energy need not be supplied by phosphorylation of ADP. Supports of the chemosmotic hypothesis envisage a primary proton pump driving cation exchange.

Mitochondrial Transporter Systems

The inner mitochondrial membrane is freely permeable to oxygen, water, CO_2, and monocarboxylate ions such as β-hydroxybutyrate, acetoacetate, and acetate. Long chain fatty acids are transported into mitochondria via the carnitine system (Fig 17–2), and there is also a special carrier for pyruvate. However, dicarboxylate and tricarboxylate anions and amino acids require specific transporter or carrier systems to facilitate their transport across the membrane. It appears that monocarboxylate anions penetrate more readily because of the lesser degree of dissociation of these acids. It is the undissociated and more lipid-soluble acid that is thought to be the molecular species that penetrates the lipid membrane.

The transport of di- and tricarboxylate anions is closely linked to that of inorganic phosphate, which penetrates readily as the $H_2PO_4^-$ ion in exchange for OH^-. The net uptake of malate by the dicarboxylate transporter requires inorganic phosphate for exchange in the opposite direction. The net uptake of citrate, isocitrate, or cis-aconitate by the tricarboxylate transporter requires malate in exchange (Fig 12–24). α-Ketoglutarate transport also requires an exchange with malate. Thus, by the use of exchange mechanisms, osmotic balance is maintained. It will be appreciated that citrate transport across the mitochondrial membrane depends not only on malate transport but on the transport of inorganic phosphate as well. The adenine nucleotide transporter allows the exchange of ATP and ADP but not AMP. It is inhibited by the poison atractyloside. Na^+ can be exchanged for H^+,

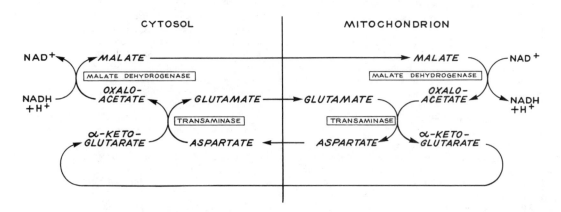

Figure 12–23. Malate shuttle for transfer of reducing equivalents from the cytosol into the mitochondrion.

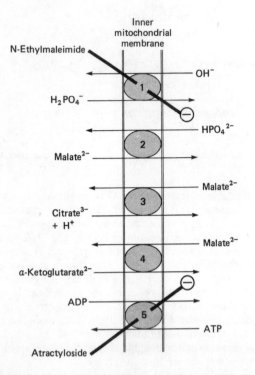

Figure 12–24. Transporter systems in the mitochondrial membrane. 1. Phosphate transporter. 2. Dicarboxylate transporter. 3. Tricarboxylate transporter. 4. α-Ketoglutarate transporter. 5. Adenine nucleotide transporter. N-ethylmaleimide and atractyloside inhibit (⊖) the indicated systems.

driven by the proton gradient. It is believed that active uptake of Ca^{2+} by mitochondria is facilitated by the membrane potential rather than by exchange with an ion of opposite charge.

Action of Ionophores

These substances are so termed because of their ability to complex specific cations and thus to facilitate cation transport through biologic membranes (Fig 31-17. This property of ionophoresis is due to their lipophilic character, which allows penetration of lipoid membranes such as the mitochondrial membrane. An example is the antibiotic **valinomycin,** which allows penetration of K^+ through the mitochondrial membrane and then discharges the membrane potential between the inside and the outside of the mitochondrion. **Nigericin** also acts as an ionophore for K^+ but in exchange for H^+. It therefore abolishes the pH gradient across the membrane. In the presence of both valinomycin and nigericin, both the membrane potential and the pH gradient are eliminated, and phosphorylation is therefore completely inhibited. The classic uncouplers such as dinitrophenol are, in fact, proton ionophores.

• • •

References

Baltscheffsky H, Baltscheffsky M: Electron transport phosphorylation. *Annu Rev Biochem* 1974;**43**:871.

Boyd GS, Smellie RMS (editors): *Biological Hydroxylation Mechanisms.* Academic Press, 1972.

Boyer PD & others: Oxidative phosphorylation and photophosphorylation. *Annu Rev Biochem* 1977;**46**:955.

Crane FL: Hydroquinone dehydrogenases. *Annu Rev Biochem* 1977;**46**:439.

DePierre JW, Ernster L: Enzyme topology of intracellular membranes. *Annu Rev Biochem* 1977;**46**:201.

Fleisher S, Packer L (editors): Biological oxidations, microsomal, cytochrome P-450, and other hemoprotein systems. In: *Methods in Enzymology.* Vol 52. Biomembranes, part C. Academic Press, 1978.

Friedovich I: Superoxide dismutases. *Annu Rev Biochem* 1975; **44**:147.

Gunsalus IC, Pederson TC, Sligar SG: Oxygenase-catalyzed biological hydroxylations. *Annu Rev Biochem* 1975;**44**:377.

Harper HA, Rodwell VW, Mayes PA: Page 276 in: *Review of Physiological Chemistry,* 17th ed. Lange, 1979.

Hayaishi O (editor): *Oxygenases.* Academic Press, 1972.

Hinkle PC, McCarty RE: How cells make ATP. *Sci Am* (March) 1978;**238**:104.

LaNoue KF, Schoolwerth AC: Metabolite transport in mitochondria. *Annu Rev Biochem* 1979;**48**:871.

Lehninger AL: *The Mitochondrion.* Benjamin, 1964.

Lemberg R, Barrett J: *Cytochromes.* Academic Press, 1973.

Lovenberg W (editor): *Iron-Sulfur Proteins.* 2 vols. Academic Press, 1973.

Mitchell P: *Chemiosmotic Coupling and Energy Transduction.* Glynn Research, Bodmin, United Kingdom, 1968.

Mitchell P: Keilin's respiratory chain concept and its chemiosmotic consequences. *Science* 1979;**206**:1148.

Racker E: From Pasteur to Mitchell: A hundred years of bioenergetics. *Fed Proc* 1980;**39**:210.

Salemme FR: Structure and function of cytochromes c. *Annu Rev Biochem* 1977;**46**:299.

Schenkman JB, Jansson I, Robie-Suh KM: The many roles of cytochrome b_5 in hepatic microsomes. *Life Sci* 1976;**19**:611.

Singer TP (editor): *Biological Oxidations.* Interscience, 1968.

Sund H (editor): *Pyridine Nucleotide Dependent Dehydrogenases.* Springer, 1970.

Wainio WW: *The Mammalian Mitochondrial Respiratory Chain.* Academic Press, 1970.

White RE, Coon MJ: Oxygen activation by cytochrome P-450. *Annu Rev Biochem* 1980;**49**:315.

Carbohydrates | 13

Peter A. Mayes, PhD, DSc

The carbohydrates are widely distributed both in animal and in plant tissues. In plants, they are produced by photosynthesis and include the cellulose of the plant framework as well as the starch of the plant cells. In animal cells, carbohydrate in the form of glucose and glycogen serves as an important source of energy for vital activities. Some carbohydrates have highly specific functions (eg, ribose in the nucleoprotein of the cells, galactose in certain lipids and the lactose of milk).

Carbohydrates may be defined chemically as aldehyde or ketone derivatives of the polyhydric (more than one OH group) alcohols or as compounds that yield these derivatives on hydrolysis.

Classification

(1) **Monosaccharides** (often called "simple sugars") are those carbohydrates that cannot be hydrolyzed into a simpler form. They may be subdivided into **trioses, tetroses, pentoses, hexoses,** or **heptoses,** depending upon the number of carbon atoms they possess; and as **aldoses** or **ketoses,** depending upon whether the aldehyde or ketone group is present. Examples are:

		Aldoses	Ketoses
Trioses	$(C_3H_6O_3)$	Glycerose	Dihydroxyacetone
Tetroses	$(C_4H_8O_4)$	Erythrose	Erythrulose
Pentoses	$(C_5H_{10}O_5)$	Ribose	Ribulose
Hexoses	$(C_6H_{12}O_6)$	Glucose	Fructose

(2) **Disaccharides** yield 2 molecules of the same or of different monosaccharide(s) when hydrolyzed. Examples are sucrose, lactose, and maltose.

(3) **Oligosaccharides** yield 3–6 monosaccharide units on hydrolysis. Maltotriose* is an example.

(4) **Polysaccharides** yield more than 6 molecules of monosaccharides on hydrolysis. Examples of polysaccharides, which may be linear or branched, are the starches and dextrins. These are sometimes designated as hexosans, pentosans, homopolysaccharides, or heteropolysaccharides depending upon the identity of the monosaccharides they yield on hydrolysis.

Structure of Glucose

Glucose is the principal sugar in blood, serving

*Note that this is not a true triose but a trisaccharide containing 3 α-glucose residues.

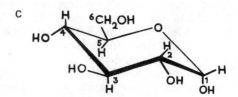

Figure 13–1. α-D-Glucose.

the tissues as a major metabolic fuel. Although the straight chain structural formula (aldohexose, Fig 13–1[A]) can account for some of its properties, a cyclic structure is favored on thermodynamic grounds and accounts completely for its chemical properties. For most purposes, the structural formula may be represented as a simple ring in perspective as proposed by Haworth (Fig 13–1[B]). X-ray diffraction analysis shows that the 6-membered ring containing one oxygen atom is actually in the form of a chair (Fig 13–1[C]).

Isomerism

Compounds that have the same structural formula but differ in spatial configuration are known as **stereoisomers.** The presence of asymmetric carbon atoms (carbon atoms attached to 4 different atoms or groups) allows the formation of isomers. The number of possible isomers of a compound depends on the

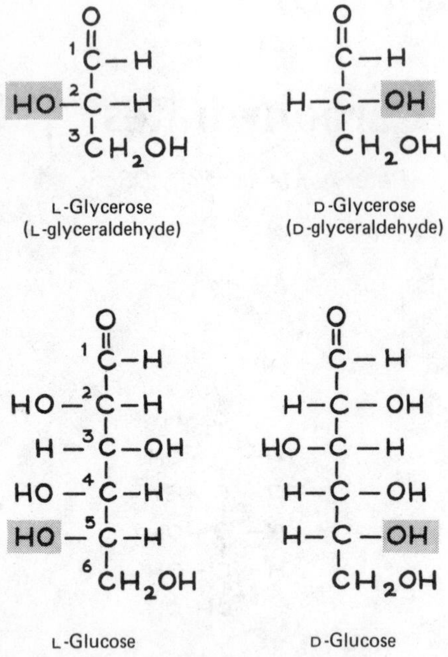

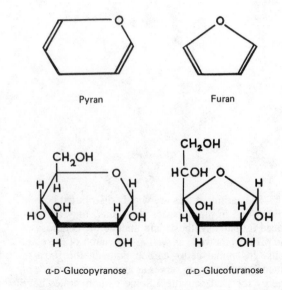

L-Glycerose
(L-glyceraldehyde)

D-Glycerose
(D-glyceraldehyde)

Pyran

Furan

L-Glucose

D-Glucose

Figure 13–2. D- and L-isomerism of glycerose and glucose.

α-D-Glucopyranose

α-D-Glucofuranose

Figure 13–3. Pyranose and furanose forms of glucose.

number of asymmetric carbon atoms (n) and is equal to 2^n. Glucose, with 4 asymmetric carbon atoms, therefore has 16 isomers. The more important types of isomerism found with glucose are as follows:

(1) D and L: The designation of an isomer as D- or of its mirror image as the L- form is determined by its spatial relationship to the parent compound of the carbohydrate family, the 3-carbon sugar glycerose. The L and D forms of this sugar are shown in Fig 13–2 together with the corresponding isomers of glucose. The orientation of the H and OH groups around the carbon atom **adjacent** to the terminal primary alcohol carbon (eg, carbon atom 5 in glucose) determines whether the sugar belongs to the D or L series. When the OH group on this carbon is on the right, the sugar is a member of the D series; when it is on the left, it is a member of the L series. Most of the monosaccharides occurring in mammalian metabolism are of the D configuration.

The presence of asymmetric carbon atoms also confers **optical activity** on the compound. When a beam of plane-polarized light is passed through a solution of an **optical isomer,** it will be rotated either to the right, dextrorotatory (+), or to the left, levorotatory (−). A compound may be designated D(−), D(+), L(−), or L(+), indicating structural relationship to D or L glycerose but not necessarily exhibiting the same optical rotation. For example, the naturally occurring form of fructose is the D(−) isomer.

When equal amounts of D and L isomers are present, the resulting mixture has no optical activity since the activities of each isomer cancel one another. Such a mixture is said to be a **racemic,** or DL mixture. Synthetically produced compounds are necessarily

racemic because the opportunities for the formation of each optical isomer are identical.

(2) Pyranose and Furanose Ring Structures: On the basis of the ring structures known to exist in glycosides (see below), Haworth proposed similar structures for the sugars. The terminology was based on the fact that the stable ring structures of monosaccharides are similar to the ring structures of either pyran or furan (Fig 13–3). Ketoses may also show ring formation (eg, D-fructofuranose or D-fructopyranose) (Fig 13–4). In the case of glucose in solution, more than 99% is in the pyranose form.

(3) α and β Anomers: The ring structure of an aldose is a hemiacetal, since it is formed by combination of an aldehyde and an alcohol group (Fig 13–5).

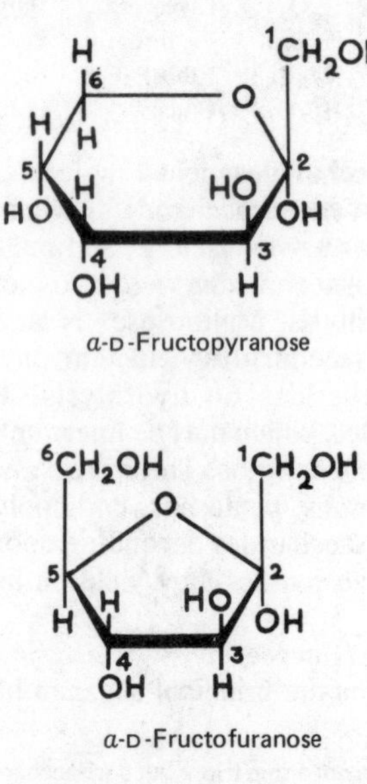

α-D-Fructopyranose

α-D-Fructofuranose

Figure 13–4. Pyranose and furanose forms of fructose.

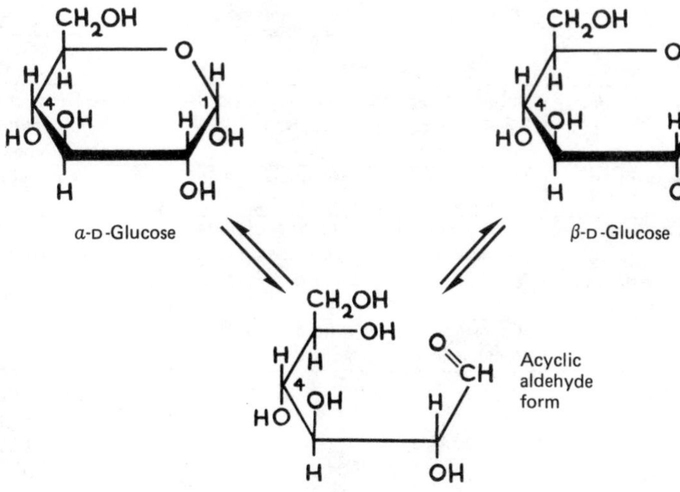

Figure 13–5. Mutarotation of glucose.

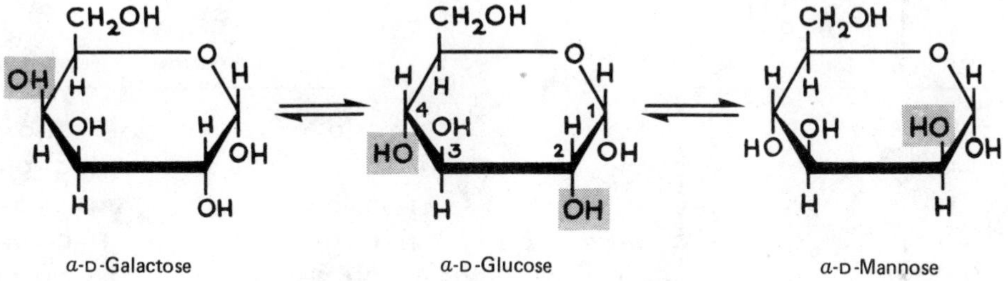

Figure 13–6. Epimerization of glucose.

Similarly, the ring structure of a ketose is a hemiketal. The cyclic structure of glucose is retained in solution, but isomerism takes place about position 1, the carbonyl or anomeric carbon atom, to give a mixture of α- and β-glucose. This equilibration is accompanied by optical rotation (**mutarotation**) as the hemiacetal ring opens and reforms with change of position of the –H and –OH groups on carbon 1. The change probably takes place via a hydrated straight-chain acyclic molecule, although polarography has indicated that glucose exists only to the extent of 0.0025% in the acyclic form.

(**4**) **Epimers:** Isomers differing as a result of variations in configuration of the –OH and –H on carbon atoms 2, 3, and 4 of glucose are known as epimers. Biologically, the most important epimers of glucose are mannose and galactose, formed by epimerization at carbons 2 and 4, respectively (Fig 13–6).

(**5**) **Aldose-Ketose Isomerism:** Fructose has the same molecular formula as glucose but differs in its structural formula since there is a potential keto group in position 2, whereas there is a potential aldehyde group in position 1 of glucose (Figs 13–3 and 13–4).

MONOSACCHARIDES

The monosaccharides include trioses, tetroses, pentoses, hexoses, and heptoses (3, 4, 5, 6, 7 carbon atoms). Derivatives of trioses are formed in the course of the metabolic breakdown of glucose by the glycolysis pathway, while derivatives of trioses, tetroses, pentoses, and of a 7-carbon sugar, sedoheptulose, are formed in the breakdown of glucose via the hexose monophosphate shunt. Pentose sugars are important constituents of nucleotides, nucleic acids, and many coenzymes (Table 13–1). Of the hexoses, glucose, galactose, fructose, and mannose are physiologically the most important (Table 13–2).

The structures of the aldo sugars are shown in Fig 13–7. Five keto sugars which are important in metabolism are shown in Fig 13–8.

HEXOSES

The hexoses are most important physiologically (Table 13–2). Examples are D-glucose, D-fructose,

Table 13—1. Examples of pentoses.

Sugar	Where Found	Importance	Reactions
D-Ribose	Nucleic acids.	Structural elements of nucleic acids and coenzymes, eg, ATP, NAD, NADP (DPN, TPN), flavoproteins.	Reduces Benedict's, Fehling's, Barfoed's, and Haynes' solutions. Forms distinctive osazones with phenylhydrazine.
D-Ribulose	Formed in metabolic processes.	Intermediates in hexose monophosphate shunt.	Those of keto sugars.
D-Arabinose	Gum arabic. Plum and cherry gums.	These sugars are used in studies of bacterial metabolism, as in fermentation tests for identification of bacteria.	With orcinol-HCl reagent gives colors: violet, blue, red, and green.
D-Xylose	Wood gums, proteoglycans, glycosaminoglycans.		With phloroglucinol-HCl gives a red color.
D-Lyxose	Heart muscle.	A constituent of a lyxoflavin isolated from human heart muscle.	

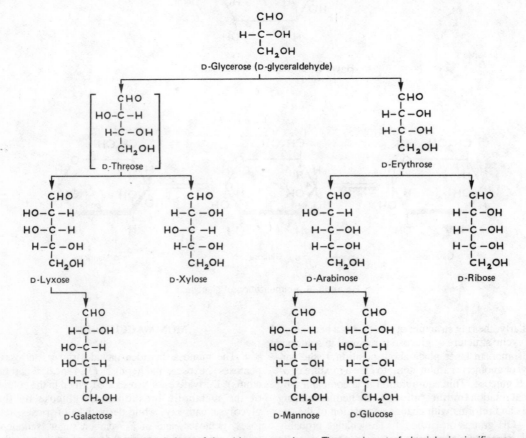

Figure 13—7. The structural relations of the aldoses, D series. D-Threose is not of physiologic significance.

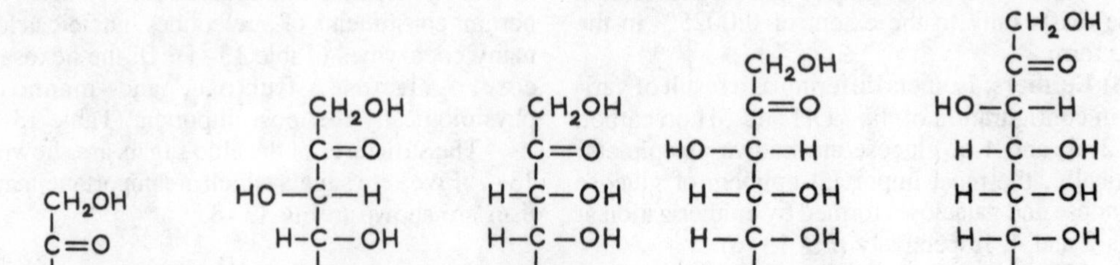

Figure 13—8. Examples of ketoses.

Table 13—2. Hexoses of physiologic importance.

Sugar	Source	Importance	Reactions
D-Glucose	Fruit juices. Hydrolysis of starch, cane sugar, maltose, and lactose.	The "sugar" of the body. The sugar carried by the blood, and the principal one used by the tissues. Glucose is usually the "sugar" of the urine when glycosuria occurs.	Reduces Benedict's, Haynes', Barfoed's reagents (a reducing sugar). Gives osazone with phenylhydrazine. Fermented by yeast. With HNO_3, forms soluble saccharic acid.
D-Fructose	Fruit juices. Honey. Hydrolysis of cane sugar and of inulin (from the Jerusalem artichoke).	Can be changed to glucose in the liver and intestine and so used in the body.	Reduces Benedict's, Haynes', Barfoed's reagents (a reducing sugar). Forms osazone identical with that of glucose. Fermented by yeast. Cherry-red color with Seliwanoff's resorcinol-HCl reagent.
D-Galactose	Hydrolysis of lactose.	Can be changed to glucose in the liver and metabolized. Synthesized in the mammary gland to make the lactose of milk. A constituent of glycolipids and glycoproteins.	Reduces Benedict's, Haynes', Barfoed's reagents (a reducing sugar). Forms osazone, distinct from above. Phloroglucinol-HCl reagent gives red color. With HNO_3, forms insoluble mucic acid. Not fermented by yeast.
D-Mannose	Hydrolysis of plant mannosans and gums.	A constituent of prosthetic polysaccharide of albumins, globulins, mucoproteins. A sugar frequently occurring in glycoproteins.	Reduces Benedict's, Haynes', Barfoed's reagents (a reducing sugar). Forms same osazone as glucose.

D-galactose, and D-mannose. Of additional significance are carboxylic acid derivatives of glucose such as D-glucuronate (important in glucuronide formation and present in glycosaminoglycans) and its metabolic derivatives, L-iduronate (present in glycosaminoglycans) and L-gulonate (a member of the uronic acid pathway; see p 180).

GLYCOSIDES

Glycosides are compounds formed from a condensation between a monosaccharide, or monosaccharide residue, and the hydroxyl group of a second compound that may, or may not (in the case of an **aglycone**), be another monosaccharide. The **glycosidic bond** is an **acetal** link because it results from a reaction between a hemiacetal group (formed from an aldehyde and an –OH group) and another –OH group. If the hemiacetal portion is glucose, the resulting compound is a **glucoside;** if galactose, a **galactoside,** etc.

A simple example is the methyl glucoside formed when a solution of glucose in boiling methyl alcohol is treated with 0.5% hydrogen chloride as a catalyst. The reaction proceeds with the formation of anomeric α- and β-glucosides (Fig 13–9).

Glycosides are found in many drugs and spices and in the constituents of animal tissues. The aglycone may be methanol, glycerol, a sterol, or a phenol. The glycosides which are important in medicine because of their action on the heart (**cardiac glycosides**) all contain steroids as the aglycone component. These include derivatives of digitalis and strophanthus such as ouabain, an inhibitor of the Na^+-K^+-ATPase of cell membranes. Other glycosides include antibiotics such as streptomycin (Fig 13–10).

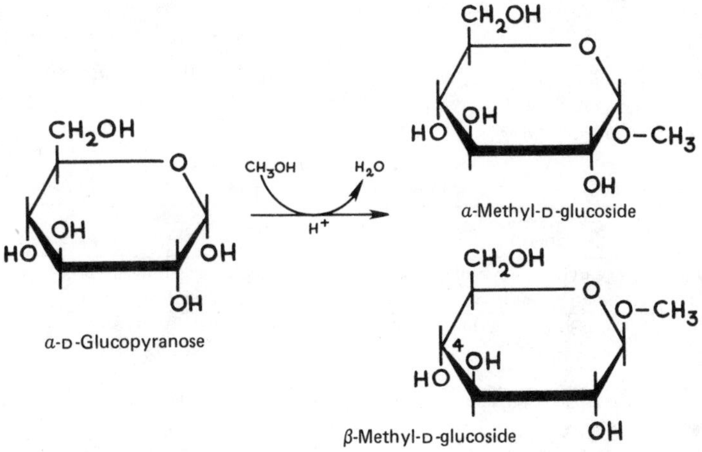

Figure 13–9. Formation of methyl glucosides.

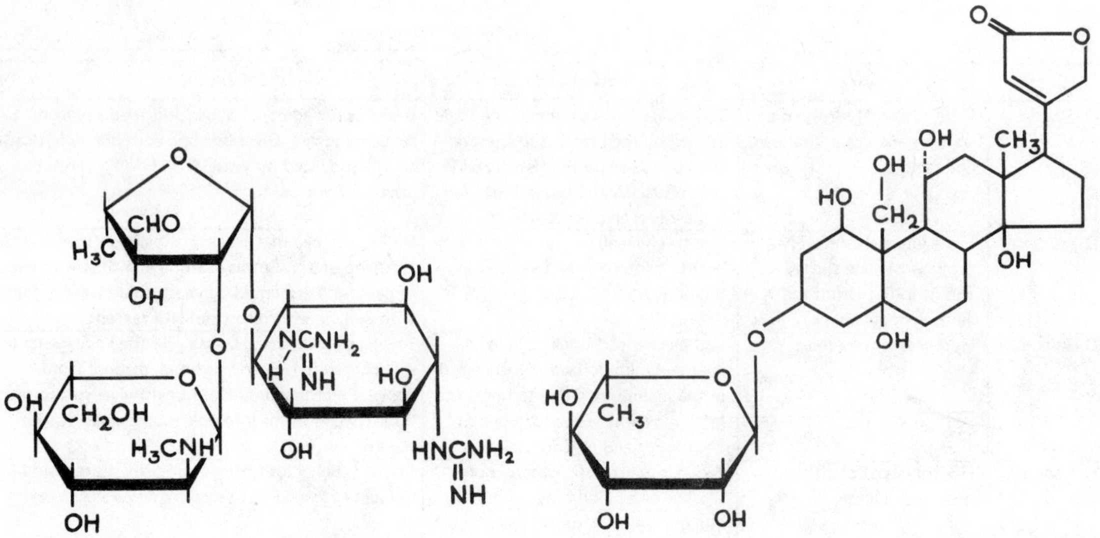

Figure 13–10. Streptomycin *(left)* and ouabain *(right)*.

DEOXY SUGARS

Deoxy sugars are those in which a hydroxyl group attached to the ring structure has been replaced by a hydrogen atom. They are obtained on hydrolysis of certain substances that are important in biologic processes. An example is the deoxyribose occurring in nucleic acids (DNA).

Also found as a carbohydrate of glycoproteins is L-fucose (see p 150), and of importance as an inhibitor of glucose metabolism is 2-deoxyglucose.

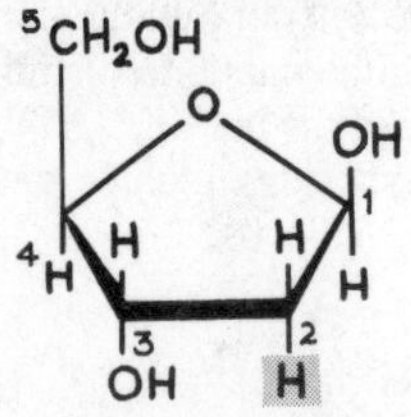

AMINO SUGARS (HEXOSAMINES)

Sugars containing an amino group are called **amino sugars.** Examples are D-glucosamine, D-galactosamine, and D-mannosamine, all of which have been identified in nature. Glucosamine is a constituent of hyaluronic acid. Galactosamine (chondrosamine) is a constituent of chondroitin. (See Chapter 32.)

Several antibiotics (erythromycin, carbomycin) contain amino sugars. Erythromycin contains a dimethylamino sugar. Carbomycin contains the first

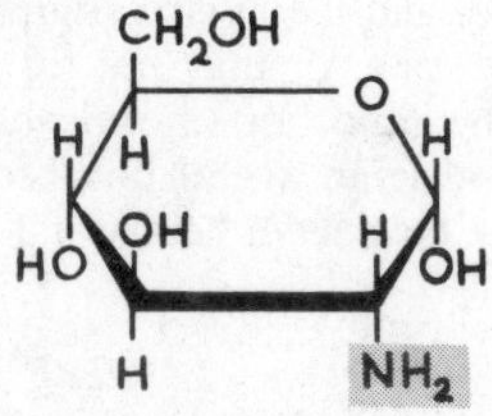

Figure 13–11. 2-Deoxy-D-ribofuranose (β form).

Figure 3–12. Glucosamine (2-amino-D-glucopyranose) (α form).

Table 13–3. Disaccharides.

Sugar	Source	Reactions
Maltose	Digestion by amylase or hydrolysis of starch. Germinating cereals and malt.	Reducing sugar. Forms osazone with phenylhydrazine. Fermentable. Hydrolyzed to D-glucose.
Lactose	Milk. May occur in urine during pregnancy.	Reducing sugar. Forms osazone with phenylhydrazine. Not fermentable by yeasts. Hydrolyzed to glucose and galactose.
Sucrose	Cane and beet sugar. Sorghum. Pineapple. Carrot roots.	Nonreducing sugar. Does not form osazone. Fermentable. Hydrolyzed to fructose and glucose.
Trehalose	Fungi and yeasts. The major sugar of insect hemolymph.	Nonreducing sugar. Does not form an osazone. Hydrolyzed to glucose.

known 3-amino sugar, 3-amino-D-ribose. The amino sugars are believed to be related to the antibiotic activity of these drugs.

DISACCHARIDES

The disaccharides are sugars composed of 2 monosaccharide residues united by a glycosidic linkage (Fig 13–13). They are named chemically according to the structures of their component monosaccharides. The suffix **-furan** or **-pyran** refers to the structural resemblances to these compounds. The physiologically important disaccharides are maltose, sucrose, lactose, and trehalose (Table 13–3).

Since sucrose has no potential carbonyl group, as the anomeric carbon atoms in both glucose and fructose residues are joined together through the acetal bond linking the 2 residues, it gives none of the reactions characteristic of "reducing" sugars. Thus, it fails to reduce alkaline copper solutions, form an osazone, or exhibit mutarotation. Hydrolysis of sucrose yields a crude mixture often called "invert sugar" because the strongly levorotatory fructose thus produced changes (inverts) the previous dextrorotatory action of the sucrose. Trehalose is also a nonreducing sugar, for similar reasons.

POLYSACCHARIDES

Polysaccharides include the following physiologically important substances:

Starch is formed of an α-glucosidic chain. Such a compound, yielding only glucose on hydrolysis, is called a **glucosan** or **glucan.** It is the most important food source of carbohydrate and is found in cereals, potatoes, legumes, and other vegetables. Natural starch is insoluble in water and gives a blue color with iodine solution. The microscopic form of the granules is characteristic of the source of the starch. The 2 chief constituents are **amylose** (15–20%), which is a nonbranching helical structure responsible for the color with iodine (Fig 13–14), and **amylopectin** (80–85%), which consists of branched chains that give only a red color with iodine because they do not coil effectively. Each chain is composed of 24–30 glucose residues. The glucose residues are united by 1→4 linkages in the chains and by 1→6 linkages at the branch points.

Glycogen is the storage polysaccharide of the animal body. It is often called animal starch. It is a more highly branched structure than amylopectin with chains of 11-18-α-D-glucopyranose residues (in $\alpha[1{\to}4]$-glucosidic linkage) with branching by means of $\alpha(1{\to}6)$-glucosidic bonds. Glycogen is nonreducing and gives a red color with iodine (Fig 13–15).

Figure 13–13 (at right). Structures of representative disaccharides. $-\alpha$ and $-\beta$ refer to the configuration at the anomeric carbon atom (*).

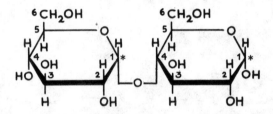

MALTOSE (a FORM)

O-a-D-Glucopyranosyl-(1→4)-a-D-glucopyranoside

SUCROSE

O-a-D-Glucopyranosyl-(1→2)-β-D-fructofuranoside

LACTOSE (β FORM)

O-β-D-Galactopyranosyl-(1→4)-β-D-glucopyranoside

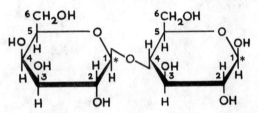

TREHALOSE (a FORM)

O-a-D-Glucopyranosyl-(1→1)-a-D-glucopyranoside

CELLOBIOSE

O-β-D-Glucopyranosyl-(1→4)-β-D-glucopyranoside

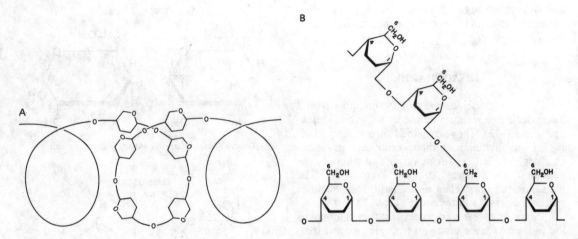

Figure 13–14. Structure of starch. *A:* Amylose, showing helical coil structure. *B:* Amylopectin, showing 1:6 branch point.

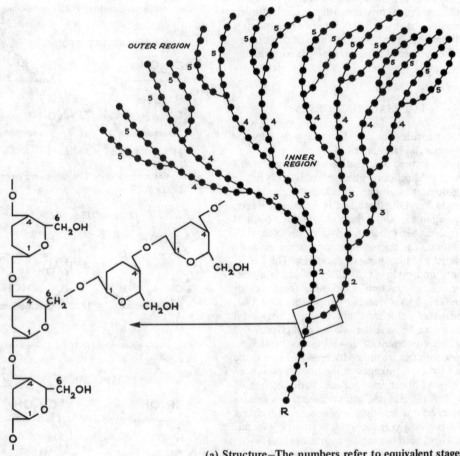

(b) Enlargement of structure at a branch point.

(a) Structure—The numbers refer to equivalent stages in the growth of the macromolecule. R, primary glucose residue with free reducing-CHO group (carbon No. 1). The branching is more variable than shown, the ratio of 1,4 to 1,6 bonds being from 12 to 18.

Figure 13–15. The glycogen molecule.

Inulin is a starch found in tubers and roots of dahlias, artichokes, and dandelions. It is hydrolyzable to fructose, and hence it is a fructosan. No color is given when iodine is added to inulin solutions. This starch is easily soluble in warm water. It is used in physiologic investigation for determination of the rate of glomerular filtration.

Dextrins are substances formed in the course of the hydrolytic breakdown of starch. The partially digested starches are amorphous. Limit dextrins that give a red color when tested with iodine are first formed as hydrolysis reaches a certain degree of branching. These are called **erythrodextrins.** As hydrolysis proceeds, the iodine color is no longer produced. These are the so-called **achroodextrins.** Finally, only reducing sugars will appear.

Cellulose is the chief constituent of the framework of plants. It gives no color with iodine and is not soluble in ordinary solvents. It consists of long, straight chains of β-D-glucopyranose units linked by β (1→4) bonds. It is not subject to attack by the digestive enzymes of humans because of the β-linkage. Thus, it is an important source of ''bulk'' in the diet.

Chitin is an important structural polysaccharide of invertebrates. It is found, for example, in the shells of crustaceans and exoskeletons of insects. Structurally, chitin consists of N-acetyl-D-glucosamine units joined by $\beta(1→4)$-glucosidic linkages (Fig 13–16).

Glycosaminoglycans (mucopolysaccharides) consist of chains of complex carbohydrates characterized by their content of amino sugars and uronic acids. When these chains are attached to a protein molecule, the compound is known as a **proteoglycan.** As the ground or packing substance, they are associated with the structural elements of the tissues such as bone, elastin, and collagen. Their property of holding large quantities of water and occupying space, thus cushioning or lubricating other structures, is assisted by the large number of –OH groups and negative charges on the molecules, which, by repulsion, keep the carbohydrate chains apart. Examples are shown in Fig 13–16, and all are discussed in detail in Chapter 32.

Glycoproteins (mucoproteins) occur in many different situations in fluids and tissues, including the cell membranes (see Chapters 31 and 32 for detailed discussions). They are proteins containing carbohydrates in varying amounts attached as short or long (up to 15 units) branched or unbranched chains. Constituent carbohydrates include

Hexoses
Mannose (Man)   Galactose (Gal)
Acetyl hexosamines
N-Acetylglucosamine   N-Acetylgalactosamine
(GlcNAc)   (GalNAc)
Pentoses
Arabinose (Ara)   Xylose (Xyl)
Methyl pentose
L-Fucose (Fuc; see Fig 13–18)
Sialic acids
N-Acyl derivatives of neuraminic acid, eg, N-acetyl-neuraminic acid (Nana; see Fig 13–17).

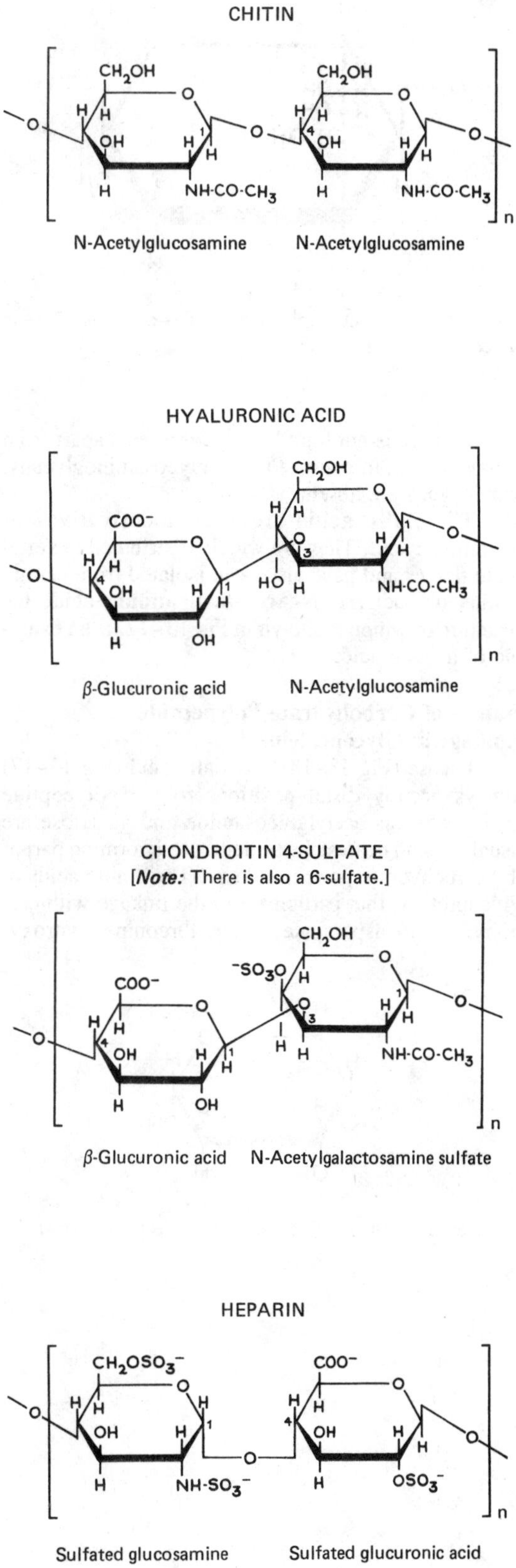

CHITIN

N-Acetylglucosamine   N-Acetylglucosamine

HYALURONIC ACID

β-Glucuronic acid   N-Acetylglucosamine

CHONDROITIN 4-SULFATE
[*Note:* There is also a 6-sulfate.]

β-Glucuronic acid   N-Acetylgalactosamine sulfate

HEPARIN

Sulfated glucosamine   Sulfated glucuronic acid

Figure 13–16. Structure of some complex polysaccharides (glycosaminoglycans).

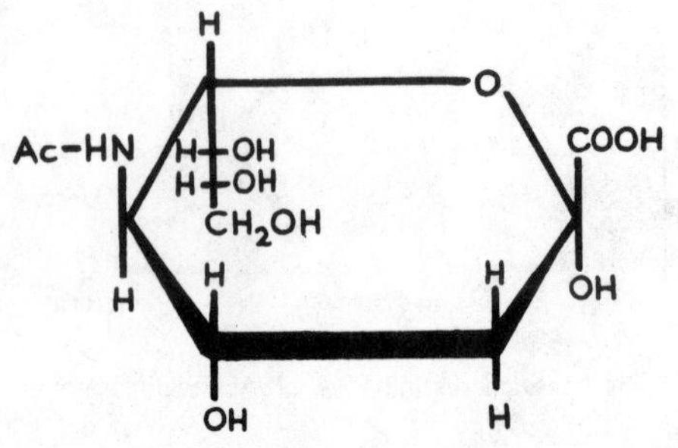

Figure 13-17. Structure of sialic acids. (Ac = CH$_3$–CO– in N-acetylneuraminic acid.)

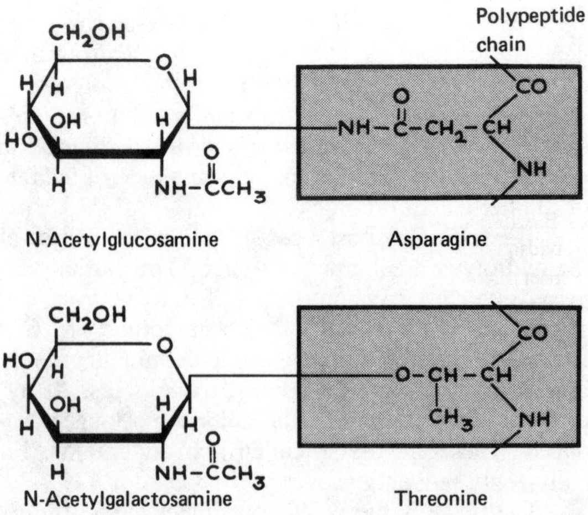

Figure 13-19. Types of linkage between carbohydrate and amino acid residues in glycoproteins.

Glucose is not found in glycoproteins apart from collagen, and, in contrast to the glycosaminoglycans, uronic acids are absent.

The **sialic acids** are N-acyl derivatives of neuraminic acid. They are widely distributed in vertebrate tissues and have also been isolated from certain strains of bacteria. **N-Acetylneuraminic acid,** the structure of which is shown in Fig 13–17, is an example of a sialic acid.

Nature of Carbohydrate-Polypeptide Linkage in Glycoproteins

Fucose (Fig 13–18) and sialic acid (Fig 13–17) always occupy distal positions to the polypeptide chain, whereas acetylglucosamine and galactose are usually found nearest the protein, often forming part of the carbohydrate-protein linkage. The amino acids of glycoproteins that participate in the linkage with carbohydrate are asparagine, serine, threonine, hydroxy-

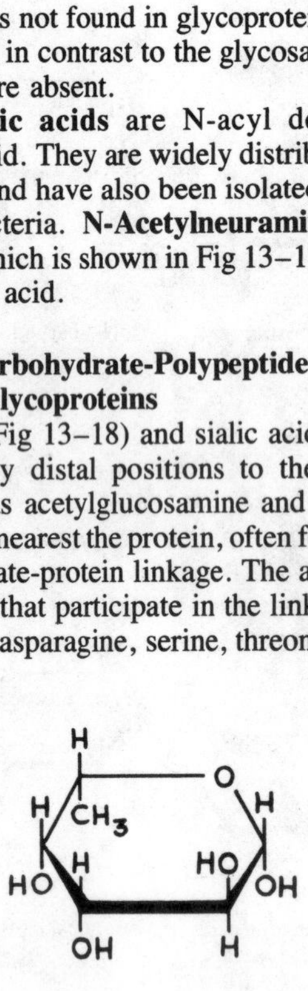

lysine, and hydroxyproline. Two examples are shown in Fig 13–19.

CARBOHYDRATES OF CELL MEMBRANES

The lipid structure of the cell membrane is described in Chapters 16 and 31. However, analysis of mammalian cell membrane components indicates that approximately 5% are carbohydrates, present in glycoproteins and glycolipids. Their presence on the outer surface of the plasma membrane has been shown with the use of plant **lectins,** protein agglutinins that bind specifically with certain glycosyl residues. For example, **concanavalin A** has a specificity towards α-glucosyl and α-mannosyl residues.

Glycophorin is a major integral membrane glycoprotein of human erythrocytes. It has 130 amino acid residues and spans the lipid membrane, having free polypeptide portions outside both the external and internal (cytoplasmic) surfaces. Carbohydrate chains are only attached to the N-terminal portion outside the external surface, via asparagine, serine, and threonine residues (see Chapter 31).

Figure 13-18. β-L-Fucose (6-deoxy-β-L-galactose).

• • •

References

Advances in Carbohydrate Chemistry. Academic Press, 1945–current.

Conn EE, Stumpf PK: *Outlines of Biochemistry,* 4th ed. Wiley, 1976.

Cook GMW, Stoddart RW: *Surface Carbohydrates of the Eukaryotic Cell.* Academic Press, 1973.

Davidson EA: *Carbohydrate Chemistry.* Holt, 1967.

Ferrier RJ, Collins PM: *Monosaccharide Chemistry.* Penguin Books, 1972.

Florkin M, Stotz E: *Comprehensive Biochemistry; Carbohydrates.* Section 2, vol 5. Elsevier, 1963.

Hughes RC: The complex carbohydrates of mammalian cell surfaces and their biological roles. *Essays Biochem* 1975;**11:**1.

Lindahl U, Höök M: Glycosaminoglycans and their binding to biological macromolecules. *Annu Rev Biochem* 1978;**47:**385.

McGilvery RW: *Biochemistry.* Saunders, 1979.

Percival EGV, Percival E: *Structural Carbohydrate Chemistry.* Prentice-Hall, 1962.

Pigman WW, Horton D (editors): *The Carbohydrates.* Vols 1A and 1B. Academic Press, 1972.

Sharon N: Lectins. *Sci Am* (June) 1977;**236:**108.

West ES.& others: *Textbook of Biochemistry,* 4th ed. Macmillan, 1966.

White A & others: *Principles of Biochemistry,* 6th ed. McGraw-Hill, 1978.

14 | The Citric Acid Cycle–The Catabolism of Acetyl-CoA

Peter A. Mayes, PhD, DSc

The citric acid cycle (Krebs cycle, tricarboxylic acid cycle) is a series of reactions in mitochondria that bring about the catabolism of acetyl residues, liberating hydrogen equivalents, which, upon oxidation, lead to the release of most of the free energy of tissue fuels. The acetyl residues are in the form of **acetyl–CoA** (CH_3–CO~S–CoA, active acetate), an ester of coenzyme A (see Chapter 10) which with other acyl thio esters of CoA is classified as a high-energy compound.

An Overview of Acetyl-CoA Metabolism

Acetyl-CoA is at the confluence of the major metabolic pathways (Fig 14–1). Nearly all carbohydrate and fat molecules form acetyl-CoA during oxidative catabolism, as do many of the amino acids resulting from the degradation of proteins. In addition, acetyl-CoA serves as the source of acetyl units in the anabolic processes responsible for the synthesis of long chain fatty acids, cholesterol and other steroids, and ketone bodies (acetoacetate, β-hydroxybutyrate, and acetone). These metabolic pathways will be the subjects of following chapters. The present chapter is concerned solely with the catabolism of acetyl-CoA and the role of the citric acid cycle.

Significance of the Citric Acid Cycle

Essentially, the cycle comprises the combination of a molecule of acetyl-CoA with the 4-carbon dicarboxylic acid oxaloacetate, resulting in the formation of a **6-carbon tricarboxylic acid, citrate.** There follows a series of reactions in the course of which 2 molecules of CO_2 are lost and oxaloacetate is regenerated (Fig 14–2). Since only a small quantity of oxaloacetate is able to facilitate the conversion of a large quantity of acetyl units to CO_2, oxaloacetate may be considered to play a **catalytic role.**

The major function of the cycle is to act as the final common pathway for the oxidation of carbohydrate, lipids, and protein, since glucose, fatty acids, and many amino acids are all metabolized to acetyl-CoA (Figs 14–1 and 14–3). Furthermore, the citric acid cycle is the mechanism by which much of the free energy liberated during the oxidation of carbohydrate, lipids, and amino acids is made available. During the course of oxidation of acetyl-CoA in the cycle, reducing equivalents in the form of hydrogen or of electrons are formed as a result of the activity of specific dehydrogenases. These reducing equivalents then enter the respiratory chain, where large amounts of high-energy

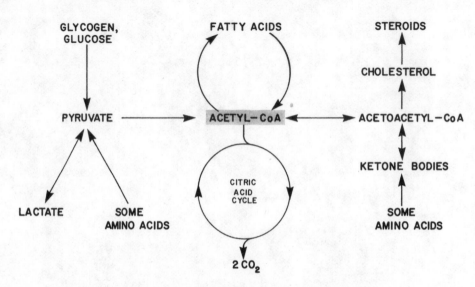

Figure 14–1. Overview of acetyl-CoA metabolism.

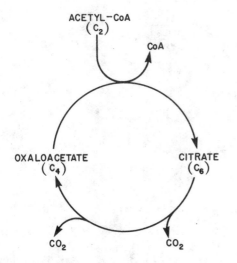

Figure 14–2. Citric acid cycle, illustrating the catalytic role of oxaloacetate.

Reactions of the Citric Acid Cycle (See Fig 14–4.)*

$$\text{Acetyl-CoA} + \text{Oxaloacetate} + H_2O \longrightarrow \text{Citrate} + \text{CoA} \cdot \text{SH}$$

The initial condensation of acetyl-CoA with oxaloacetate to form citrate is catalyzed by a condensing enzyme, **citrate synthase,** which effects a carbon-to-carbon bond between the methyl carbon of acetyl-CoA and the carbonyl carbon of oxaloacetate. The condensation reaction is followed by hydrolysis of the thioester bond of CoA, which is accompanied by considerable loss of free energy as heat, ensuring that the reaction goes to completion.

Citrate is converted to isocitrate by the enzyme **aconitase** (aconitate hydratase), which contains iron in the Fe^{2+} state. This conversion takes place in 2 steps: dehydration to *cis*-aconitate, some of which remains bound to the enzyme, and rehydration to isocitrate.

$$\text{Citrate} \xrightleftharpoons{\quad} \underset{H_2O}{\overset{\textit{Cis}\text{-aconitate}}{\text{(enzyme bound)}}} \xrightleftharpoons{\quad} \underset{H_2O}{\text{Isocitrate}}$$

phosphate are generated in the process of oxidative phosphorylation (Fig 14–3; see also Chapter 12).

It is noteworthy that the enzymes of the citric acid cycle are located in the **mitochondrial matrix,** either free or attached to the inner surface of the inner mitochondrial membrane, which facilitates the **transfer of reducing equivalents to the adjacent enzymes of the respiratory chain,** situated in the inner mitochondrial membrane.

It is of further significance that the citric acid cycle has a dual or **amphibolic** role, as it is a source of molecules for anabolic processes such as fatty acid and amino acid synthesis and gluconeogenesis.

Historical Aspects

By 1935, it was known that certain dicarboxylic and tricarboxylic acids were actively oxidized by respiring aerobic tissues. Szent-Györgyi had established that succinate was converted to oxaloacetate via fumarate and malate, and Martius and Knoop showed that succinate could be formed from citrate via α-ketoglutarate. In 1937, Krebs supplied a conceptual basis for these reactions by suggesting that they were arranged in a cyclic sequence termed the "citric acid cycle." Krebs came to this conclusion in the course of investigations on pigeon breast muscle, a very actively respiring tissue, in which he showed that oxidation of pyruvate or of endogenous carbohydrate was stimulated by only small amounts of citric acid cycle intermediates, ie, in a catalytic manner. In other experiments where malonate was added as an inhibitor of succinate dehydrogenase, it was noted that succinate accumulated after addition of pyruvate or any of the other intermediates of the citric acid cycle. The block in pyruvate utilization could be relieved by the addition of oxaloacetate on a mole-for-mole basis, thus establishing the existence of the initial condensation reaction that forms citrate.

The reaction is inhibited by the presence of **fluoroacetate,** which, in the form of fluoroacetyl-CoA, condenses with oxaloacetate to form fluorocitrate. The latter inhibits aconitase, causing citrate to accumulate.

Experiments using ^{14}C-labeled intermediates indicate that citrate reacts with aconitase in an asymmetric manner, with the result that aconitase always acts on that part of the citrate molecule that is derived from oxaloacetate. Ogston suggested that this was due to a 3-point attachment of the enzyme to the substrate. The 3-point attachment would enable aconitase to differentiate the two $-CH_2COOH$ groups in citrate, thus conferring asymmetry on an apparently symmetric molecule. However, the 3-point attachment hypothesis is not necessary to explain the asymmetric action of aconitase. It is now realized that the two $-CH_2COOH$ groups are not identical in space with respect to the $-OH$ and $-COOH$ groups. The consequences of the asymmetric action of aconitase may be appreciated by reference to the fate of labeled acetyl-CoA in the citric acid cycle as shown in Fig 14–4. It is possible that *cis*-aconitate may not be an obligatory intermediate between citrate and isocitrate but may in fact be a side branch from the main pathway.

Isocitrate undergoes dehydrogenation in the presence of **isocitrate dehydrogenase** to form oxalosuccinate. Three different enzymes have been described. One, which is NAD-specific, is found only in mitochondria. The other 2 enzymes are NADP-specific and are found in the mitochondria and the cytosol, respectively. Respiratory chain-linked oxida-

---

*From Circular No. 200 of the Committee of Editors of Biochemical Journals Recommendations (1975): "According to standard biochemical convention, the ending ate *in, eg, palmitate, denotes any mixture of free acid and the ionized form(s) (according to pH) in which the cations are not specified." The same convention is adopted in this text for all carboxylic acids.*

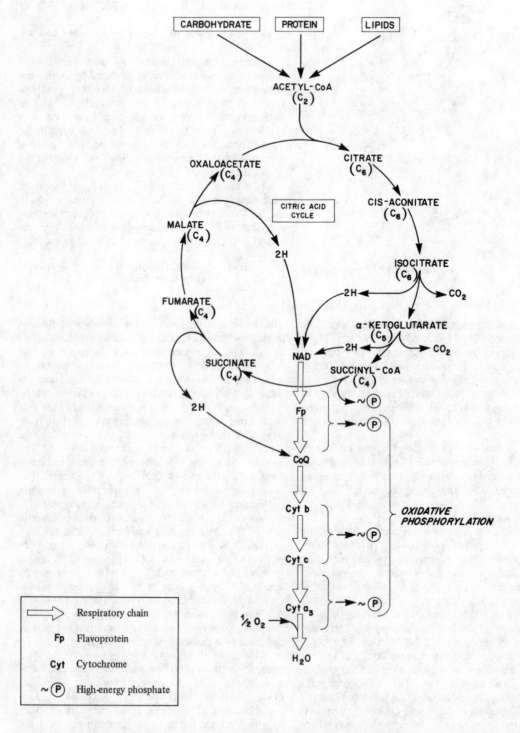

Figure 14–3. The citric acid cycle: the major catabolic pathway in aerobic organisms. The diagram shows how acetyl-CoA, the product of carbohydrate, protein, and lipid catabolism, is oxidized by the cycle to CO_2 with the release of reducing equivalents (2H). In turn, oxidation of 2H in the respiratory chain leads to coupled phosphorylation of ADP to ATP. For one turn of the cycle, 11 ~Ⓟ are generated via oxidative phosphorylation and one ~Ⓟ arises at substrate level from the conversion of succinyl-CoA to succinate.

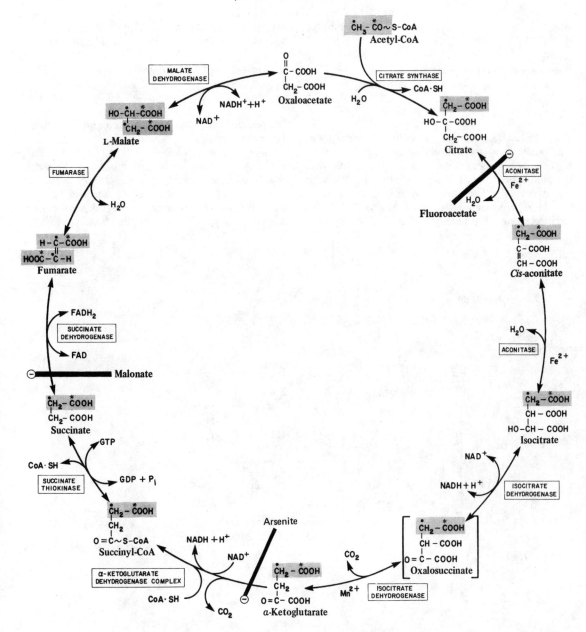

Figure 14–4. The citric acid (Krebs) cycle. Oxidation of NADH and FADH$_2$ in the respiratory chain leads to the generation of ATP via oxidative phosphorylation. In order to follow the passage of acetyl-CoA through the cycle, the 2 carbon atoms of the acetyl radical are shown labeled on the carboxyl carbon (using the designation [*]) and on the methyl carbon (using the designation [•]). Although 2 carbon atoms are lost as CO$_2$ in one revolution of the cycle, these particular atoms are not derived from the acetyl-CoA that has immediately entered the cycle but arise from that portion of the citrate molecule which was derived from oxaloacetate. However, on completion of a single turn of the cycle, the oxaloacetate that is regenerated is now labeled, which leads to labeled CO$_2$ being evolved during the second turn of the cycle. It is to be noted that because succinate is a symmetric compound and because succinate dehydrogenase does not differentiate between its 2 carboxyl groups, "randomization" of label occurs at this step such that all 4 carbon atoms of oxaloacetate appear to be labeled after one turn of the cycle. When gluconeogenesis takes place, some of the label in oxaloacetate makes its way into glucose and glycogen (see p 178). In this process, oxaloacetate is decarboxylated in the carboxyl group adjacent to the CH$_2$ group. As a result of recombination of the resulting 3-carbon residues in a process that is essentially a reversal of glycolysis, the eventual location of label from acetate in glucose (or glycogen) is distributed in a characteristic manner. Thus, if oxaloacetate leaves the citric acid cycle after only one turn from the entry of labeled acetyl-CoA (acetate), label from the carboxyl carbon of acetate is found in carbon atoms 3 and 4 of glucose, whereas label from the methyl carbon of acetate is found in carbon atoms 1, 2, 5, and 6. For a discussion of the stereochemical aspects of the citric acid cycle, see Greville (1968). The sites of inhibition (⊖) by fluoroacetate, malonate, and arsenite are indicated.

tion of isocitrate proceeds almost completely through the NAD-dependent enzyme.

Isocitrate + NAD$^+$ ⟷ Oxalosuccinate ⟷
(enzyme bound)

α-Ketoglutarate + CO$_2$ + NADH + H$^+$

There follows a decarboxylation to α-ketoglutarate, also catalyzed by isocitrate dehydrogenase. Mn^{2+} is an important component of the decarboxylation reaction. It would appear that oxalosuccinate remains bound to the enzyme as an intermediate in the overall reaction.

Next, α-ketoglutarate undergoes **oxidative decarboxylation** in a manner that is analogous to the

oxidative decarboxylation of pyruvate (see p 166), both substrates being α-keto acids (Fig 14–5).

α-Ketoglutarate + NAD$^+$ + CoA·SH ⟶

Succinyl-CoA + CO$_2$ + NADH + H$^+$

The reaction catalyzed by an α-**ketoglutarate dehydrogenase** complex also requires identical cofactors—eg, thiamin diphosphate, lipoate, NAD$^+$, FAD, and CoA—and results in the formation of succinyl-CoA, a thioester containing a high-energy bond. The equilibrium of this reaction is so much in favor of succinyl-CoA formation that the reaction must be considered as physiologically unidirectional. As in the

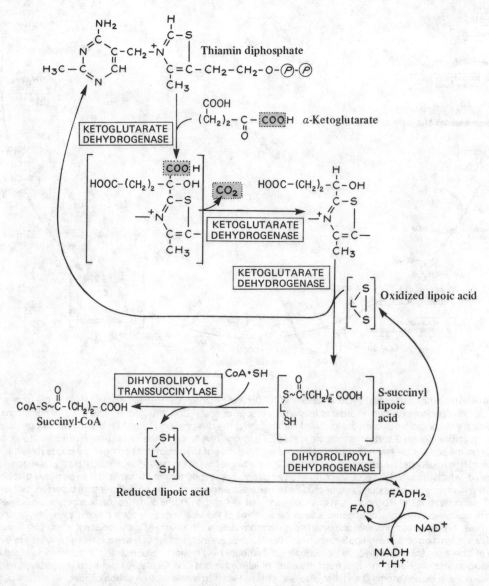

Figure 14–5. Oxidative decarboxylation of α-ketoglutarate. This series of reactions is analogous to those described for the oxidative decarboxylation of pyruvate, discussed in greater detail on p 165.

case of pyruvate oxidation (see p 165), arsenite inhibits the reaction, causing the substrate, α-**ketoglutarate,** to accumulate.

To continue the cycle, succinyl-CoA is converted to succinate by the enzyme **succinate thiokinase (succinyl-CoA synthetase).**

$$\text{Succinyl-CoA} + P_i + \text{GDP} \longleftrightarrow \text{Succinate} + \text{GTP} + \text{CoA·SH}$$

This reaction requires GDP or IDP, which is converted in the presence of inorganic phosphate to either GTP or ITP. This is the only example in the citric acid cycle of the **generation of a high-energy phosphate at the substrate level** and arises because the release of free energy from the oxidative decarboxylation of α-ketoglutarate is sufficient to generate a high-energy bond in addition to the formation of NADH (equivalent to $3 \sim \text{ⓟ}$). By means of a phosphokinase, ATP may be formed from either GTP or ITP,

$$\text{eg, GTP} + \text{ADP} \longleftrightarrow \text{GDP} + \text{ATP}$$

An alternative reaction in extrahepatic tissues, which is catalyzed by **succinyl-CoA-acetoacetate CoA transferase (thiophorase),** is the conversion of succinyl-CoA to succinate coupled with the conversion of acetoacetate to acetoacetyl-CoA. In liver there is also deacylase activity, causing some hydrolysis of succinyl-CoA to succinate plus CoA.

Succinate is metabolized further by undergoing a dehydrogenation followed by the addition of water, and subsequently by a further dehydrogenation which regenerates oxaloacetate.

$$\text{Succinate} + \text{FAD} \longleftrightarrow \text{Fumarate} + \text{FADH}_2$$

The first dehydrogenation reaction is catalyzed by **succinate dehydrogenase,** which is bound to the inner surface of the inner mitochondrial membrane. It is the only dehydrogenation in the citric acid cycle that involves the **direct transfer of hydrogen from the substrate to a flavoprotein without the participation of NAD.** The enzyme contains FAD and Fe:S protein. Fumarate is formed as a result of the dehydrogenation. Isotopic experiments have shown that the enzyme is stereospecific for the *trans* hydrogen atoms of the methylene carbons of succinate. Addition of malonate or oxaloacetate inhibits succinate dehydrogenase competitively, resulting in succinate accumulation.

Under the influence of **fumarase (fumarate hydratase),** water is added to fumarate to give malate.

$$\text{Fumarate} + H_2O \longleftrightarrow \text{L-Malate}$$

In addition to being specific for the L-isomer of malate, fumarase catalyzes the addition of the elements of water to the double bond of fumarate in the *trans* configuration. Malate is converted to oxaloacetate by **malate dehydrogenase,** a reaction requiring NAD⁺.

$$\text{L-Malate} + \text{NAD}^+ \longleftrightarrow \text{Oxaloacetate} + \text{NADH} + H^+$$

Although the equilibrium of this reaction is much in favor of malate, the net flux is toward the direction of oxaloacetate because this compound together with the other product of the reaction (NADH) is removed continuously in further reactions.

The enzymes participating in the citric acid cycle are also found outside the mitochondria except for the α-ketoglutarate and succinate dehydrogenases. While they may catalyze similar reactions, some of the enzymes, eg, malate dehydrogenase, may not in fact be the same proteins as the mitochondrial enzymes of the same name.

Energetics of the Citric Acid Cycle

As a result of oxidation catalyzed by dehydrogenase enzymes of the citric acid cycle, **3 molecules of NADH** and **one of FADH₂** are produced for each molecule of acetyl-CoA catabolized in one revolution of the cycle. These reducing equivalents are transferred to the respiratory chain in the inner mitochondrial membrane (Fig 14–3). During passage along the chain, reducing equivalents from NADH will generate 3 high-energy phosphate bonds by the esterification of ADP to ATP in the process of oxidative phosphorylation (see Chapter 12). However, FADH₂ produces only 2 high-energy phosphate bonds because it transfers its reducing power to Q, thus bypassing the first site for oxidative phosphorylation in the respiratory chain (see p 130). A further high-energy phosphate is generated at the level of the cycle itself (ie, at substrate level) during the conversion of succinyl-CoA to succinate. Thus, **12 new high-energy phosphate bonds are generated for each turn of the cycle** (Table 14–1).

Table 14–1. Generation of high-energy phosphate bonds by the citric acid cycle.

Reaction Catalyzed By	Method of $\sim$ ⓟ Production	Number of $\sim$ ⓟ Formed
Isocitrate dehydrogenase	Respiratory chain oxidation of NADH	3
α-Ketoglutarate dehydrogenase	Respiratory chain oxidation of NADH	3
Succinate thiokinase	Oxidation at substrate level	1
Succinate dehydrogenase	Respiratory chain oxidation of FADH₂	2
Malate dehydrogenase	Respiratory chain oxidation of NADH	3
		Net 12

AMPHIBOLIC ROLE OF THE CITRIC ACID CYCLE

Some metabolic pathways end in a constituent of the cycle while other pathways originate from the cycle. These pathways concern the processes of gluconeogenesis, transamination, deamination, and fatty acid synthesis. Although these will be discussed in greater detail in subsequent chapters, their relationships with the cycle are summarized below.

Gluconeogenesis, Transamination, & Deamination

All major members of the cycle, from citrate to oxaloacetate, are potentially glucogenic since they can give rise to a net production of glucose in the liver or kidney, the organs that contain a complete set of enzymes necessary for gluconeogenesis (see p 177). The key enzyme that facilitates the net transfer out of the cycle into the main pathway of gluconeogenesis is **phosphoenolpyruvate carboxykinase,** which catalyzes the decarboxylation of oxaloacetate to phosphoenolpyruvate, GTP acting as the source of high-energy phosphate (Fig 14–6).

$$\text{Oxaloacetate} + \text{GTP} \longrightarrow \text{Phosphoenolpyruvate} + CO_2 + \text{GDP}$$

Net transfer into the cycle (anaplerotic reactions) occurs as a result of several different reactions. Among the most significant is the formation of oxaloacetate by the carboxylation of pyruvate, catalyzed by **pyruvate carboxylase.**

$$\text{ATP} + CO_2 + H_2O + \text{Pyruvate} \longrightarrow \text{Oxaloacetate} + \text{ADP} + P_i$$

This reaction is considered important in maintaining adequate concentrations of oxaloacetate for the condensation reaction with acetyl-CoA. If acetyl-CoA accumulates, it acts as an allosteric activator of pyruvate carboxylase, thereby ensuring a supply of oxaloacetate. Lactate, an important substrate for gluconeogenesis, enters the cycle via conversion to pyruvate and oxaloacetate.

Transaminase reactions produce pyruvate from alanine, oxaloacetate from aspartate, and α-ketoglutarate from glutamate. Because these reactions are reversible, the cycle also serves as a source of carbon skeletons for the synthesis of nonessential amino acids, eg,

$$\text{Aspartate} + \text{Pyruvate} \longleftrightarrow \text{Oxaloacetate} + \text{Alanine}$$

$$\text{Glutamate} + \text{Pyruvate} \longleftrightarrow \alpha\text{-Ketoglutarate} + \text{Alanine}$$

Other amino acids contribute to gluconeogenesis because all or part of their carbon skeletons are fed into the citric acid cycle after deamination or transamination. Examples are alanine, cysteine, glycine, hy-

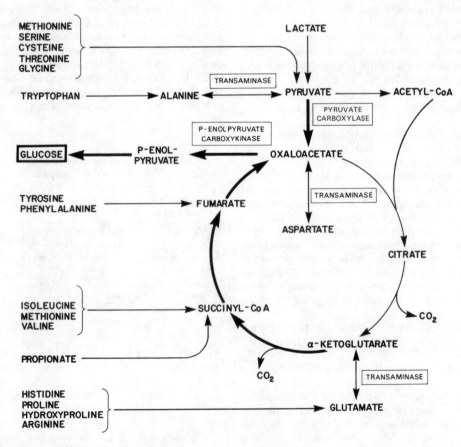

Figure 14–6. Involvement of the citric acid cycle in transamination and gluconeogenesis. The bold arrows indicate the main pathway of gluconeogenesis.

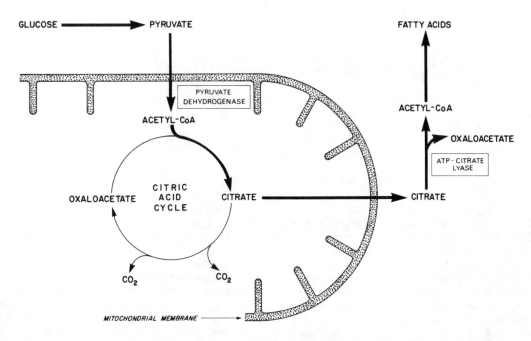

Figure 14–7. Participation of the citric acid cycle in fatty acid synthesis from glucose. See also Fig 17–8.

droxyproline, serine, threonine, and tryptophan, which form pyruvate; arginine, histidine, glutamate, and proline, which form α-ketoglutarate via glutamate; isoleucine, methionine, and valine, which form succinyl-CoA; and tyrosine and phenylalanine, which form fumarate. (See Fig 14–6.) It should be noted that substances forming pyruvate have the option of complete oxidation to CO_2 if they follow the pyruvate dehydrogenase pathway to acetyl-CoA, or they may follow the gluconeogenic pathway via carboxylation to oxaloacetate.

Of particular significance to ruminants is the conversion of propionate, the major glucogenic product of rumen fermentation, to succinyl-CoA via the methylmalonyl-CoA pathway (see p 179).

Fatty Acid Synthesis (See Fig 14–7.)
Acetyl-CoA formed from pyruvate by the action

of pyruvate dehydrogenase is the major building block for long chain fatty acid synthesis in nonruminants. (In ruminants, acetyl-CoA is derived directly from acetate.) As pyruvate dehydrogenase is a mitochondrial enzyme and the enzymes responsible for fatty acid synthesis are extramitochondrial, the cell has the problem of transporting acetyl-CoA through the mitochondrial membrane into the cytosol. This is achieved by allowing **acetyl-CoA to form citrate** in the citric acid cycle, **transporting citrate** out of the mitochondria, and finally making acetyl-CoA available in the cytosol by **cleaving citrate** in a reaction catalyzed by the enzyme **ATP-citrate lyase,** as shown below.

Citrate + ATP + CoA → Acetyl-CoA + Oxaloacetate + ADP + P$_i$

Regulation of the Citric Acid Cycle
This is discussed in Chapter 19.

•   •   •

References

Boyer PD (editor): *The Enzymes,* 3rd ed. Academic Press, 1971.
Goodwin TW (editor): *The Metabolic Roles of Citrate.* Academic Press, 1968.
Greville GD: Vol 1, p 297, in: *Carbohydrate Metabolism and Its Disorders.* Dickens F, Randle PJ, Whelan WJ (editors). Academic Press, 1968.

Lowenstein JM (editor): *Citric Acid Cycle: Control and Compartmentation.* Dekker, 1969.
Lowenstein JM (editor): *Citric Acid Cycle.* Vol 13 in: *Methods in Enzymology.* Academic Press, 1969.
Lowenstein JM: Vol 1, p 146, in: *Metabolic Pathways,* 3rd ed. Greenberg DM (editor). Academic Press, 1967.

15 | Metabolism of Carbohydrate

Peter A. Mayes, PhD, DSc

Although the human diet is variable, in most instances carbohydrate accounts for a large proportion of the daily intake. However, some of the dietary carbohydrate is converted to fat and consequently is metabolized as fat. The extent of this process (lipogenesis) depends on whether or not the animal is a "meal eater" or a more continual feeder. It is possible that in humans the frequency of taking meals and the extent to which carbohydrates are converted to fat could have a bearing on disease states such as atherosclerosis, obesity, and diabetes mellitus. In herbivores, especially ruminants, much of the intake of carbohydrate is fermented by microorganisms to lower molecular weight fatty acids prior to absorption from the alimentary tract.

The major function of carbohydrate in metabolism is as a fuel to be oxidized and provide energy for other metabolic processes. In this role, carbohydrate is utilized by cells mainly in the form of glucose. The 3 principal monosaccharides resulting from the digestive processes are **glucose, fructose,** and **galactose.** Fructose may assume considerable quantitative importance if there is a large intake of sucrose. Galactose is of major quantitative significance only when lactose is the principal carbohydrate of the diet. Both fructose and galactose are readily converted to glucose by the liver.

Pentose sugars such as xylose, arabinose, and ribose may be present in the diet, but their fate after absorption is obscure. D-Ribose is synthesized in the body for incorporation into nucleotides.

INTERMEDIARY METABOLISM OF CARBOHYDRATE

The metabolism of carbohydrate in the mammalian organism may be subdivided as follows:

(1) Glycolysis: The oxidation of glucose or glycogen to pyruvate and lactate by the Embden-Meyerhof pathway (Fig 15–1).

(2) Glycogenesis: The synthesis of glycogen from glucose.

(3) Glycogenolysis: The breakdown of glycogen. Glucose is the main end product of glycogenolysis in the liver, and pyruvate and lactate are the main products in muscle.

(4) The oxidation of pyruvate to acetyl-CoA: This is a necessary step prior to the entrance of the products of glycolysis into the citric acid cycle, which is the final common pathway for the oxidation of carbohydrate, fat, and protein.

(5) The hexose monophosphate shunt (pentose phosphate pathway, phosphogluconate oxidative pathway, direct oxidative pathway): An alternative pathway to the Embden-Meyerhof pathway for the oxidation of glucose. Its primary function is the synthesis of important intermediates such as NADPH and ribose.

(6) Gluconeogenesis: The formation of glucose or glycogen from noncarbohydrate sources. The pathways involved in gluconeogenesis are mainly the citric acid cycle and the reversal of glycolysis. The principal substrates for gluconeogenesis are glucogenic amino acids, lactate, and glycerol, and, in the ruminant, propionate (Fig 15–2).

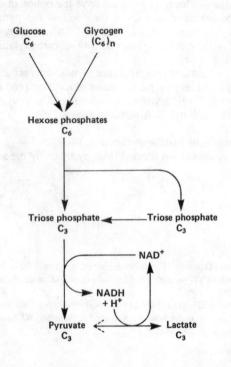

Figure 15–1. Summary of glycolysis.

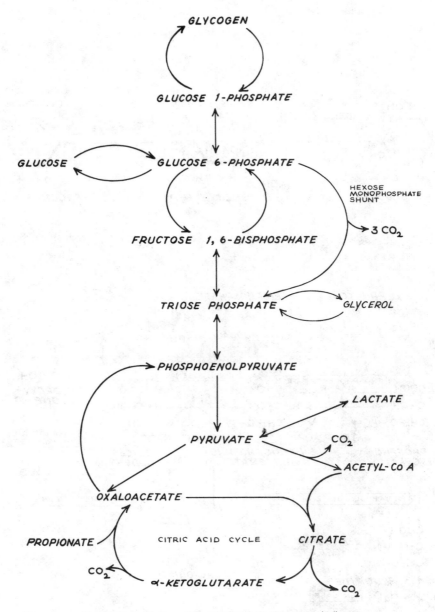

Figure 15-2. Major pathways of carbohydrate metabolism.

GLYCOLYSIS

At an early period in the course of investigations on carbohydrate metabolism it was realized that the process of fermentation in yeast was similar to the breakdown of glycogen in muscle. Although many of the early investigations of the glycolytic pathway were carried out on these 2 systems, the process is now known to occur in virtually **all tissues.**

In many of the first studies on the biochemical changes that occur during muscular contraction it was noted that when a muscle contracts in an anaerobic medium, ie, one from which oxygen is excluded, glycogen disappears and pyruvate and lactate appear as the principal end products. When oxygen is admitted,

aerobic recovery takes place and glycogen reappears, while pyruvate and lactate disappear. However, if contraction takes place under aerobic conditions, lactate does not accumulate and pyruvate is oxidized further to CO_2 and water. As a result of these observations, it has been customary to separate carbohydrate metabolism into anaerobic and aerobic phases. However, this distinction is arbitrary since the reactions in glycolysis are the same in the presence of oxygen as in its absence except in extent and end products. When oxygen is in short supply, reoxidation of NADH formed during glycolysis is impaired. Under these circumstances NADH is reoxidized by being coupled to the reduction of pyruvate to lactate, the NAD so formed being used to allow further glycolysis to proceed (Fig 15–1).

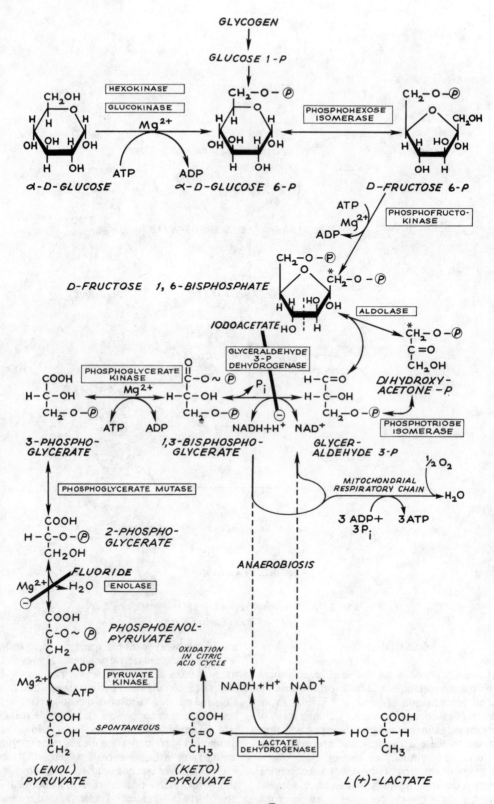

Figure 15–3. Embden-Meyerhof pathway of glycolysis. (P) = $-PO_3^{2-}$; P_i = $HOPO_3^{2-}$; $\ominus$ = inhibition.)

Thus, glycolysis can take place under anaerobic conditions, but this limits the amount of energy liberated per mole of glucose oxidized. Consequently, **to provide a given amount of energy, more glucose must undergo glycolysis under anaerobic as compared with aerobic conditions.**

The overall equation for glycolysis to lactate is

$$\text{Glucose} + 2\,\text{ADP} + 2\,\text{P}_i \rightarrow 2\,\text{L-Lactate} + 2\,\text{ATP} + 2\,\text{H}_2\text{O}$$

Sequence of Reactions in Glycolysis

All of the enzymes of the Embden-Meyerhof pathway (Fig 15–3) are found in the extramitochondrial soluble fraction of the cell, the cytosol. They catalyze the reactions involved in the glycolysis of glucose to pyruvate and lactate, which are as follows:

Glucose enters into the glycolytic pathway by phosphorylation to glucose 6-phosphate. This is accomplished by the enzyme **hexokinase** and by an additional enzyme in the liver, **glucokinase,** whose activity is inducible and affected by changes in the nutritional state. The reaction is accompanied by considerable loss of free energy as heat and is therefore a ''nonequilibrium'' type reaction, which, under physiologic conditions, may be regarded for practical purposes as irreversible. ATP is required as phosphate donor, and, as in many reactions involving phosphorylation, it reacts as the Mg-ATP complex. One high-energy phosphate bond of ATP is utilized, and ADP is produced. Hexokinase is inhibited in an allosteric manner by the product, glucose 6-phosphate.

$$\alpha\text{-D-Glucose} + \text{ATP} \xrightarrow{\text{Mg}^{2+}} \alpha\text{-D-Glucose 6-phosphate} + \text{ADP}$$

Hexokinase has a high affinity (low K_m) for its substrate, glucose. Its function is to ensure a supply of glucose for the tissues even in the presence of low blood glucose concentrations. It acts on both the α- and β-anomer of glucose and will also catalyze the phosphorylation of other hexoses but at a much slower rate than glucose. The function of glucokinase is to remove glucose from the blood following a meal. In contrast to hexokinase, it has a high K_m for glucose and operates optimally at blood glucose concentrations above 100 mg/dL.

Glucose 6-phosphate is an important compound, being at the junction of several metabolic pathways (glycolysis, gluconeogenesis, the hexose monophosphate shunt, glycogenesis, and glycogenolysis) (Fig 15–2). In glycolysis it is converted to fructose 6-phosphate by **phosphohexose isomerase,** which involves an aldose-ketose isomerization. Only the α-anomer of glucose 6-phosphate is acted upon.

$$\alpha\text{-D-Glucose 6-phosphate} \longleftrightarrow \alpha\text{-D-Fructose 6-phosphate}$$

This reaction is followed by another phosphorylation with ATP catalyzed by the enzyme **phosphofructokinase** to produce fructose 1,6-bisphosphate. Phosphofructokinase is another inducible enzyme whose activity is considered to play a major role in the regulation of the rate of glycolysis. The phosphofructokinase reaction is another that may be considered to be functionally irreversible under physiologic conditions.

$$\text{D-Fructose 6-phosphate} + \text{ATP} \rightarrow \text{D-Fructose 1,6-bisphosphate}$$

The hexose phosphate, fructose 1,6-bisphosphate, is split by **aldolase** (fructose 1,6-bisphosphate aldolase) into 2 triose phosphates, glyceraldehyde 3-phosphate and dihydroxyacetone phosphate.

$$\text{D-Fructose 1,6-bisphosphate} \longleftrightarrow \text{D-Glyceraldehyde 3-phosphate} + \text{Dihydroxyacetone phosphate}$$

Several different aldolases have been detected, all of which contain 4 subunits. Aldolase A occurs in most tissues, and, in addition, aldolase B occurs in liver and kidney. The fructose phosphates exist in the cell mainly in the furanose form, but they react with phosphohexose isomerase, phosphofructokinase, and aldolase in the open chain configuration.

Glyceraldehyde 3-phosphate and dihydroxyacetone phosphate are interconverted by the enzyme **phosphotriose isomerase.**

$$\text{D-Glyceraldehyde 3-phosphate} \longleftrightarrow \text{Dihydroxyacetone phosphate}$$

Glycolysis proceeds by the oxidation of glyceraldehyde 3-phosphate to 1,3-bisphosphoglycerate, and, because of the activity of phosphotriose isomerase, the dihydroxyacetone phosphate is also oxidized to 1,3-diphosphoglycerate via glyceraldehyde 3-phosphate.

$$\text{D-Glyceraldehyde 3-phosphate} + \text{NAD}^+ + \text{P}_i \longleftrightarrow 1,3\text{-Bisphosphoglycerate} + \text{NADH} + \text{H}^+$$

The enzyme responsible for the oxidation, **glyceraldehyde-3-phosphate dehydrogenase,** is NAD-dependent. Structurally, it consists of 4 identical polypeptides (monomers) forming a tetramer. Four SH groups are present on each polypeptide, probably derived from cysteine residues within the polypeptide chain. One of the SH groups is found at the active site of the enzyme. It is believed that the SH group participates in the reaction in which glyceraldehyde 3-phosphate is oxidized. The substrate initially combines with a cysteinyl moiety on the dehydrogenase forming a thiohemiacetal that is converted to a thiol ester by oxidation, the hydrogens removed in this oxidation being transferred to NAD bound to the enzyme. The NADH produced on the enzyme is not so firmly bound to the enzyme as is NAD. Consequently, NADH is easily displaced by a molecule of NAD. Finally, by phosphorolysis, inorganic phosphate (P_i) is added, forming 1,3-bisphosphoglycerate, and the free enzyme with a reconstituted SH group is liberated (Fig 15–4). Energy released during the oxidation is retained by the formation of a high-energy sulfur bond that becomes, after phosphorolysis, a high-energy phosphate bond in position 1 of 1,3-bisphosphoglycer-

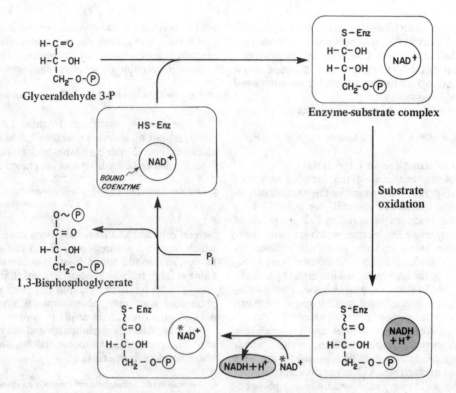

Figure 15–4. Oxidation of glyceraldehyde 3-phosphate. (Enz = glyceraldehyde-3-phosphate dehydrogenase.) The enzyme is inhibited by the –SH poison **iodoacetate,** which is thus able to inhibit glycolysis.

ate. This high-energy phosphate is captured as ATP in a further reaction with ADP catalyzed by **phosphoglycerate kinase,** leaving 3-phosphoglycerate.

1,3-Bisphosphoglycerate + ADP ⟷ 3-Phosphoglycerate + ATP

Since 2 molecules of triose phosphate are formed per molecule of glucose undergoing glycolysis, 2 molecules of ATP are generated at this stage per molecule of glucose, an example of phosphorylation "at the substrate level."

If arsenate is present, it will compete with inorganic phosphate (P_i) in the above reactions to give 1-arseno-3-phosphoglycerate, which hydrolyzes spontaneously to give 3-phosphoglycerate without generating ATP. This is an important example of the ability of arsenate to accomplish uncoupling of oxidation and phosphorylation.

3-Phosphoglycerate arising from the above reactions is converted to 2-phosphoglycerate by the enzyme **phosphoglycerate mutase.** It is likely that 2,3-bisphosphoglycerate (diphosphoglycerate, DPG) is an intermediate in this reaction.

3-Phosphoglycerate ⟷ 2-Phosphoglycerate

The subsequent step is catalyzed by **enolase** and involves a dehydration and redistribution of energy within the molecule, raising the phosphate on position 2 to the high-energy state, thus forming phosphoenol-

pyruvate. Enolase is inhibited by **fluoride,** a property that can be made use of when it is required to prevent glycolysis prior to the estimation of blood glucose. The enzyme is also dependent on the presence of either Mg^{2+} or Mn^{2+}.

2-Phosphoglycerate ⟷ Phosphoenolpyruvate + H_2O

The high-energy phosphate of phosphoenolpyruvate is transferred to ADP by the enzyme **pyruvate kinase** to generate, at this stage, 2 mol of ATP per mole of glucose oxidized. Enolpyruvate formed in this reaction is converted spontaneously to the keto form of pyruvate. This is another nonequilibrium reaction that is accompanied by considerable loss of free energy as heat and must be regarded as physiologically irreversible.

Phosphoenolpyruvate + ADP → Pyruvate + ATP

The redox state of the tissue now determines which of 2 pathways is followed. If **anaerobic** conditions prevail, the reoxidation of NADH by transfer of reducing equivalents through the respiratory chain to oxygen is prevented. Pyruvate is reduced by the NADH to lactate, the reaction being catalyzed by **lactate dehydrogenase.**

Pyruvate + NADH + H^+ ⟷ L-Lactate + NAD^+

Several isozymes of this enzyme are described in Chapter 8. The reoxidation of NADH via lactate formation allows glycolysis to proceed in the absence of oxygen by **regenerating sufficient NAD$^+$** for another cycle of the reaction catalyzed by glyceraldehyde-3-phosphate dehydrogenase. Thus, tissues that function under **hypoxic circumstances tend to produce lactate** (Fig 15–3). This is particularly true of skeletal muscle, where the rate at which the organ performs work is not limited by its capacity for oxygenation. The additional quantities of lactate produced may be detected in the tissues and in the blood and urine. Glycolysis in erythrocytes, even under aerobic conditions, always terminates in lactate, because mitochondria that contain the enzymatic machinery for the aerobic oxidation of pyruvate are absent. The mammalian erythrocyte is unique in that about 90% of its total energy requirement is provided by glycolysis.

In the erythrocytes of many mammalian species, there is a bypass of the step catalyzed by phosphoglycerate kinase. Another enzyme, **bisphosphoglycerate mutase,** catalyzes the conversion of 1,3-bisphosphoglycerate to 2,3-bisphosphoglycerate. The latter is converted to 3-phosphoglycerate by **2,3-bisphosphoglycerate phosphatase,** an activity also attributed to phosphoglycerate mutase. 2,3-Bisphosphoglycerate combines with hemoglobin, causing a decrease in affinity for oxygen and a displacement of the oxyhemoglobin dissociation curve to the right. Thus, its presence in the red cells aids oxyhemoglobin to unload oxygen (see Chapter 5).

Although most of the glycolytic reactions are reversible, 3 of them are markedly exergonic and must therefore be considered physiologically irreversible. These reactions are catalyzed by **hexokinase** (and glucokinase), **phosphofructokinase,** and **pyruvate kinase.** Cells that are capable of effecting a net movement of metabolites in the synthetic direction of the glycolytic pathway (gluconeogenesis) do so because of the presence of different enzyme systems which provide alternative routes around the irreversible reactions catalyzed by the above mentioned enzymes. These will be discussed under gluconeogenesis.

OXIDATION OF PYRUVATE TO ACETYL–CoA

Before pyruvate can enter the citric acid cycle, it must be transported into the mitochondrion via a special pyruvate transporter that aids its passage across the inner mitochondrial membrane. Within the mitochondrion, it is oxidatively decarboxylated to acetyl-CoA. This reaction is catalyzed by several different enzymes working sequentially in a multienzyme complex. They are collectively designated as the **pyruvate dehydrogenase** complex and are analogous to the α-ketoglutarate dehydrogenase complex of the citric acid cycle (see p 156). Pyruvate is decarboxylated in the presence of thiamin diphosphate to a hydroxyethyl derivative of the thiazole ring of enzyme-bound

thiamin diphosphate, which in turn reacts with oxidized lipoate to form S-acetyl lipoate, all catalyzed by pyruvate dehydrogenase (Fig 15–5). In the presence of **dihydrolipoyl transacetylase,** S-acetyl lipoate reacts with coenzyme A to form acetyl-CoA and reduced lipoate. The cycle of reaction is completed when the latter is reoxidized by a flavoprotein in the presence of **dihydrolipoyl dehydrogenase.** Finally, the reduced flavoprotein is oxidized by NAD, which in turn transfers reducing equivalents to the respiratory chain.

Pyruvate + NAD$^+$ + CoA → Acetyl-CoA + NADH + H$^+$ + CO$_2$

The pyruvate dehydrogenase complex consists of about 29 mol of pyruvate dehydrogenase and about 8 mol of flavoprotein (dihydrolipoyl dehydrogenase) distributed around 1 mol of transacetylase. Movement of the individual enzymes appears to be restricted, and the metabolic intermediates do not dissociate freely but remain bound to the enzymes.

It is to be noted that the pyruvate dehydrogenase system is sufficiently electronegative with respect to the respiratory chain that, in addition to generating a reduced coenzyme (NADH), it also generates a high-energy thio ester bond in acetyl-CoA.

Arsenite or mercuric ions complex the –SH groups of lipoic acid and inhibit pyruvate dehydrogenase as does a dietary deficiency of thiamin, allowing pyruvate to accumulate. Nutritionally deprived alcoholics are particularly susceptible to thiamin deficiency and if administered glucose exhibit rapid accumulation of pyruvate and lactic acidosis, which can be life-threatening. Mutations have been reported for virtually all of the enzymes of carbohydrate metabolism, each associated with human disease (Blass, 1979).

Energetics of Carbohydrate Oxidation

When 1 mol of glucose is combusted in a calorimeter to CO$_2$ and water, approximately 2870 kJ are liberated as heat. When oxidation occurs in the tissues, some of this energy is not lost immediately as heat but is "captured" in high-energy phosphate bonds. On the order of 38 high-energy phosphate bonds are generated per molecule of glucose oxidized to CO$_2$ and water. Assuming each high-energy bond to be equivalent to 36.8 kJ, the total energy captured in ATP per mol of glucose oxidized is 1398 kJ, or approximately 48.7% of the energy of combustion. Most of the ATP is formed as a consequence of oxidative phosphorylation resulting from the reoxidation of reduced coenzymes by the respiratory chain. The remainder is generated by phosphorylation at the "substrate level." (See Chapter 12.) Table 15–1 indicates the reactions responsible for the generation of high-energy phosphate during oxidation of glucose and the net production under aerobic and anaerobic conditions.

Table 15—1. Generation of high-energy bonds in the catabolism of glucose.

Pathway	Reaction Catalyzed By	Method of ~(P)Production	Number of ~(P) Formed per Mole Glucose
Glycolysis	Glyceraldehyde-3-phosphate dehydrogenase	Respiratory chain oxidation of 2 NADH	6*
	Phosphoglycerate kinase	Oxidation at substrate level	2
	Pyruvate kinase	Oxidation at substrate level	2
			10
	Allow for consumption of ATP by reactions catalyzed by hexokinase and phosphofructokinase		−2
			Net 8
Citric acid cycle	Pyruvate dehydrogenase	Respiratory chain oxidation of 2 NADH	6
	Isocitrate dehydrogenase	Respiratory chain oxidation of 2 NADH	6
	a-Ketoglutarate dehydrogenase	Respiratory chain oxidation of 2 NADH	6
	Succinate thiokinase	Oxidation at substrate level	2
	Succinate dehydrogenase	Respiratory chain oxidation of 2 $FADH_2$	4
	Malate dehydrogenase	Respiratory chain oxidation of 2 NADH	6
			Net 30
	Total per mole of glucose under aerobic conditions		38
	Total per mole of glucose under anaerobic conditions		2

*It is assumed that NADH formed in glycolysis is transported into mitochondria via the malate shuttle (p 139). If the glycerophosphate shuttle is used, only 2~(P) would be formed per mol of NADH, the total net production being 36 instead of 38.

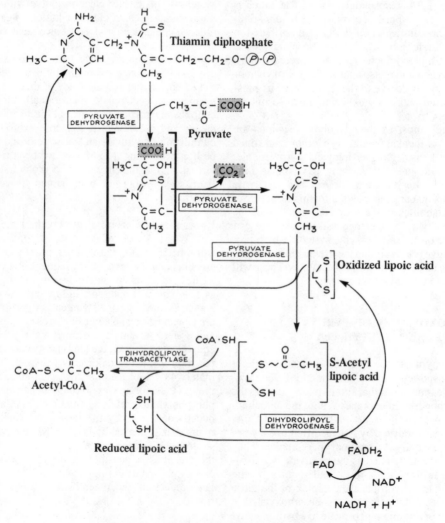

Figure 15—5. Oxidative decarboxylation of pyruvate.

GLYCOGEN FORMATION & DEGRADATION

The synthesis (glycogenesis) and degradation of glycogen (glycogenolysis) are not simply the reversal of one series of reactions. Instead, each process is an entirely separate metabolic pathway catalyzed by a different set of enzymes (Fig 15–6).

The formation of glycogen occurs in practically every tissue of the body but chiefly in liver and muscle (Table 15–2). In humans, the liver may contain as much as 6% of its wet weight as glycogen when analyzed shortly after a meal high in carbohydrate. After 12–18 hours of fasting, the liver becomes almost totally depleted of glycogen. Muscle glycogen is only rarely elevated above 1% and is only depleted significantly after prolonged vigorous exercise. Higher concentrations of muscle glycogen can be induced by feeding high-carbohydrate diets after depletion by exercise.

The function of muscle glycogen is to act as a readily available source of hexose units for glycolysis within the muscle itself. Liver glycogen is largely concerned with export of hexose units for maintenance of the **blood glucose,** particularly between meals.

Table 15–2. Storage of carbohydrate in postabsorptive normal adult man (70 kg).

Liver glycogen	4.0% =	72 g*
Muscle glycogen	0.7% =	245 g†
Extracellular glucose	0.1% =	10 g‡
Total:		327 g

*Liver weight 1800 g.
†Muscle mass, 35 kg.
‡Total volume, 10 L.

GLYCOGENESIS

Glucose is phosphorylated to glucose 6-phosphate, a reaction that is common to the first reaction in the pathway of glycolysis from glucose. Glucose

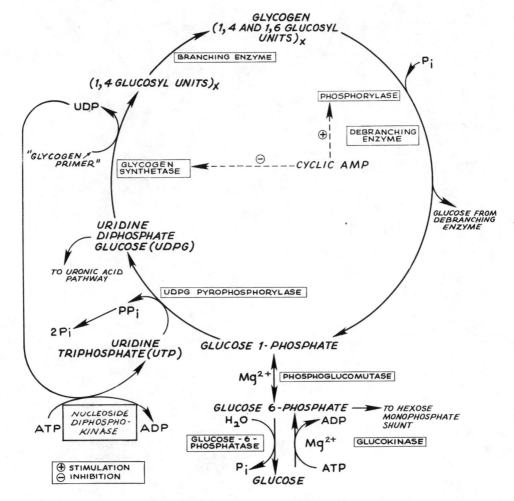

Figure 15–6. Pathway of glycogenesis and of glycogenolysis in the liver. Two high-energy phosphate bonds are used in the incorporation of 1 mol of glucose into glycogen.

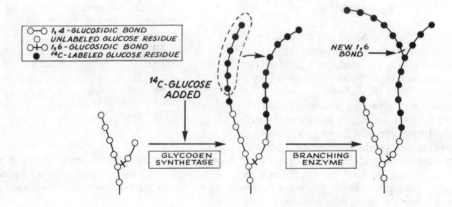

(a) Synthesis.

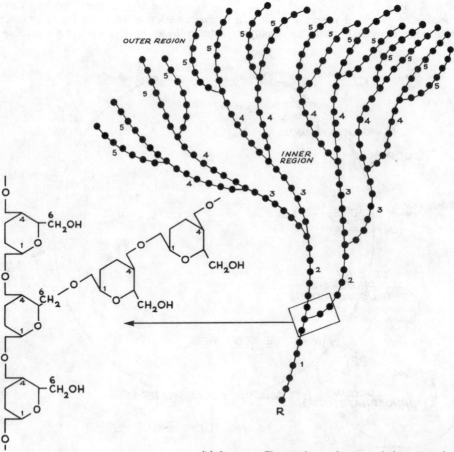

(b) Structure—The numbers refer to equivalent stages in the growth of the macromolecule. Thus, primary chain 1 branched into chains 2, which were synthesized simultaneously before branching into chains 3, etc. R, primary glucose residue. The branching is, in fact, more variable than shown, the ratio of 1,4 to 1,6 bonds being from 12 to 18.

(c) Enlargement of structure at a branch point.

Figure 15–7. The glycogen molecule.

6-phosphate is then converted to glucose 1-phosphate in a reaction catalyzed by the enzyme **phosphoglucomutase.** The enzyme itself is phosphorylated and the phospho- group takes part in a reversible reaction in which glucose 1,6-bisphosphate is an intermediate.

Enz-P + Glucose 6-phosphate ⟷ Enz + Glucose 1,6-
bisphosphate ⟷ Enz-P + Glucose 1-phosphate

Next, glucose 1-phosphate reacts with uridine triphosphate (UTP) to form the active nucleotide **uridine diphosphate glucose (UDPG).***

Uridine diphosphate glucose (UDPG)

The reaction between glucose 1-phosphate and uridine triphosphate is catalyzed by the enzyme **UDPG pyrophosphorylase.**

UTP + Glucose 1-phosphate ⟷ UDPG + PP$_i$

The subsequent hydrolysis of inorganic pyrophosphate by **inorganic pyrophosphatase** pulls the reaction to the right of the equation.

By the action of the enzyme **glycogen synthetase** (or **glucosyl transferase**), the C_1 of the activated glucose of UDPG forms a glycosidic bond with the C_4 of a terminal glucose residue of glycogen, liberating uridine diphosphate (UDP) (Fig 15–6). A preexisting glycogen molecule or "primer" must be present to initiate this reaction. The glycogen primer may in turn be formed on a protein backbone, which may be a process similar to the synthesis of other glycoproteins (see Chapter 32).

$$\text{UDPG} + (C_6)_n \longrightarrow \text{UDP} + (C_6)_{n+1}$$
$$\text{glycogen} \qquad\qquad \text{glycogen}$$

The addition of a glucose residue to a preexisting glycogen chain, or "primer" occurs at the nonreducing, outer end of the molecule so that the "branches"

*Other nucleoside diphosphate sugar compounds are known, eg, UDPGal. In addition, the same sugar may be linked to different nucleotides. For example, glucose may be linked to uridine (as shown above) as well as to guanosine, thymidine, adenosine, or cytidine nucleotides.

of the glycogen "tree" become elongated as successive **-1,4- linkages** occur (Fig 15–7). When the chain has been lengthened to between 6 and 11 glucose residues, a second enzyme, the **branching enzyme (amylo-1,4→1,6-transglucosidase)** acts on the glycogen. This enzyme transfers a part of the -1,4-chain (minimum length 6 glucose residues) to a neighboring chain to form a **-1,6- linkage,** thus establishing a **branch point** in the molecule.

The action of the branching enzyme has been studied in the living animal by feeding ^{14}C-labeled glucose and examining the liver glycogen at intervals thereafter. At first only the outer branches of the chain are labeled, indicating that the new glucose residues are added at this point. Later, some of these outside chains are transferred to the inner portion of the molecule, appearing as labeled -1,6- linked branches (Fig 15–7). Thus, under the combined action of glycogen synthetase and branching enzyme, the glycogen molecule is assembled.

The structure of glycogen is shown in Fig 15–7. It will be seen to be a branched polysaccharide composed entirely of α-D-glucose units. These glucose units are connected to one another by glucosidic linkages between the first and fourth carbon atoms except at branch points, where the linkages are between carbon atoms 1 and 6. The molecular weight of glycogen may vary from 1 million to 4 million or more. If glycogen is a regularly branched structure as shown in Fig 15–7, a maximum molecular weight of $10–20 \times 10^6$ would be possible because of the fact that the molecule becomes more dense toward the periphery. However, if some of the glucose chains terminate in the interior, a larger molecule is theoretically possible.

Glycogen Synthetase Activation & Inactivation

In muscle (and possibly liver), **glycogen synthetase** is present in 2 interconvertible forms: **synthetase D** (dependent), which is totally dependent for its activity on the presence of glucose 6-phosphate; and **synthetase I** (independent), whose K_m for UDPG decreases in the presence of glucose 6-phosphate (Fig 15–8). However, only the latter effect occurs with physiologic concentrations of glucose 6-phosphate, implying that synthetase I is the active form of the enzyme. Synthetase D is converted to synthetase I by **synthetase phosphatase,** a reaction involving dephosphorylation of a serine residue within the enzyme protein. Synthetase I is phosphorylated to form synthetase D, with ATP acting as a phosphate donor, by an enzyme of rather wide specificity, **cAMP-dependent protein kinase** (synthetase kinase), which is active only in the presence of 3',5'-cyclic adenylic acid or cyclic AMP (cAMP).

cAMP is the intracellular intermediate compound (second messenger) through which many hormones appear to act. It is formed from ATP by an enzyme, **adenylate cyclase,** occurring in cell membranes. Adenylate cyclase is activated by hormones such as epinephrine, norepinephrine, and glucagon, all of which lead to an increase in cAMP. cAMP is destroyed by a

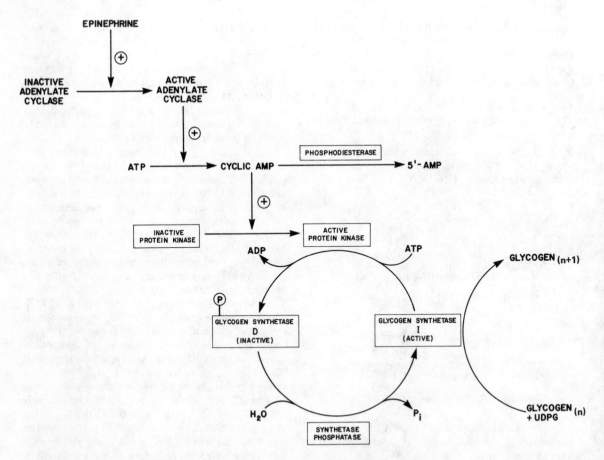

Figure 15–8. Control of glycogen synthetase in muscle (n = number of glucose residues). The sequence of reactions arranged in a cascade allows amplification at each step, allowing only nmol quantities of hormone to cause major changes in glycogen concentration.

phosphodiesterase, and it is the activity of this enzyme that maintains the level of cAMP at its normally low level. Insulin has been reported to increase its activity in liver. Thyroid hormones may increase the synthesis of adenylate cyclase, thus potentiating the effects of epinephrine in stimulating the formation of cAMP.

In liver, glycogen synthetase also exists in an active **a** form as well as an inactive **b** form; **b** is formed from **a** by phosphorylation of the enzyme protein in a reaction catalyzed by cAMP-dependent protein kinase, and **a** is formed from **b** by the action of **synthetase phosphatase.**

The reactions of glycogenesis in liver are summarized in Fig 15–6.

GLYCOGENOLYSIS

The breakdown of glycogen is initiated by the action of the enzyme **phosphorylase,** which is specific for the phosphorylytic breaking (phosphorolysis) of the -1,4- linkages of glycogen to yield glucose 1-phosphate (Fig 15–6).

Phosphorylase Activation & Inactivation
(Fig 15–9.)

In liver, the enzyme exists in both an active and an inactive form. Active phosphorylase (**phosphorylase a** or **phosphophosphorylase**) has one of its serine hydroxyl groups phosphorylated in an ester linkage.

3′,5′-Adenylic acid (cyclic AMP; cAMP)

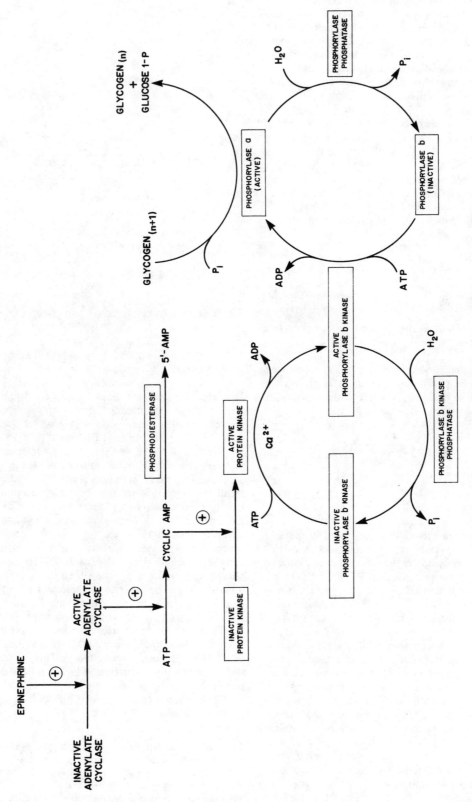

Figure 15—9. Control of phosphorylase in muscle (n = number of glucose residues).

By the action of a specific phosphatase (**phosphorylase phosphatase**), the enzyme is inactivated to **dephosphophosphorylase** in a reaction which involves hydrolytic removal of the phosphate from the serine residue. Reactivation requires rephosphorylation with ATP and a specific enzyme, **phosphorylase b kinase** or **dephosphophosphorylase kinase.**

Muscle phosphorylase is immunologically distinct from that of liver. It is present in 2 forms: **phosphorylase a,** which is active in the absence of 5′-AMP, and **phosphorylase b,** which is active only in the presence of 5′-AMP. Phosphorylase a is the physiologically active form of the enzyme. It is a tetramer containing 4 mol of pyridoxal phosphate. When it is hydrolytically converted to a dimer by **phosphorylase phosphatase,** which removes phosphate from phosphoserine residues, phosphorylase b is formed. This contains 2 mol of pyridoxal phosphate.

$$\text{Phosphorylase a} + 4H_2O \xrightarrow{\substack{\text{Phosphorylase} \\ \text{phosphatase}}}$$
$$\text{(Active tetramer)}$$
$$\text{2 Phosphorylase b} + 4\ P_i$$
$$\text{(Inactive dimer)}$$

Conversion of phosphorylase b to phosphorylase a is considered to be the mechanism for increasing glycogenolysis.

Two dimers of phosphorylase b may recondense to an active phosphorylase a tetramer in the presence of **phosphorylase b kinase,** which rephosphorylates the serine residues at the expense of ATP.

$$\text{2 Phosphorylase b} + 4\ \text{ATP} \xrightarrow[\text{Mg}^{2+}]{\substack{\text{Phosphorylase} \\ \text{b kinase}}}$$
$$\text{Phosphorylase a} + 4\ \text{ADP}$$

Phosphorylase in muscle is activated by epinephrine (Fig 15–9). However, this occurs not as a direct effect but rather by way of the action of epinephrine on adenylate cyclase to form cAMP. Phosphorylase b kinase is then **activated** by a second protein kinase system considered to be identical to the cAMP-dependent protein kinase responsible for **inactivation** of glycogen synthetase I (Fig 15–8). In this way, glycogen catabolism is activated while, simultaneously, glycogen synthesis is inhibited. Activation of phosphorylase b kinase is also caused by muscular contraction, an effect due to Ca^{2+} rather than cAMP.

The reactions for the inactivation of muscle phosphorylase are in some respects similar to those of the liver enzyme except that no cleavage of the protein molecular structure is involved in the case of liver phosphorylase. Furthermore, skeletal muscle phosphorylase is not affected by glucagon although heart muscle is. Another important difference is that liver synthetase phosphatase is inhibited by the active form of phosphorylase.

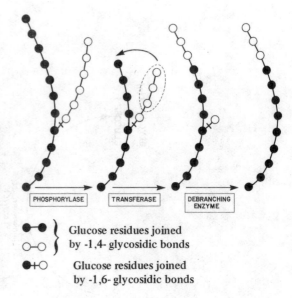

●—● } Glucose residues joined
○—○ } by -1,4- glycosidic bonds

●+○   Glucose residues joined
      by -1,6- glycosidic bonds

Figure 15–10. Steps in glycogenolysis.

It is the step catalyzed by phosphorylase that is rate-limiting in glycogenolysis.

$$(C_6)_n + P_i \rightarrow (C_6)_{n-1} + \text{Glucose 1-phosphate}$$
$$\text{glycogen} \qquad \text{glycogen}$$

This enzyme catalyzes the removal of 1,4-glucosyl residues from the outermost chains of the glycogen molecule until approximately 4 glucose residues remain on either side of a -1,6- branch (Fig 15–10). Another enzyme (α-**1,4**→α-**1,4 glucan transferase**) transfers a trisaccharide unit from one side to the other, thus exposing the -1,6- branch points. The hydrolytic splitting of the -1,6- linkages requires the action of a specific **debranching enzyme (amylo-1,6-glucosidase).*** With the removal of the branch, further action by phosphorylase can proceed. The combined action of phosphorylase and these other enzymes converts glycogen to glucose 1-phosphate. The action of phosphoglucomutase is reversible, so that glucose 6-phosphate can be formed from glucose 1-phosphate. In **liver** and **kidney** (but not in muscle), there is a specific enzyme, **glucose-6-phosphatase,** that removes phosphate from glucose 6-phosphate, enabling the free glucose to diffuse from the cell into the extracellular spaces, including the blood. This is the final step in hepatic glycogenolysis, which is reflected by a rise in the blood glucose.

The regulation of glycogen metabolism is discussed on p 250.

The regulation of glycogen metabolism is discussed on p 250.

---

*Because the -1,6- linkage is hydrolytically split, 1 mol of free glucose is produced rather than 1 mol of glucose 1-phosphate. In this way it is possible for some rise in the blood glucose to take place even in the absence of glucose-6-phosphatase, as occurs in type I glycogen storage disease (von Gierke's disease; see below) after glucagon or epinephrine is administered.

Diseases of Glycogen Storage

The term "glycogen storage disease" is a generic one intended to describe a group of inherited disorders characterized by deposition of an abnormal type or quantity of glycogen in the tissues.

In **type I glycogenosis (von Gierke's disease),** both the liver cells and the cells of the renal convoluted tubules are characteristically loaded with glycogen. However, these glycogen stores seem to be metabolically unavailable, as evidenced by the occurrence of hypoglycemia and a lack of glucose release under stimulus by epinephrine or glucagon. Ketosis and hyperlipemia are also present in these patients, as would be characteristic of an organism deprived of carbohydrate. In liver, kidney, and intestinal tissue, the activity of glucose-6-phosphatase is either extremely low or entirely absent.

Other types of glycogen storage disease include the following: **type II (Pompe's disease),** which is characterized by a deficiency of lysosomal α-1,4-glucosidase (acid maltase) whose function is to degrade glycogen, which otherwise accumulates in the lysosomes; **type III (limit dextrinosis),** characterized by the absence of debranching enzyme, which causes the accumulation of a polysaccharide of the limit dextrin type; and **type IV (amylopectinosis),** characterized by the absence of branching enzyme, with the result that a polysaccharide having few branch points accumulates.

An absence of muscle phosphorylase (myophosphorylase) is the cause of **type V glycogenosis (myophosphorylase deficiency glycogenosis; McArdle's syndrome).** Patients with this disease exhibit a markedly diminished tolerance to exercise. Although their skeletal muscles have an abnormally high content of glycogen (2.5–4.1%), little or no lactate is detectable in their blood after exercise. A rise in blood sugar does occur, however, after administration of glucagon or epinephrine, which indicates that hepatic phosphorylase activity is normal. In some of the reported cases, myoglobinuria has been an associated finding.

Also described among the glycogen storage diseases are **type VI glycogenosis,** involving phosphoglucomutase deficiency in the liver, and **type VII glycogenosis,** characterized by a deficiency of phosphofructokinase in the muscles.

THE HEXOSE MONOPHOSPHATE SHUNT OR PENTOSE PHOSPHATE PATHWAY

Functions of the Hexose Monophosphate Shunt

A major function of the hexose monophosphate shunt is the provision of reduced NADP (NADPH) required by anabolic processes outside the mitochondria, such as the synthesis of fatty acids and steroids. Another important function is to provide ribose for nucleotide and nucleic acid synthesis.

Sequence of Reactions

This pathway for the oxidation of glucose occurs in certain tissues, notably liver, lactating mammary gland, and adipose tissue, in addition to the Embden-Meyerhof pathway of glycolysis. It is in effect a multicyclic process whereby 3 molecules of glucose 6-phosphate give rise to 3 molecules of CO_2 and three 5-carbon residues. The latter are rearranged to regenerate 2 molecules of glucose 6-phosphate and one molecule of glyceraldehyde 3-phosphate. Since 2 molecules of glyceraldehyde 3-phosphate can regenerate a molecule of glucose 6-phosphate by reactions which are essentially a reversal of glycolysis, the pathway can account for the complete oxidation of glucose. As in the Embden-Meyerhof glycolysis pathway, oxidation is achieved by dehydrogenation; but in the case of the shunt pathway, NADP and not NAD is used as a hydrogen acceptor. The enzymes of the shunt pathway are found in the **extramitochondrial** soluble portion of the cell.

A summary of the reactions of the hexose monophosphate shunt is shown below.

$$3 \text{ Glucose 6-P} + 6 \text{ NADP}^+ \rightarrow 3 \text{ CO}_2 + 2 \text{ Glucose 6-P} +$$
$$\text{Glyceraldehyde 3-P} + 6 \text{ NADPH} + 6 \text{ H}^+$$

The sequence of reactions of the shunt pathway may be divided into 2 phases. In the first, glucose 6-phosphate undergoes dehydrogenation and decarboxylation to give the pentose, ribulose 5-phosphate. In the second phase, ribulose 5-phosphate is converted back to glucose 6-phosphate by a series of reactions involving mainly 2 enzymes: **transketolase** and **transaldolase** (Fig 15–11).

Dehydrogenation of glucose 6-phosphate to 6-phosphogluconate occurs via the formation of 6-phosphogluconolactone catalyzed by **glucose-6-phosphate dehydrogenase,** an NADP-dependent enzyme. The hydrolysis of 6-phosphogluconolactone is accomplished by the enzyme **gluconolactone hydrolase.** A second oxidative step is catalyzed by **6-phosphogluconate dehydrogenase,** which also requires NADP$^+$ as hydrogen acceptor. Decarboxylation follows with the formation of the ketopentose, ribulose 5-phosphate. The reaction probably takes place in 2 steps through the intermediate 3-keto-6-phosphogluconate.

Ribulose 5-phosphate now serves as substrate for 2 different enzymes. **Ribulose-5-phosphate epimerase** alters the configuration about carbon 3, forming the epimer, xylulose 5-phosphate, another ketopentose. **Ribose-5-phosphate ketoisomerase** converts ribulose 5-phosphate to the corresponding aldopentose, ribose 5-phosphate. This reaction is analogous to the interconversion of fructose 6-phosphate and glucose 6-phosphate in the Embden-Meyerhof pathway.

Transketolase transfers the 2-carbon unit comprising carbons 1 and 2 of a ketose to the aldehyde carbon of an aldose sugar. It therefore effects the conversion of a ketose sugar into an aldose with 2 carbons less, and simultaneously converts an aldose sugar into a ketose with 2 carbons more. In addition to the enzyme transketolase, the reaction requires

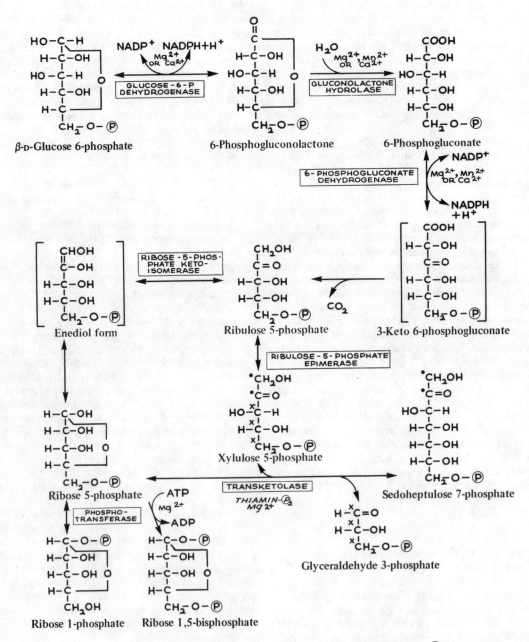

Figure 15-11. The hexose monophosphate shunt (pentose phosphate pathway). ($\textcircled{P}$ = $-PO_3^{2-}$.)

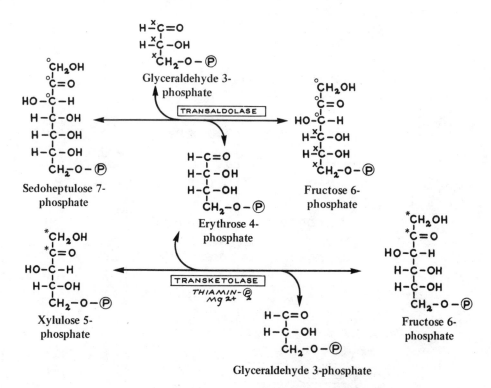

Figure 15–11 (cont'd). The hexose monophosphate shunt.

thiamin diphosphate as coenzyme and Mg^{2+} ions. The 2-carbon moiety transferred is probably glycolaldehyde bound to thiamin diphosphate, ie, "active glycolaldehyde." In the hexose monophosphate shunt, transketolase catalyzes the transfer of the 2-carbon unit from xylulose 5-phosphate to ribose 5-phosphate, producing the 7-carbon ketose sedoheptulose 7-phosphate and the aldose glyceraldehyde 3-phosphate. These 2 products then enter another reaction known as transaldolation. Transaldolase allows the transfer of a 3-carbon moiety, "active dihydroxyacetone" (carbons 1–3), from the ketose sedoheptulose 7-phosphate to the aldose glyceraldehyde 3-phosphate to form the ketose fructose 6-phosphate and the 4-carbon aldose erythrose 4-phosphate.

A further reaction takes place, again involving transketolase, in which xylulose 5-phosphate serves as a donor of "active glycolaldehyde." In this case the erythrose 4-phosphate formed above acts as acceptor, and the products of the reaction are fructose 6-phosphate and glyceraldehyde 3-phosphate.

In order to oxidize glucose completely to CO_2 via the shunt pathway, it is necessary that the enzymes are present in the tissue to convert glyceraldehyde 3-phosphate to glucose 6-phosphate. This involves the enzymes of the Embden-Meyerhof pathway working in a reverse direction and, in addition, the enzyme **fructose-1,6-diphosphatase.** A summary of the reactions of the direct oxidative pathway is shown in Fig 15–12. Most of the reactions shown in that illustration

are reversible, but the complete pathway is probably irreversible at the gluconolactone hydrolase step.

Metabolic Significance of the Hexose Monophosphate Shunt

It is clear that this is markedly different from the Embden-Meyerhof pathway of glycolysis. Oxidation occurs in the first reactions, and CO_2, which is not produced at all in the Embden-Meyerhof pathway, is a characteristic product.

Estimates of the activity of the shunt pathway in various tissues give an indication of its metabolic significance. It is active in liver, adipose tissue, adrenal cortex, thyroid, erythrocytes, testis, and lactating mammary gland. It is not active in nonlactating mammary gland, and its activity is low in skeletal muscle. Most of the tissues in which the pathway is active use NADPH from the shunt in the synthesis of fatty acids or steroids and in the synthesis of amino acids via glutamate dehydrogenase. It is probable that the presence of active lipogenesis or of a system which utilizes NADPH stimulates an active degradation of glucose via the shunt pathway. The synthesis of glucose-6-phosphate dehydrogenase and 6-phosphogluconate dehydrogenase may also be induced during conditions associated with the "fed state."

The hexose monophosphate shunt in the erythrocyte provides NADPH for the reduction of oxidized glutathione (G–S–S–G) to reduced glutathione (2G–SH), catalyzed by **glutathione reductase.** In turn, reduced glutathione removes H_2O_2 from the eryth-

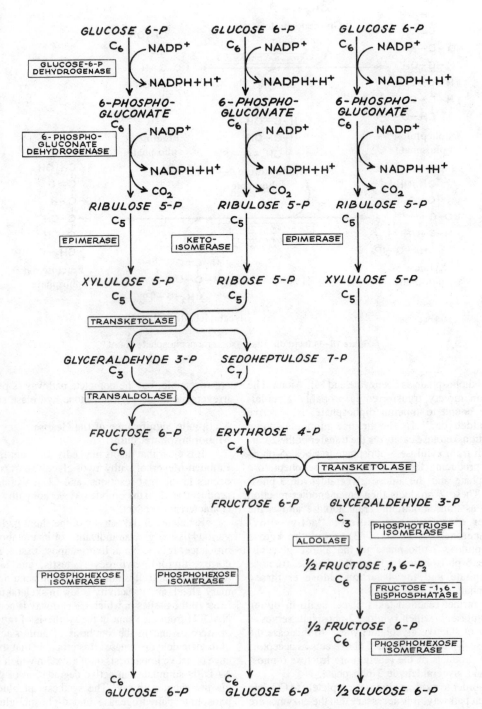

Figure 15–12. Flow chart of hexose monophosphate shunt and its connections with the Embden-Meyerhof pathway of glycolysis.

rocyte in a reaction catalyzed by **glutathione peroxidase**

$$2G-SH + H_2O_2 \longrightarrow G-S-S-G + 2H_2O$$

This reaction is important since accumulation of H_2O_2 may decrease the life span of the erythrocyte by increasing the rate of oxidation of hemoglobin to methemoglobin. An inverse correlation has been found between the activity of glucose-6-phosphate dehydrogenase and the fragility of red cells (susceptibility to hemolysis). A mutation present in some populations causes a deficiency in this enzyme that is manifested as red cell hemolysis when the susceptible individual is subjected to oxidants such as the antimalarial primaquine, aspirin, or sulfonamides, or when the susceptible individual has eaten fava beans (*Vicia fava* —favism).

The hexose monophosphate shunt provides pentoses for nucleotide and nucleic acid synthesis. The source of the ribose is the ribose 5-phosphate intermediate. This compound may be isomerized to the 1-phosphate (cf glucose 6-phosphate ⟷ glucose 1-phosphate interconversion, p 169), or it can react with ATP to give ribose 1,5-bisphosphate (cf fructose 6-phosphate → fructose 1,6-bisphosphate). Muscle tissue contains very small amounts of glucose-6-phosphate dehydrogenase and 6-phosphogluconate dehydrogenase. Nevertheless, skeletal muscle is capable of synthesizing ribose. This is probably accomplished by a reversal of the shunt pathway utilizing fructose 6-phosphate, glyceraldehyde 3-phosphate, and the enzymes transketolase and transaldolase. Thus, it is not necessary to have a completely functioning shunt pathway in order that a tissue may synthesize ribose. In human tissues, ribose seems to be derived primarily by way of the oxidative reactions of the shunt pathway, whereas in the rat and mouse—except in muscle—the nonoxidative reactions appear to play a larger role than the oxidative.

GLUCONEOGENESIS

The Basal Requirement for Glucose

Gluconeogenesis meets the needs of the body for glucose when carbohydrate is not available in sufficient amounts from the diet. A continual supply of glucose is necessary as a source of energy, especially for the nervous system and the erythrocytes. Glucose is also required in adipose tissue as a source of glyceride-glycerol, and it probably plays a role in maintaining the level of intermediates of the citric acid cycle in many tissues. It is clear that even under conditions where fat may be supplying most of the caloric requirement of the organism, there is always a certain basal requirement for glucose. In addition, glucose is the only fuel that will supply energy to skeletal muscle under anaerobic conditions. It is the precursor of milk sugar (lactose) in the mammary gland and it is taken up actively by the fetus. It is not surprising, therefore, to find that enzymatic pathways have been developed in certain specialized tissues for the conversion of **noncarbohydrates to glucose,** ie, **gluconeogenesis.** In addition, these gluconeogenic mechanisms are used to clear the products of the metabolism of other tissues from the blood, eg, lactate, produced by muscle and erythrocytes, and glycerol, which is continuously produced by adipose tissue. Propionate, the principal glucogenic fatty acid produced in the digestion of carbohydrates by ruminants, is a major substrate for gluconeogenesis in these species.

In mammals, the **liver** and the **kidney** are the principal organs responsible for gluconeogenesis. As the main pathway for gluconeogenesis is essentially a reversal of glycolysis, this can explain why the glycolytic activity of liver and kidney is low when there is active gluconeogenesis.

Metabolic Pathways Involved in Gluconeogenesis
(Fig 15–13.)

These pathways are modifications and adaptations of the Embden-Meyerhof pathway and the citric acid cycle. They are concerned with the conversion of glucogenic amino acids, lactate, glycerol, and, in ruminants, propionate, to glucose or glycogen. It has been pointed out by Krebs that energy barriers obstruct a simple reversal of glycolysis (1) between pyruvate and phosphoenolpyruvate, (2) between fructose 1,6-bisphosphate and fructose 6-phosphate, (3) between glucose 6-phosphate and glucose, and (4) between glucose 1-phosphate and glycogen. These barriers are circumvented by special reactions described below:

(1) Present in mitochondria is an enzyme, **pyruvate carboxylase,** which in the presence of ATP, biotin, and CO_2 converts pyruvate to oxaloacetate. The function of the biotin is to bind CO_2 from bicarbonate onto the enzyme prior to the addition of the CO_2 to pyruvate (see Chapter 10). In the extramitochondrial part of the cell is found a second enzyme, **phosphoenolpyruvate carboxykinase,** which catalyzes the conversion of oxaloacetate to phosphoenolpyruvate. High-energy phosphate in the form of GTP or ITP is required in this reaction, and CO_2 is liberated. Thus, with the help of these 2 enzymes and lactate dehydrogenase, lactate can be converted to phosphoenolpyruvate.

However, oxaloacetate does not diffuse readily from mitochondria. Alternative means are available to achieve the same end by converting oxaloacetate into compounds that can diffuse from the mitochondria, followed by their reconversion to oxaloacetate in the extramitochondrial portion of the cell. Such a compound is malate, but conversion via aspartate, α-ketoglutarate, glutamate, and citrate has also been proposed. Their formation from oxaloacetate within mitochondria and their conversion back to oxaloacetate in the extramitochondrial compartment involve citric acid cycle reactions and transaminations. There are species differences with regard to the distribution of phosphoenolpyruvate carboxykinase. The extramitochondrial location is true for the rat and mouse; but in

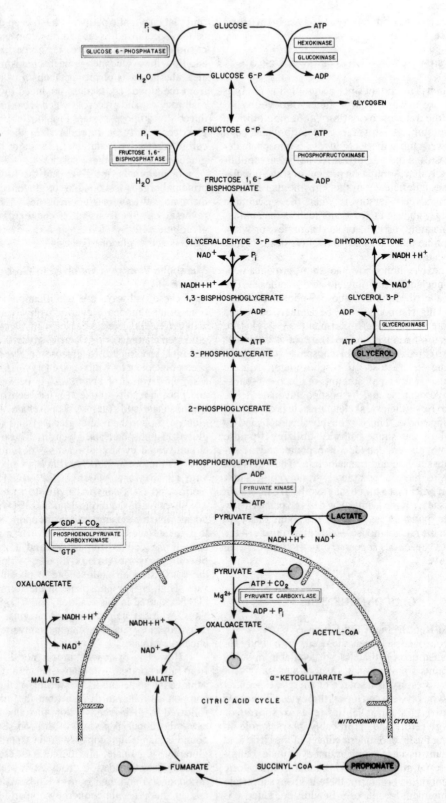

Figure 15-13. Major pathways of gluconeogenesis in the liver. Entry points of glucogenic amino acids after transamination are indicated by 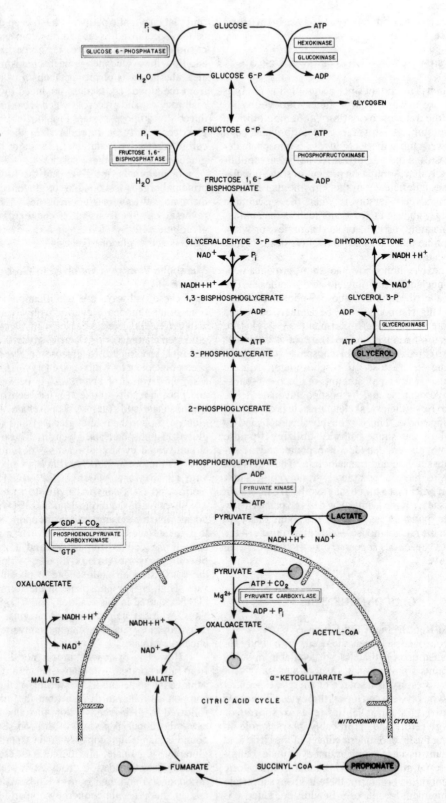→. (See also Fig 14 –6.) The key gluconeogenic enzymes are shown thus ▭. The ATP required for gluconeogenesis is supplied by the oxidation of acetyl-CoA derived mainly from long chain fatty acids or lactate (via pyruvate and pyruvate dehydrogenase). Propionate is of quantitative importance only in ruminants.

the rabbit and chicken the enzyme is located in the mitochondria, and in the guinea pig and human it is found in both the mitochondria and cytosol.

(2) The conversion of fructose 1,6-bisphosphate to fructose 6-phosphate, necessary to achieve a reversal of glycolysis, is catalyzed by a specific enzyme, **fructose-1,6-bisphosphatase.** This is a key enzyme in the sense that its presence determines whether or not a tissue is capable of resynthesizing glycogen from pyruvate and triosephosphates. It is present in liver and kidney and has been demonstrated in striated muscle. It is held to be absent from adipose tissue, heart muscle, and smooth muscle.

(3) The conversion of glucose 6-phosphate to glucose is catalyzed by another specific phosphatase, **glucose-6-phosphatase.** It is present in intestine, platelets, liver, and kidney, where it allows these particular tissues to add glucose to the blood. The enzyme, which is microsomal, also possesses pyrophosphatase activity. It is absent from muscle and adipose tissue.

(4) The breakdown of glycogen to glucose 1-phosphate is carried out by phosphorylase. The synthesis of glycogen involves an entirely different pathway through the formation of uridine diphosphate glucose and the activity of **glycogen synthetase** (Fig 15–6).

The relationships between these key enzymes of gluconeogenesis and the Embden-Meyerhof glycolytic pathway are shown in Fig 15–13. After transamination or deamination, glucogenic amino acids form either pyruvate or members of the citric acid cycle. Therefore, the reactions described above can account for the conversion of both glucogenic amino acids and lactate to glucose or glycogen. Thus, lactate forms pyruvate and enters the mitochondria before conversion to oxaloacetate and ultimate conversion to glucose. Propionate, which is a major source of glucose in ruminants, enters the main gluconeogenic pathway via the citric acid cycle after conversion to succinyl-CoA. Propionate, as with other fatty acids, is first activated

with ATP and CoA by an appropriate **thiokinase.** Propionyl-CoA, the product of this reaction, undergoes a CO_2 fixation reaction to form D-methylmalonyl-CoA, catalyzed by **propionyl-CoA carboxylase** (Fig 15–14). This reaction is analogous to the fixation of CO_2 in acetyl-CoA by acetyl-CoA carboxylase (see Chapter 17) in that it forms a malonyl derivative and requires biotin as a coenzyme. D-Methylmalonyl-CoA must be converted to its stereoisomer, L-methylmalonyl-CoA, by **methylmalonyl-CoA racemase** before its final isomerization to succinyl-CoA by the enzyme **methylmalonyl-CoA isomerase,** which requires vitamin B_{12} as a coenzyme. Vitamin B_{12} deficiency in humans and animals results in the excretion of large amounts of methylmalonate (methylmalonic aciduria).

Although the pathway to succinate is its main route of metabolism, propionate may also be used as the priming molecule for the synthesis—in adipose tissue and mammary gland—of fatty acids that have an odd number of carbon atoms in the molecule. C 15 and C 17 fatty acids are found particularly in the lipids of ruminants.

Glycerol is a product of the metabolism of adipose tissue, and only tissues that possess the activating enzyme, **glycerokinase,** can utilize it. This enzyme, which requires ATP, is found in liver and kidney, among other tissues. Glycerokinase catalyzes the conversion of glycerol to glycerol 3-phosphate. This pathway connects with the triosephosphate stages of the Embden-Meyerhof pathway because glycerol 3-phosphate may be oxidized to dihydroxyacetone phosphate by NAD^+ in the presence of another enzyme, **glycerol-3-phosphate dehydrogenase,** although the equilibrium constant is very much in favor of glycerol 3-phosphate formation. Thus, liver and kidney are able to convert glycerol to blood glucose by making use of the above enzymes, some of the enzymes of the Embden-Meyerhof pathway, and the specific enzymes of the gluconeogenic pathway, fructose-1,6-bisphosphatase and glucose-6-phosphatase (Fig 15–13).

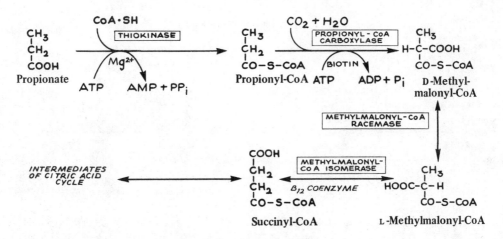

Figure 15–14. Metabolism of propionate.

METABOLISM OF HEXOSES

Phosphorylation

The hexoses of metabolic importance—glucose, fructose, and galactose—enter most metabolic pathways, including glycolysis, after phosphorylation. As mentioned previously, glucose is phosphorylated by ATP in the presence of the enzyme **hexokinase;** but in liver there is in addition a more specific **glucokinase.** Some studies indicate that only glucokinase, and not hexokinase, is present in hepatic cells. Hexokinase differs from glucokinase in that it is inhibited by glucose 6-phosphate (allosteric inhibition); it does not change in activity as a response to the nutritional or hormonal state of the animal; and it has a high affinity for glucose (low K_m). When glucose is the substrate, the product of the reaction with glucokinase or hexokinase is glucose 6-phosphate.

Fructose and galactose are not phosphorylated in the presence of glucokinase, but they have their own specific enzymes, **fructokinase** and **galactokinase,** which carry out phosphorylation in the liver. These enzymes always convert the hexose to the corresponding hexose 1-phosphate.

MINOR PATHWAYS OF GLUCOSE METABOLISM

THE URONIC ACID PATHWAY

Besides the major pathways of metabolism of glucose 6-phosphate that have been described, there exists a pathway for the conversion of glucose to

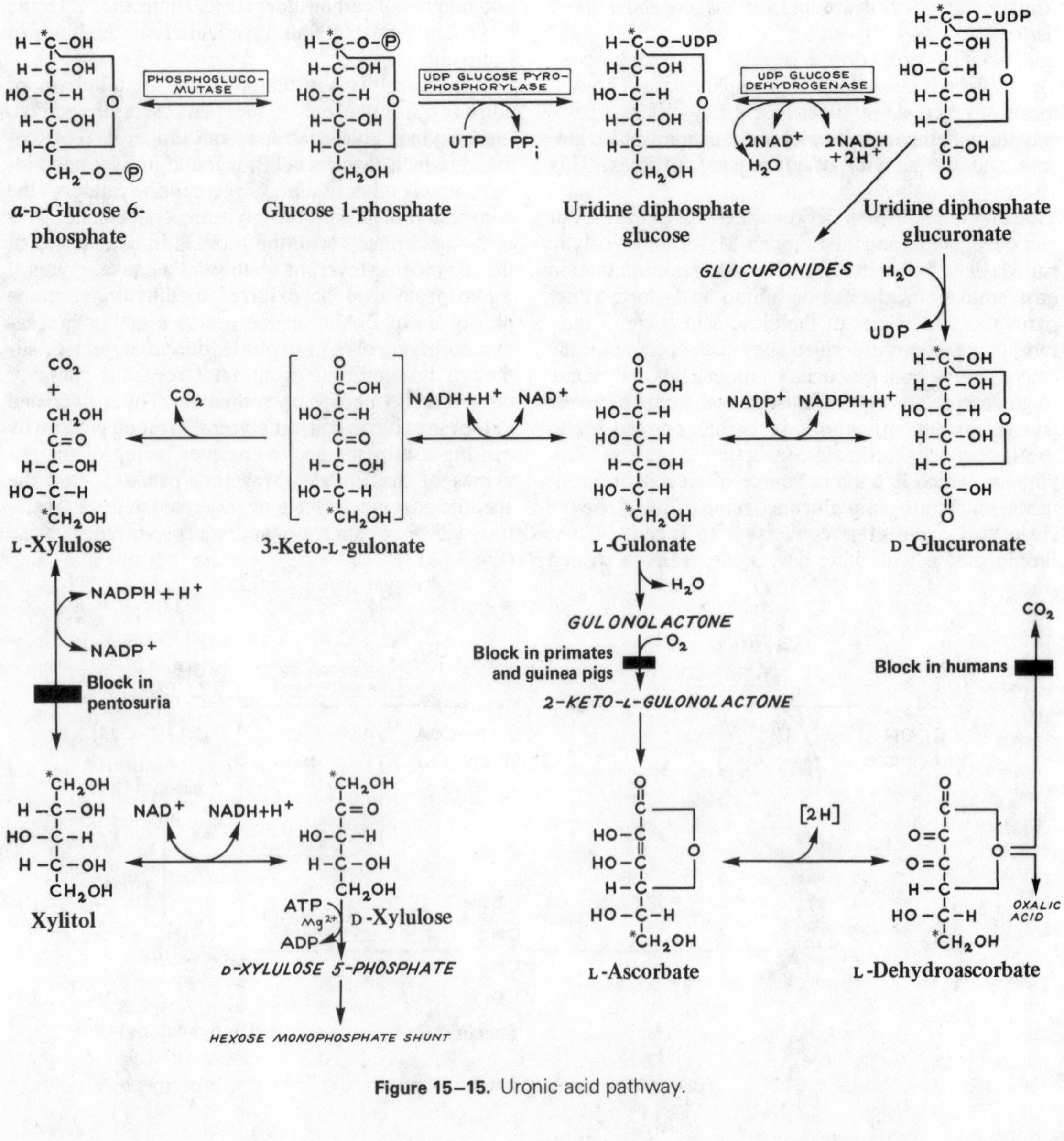

Figure 15–15. Uronic acid pathway.

glucuronic acid, ascorbic acid, and pentoses that is referred to as the **uronic acid pathway.** It is also an alternative oxidative pathway for glucose.

In the uronic acid pathway, glucuronic acid is formed from glucose by the reactions shown in Fig 15–15. Glucose 6-phosphate is converted to glucose 1-phosphate, which then reacts with uridine triphosphate (UTP) to form the active nucleotide, uridine diphosphate glucose (UDPG). This latter reaction is catalyzed by the enzyme **UDPG pyrophosphorylase.** All of the steps up to this point are those previously indicated as in the pathway of glycogenesis in the liver. Uridine diphosphate glucose is now oxidized at carbon 6 by a 2-step process to glucuronate. The product of the oxidation, which is catalyzed by an NAD-dependent **UDPG dehydrogenase,** is therefore UDP-glucuronate.

Galacturonate is an important constituent of many natural products such as the pectins. It may be formed from UDP-glucuronate by inversion around carbon 4, as occurs when UDP-glucose is converted to UDP-galactose.

UDP-glucuronate is the "active" form of glucuronate for reactions involving incorporation of glucuronic acid into chondroitin sulfate or for reactions in which glucuronate is conjugated to such substrates as steroid hormones, certain drugs, or bilirubin (formation of "direct" bilirubin). (See p 316.)

The further metabolism of glucuronate is shown in Fig 15–15. In an NADPH-dependent reaction, glucuronate is reduced to L-gulonate. This latter compound is the direct precursor of ascorbate in those animals which are capable of synthesizing this vitamin. In humans and other primates as well as in guinea pigs, ascorbic acid cannot be synthesized and gulonate is oxidized to 3-keto-L-gulonate, which is then decarboxylated to the pentose, L-xylulose.

Xylulose is a constituent of the hexose monophosphate shunt pathway; but in the reactions shown in Fig 15–15, the L-isomer of xylulose is formed from ketogulonate. If the 2 pathways are to connect, it is therefore necessary to convert L-xylulose to the D-isomer. This is accomplished by an NADPH-dependent reduction to xylitol, which is then oxidized in an NAD-dependent reaction to D-xylulose; this latter compound, after conversion to D-xylulose 5-phosphate with ATP as phosphate donor, is further metabolized in the hexose monophosphate shunt.

In the rare hereditary disease termed **"essential pentosuria,"** considerable quantities of L-xylulose appear in the urine. It is now believed that this may be explained by the absence in pentosuric patients of the enzyme necessary to accomplish reduction of L-xylulose to xylitol, and hence inability to convert the L-form of the pentose to the D-form.

Various drugs markedly increase the rate at which glucose enters the uronic acid pathway. For example, administration of barbital or of chlorobutanol to rats results in a significant increase in the conversion of glucose to glucuronate, L-gulonate, and ascorbate. This effect on L-ascorbic acid biosynthesis is shown by

many drugs, including various barbiturates, aminopyrine, and antipyrine. It is of interest that these last 2 drugs have also been reported to increase the excretion of L-xylulose in pentosuric subjects.

METABOLISM OF FRUCTOSE

Fructose may be phosphorylated to form fructose 6-phosphate, catalyzed by the same enzyme, hexokinase, that accomplishes the phosphorylation of glucose (or mannose). (See Fig 15–16.) However, the affinity of the enzyme for fructose is very small compared with its affinity for glucose. It is unlikely, therefore, that this is a major pathway for fructose utilization.

Another enzyme, **fructokinase,** is present in liver that effects the transfer of phosphate from ATP to fructose, forming fructose 1-phosphate. It has also been demonstrated in kidney and intestine. This enzyme will not phosphorylate glucose, and, unlike glucokinase, its activity is not affected by fasting or by insulin, which may explain why fructose disappears from the blood of diabetic patients at a normal rate. The K_m for fructose of the enzyme in liver is very low, indicating a very high affinity of the enzyme for its substrate. It seems probable that this is the major route for the phosphorylation of fructose.

Fructose 1-phosphate is split into D-glyceraldehyde and dihydroxyacetone phosphate by **aldolase B,** an enzyme found in the liver. The enzyme also attacks fructose 1,6-bisphosphate. Absence of this enzyme leads to a **hereditary fructose intolerance.** D-Glyceraldehyde may gain entry to the glycolysis sequence of reactions via 3 possible routes. One is by the action of **alcohol dehydrogenase** to form glycerol, which, in the presence of **glycerokinase,** forms glycerol 3-phosphate. A second alternative involves **aldehyde dehydrogenase** which forms D-glycerate from D-glyceraldehyde. In rat liver, **D-glycerate kinase** catalyzes the formation of 2-phosphoglycerate, but this enzyme is not active in human liver. Another enzyme present in liver, **triokinase,** catalyzes the phosphorylation of D-glyceraldehyde to glyceraldehyde 3-phosphate. This appears to be the major pathway for the further metabolism of D-glyceraldehyde. The 2 triose phosphates, dihydroxyacetone phosphate and glyceraldehyde 3-phosphate, may be degraded via the Embden-Meyerhof pathway or they may combine under the influence of aldolase and be converted to glucose. The latter is the fate of much of the fructose metabolized in the liver.

One consequence of hereditary fructose intolerance and of another condition due to **fructose-1,6-bisphosphatase deficiency** is a fructose-induced hypoglycemia despite the presence of high glycogen reserves. Apparently the accumulation of fructose 1-phosphate and fructose 1,6-bisphosphate inhibits the activity of liver phosphorylase.

If the liver and intestines of an experimental animal are removed, the conversion of injected fructose to

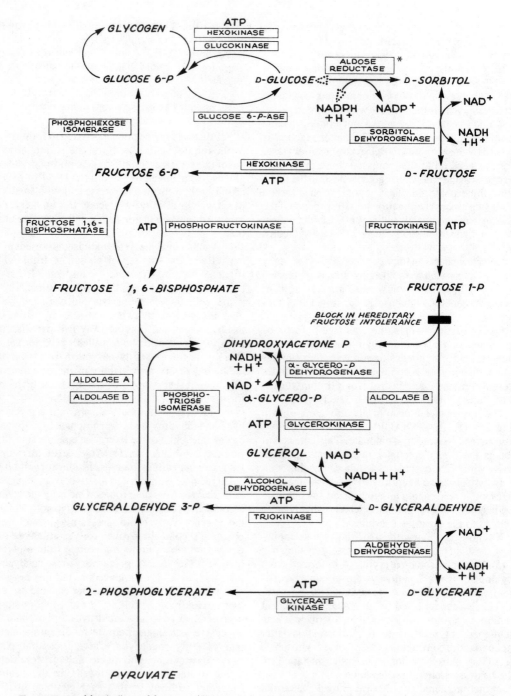

Figure 15–16. Metabolism of fructose. (*In seminal vesicles and the placenta of ungulates and whales.)

glucose does not take place and the animal succumbs to hypoglycemia unless glucose is administered. It appears that brain and muscle can utilize significant quantities of fructose only after its conversion to glucose in the liver. In humans but not in the rat, a significant amount of the fructose resulting from the digestion of sucrose is converted to glucose in the intestinal wall prior to passage into the portal circulation. Fructose is more rapidly glycolyzed by the liver than glucose. This is due most probably to the fact that it bypasses the steps in glucose metabolism catalyzed by glucokinase and phosphofructokinase, at which points metabolic control is exerted on the rate of catabolism of glucose.

Studies have indicated that fructose is metabolized by adipose tissue and that it is metabolized independently of glucose. At low concentrations, fructose is utilized by epididymal adipose tissue of the rat more slowly than glucose; at high concentrations, fructose is metabolized at a faster rate than glucose.

Free fructose is found in seminal plasma and is secreted in quantity into the fetal circulation of ungulates and whales, where it accumulates in the amniotic and allantoic fluids. Experiments demonstrated that glucose was the precursor of fructose. However, there is no evidence that the liver can convert glucose to fructose. One pathway proposed for the former conversion is via sorbitol. In seminal vesicles of sheep, glucose undergoes reduction to sorbitol catalyzed by **aldose reductase** (polyol dehydrogenase) and NADPH, followed by oxidation of sorbitol to fructose in the presence of NAD and **ketose reductase** (sorbitol dehydrogenase). Aldose reductase is found in the placenta of the ewe and is responsible for the secretion of sorbitol into the fetal blood. As in adult liver, the presence of ketose reductase in fetal liver is responsible for the conversion of sorbitol into fructose. When sorbitol is administered to the whole animal, it is converted to fructose rather than to glucose, although if given by mouth, much escapes absorption from the gut and is fermented in the colon by bacteria to products such as acetate and H_2.

METABOLISM OF GALACTOSE

Galactose (Fig 13–13) is derived from the hydrolysis in the intestine of the disaccharide **lactose, the sugar of milk.** It is readily converted in the liver to glucose. The ability of the liver to accomplish this conversion may be used as a test of hepatic function in the galactose tolerance test. The pathway by which galactose is converted to glucose is shown in Fig 15–17.

In reaction ①, galactose is phosphorylated with the aid of **galactokinase,** using ATP as phosphate donor. The product, galactose 1-phosphate, reacts with **uridine diphosphate glucose** (UDPG) to form **uridine diphosphate galactose** and glucose 1-phosphate. In this step (reaction ②), which is catalyzed by an enzyme called **galactose-1-phosphate uridyl transferase,** galactose is transferred to a position on UDPG, replacing glucose. The conversion of galactose to glucose takes place (reaction ③) in a reaction of the galactose-containing nucleotide that is catalyzed by an **epimerase.** The product is uridine diphosphate glucose, UDPG. Epimerization probably involves an oxidation and reduction at carbon 4 with NAD as

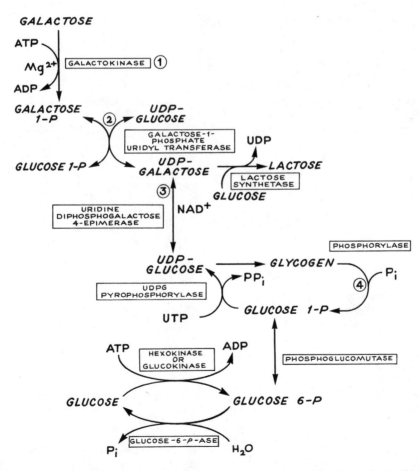

Figure 15–17. The pathway for conversion of galactose to glucose and for the synthesis of lactose.

coenzyme. Finally (reaction ④), glucose is liberated from UDPG as glucose 1-phosphate, probably after incorporation into glycogen followed by phosphorolysis.

Reaction ③ is freely reversible. In this manner glucose can be converted to galactose, so that preformed galactose is not essential in the diet. It will be recalled that galactose is required in the body not only in the formation of milk but also as a constituent of glycolipids (cerebrosides), proteoglycans, and glycoproteins.

Galactokinase is an adaptive enzyme, responding with an increased activity upon the feeding of galactose. Young animals show higher activity than adults.

In the synthesis of lactose in the mammary gland, glucose is converted to UDP-galactose by the enzymes described above. UDP-galactose condenses with glucose to yield lactose, catalyzed by **lactose synthetase.**

Inability to metabolize galactose occurs in the **galactosemias,** which may be caused by inherited defects in any of the 3 enzymes marked ①, ②, and ③ in Fig 15–17, although a deficiency in the uridyl transferase (②) is the best known. Galactose, which increases in concentration in the blood, is reduced by aldose reductase in the eye to the corresponding polyol (galacticol), which accumulates, causing cataract. The general condition is more severe if it is due to a defect in the uridyl transferase, since galactose 1-phosphate accumulates and depletes the liver of inorganic phosphate. Ultimately, liver failure and mental deterioration result.

In inherited galactose-1-phosphate uridyl transferase deficiency in the liver and red blood cells (reaction②), the epimerase (reaction③) is, however, present in adequate amounts, so that the galactosemic individual can still form UDP-galactose from glucose.

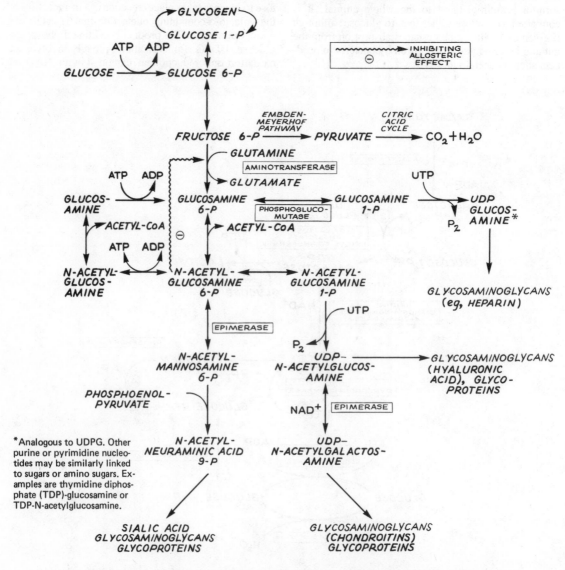

*Analogous to UDPG. Other purine or pyrimidine nucleotides may be similarly linked to sugars or amino sugars. Examples are thymidine diphosphate (TDP)-glucosamine or TDP-N-acetylglucosamine.

Figure 15–18. A summary of the interrelationships in metabolism of amino sugars.

This explains how it is possible for normal growth and development of affected children to occur regardless of the galactose-free diets used to control the symptoms of the disease. Several different genetic defects have been described that cause reduced rather than total transferase deficiency. As the enzyme is normally present in excess, a reduction in activity to 50% or even less does not cause clinical manifestation of the disease, which is apparent only in homozygotes.

The epimerase has been found deficient in erythrocytes but present in liver and elsewhere, and this third condition appears to be symptom-free.

Metabolism of Amino Sugars (Hexosamines)
(See Fig 15–18.)

Amino sugars are important components of the carbohydrate that is widely distributed throughout the body as a part of the structural elements of the tissues. The glycosaminoglycans (mucopolysaccharides; see Chapter 32) are examples of these "structural" carbohydrates. In contrast to glycogen, in which each unit of the polysaccharide is identical (a glucosyl unit), the glycosaminoglycans consist of units of 2 monosaccharides, one of which is an amino sugar.

A summary of the interrelationships in the metabolism of the amino sugars is shown in Fig 15–18. Note the pathways for the synthesis from glucose of N-acetylglucosamine and N-acetylgalactosamine as their active uridine diphosphate derivatives. Also note the pathway of synthesis of N-acetylneuraminic acid, another important amino sugar in glycoproteins and mucopolysaccharides.

● ● ●

References

Blass JP: Disorders of pyruvate metabolism. *Neurology* 1979;**29**:280.

Boyer PD (editor): *The Enzymes,* 3rd ed. Vols 5–9. Academic Press, 1972.

Busby JW, Radda GK: Page 89 in: *Current Topics in Cellular Regulation.* Vol 10. Academic Press, 1976.

Dickens F, Randle PJ, Whelan WJ (editors): *Carbohydrate Metabolism and Its Disorders.* 2 vols. Academic Press, 1968.

Greenberg DM (editor): *Metabolic Pathways,* 3rd ed. Vol 1. Academic Press, 1967.

Hers HG: The control of glycogen metabolism in the liver. *Annu Rev Biochem* 1976;**45**:167.

Hers HG: *Rev internat d'hépatol* 1959;**9**:35.

Huijing F: Galactose metabolism and galactosemia. *Trends Biochem Sci* (June) 1978:129.

Krebs EG: Page 99 in: *Current Topics in Cellular Regulation.* Vol 5. Academic Press, 1972.

Krebs HA: Gluconeogenesis. *Proc R Soc Lond* [*Biol*] 1964;**159**:545.

Lindahl U, Höök M: Glycosaminoglycans and their binding to biological macromolecules. *Annu Rev Biochem* 1978;**47**:385.

Marshall RD: Glycoproteins. *Annu Rev Biochem* 1972;**41**:673.

Rapoport S: Page 69 in: *Essays in Biochemistry.* Vol 4. Campbell PN, Greville GD (editors). Academic Press, 1968.

Stanbury JB, Wyngaarden JB, Fredrickson DS (editors): *The Metabolic Basis of Inherited Disease,* 4th ed. McGraw-Hill, 1978.

Weber G: Page 263 in: *The Biological Basis of Medicine.* Vol 2. Bittar EE, Bittar N (editors). Academic Press, 1968.

Whelan WJ (editor): *Control of Glycogen Metabolism.* Academic Press, 1968.

Whelan WJ: On the origin of primer for glycogen synthesis. *Trends Biochem Sci* (Jan) 1976:13.

16 | Lipids

Peter A. Mayes, PhD, DSc

The lipids are a heterogeneous group of compounds related, either actually or potentially, to the fatty acids. They have the common property of being (1) relatively insoluble in water and (2) soluble in nonpolar solvents such as ether, chloroform, and benzene. Thus, the lipids include fats, oils, waxes, and related compounds.

A lipoid is a "fatlike" substance that may not actually be related to the fatty acids, although occasionally the terms "lipid" and "lipoid" are used synonymously.

Lipids are important dietary constituents not only because of their high energy value but also because of the fat-soluble vitamins and the essential fatty acids contained in the fat of natural foods. In the body, fat serves as an efficient source of energy—both directly and potentially, when stored in adipose tissue. It serves as a thermal insulator in the subcutaneous tissues and around certain organs, and nonpolar lipids act as electrical insulators allowing rapid propagation of depolarization waves along myelinated nerves. The fat content of nerve tissue is particularly high. Combinations of fat and protein (lipoproteins) are important cellular constituents, occurring both in the cell membrane and in the mitochondria within the cytoplasm, and serving also as the means of transporting lipids in the blood.

Classification

The following classification of lipids has been proposed by Bloor:

A. Simple Lipids: Esters of fatty acids with various alcohols.

1. Fats–Esters of fatty acids with glycerol. A fat in the liquid state is known as an oil.

2. Waxes–Esters of fatty acids with higher molecular weight monohydric alcohols.

B. Compound Lipids: Esters of fatty acids containing groups in addition to an alcohol and a fatty acid.

1. Phospholipids–Lipids containing, in addition to fatty acids and an alcohol, a phosphoric acid residue. They also have nitrogen-containing bases and other substituents. In many phospholipids—eg, the glycerophospholipids—the alcohol is glycerol, but in others—eg, the sphingophospholipids—it is sphingosine.

2. Glycolipids–Compounds of the fatty acids with carbohydrate, containing nitrogen but no phosphoric acid.

3. Other compound lipids, such as sulfolipids and aminolipids. Lipoproteins may also be placed in this category.

C. Derived Lipids: Substances derived from the above groups by hydrolysis. These include fatty acids (both saturated and unsaturated), glycerol, steroids, alcohols in addition to glycerol and sterols, fatty aldehydes, and ketone bodies (see Ketosis, p 233).

Because they are uncharged, glycerides (acylglycerols), cholesterol, and cholesteryl esters are termed **neutral lipids.**

FATTY ACIDS

Fatty acids are obtained from the hydrolysis of fats. Fatty acids that occur in natural fats usually contain an **even number** of carbon atoms (because they are synthesized from 2-carbon units) and are straight-chain derivatives. The chain may be saturated (containing no double bonds) or unsaturated (containing one or more double bonds).

Nomenclature

The most frequently used systematic nomenclature is based on naming the fatty acid after the hydrocarbon with the same number of carbon atoms, **-oic** being substituted for the final **e** in the name of the hydrocarbon (Genevan system). Thus, saturated acids end in **-anoic,** eg, octanoic acid, and unsaturated acids with double bonds end in **-enoic,** eg, octadecenoic acid (oleic acid). Carbon atoms are numbered from the carboxyl carbon (carbon No. 1). The carbon atom adjacent to the carboxyl carbon (No. 2) is also known as the α-carbon. Carbon atom No. 3 is the β-carbon, and the end methyl carbon is known as the ω-carbon. Various conventions are in use for indicating the number and position of the double bonds, eg, Δ^9 indicates a double bond between carbon atoms 9 and 10 of the fatty acid. A widely used convention is to indicate the number of carbon atoms, the number of double bonds, and the positions of the double bonds as shown in Figs 16–1 and 16–2.

A closer examination of the position of the double bonds in naturally occurring fatty acids reveals that

18:1; 9

$$CH_3(CH_2)_7 \overset{10}{C}H = \overset{9}{C}H(CH_2)_7 COOH$$

or

ω-9, C18:1

$$\overset{\omega}{C}H_3 \overset{2}{C}H_2 \overset{3}{C}H_2 \overset{4}{C}H_2 \overset{5}{C}H_2 \overset{6}{C}H_2 \overset{7}{C}H_2 \overset{8}{C}H_2 \overset{9}{C}H = CH(CH_2)_7 COOH$$

Figure 16–1. Oleic acid.

18:2; 9, 12

$$CH_3(CH_2)_4 \overset{13}{C}H = \overset{12}{C}HCH_2 \overset{10}{C}H = \overset{9}{C}H(CH_2)_7 COOH$$

or

ω-6, C18:2

$$\overset{\omega}{C}H_3 \overset{2}{C}H_2 \overset{3}{C}H_2 \overset{4}{C}H_2 \overset{5}{C}H_2 \overset{6}{C}H = CHCH_2 CH = CH(CH_2)_7 COOH$$

Figure 16–2. Linoleic acid.

they are related to the –CH_3 or ω-end of the fatty acid rather than the carboxyl group. Thus, a series of fatty acids of increasing chain length or increasing desaturation based on oleic acid are ω-9 acids, series based on linoleic acid are ω-6 acids, and a series based on linolenic acid are ω-3 acids. In animals, additional double bonds are introduced only **between the existing double bond (eg, ω-9, ω-6, or ω-3, respectively) and the carboxyl carbon** (Figs 16–1 and 16–2).

Table 16–1. Saturated fatty acids.

Acetic	CH_3COOH	Major end product of carbohydrate fermentation by rumen organisms
Propionic	C_2H_5COOH	An end product of carbohydrate fermentation by rumen organisms
Butyric	C_3H_7COOH	In certain fats in small amounts (especially butter). An end product of carbohydrate fermentation by rumen organisms.
Caproic	$C_5H_{11}COOH$	
Caprylic (octanoic)	$C_7H_{15}COOH$	In small amounts in many fats (including butter), especially those of plant origin
Decanoic (capric)	$C_9H_{19}COOH$	
Lauric	$C_{11}H_{23}COOH$	Spermaceti, cinnamon, palm kernel, coconut oils, laurels
Myristic	$C_{13}H_{27}COOH$	Nutmeg, palm kernel, coconut oils, myrtles
Palmitic	$C_{15}H_{31}COOH$	Common in all animal and plant fats
Stearic	$C_{17}H_{35}COOH$	
Arachidic	$C_{19}H_{39}COOH$	Peanut (arachis) oil
Behenic	$C_{21}H_{43}COOH$	Seeds
Lignoceric	$C_{23}H_{47}COOH$	Cerebrosides, peanut oil

Saturated Fatty Acids

Saturated fatty acids may be envisaged as based on acetic acid as the first member of the series. Examples of the acids in this series are shown in Table 16–1.

Other higher members of the series are known to occur, particularly in waxes. A few branched-chain fatty acids have also been isolated from both plant and animal sources.

Unsaturated Fatty Acids

These may be further subdivided according to degree of unsaturation.

A. Monounsaturated (Monoethenoid) Acids: *Examples:* Oleic acid, palmitoleic acid, found in nearly all fats.

B. Polyunsaturated (Polyethenoid) Acids:

1. Two double bonds. *Example:* Linoleic acid* (18:2; 9, 12). Occurs in many seed oils, eg, corn, peanut, cottonseed, soybean oils.

2. Three double bonds. *Example:* Linolenic acid* (18:3; 9, 12, 15). Found frequently with linoleic acid but particularly in linseed oil.

3. Four double bonds. *Example:* Arachidonic acid* (20:4; 5, 8, 11, 14). Found in small quantities with linoleic and linolenic acids but particularly in peanut oil. (See p 209.)

C. Prostaglandins (PG) were originally discovered in seminal plasma but are now known to exist in virtually every mammalian tissue and have important physiologic and pharmacologic activities. They are synthesized in vivo by cyclization of the center of the carbon chain of 20-C (eicosanoic) polyunsaturated fatty acids (eg, arachidonic acid) to form a cyclopentane ring (Fig 16–3). A related series of compounds, the **thromboxanes** (TX), discovered in platelets, have the cyclopentane ring interrupted with an oxygen atom (oxane ring). Three eicosanoic fatty acids give rise to 3 series of prostaglandins characterized by the number of double bonds in the acyl side chains, ie, PG_1, PG_2, PG_3 series. Variations in the substituent groups attached to the rings give rise to different types in each series of prostaglandins and thromboxanes, labeled A, B, etc. For example, the "E" type of prostaglandin (as in PGE_2) has a keto group in position 9, whereas the "F" type has a hydroxyl group in this position. PGI_2 is known as **prostacyclin.**

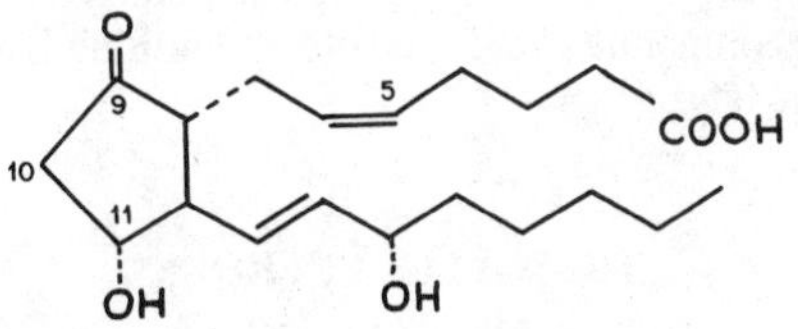

Figure 16–3. Prostaglandin E_2 (PGE_2).

*Linoleic, linolenic, and arachidonic are the so-called essential fatty acids (see p 210), but arachidonic acid can be synthesized from linoleic acid by humans since they are both of the ω-6 series.

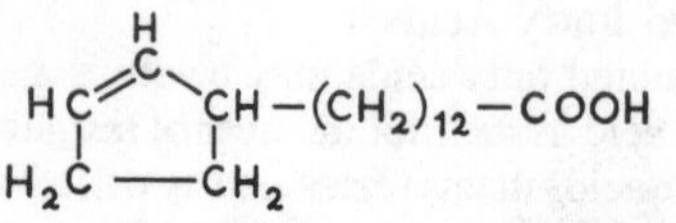

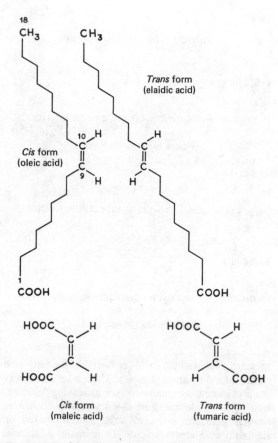

Figure 16–4. Chaulmoogric acid.

D. Many other fatty acids have been detected in biologic material. For example, fish oil contains 22:5 and 22:6 unsaturated fatty acids. Various other structures, such as hydroxy groups (ricinoleic acid) or cyclic groups, have been found in nature. An example of the latter is chaulmoogric acid (Fig 16–4).

Isomerism in Unsaturated Fatty Acids

Variations in the location of the double bonds in unsaturated fatty acid chains produce isomers. Thus, oleic acid could have 15 different positional isomers.

Geometric isomerism depends on the orientation of atoms or groups around the axis of double bonds. Some compounds differ only in the orientation of their parts around this axis. This is noteworthy in the chemistry of steroids. If the radicals that are being considered are on the same side of the bond, the compound is called *cis*; if on opposite sides, *trans*. This can be illustrated with oleic and elaidic acids or with dicarboxylic acids such as fumaric and maleic acids (Fig 16–5).

In acids with a greater degree of unsaturation, there are, of course, more geometric isomers. Naturally occurring unsaturated long chain fatty acids are nearly all of the *cis* **configuration,** the molecule being "bent" at the position of the double bond. Thus, arachidonic acid, having 4 double bonds, is U-shaped.

Alcohols

Alcohols found in lipid molecules include glycerol, cholesterol, and higher alcohols (eg, cetyl alcohol, $C_{16}H_{33}OH$), usually found in the waxes.

Among the unsaturated alcohols found in fats are a number of important pigments. These include phytol (phytyl alcohol), which is also a constituent of chlorophyll, and lycophyll ($C_{40}H_{56}O_2$), a polyunsaturated dihydroxy alcohol that occurs in tomatoes as a purple pigment.

Fatty Aldehydes

The fatty acids may be reduced to fatty aldehydes. These compounds are found either combined or free in natural fats.

TRIACYLGLYCEROLS*
(Triglycerides)

The triacylglycerols, or so-called neutral fats, are esters of the alcohol glycerol and fatty acids. In naturally occurring fats, the proportion of triacylglycerol

*See explanatory note on p 199.

Figure 16–5. Geometric isomerism of oleic and elaidic acids and of maleic and fumaric acids.

molecules containing the same fatty acid residue in all 3 ester positions is very small. They are nearly all **mixed acylglycerols.**

In Fig 16–6, if all 3 fatty acids were the same and if R were $C_{17}H_{35}$, the fat would be known as tristearin, since it consists of 3 stearic acid residues esterified with glycerol. In a mixed acylglycerol, more than one fatty acid is involved (Figs 16–7 and 16–8).

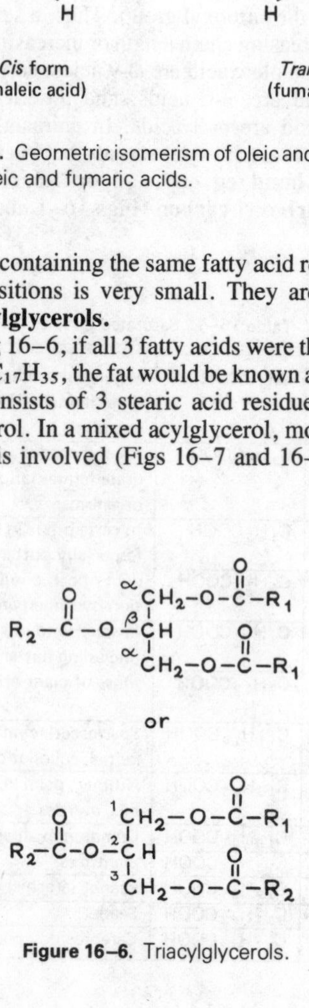

Figure 16–6. Triacylglycerols.

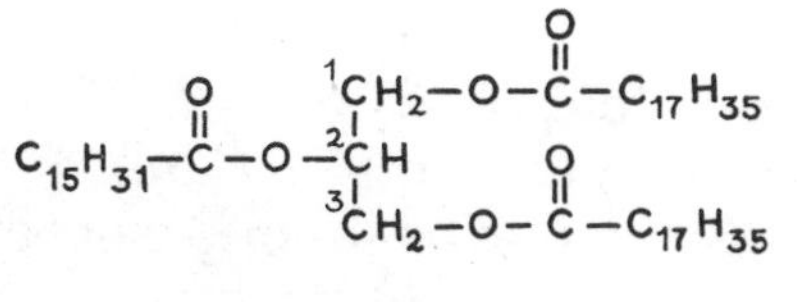

Figure 16–7. 1,3-Distearopalmitin (or α,α'-distearopalmitin).

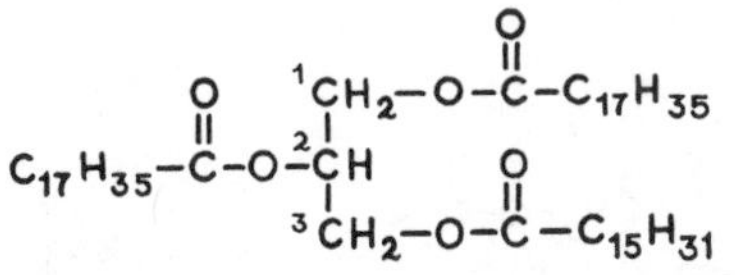

Figure 16–8. 1,2-Distearopalmitin (or α,β-distearopalmitin).

Nomenclature

The numbering system shown above has largely superseded the older α-, β- nomenclature. When it is required to number the carbon atoms of glycerol unambiguously, the -sn- (stereochemical numbering) system is used, eg, 1,2-distearyl-3-palmityl-sn-glycerol (as above, or more generally as a projection formula shown in Fig 16–9).

Partial acylglycerols consisting of mono- and diacylglycerols wherein a single fatty acid or 2 fatty acids are esterified with glycerol are also found in the tissues. These are of particular significance in the synthesis and hydrolysis of triacylglycerols.

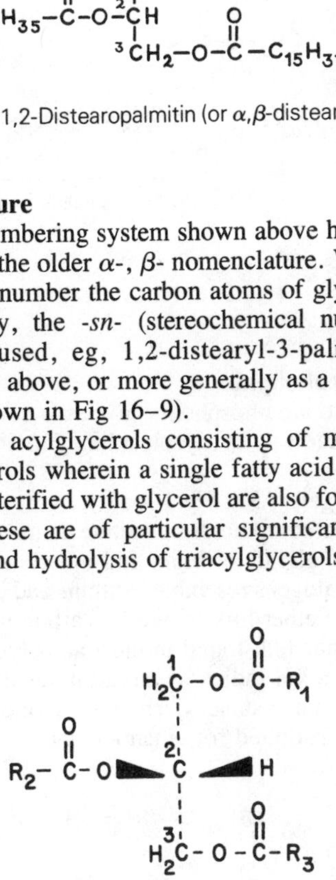

Figure 16–9. Triacyl-sn-glycerol.

Waxes

If the fatty acid is esterified with a monohydric alcohol of high molecular weight instead of with glycerol, the resulting compound is called a wax.

PHOSPHOLIPIDS

The phospholipids include the following: (1) phosphatidic acid and phosphatidylglycerols, (2) phosphatidylcholine, (3) phosphatidylethanolamine, (4) phosphatidylinositol, (5) phosphatidylserine, (6) lysophospholipids, (7) plasmalogens, and (8) sphingomyelins.

Phosphatidic Acid & Phosphatidylglycerols

Phosphatidic acid is important as an intermediate in the synthesis of triacylglycerols and phospholipids but is not found in any great quantity in tissues (Fig 16–10).

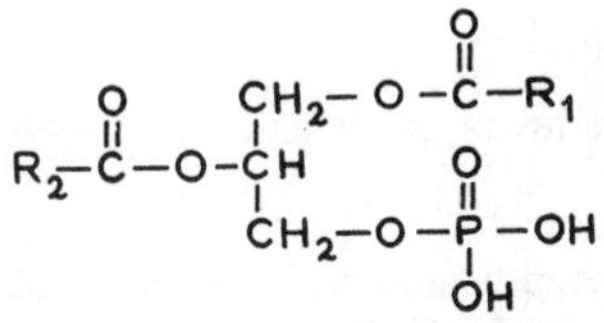

Figure 16–10. Phosphatidic acid.

Cardiolipin is a phospholipid that is found in membranes of mitochondria. It is formed from **phosphatidylglycerol** (Fig 16–11).

Phosphatidylcholine (Lecithin)

The lecithins contain glycerol and fatty acids, as do the simple fats, but they also contain phosphoric acid and choline. The lecithins are widely distributed in the cells of the body, having both metabolic and structural functions in membranes. Dipalmityl lecithin is a very effective surface active agent, preventing adherence, due to surface tension, of the inner surfaces of the lungs. However, most phospholipids have a

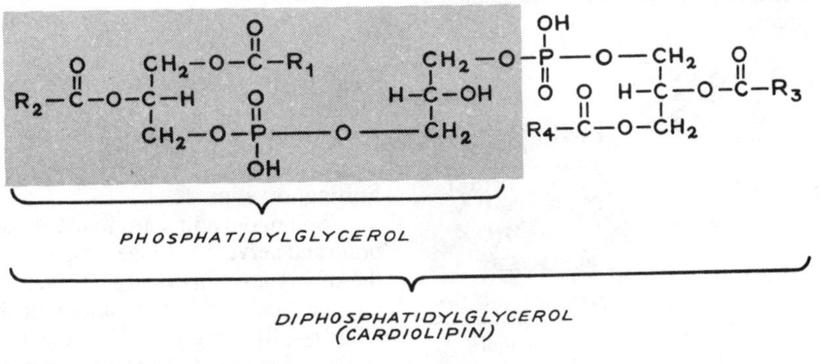

Figure 16–11. Diphosphatidylglycerol (cardiolipin).

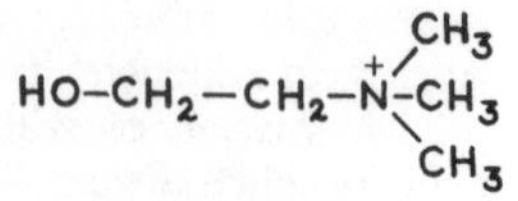

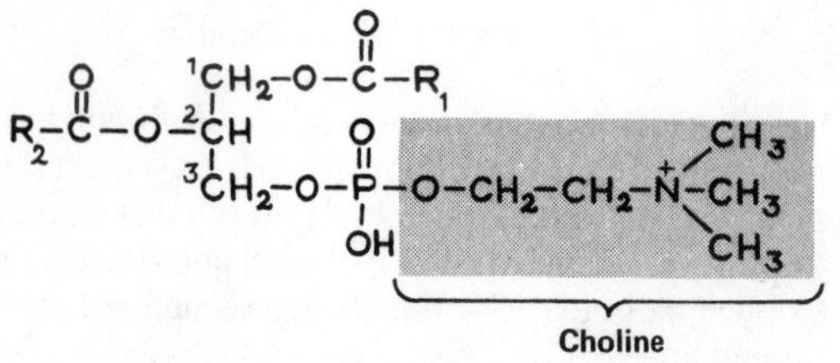

Figure 16–12. 3-Phosphatidylcholine.

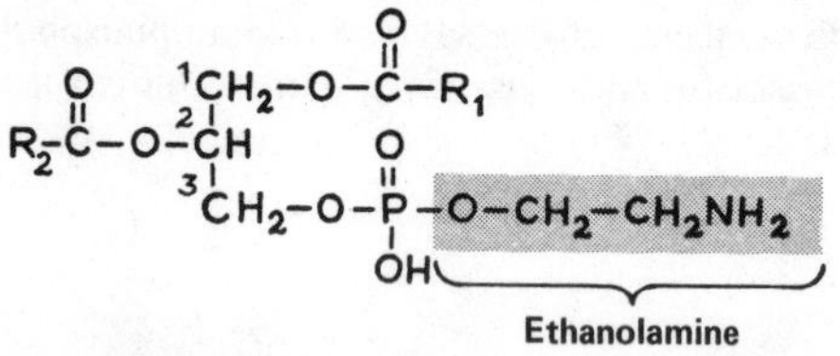

Figure 16–13. 3-Phosphatidylethanolamine.

saturated acyl radical in the C_1 position and an unsaturated radical in the C_2 position (Fig 16–12).

Phosphatidylethanolamine (Cephalin)

The cephalins differ from lecithins only in that ethanolamine replaces choline (Fig 16–13).

Phosphatidylinositol

Inositol as a constituent of lipids was first discovered in acid-fast bacteria. Later it was found to occur in phospholipids of brain tissue and of soybeans as well as in other plant phospholipids. The inositol is present as the stereoisomer, myo-inositol (Fig 16–14).

Phosphatidylserine (See Fig 16–15.)

A cephalinlike phospholipid, phosphatidylserine, which contains the amino acid serine rather than ethanolamine, has been found in tissues. In addition, phospholipids containing threonine have been isolated from natural sources.

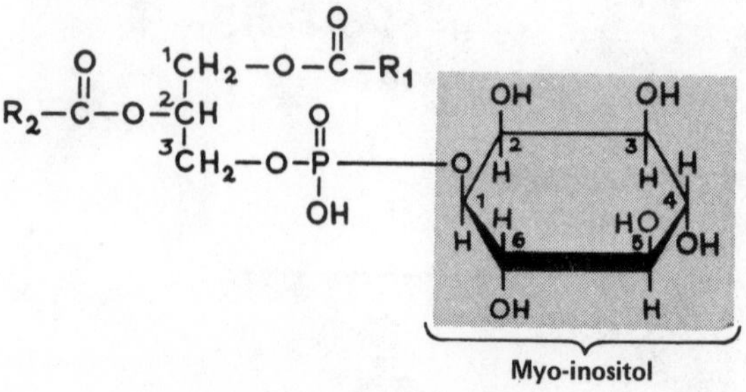

Figure 16–14. 3-Phosphatidylinositol.

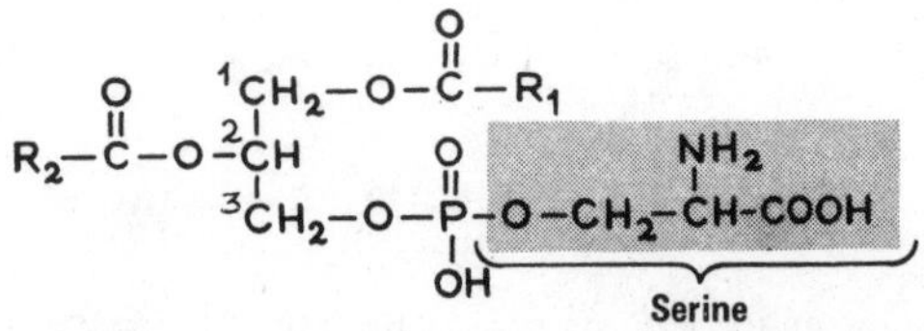

Figure 16–15. 3-Phosphatidylserine.

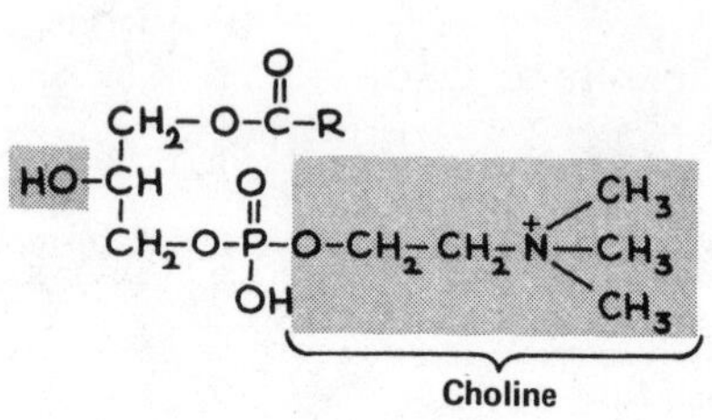

Figure 16–16. Lysolecithin.

Lysophospholipids

These are phosphoacylglycerols containing only one acyl radical, eg, lysolecithin (Fig 16–16).

Plasmalogens (See Fig 16–17.)

These compounds constitute as much as 10% of the phospholipids of brain and muscle. Structurally, the plasmalogens resemble lecithins and cephalins but possess an ether link on the C_1 carbon instead of the normal ester link found in most acylglycerols. Typically, the alkyl radical is an unsaturated alcohol.

In some instances, choline, serine, or inositol may be substituted for ethanolamine.

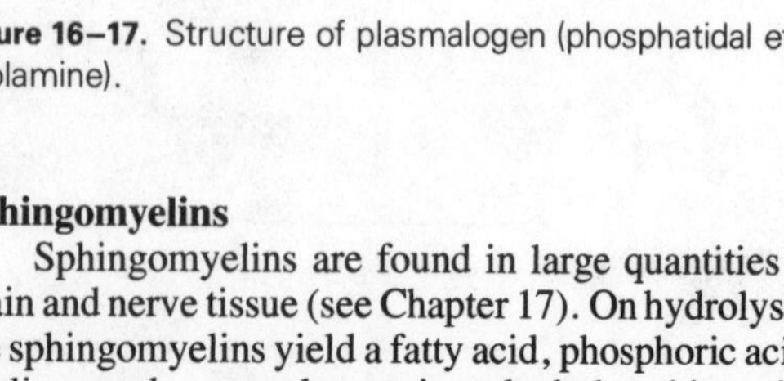

Figure 16–17. Structure of plasmalogen (phosphatidal ethanolamine).

Sphingomyelins

Sphingomyelins are found in large quantities in brain and nerve tissue (see Chapter 17). On hydrolysis, the sphingomyelins yield a fatty acid, phosphoric acid, choline, and a complex amino alcohol, sphingosine (Fig 16–18). No glycerol is present. The combination sphingosine plus fatty acid is known as **ceramide,** a structure also found in the glycolipids (see below).

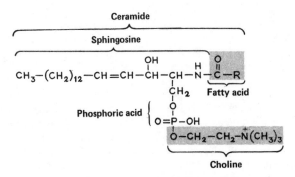

Figure 16–18. Structure of a sphingomyelin.

GLYCOLIPIDS
(Glycosphingolipids)

Glycolipids contain **ceramide** plus **galactose.** Therefore, they may also be classified with the sphingomyelins as **sphingolipids.** Simple glycolipids contain only galactose, a high molecular weight fatty acid, and sphingosine. They are known as **cerebrosides.** Individual cerebrosides are differentiated by the type of fatty acid in the molecule. These are **kerasin,** containing lignoceric acid; **cerebron,** with a hydroxy lig-

$$CH_3-(CH_2)_{22}-COOH$$
LIGNOCERIC ACID

$$CH_3-(CH_2)_{21}-CH(OH)-COOH$$
CEREBRONIC ACID

$$CH_3-(CH_2)_7-CH=CH-(CH_2)_{13}-COOH$$
NERVONIC ACID

$$CH_3-(CH_2)_7-CH=CH-(CH_2)_{12}-CH(OH)-COOH$$
OXYNERVONIC ACID

Figure 16–19. Characteristic fatty acids of cerebrosides.

noceric acid (cerebronic acid); **nervon,** containing an unsaturated homolog of lignoceric acid called nervonic acid; and **oxynervon,** having the hydroxy derivative of nervonic acid as its constituent fatty acid (Fig 16–19). Stearic acid is a major component of the fatty acids of rat brain cerebrosides. The cerebrosides are found in many tissues besides brain and the myelin of nerve fibers.

Sulfatides are cerebrosides in which the galactose residue is sulfated (Fig 16–20).

Gangliosides (Fig 16–21) are more complex glycolipids that occur in the brain. They contain **sialic acid,** eg, N-acetylneuraminic acid (Nana; see p 150), **ceramide** (containing fatty acids of which 80–90% are of C-18 chain length), and **3 molecules of hexose** (glucose and galactose). Hexosamine is a common constituent of virtually all naturally occurring gangliosides; the N-acetylneuraminic acid (Nana) content varies between 1 and 5 molecules per molecule of ganglioside, giving rise to di-, trisialogangliosides, etc.

```
Ceramide—Glucose—Galactose—N—Acetylgalactosamine—Galactose
 (Acyl-                       |
sphingo-                     Nana
 sine)
              or

     Cer—Glc—Gal—GalNAc—Gal
                   |
                 Nana
```

Figure 16–21. G$_{M1}$ ganglioside, a monosialoganglioside.

STEROIDS

The steroids are often found in association with fat. They may be separated from the fat after saponification (see p 195), since they occur in the "unsaponifiable residue." All of the steroids have a similar cyclic

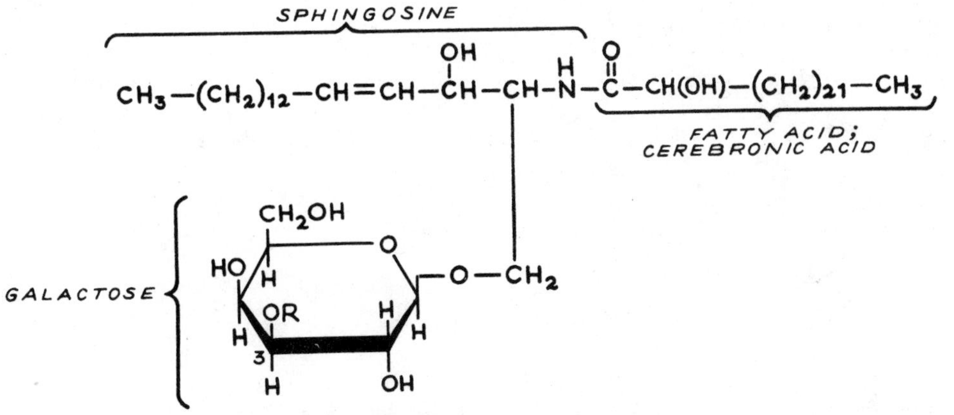

Figure 16–20. Structure of a cerebroside (R = H) and a sulfatide (cerebroside sulfate, R = SO$_4^{2-}$).

nucleus resembling phenanthrene (rings A, B, and C) to which a cyclopentane ring (D) is attached. However, the rings are not uniformly saturated, so the parent (completely saturated) substance is better designated as cyclopentanoperhydrophenanthrene. The carbon positions on the steroid nucleus are numbered as shown in Fig 16-22.

It is important to realize that in structural formulas of steroids, a simple hexagonal ring denotes a completely saturated 6-carbon ring with all valences satisfied by hydrogen bonds unless shown otherwise, ie, it is not a benzene ring. All double bonds are shown as such. Methyl side chains are shown as single bonds unattached at the farther (methyl) end. These occur typically at positions 10 and 13 (constituting C atoms 19 and 18). A side chain at position 17 is usual (as in cholesterol). If the compound has one or more hydroxyl groups and no carbonyl or carboxyl groups, it is a **sterol,** and the name terminates in -ol.

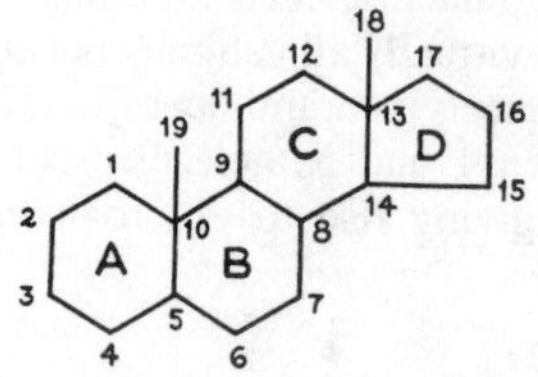

Stereochemical Aspects

Because of their complexity and the possibilities of asymmetry in the molecule, steroids have many potential stereoisomers. Each of the 6-carbon rings of the steroid nucleus is capable of existing in the 3-dimensional conformation either of a "chair" or a "boat" (Fig 16-23).

In naturally occurring steroids, virtually all the rings are in the "chair" form, which is the more stable conformation. With respect to each other, the rings can be either -*cis* or -*trans* (Fig 16-24).

The junction between the A and B rings can be -*cis* or -*trans* in naturally occurring steroids. That between B and C is -*trans* and the C/D junction is -*trans* except in cardiac glycosides and toad poisons. Bonds attaching substituent groups above the plane of the rings are shown with bold solid lines (β), whereas those bonds attaching groups below are indicated with broken lines (α). The A ring of a 5α steroid is always -*trans* to the B ring, whereas it is -*cis* in a 5β steroid. The methyl groups attached to C$_{10}$ and C$_{13}$ are invariably in the β configuration.

Cholesterol (See Fig 16-25.)

Cholesterol is widely distributed in all cells of the

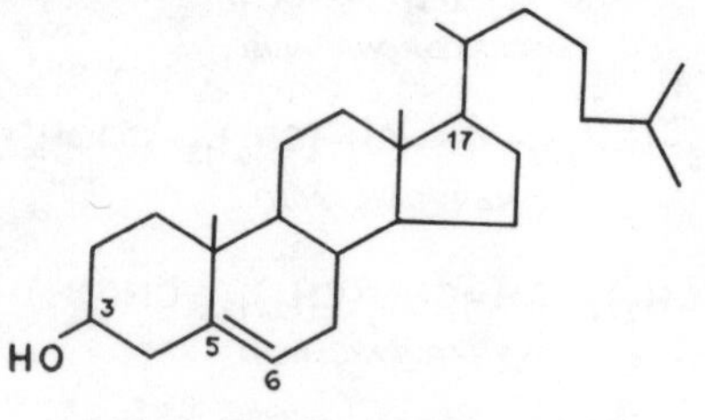

Figure 16-22. Cyclopentanoperhydrophenanthrene nucleus.

"Chair" form

"Boat" form

Figure 16-23. Conformations of stereoisomers.

Figure 16-25. Cholesterol.

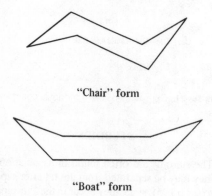

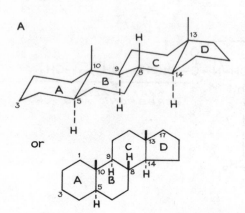

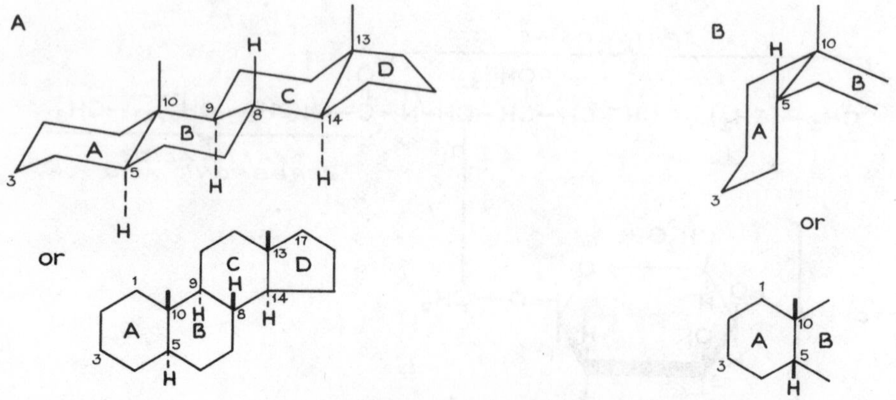

Figure 16-24. Generalized steroid nucleus, showing (A) an all-*trans* configuration between adjacent rings and (B) a *cis* configuration between rings A and B.

body, but particularly in nervous tissue. It is the parent compound of all steroids synthesized in the body. It occurs in animal fats but not in plant fats. The metabolism of cholesterol is discussed on p 237. Cholesterol is designated as 3-hydroxy-5,6-cholestene.

Ergosterol (See Fig 16–26.)

Ergosterol occurs in plants and yeast. It is important as a precursor of vitamin D. When irradiated with ultraviolet light, it acquires antirachitic properties consequent to the opening of ring B.

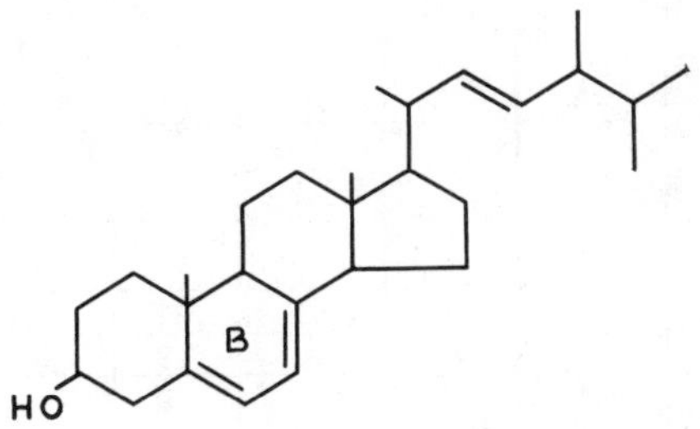

Figure 16–26. Ergosterol.

Coprosterol

Coprosterol (coprostanol) occurs in feces as a result of the reduction of the double bond of cholesterol between C_5 and C_6 by bacteria in the intestine. The orientation of rings A and B (between carbon atoms 5 and 10), which is *trans* in cholesterol, is *cis* in coprosterol.

Other Important Sterols & Steroids

These include the bile acids, adrenocortical hormones, sex hormones, D vitamins, cardiac glycosides, sitosterols of the plant kingdom, and some alkaloids.

Polyprenoid Compounds

Although not steroids, these compounds are related because they are synthesized, like cholesterol (see p 237), from 5-carbon isoprene units (Fig 16–27). They include **ubiquinone** (see p 131), a member of the respiratory chain in mitochondria, and the long chain alcohol **dolichol** (see Chapter 32), which takes part in glycoprotein synthesis by transferring carbohydrate residues to asparagine residues of the polypeptide. Plant-derived isoprenoid compounds include rubber, camphor, the fat-soluble vitamins (see Chapter 10), and β-carotene (provitamin A).

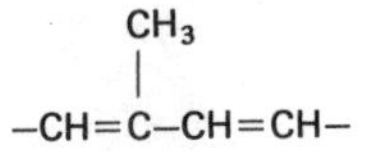

Figure 16–27. Isoprene unit.

THE PLASMA LIPIDS & LIPOPROTEINS

Extraction of the plasma lipids with a suitable lipid solvent and subsequent separation of the extract into various classes of lipids shows the presence of triacylglycerols, phospholipids, cholesterol and cholesteryl esters, and, in addition, the existence of a much smaller fraction of unesterified long chain fatty acids (free fatty acids, FFA) that accounts for less than 5% of the total fatty acid present in the plasma. This latter fraction, the **free fatty acids,** is now known to be metabolically the most active of the plasma lipids. An analysis of blood plasma showing the major lipid classes is given in Table 16–2.

Since lipids account for much of the energy expenditure of the body, the problem is presented of transporting a large quantity of hydrophobic material (lipid) in an aqueous environment (blood plasma). This is solved by associating the more insoluble lipids with more polar ones such as phospholipids and then combining them with cholesterol and protein to form a **hydrophilic lipoprotein complex.** It is in this way that triacylglycerols derived from intestinal absorption of fat or from the liver are transported in the blood as chylomicrons and very low density lipoproteins. Fat is released from adipose tissue in the form of free fatty acids and carried in the unesterified state in the plasma as an albumin–free fatty acid complex. Many classes of lipids are, therefore, transported in the blood as lipoproteins.

Pure fat is less dense than water; it follows that as the proportion of lipid to protein in lipoproteins increases, the density decreases. Use is made of this property in separating the various lipoproteins in plasma by ultracentrifugation. The rate at which each lipoprotein floats through a solution of NaCl (specific gravity 1.063) may be expressed in Svedberg (Sf) units of flotation. One Sf unit is equal to 10^{-13} cm/s/dyne/g at 26 C. The composition of the various lipoprotein

Table 16–2. Lipids of the blood plasma in humans.

Lipid	mg/dL	
	Mean	Range
Total lipid	570	360–820
Triacylglycerol	142	80–180*
Total phospholipid†	215	123–390
Lecithin		50–200
Cephalin		50–130
Sphingomyelins		15–35
Total cholesterol	200	107–320
Free cholesterol (nonesterified)	55	26–106
Free fatty acids (nonesterified)	12	6–16*

Total fatty acids (as stearic) range from 200–800 mg/dL; 45% are triacylglycerols, 35% phospholipids, 15% cholesteryl ester, and less than 5% free fatty acids.

*Varies with nutritional state.
†Analyzed as lipid phosphorus; mean lipid phosphorus = 9.2 mg/dL (range, 6.1–14.5). Lipid phosphorus × 25 = phospholipid as lecithin (4% phosphorus).

Table 16–3. Composition of the lipoproteins in plasma of man. (Adapted from Olson & Vester, 1960.)

Fraction	Source	Diameter (nm)	Density	Sf	Protein (%)	Total Lipid (%)	Triacyl-glycerol	Phospho-lipid	Choles-teryl Ester	Choles-terol (Free)	Free Fatty Acids
								Percentages of Total Lipid			
Chylomicrons	Intestine	100–1000	< 0.96	> 400	1–2	98–99	88	8	3	1	...
Very low density lipoproteins (VLDL)	Liver and intestine	30–80	0.96–1.006	20–400	7–10	90–93	56	20	15	8	1
Low density lipoproteins LDL 1 or IDL	VLDL chylo-microns	25–30	1.006–1.019	12–20	11	89	29	26	34	9	1
LDL 2		20–25	1.019–1.063	2–12	21	79	13	28	48	10	1
High density lipoproteins HDL 1*	Liver; ? intestine	20	1.063	0–2							
HDL 2		10–20	1.063–1.125		33	67	16	43	31	10	...
HDL 3		7.5–10	1.125–1.210		57	43	13	46	29	6	6
Albumin-FFA	Adipose tissue		> 1.2810		99	1	0	0	0	0	100

IDL, intermediate density lipoprotein; FFA, free fatty acids.
*This fraction is quantitatively insignificant.

fractions obtained by centrifugation is shown in Table 16–3; the density of lipoproteins increases as the protein content rises and the lipid content falls and as the size of the particle becomes smaller. The various chemical classes of lipids are seen to occur in varying amounts in most of the lipoprotein fractions. Since the fractions represent the physiologic entities present in the plasma, mere chemical analysis of the plasma lipids (apart from free fatty acids) yields little information on their physiology.

In addition to the use of technics depending on their density, lipoproteins may be separated according to their electrophoretic properties (Fig 16–28) and

may be identified more accurately by means of immunoelectrophoresis. Apart from FFA, 4 major groups of lipoproteins have been identified that are important physiologically and in clinical diagnosis. These are **chylomicrons,** very low density lipoproteins (**VLDL** or pre-β-lipoproteins), low density lipoproteins (**LDL** or β-lipoproteins), and high density lipoproteins (**HDL** or α-lipoproteins). Triacylglycerol is the predominant lipid in chylomicrons and VLDL, whereas cholesterol and phospholipid are the predominant lipids in LDL and HDL, respectively (Table 16–3).

The protein moiety of lipoproteins is known as an apolipoprotein or apoprotein, constituting nearly 60% of some HDL and as little as 1% of chylomicrons. Many lipoproteins contain more than one type of apoprotein polypeptide. They differ in their amino acid content and may be identified from their terminal amino acid residues by polyacrylamide gel electrophoresis or by immunochemical methods. Apoproteins are prepared by delipidation of isolated lipoproteins. The lipid-free apoproteins may be purified by gel filtration or by ion-exchange chromatography.

The larger lipoproteins—such as chylomicrons and VLDL—consist of a **lipid core** of **nonpolar triacylgylcerol** and **cholesteryl ester** surrounded by more polar phospholipid, cholesterol, and apoproteins that can solubilize the particle in the surrounding aqueous plasma.

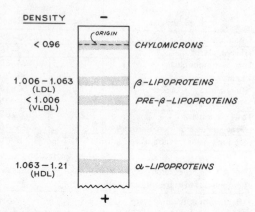

Figure 16–28. Separation of plasma lipoproteins by electrophoresis.

REACTIONS & PROPERTIES OF LIPIDS

Hydrolysis

Hydrolysis of a lipid such as a triacylglycerol may be accomplished enzymatically through the action of lipases, yielding fatty acids and glycerol. Use may be made of the property of pancreatic lipase to attack the ester bonds in positions 1 and 3 preferentially to position 2 of triacylglycerols. **Phospholipases** attack the various ester linkages in phospholipids. Their specificity may be used to analyze the components of phospholipids. The sites of action of the various phospholipases are discussed on p 217.

Saponification

Hydrolysis of a fat by alkali is called **saponification.** The products are glycerol and the alkali salts of the fatty acids, which are called **soaps.** Acid hydrolysis of a fat yields the free fatty acids and glycerol. Soaps are cleansing agents because of their emulsifying action. Some soaps of high molecular weight and a considerable degree of unsaturation are selective germicides. Others, such as sodium ricinoleate, have detoxifying activity against diphtheria and tetanus toxins.

Unsaponifiable Matter

Unsaponifiable matter includes substances in natural fats that cannot be saponified by alkali but are soluble in ether or petroleum ether. Since soaps are not ether-soluble, they may be separated from lipid mixtures by extraction with these solvents following saponification of the fat. Ketones, hydrocarbons, high molecular weight alcohols, and the steroids are examples of unsaponifiable residues of natural fats.

Hydrogenation

Hydrogenation of unsaturated fats in the presence of a catalyst (nickel) is known as "hardening." It is commercially valuable as a method of converting these liquid fats, usually of plant origin, into solid fats as lard substitutes or margarines.

Rancidity

Rancidity is a chemical change that results in unpleasant odors and taste in a fat. The oxygen of the air is believed to attack the double bond in fatty acids to form a peroxide linkage. Lead or copper catalyzes rancidity; exclusion of oxygen or the addition of an antioxidant delays the process. Free radicals are produced during peroxide formation, and these can damage living tissues unless antioxidants, eg, tocopherols (vitamin E), are present. Peroxidation is also catalyzed in vivo by heme compounds and by the enzyme **lipoxygenase** found in platelets.

Spontaneous Oxidation

Oils that contain highly unsaturated fatty acids (eg, linseed oil) are spontaneously oxidized by atmospheric oxygen at ordinary temperatures and form a hard, waterproof material. Such oils are added for this purpose to paints and shellacs. They are then known as "drying oils."

TWO MODERN METHODS FOR SEPARATING & IDENTIFYING LIPIDS IN BIOLOGIC MATERIAL

The older methods of separation and identification of lipids, based on classic chemical procedures of crystallization, distillation, and solvent extraction, have now been largely supplanted by chromatographic procedures. Particularly useful for the separation of the various lipid classes is **thin layer chromatography** (TLC) and for the separation of the individual fatty acids, **gas-liquid chromatography** (GLC; Fig 16–29). Before these technics are applied to wet tissues, the lipids are extracted by a solvent system based usually on a mixture of chloroform-methanol (2:1).

Gas-liquid chromatography involves the physical separation of a moving gas phase by adsorption onto a stationary phase consisting of an inert solid such as silica gel or inert granules of ground firebrick coated with a nonvolatile liquid (eg, lubricating grease or silicone oils). In practice, a glass or metal column is packed with the inert solid and a mixture of the methyl esters of fatty acids is evaporated at one end of the column, the entire length of which is kept at temperatures of 170–225 C (Fig 16–29). A constantly flowing stream of an inert gas such as argon or helium keeps the volatilized esters moving through the column. As with other types of chromatography, separation of the vaporized fatty acid esters is dependent upon the different affinities of the components of the gas mixture for the stationary phase. Gases that are strongly attracted to the stationary phase move through the column at a slower rate and therefore emerge at the end of the column later than those that are relatively less attracted. As the individual fatty acid esters emerge from the column, they are detected by physical or chemical

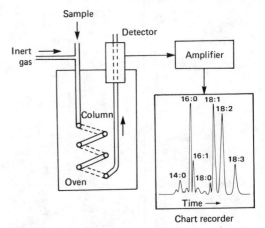

Figure 16–29. Diagrammatic representation of a gas-liquid chromatography apparatus and the separation of long chain fatty acids (as methyl esters). (A section of the record of a chromatogram is shown at right.)

means and recorded automatically as a series of peaks that appear at different times according to the tendency of each fatty acid ester to be retained by the stationary phase (Fig 16–29). The area under each peak is proportionate to the concentration of a particular component of the mixture. The identity of each component is established by comparison with the gas chromatographic pattern of a related standard mixture of known composition. A detector of radioactivity may also be incorporated into the gas stream, together with the mass detector. Thus, a measure of the specific radioactivity of each component separated is obtained.

The advantages of gas-liquid chromatography are its extreme sensitivity, which allows very small quantities of mixtures to be separated, and the fact that the columns may be used repeatedly. Application of the technic has shown that natural fats contain a wide variety of hitherto undetected fatty acids.

Thin layer chromatography (TLC) is carried out on glass plates coated with a thin slurry of adsorbent, usually silica gel. This is allowed to dry and is then heated in an oven at a standard temperature and for a standard time. After cooling, the "activated" plate is "spotted" with the lipid mixture contained in a suitable solvent. The solvent is evaporated, the edge of the plate nearest the spots is dipped in an appropriate solvent mixture, and the plate is run inside a closed tank until the solvent front arrives near the top edge of the plate. The plate is dried of solvent, and the position of the spots is determined by "charring" (spraying with sulfuric acid followed by heating) or by fluorescence (with dichlorofluorescein) or by reacting with iodine vapor (Fig 16–30). Greater resolution of mixtures can be achieved by 2-dimensional development, using first one solvent in one direction and then, after drying, running the plate in a second solvent in a direction at right angles to the first. As well as being used for analytic purposes, thin layer chromatography

may be used in purifying lipids; milligram quantities of lipid may be applied as a band to one plate. For recent reviews of general analytic methods applicable to lipids, see Lowenstein (1969) and Christie (1973).

Membranes, Micelles, Liposomes, & Emulsions

In general, lipids are insoluble in water since they contain a predominance of nonpolar (hydrocarbon) groups. However, fatty acids, some phospholipids, and sphingolipids (the polar lipids) also contain a large proportion of polar groups and are therefore partly soluble in water and partly soluble in nonpolar solvents (Fig 16–31). The molecules thus become oriented at oil-water interfaces with the **polar group in the water phase** and the **nonpolar group in the oil phase.** A bilayer of such polar lipids has been regarded as a basic structure in biologic membranes, being some 5–10 nm in thickness. When a critical concentration of polar lipids is present in an aqueous medium, they form **micelles.** Aggregations of bile salts into micelles and the formation of mixed micelles with the products of fat digestion are important in facilitating absorption of lipids from the intestine. **Liposomes** are formed by sonicating a lipid in an aqueous medium. They consist of spheres of lipid bilayers that enclose part of the aqueous medium. Emulsions are much larger particles, formed usually by nonpolar lipids in an aqueous medium. These are stabilized by emulsifying agents such as polar lipids (eg, lecithin), which form a surface layer separating the main bulk of the nonpolar material from the aqueous phase (Fig 16–31).

THE CELL MEMBRANES
(See Chapter 31.)

The plasma membrane of the living cell is a permeability barrier controlling the transfer of water and solutes between the external and internal environments. It was recognized (Overton) that the penetration of the cell by many classes of compounds was proportionate to their solubility in lipids rather than to molecular size. This led to the concept that the cell membrane is lipoid in nature. Gorter and Grendel observed in experiments using the Langmuir trough that the area occupied by lipids extracted from erythrocytes and spread as a monomolecular film on water was twice the surface area of the cells before extraction. This finding suggested that the membrane lipids were arranged in a bimolecular layer (bilayer), with the nonpolar ends of the molecules toward each other within the membrane and the polar ends oriented toward the aqueous phase inside and outside the cell (Fig 16–31).

To overcome thermodynamic objections to the traditional concept of the simple lipid bilayer model of the plasma membrane, Singer and Nicolson (1972) proposed a **fluid mosaic model** (Fig 16–32). This consists of a mosaic of globular proteins in a phospholipid bilayer, all of which are in a dynamic and fluid state.

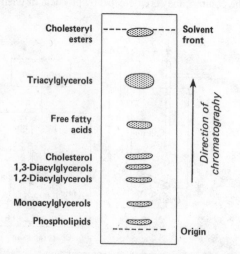

Figure 16–30. Separation of major lipid classes by thin layer chromatography. A suitable solvent system for the above would be hexane–diethyl ether–formic acid (80:20:2 v/v/v).

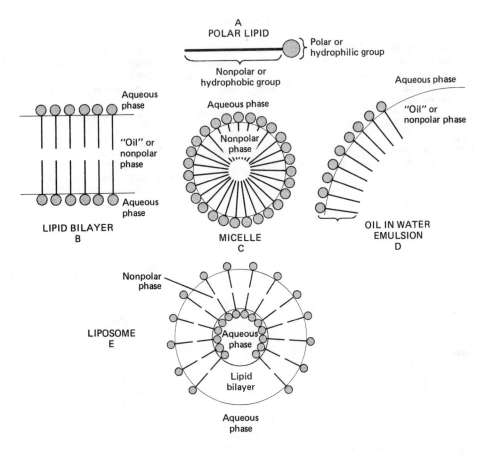

Figure 16–31. Formation of lipid membranes, micelles, emulsions, and liposomes from polar lipids, eg, phospholipids.

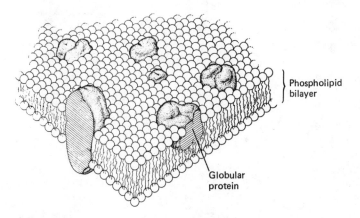

Figure 16–32. Fluid mosaic model. Schematic 3-dimensional cross-section.

References

Ansell GB, Dawson RMC, Hawthorne JN (editors): *Form and Function of Phospholipids,* 2nd ed. Elsevier, 1973.

Christie WW: *Lipid Analysis.* Pergamon Press, 1973.

Gunstone FD: *An Introduction to the Chemistry and Biochemistry of Fatty Acids and Their Glycerides,* 2nd ed. Chapman & Hall, 1967.

Gurr AI, James AT: *Lipid Biochemistry: An Introduction,* 2nd ed. Wiley, 1975.

Hanahan DJ: *Lipide Chemistry.* Wiley, 1960.

Hilditch TP, Williams PN: *The Chemical Constitution of Natural Fats,* 4th ed. Chapman & Hall, 1964.

Johnson AR, Davenport JB: *Biochemistry and Methodology of Lipids.* Wiley, 1971.

Klyne W: *The Chemistry of the Steroids.* Methuen, 1965.

Lowenstein JM (editor): *Methods in Enzymology.* Vol 14. Academic Press, 1969.

Marsh D: Spectroscopic studies of membrane structure. *Essays Biochem* 1975;**11**:139.

Pecsok RL (editor): *Principles and Practice of Gas Chromatography.* Wiley, 1959.

Ralston AW: *Fatty Acids and Their Derivatives.* Wiley, 1948.

Rothfield LI (editor): *Structure and Function of Biological Membranes.* Academic Press, 1971.

Singer SJ, Nicolson GL: The fluid mosaic model of the structure of cell membranes. *Science* 1972;**175**:720.

Metabolism of Lipids: I. Fatty Acids | 17

Peter A. Mayes, PhD, DSc

The lipids of metabolic significance in the mammalian organism include triacylglycerols (triglycerides,* neutral fat), phospholipids, and steroids, together with products of their metabolism such as long chain fatty acids (free fatty acids), glycerol, and ketone bodies. An overview of their metabolic interrelationships and their relationship to carbohydrate metabolism is shown in Fig 17–1.

For many years the tissue lipids were considered to be inactive storehouses of calorigenic material, called upon only in times of shortage of energy-yielding foods. However, Schoenheimer and Ritten-

*According to the current standardized terminology of the International Union of Pure and Applied Chemistry (IUPAC) and the International Union of Biochemistry (IUB), the monoglycerides, diglycerides, and triglycerides are to be designated monoacylglycerols, diacylglycerols, and triacylglycerols, respectively. The older terminology may, however, be used occasionally in this book.

berg showed by experiments in which deuterium-labeled fatty acids were fed to mice in caloric equilibrium that in only 4 days a considerable proportion of the depot lipid had been formed from the dietary lipid. Since the total mass of triacylglycerol in the depots remained constant, a corresponding quantity of triacylglycerol must have been mobilized during this period. These investigations demonstrated the dynamic state of body fat, a concept that forms the basis of present understanding of lipid metabolism.

A variable amount of the carbohydrate of the diet is converted to triacylglycerol before it is utilized for the purpose of providing energy. As a result, fatty acids derived from triacylglycerol may be the major source of energy for many tissues; indeed, there is evidence that in certain organs fatty acids may be used as fuel in preference to carbohydrate.

As the principal form in which energy is stored in the body, triacylglycerol has definite advantages over

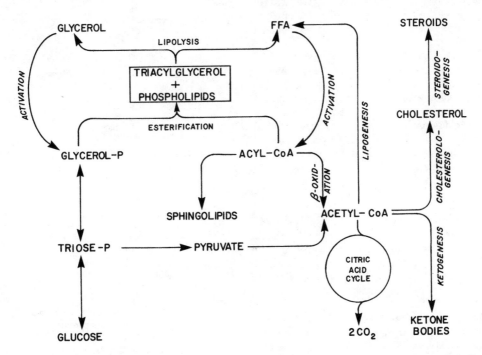

Figure 17–1. Overview of the principal pathways of lipid metabolism and their relationship to glucose metabolism. FFA = free fatty acids (nonesterified long chain fatty acids).

carbohydrate or protein. Its caloric value per unit mass is over twice as great (38.9 kJ/g), and it is associated with less water in storage. Triacylglycerol is therefore the most concentrated form in which potential energy can be stored. In addition, fatty acids provide more metabolic water upon oxidation than other metabolic fuels, which is advantageous to mammals occupying dry environments.

A minimal amount of lipid is essential in the diet to provide an adequate supply of certain polyunsaturated fatty acids (the essential fatty acids) and of fat-soluble vitamins that cannot be synthesized in adequate amounts for optimal body function. As well as acting as a carrier of these essential compounds, dietary lipid is necessary for their efficient absorption from the gastrointestinal tract. Apart from these functions, it is not certain how essential lipid is as a constituent of the diet. As a source of energy, it can be replaced completely by either carbohydrate or protein, although the efficiency with which foodstuffs are utilized may suffer as a consequence.

OXIDATION OF FATTY ACIDS

Activation of Fatty Acids

As in the metabolism of glucose, fatty acids must first be converted in a reaction with ATP to an active intermediate before they will react with the enzymes responsible for their further metabolism. This is the only step in the complete degradation of a fatty acid that requires energy from ATP. In the presence of ATP and coenzyme A, the enzyme **thiokinase** (acyl-CoA synthetase) catalyzes the conversion of a fatty acid (or free fatty acid) to an ''active fatty acid'' or acyl-CoA, accompanied by the expenditure of one high-energy phosphate bond.

$$Fatty\ acid\ +\ ATP\ +\ CoA\ \rightarrow\ Acyl\text{-}CoA\ +\ PP_i\ +\ AMP$$

The presence of **inorganic pyrophosphatase** ensures that activation goes to completion by facilitating the loss of the additional high-energy phosphate bond of pyrophosphate. Thus, in effect, 2 high-energy phosphate bonds are expended during the activation of each fatty acid molecule.

$$PP_i\ +\ H_2O\ \rightarrow\ 2\ P_i$$

Thiokinases are found both inside and outside the mitochondria. Several thiokinases have been described, each specific for fatty acids of different chain length. In addition, there is a GTP-specific mitochondrial thiokinase which, unlike the ATP-specific enzyme, forms GDP + Pi as products and not pyrophosphate.

Role of Carnitine in Fatty Acid Oxidation

Carnitine (β-hydroxy-γ-trimethylammonium butyrate), $(CH_3)_3N^+\text{-}CH_2\text{-}CH(OH)\text{-}CH_2\text{-}COO^-$, stimulates the oxidation of long chain fatty acids by mitochondria. It is widely distributed, being particu-

larly abundant in muscle. Activation of long chain fatty acids to acyl-CoA occurs in microsomes and on the outer membranes of mitochondria. Activation of lower fatty acids may occur within the mitochondria, independently of carnitine. Long chain acyl-CoA **will not penetrate mitochondria** and become oxidized unless carnitine is present. An enzyme, **carnitine acyltransferase I,** is associated with the outer side of the inner mitochondrial membrane and allows long chain acyl groups (as acylcarnitine) to penetrate the

Acyl-CoA + Carnitine ⟷ Acylcarnitine + CoA

| Carnitine |
| acyltransferase I |

mitochondria and gain access to the β-oxidation system of enzymes. A possible mechanism to account for the action of carnitine in facilitating the oxidation of fatty acids by mitochondria is shown in Fig 17–2. In addition, another enzyme, **carnitine-acetyl acyltransferase,** is present within mitochondria and catalyzes the transfer of short chain acyl groups between CoA and carnitine. The function of this enzyme

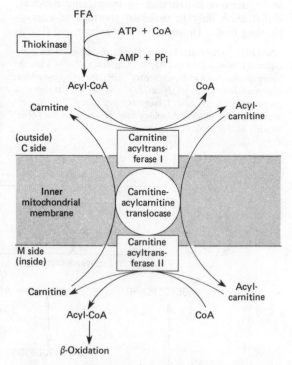

Figure 17–2. Role of carnitine in the transport of long chain fatty acids through the inner mitochondrial membrane (Pande and Parvin, 1980). Long chain acyl-CoA cannot pass through the inner mitochondrial membrane, but its metabolic product, acylcarnitine, can. **Carnitine-acylcarnitine translocase** acts as a membrane carnitine exchange transporter. Acylcarnitine is transported in, coupled with the transport out of one molecule of carnitine. The acylcarnitine then reacts with CoA, catalyzed by **carnitine acyltransferase II,** attached to the inside of the inner membrane. Acyl-CoA is re-formed in the mitochondrial matrix, and carnitine is liberated.

is obscure, but it may facilitate transport of acetyl groups out through the mitochondrial membrane, acetyl-carnitine exchanging with carnitine, allowing all of the carnitine of the cell to buffer acetyl groups formed in fatty acid oxidation. This releases CoA for further reactions within the mitochondrion. A deficiency of carnitine impairs fatty acid oxidation, and triacylglycerol accumulates. Carnitine is synthesized from lysine in liver and kidney.

$$\text{Acetyl-CoA + Carnitine} \longleftrightarrow \text{Acetyl-carnitine + CoA}$$

$$\boxed{\text{Carnitine-acetyl acyltransferase}}$$

β-Oxidation of Fatty Acids

Several enzymes, known collectively as "fatty acid oxidase," are found in the mitochondrial matrix adjacent to the respiratory chain (which is found in the inner membrane). These catalyze the oxidation of acyl-CoA to acetyl-CoA, the system being coupled with the phosphorylation of ADP to ATP (Fig 17–3).

After the formation of acyl-CoA and the penetration of the acyl moiety through the mitochondrial membrane via the carnitine transporter system, there follows the removal of 2 hydrogen atoms from the α and β carbons, catalyzed by **acyl-CoA dehydrogenase.** This results in the formation of α,β-unsaturated or Δ^2-unsaturated acyl-CoA. The coenzyme for the dehydrogenase is a flavoprotein, containing FAD as prosthetic group, whose reoxidation by the respiratory chain requires the mediation of another flavoprotein, termed electron-transferring flavoprotein (see p 127). Water is added to saturate the double bond and form β-hydroxyacyl-CoA, catalyzed by the enzyme Δ^2-**enoyl-CoA hydratase** (crotonase). The β-hydroxy derivative undergoes further dehydrogenation on the β carbon (β-**hydroxyacyl-CoA dehydrogenase**) to form the corresponding β-ketoacyl-CoA compound. In this case, NAD is the coenzyme involved in the dehydrogenation. Finally, β-ketoacyl-CoA is split at the β position by **thiolase** (β-ketothiolase or acetyl-CoA acyltransferase), which catalyzes a thiolytic cleavage involving another molecule of CoA. The products of this reaction are acetyl-CoA and an acyl-CoA derivative containing 2 carbons less than the original acyl-CoA molecule that underwent oxidation. The acyl-CoA formed in the cleavage reaction reenters the oxidative pathway at reaction (2) (Fig 17–3). In this way, a long chain fatty acid may be degraded completely to acetyl-CoA (C_2-units). As acetyl-CoA can be oxidized to CO_2 and water via the citric acid cycle (which is also found within the mitochondria), the complete oxidation of fatty acids is achieved.

Fatty acids with an odd number of carbon atoms are oxidized by the pathway of β-oxidation until a 3-carbon (propionyl-CoA) residue remains. This compound is converted to succinyl-CoA, a constituent of the citric acid cycle (see also p 179).

Energetics of Fatty Acid Oxidation

Transport in the respiratory chain of electrons from reduced flavoprotein and NAD will lead to the synthesis of 5 high-energy phosphate bonds (see Chapter 12) for each of the first 7 acetyl-CoA molecules formed by β-oxidation of palmitate ($7 \times 5 = 35$). A total of 8 mol of acetyl-CoA is formed, and each will give rise to 12 high-energy bonds on oxidation in the citric acid cycle, making $8 \times 12 = 96$ high-energy bonds derived from the acetyl-CoA formed from palmitate, minus 2 for the initial activation of the fatty acid, yielding a net gain of 129 high-energy bonds/mol, or $129 \times 36.8 = 4747$ kJ. As the free energy of combustion of palmitic acid is 9791 kJ/mol, the process captures as high-energy phosphate on the order of 48% of the total energy of combustion of the fatty acid.

α- & ω-Oxidation of Fatty Acids

Quantitatively, β-oxidation is the most important pathway for fatty acid oxidation. However, α-oxidation, ie, the removal of one carbon at a time from the carboxyl end of the molecule, has been detected in brain tissue. It does not require CoA intermediates and does not generate high-energy phosphates. Persons with **Refsum's disease** have an inherited defect in α-oxidation that prevents them from oxidizing phytanic acid, formed from phytol present in plant foodstuffs. Phytanic acid contains a $-CH_3$ group on the β-carbon that blocks β-oxidation. Normal persons can overcome the block by employing an initial α-oxidation.

ω-Oxidation is brought about by hydroxylase enzymes involving cytochrome P-450 in microsomes (see p 127). The $-CH_3$ group is converted to a $-CH_2OH$ group that subsequently is oxidized to $-COOH$, thus forming a dicarboxylic acid.

Oxidation of Unsaturated Fatty Acids

The CoA esters of these acids are degraded by the enzymes normally responsible for β-oxidation until either a Δ^3-*cis*-acyl-CoA compound or a Δ^2-*cis*-acyl-CoA compound is formed, depending upon the position of the double bonds (Fig 17–4). The former compound is isomerized (Δ^3-*cis*-Δ^2-*trans*-enoyl-CoA isomerase) to the corresponding Δ^2-*trans*-CoA stage, which in turn is hydrated by Δ^2-enoyl hydratase to $L(+)$-β-hydroxy-acyl-CoA. The Δ^2-*cis*-acyl-CoA compound is first hydrated by Δ^2-enoyl hydratase to the $D(-)$-β-hydroxy-acyl-CoA derivative. This undergoes epimerization ($D[-]$-β-hydroxy-acyl-CoA epimerase) to give the normal $L(+)$-β-hydroxy-acyl-CoA stage in β-oxidation (Fig 17–4).

Microsomal Peroxidation of Polyunsaturated Fatty Acids

Lipid peroxidation results in vivo in the destruction of polyunsaturated fatty acids in membrane lipids. Initially, a hydrogen atom is removed, leaving a lipid-free radical. After rearrangement of the double bonds, molecular oxygen is added to form a lipid hydroperoxide or endoperoxide. If the original fatty acid contained at least 3 double bonds, malondialdehyde may be detected as a final product. NADPH-dependent

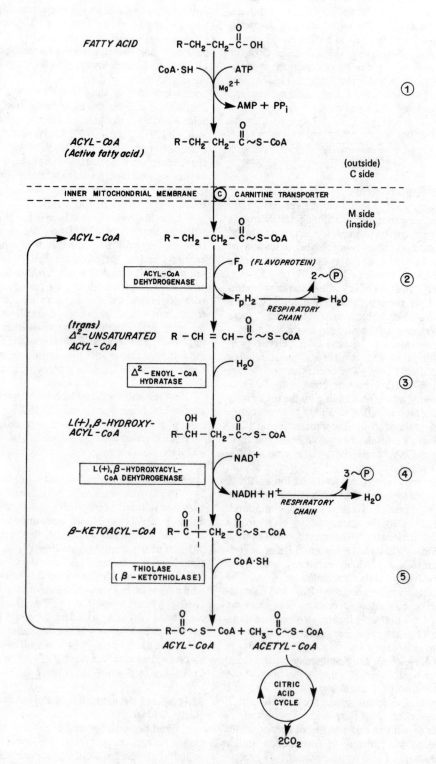

Figure 17–3. β-Oxidation of fatty acids. Long chain acyl-CoA is cycled through reactions ②–⑤, acetyl-CoA being split off each cycle by thiolase (reaction ⑤). When the acyl radical is only 4 carbon atoms in length, 2 acetyl-CoA molecules are formed in reaction ⑤.

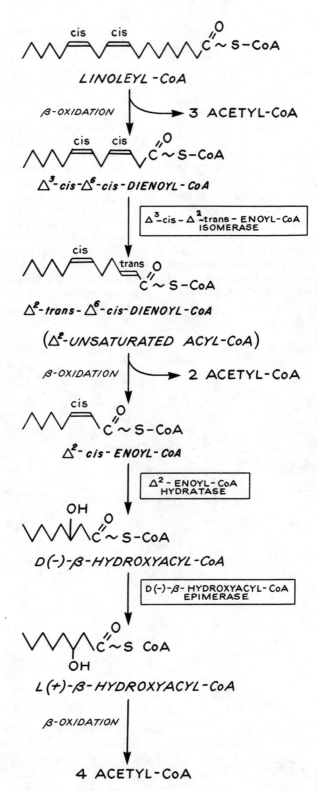

Figure 17–4. Sequence of reactions in the oxidation of unsaturated fatty acids, eg, linoleic acid.

peroxidation of unsaturated fatty acids is catalyzed by microsomal enzymes (see p 129). The antioxidants BHT (butylated hydroxytoluene) and α-tocopherol (vitamin E) inhibit microsomal lipid peroxidation.

BIOSYNTHESIS OF SATURATED FATTY ACIDS

Like many other degradative and synthetic processes (eg, glycogenolysis and glycogenesis), fatty acid synthesis was formerly considered to be merely the reversal of oxidation. However, it now seems clear that a mitochondrial system for fatty acid synthesis, involving some modification of the β-oxidation sequence, is responsible only for elongation of existing fatty acids of moderate chain length, whereas a radically different and highly active **extramitochondrial** system is responsible for the complete synthesis of palmitate from acetyl-CoA. An active system for chain elongation is also present in liver microsomes.

Extramitochondrial System for De Novo Synthesis of Fatty Acids (Lipogenesis)

This system has been found in the soluble (cytosol) fraction of many tissues, including liver, kidney, brain, lung, mammary gland, and adipose tissue. Its cofactor requirements include NADPH, ATP, Mn^{2+}, and HCO_3^- (as a source of CO_2). Acetyl-CoA is the substrate, and free palmitate is the end product. These characteristics contrast markedly with those of β-oxidation.

Bicarbonate as a source of CO_2 is required in the initial reaction for the carboxylation of acetyl-CoA to **malonyl-CoA** in the presence of ATP and **acetyl-CoA carboxylase.** Acetyl-CoA carboxylase has a requirement for the vitamin **biotin.** As acyl-CoA derivatives are inactive in the system—unlike the situation in the mitochondria—it was concluded that acyl derivatives of CoA were not intermediates in the extramitochondrial pathway during the synthesis of palmitate, and it was proposed that the acyl moiety remained attached to the enzyme as an acyl-S-enzyme complex (Fig 17–6).

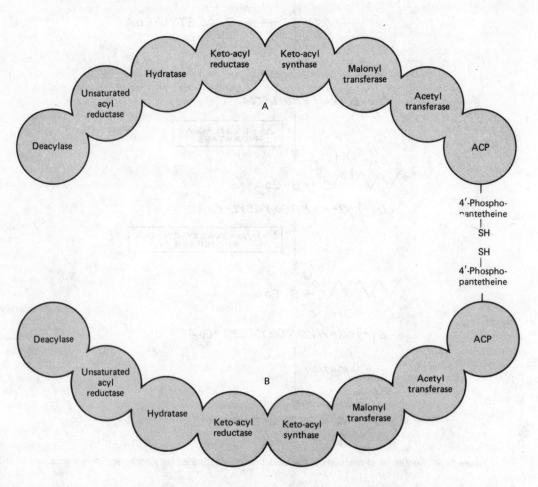

Figure 17–5. Fatty acid synthetase multienzyme complex. The complex is a dimer of 2 identical polypeptide monomers A and B, each consisting of 7 separate enzyme activities and the acyl carrier protein (ACP).

There appear to be 2 types of fatty acid synthetase systems found in the soluble portion of the cell. In bacteria, plants, and lower forms like *Euglena,* the individual enzymes of the system may be separate, and the acyl radicals are found in combination with a protein called the **acyl carrier protein (ACP).** However, in yeast, mammals, and birds, the synthetase system is a multienzyme complex that may not be subdivided without loss of activity, and ACP is part of this complex. Both ACP of bacteria and the multienzyme complex contain the vitamin pantothenic acid in the form of 4'-phosphopantetheine (see p 105).

Recent investigations have shown that the fatty acid synthetase complex is a dimer, each monomer having a molecular weight of about 250,000. In animals, it would appear that each monomer is identical, consisting of one remarkable polypeptide chain containing all the 7 enzymes of fatty acid synthetase and a terminal ACP with a 4'-phosphopantetheine-SH group. Only the dimer is active (Fig 17–5). It is envisaged that the −SH groups alternate in their function, carrying first an acyl group and then a malonyl group, functioning together in a coordinated manner (see Bloch, 1977; Guy, 1978).

Initially, a priming molecule of acetyl-CoA combines with an −SH group of ACP on one of the polypeptide monomers of fatty acid synthetase, catalyzed by **acetyl transferase** (Fig 17–6). Malonyl-CoA combines with the −SH group of the other monomer, catalyzed by **malonyl transferase,** to form **acyl-malonyl enzyme.** The acetyl group attacks the methylene group of the malonyl residue to liberate CO_2 and to form a β-**ketoacyl enzyme** (acetoacetyl enzyme), freeing the −SH group hitherto occupied by the acetyl group. This decarboxylation allows the reaction to go to completion and acts as a driving force for the whole sequence of reactions. The β-ketoacyl group is reduced, dehydrated, and reduced again to form the corresponding saturated acyl-S-enzyme. These reactions are analogous to those in β-oxidation, except that the β-hydroxy acid is the D(−) isomer instead of the L(+) isomer, and NADPH, rather than NADH, serves as the hydrogen donor for both reductions. The sequence of reactions is then repeated 6 times, a new malonyl residue being attached to the free −SH group after each sequence. It will be appreciated how the 2 −SH groups alternate in function, first as an acyl carrier than as a malonyl carrier. Finally, when a saturated 16-carbon acyl radical (ie, palmityl) has been assembled, it is liberated by hydrolysis from the enzyme catalyzed by a seventh enzyme present in the complex, **deacylase.** The free palmitate must be activated to acyl-CoA before it can proceed via any other metabolic pathway. Its usual fate is esterification into acylglycerols.

The aggregation of all the enzymes of a particular pathway into one multienzyme functional unit offers great efficiency and freedom from interference by competing processes, thus achieving the effect of compartmentalization of the process within the cell, without the erection of permeability barriers.

The equation for the overall synthesis of palmitate from acetyl-CoA and malonyl-CoA is shown below:

$$CH_3CO\cdot S\cdot CoA + 7HOOC\cdot CH_2CO\cdot S\cdot CoA + 14NADPH + 14H^+$$
$$\longrightarrow CH_3(CH_2)_{14}COOH + 7CO_2 + 6H_2O + 8CoA\cdot SH + 14NADP^+$$

The acetyl-CoA used as a primer forms carbon atoms 15 and 16 of palmitate. The addition of all the subsequent C_2 units is via malonyl-CoA formation. Butyryl-CoA may act as a primer molecule in mammalian liver and mammary gland. If propionyl-CoA acts as primer, long chain fatty acids having an odd number of carbon atoms result. These are found particularly in ruminants, where propionate is formed by microbial action in the rumen.

Source of reducing equivalents and acetyl-CoA. NADPH is involved as coenzyme in both the reduction of the β-ketoacyl and of the α,β-unsaturated acyl derivatives. The oxidative reactions of the **hexose monophosphate shunt** are the chief source of the hydrogen required for the reductive synthesis of fatty acids. It is significant that tissues which possess an active hexose monophosphate shunt are also the tissues specializing in active lipogenesis, ie, liver, adipose tissue, and the lactating mammary gland. Moreover, both metabolic pathways are found in the extramitochondrial region of the cell, so that there are no membranes or permeability barriers for the transfer of NADPH/NADP from one pathway to the other. Other sources of NADPH include the extramitochondrial **isocitrate dehydrogenase** reaction (probably not a substantial source) and the reaction that converts malate to pyruvate catalyzed by the **"malic enzyme"** (NADP malate dehydrogenase) (Fig 17–8).

Acetyl-CoA, the main building block for fatty acids, is formed from carbohydrate via the oxidation of pyruvate within the mitochondria, but acetyl-CoA does not diffuse readily into the extramitochondrial compartment, the principal site of fatty acid synthesis. The activity of the extramitochondrial **ATP-citrate lyase (citrate cleavage enzyme),** like the "malic enzyme," increases in activity in the well-fed state, closely paralleling the activity of the fatty acid synthesizing system. It is now believed that utilization of pyruvate for lipogenesis is by way of citrate. The pathway involves glycolysis followed by the oxidative decarboxylation of pyruvate to acetyl-CoA, catalyzed by pyruvate dehydrogenase, within the mitochondria, and subsequent condensation with oxaloacetate to form citrate, as part of the citric acid cycle. This is followed by the translocation of citrate into the extramitochondrial compartment, where in the presence of CoA and ATP, it undergoes cleavage to acetyl-CoA and oxaloacetate catalyzed by ATP-citrate lyase. The acetyl-CoA is then available for malonyl-CoA formation and synthesis to palmitate (Fig 17–8). The oxaloacetate can form malate via NADH-linked malate dehydrogenase, followed by the generation of NADPH via the malic enzyme. In turn, the NADPH becomes available for lipogenesis. This pathway is a means of transferring reducing equivalents from

1. SYNTHESIS OF MALONYL-CoA:

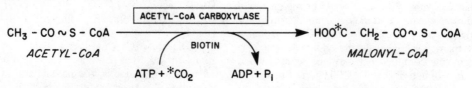

2. SYNTHESIS OF PALMITATE:

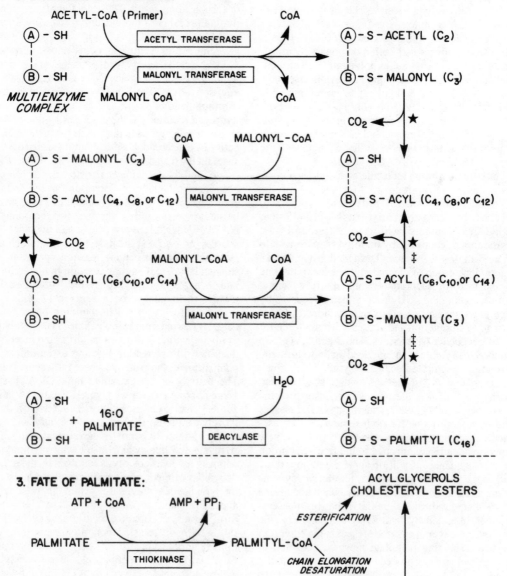

3. FATE OF PALMITATE:

Figure 17–6. Overall scheme for long chain fatty acid synthesis in mammals. ★ represents steps ① to ④ in Fig 17–7 ‡ takes place after passing twice ‡.

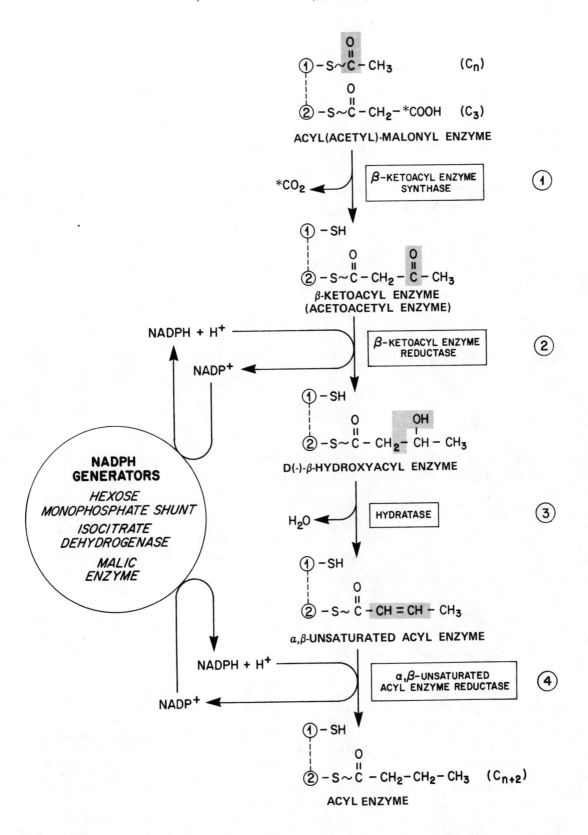

Figure 17–7. Biosynthesis of long chain fatty acids. Details of how addition of a malonyl residue causes the acyl chain to grow by 2 carbon atoms.

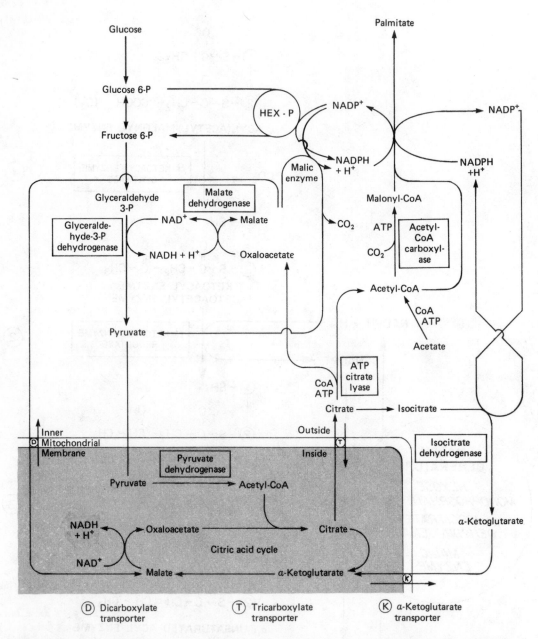

Figure 17–8. The provision of acetyl-CoA and NADPH for lipogenesis. (Hex-P, hexose monophosphate shunt.)

extramitochondrial NADH to NADP. Alternatively, malate can be transported into the mitochondrion where it is able to re-form oxaloacetate. It is to be noted that the citrate (tricarboxylate) transporter in the mitochondrial membrane requires malate to exchange with citrate (see p 140).

There is little ATP-citrate lyase or malic enzyme in ruminants, probably because in these species acetate (derived from the rumen) is the main source of acetyl-CoA. Since the acetate is activated to acetyl-CoA extramitochondrially, there is no necessity for it to enter mitochondria and form citrate prior to incorporation into long chain fatty acids. Generation of

NADPH via extramitochondrial isocitrate dehydrogenase is more important in these species.

Microsomal System for Chain Elongation

This is probably the main site for the elongation of existing long chain fatty acid molecules. The pathway converts acyl-CoA compounds of fatty acids to higher derivatives, using malonyl-CoA as acetyl donor and NADPH as reductant. Intermediates in the process are the CoA thioesters. The end product is the next higher homolog of the primer acyl-CoA molecule. The acyl groups that may act as a primer molecule include the saturated series from $C_{10}–C_{16}$, as well as some unsatu-

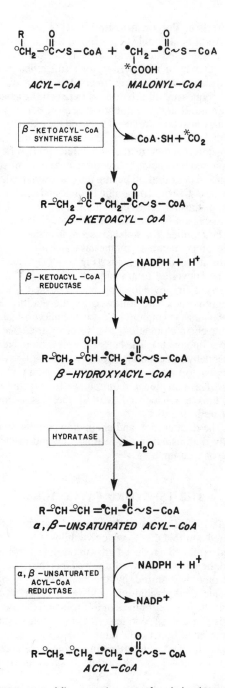

Figure 17–9. Microsomal system for chain elongation.

rated C_{18} fatty acids. Fasting largely abolishes chain elongation. Elongation of stearoyl-CoA in brain increases rapidly during myelination in order to provide C_{22} and C_{24} fatty acids that are present in sphingolipids (Fig 17–9).

Mitochondrial System for Chain Elongation

The enzymes are probably the same as those involved in β-oxidation except for the conversion of the α,β-unsaturated acyl-CoA to the corresponding satu-

rated compound catalyzed by α,β-**unsaturated acyl-CoA reductase** (enoyl-CoA reductase), requiring NADPH. A role for pyridoxal phosphate has been suggested as a coenzyme for the enzyme condensing acetyl-CoA with acyl-CoA; thus, thiolase may not be used in this synthetic pathway. The physiologic significance of this pathway is uncertain, since it will operate only when the [NADH]/[NAD⁺] ratio in mitochondria is high, ie, under anaerobic conditions, or in the liver, in the presence of excessive ethanol oxidation.

METABOLISM OF UNSATURATED FATTY ACIDS

The long chain unsaturated fatty acids of metabolic significance in mammals are as follows:

Nonessential Fatty Acids

$$CH_3 (CH_2)_5 CH=CH(CH_2)_7 COOH$$
Palmitoleic acid (16:1)

$$CH_3 (CH_2)_7 CH=CH(CH_2)_7 COOH$$
Oleic acid (18:1)

Essential Fatty Acids

$$CH_3 (CH_2)_4 CH=CHCH_2 CH=CH(CH_2)_7 COOH$$
Linoleic acid (18:2)

$$CH_3 CH_2 CH=CHCH_2 CH=CHCH_2 CH=CH(CH_2)_7 COOH$$
Linolenic acid (18:3)

$$CH_3 (CH_2)_4 (CH=CHCH_2)_4 (CH_2)_2 COOH$$
Arachidonic acid (20:4)

Other C_{20}, C_{22}, and C_{24} polyenoic fatty acids may be detected by gas-liquid chromatography. These are derived from linoleic and linolenic acids by chain elongation. It is to be noted that all double bonds present in naturally occurring unsaturated fatty acids of mammals are of the *cis* **configuration.**

Palmitoleic and oleic acids are not essential in the diet because the tissues are capable of introducing one double bond into the corresponding saturated fatty acid. Experiments with labeled palmitate have demonstrated that the label enters freely into palmitoleic and oleic acids but is absent from linoleic, linolenic, and arachidonic acids. Linoleic, linolenic, and arachidonic acids are the only fatty acids known to be essential for the complete nutrition of many species of animals, including the human infant, and must therefore be supplied in the diet; as a consequence, they are known as the **nutritionally essential fatty acids.** Although linoleic acid cannot be synthesized and therefore must be supplied preformed in the diet, arachidonic acid can be formed from linoleic acid in the animal body.

Synthesis of Monounsaturated Fatty Acids
(Fig 17–10.)

It is a common finding in the husbandry of animals that the degree of saturation of the fat laid down in the depots can be altered by dietary means. If, for example, an animal is fed a diet containing a large quantity of vegetable oil (ie, a high proportion of the unsaturated fatty acids), the animal lays down a soft type of depot fat. The converse situation is found in ruminants, where a characteristic hard, saturated fat is laid down as a result of the action of microorganisms in the rumen, which saturate the unsaturated fatty acids of the diet. As far as the nonessential monounsaturated fatty acids are concerned, the liver is considered to be the main organ responsible for their interconversion with the saturated fatty acids. An enzyme system in liver microsomes (endoplasmic reticulum) will catalyze the conversion of stearyl-CoA to oleyl-CoA. Oxygen, NADPH, or NADH is necessary for the reaction. The enzymes appear to be those of a typical mono-oxygenase system involving cytochrome b_5 (hydroxylase). In the case of saturated fatty acids, eg, palmitic and stearic acids, it is specific for introducing a double bond in the Δ^9 position.

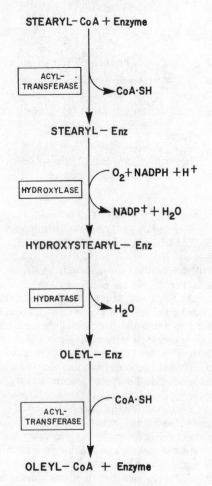

Figure 17–10. Microsomal desaturase system.

Synthesis of Polyunsaturated Fatty Acids

Additional double bonds introduced into existing monounsaturated fatty acids are always separated from each other by a methylene group (methylene interrupted), except in bacteria. In animals, the additional double bonds are **all introduced between the existing double bond and the carboxyl group,** but in plants they may also be introduced between the existing double bond and the ω-carbon. Thus, animals are able to completely synthesize the ω-9 (oleic acid) series of unsaturated fatty acids by a combination of chain elongation and desaturation but are unable to synthesize de novo the ω-6 series containing linoleic and arachidonic acids, or the ω-3 series containing linolenic acid. It is for this reason that at least linoleic and linolenic acid must be supplied in the diet to accomplish the synthesis of the other members of the ω-6 and ω-3 series of polyunsaturated fatty acids (Fig 17–11). Linoleate may be converted to arachidonate (Fig 17–12). The pathway is first by dehydrogenation of the CoA ester through γ-linolenate followed by the addition of a 2-carbon unit via malonyl-CoA in the microsomal system for chain elongation, to give eicosatrienoate (dihomo γ-linolenate). The latter forms arachidonate by a further dehydrogenation. The dehydrogenating system is similar to that described above for saturated fatty acids. The nutritional requirement for arachidonate may thus be dispensed with if there is adequate linoleate in the diet.

The desaturation and chain elongation system is greatly diminished in the fasting state and in the absence of insulin.

THE ESSENTIAL FATTY ACIDS

In 1928, Evans and Burr noticed that rats fed on a purified nonlipid diet to which vitamins A and D were added exhibited a reduced growth rate and a reproductive deficiency. Later work showed that the deficiency syndrome was cured by the addition of linoleic, linolenic, and arachidonic acids to the diet. Further diagnostic features of the syndrome include scaly skin, necrosis of the tail, and lesions in the urinary system, but the condition is not fatal. These fatty acids are found in high concentrations in various vegetable oils (see p 187 and Table 18–2) and in small amounts in animal carcasses.

The functions of the essential fatty acids appear to be various, though not well defined, apart from prostaglandin formation (see below). Essential fatty acids are found in the structural lipids of the cell, are concerned with the structural integrity of the mitochondrial membrane, and occur in high concentration in the reproductive organs. In many of their structural functions, essential fatty acids are present in phospholipids, mainly in the 2 position. The roles of essential fatty acids in the genesis of fatty livers and in the metabolism of cholesterol are discussed later.

A deficiency of essential fatty acids has been produced in animals as well as in humans using diets

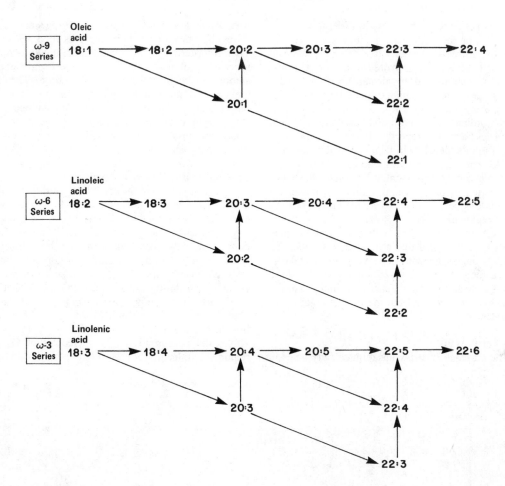

Figure 17–11. Biosynthesis of the ω-9, ω-6, and ω-3 series of polyunsaturated fatty acids. Each step is catalyzed by the microsomal chain elongation or desaturase system.

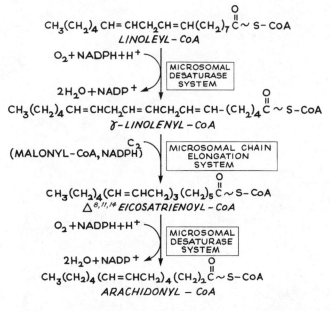

Figure 17–12. Conversion of linoleate to arachidonate.

restricted in essential fatty acids. In experimental animals, signs of the deficiency include poor growth, dermatitis, decreased capacity to reproduce, lessened resistance to stress, and impaired transport of lipids. The skin symptoms and impairment of lipid transfer have also been noted in human subjects ingesting a diet lacking in essential fatty acids. In human adults subsisting on ordinary diets, no signs of essential fatty acid deficiencies have been reported. However, infants receiving formula diets low in fat developed skin symptoms that were cured by giving linoleate. Deficiencies attributable to a lack of essential fatty acids have also been reported to occur among patients being maintained for long periods exclusively by intravenous nutritional regimens.

The results of studies with animals or human subjects have indicated that a deficiency of essential fatty acids can be prevented by a very small intake — within a range of about 1–2% of the total caloric intake—of essential fatty acids. This quantity is easily obtained in the diet in all but the most extraordinary circumstances.

Trans-Fatty Acids

The presence of *trans*-unsaturated fatty acids in partially hydrogenated vegetable oils (eg, margarine) raises the question of their safety as food additives. Their long-term effects in humans are not known, but up to 15% of tissue fatty acids have been found at autopsy to be in the *trans* configuration. They are metabolized more like saturated than like the *cis*-unsaturated fatty acids. This may be due to their similar straight chain conformation (see Chapter 16). *Trans*-polyunsaturated fatty acids do not possess essential fatty acid activity.

Prostaglandins & Thromboxanes

Isotopic experiments have indicated that arachidonate and some related C_{20} fatty acids with methylene-interrupted bonds give rise to the group of physiologically and pharmacologically active compounds known as **prostaglandins** and **thromboxanes** (see p 187). Their physiologic role is at present under intensive investigation. The 3 main series of prostaglandins and thromboxanes, PG_1, PG_2, and PG_3, are synthesized in the body from each of the essential fatty acids, respectively, linoleate, arachidonate, and linolenate (Fig 17–13). Prostaglandin synthesis involves the consumption of 2 molecules of O_2 and requires 2 molecules of reduced glutathione, although

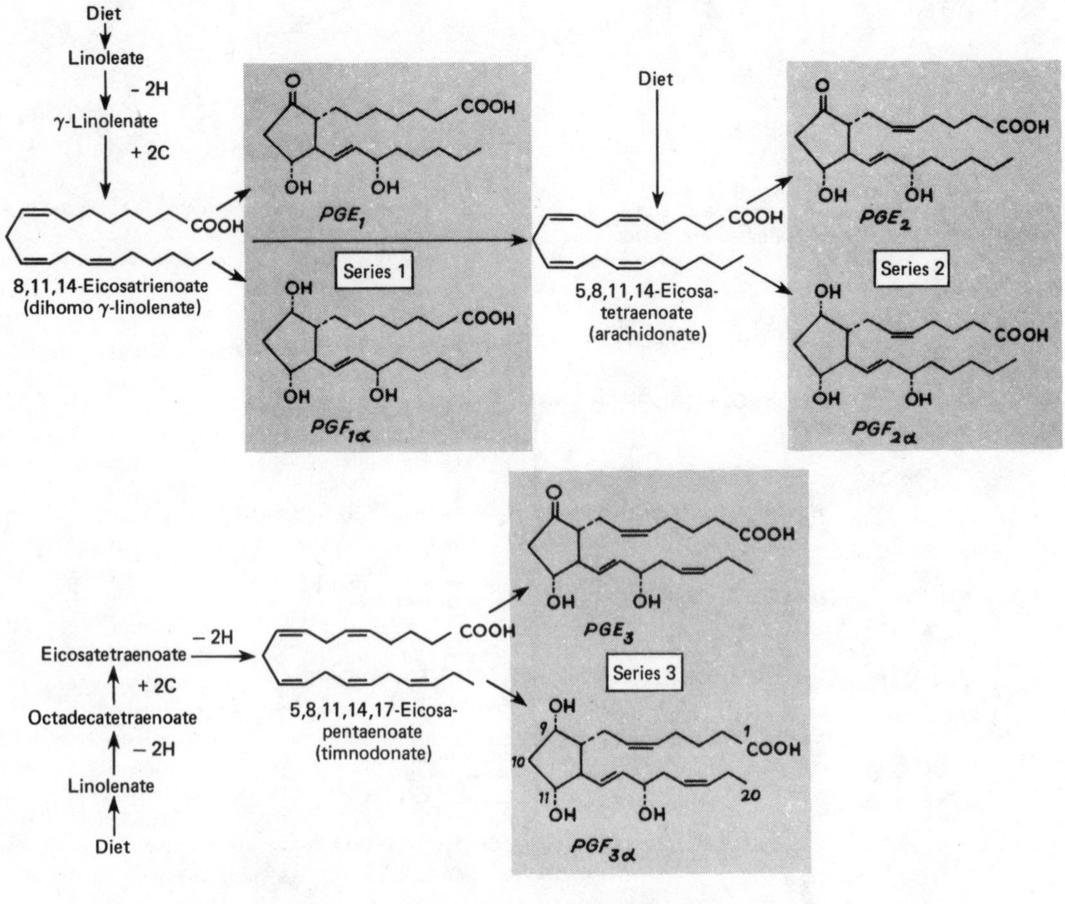

Figure 17–13. The 3 series of prostaglandins and their biosynthetic origins. (PG, prostaglandin.)

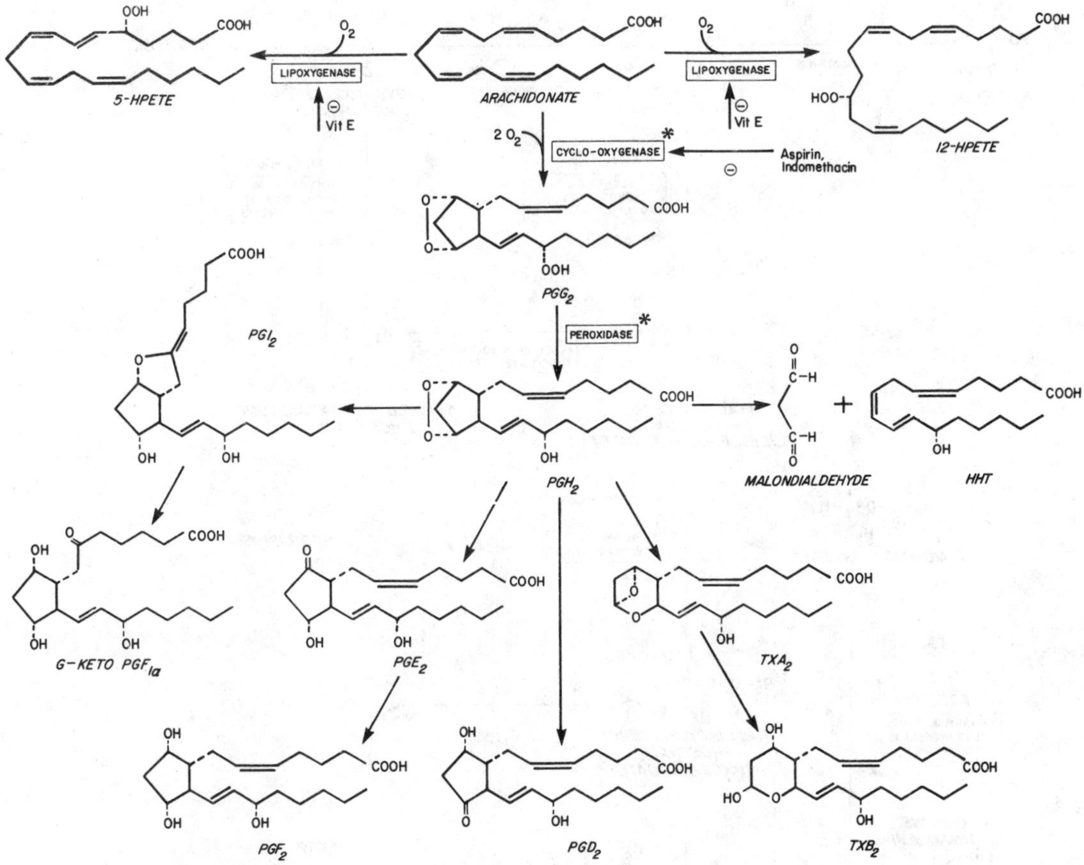

Figure 17–14. Conversion of arachidonic acid to prostaglandins and thromboxanes of series 2. (PG, prostaglandin; TX, thromboxane; PGI, prostacyclin; HPETE, hydroperoxyeicosatri- or -tetraenoate; HHT, hydroxyheptadecatrienoate.) *Both of these activities are attributed to one enzyme—prostaglandin endoperoxide synthase. Similar conversions occur in series 1 and 3.

the glutathione is not oxidized in the reaction, which is catalyzed by **prostaglandin endoperoxide synthase,** which possesses 2 separate enzyme activities, **cyclo-oxgenase** and **peroxidase. Aspirin inhibits the cyclo-oxygenase** (Lands, 1979) as does indomethacin. The product, an endoperoxide (PGH), is converted to prostaglandins by other enzymes (Fig 17–14). One series of derivatives causes the aggregation of platelets—the **thromboxanes.** Another series, called **prostacyclins,** antagonizes the action of thromboxanes; they are formed in the walls of blood vessels. Peroxidation of polyunsaturated fatty acids can occur in competition to the cyclo-oxygenase pathway to prostaglandins. This is promoted by **lipoxygenases,** which are inhibited by vitamin E. When peroxidation of polyunsaturated fatty acids takes place, malondialdehyde (also formed by breakdown of cyclic endoperoxides like PGH_2), unconjugated dienes, ethane (from ω-3), and pentane (from ω-6 series fatty acids) are among the many products.

The prostaglandins are among the most potent biologically active substances yet discovered. As little as 1 ng/mL causes contraction of smooth muscle in animals. Potential therapeutic uses include prevention of conception, induction of labor at term, termination of pregnancy, prevention or alleviation of gastric ulcers, control of inflammation and of blood pressure, and relief of asthma and nasal congestion.

Prostaglandins increase cAMP in platelets, thyroid, corpus luteum, fetal bone, adenohypophysis, and lung but lower cAMP in adipose tissue (see p 225).

Although the prostaglandins are synthesized from the "essential fatty acids," these compounds do not relieve symptoms of essential fatty acid deficiency, possibly because they are too rapidly metabolized. However, there is a marked correlation between essential fatty acid activity of various fatty acids and their ability to be converted to prostaglandins. It is therefore an open question whether essential fatty acids exert all of their physiologic effects via prostaglandin synthesis. The role of essential fatty acids in membrane formation does not, however, seem to be related to prostaglandin formation.

The presence of the enzyme **15-hydroxyprosta-**

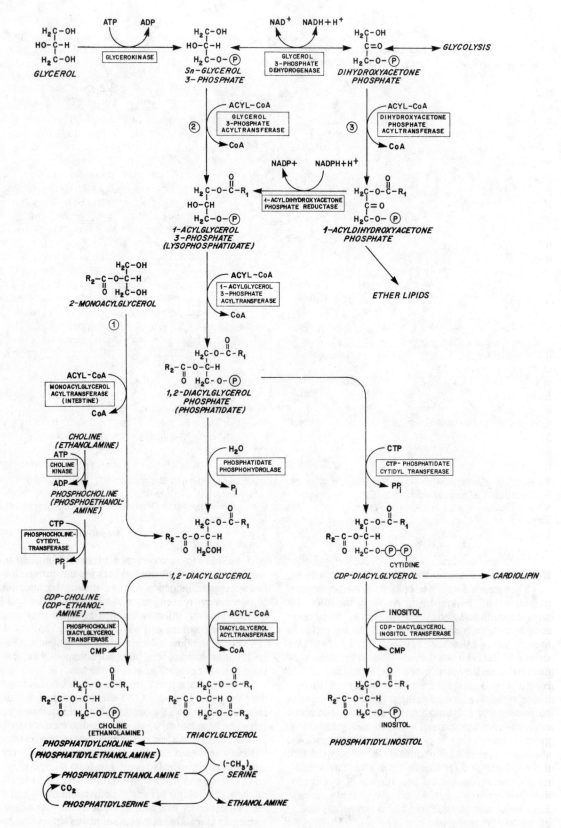

Figure 17–15. Biosynthesis of triacylglycerol and phospholipids. ① Monoacylglycerol pathway. ② Glycerol phosphate pathway. ③ Dihydroxyacetone phosphate pathway.

glandin dehydrogenase in most mammalian tissues is probably the principal cause of the rapid metabolism of prostaglandins. It has been shown that blocking the action of this enzyme can prolong the half-life of prostaglandins in the body from 2- to 10-fold. Several analogs have been developed to bring about impairment of the action of the dehydrogenase. Furthermore, modifications to produce enzyme blocking also increase the tissue specificity of the action of the modified compound. Initial studies of prostaglandin analogs indicate that the introduction of a methyl group at the C_{15} position blocks the action of 15-hydroxyprostaglandin dehydrogenase while showing little effect on either contraction of smooth muscle or lowering of blood pressure.

The synthesis and metabolism of prostaglandins has been reviewed extensively by Samuelsson and others (1978) and Lands (1979).

METABOLISM OF ACYLGLYCEROLS

Catabolism of Triacylglycerol

Triacylglycerols must be hydrolyzed by lipases to their constituent fatty acids and glycerol before further catabolism can proceed. Much of this hydrolysis occurs in adipose tissue (see p 223) with release of free fatty acids into the plasma, where they are found combined with serum albumin. This is followed by free fatty acid uptake into tissues and subsequent oxidation. Many tissues (including liver, heart, kidney, muscle, lung, testis, brain, and adipose tissue) have the ability to oxidize long chain fatty acids although brain cannot extract them from the blood. The utilization of glycerol depends upon whether such tissues possess the necessary activating enzyme, **glycerokinase** (Fig 17–15). The enzyme has been found in significant amounts in liver, kidney, intestine, brown adipose tissue, and lactating mammary gland.

Biosynthesis of Acylglycerols

Although reactions involving the hydrolysis of triacylglycerols by lipase can be reversed, this does not seem to be the mechanism by which ester bonds of acylglycerols are synthesized in tissues. Tietz and Shapiro showed that ATP was required for the synthesis of neutral fat from free fatty acids, and indeed both glycerol and fatty acids must be activated by ATP before they become incorporated into acylglycerols. If the tissue is liver, kidney, lactating mammary gland, or intestinal mucosa, the enzyme glycerokinase will catalyze the activation, by phosphorylation, of glycerol to *sn*-glycerol 3-phosphate. If this enzyme is absent—or low in activity, as it is in muscle or adipose tissue—most of the glycerol 3-phosphate must be derived from an intermediate of the glycolytic system, dihydroxyacetone phosphate, which forms glycerol 3-phosphate by reduction with NADH catalyzed by **glycerol-3-phosphate dehydrogenase** (Fig 17–15).

A. Triacylglycerol: Fatty acids are activated to acyl-CoA by the enzyme **thiokinase**, utilizing ATP

and CoA. Two molecules of acyl-CoA combine with glycerol 3-phosphate to form 1,2-diacylglycerol phosphate (phosphatidate). This takes place in 2 stages via lysophosphatidate, catalyzed first by **glycerol-3-phosphate acyltransferase** and then by **1-acyl glycerol-3-phosphate acyltransferase** (lysophosphatidate acyltransferase). Phosphatidate is converted by a phosphatase **(phosphatidate phosphohydrolase)** to a 1,2-diacylglycerol. In intestinal mucosa, a monoacylglycerol pathway exists whereby monoacylglycerol is converted to 1,2-diacylglycerol as a result of the presence of **monoacylglycerol acyltransferase.** A further molecule of acyl-CoA is esterified with the diacylglycerol to form a triacylglycerol, catalyzed by **diacylglycerol acyltransferase.** Most of the activity of these enzymes resides in the microsomal fraction of the cell, but some is found also in mitochondria; phosphatidate phosphohydrolase activity is found mainly in the particle-free supernatant fraction. It has been reported that dihydroxyacetone phosphate may be acylated and converted to lysophosphatidate after reduction by NADPH. The quantitative significance of this pathway remains in dispute. The pathway appears to be more important in mitochondria than in microsomes.

B. Phospholipids: Phospholipids are synthesized either from phosphatidate, eg, phosphatidylinositol, or from 1,2-diacylglycerol, eg, phosphatidylcholine or phosphatidylethanolamine. In the synthesis of phosphatidylinositol, cytidine triphosphate (CTP) reacts with phosphatidate to form a cytidine-diphosphate-diacylglycerol (CDP-diacylglycerol). Finally, this compound reacts with inositol, catalyzed by the enzyme **CDP-diacylglycerol inositol transferase,** to form a phosphatidylinositol (Fig 17–15).

In the biosynthesis of phosphatidylcholine and phosphatidylethanolamine (lecithins and cephalins) (Fig 17–15), choline or ethanolamine must first be converted to "active choline" or "active ethanolamine," respectively. This is a 2-stage process involving, first, a reaction with ATP to form the corresponding monophosphate, followed by a further reaction with CTP to form either cytidine diphosphocholine (CDP-choline) or cytidine diphosphoethanolamine (CDP-ethanolamine). In this form, choline or ethanolamine reacts with 1,2-diacylglycerol so that a phosphorylated base (either phosphocholine or phosphoethanolamine) is transferred to the diacylglycerol to form either phosphatidylcholine or phosphatidylethanolamine, respectively. The enzyme responsible for the formation of phosphatidylethanolamine, **phosphoethanolamine-acylglycerol transferase,** is not present in liver. Phosphatidylserine is formed from phosphatidylethanolamine directly by reaction with serine. Phosphatidylserine may re-form phosphatidylethanolamine by decarboxylation. An alternative pathway enables phosphatidylethanolamine to give rise directly to phosphatidylcholine by progressive methylation of the ethanolamine residue utilizing S-adenosylmethionine as the methyl donor.

A phospholipid present in mitochondria is **car-**

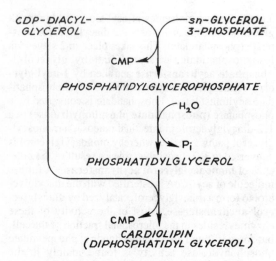

Figure 17–16. Biosynthesis of cardiolipin.

diolipin (diphosphatidylglycerol). It is formed from phosphatidylglycerol, which in turn is synthesized from CDP-diacylglycerol (Fig 17–15) and glycerol 3-phosphate according to the scheme shown in Fig 17–16.

C. Glycerol Ether Phospholipids and Plasmalogens: A plasmalogenic diacylglycerol is one in which the 1 (or 2) position has an alkenyl residue

containing the vinyl ether aldehydogenic linkage ($-CH_2-O-CH=CH-R'$). It appears that dihydroxyacetone phosphate is the precursor of the glycerol moiety (Fig 17–17). This compound combines with acyl-CoA to give 1-acyl-dihydroxyacetone phosphate. An exchange reaction takes place between the acyl group and a long chain alcohol to give a 1-alkyl-dihydroxyacetone phosphate (containing the ether link) which in the presence of NADPH is converted to 1-alkyl-glycerol 3-phosphate. After further acylation in the 2 position, the resulting 1-alkyl, 2-acyl glycerol 3-phosphate (analogous to phosphatidate in Fig 17–15) is hydrolyzed to give the free glycerol derivative. Plasmalogens are formed by desaturation of the analogous glycerol ether lipid (Fig 17–17). Much of the phospholipid in mitochondria consists of plasmalogens.

Degradation & Turnover of Phospholipids

Degradation of many complex molecules in tissues is complete, eg, proteins. Thus, a turnover time can be determined for such a molecule. Although phospholipids are actively degraded, each portion of the molecule turns over at a different rate, eg, the turnover time of the phosphate group is different from that of the 1-acyl group. This is due to the presence of enzymes which allow partial degradation followed by resynthesis (Fig 17–19). **Phospholipase A_2** catalyzes the hydrolysis of the ester bond in position 2 of

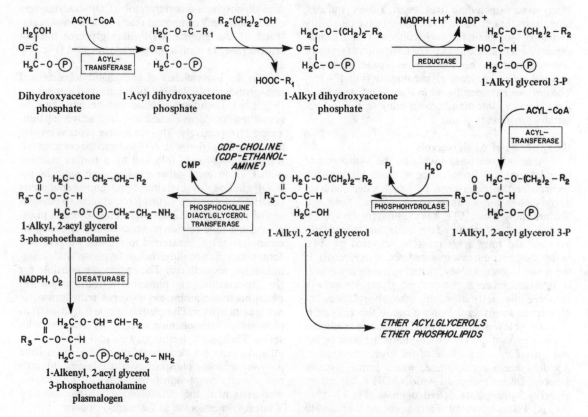

Figure 17–17. Biosynthesis of ether lipids and plasmalogens.

glycerophospholipids to form a free fatty acid and lysophospholipid which, in turn, may be reacylated by acyl-CoA in the presence of an acyltransferase. Alternatively, lysophospholipid (eg, lysolecithin) is attacked by **lysophospholipase** (phospholipase B), removing the remaining 1-acyl group and forming the corresponding glyceryl phosphoryl base, which in turn may be split by a hydrolase liberating glycerol 3-phosphate plus base (Fig 17–18). **Phospholipase A₁** attacks the ester bond in position 1 of phospholipids. **Phospholipase C** attacks the ester bond in position 3, liberating 1,2-diacylglycerol plus a phosphoryl base. **Phospholipase D** is an enzyme, described mainly in plants, that hydrolyzes the nitrogenous base from phospholipids (Fig 17–19).

Lysolecithin may be formed by an alternative route involving **lecithin:cholesterol acyltransferase (LCAT)**. This enzyme, found in plasma and possibly in liver, catalyzes the transfer of a fatty acid residue from the 2 position of lecithin to cholesterol to form cholesteryl ester and is considered to be responsible for much of the cholesteryl ester in plasma lipoproteins.

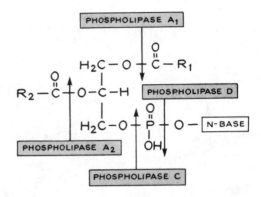

Figure 17–19. Sites of the hydrolytic activity of phospholipases on a phospholipid substrate.

Lecithin + Cholesterol ⟶ Lysolecithin + Cholesteryl ester

Lecithin:-
cholesterol
acyltransferase

Long chain saturated fatty acids are found predominantly in the 1 position of phospholipids, whereas the polyunsaturated acids (eg, the precursors of prostaglandins) are incorporated more into the 2 position. The incorporation of fatty acids into lecithin occurs by complete synthesis of the phospholipid, by transacylation between cholesteryl ester and lysolecithin, and by direct acylation of lysolecithin by acyl-CoA. Thus, a continuous exchange of the fatty acids is possible, particularly with regard to introducing essential fatty acids into phospholipid molecules.

METABOLISM OF SPHINGOLIPIDS

The **sphingomyelins** are phospholipids containing a fatty acid, phosphoric acid, choline, and a complex amino alcohol, sphingol (sphingosine). No glycerol is present.

The synthesis of **sphingosine** (Fig 17–20) has been studied in microsomes. Following activation by combination with pyridoxal phosphate, the amino acid serine combines with palmityl-CoA to form 3-ketodihydrosphingosine after loss of CO_2. Sphingosine itself is formed after 2 reductive steps, one of which is known to utilize NADPH as H donor and the other to involve a flavoprotein enzyme, analogous to the acyl-CoA dehydrogenase step in β-oxidation.

In vivo, sphingomyelin is synthesized from sphingosine phosphorylcholine (Fig 17–21). This is formed by the reaction of sphingosine with CDP-choline. Sphingosine phosphorylcholine is acylated at the amino group by an acyl-CoA of a long chain fatty acid to form sphingomyelin. Alternatively, sphingomyelin may be synthesized from sphingosine via the formation of ceramide (N-acyl sphingosine), which in turn reacts with CDP-choline, giving CMP and sphingomyelin (Fig 17–21).

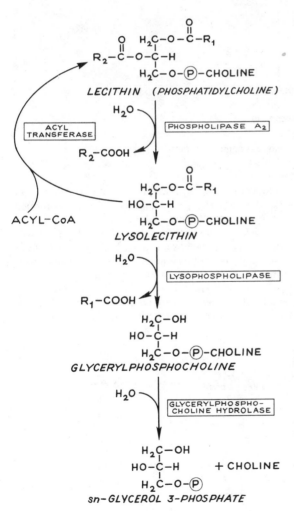

Figure 17–18. Metabolism of lecithin (phosphatidylcholine).

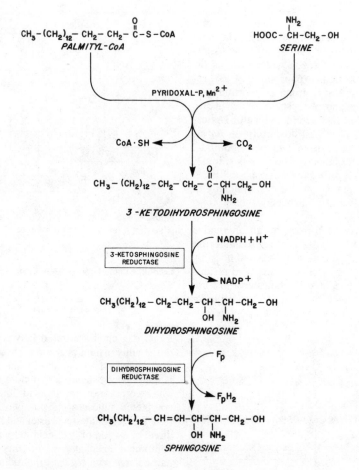

Figure 17–20. Biosynthesis of sphingosine. (Fp, flavoprotein.)

Cerebrosides, Sulfatides, & Gangliosides

The cerebrosides are glycolipids that contain the sphingosine-fatty acid combination (ceramide) found in the sphingomyelins, but a **galactose** moiety is attached to the ceramide in the place of the phosphorylcholine residue found in sphingomyelin. Characteristically, C_{24} fatty acids occur in cerebrosides (lignoceric, cerebronic, and nervonic acids). Lignoceric acid ($C_{23}H_{47}COOH$) is completely synthesized from acetate. Cerebronic acid, the 2-hydroxy derivative of

lignoceric acid, is formed from it. Nervonic acid ($C_{23}H_{45}COOH$), a monounsaturated acid, is formed by elongation of oleic acid.

The requirement for galactose in the formation of cerebrosides, chondromucoids, and mucoproteins is the only known physiologic role of this sugar other than in the formation of lactose in milk.

The biosynthesis of the complete cerebroside molecule is catalyzed by an enzyme preparation obtained from young rat brain (Fig 17–22). **Uridine**

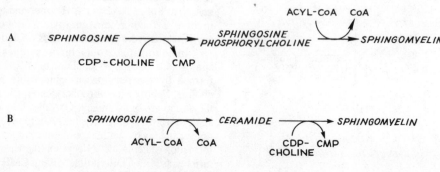

Figure 17–21. Biosynthesis of sphingomyelin.

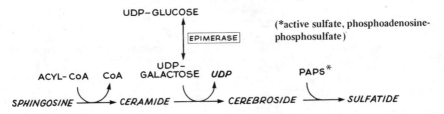

Figure 17–22. Biosynthesis of cerebrosides and sulfatides.

diphosphogalactose epimerase utilizes uridine diphosphate glucose as substrate and accomplishes epimerization of the glucose moiety to galactose, thus forming uridine diphosphogalactose. The reaction in brain is similar to that described on p 183 for the liver and mammary gland.

In one reaction sequence shown in Fig 17–22, acyl-CoA represents the CoA derivative of a fatty acid that is to be incorporated into the cerebroside. Examples would be lignoceric, cerebronic, and nervonic acids or stearic acid, which is a major component among the fatty acids of the cerebrosides in rat brain. The cerebrosides are found in high concentration in the myelin sheaths of nerves. **Sulfatides** are formed from cerebrosides after reaction with 3'-phosphoadenosine-5'-phosphosulfate (''active sulfate''). Gangliosides are synthesized from ceramide (acylsphingosine) by the stepwise addition of the activated sugars (eg,

UDPG and UDPGal) and N-acetylneuraminic acid (Fig 17–23). A large number of gangliosides of increasing molecular weight may be formed.

Although glycosphingolipids are recognized as constituents of cell membranes, it is now realized that they are involved as determinants in immunologic reactions such as in blood group substances.

PHOSPHOLIPIDS & SPHINGOLIPIDS IN DISEASE (Lipidoses)

Certain diseases are characterized by abnormal quantities of these lipids in the tissues, often in the nervous system. They may be classified into 3 groups: (1) true demyelinating diseases, (2) sphingolipidoses, and (3) leukodystrophies.

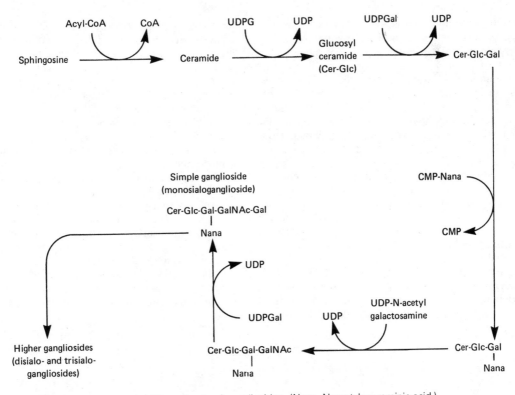

Figure 17–23. Biosynthesis of gangliosides. (Nana, N-acetylneuraminic acid.)

Table 17—1. Summary of the sphingolipidoses.
(Adapted from Brady, 1978.)

Disease	Enzyme Deficiency	Lipid Accumulating; Deficient Site of Enzymatic Reaction	Clinical Symptoms
Fucosidosis	α-Fucosidase	Cer – Glc – Gal – GalNAc – Gal ⫶ Fucose H-Isoantigen	Cerebral degeneration, muscle spasticity, thick skin.
Generalized gangliosidosis	G_{M1}-β-galactosidase	Cer – Glc – Gal (Nana)* – GalNAc ⫶ Gal G_{M1} Ganglioside	Mental retardation, liver enlargement, skeletal deformation.
Tay-Sachs disease	Hexosaminidase A	Cer – Glc – Gal (Nana) ⫶ GalNAc G_{M2} Ganglioside	Mental retardation, blindness, muscular weakness.
Tay-Sachs variant	Hexosaminidase A and B	Cer – Glc – Gal – Gal ⫶ GalNAc Globoside plus GM_2 ganglioside	Same as Tay-Sachs but progressing more rapidly.
Fabry's disease	Ceramide trihexosidase	Cer – Glc – Gal ⫶ Gal Ceramide trihexoside	Skin rash, kidney failure (full symptoms only in males; X-linked recessive).
Ceramide lactoside lipidosis	Ceramide lactosidase (β-galactosidase)	Cer – Glc ⫶ Gal Ceramide lactoside	Progressing brain damage, liver and spleen enlargement.
Metochromatic leukodystrophy	Sulfatidase	Cer – Gal ⫶ OSO_3 Sulfatide	Mental retardation and psychologic disturbances in adults.
Krabbe's disease	Galactocerebrosidase	Cer ⫶ Gal Galactocerebroside	Mental retardation; myelin almost absent.
Gaucher's disease	Glucocerebrosidase	Cer ⫶ Glc Glucocerebroside	Enlarged liver and spleen, erosion of long bones, mental retardation in infants.
Niemann-Pick disease	Sphingomyelinase	Cer ⫶ (P)-choline Sphingomyelin	Enlarged liver and spleen, mental retardation; fatal in early life.
Farber's disease	Ceramidase	Acyl ⫶ sphingosine Ceramide	Hoarseness, dermatitis, skeletal deformation, mental retardation.

*Nana = N-acetylneuraminic acid; Cer = ceramide; Glc = glucose; Gal = galactose.

In **multiple sclerosis,** which is a demyelinating disease, there is loss both of phospholipids, particularly ethanolamine plasmalogen, and of sphingolipids from white matter, such that an analysis of it resembles more the composition of gray matter. Cholesteryl esters are also found, though normally absent. The cerebrospinal fluid shows raised phospholipid levels.

The **sphingolipidoses** are a group of inherited diseases that are often manifested in childhood. These diseases are part of a larger group of lysosomal disorders (Neufeld, 1975).

Lipid storage diseases exhibit several constant features: (1) The accumulation in various tissues of complex lipids that have a portion of their structure in common. This portion is **ceramide** (an N-fatty acyl derivative of sphingosine, Fig 17–21). (2) The rate of **synthesis** of the stored lipid is comparable to that in normal humans. (3) The enzymatic defect in each of these diseases is **a deficiency of a specific hydrolytic enzyme necessary to break down the lipid.** (4) The extent to which the activity of the affected enzyme is decreased is similar in all of the tissues of the affected individual. As a result of these unifying basic considerations, procedures for the diagnosis of patients with these disorders have been developed. It has also become possible to detect heterozygous carriers of the genetic abnormalities responsible for these diseases as well as to discover in the unborn fetus the fact that a sphingolipodystrophy is present. A summary of the more important lipidoses is shown in Table 17–1. It will be noted that a specific disease, corresponding to virtually every step in the catabolism of a complex sphingolipid, can occur. Individuals heterozygous for the Tay-Sachs mutant gene can be detected by an assay for the enzyme in serum. Cultured skin fibroblasts have also been used for assay of the enzyme activity. Using the technic of amniocentesis, prenatal diagnosis of many of the sphingolipidoses has been possible in cases where there is a risk that a pregnant woman may be carrying an affected child.

In **metachromatic leukodystrophy,** there is general demyelination characterized by the accumulation of sulfatides containing galactose rather than glucose.

• • •

References

Ansell GB, Hawthorne JN, Dawson RMC (editors): *Form and Function of Phospholipids*. Elsevier, 1973.

Bell RM, Coleman RA: Enzymes of glycerolipid synthesis in eukaryotes. *Annu Rev Biochem* 1980;**49**:459.

Bloch K, Vance D: Control mechanisms in the synthesis of saturated fatty acids. *Annu Rev Biochem* 1977;**46**:263.

Brady RO: Sphingolipidoses. *Annu Rev Biochem* 1978;**47**:687.

Buege JA, Aust SD: Microsomal lipid peroxidation. Page 302 in: *Methods in Enzymology*. Vol 52. Biomembranes, part C. Fleischer S, Packer L (editors). Academic Press, 1978.

Florkin M, Stotz EH (editors): *Comprehensive Biochemistry*. Vol 18. Elsevier, 1970.

Gurr MI, James AT: *Lipid Biochemistry*. Chapman and Hall, 1975.

Guy P, Law S, Hardie G: Mammalian fatty acid synthetase. *FEBS Lett* 1978;**94**:33.

Harris RH, Ramwell PW: Cellular mechanisms of prostaglandin action. *Annu Rev Physiol* 1979;**41**:553.

Henderson LM, Hulse JD, Henderson LL: Page 35 in: *Carnitine Biosynthesis, Metabolism, and Functions*. Frenkel RA, McGarry JD (editors). Academic Press, 1980.

Holub BJ, Kuksis A: Metabolism of molecular species of diacylglycerophospholipids. *Adv Lipid Res* 1978;**16**:1.

Horton EW: Prostaglandins: A biochemical triumph in medicine. *Trends in Biochemical Science* (April) 1978;**N75**.

Houtsmuller UMT: Biochemical aspects of fatty acids with *trans* double bonds. *Fette Seifen Anstrichmittel* 1978;**80**:162.

Jeffcoat R: The physiological role and control of mammalian fatty acyl-coenzyme A desaturases. *Biochem Soc Trans* 1977;**5**:811.

Kuehl FA, Egan RW: Prostaglandins, arachidonic acid, and inflammation. *Science* 1980;**210**:978.

Lands WEM: The biosynthesis and metabolism of prostaglandins. *Annu Rev Physiol* 1979;**41**:633.

Marx JL: Blood clotting: The role of the prostaglandins. *Science* 1977;**196**:1072.

Neufeld EF, Lim TW, Shapiro LJ: Inherited disorders of lysosomal metabolism. *Annu Rev Biochem* 1975;**44**:357.

Pande SV, Parvin R: Page 143 in: *Carnitine Biosynthesis, Metabolism, and Functions*. Frenkel RA, McGarry JD (editors). Academic Press, 1980.

Ramwell PW (editor): *The Prostaglandins*. Vols 1–3. Plenum Press, 1973–1978.

Samuelsson B & others: Prostaglandins and thromboxanes. *Annu Rev Biochem* 1978;**47**:997.

Wakil S (editor): *Lipid Metabolism*. Academic Press, 1970.

Various authors: Disorders characterized by evidence of abnormal lipid metabolism. In: *The Metabolic Basis of Inherited Disease*, 4th ed. Stanbury JB, Wyngaarden JB, Fredrickson DS (editors). McGraw-Hill, 1978.

18 | Metabolism of Lipids: II. Role of the Tissues

Peter A. Mayes, PhD, DSc

In the previous chapter, the metabolism of the fatty acids was described from a mainly chemical viewpoint. However, while certain metabolic sequences, eg, β-oxidation, are common to many tissues, some tissues have distinct and specialized functions in the transport and utilization of lipids in the mammalian organism. The major routes for the disposition of fatty acids between the intestinal tract, the liver, adipose tissue, and the extrahepatic tissues

are shown in Fig 18–1. Lipoprotein triacylglycerol in chylomicrons or in very low density lipoprotein (VLDL) cannot be taken up intact by tissues but must first undergo hydrolysis by lipoprotein lipase, an enzyme situated in the capillary endothelium of extrahepatic tissues. The released free fatty acids are then taken up into the tissues where they are reesterified to triacylglycerol or oxidized as fuel. Free fatty acids are also released from adipose tissue and taken up by the

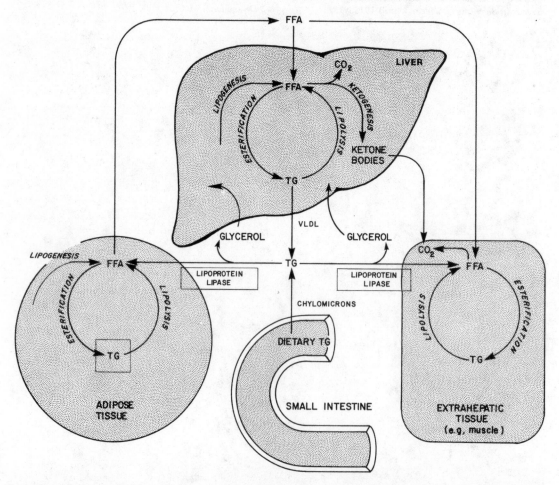

Figure 18–1. Overview of lipid metabolism in the whole animal. VLDL, very low density lipoproteins; FFA, free fatty acids; TG, triacylglycerol.

liver and other tissues and esterified or oxidized. In the liver, an additional pathway (ketogenesis) allows fatty acids to form ketone bodies, which in turn are transported via the circulation to other tissues for oxidation to CO_2.

As shown in Fig 18–1, there are 2 main entry points for fatty acids in this system. One is from chylomicrons, resulting from digestion and absorption of dietary triacylglycerol; the other is from de novo synthesis of fatty acids (lipogenesis) in the liver and adipose tissue.

Before their ultimate oxidation to CO_2, fatty acids may undergo several journeys through the circulation, either as free fatty acids or esterified as lipoprotein acylglycerol. This involves alternation of lipolysis (hydrolysis) and esterification. Both processes may take place in the same tissue; thus, the balance in activities between lipolysis and esterification determines the rate of release of free fatty acids from adipose tissue.

METABOLISM OF ADIPOSE TISSUE & MOBILIZATION OF FAT

The triacylglycerol stores in adipose tissue are continually undergoing lipolysis (hydrolysis) and reesterification (Fig 18–2). These 2 processes are not the forward and reverse phases of the same reaction. Rather, they are entirely different pathways involving different reactants and enzymes. Many of the nutritional, metabolic, and hormonal factors that regulate the metabolism of adipose tissue act either upon the process of esterification or on lipolysis. The resultant

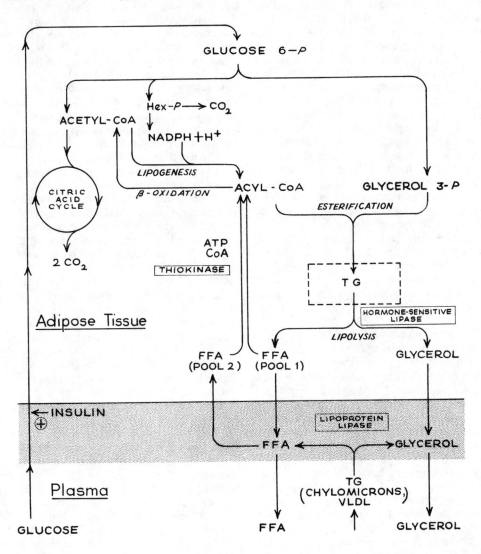

Figure 18–2. Metabolism of adipose tissue. Hormone-sensitive lipase is activated by ACTH, TSH, glucagon, epinephrine, norepinephrine, and vasopressin and inhibited by insulin, prostaglandin E_1, and nicotinic acid. Shaded area represents lipoprotein lipase region of the capillary wall. (Hex-*P*, hexose monophosphate shunt; TG, triacylglycerol; FFA, free fatty acids; VLDL, very low density lipoproteins.).

of these 2 processes determines the magnitude of the free fatty acid pool in adipose tissue, which in turn is the source and determinant of the level of free fatty acids circulating in the plasma. Since the level of plasma free fatty acids has most profound effects upon the metabolism of other tissues, particularly liver and muscle, the factors operating in adipose tissue that regulate the outflow of free fatty acids exert an influence far beyond the tissue itself.

Metabolic Pathways

In adipose tissue, triacylglycerol is synthesized from acyl-CoA and glycerol 3-phosphate according to the mechanism shown in Fig 17–15. Because the enzyme **glycerokinase** is low in activity in adipose tissue, glycerol cannot be utilized to any great extent in the esterification of acyl-CoA. For the provision of glycerol 3-phosphate needed in this reaction, the tissue is dependent on a supply of glucose. The triacylglycerol undergoes hydrolysis by a **hormone-sensitive lipase*** or **mobilizing lipase** to form free fatty acids and glycerol. Since glycerol cannot be utilized readily in this tissue, it diffuses out into the plasma, from where it is utilized by such tissues as liver and kidney, which possess an active glycerokinase. The free fatty acids formed by lipolysis can be resynthesized in the tissue to acyl-CoA by a **thiokinase** and reesterified with glycerol 3-phosphate to form triacylglycerol. Thus, there is a continual cycle within the tissue of lipolysis and reesterification. However, when the rate of reesterification is not sufficient to match the rate of lipolysis, free fatty acid accumulates and diffuses into the plasma, where it raises the level of free fatty acids.

When the utilization of glucose by adipose tissue in vitro is increased, the free fatty acid outflow decreases. However, the release of glycerol continues, demonstrating that the effect of glucose is not mediated by reducing the rate of lipolysis. It is believed that the effect is due to the provision of glycerol 3-phosphate, which enhances esterification of free fatty acids via acyl-CoA.

Glucose can take several pathways in adipose tissue, including oxidation to CO_2 via the citric acid cycle, oxidation in the hexose monophosphate shunt, conversion to long chain fatty acids, and formation of acylglycerol via glycerol 3-phosphate (Fig 18–2). When glucose utilization is high, a larger proportion of the uptake is oxidized to CO_2 and converted to fatty acids. However, as total glucose utilization decreases, the greater proportion of the glucose is directed to the formation of glycerol 3-phosphate and acylglycerol, which helps to minimize the efflux of free fatty acids.

Thus, when carbohydrate is abundant, adipose tissue tends to emphasize the utilization of glucose for oxidation and to esterify free fatty acids; on the other hand, when carbohydrate is in short supply, it conserves glucose for esterification via glycerol 3-phos-

phate formation and utilizes fatty acids as a source of energy.

There is more than one free fatty acid pool within adipose tissue. Dole has shown that the free fatty acid pool (Fig 18–2, pool 1) formed by lipolysis of triacylglycerol is the same pool that supplies fatty acids for reesterification; also, it releases them into the external medium (plasma). This latter process is not reversible, since labeled fatty acids taken up from the external medium do not label pool 1 before they are incorporated into triacylglycerol. It is necessary to postulate the existence of a second free fatty acid pool (pool 2) through which free fatty acids pass after uptake before they are incorporated into triacylglycerol or oxidized to CO_2. This second pool must be small and have a high turnover rate.

Role of Hormones in Fat Mobilization

Insulin: The rate of release of free fatty acids from adipose tissue is affected by many hormones that influence either the rate of esterification or the rate of lipolysis. Insulin administration is followed by a fall in circulating plasma free fatty acids. In vitro, it inhibits the release of free fatty acids from adipose tissue, enhances lipogenesis and the synthesis of acylglycerol, and increases the oxidation of glucose to CO_2 via the hexose monophosphate shunt. All of these effects are dependent on the presence of glucose in the medium and can be explained, to a large extent, on the basis of the ability of insulin to enhance the uptake of glucose into adipose tissue cells. Insulin has also been shown to increase the activity of pyruvate dehydrogenase, acetyl-CoA carboxylase, and glycerol phosphate acyltransferase, which could explain the enhancement of fatty acid and acylglycerol synthesis. These 3 enzymes are now known to be regulated by covalent modification, ie, by phosphorylation-dephosphorylation mechanisms. A principal action of insulin in adipose tissue is to inhibit the activity of the hormone-sensitive lipase, reducing the release not only of free fatty acids but of glycerol as well. Adipose tissue is much more sensitive to insulin than are many other tissues, which points to adipose tissue as a major site of insulin action in vivo. Both glucose oxidation and lipogenesis are reduced to the extent of 80–90% in adipose tissue from alloxan-diabetic rats. These metabolic effects are reversed by the addition of insulin in vitro.

Lipolytic hormones: Other hormones accelerate the release of free fatty acids from adipose tissue and raise the plasma free fatty acid concentration by increasing the rate of lipolysis of the triacylglycerol stores. These include epinephrine, norepinephrine, glucagon, adrenocorticotropic hormone (ACTH), α- and β-melanocyte-stimulating hormones (MSH), thyroid-stimulating hormone (TSH), growth hormone (GH), and vasopressin. Many of these activate the hormone-sensitive lipase and increase glucose utilization as well. The latter process has been attributed to stimulation of esterification by the increased production of free fatty acids. For an optimum effect, most of

---

*This lipase is distinct from lipoprotein lipase that catalyzes lipoprotein triacylglycerol hydrolysis prior to its uptake into extrahepatic tissues (see p 229).

these lipolytic processes require the presence of glucocorticoids and thyroid hormones. On their own, these particular hormones do not increase lipolysis markedly but act in a facilitatory or permissive capacity with respect to other lipolytic endocrine factors.

Adipose tissue contains a number of lipases, one of which is a hormone-sensitive triacylglycerol lipase. In addition, there is present a diacylglycerol lipase and monoacylglycerol lipase, which are not hormone-sensitive in mammals, but they are considerably more active than the hormone-sensitive triacylglycerol lipase; therefore, the latter is considered to catalyze the rate-limiting step in lipolysis (Fig 18–3). All of these hydrolase enzymes may be part of an enzyme complex together with a hormone-sensitive cholesteryl ester hydrolase. The hormones that act rapidly in promoting lipolysis, ie, catecholamines and glucagon, do so by stimulating the activity of adenylate cyclase, the enzyme that converts ATP to cAMP. The mechanism is analogous to that responsible for hormonal stimulation of glycogenolysis (see p 170). It appears that cAMP, by stimulating **cAMP-dependent protein kinase**, converts inactive hormone-sensitive triacylglycerol lipase into active lipase. Lipolysis is controlled largely by the amount of cAMP present in the tissue. It follows that processes that destroy or preserve cAMP have an effect on lipolysis. cAMP is degraded to 5'-AMP by the enzyme **cyclic 3',5'-nucleotide phosphodiesterase.** This enzyme is inhibited by methyl xanthines such as caffeine and theophylline. Thus, at concentrations at which caffeine itself does not cause any increase in cAMP in isolated fat cells, and in the presence of a lipolytic hormone such as epinephrine, caffeine acts synergistically to cause a considerable increase in cAMP over that which would be caused by the epinephrine alone. It is significant that the drinking of coffee or the administration of caffeine causes marked and prolonged elevation of plasma free fatty acids in humans.

Insulin has a pronounced antilipolytic effect both in vivo and in vitro and antagonizes the effect of the lipolytic hormones. It is now considered that lipolysis may be more sensitive to changes in concentration of insulin than are glucose utilization and esterification. The antilipolytic effects of insulin, nicotinic acid, and prostaglandin E_1 may be accounted for by inhibition of the synthesis of cAMP, possibly at the adenylate cyclase site or by stimulating phosphodiesterase. Prosta-

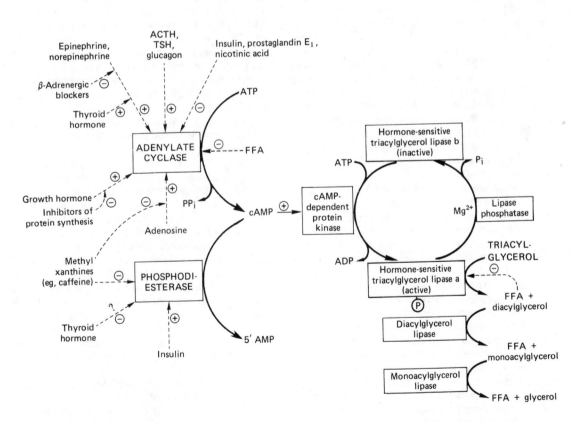

Figure 18–3. Control of adipose tissue lipolysis. (TSH, thyroid-stimulating hormone; FFA, free fatty acids.) Note the cascade sequence of reactions affording amplification at each step. The lipolytic stimulus is "switched off" by the action of lipase phosphatase, the inhibition of the lipase and adenylate cyclase by high concentrations of FFA, the inhibition of adenylate cyclase by adenosine, and the removal of cAMP by the action of phosphodiesterase. Positive (+) and negative (−) regulatory effects are represented by broken lines and substrate flow by solid lines.

glandin synthesis in adipose tissue is increased by lipolytic hormones and is reduced by essential fatty acid deficiency. When infused in vivo at low concentration, prostaglandin E_1 causes the release of catecholamines with consequent increase in free fatty acid mobilization. However, when infused at high concentration, it inhibits mobilization, as it does in vitro. Possible sites for the action of thyroid hormones include an augmentation of the level of cAMP by facilitation of the passage of the stimulus from the receptor site on the outside of the cell membrane to the adenylate cyclase site on the inside of the membrane (see p 464) and an inhibition of phosphodiesterase activity. The effect of growth hormone and glucocorticoids in promoting lipolysis is slow. It is dependent on new formation of proteins involved in the formation of cAMP. This finding also helps to explain the role of the pituitary gland and the adrenal cortex in enhancing fat mobilization.

Besides the recognized hormones, certain other adipokinetic principles have been isolated from pituitary glands. A "fat mobilizing substance" has been isolated from the urine of several fasting species, including humans, provided the pituitary gland is intact. This substance is highly active both in vivo and in vitro.

The sympathetic nervous system, through liberation of norepinephrine in adipose tissue, plays a central role in the mobilization of free fatty acids by exerting a tonic influence even in the absence of augmented nervous activity. Thus, the increased lipolysis caused by many of the factors described previously can be reduced or abolished by denervation of adipose tissue, by ganglionic blockade with hexamethonium, or by depleting norepinephrine stores with reserpine.

In older rats (> 350 g), a much greater proportion of the glucose metabolized in adipose tissue is converted to glycerol of acylglycerol and much less is synthesized into fatty acids, implying that there is a shift in lipogenesis from adipose to other tissues such as the liver. The tissue is also less sensitive to insulin. These changes in adipose tissue of the older rat are related to adiposity rather than age, since weight reduction is followed by a return in adipose tissue metabolism to a pattern similar to that of the young rat. Human adipose tissue may not be an important site of lipogenesis. This is indicated by the observation that there is not significant incorporation of label into long chain fatty acids from labeled glucose or pyruvate and that ATP-citrate lyase, a key enzyme in lipogenesis, does not appear to be present. Other enzymes—eg, glucose-6-phosphate dehydrogenase, the malic enzyme—which in the rat undergo adaptive changes coincident with increased lipogenesis, do not undergo similar changes in human adipose tissue. Indeed, it has been suggested that in humans there is a "carbohydrate excess syndrome" due to a unique limitation in ability to dispose of excess carbohydrate by lipogenesis (Björntorp and Sjöström, 1978).

Human adipose tissue is unresponsive to most of the lipolytic hormones apart from the catecholamines.

Of further interest is the lack of lipolytic response to epinephrine in the rabbit, guinea pig, pig, and chicken, the pronounced lipolytic effect of glucagon in birds, and the lack of acylglycerol glycerol synthesis from glucose in the pigeon. It would appear that, in the various species studied, a variety of mechanisms have been evolved for fine control of adipose tissue metabolism.

On consideration of the profound derangement of metabolism in diabetes mellitus (which is due mainly to increased release of free fatty acids from the depots) and the fact that insulin to a large extent corrects the condition, it must be concluded that **insulin plays a prominent role in the regulation of adipose tissue metabolism.** To reach as firm a conclusion with respect to the role of the pituitary hormones is more difficult, since the rate of free fatty acid mobilization is only slightly depressed in fasting hypophysectomized animals. This depression could be accounted for by the reduced facilitatory or potentiating influence of the secretion of the thyroid and adrenal glands. Under physiologic conditions, it is likely that the main lipolytic stimulus in adipose tissue is due to liberation of norepinephrine through sympathetic activity.

Role of Brown Adipose Tissue in Thermogenesis

Brown adipose tissue is involved in metabolism particularly at times when heat generation is necessary. Thus, the tissue is extremely active in arousal from hibernation, in animals exposed to cold, and in heat production in the newborn animal. Recently, it has been shown to be active in normal humans but absent from the obese. Brown adipose tissue is characterized by a high content of mitochondria, cytochromes, and a well developed blood supply. Metabolic emphasis is placed on oxidation of both glucose and fatty acids.

Norepinephrine liberated from sympathetic nerve endings is important in increasing lipolysis in the tissue. Addition of dinitrophenol has no effect, and there is no respiratory control by ADP. These experiments indicate that oxidation and phosphorylation are not coupled in mitochondria of this tissue. The phosphorylation that does occur appears to be at the substrate level. Thus, oxidation produces much heat, and little free energy is trapped in ATP. In terms of the **chemosmotic hypothesis** (see p 134), it would appear that the proton gradient normally present across the inner mitochondrial membrane of coupled mitochondria is continually dissipated in brown adipose tissue by a thermogenic proton conductance pathway through the membrane. This would explain the apparent lack of effect of uncouplers.

Glycerol 3-phosphate is oxidized readily via the mitochondrial flavoprotein-linked glycerol-3-phosphate dehydrogenase. If substrate level phosphorylation is important in brown adipose tissue, this pathway would be a means of maintaining glycolysis by transporting reducing equivalents generated in glycolysis into the mitochondria for oxidation in the respiratory chain. The presence of glycerokinase would enable free glycerol resulting from lipolysis to be converted to glycerol 3-phosphate and be oxidized directly in the tissue. It does not appear that much heat is generated by the energy-consuming futile cycle of lipolysis followed by resynthesis of triacylglycerol.

METABOLISM OF THE PLASMA LIPOPROTEINS

For the chemistry and composition of lipoproteins, see p 193.

Five groups of lipoproteins having major roles in the transport and metabolism of lipids are present in plasma: (1) **chylomicrons,** derived from intestinal absorption of triacylglycerol; (2) **very low density lipoproteins** (VLDL, or pre-β-lipoproteins), also formed to a lesser extent from dietary lipids but mainly derived from the liver for the export of triacylglycerol; (3) **low density lipoproteins** (LDL, or β-lipoproteins), representing a final stage in the catabolism of VLDL and possibly chylomicrons; (4) **high density lipoproteins** (HDL or α-lipoproteins), involved in VLDL and chylomicron metabolism and also in cholesterol metabolism; and (5) **free fatty acids** (FFA), not generally classified with the other plasma lipoproteins since their structure is different, consisting of long chain fatty acids attached to serum albumin.

Free Fatty Acids

The free fatty acids (nonesterified fatty acids, unesterified fatty acids) arise in the plasma from lipolysis of triacylglycerol in adipose tissue or as a result of the action of lipoprotein lipase during uptake of plasma triacylglycerols into tissues. They are found in combination with serum albumin in concentrations varying between 0.1 and 2 μEq/mL plasma and comprise the long chain fatty acids found in adipose tissue, ie, palmitic, stearic, oleic, palmitoleic, linoleic, and other polyunsaturated acids, and smaller quantities of other long chain fatty acids. Binding sites on albumin of varying affinity for the fatty acids have been described. Low levels of free fatty acids are recorded in the fully fed condition, rising to about 0.5 μEq/mL in the postabsorptive and between 0.7 and 0.8 μEq/mL in the fully fasting state. In uncontrolled diabetes mellitus, the level may rise to as much as 2 μEq/mL. In meal eaters, the level falls just after eating and rises again prior to the next meal, whereas in such continual feeders as ruminants—where there is a continual influx of nutrient from the intestine—the free fatty acids remain relatively constant and at a low level.

The rate of removal of free fatty acids from the blood is extremely rapid. Estimates suggest that the free fatty acids supply about 25–50% of the energy requirements in fasting. The remainder of the uptake is esterified and, according to evidence using radioactive free fatty acids, eventually recycled. In starvation, the respiratory quotient (RQ) would indicate that considerably more fat is being oxidized than can be traced to the oxidation of free fatty acids. This difference may

be accounted for by the oxidation of esterified lipids from the circulation or of those present in tissues. The latter are thought to occur particularly in heart and skeletal muscle, where considerable stores of lipid are to be found in the muscle cells. The free fatty acid turnover is related directly to free fatty acid concentration. Thus, the rate of free fatty acid production in adipose tissue controls the free fatty acid concentration in plasma, which in turn determines the free fatty acid uptake by other tissues. The nutritional condition does not appear to have a great effect on the fractional uptake of free fatty acids by tissues. It does, however, alter the proportion of the uptake which is oxidized to CO_2 compared to the fraction which is esterified, more being oxidized in the fasting than in the fed state.

A **fatty acid–binding protein** or **Z-protein** has been reported to occur in the cytosol of many of the major tissues. It presumably fulfills a similar role, intracellularly, to serum albumin in the extracellular transport of long chain fatty acids.

The Apolipoproteins (Apoproteins)

The lipoproteins are characterized by the presence of one or more proteins or polypeptides known as apoproteins. According to the ABC nomenclature, the 2 major apoproteins of HDL are designated A-I and A-II, respectively. The main apoprotein of LDL is apoprotein B, which is found also in VLDL and chylomicrons. Apoproteins C-I, C-II, and C-III are smaller polypeptides found in VLDL, HDL, and chylomicrons (Table 18-1). Carbohydrates account for approximately 5% of apoprotein B and include mannose, galactose, fucose, glucose, glucosamine, and sialic acid. Thus, some lipoproteins are also glycoproteins (Table 18–1). The C apoproteins seem to be freely transferable between VLDL and chylomicrons on the one hand and HDL on the other. C-II is an important activator of extrahepatic lipoprotein lipase, involved in the clearance of triacylglycerol from the circulation.

Several apoproteins other than apo-A, -B, or -C have been found in plasma lipoproteins. One is the arginine-rich apoprotein E isolated from VLDL; it contains arginine to the extent of 10% of the total amino acids and accounts for 5–10% of total VLDL apoproteins in normal subjects but is present in excess in the broad β-VLDL of patients with type III hyperlipoproteinemia. Animals made hypercholesterolemic by cholesterol feeding also have increased quantities of this apoprotein.

Formation of Chylomicrons & Very Low Density Lipoproteins (VLDL)

By definition, **chylomicrons** are found in chyle formed only by the lymphatic system **draining the intestine.** However, it is now realized that a smaller and denser particle having the characteristics of VLDL is also to be found in chyle. Chylomicron formation fluctuates with the load of triacylglycerol absorbed, whereas VLDL formation is quantitatively less but is more constant and occurs even in the fasting state.

Table 18–1. Apoproteins of human plasma lipoproteins.

Apoprotein	Lipoprotein	C-Terminal Amino Acid	Number of Amino Acid Residues	Molecular Weight	Presence of Carbohydrate Residues	Additional Remarks
A-I	HDL, chylomicrons, intestinal VLDL	Glutamine	245	28,300	+	Activator of lecithin:cholesterol acyltransferase (LCAT).
A-II	HDL	Glutamine	77 X 2	17,000	–	Structure is 2 identical monomers joined by a disulfide bridge.
B	LDL, VLDL, IDL, chylomicrons, chylomicron remnants	?	?	?	+	
C-I	VLDL, HDL, chylomicrons	Serine	57	6631	–	Possible activator of LCAT.
C-II	VLDL, HDL, chylomicrons	Glutamic acid	?	8837	–	Activator of extrahepatic lipoprotein lipase.
C-III	VLDL, HDL, chylomicrons	Alanine	79	8764	+	Several polymorphic forms depending on content of sialic acids.
D	Subfraction of HDL	?	?	20,000	+	Catalyzes transfer of cholesteryl esters among lipoproteins
E (Arginine-rich)	VLDL, HDL, chylomicrons, chylomicron remnants	Alanine (?)	?	33,000 (?)	+	Present in excess in the β-VLDL of patients with type III hyperlipoproteinemia.

However, the bulk of the plasma **VLDL** is of hepatic origin, being the vehicle of transport of **triacylglycerol from the liver to the extrahepatic tissues.**

There are many similarities in the mechanism of formation of chylomicrons by intestinal cells and of VLDL by hepatic parenchymal cells (Fig 18–4). Apoprotein B is synthesized by ribosomes in the rough endoplasmic reticulum and is incorporated into lipo-

proteins in the smooth endoplasmic reticulum, which is the main site of synthesis of triacylglycerol, phospholipids, and cholesterol. Lipoproteins are also found in the Golgi apparatus, where, it is thought, carbohydrate residues are added to the lipoprotein. The chylomicrons and VLDL are released from either the intestinal or hepatic cell by fusion of the secretory vacuole with the cell membrane (reverse pinocytosis).

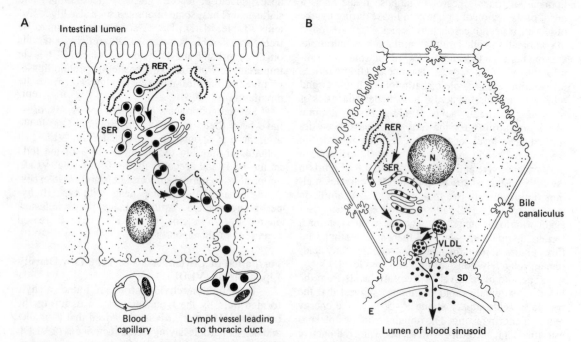

Figure 18–4. The formation and secretion of (A) chylomicrons by an intestinal cell and (B) very low density lipoproteins by a hepatic cell. (RER, rough endoplasmic reticulum; SER, smooth endoplasmic reticulum; G, Golgi complex; N, nucleus; C, chylomicrons; VLDL, very low density lipoproteins; E, endothelium; SD, space of Disse, containing blood plasma.) The figure is a diagrammatic representation of events that can be seen with electron microscopy.

Chylomicrons pass into the spaces between the intestinal cells, eventually making their way into the lymphatic system (lacteals) draining the intestine. VLDL are secreted by hepatic parenchymal cells into the space of Disse and then into the hepatic sinusoids. The similarities between the 2 processes and the anatomic mechanisms are striking, for—apart from the mammary gland—the intestine and liver are the only tissues from which particulate lipid is secreted. The inability of particulate lipid to pass through endothelial cells of the capillaries without prior hydrolysis is probably the reason dietary fat enters the circulation via the lymphatics (thoracic duct) and not via the hepatic portal system.

Apoprotein B is essential for chylomicron and VLDL formation. In abetalipoproteinemia (a rare disease), apoprotein B is not synthesized; lipoproteins containing this apoprotein are not formed, and lipid droplets accumulate in the intestine and liver. Although both chylomicrons and VLDL isolated from blood contain apoprotein C, the newly secreted or "nascent" lipoproteins contain little or none, and it would appear that the complement of apoprotein C polypeptides is taken up by transfer from HDL once the chylomicrons and VLDL have entered the circulation (Figs 18–5 and 18–6). A more detailed account of the factors controlling hepatic VLDL secretion is given on p 231.

Catabolism of Chylomicrons & Very Low Density Lipoproteins

The clearance of labeled chylomicrons from the blood is rapid, the half-time of disappearance being of the order of minutes in small animals like rats but longer in larger animals like humans, where it is still under 1 hour. Larger particles are catabolized more quickly than smaller ones. When chylomicrons labeled in the triacylglycerol fatty acids are administered intravenously, some 80% of the label is found in adipose tissue, heart, and muscle and approximately 20% in the liver. As experiments with the perfused organ have shown that the liver does not metabolize native chylomicrons or VLDL significantly, the label in the liver must result secondarily from their metabolism in extrahepatic tissues.

A. Role of Lipoprotein Lipase: There is a significant correlation between the ability of a tissue to incorporate lipoprotein triacylglycerol fatty acids and the activity of the enzyme **lipoprotein lipase** (clearing factor lipase). It is located in the **walls of blood capillaries** and has been found in extracts of heart, adipose tissue, spleen, lung, renal medulla, aorta, diaphragm, and lactating mammary gland. Normal blood does not contain appreciable quantities of the enzyme; however, following injection of heparin, lipoprotein lipase is released from the tissues into the circulation and is accompanied by the clearing of lipemia. A lipase is also released from the liver by large quantities of heparin, but this enzyme has properties different from those of lipoprotein lipase and does not react readily with chylomicrons.

Both phospholipids and apolipoprotein C-II are required as cofactors for lipoprotein lipase activity. Thus, chylomicrons and VLDL provide the enzyme with both its substrate and cofactors. Hydrolysis takes place while the lipoproteins are attached to the enzyme on the endothelium. The triacylglycerol is hydrolyzed progressively through a diacylglycerol to a monoacylglycerol which is finally hydrolyzed by a separate monoacylglycerol hydrolase. Some of the released free fatty acids return to the circulation, but the bulk are transported into the tissue (Figs 18–5 and 18–6).

Reaction with lipoprotein lipase results in the loss of approximately 90% of the triacylglycerol of chylomicrons and in the loss of the apoprotein-C polypeptides that return to HDL. The resulting lipoprotein or **remnant** is about half the diameter of the parent chylomicron and in terms of the percentage composition becomes relatively enriched in cholesterol and cholesteryl esters because of the loss of triacylglycerol.

B. Role of the Liver: Chylomicron remnants are taken up by the liver in vivo and by the perfused liver, in which system it has been shown that the cholesteryl esters of remnants are hydrolyzed and the triacylglycerol fatty acids metabolized (Gardner, 1978). The latter are incorporated mainly into phospholipids that are released from the liver as a phospholipid-rich lipoprotein of density < 1.006 (ie, a "remnant" remnant) whose metabolic fate is under investigation.

When ^{125}I-VLDL were injected into humans, labeled apoprotein C was found in HDL as it became distributed between VLDL and HDL (Eisenberg, 1975). On the other hand, labeled apoprotein B disappeared from VLDL and appeared in a lipoprotein of intermediate density (1.006–1.019, IDL). Finally, the radioactivity was found in apoprotein B of LDL, showing that the B apoprotein of VLDL is the precursor of apoprotein B of LDL. The role of the liver in this process is speculative. However, the IDL may represent the end of the degradation of VLDL by lipoprotein lipase and may correspond to chylomicron remnants. Only one IDL particle is formed from each VLDL particle (Fig 18–6). In humans, virtually all of the VLDL is converted to LDL, but in the rat most of the apo-B from VLDL appears in the liver and only a small percentage in LDL.

Metabolism of LDL

LDL does not appear to be secreted as such from either the liver or intestines. Rather, it seems to be formed from VLDL and possibly chylomicrons, as described above. The half-time of disappearance from the circulation of apoprotein B in LDL is approximately 2½ days.

Studies on cultured human fibroblasts, lymphocytes, and arterial smooth muscle cells have shown the existence of specific binding sites for LDL, which are defective in familial hypercholesterolemia (Goldstein, 1977). In normal cells, the LDL is internalized, the apoprotein is broken down in lysosomes, choles-

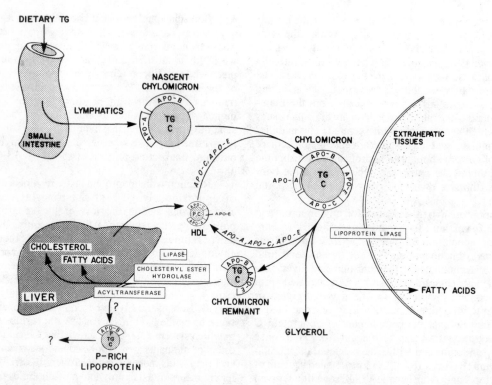

Figure 18–5. Metabolic fate of chylomicrons. (APO-A, apolipoprotein A; APO-B, apolipoprotein B; APO-C, apolipoprotein C; APO-E, apolipoprotein E; HDL, high density lipoprotein; TG, triacylglycerol; C, cholesterol and cholesteryl ester; P, phospholipid.) Only the predominant lipids are shown.

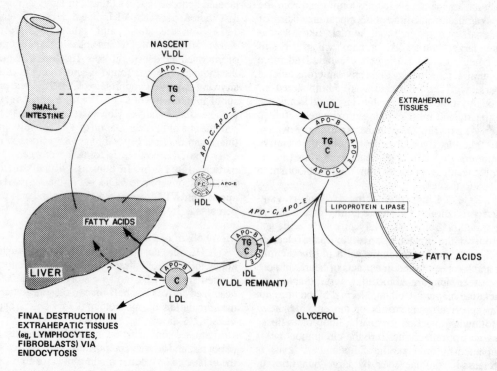

Figure 18–6. Metabolic fate of very low density lipoproteins (VLDL). (APO-A, apolipoprotein A; APO-B, apolipoprotein B; APO-C, apolipoprotein C; APO-E, apolipoprotein E; HDL, high density lipoprotein; TG, triacylglycerol; IDL, intermediate density lipoprotein; LDL, low density lipoprotein; C, cholesterol and cholesteryl ester; P, phospholipid.) Only the predominant lipids are shown.

terol is reesterified, and the activity of HMG-CoA reductase (see p 237) is repressed, thus inhibiting cholesterol synthesis within the cell. It appears that the number of LDL binding sites on the cell surface is regulated by the need for cholesterol by the cell for membrane and steroid hormone synthesis.

Metabolism of HDL

HDL is synthesized and secreted from both liver and intestine. However, nascent HDL from intestine does not contain apoprotein C but only apoprotein A. Thus, apoprotein C seems to be synthesized in the liver only and is transferred to intestinal HDL when the latter enters the plasma. Nascent HDL formed by the liver consists of discoid phospholipid bilayers containing apoprotein and free cholesterol (Hamilton, 1976). These lipoproteins are similar to the particles found in the plasma of patients with a deficiency of the plasma enzyme **lecithin:cholesterol acyltransferase (LCAT)** and in the plasma of patients with obstructive jaundice. Hamilton and others proposed that LCAT—and possibly the LCAT activator apoprotein A-I—bind to the disk. Catalysis by LCAT converts surface phospholipid and free cholesterol into cholesteryl esters and lysolecithin. The nonpolar cholesteryl esters move into the hydrophobic interior of the bilayer, whereas lysolecithin is transferred to plasma albumin. The reaction continues generating a nonpolar core that pushes the bilayer apart until a spherical, pseudomicellar HDL is formed, covered by a surface film of polar lipids and apoproteins. In LCAT deficiency, all lipoproteins contain abnormally low amounts of cholesteryl esters and high concentrations of free cholesterol and lecithin. In normal persons it is considered that the esterified cholesterol can be transferred nonenzymically from HDL to the lower density lipoproteins, eg, VLDL and LDL. The LCAT system may be involved more with the removal of excess unesterified cholesterol from lipoproteins. In LCAT deficiency, a large LDL particle accumulates which is rich in unesterified cholesterol. The liver and possibly the intestines seem to be the final sites of degradation of HDL apoproteins.

ROLE OF THE LIVER IN LIPID METABOLISM

Much of the lipid metabolism of the body was formerly thought to be the prerogative of the liver. The discovery that most tissues have the ability to oxidize fatty acids completely and the knowledge that has accumulated showing that adipose tissue is extremely active metabolically have tended to modify the former emphasis on the role of the liver. Nonetheless, the concept of a central and unique role for the liver in lipid metabolism is still an important one. Apart from its role in facilitating the digestion and absorption of lipids by the production of bile, which contains cholesterol and bile salts synthesized within the liver, the liver has active enzyme systems for synthesizing and

oxidizing fatty acids, for synthesizing triacylglycerols, phospholipids, cholesterol, and plasma lipoproteins, and for converting fatty acids to ketone bodies (ketogenesis). Some of these processes have already been described.

Triacylglycerol Synthesis & the Formation of VLDL

Experiments involving a comparison between hepatectomized and intact animals have shown that the liver is the main source of plasma lipoproteins derived from endogenous sources. Hepatic triacylglycerols are the immediate precursors of triacylglycerols contained in plasma VLDL. The fatty acids used in the synthesis of hepatic triacylglycerols are derived from 2 possible sources: (1) synthesis within the liver from acetyl-CoA derived in the main from carbohydrate and (2) uptake of free fatty acids from the circulation. The first source would appear to be predominant in the well-fed condition, when fatty acid synthesis is high and the level of circulating free fatty acids is low. As triacylglycerol does not normally accumulate in the liver under this condition, it must be inferred that it is transported from the liver as rapidly as it is synthesized. On the other hand, during fasting, during the feeding of high-fat diets, or in diabetes mellitus, the level of circulating free fatty acids is raised and more is abstracted into the liver. Under these conditions, free fatty acids are the main source of triacylglycerol fatty acids in the liver and in plasma lipoproteins because lipogenesis from acetyl-CoA is depressed. The enzyme mechanism responsible for the synthesis of triacylglycerols and phospholipids has been described on p 215. Factors that enhance both the synthesis of triacylglycerol and the secretion of VLDL by the liver include the feeding of diets high in carbohydrate (particularly if they contain sucrose or fructose), high levels of circulating free fatty acids, ingestion of ethanol, and the presence of high concentrations of insulin and low concentrations of glucagon.

Fatty Livers & Lipotropic Factors (Fig 18–7)

For a variety of reasons, lipid—mainly as triacylglycerol—can accumulate in the liver. Extensive accumulation is regarded as a pathologic condition. When accumulation of lipid in the liver becomes chronic, fibrotic changes occur in the cells which progress to cirrhosis and impaired liver function.

Fatty livers fall into 2 main categories. The first type is associated with **raised levels of plasma free fatty acids** resulting from mobilization of fat from adipose tissue or from the hydrolysis of lipoprotein or chylomicron triacylglycerol by lipoprotein lipase in extrahepatic tissues. Increasing amounts of free fatty acids are taken up by the liver and esterified. The production of plasma lipoprotein does not keep pace with the influx of free fatty acids, allowing triacylglycerol to accumulate, causing a fatty liver. The quantity of triacylglycerol present in the liver is significantly increased during starvation and the feeding of high-fat diets. In many instances (eg, in starvation), the ability

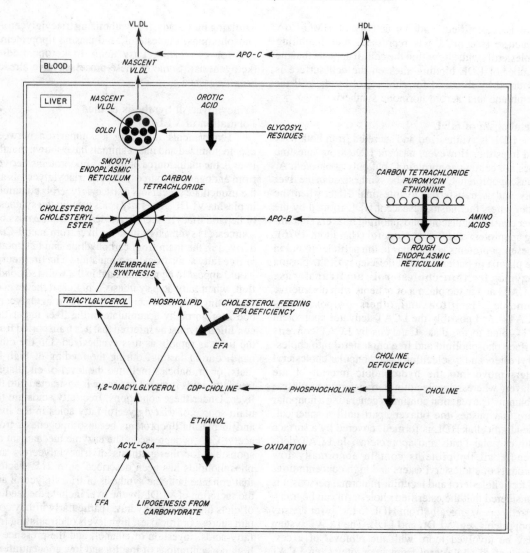

Figure 18–7. The synthesis of very low density lipoprotein (VLDL) and the possible loci of action of factors causing accumulation of triacylglycerol and a fatty liver. (EFA, essential fatty acids; FFA, free fatty acids; LDL, low density lipoproteins; HDL, high density lipoproteins; APO-B, apolipoprotein B; APO-C, apolipoprotein C.)

to secrete VLDL is also impaired. In uncontrolled diabetes mellitus, pregnancy, toxemia of ewes, or ketosis in cattle, fatty infiltration is sufficiently severe to cause visible pallor or fatty appearance and enlargement of the liver.

The second type of fatty liver is usually due to a **metabolic block in the production of plasma lipoproteins.** Theoretically, the lesion may be due to a block in lipoprotein apoprotein synthesis, a block in the synthesis of the lipoprotein from lipid and apoprotein, a failure in provision of phospholipids that are found in lipoproteins, or a failure in the secretory mechanism itself. It is often associated with deficiency of a substance known as a **lipotropic factor.** The deficiency causes triacylglycerol to accumulate even though only a normal rate of fatty acid synthesis and uptake of free fatty acids may be occurring. One type

of fatty liver that has been studied extensively is due to a deficiency of choline. As choline may be synthesized using labile methyl groups donated by methionine in the process of **transmethylation** (see Chapters 22 and 23), the deficiency is basically due to a shortage of the type of methyl group donated by methionine. Thus, choline, methionine, and betaine can all act as lipotropic agents in curing fatty livers due to choline deficiency, and, conversely, processes that utilize methyl groups excessively or diets poor in protein (containing methionine) or lecithin (containing choline) will all tend to favor the production of fatty livers.

Several mechanisms have been suggested to explain the role of choline as a lipotropic agent. The VLDL are virtually absent from the blood of choline-deficient rats, indicating that the defect lies in the formation of VLDL from triacylglycerol. In the perfused rat liver, the uptake of labeled free fatty acids and their oxidation is not decreased in choline-deficient livers; however, more of the label is incorporated into liver triacylglycerol and non-choline-containing phospholipids, and significantly less is incorporated into the choline-containing phospholipids. Mookerjea has suggested that, in addition to causing an impairment in synthesis of lipoprotein phospholipids containing choline, a choline deficiency may impair availability of phosphocholine, which stimulates incorporation of glucosamine into glycolipoproteins. Deficiency of phospholipids containing choline may impair synthesis of intracellular membranes concerned in lipoprotein synthesis. It has been suggested that depression of long chain fatty acid oxidation, which may occur in choline deficiency, may be due to depressed levels of carnitine (carnitine synthesis also being dependent on the provision of methyl groups). Decreased oxidation of fatty acids would be expected to enhance triacylglycerol formation.

It is to be noted that the antibiotic puromycin, which inhibits protein synthesis, causes a fatty liver and a marked reduction in concentration of plasma esterified fatty acids in rats. Other substances that cause fatty livers include ethionine (α-amino-γ-ethylmercaptobutyric acid), carbon tetrachloride, chloroform, phosphorus, lead, and arsenic. Choline will not protect the organism against these agents but appears to aid in recovery. The action of most of these substances is associated with inhibition of hepatic protein synthesis. The rapidity of action of carbon tetrachloride (within minutes), compared with the several hours required to elicit an effect with ethionine, indicates some difference in mode of action. It is very likely that carbon tetrachloride also affects the secretory mechanism itself or the conjugation of the lipid with lipoprotein apoprotein. Its effect is not direct but depends rather on further transformation of the molecule. This probably involves formation of free radicals that may disrupt lipid membranes in the endoplasmic reticulum, with formation of lipid peroxides. Some protection against carbon tetrachloride–induced lipid peroxidation is provided by vitamin E–supplemented diets. The action of ethionine is thought to be due to a reduction in availability of ATP. This results when ethionine, replacing methionine in S-adenosylmethionine, traps available adenine and prevents synthesis of ATP. This hypothesis is supported by the fact that the effect of ethionine may be reversed by administration of ATP or adenine. Administration of orotic acid also causes fatty livers. As VLDL accumulate in the Golgi, it is considered that orotic acid interferes with glycosylation of the lipoprotein, thus inhibiting its release and accounting for the marked decrease in plasma lipoproteins containing apo-B.

A deficiency of vitamin E enhances the hepatic necrosis of the choline deficiency type of fatty liver. Added vitamin E or a source of selenium (see Chapter 10) has a protective effect. In addition to protein deficiency, essential fatty acid and vitamin deficiencies

(eg, pyridoxine and pantothenic acid) can cause fatty infiltration of the liver. A deficiency of essential fatty acids is thought to depress the synthesis of phospholipids; therefore, other substances such as cholesterol which compete for available essential fatty acids for esterification can also cause fatty livers.

Ethanol Metabolism

Alcoholism also leads to fat accumulation in the liver, hyperlipidemia, and ultimately cirrhosis. The exact mechanism of action of alcohol in this respect is still uncertain. Whether or not extra free fatty acid mobilization plays some part in causing the accumulation of fat is not clear, but several studies have demonstrated elevated levels of free fatty acids in the rat after administration of a single intoxicating dose of ethanol. There is good evidence of increased hepatic triacylglycerol synthesis, decreased fatty acid oxidation, and decreased citric acid cycle activity, caused possibly by an increased [NADH]/[NAD$^+$] ratio generated by the oxidation of ethanol by **alcohol dehydrogenase.**

$$CH_3-CH_2-OH + NAD^+ \xrightarrow{\boxed{\text{Alcohol dehydrogenase}}} CH_3-CHO + NADH + H^+$$

This causes a shift to the left in the equilibrium malate $\rightleftharpoons$ oxaloacetate, which may reduce activity of the citric acid cycle. The net effect of inhibiting fatty acid oxidation is to cause increased esterification of fatty acids in triacylglycerol, which appears to be the cause of the fatty liver. Oxidation of ethanol leads to the formation of acetaldehyde, which is oxidized by **aldehyde dehydrogenase** in mitochondria, acetate being the end product. Other effects of alcohol may include increased lipogenesis and cholesterol synthesis from acetyl-CoA. The increased [NADH]/[NAD$^+$] ratio also causes an increased [lactate]/[pyruvate] ratio that results in hyperlactacidemia, which in turn decreases the capacity of the kidney to excrete uric acid. The latter is probably the cause of aggravation of gout by drinking alcohol. Although the major route for ethanol metabolism is via the alcohol dehydrogenase pathway, some metabolism takes place via a microsomal ethanol oxidizing system involving NADPH and O_2.

$$CH_2-CH_2-OH + NADPH + H^+ + O_2 \longrightarrow CH_3-CHO + NADP^+ + 2H_2O$$

Alcohol consumption over a long period leads to the accumulation of fatty acids in the liver that are derived from endogenous synthesis rather than from adipose tissue. There is no impairment of hepatic synthesis of protein after ethanol ingestion.

KETOSIS

Under certain metabolic conditions associated with a high rate of fatty acid oxidation, the liver pro-

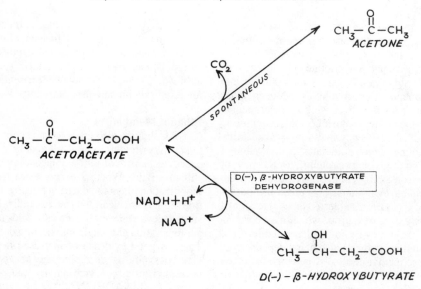

Figure 18–8. Interrelationships of the ketone bodies. D(–),β-Hydroxybutyrate dehydrogenase is a mitochondrial enzyme.

duces considerable quantities of acetoacetate and D(–)-β-hydroxybutyrate which pass by diffusion into the blood. Acetoacetate continually undergoes spontaneous decarboxylation to yield acetone. These 3 substances are collectively known as the **ketone bodies** (also called acetone bodies or "ketones") (Fig 18–8). Acetoacetate and β-hydroxybutyrate are in equilibrium with each other, the equilibrium being controlled by the mitochondrial ratio of [NAD$^+$] to [NADH], ie, the **redox state.** The ratio [β-hydroxybutyrate]/[acetoacetate] in blood varies between 1:1 and 10:1.

The concentration of total ketone bodies in the blood of well-fed mammals does not normally exceed 1 mg/dL (as acetone equivalents). It is somewhat higher than this in ruminants. Loss via the urine is usually less than 1 mg/24 h in humans. Higher than normal quantities present in the blood or urine constitute **ketonemia** (hyperketonemia) or **ketonuria,** respectively. The overall condition is called **ketosis.** Acetoacetic and β-hydroxybutyric acids are both moderately strong acids and are buffered when present in blood or the tissues. However, their continual excretion in quantity entails some loss of buffer cation (in spite of ammonia production by the kidney) which progressively depletes the alkali reserve, causing **ketoacidosis.** This may be fatal in uncontrolled diabetes mellitus.

The simplest form of ketosis occurs in starvation and involves depletion of available carbohydrate coupled with mobilization of free fatty acids. No other condition in which ketosis occurs seems to differ qualitatively from this general pattern of metabolism, but quantitatively it may be exaggerated to produce the pathologic states found in diabetes mellitus, pregnancy toxemia in sheep, and ketosis in lactating cattle. Other nonpathologic forms of ketosis are found under conditions of high-fat feeding and after severe exercise in the postabsorptive state.

In vivo, the liver appears to be the only organ in nonruminants to add significant quantities of ketone bodies to the blood. Extrahepatic tissues utilize them as respiratory substrates. In ruminants, the rumen wall converts butyric acid, formed as a result of ruminal fermentation, to β-hydroxybutyrate, which enters the bloodstream. The ruminant lactating mammary gland is also reported to produce ketone bodies. These extrahepatic sources of ketone bodies do not contribute significantly to the occurrence of ketosis in these species.

Enzymatic Mechanism for Ketogenesis in the Liver & for the Utilization of Ketone Bodies in Extrahepatic Tissues

The net flow of ketone bodies from the liver to the extrahepatic tissues results from an active enzymatic mechanism in the liver for the production of ketone bodies coupled with very low activity of enzymes responsible for their utilization. The reverse situation occurs in extrahepatic tissues (Fig 18–9).

Ketogenesis

Enzymes responsible for ketone body formation are associated mainly with the mitochondria. Originally it was thought that only one molecule of acetoacetate was formed from the terminal 4 carbons of a fatty acid upon oxidation. Later, to explain both the production of more than one equivalent of acetoacetate from a long chain fatty acid and the formation of ketone bodies from acetic acid, it was proposed that C$_2$ units formed in β-oxidation condensed with one another to form acetoacetate. This may occur by a reversal of the **thiolase** reaction whereby 2 molecules of acetyl-CoA condense to form acetoacetyl-CoA. Thus, acetoacetyl-CoA, which is the starting material for ketogenesis, arises either directly during the course of β-oxidation or as a result of the condensation of

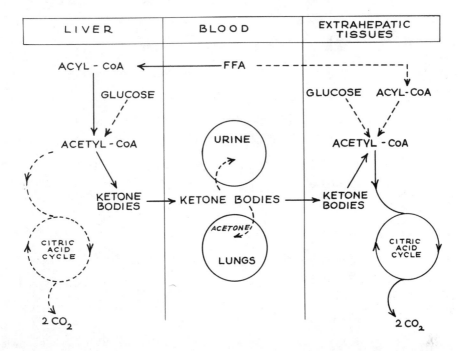

Figure 18–9. Formation, utilization, and excretion of ketone bodies. (The main pathway is indicated by the solid arrows.)

acetyl-CoA (Fig 18–10). Two pathways for the formation of acetoacetate from acetoacetyl-CoA have been proposed. The first is by simple deacylation catalyzed by the enzyme **acetoacetyl-CoA deacylase.** The second pathway (Fig 18–11) involves the condensation of acetoacetyl-CoA with another molecule of acetyl-CoA to form β-hydroxy-β-methylglutaryl-CoA (HMG-CoA), catalyzed by β-**hydroxy-β-methylglutaryl-CoA synthase.** The presence of another enzyme in the mitochondria, β-**hydroxy-β-methylglutaryl-CoA lyase,** causes acetyl-CoA to split off from the β-hydroxy-β-methylglutaryl-CoA, leaving free acetoacetate. The carbon atoms split off in the acetyl-CoA molecule are derived from the original acetoacetyl-CoA molecule (Fig 18–11). Both of these enzymes must be present in mitochondria for ketogenesis to take place. This occurs solely in liver and rumen epithelium.

Present opinion favors the β-hydroxy-β-methylglutaryl-CoA pathway as the major route of ketone body formation. Although there is a marked increase in activity of HMG-CoA lyase in fasting, evidence does not suggest that this enzyme is rate-limiting in ketogenesis.

Acetoacetate may be converted to D(–)-β-hydroxybutyrate by D(–)-β-**hydroxybutyrate dehydrogenase,** which is present in many tissues, including the liver. D(–)-β-Hydroxybutyrate is quantitatively the predominant ketone body present in the blood and urine in ketosis.

Utilization of Ketone Bodies

While the liver is equipped with an active enzy-

matic mechanism for the production of acetoacetate from acetoacetyl-CoA, acetoacetate once formed cannot be reactivated directly in the liver. This accounts for the net production of ketone bodies by the liver.

Two reactions shown below take place in extrahepatic tissues. These will activate acetoacetate to acetoacetyl-CoA. The enzymes responsible are absent from liver. One mechanism involves succinyl-CoA and the enzyme **succinyl-CoA-acetoacetate-CoA transferase** (thiophorase). Acetoacetate reacts with succinyl-CoA, the CoA being transferred to form acetoacetyl-CoA and succinate.

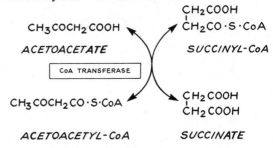

The other reaction involves the activation of acetoacetate with ATP in the presence of CoA catalyzed by acetoacetic thiokinase.

$$CH_3COCH_2COOH + ATP + CoA \cdot SH \xrightarrow{\boxed{\text{Acetoacetic thiokinase}}}$$
Acetoacetate

$$CH_3COCH_2CO \cdot S \cdot CoA + AMP + PP_i$$
Acetoacetyl-CoA

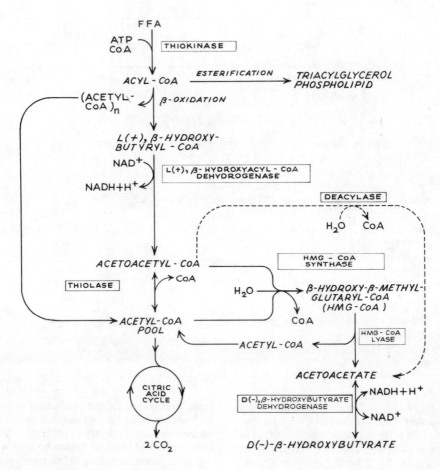

Figure 18–10. Pathways of ketogenesis in the liver. (FFA, free fatty acids; HMG, β-hydroxy-β-methylglutaryl.)

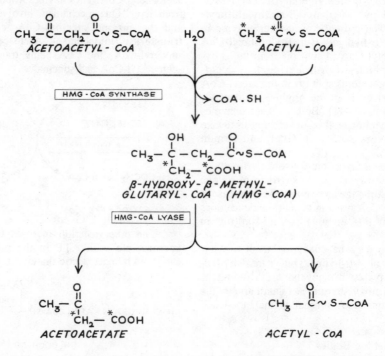

Figure 18–11. Formation of acetoacetate through intermediate production of HMG-CoA.

D(−)-β-Hydroxybutyrate may be activated directly in extrahepatic tissues by a thiokinase; however, conversion to acetoacetate with D(−)-β-hydroxybutyrate dehydrogenase and NAD^+, followed by activation to acetoacetyl-CoA, is the more important route leading to its further metabolism. The acetoacetyl-CoA formed by these reactions is split to acetyl-CoA by thiolase and oxidized in the citric acid cycle as shown in Fig 18–10.

Ketone bodies are oxidized in extrahepatic tissues proportionately to their concentration in the blood. They are also oxidized in preference to glucose and to FFA. If the blood level is raised, oxidation of ketone bodies increases until, at a concentration of approximately 70 mg/dL, they saturate the oxidative machinery; any further increase in the rate of ketogenesis serves merely to raise the blood concentration and the rate of urinary excretion precipitously. When this occurs, a large proportion of the oxygen consumption of the animal may be accounted for by the oxidation of ketone bodies.

Most of the evidence suggests that ketonemia is due to increased production of ketone bodies by the liver rather than to a deficiency in their utilization by extrahepatic tissues. However, the results of experiments on depancreatized rats support the possibility that ketosis in the severe diabetic may be enhanced by a reduced ability to catabolize ketone bodies.

In moderate ketonemia, the loss of ketone bodies via the urine is only a few percent of the total ketone body production and utilization. As there are renal thresholdlike effects (there is not a true threshold) that vary between species and individuals, measurement of the ketonemia, not the ketonuria, is the preferred method of assessing the severity of ketosis.

While acetoacetate and D(−)-β-hydroxybutyrate are readily oxidized by extrahepatic tissues, acetone is difficult to oxidize in vivo. When acetone is injected into human subjects, its concentration in the blood rises sharply and is maintained at a high level for several hours, indicating a very slow rate of utilization.

CHOLESTEROL METABOLISM

The greater part of the cholesterol of the body arises by **synthesis** (about 1 g/d), whereas only about 0.3 g/d are provided by the average diet. Cholesterol is eliminated via 2 main pathways: conversion to bile acids and excretion of neutral sterols in the feces. The synthesis of steroid hormones from cholesterol and the elimination of their products of degradation in the urine are of minor quantitative significance. **Cholesterol is typically a product of animal metabolism** and occurs therefore in foods of animal origin such as meat, liver, brain, and egg yolk (a particularly rich source).

Synthesis of Cholesterol

Virtually all tissues containing nucleated cells are capable of synthesizing cholesterol, particularly the

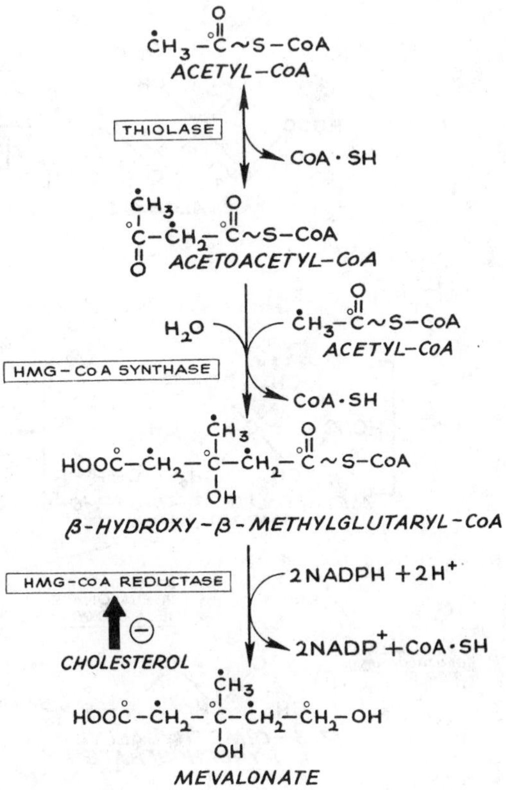

Figure 18–12. Biosynthesis of mevalonate. (HMG, β-hydroxy-β-methylglutaryl.)

liver, adrenal cortex, skin, intestines, testis, and aorta. The microsomal and cytosol fraction of the cell is responsible for cholesterol synthesis.

Acetyl-CoA is the source of all the carbon atoms in cholesterol. The manner of synthesis of this complex molecule has been the subject of investigation by many workers, with the result that it is possible at the present time to chart the origin of all parts of the cholesterol molecule (Figs 18–12, 18–13, and 18–14). Synthesis takes place in several stages. The first is the synthesis of mevalonate, a 6-carbon compound, from acetyl-CoA (Fig 18–12). The next major stage is the formation of isoprenoid units from mevalonate by loss of CO_2 (Fig 18–13). The isoprenoid units may be regarded as the building blocks of the steroid skeleton. Six of these units condense to form the intermediate, squalene, which in turn gives rise to the parent steroid, lanosterol. Cholesterol is formed from lanosterol after several further steps, including the loss of 3 methyl groups (Fig 18–14).

Two separate pathways have been described for the formation of mevalonate. One involves the intermediate β-hydroxy-β-methylglutaryl-CoA and the other is through a β-hydroxy-β-methylglutaryl-S-enzyme complex. The pathway through β-hydroxy-β-methylglutaryl-CoA is considered to be quantitatively the more significant and follows the same se-

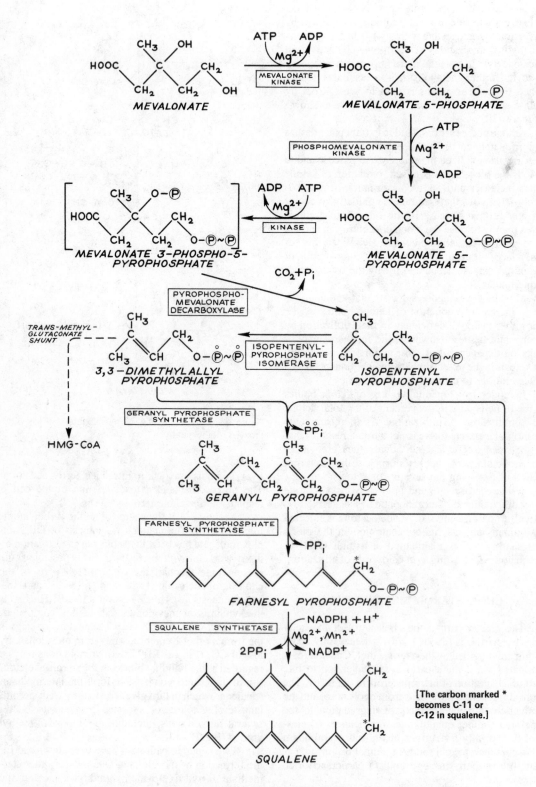

Figure 18—13. Biosynthesis of squalene. (HMG, β-hydroxy-β-methylglutaryl.)

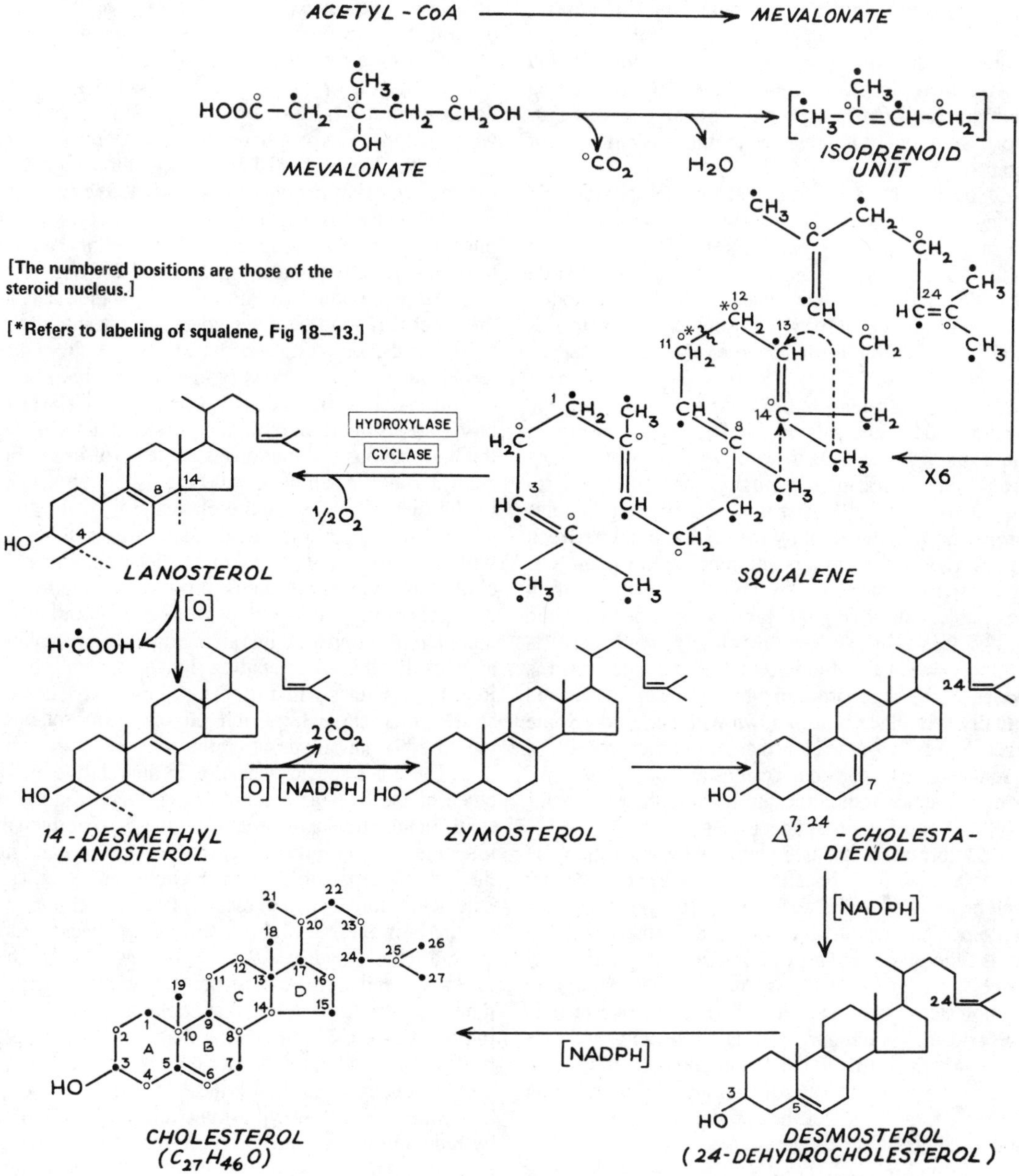

Figure 18–14. Biosynthesis of cholesterol.

quence of reactions described previously for the synthesis in mitochondria of ketone bodies. However, since cholesterol synthesis is extramitochondrial, the 2 pathways are distinct.

β-Hydroxy-β-methylglutaryl-CoA is converted to mevalonate in a 2-stage reduction by NADPH catalyzed by **β-hydroxy-β-methylglutaryl-CoA reductase** (Fig 18–12).

In the second stage, mevalonate is phosphorylated by ATP to form several active phosphorylated intermediates. By means of a decarboxylation, the active isoprenoid unit, isopentenylpyrophosphate, is

formed. The next stage involves the condensation of molecules of isopentenylpyrophosphate to form farnesyl pyrophosphate. This occurs via an isomerization of isopentenylpyrophosphate to form the 10-carbon intermediate, geranyl pyrophosphate. A further condensation with isopentenylpyrophosphate forms farnesyl pyrophosphate. Two molecules of farnesyl pyrophosphate condense at the pyrophosphate end in a reaction involving a reduction with NADPH with elimination of the pyrophosphate radicals. The resulting compound is squalene. Recently, evidence has been provided that an alternative pathway known as the "*trans*-methylglutaconate shunt" may be present. This pathway removes a significant proportion (20%) of the dimethylallyl pyrophosphate and returns it, via *trans*-3-methylglutaconate-CoA, to β-hydroxy-β-methylglutaryl-CoA. This pathway may have regulatory potential with respect to the overall rate of cholesterol synthesis.

Squalene has a structure that resembles the steroid nucleus very closely (Fig 18–14). It is converted to lanosterol by ring closures. Before closure occurs, the methyl group on C_{14} is transferred to C_{13} and that on C_8 to C_{14} and C_3 is hydroxylated. The latter reaction involves molecular oxygen, and the reaction is catalyzed by a microsomal hydroxylase system.

The last stage (Fig 18–14), the formation of cholesterol from lanosterol, involves changes to the steroid nucleus and side chain. The methyl group on C_{14} is oxidized to CO_2 to form 14-desmethyl lanosterol. Likewise, 2 more methyl groups on C_4 are removed to produce zymosterol. $\Delta^{7,24}$-Cholestadienol is formed from zymosterol by the double bond between C_8 and C_9, moving to a position between C_8 and C_7. Desmosterol is formed at this point by a further shift in the double bond in ring B to take up a position between C_5 and C_6, as in cholesterol. Finally, cholesterol is produced when the double bond of the side chain is reduced. The exact order in which the steps described actually take place is not known with certainty. Some investigators favor the view that the double bond at C_{24} is reduced early and that desmosterol is not the immediate precursor of cholesterol. More than one pathway may operate simultaneously.

It is probable that the intermediates from squalene to cholesterol may be attached to a special carrier protein known as the **squalene and sterol carrier protein.** This protein binds sterols and other insoluble lipids, allowing them to react in the aqueous phase of the cell. In addition, it seems likely that it is in the form of cholesterol-sterol carrier protein that cholesterol is converted to steroid hormones and bile acids and participates in the formation of membranes and of lipoproteins. It is also as cholesterol-sterol carrier protein that cholesterol might affect the activity of β-hydroxy-β-methylglutaryl-CoA reductase (see below).

Control of cholesterol synthesis is exerted near the beginning of the pathway. There is a marked decrease in the activity of β-hydroxy-β-methylglutaryl-CoA reductase in fasting rats, which might explain the reduced synthesis of cholesterol during fasting. On the other hand, the activity of this enzyme was not reduced in the livers of diabetic rats, which correlates well with the continued synthesis of cholesterol observed in the diabetic state. Siperstein has proposed a feedback mechanism whereby β-hydroxy-β-methylglutaryl-CoA reductase in liver is inhibited by cholesterol. Since a direct inhibition of the enzyme by cholesterol cannot be demonstrated, cholesterol may act either by repression of the synthesis of new reductase or by inducing the synthesis of enzymes that degrade existing reductase. A diurnal variation occurs in both cholesterol synthesis and reductase activity. However,

other work indicates more rapid effects of cholesterol on reductase activity than can be explained solely by changes in the rate of protein synthesis. Administration of insulin or thyroid hormone increases β-hydroxy-β-methylglutaryl-CoA reductase activity, whereas glucagon or glucocorticoids decrease it. Recent work (Nordstrom, 1977) has demonstrated that the enzyme exists in both active and inactive forms that may be reversibly modified by phosphorylation-dephosphorylation mechanisms (cf phosphorylase and hormone-sensitive lipase, pp 170 and 225).

After the administration of ^{14}C-labeled acetate, the label can soon be detected in the plasma cholesterol. Synthesis takes place in the liver, and the cholesterol is incorporated into very low density lipoproteins and ultimately into low density lipoproteins. The effect of variations in the amount of cholesterol in the diet on the endogenous production of cholesterol in rats has been studied. When there was only 0.05% cholesterol in the diet, 70–80% of the cholesterol of the liver, small intestine, and adrenal gland was synthesized within the body, whereas on a diet containing 2% cholesterol the endogenous production fell to 10–30%. However, endogenous production could not be completely suppressed by raising the dietary intake. It appears that it is only hepatic synthesis which is inhibited. Experiments with the perfused liver have demonstrated that cholesterol-rich chylomicron remnants (see p 229) inhibit sterol synthesis.

There is a species variation in the relative importance of the liver as a source of endogenous cholesterol. In humans, extrahepatic synthesis, mainly in the intestine, is more important, whereas in dogs and rats the liver is responsible for most cholesterol synthesis. Bile acids, rather than cholesterol, inhibit cholesterol synthesis in the intestine. A similar feedback control system at the β-hydroxy-β-methylglutaryl-CoA reductase step seems also to operate. More recent experiments in vitro have shown that cholesterol synthesis is inhibited by cAMP, indicating that one or more reactions in the synthetic pathway may be controlled by a cAMP-dependent protein kinase.

Attempts to lower plasma cholesterol in humans by reducing the amount of cholesterol in the diet are effective. An increase of 100 mg in dietary cholesterol causes a rise of 5 mg cholesterol per 100 mL serum.

Transport

Cholesterol in the diet is absorbed from the intestine and, in company with other lipids, including cholesterol synthesized in the intestines, incorporated into chylomicrons and VLDL. Of the cholesterol absorbed, 80–90% in the lymph is esterified with long chain fatty acids. Esterification may occur in the intestinal mucosa. The plant sterols (sitosterols) are poorly absorbed. When chylomicron remnants react with the liver, much of their cholesteryl esters are hydrolyzed and the cholesterol taken up by the liver. VLDL formed in the liver transport cholesterol into the plasma.

In humans, the total plasma cholesterol is about

200 mg/dL, rising with age, although there are wide variations between individuals. The greater part is found in the esterified form. It is transported as lipoprotein in the plasma, the highest proportion of cholesterol being found in the LDL (β-lipoproteins), which are formed from VLDL. However, under conditions where the VLDL are quantitatively predominant, an increased proportion of the plasma cholesterol will continue to reside in this fraction. Ultimately, LDL are broken down, probably in extrahepatic tissues, and the cholesterol is then taken up.

Dietary cholesterol takes several days to equilibrate with cholesterol in the plasma and several weeks to equilibrate with cholesterol of the tissues. The turnover of cholesterol in the liver is relatively fast compared with the half-life of the total body cholesterol, which is several weeks. Free cholesterol in plasma and liver equilibrates in a matter of hours.

Equilibration of cholesteryl ester with free cholesterol in plasma takes several days in humans. In general, free cholesterol exchanges readily between tissues and lipoproteins, whereas cholesteryl ester does not exchange freely. Some plasma cholesteryl ester may be formed in HDL as a result of the transesterification reaction in plasma between cholesterol and the fatty acid in position 2 of phosphatidylcholine, catalyzed by **lecithin:cholesterol acyltransferase (LCAT)** (see p 217). A familial deficiency of this enzyme has been described. In affected subjects, the plasma concentration of cholesteryl esters and lysolecithin is low whereas the concentration of cholesterol and lecithin is raised. The plasma tends to be turbid. Abnormalities are also found in the lipoproteins. One HDL fraction contains disk-shaped structures in stacks or rouleaux, and LDL contains a larger particle having a lipid composition somewhat similar to VLDL. Also present as an abnormal LDL subfraction is lipoprotein-X, otherwise found only in patients with cholestasis. VLDL are also abnormal, migrating as β-lipoproteins upon electrophoresis. Patients with parenchymal liver disease also show a decrease of lecithin:cholesterol acyltransferase activity and abnormalities in the serum lipids and lipoproteins. It would appear that lecithin:cholesterol acyltransferase is necessary for the normal metabolism of the plasma lipoproteins.

Thus, HDL is the probable vehicle, in combination with LCAT, for transporting cholesterol, as ester, from extrahepatic tissues back to the liver. Some of the cholesterol of HDL may be transferred to VLDL and chylomicrons and be recycled. Ultimately, all cholesterol destined for excretion from the body must enter the liver and be excreted in the bile, either as cholesterol or as cholic acid in the bile salts.

Excretion of Cholesterol

Approximately half of the cholesterol eliminated from the body is excreted in the feces after conversion to bile salts. The remainder is excreted as neutral steroids. Much of the cholesterol secreted in the bile is reabsorbed, and it is believed that the cholesterol that serves as precursor for the fecal sterols is derived from the intestinal mucosa. Coprostanol is the principal sterol in the feces; it is formed from cholesterol in the lower intestine by the bacterial flora therein. A large proportion of the biliary excretion of bile salts is reabsorbed into the portal circulation, taken up by the liver, and reexcreted in the bile. This is known as the **enterohepatic circulation.** The bile salts not reabsorbed, or their derivatives, are excreted in the feces. Bile salts undergo changes brought about by intestinal bacteria. The rate of production of bile acids from cholesterol in the liver is reduced by infusion of bile salts, indicating the existence of another feedback control mechanism initiated by the product of the reaction.

Cholesterol, Coronary Heart Disease, & Atherosclerosis

Many investigators have demonstrated a correlation between raised serum lipid levels and the incidence of coronary heart disease and atherosclerosis in humans. Of the serum lipids, cholesterol has been the one most often singled out as being chiefly concerned in the relationship. However, other parameters—such as the cholesterol:phospholipid ratio, Sf 12–400 lipoprotein concentration, serum triacylglycerol concentration, etc—show similar correlations. Patients with arterial disease can have any one of the following abnormalities: (1) elevated concentrations of VLDL (mainly triacylglycerols), with normal concentrations of LDL (D = 1.019–1.063) containing chiefly cholesterol; (2) elevated low density lipoproteins (cholesterol) with normal VLDL (triacylglycerols); (3) elevation of both lipoprotein fractions (cholesterol plus triacylglycerols). There is also an inverse relationship between HDL concentrations and coronary heart disease, and some consider that the most predictive relationship is the LDL/HDL cholesterol ratio. This relationship is explainable in terms of the proposed roles of LDL in transporting cholesterol to the tissues and of HDL acting as the scavenger of cholesterol.

Atherosclerosis is characterized by the deposition of cholesteryl ester and other lipids in the connective tissue of the arterial walls. Diseases in which prolonged elevated levels of low and very low density lipoproteins occur in the blood (eg, diabetes mellitus, lipid nephrosis, hypothyroidism, and other conditions of hyperlipidemia) are often accompanied by premature or more severe atherosclerosis.

Experiments on the induction of atherosclerosis in animals indicate a wide species variation in susceptibility. The rabbit, pig, monkey, and humans are species in which atherosclerosis can be induced by feeding cholesterol. The rat, dog, and cat are resistant. Thyroidectomy or treatment with thiouracil drugs will allow induction of atherosclerosis in the dog and rat. Low blood cholesterol is a characteristic of hyperthyroidism. However, hyperthyroidism is associated with an increased rate of cholesterol synthesis. The fall in level of plasma cholesterol may be due to an increased rate of turnover and excretion.

Of the factors that lower blood cholesterol, the

Table 18—2. Typical fatty acid analyses of some fats of animal and plant origin.*
(All values in weight percentages of component fatty acids.)

	Saturated			Unsaturated		
	Palmitic	Stearic	Other	Oleic	Linoleic	Other
Animal fats						
Lard	29.8	12.7	1.0	47.8	3.1	5.6
Chicken	25.6	7.0	0.3	39.4	21.8	5.9
Butterfat	25.2	9.2	25.6	29.5	3.6	7.2
Beef fat	29.2	21.0	3.4	41.1	1.8	3.5
Vegetable oils						
Corn	8.1	2.5	0.1	30.1	56.3	2.9
Peanut	6.3	4.9	5.9	61.1	21.8	. . .
Cottonseed	23.4	1.1	2.7	22.9	47.8	2.1
Soybean	9.8	2.4	1.2	28.9	50.7	7.0†
Olive	10.0	3.3	0.6	77.5	8.6	. . .
Coconut	10.5	2.3	78.4	7.5	trace	1.3

*Reproduced from NRC Publication No. 575: *The Role of Dietary Fat in Human Health: A Report.* Food and Nutrition Board, National Academy of Sciences.
†Mostly linolenic acid.

substitution in the diet of polyunsaturated fatty acids for some of the saturated fatty acids has been the most intensely studied. Naturally occurring oils that are beneficial in lowering plasma cholesterol include peanut, cottonseed, corn, and soybean oil, whereas butterfat and coconut oil raise the level. Table 18–2 shows the high proportion of linoleic acid in the first group of oils and its relative deficiency or absence in butterfat or coconut oil, respectively. Sucrose and fructose have a greater effect in raising blood lipids than other carbohydrates. A correlation between the increased consumption of sucrose and atherosclerosis has been claimed.

The reason for the cholesterol lowering effect of polyunsaturated fatty acids is still not clear. However, several hypotheses have been advanced to explain the effect, including the stimulation of cholesterol excretion into the intestine and the stimulation of the oxidation of cholesterol to bile acids. It is possible that cholesteryl esters of polyunsaturated fatty acids are more rapidly metabolized by the liver and other tissues, which might enhance their rate of turnover and excretion. There is other evidence that the effect is largely due to a shift in distribution of cholesterol from the plasma into the tissues. Saturated fatty acids cause the formation of smaller VLDL particles that contain relatively more cholesterol, and they are utilized by extrahepatic tissues at a slower rate than are larger particles. All of these tendencies may be regarded as atherogenic.

Additional factors considered to play a part in atherosclerosis include high blood pressure, smoking, obesity, lack of exercise, and drinking soft as opposed to hard water. Elevation of plasma free fatty acids will also lead to increased VLDL secretion by the liver, involving extra triacylglycerol and cholesterol output into the circulation. Factors leading to higher or fluctuating levels of free fatty acids include emotional stress, nicotine from cigarette smoking, coffee drinking, and partaking of few large meals rather than more

continuous feeding. Premenopausal women appear to be protected against many of these deleterious factors, possibly because they have higher concentrations of HDL than men.

Hypolipidemic Drugs

When dietary measures fail to achieve reduced serum lipid levels, the use of hypolipidemic drugs may be resorted to. Several drugs are known that block the formation of cholesterol at various stages in the biosynthetic pathway. Many of these drugs have harmful effects, and it is now considered that direct interference with cholesterol synthesis is to be avoided. **Sitosterol** is a hypocholesterolemic agent that acts by blocking the absorption of cholesterol in the gastrointestinal tract. Drugs that are considered to increase the fecal excretion of cholesterol and bile acids include **dextrothyroxine** (Choloxin), **neomycin,** and possibly **clofibrate** (Atromid S). On the other hand, **cholestyramine** (Cuemid, Questran) prevents the reabsorption of bile salts by combining with them, thereby increasing their fecal loss. Clofibrate exerts at least part of its hypolipidemic effect by diverting the hepatic inflow of free fatty acids from the pathways of esterification into those of oxidation, thus decreasing the secretion of triacylglycerol and cholesterol containing VLDL by the liver (Laker, 1979). Other hypocholesterolemic drugs include **nicotinic acid** and **estrogens.**

Disorders of the Plasma Lipoproteins

A few individuals in the population exhibit inherited defects in their lipoproteins leading to the primary condition of either hypo- or hyperlipoproteinemia. Many others having defects such as diabetes mellitus, hypothyroidism, and atherosclerosis show abnormal lipoprotein patterns that are very similar to one or the other of the primary inherited conditions. Virtually all of these diseases are due to a defect at one or another stage in the course of lipoprotein formation, transport, or destruction (Figs 18–5 and 18–6).

A. Hypolipoproteinemia:

1. Abetalipoproteinemia–This is a rare inherited disease characterized by absence of β-lipoprotein (LDL) in plasma. Most of the blood lipids are present in low concentrations—especially acylglycerols, which are virtually absent since no chylomicrons or pre-β-lipoproteins (VLDL) are formed. Both the intestine and the liver accumulate acylglycerols. It is most likely due to a defect in apoprotein B synthesis.

2. Familial hypobetalipoproteinemia–In hypobetalipoproteinemia, LDL or β-lipoprotein concentration is between 10 and 50% of normal, but chylomicron formation occurs. It must be concluded that β-lipoprotein is essential for triacylglycerol transport. Most individuals are healthy and long-lived.

3. Familial alpha-lipoprotein deficiency (Tangier disease)–In the homozygous individual, there is near absence of plasma HDL or α-lipoproteins and accumulation of cholesteryl esters in the tissues. There is no impairment of chylomicron formation or secretion of endogenous triacylglycerol by the liver. However, on electrophoresis, there is no pre-β-lipoprotein, but a broad β-band is found containing the endogenous triacylglycerol. This finding provides evidence that the normal pre-β-band contains other apoproteins normally provided by HDL. Although α-lipoprotein does not appear to be essential for acylglycerol transport, clearance from the plasma is slow when it is absent, the patients tending to develop hypertriacylglycerolemia, presumably as a result of the absence of apo-C–II, which activates lipoprotein lipase.

B. Hyperlipoproteinemia:

1. Familial lipoprotein lipase deficiency (type I)–Characterized by very slow clearing of chylomicrons from the circulation, leading to abnormally raised levels of chylomicrons. Pre-β-lipoproteins may be raised, but there is a decrease in α- and β-lipoproteins. Thus, the condition is fat-induced. It may be corrected by reducing the quantity of fat in the diet, but high-carbohydrate diets lead to raised levels of pre-β-lipoproteins due to synthesis in the liver. A variation of this disease is caused by a deficiency in apo-C–II, required as a cofactor for lipoprotein lipase.

2. Familial hypercholesterolemia (type II)–Characterized by hyperbetalipoproteinemia (LDL), which is associated with increased plasma total cholesterol. There may also be a tendency for the VLDL to be elevated in type IIb. Therefore, the patient may have somewhat elevated triacylglycerol levels but the plasma—as is not true in the other types of hyperlipoproteinemia—remains clear. Lipid deposition in the tissue (eg, xanthomas, atheromas) is common. A type II pattern may also arise as a secondary result of hypothyroidism. The disease appears to be associated with reduced rates of clearance of β-lipoprotein (LDL) from the circulation due to defective LDL receptors and is associated with an increased incidence of atherosclerosis. Reduction of dietary cholesterol and saturated fats may be of use in treatment. A disease producing hypercholesterolemia but due to a different cause is **Wolman's disease** (cholesteryl ester storage disease). This is due to a deficiency of cholesteryl ester hydrolase in lysosomes of cells such as fibroblasts that normally metabolize LDL.

3. Familial type III hyperlipoproteinemia (broad beta disease, remnant removal disease)–Characterized by an increase in both β- and pre-β-lipoproteins, thought to be chylomicron and VLDL remnants; these appear as a broad β-band on electrophoresis, causing hypercholesterolemia and hypertriacylglycerolemia. Xanthomas and atherosclerosis of both peripheral and coronary arteries are present. Treatment by weight reduction and low-carbohydrate diets containing unsaturated fats and little cholesterol is recommended. The disease is probably caused by a deficiency in remnant metabolism by the liver.

4. Familial hypertriacylglycerolemia (type IV)–Characterized by hyperprebetalipoproteinemia with associated high levels of endogenously produced triacylglycerol (VLDL). Cholesterol levels rise in proportion to the hypertriacylglycerolemia, and glucose intolerance is frequently present. Both α- and β-lipoproteins are subnormal in quantity. This lipoprotein pattern is also commonly associated with coronary heart disease, maturity onset diabetes, obesity, and many other conditions, including alcoholism and the taking of progestational hormones. Treatment of primary type IV hyperlipoproteinemia is by weight reduction, replacement of much of the carbohydrate in the diet with unsaturated fat, low-cholesterol diets, and hypolipidemic agents.

5. Familial type V hyperlipoproteinemia–The lipoprotein pattern is complex since both chylomicrons and pre-β-lipoproteins are elevated, causing both triacylglycerolemia and cholesterolemia. Concentrations of α- and β-lipoproteins are low. Xanthomas are frequently present, but the incidence of atherosclerosis is apparently not striking. Glucose tolerance is abnormal and frequently associated with obesity and diabetes. The reason for the condition, which is familial, is not clear. Treatment has consisted of weight reduction followed by a diet not too high in either carbohydrate or fat.

● ● ●

References

Björntorp P, Sjöström L: Carbohydrate storage in man: Speculations and some quantitative considerations. *Metabolism* 1978;**27**:1853.

Crepaldi G, Lefebvre PJ, Alberti KGMM (editors): *Diabetes, Obesity and Hyperlipidemias.* Academic Press, 1978.

Dietschy JM, Gotto AM, Ontko JA (editors): *Disturbances in Lipid and Lipoprotein Metabolism.* American Physiological Society, 1978.

Eisenberg S, Levy RI: Lipoprotein metabolism. *Adv Lipid Res* 1975;**13**:1.

Florkin M, Stotz EH (editors): *Comprehensive Biochemistry.* Vol 18. Elsevier, 1970.

Gardner RS, Mayes PA: *Biochem J* 1978;**170**:47.

Goldstein JL, Brown MS: The low-density lipoprotein pathway and its relation to atherosclerosis. *Annu Rev Biochem* 1977;**46**:897.

Hamilton RL & others: *J Clin Invest* 1976;**58**:667.

Jeanrenaud B, Hepp D (editors): *Adipose Tissue Regulation and Metabolic Functions.* Academic Press, 1970.

Kuksis A, Mookerjea S: Choline. *Nutr Rev* 1978;**36**:201.

Laker ME, Mayes PA: *Biochem Pharmacol* 1979;**28**:2813.

Levy RI: The effect of hypolipidemic drugs on plasma lipoproteins. *Annu Rev Pharmacol* 1977;**17**:499.

Lewis B: *The Hyperlipidaemias.* Blackwell, 1976.

Lieber CS & others: Differences in hepatic and metabolic changes after acute and chronic alcohol consumption. *Fed Proc* 1975;**34**:2060.

Morrisett JD, Jackson RL, Gotto AM: Lipoproteins: Structure and function. *Annu Rev Biochem* 1975;**44**:183.

Nordstrom JL, Rodwell VW, Mitschelen JJ: Interconversion of active and inactive forms of rat liver HMG-CoA reductase. *J Biol Chem* 1977;**252**:8924.

Renold AE, Cahill GF (editors): *Handbook of Physiology.* Section 5. American Physiological Society, 1965.

Scallen TJ & others: Sterol carrier protein hypothesis. *Fed Proc* 1974;**33**:1733.

Smith LC, Pownall HJ, Gotto AM: The plasma lipoproteins: Structure and metabolism. *Annu Rev Biochem* 1978;**47**:751.

Starr P: Atherosclerosis, hypothyroidism, and thyroid hormone therapy. *Adv Lipid Res* 1978;**16**:345.

Steinberg D: Interconvertible enzymes in adipose tissue regulated by cyclic AMP-dependent protein kinase. *Adv Cyclic Nucleotide Res* 1976;**7**:157.

Wakil S (editor): *Lipid Metabolism.* Academic Press, 1970.

Various authors: Disorders characterized by evidence of abnormal lipid metabolism. In: *The Metabolic Basis of Inherited Disease,* 4th ed. Stanbury JB, Wyngaarden JB, Fredrickson DS (editors). McGraw-Hill, 1978.

Regulation of Carbohydrate & Lipid Metabolism | 19

Peter A. Mayes, PhD, DSc

The concept of respiratory control of the rate of oxidation of substrate provides a mechanism for the orderly burning of fuel molecules by each individual cell. It explains, in terms of availability of ADP, why the metabolic fuel is not burned in an uncontrolled or explosive fashion but rather at just that precise rate necessary to provide the immediate energy requirements of the cell in the form of high-energy phosphate. For such a mechanism to function efficiently, a continuous supply of substrate or respiratory fuel molecules must always be available. Regulation of the metabolic pathways that provide these fuel molecules is essential if the supply is to be maintained under the variety of nutritional, metabolic, and pathologic conditions that are encountered in vivo. The term **caloric homeostasis** has been given to this type of metabolic regulation. It involves provision of the special fuel needs of each tissue, including the making available of alternative fuels. It also involves transport of various fuels about the body together with mechanisms to control their concentration in the blood.

GENERAL PRINCIPLES OF REGULATION OF METABOLIC PATHWAYS

Regulation of the overall flux along a metabolic pathway is often concerned with the control of only one or perhaps 2 key reactions in the pathway, catalyzed by "regulatory enzymes." The physicochemical factors that control the rate of an enzyme-catalyzed reaction, eg, substrate concentration (see Chapter 8), are of primary importance in the control of the overall rate of a metabolic pathway. However, temperature and pH, factors that can influence enzyme activity, are held constant in warm-blooded vertebrates and have little regulatory significance.

Equilibrium & Nonequilibrium Reactions

In a reaction at equilibrium, the forward and reverse reactions take place at equal rates, and there is therefore no net flux in either direction. Many reactions in metabolic pathways are of this type, ie, "equilibrium reactions":

$$A \longleftrightarrow B \longleftrightarrow C \longleftrightarrow D$$

In vivo, under "steady state" conditions, there would probably be a net flux from left to right owing to continuous supply of A and continuous removal of D. Such a pathway could function, but there would be little scope for control of the flux via regulation of enzyme activity since an increase in activity would only serve to speed up attainment of the equilibrium.

In practice, there are invariably one or more "nonequilibrium" type reactions in a metabolic pathway, where the reactants are present in concentrations that are far from equilibrium. In attempting to reach equilibrium, large losses of free energy occur as heat, making this type of reaction essentially nonreversible, eg,

$$A \longleftrightarrow B \overset{\text{Heat}}{\longrightarrow} C \longleftrightarrow D$$

Nonequilibrium reaction

Such a pathway has both flow and direction and would exhaust itself if control were not exerted. The enzymes catalyzing nonequilibrium reactions are usually low in concentration and are subject to other controlling mechanisms. This is similar to the opening and shutting of a "one-way" valve, making it possible to control the net flow.

METABOLIC CONTROL OF AN ENZYME–CATALYZED REACTION

A hypothetical metabolic pathway, A,B,C,D, is shown in Fig 19–1, in which reactions A $\longleftrightarrow$ B and C $\longleftrightarrow$ D are equilibrium reactions and B $\rightarrow$ C is a nonequilibrium reaction. The flux through such a pathway can be regulated by the availability of substrate A. This might depend on its supply from the blood and on its ability to permeate the cell membrane. The flux will also be determined by the efficiency of removal of the end product D and on the availability of cosubstrate or cofactors represented by X and Y.

Enzymes catalyzing nonequilibrium reactions are often allosteric proteins subject to the action of "feedback" or "feed-forward" control by allosteric modifiers (see Chapter 8). Other control mechanisms depend on the action of hormones. These act by several

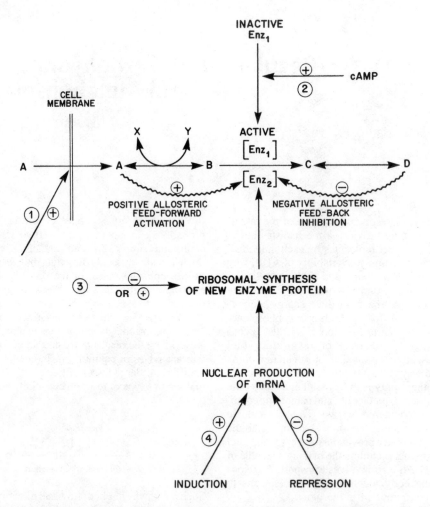

Figure 19–1. Mechanisms of control of an enzyme-catalyzed reaction. Circled numbers indicate possible sites of action of hormones. ① Alteration of membrane permeability, ② conversion of an inactive to an active enzyme, ③ alteration of the rate of translation of mRNA at the ribosomal level, ④ induction of new mRNA formation, and ⑤ repression of mRNA formation.

different mechanisms (see Chapter 34). One is **covalent modification** of the enzyme by phosphorylation and dephosphorylation. This is rapid and is often mediated through the formation of cAMP, which in turn causes the conversion of an inactive enzyme into an active enzyme. This change is brought about via the activity of a cAMP-dependent protein kinase that phosphorylates the enzyme. The active form of the enzyme can be either the phosphorylated enzyme (eg, phosphorylase a) or the dephosphorylated enzyme (eg, glycogen synthetase I). Some regulatory enzymes can be phosphorylated without the mediation of cAMP and cAMP-dependent protein kinase. These enzymes respond to other metabolic signals such as the [ATP]/[ADP] ratio, eg, pyruvate dehydrogenase (Fig 19–2). Besides the enzymes mentioned, many others are known to undergo phosphorylation-dephosphorylation.

The synthesis of rate-controlling enzymes can be affected by hormones. Because this involves new pro-

tein synthesis, it is not a rapid change but is often a response to a change in nutritional state. Hormones can act as inducers or repressors of mRNA formation in the nucleus or as stimulators of the translation stage of protein synthesis at the ribosomal level (see Chapters 30 and 34).

REGULATION OF CARBOHYDRATE METABOLISM

It is convenient to divide the regulation of carbohydrate metabolism into 2 parts: (1) the regulation of carbohydrate metabolism at the cellular and enzymatic level, and (2) factors affecting the blood glucose. However, this is an arbitrary division as the 2 parts are functionally related.

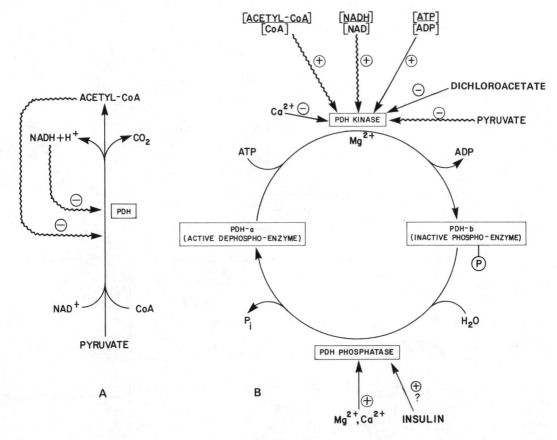

Figure 19–2. Regulation of pyruvate dehydrogenase (PDH). Arrows with wavy shafts indicate allosteric effects. *A:* Regulation by end product inhibition. *B:* Regulation by interconversion of active and inactive forms.

REGULATION OF CARBOHYDRATE METABOLISM AT THE CELLULAR & ENZYMATIC LEVEL

Gross effects on metabolism of changes in nutritional state or in the endocrine balance of an animal may be studied by observing changes in the concentration of blood metabolites. By such technics as catheterization, it is also possible to study effects on individual organs by measuring arteriovenous differences, etc. However, the changes which occur in the metabolic balance of the intact animal are due to shifts in the pattern of metabolism in individual tissues that are usually associated with changes in availability of metabolites or changes in activity of key enzymes.

Changes in availability of substrates are either directly or indirectly responsible for most changes in metabolism. The concentration of glucose, fatty acids, and amino acids in blood influences their rate and pattern of metabolism in many tissues. Fluctuations in their blood concentrations due to changes in dietary availability may alter the rate of secretion of hormones that influence, in turn, the pattern of metabolism in metabolic pathways—often by affecting the activity of key enzymes which attempt to compensate for the original change in substrate availability. Three types of

mechanisms can be identified as responsible for regulating the activity of enzymes concerned in carbohydrate metabolism: (1) changes in the rate of enzyme synthesis, (2) conversion of an inactive to an active enzyme, and (3) allosteric effects.

Regulation of Glycolysis, Gluconeogenesis, & the Hexose Monophosphate Shunt (Fig 19–3)

Some of the better-documented changes in enzyme activity that are considered to occur under various metabolic conditions are listed in Table 19–1. The information in this table applies mainly to the liver. The enzymes involved catalyze nonequilibrium reactions that may be regarded physiologically as "one-way" rather than balanced reactions. Often the effect is reinforced for the reason that the activity of the enzyme catalyzing the change in the opposite direction varies reciprocally. Thus, glucokinase catalyzes the conversion of glucose to glucose 6-phosphate. In the same compartment of the cell (the extramitochondrial region) is found glucose-6-phosphatase, the enzyme catalyzing the same interconversion but in the reverse direction. Under conditions of a plentiful supply of carbohydrate, glucokinase activity is high whereas glucose-6-phosphatase activity is depressed. In starvation, glucokinase activity falls relative to glucose-6-

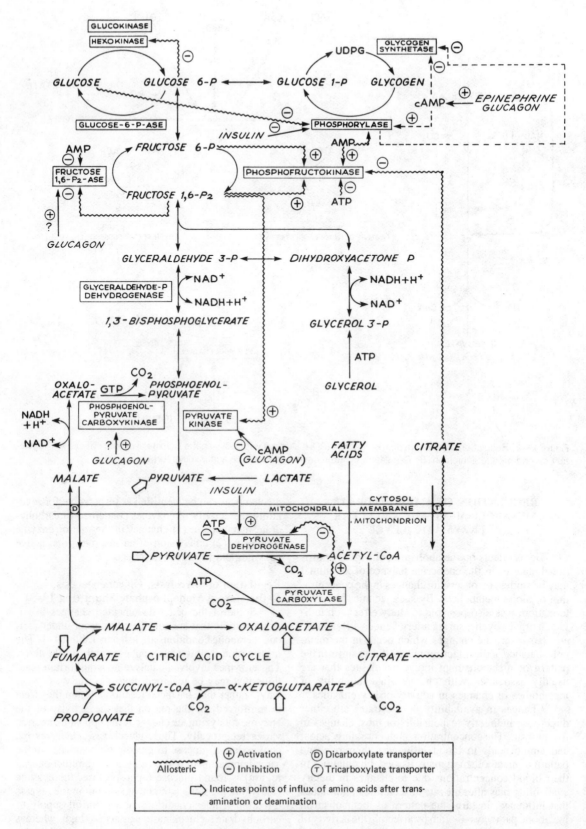

Figure 19–3. Key enzymes in the control of glycolysis, gluconeogenesis, and glycogen metabolism in liver. Indications of hormone action do not necessarily imply a direct action on the enzymes concerned.

Table 19—1. Regulatory and adaptive enzymes of the rat (mainly liver).

	Activity In Carbo-hydrate Feeding	Activity In Starva-tion* and Diabetes	Inducer	Repressor	Activator [* = allosteric]	Inhibitor [* = allosteric]
Enzymes of glycolysis and glycogenesis						
Hexokinase						*Glucose 6-phosphate
Glucokinase	↑	↓	Insulin			
Glycogen synthetase system	↑	↓	Insulin		Insulin	cAMP, phosphorylase, glycogen
Phosphofructokinase	↑	↓	Insulin		*cAMP, *AMP, *fructose 6-P, *Pi, *fructose 1,6-bisphosphate	*Citrate (fatty acids, ketone bodies), *ATP
Pyruvate kinase	↑	↓	Insulin, fructose		*Fructose 1,6-bisphosphate	ATP, alanine, glucagon, epinephrine
Pyruvate dehydrogenase	↑	↓			CoA, NAD, insulin, ADP, pyruvate	Acetyl-CoA, NADH ATP
Enzymes of gluconeogenesis						
Pyruvate carboxylase	↓	↑	Glucocorticoids, glucagon, epinephrine	Insulin	*Acetyl-CoA	*ADP
Phosphoenolpyruvate carboxykinase	↓	↑	Glucocorticoids	Insulin	Glucagon?	
Fructose-1,6-bisphosphatase	↓	↑	Glucocorticoids, glucagon, epinephrine	Insulin	Glucagon?	*Fructose 1,6-bisphosphate, *AMP
Glucose-6-phosphatase	↓	↑	Glucocorticoids, glucagon, epinephrine	Insulin		
Enzymes of the hexose monophosphate shunt, lipogenesis, and cholesterol synthesis						
Glucose-6-phosphate dehydrogenase	↑	↓	Insulin			
6-Phosphogluconate dehydrogenase	↑	↓	Insulin			
"Malic enzyme"	↑	↓	Insulin			
ATP-citrate lyase	↑	↓	Insulin			ADP
Acetyl-CoA carboxylase	↑	↓	Insulin?		*Citrate, insulin	Long chain acyl-CoA, cAMP?, glucagon
Fatty acid synthetase	↑	↓	Insulin?			
HMG-CoA reductase	↓*	↑			Insulin	Cholesterol

phosphatase activity. In this way a so-called ''substrate cycle'' or ''futile cycle'' whose net result would be hydrolysis of ATP is minimized. However, it appears that some recycling does occur in the glucokinase/glucose-6-phosphatase cycle that may have the physiologic advantage of allowing large changes in net flux of metabolites in either direction, controlled by substrate concentration only. It is also of importance that the key enzymes involved in a metabolic pathway are all activated or depressed in a coordinated manner. Table 19–1 shows that this is clearly the case. The enzymes involved in the utilization of glucose are all activated under the circumstance of a superfluity of glucose, and under these conditions the enzymes responsible for producing glucose by the pathway of gluconeogenesis are all low in activity. The secretion of insulin, which is responsive to the blood glucose concentration, controls the activity of the enzymes responsible for glycolysis and those responsible for gluconeogenesis. All of these effects, which can be explained on the basis of new enzyme synthesis, can be prevented by agents that block the synthesis of new protein, such as puromycin and ethionine.

Both dehydrogenases of the hexose monophosphate pathway can be classified as adaptive enzymes since they increase in activity in the well-fed animal and when insulin is given to a diabetic animal. Activity is low in diabetes or fasting. ''Malic enzyme'' and ATP-citrate lyase behave similarly, indicating that these 2 enzymes are probably involved in lipogenesis rather than gluconeogenesis.

Pyruvate dehydrogenase may be regulated by phosphorylation involving an ATP-specific kinase that causes a decrease in activity, and by dephosphorylation by a phosphatase that causes an increase in activity of the dehydrogenase. The kinase is activated by increases in the [acetyl-CoA]/[CoA], [NADH]/[NAD⁺], or [ATP]/[ADP] ratios. Thus, pyruvate dehydrogenase—and therefore glycolysis—is inhibited under conditions of fatty acid oxidation, which leads to increases in these ratios (Fig 19–2). An increase in activity occurs after administration of insulin and a decrease occurs in starvation.

Several examples are available from carbohydrate metabolism to illustrate allosteric control of the activity of an enzyme. In gluconeogenosis, the synthesis of oxaloacetate from bicarbonate and pyruvate, catalyzed by the enzyme **pyruvate carboxylase,** requires the presence of acetyl-CoA as an allosteric activator. The addition of acetyl-CoA results in a change in the tertiary structure of the protein, lowering the K_m value for bicarbonate. This effect has important implications for the self-regulation of intermediary metabolism, for, as acetyl-CoA is formed from pyruvate, it automatically ensures the provision of oxaloacetate and its further oxidation in the citric acid cycle by activating pyruvate carboxylase. The activation of pyruvate carboxylase and the inhibition of pyruvate dehydrogenase by acetyl-CoA formed from the oxidation of fatty acids helps to explain the sparing action of fatty acid oxidation on the oxidation of pyruvate and the stimulation of gluconeogenesis in the liver (Fig 19–3). Probably the main role of fatty acid oxidation in promoting gluconeogenesis is to supply ATP required in the pyruvate carboxylase and phosphoenolpyruvate carboxykinase reactions. Glucagon promotes gluconeogenesis in the liver probably by increasing cAMP concentrations that stimulate the flux of substrates through the phosphoenolpyruvate carboxykinase reaction and inhibit pyruvate kinase. Another site of action of glucagon at fructose bisphosphatase is claimed in order to account for the stimulation of glycerol metabolism.

Another enzyme that is subject to feedback control is **phosphofructokinase.** It occupies a key position in regulating glycolysis. Phosphofructokinase is inhibited by citrate and by ATP and is activated by AMP. The presence of **adenylate kinase** in liver and many other tissues allows rapid equilibration of the reaction:

$$ATP + AMP \rightleftharpoons 2\,ADP$$

Thus, when ATP is used in energy-requiring processes resulting in formation of ADP, [AMP] rises. As [ATP] may be 50 times that of [AMP] at equilibrium, a small fractional decrease in [ATP] will cause a several-fold increase in [AMP]. Thus, a large change in [AMP] acts as a metabolic amplifier of a small change in [ATP]. This mechanism may allow the activity of phosphofructokinase to be highly sensitive to even small changes in energy status of the cell and may control the quantity of carbohydrate undergoing glycolysis prior to its entry into the citric acid cycle. The increase in [AMP] can also explain why glycolysis is increased during anoxia when [ATP] decreases. Simultaneously, AMP activates phosphorylase, increasing glycogenolysis. The inhibition of phosphofructokinase by citrate and ATP could be another explanation of the sparing action of fatty acid oxidation on glucose oxidation and also of the **Pasteur effect** whereby aerobic oxidation (via the citric acid cycle) inhibits the anaerobic degradation of glucose. A consequence of the inhibition of phosphofructokinase is an accumulation of glucose 6-phosphate which, in turn, inhibits further uptake of glucose by allosteric inhibition of hexokinase. There appears to be a reciprocal relationship between the

regulation of pyruvate dehydrogenase and pyruvate carboxylase in both liver and kidney, which alters the metabolic fate of pyruvate as the tissue changes from carbohydrate oxidation, via glycolysis, to gluconeogenesis.

Regulation of Glycogen Metabolism

Regulation of glycogen metabolism is effected by a balance in activities between the enzymes of glycogen synthesis and of breakdown that are under substrate (through allosteric activity) as well as hormonal control. Not only is phosphorylase activated by a rise in concentration of cAMP, but glycogen synthetase is at the same time converted to the inactive form (see Chapter 15). Cyclic AMP–dependent protein kinase both activates phosphorylase b kinase and inactivates glycogen synthetase (Figs 15–8 and 15–9). Thus, inhibition of glycogenolysis enhances net glycogenesis and inhibition of glycogenesis enhances net glycogenolysis. Cohen has shown that both phosphorylase b kinase and glycogen synthetase may be reversibly phosphorylated in more than one site by separate kinases and phosphatases. These secondary phosphorylations modify the sensitivity of the primary sites to phosphorylation and dephosphorylation. Pyruvate dehydrogenase also shows evidence of **multisite phosphorylation.**

According to Hers, the major factor that controls glycogen metabolism in the liver is the concentration of phosphorylase a. Not only does this enzyme control the rate-limiting step in glycogenolysis; it also inhibits the activity of synthetase phosphatase and thereby controls glycogen synthesis (Fig 19–3). Inactivation of phosphorylase is caused by glucose, and activation is caused by 5′-AMP. Several observations have suggested that catecholamines, including epinephrine, stimulate glycogenolysis by an additional mechanism not involving cAMP but via α-adrenergic receptors. These mechanisms possibly involve direct stimulation of phosphorylase kinase by Ca^{2+}. cAMP-independent glycogenolysis is also caused by vasopressin, oxytocin, and angiotensin II. Administration of insulin causes an immediate inactivation of phosphorylase followed by activation of glycogen synthetase. The effects of insulin require the presence of glucose.

Regulation of the Citric Acid Cycle
(Fig 14–4)

The identification of regulatory enzymes of the citric acid cycle is difficult because of the many pathways with which the cycle interacts as well as its location within the mitochondrion wherein measurement of enzyme activity and substrate levels is relatively uncertain. In most tissues, where the primary function of the citric acid cycle is to provide energy, there is little doubt that respiratory control via the respiratory chain and oxidative phosphorylation is the overriding control on citric acid cycle activity. Thus, activity is immediately dependent on the supply of oxidized dehydrogenase cofactors (eg, NAD), which in turn is dependent on the availability of ADP and ultimately, therefore, on the rate of utilization of ATP. In addition to this overall or coarse control, the properties of some of the enzymes of the cycle indicate that control might also be exerted at the level of the cycle itself. In a tissue such as brain, which is largely dependent on carbohydrate to supply acetyl-CoA, control of the citric acid cycle may occur at the pyruvate dehydrogenase step. In the cycle proper, control may be exercised by allosteric inhibition of citrate synthase by ATP or long chain fatty acyl-CoA. Allosteric activation of mitochondrial NAD-dependent isocitrate dehydrogenase by ADP is counteracted by ATP and NADH. The α-ketoglutarate dehydrogenase complex appears to be under control analogous to that of pyruvate dehydrogenase. Succinate dehydrogenase is inhibited by oxaloacetate, and the availability of oxaloacetate, as controlled by malate dehydrogenase, depends on the [NADH]/[NAD⁺] ratio. In the heart the cycle is controlled by the [NADH]/[NAD⁺] ratio via the availability of oxaloacetate and by the [ATP]/[ADP] ratio via inhibition of citrate synthetase by succinyl-CoA in competition with acetyl-CoA. An increased [ATP]/[ADP] ratio is considered to raise the [GTP]/[GDP] ratio at the succinate thiokinase step, thereby increasing the concentration of succinyl-CoA. Which (if any) of these mechanisms operates in vivo has still to be resolved.

THE BLOOD GLUCOSE

Sources of Blood Glucose

A. From Carbohydrates of the Diet: Most carbohydrates in the diet form glucose, galactose, or fructose upon digestion. These are absorbed into the portal vein. Galactose and fructose are readily converted to glucose in the liver (Figs 15–16 and 15–17).

B. From Various Glucogenic Compounds That Undergo Gluconeogenesis: These compounds fall into 2 categories—those which involve a direct net conversion to glucose without significant recycling, such as some amino acids and propionate; and those which are the products of the partial metabolism of glucose in certain tissues and which are conveyed to the liver and kidney, where they are resynthesized to glucose. Thus, lactate, formed by the oxidation of glucose in skeletal muscle and by erythrocytes, is transported to the liver and kidney where it re-forms glucose, which again becomes available via the circulation for oxidation in the tissues. This process is known as the **Cori cycle** or lactic acid cycle (Fig 19–4). Glycerol for the triacylglycerols of adipose tissue is derived initially from the blood glucose since free glycerol cannot be utilized readily for the synthesis of triacylglycerols in this tissue. Acylglycerols of adipose tissue are continually undergoing hydrolysis to form free glycerol, which diffuses out of the tissue into the blood. It is converted back to glucose by gluconeogenic mechanisms in the liver and kidney. Thus, a continuous cycle exists in which glucose is transported from the liver and kidney to adipose tissue and whence glycerol is returned to be synthesized into glucose by the liver and kidney.

It has been noted that, of the amino acids transported from muscle to the liver during starvation, alanine predominates. This has led to the postulation of a **glucose-alanine cycle,** as shown in Fig 19–4, which has the effect of cycling glucose from liver to muscle and alanine from muscle to liver, effecting a net transfer of amino nitrogen from muscle to liver and of free energy from liver to muscle. The energy required for the hepatic synthesis of glucose from pyruvate is derived from the oxidation of fatty acids.

C. From liver glycogen by glycogenolysis.

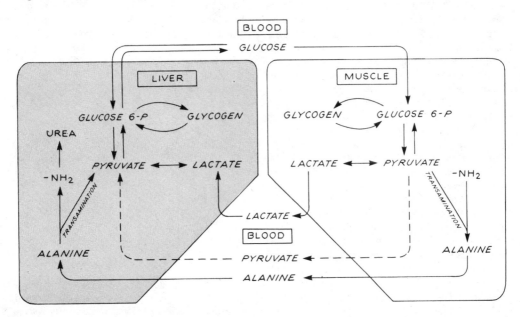

Figure 19–4. The lactic acid (Cori) cycle and glucose-alanine cycle.

The Concentration of the Blood Glucose

In the postabsorptive state, the blood glucose concentration of humans varies between 80 and 100 mg/dL. After the ingestion of a carbohydrate meal it may rise to 120–130 mg/dL. During fasting, the level falls to around 60–70 mg/dL. Under normal circumstances, the level is controlled within these limits. The normal blood glucose level of ruminants is considerably lower, being approximately 40 mg/dL in sheep and 60 mg/dL in cattle. These lower normal levels appear to be associated with the fact that ruminants ferment virtually all dietary carbohydrate to lower (volatile) fatty acids, and these largely replace glucose as the main metabolic fuel of the tissues in the fed condition.

Regulation of the Blood Glucose

The maintenance of stable levels of glucose in the blood is one of the most finely regulated of all homeostatic mechanisms and one in which the liver, the extrahepatic tissues, and several hormones play a part. **Liver cells appear to be freely permeable to glucose** whereas cells of **extrahepatic tissues are relatively impermeable.** As a result, the passage through the cell membrane is the rate-limiting step in the uptake of glucose in extrahepatic tissues, and it is rapidly phosphorylated by hexokinase on entry into the cells. On the other hand, it is probable that the activity of certain enzymes and the concentration of key intermediates exert a much more direct effect on the uptake or output of glucose from liver. Nevertheless, the concentration of glucose in the blood is an important factor controlling the rate of uptake of glucose in both liver and extrahepatic tissues. It is to be noted that hexokinase is inhibited by glucose 6-phosphate, so that some feedback control may be exerted on glucose uptake in extrahepatic tissues that are dependent on hexokinase for glucose phosphorylation. The liver is not subject to this constraint, because glucokinase is not affected by glucose 6-phosphate. Glucokinase, which has a higher K_m for glucose than does hexokinase, increases in activity over the physiologic range of glucose concentrations (Fig 19–5) and seems to be specifically concerned with glucose uptake into the liver at the higher concentrations found in the hepatic portal vein after a carbohydrate meal. Its absence in ruminants, which have low blood glucose concentrations, is compatible with this function.

At normal blood glucose concentrations (80–100 mg/dL), the liver appears to be a net producer of glucose. However, as the glucose level rises, the output of glucose ceases, so that at high levels there is a net uptake. In the rat, it has been estimated that the rate of uptake of glucose and the rate of output are equal at a hepatic portal vein blood glucose concentration of 150 mg/dL. In dogs the blood glucose level at which there is net uptake by the liver varies with the type of diet. Thus, infusion of glucose into dogs maintained on a high-protein diet resulted in a rise in blood glucose, with a cessation of net hepatic glucose production only at hyperglycemic levels. In contrast, in carbohydrate-fed dogs, the blood glucose concentration increased very little upon glucose infusion, and there was an immediate net uptake of glucose by the liver. An explanation of these differences due to changes in diet is probably to be found in changes in activity of enzymes in the liver concerned with glycolysis and gluconeogenesis.

In addition to the direct effects of hyperglycemia in enhancing the uptake of glucose into both the liver and peripheral tissues, the hormone **insulin** plays a central role in the regulation of the blood glucose concentration. It is produced by the beta cells of the islets of Langerhans in the pancreas and is secreted into the blood as a direct response to hyperglycemia. Its concentration in the blood parallels that of the blood glucose, and its administration results in prompt hypoglycemia. Substances causing release of insulin include also amino acids, free fatty acids, ketone bodies, glucagon, secretin, and tolbutamide. Epinephrine and norepinephrine block the release of insulin. In vitro (and probably in vivo), insulin has an immediate effect on tissues such as adipose tissue and muscle of increasing the rate of glucose uptake. It is considered that this action is due to an enhancement of glucose transport through the cell membrane. In contrast, it is not easy to demonstrate an immediate effect of insulin on glucose uptake by liver tissue. This agrees with other findings which show that glucose penetration of hepatic cells is not rate-limited by their permeability to glucose. Unequivocal evidence that insulin does have a direct effect on glucose metabolism in the liver has been obtained in experiments with the isolated perfused liver where it has been demonstrated that insulin reduces glucose production and diminishes oxidation of ^{14}C-glucose to $^{14}CO_2$.

The **anterior pituitary gland** secretes hormones that tend to elevate the blood glucose and therefore antagonize the action of insulin. These are growth hormone, ACTH (corticotropin), and possibly other "diabetogenic" principles. Growth hormone secre-

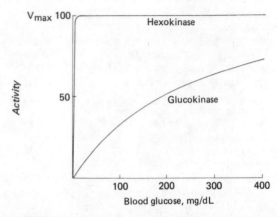

Figure 19–5. Variation in glucose phosphorylating activity of hexokinase and glucokinase with increase of blood glucose concentration. The K_m for glucose of hexokinase is 0.05 mM (0.9 mg/dL) and of glucokinase is 10 mM (180 mg/dL).

tion is stimulated by hypoglycemia. Growth hormone decreases glucose uptake in certain tissues, eg, muscle. Some of this effect may not be direct since it mobilizes free fatty acids from adipose tissue which themselves inhibit glucose utilization. Chronic administration of growth hormone leads to diabetes. By producing hyperglycemia it stimulates secretion of insulin, eventually causing beta cell exhaustion. Although ACTH could have an indirect effect upon glucose utilization, since it enhances the release of free fatty acids from adipose tissue, its major effect on carbohydrate metabolism is due to its stimulation of the secretion of hormones of the adrenal cortex.

The **adrenal cortex** secretes a number of steroid hormones of which the glucocorticoids (11-oxysteroids) are important in carbohydrate metabolism. Upon administration, the glucocorticoids lead to gluconeogenesis. This is as a result of increased protein catabolism in the tissues, increased hepatic uptake of amino acids, and increased activity of transaminases and other enzymes concerned with gluconeogenesis in the liver. In addition, glucocorticoids inhibit the utilization of glucose in extrahepatic tissues. In all these actions, glucocorticoids act in a manner antagonistic to insulin.

Epinephrine, as secreted by the adrenal medulla, stimulates glycogen breakdown in muscle. However, administration of epinephrine leads to an outpouring of glucose from the liver provided glycogen is present, owing to stimulation of phosphorylase. In muscle, as a result of the absence of glucose-6-phosphatase, glycogenolysis ensues with the formation of lactate. The lactate that diffuses into the blood is converted by the gluconeogenic mechanisms back to glycogen in the liver (Cori cycle). Hypoglycemia causes a neural sympathetic discharge that increases epinephrine secretion stimulating glycogenolysis, which is followed by an increase in the blood glucose concentration.

Glucagon is the hormone produced by the alpha cells of the islets of Langerhans of the pancreas. Its secretion is stimulated by hypoglycemia, and, when it reaches the liver (via the portal vein), it causes glycogenolysis by activating phosphorylase in a manner similar to epinephrine. Most of the endogenous glucagon is cleared from the circulation by the liver. Unlike epinephrine, glucagon does not have an action on muscle phosphorylase. Glucagon also enhances gluconeogenesis from amino acids and lactate.

Thyroid hormone should also be considered as affecting the blood sugar. There is experimental evidence that thyroxine has a diabetogenic action and that thyroidectomy inhibits the development of diabetes. It has also been noted that there is a complete absence of glycogen from the livers of thyrotoxic animals. In humans, the fasting blood glucose is elevated in hyperthyroid patients and decreased in hypothyroid patients. However, hyperthyroid patients apparently utilize glucose at a normal or increased rate, whereas hypothyroid patients have a decreased ability to utilize glucose. In addition, hypothyroid patients are much less sensitive to insulin than normal or hyperthyroid

individuals. These effects of thyroid hormone on carbohydrate metabolism may be related to differences in end organ response, rates of destruction of insulin, or both.

The Renal Threshold for Glucose

When the blood glucose rises to relatively high levels, the kidney also exerts a regulatory effect. Glucose is continually filtered by the glomeruli but is ordinarily returned completely to the blood by the reabsorptive system of the renal tubules. The reabsorption of glucose is linked to oxidative phosphorylation and the provision of ATP in the tubular cells, a process similar to that responsible for the absorption of this sugar from the intestine. The capacity of the tubular system to reabsorb glucose is limited to a rate of about 350 mg/min. When the blood levels of glucose are elevated, the glomerular filtrate may contain more glucose than can be reabsorbed; the excess passes into the urine to produce **glycosuria**. In normal individuals, glycosuria occurs when the venous blood sugar exceeds 170–180 mg/dL. This level of the venous blood sugar is termed the **renal threshold** for glucose.

Glycosuria may be produced in experimental animals with phlorhizin, which inhibits the glucose reabsorptive system in the tubule. This is known as **renal glycosuria**. Glycosuria of renal origin may result from inherited defects in the kidney, or it may be acquired as a result of disease processes.

Carbohydrate Tolerance

The ability of the body to utilize carbohydrates may be ascertained by measuring its **carbohydrate tolerance**. It is indicated by the nature of the blood glucose curve following the administration of glucose. **Diabetes mellitus** ("sugar" diabetes) is characterized by decreased tolerance to carbohydrate due to decreased secretion of insulin. This is manifested by elevated blood glucose levels (hyperglycemia) and accompanying glycosuria and may be accompanied by changes in fat metabolism. Tolerance to carbohydrate declines not only in diabetes but also in conditions where the liver is damaged, in some infections, in obesity, and sometimes in atherosclerosis. It would also be expected to occur in the presence of hyperactivity of the pituitary or adrenal cortex because of the antagonism of the hormones of these endocrine glands to the action of insulin.

Insulin, the hormone of the islets of Langerhans of the pancreas, increases tolerance to carbohydrate. Injection of insulin lowers the content of the glucose in the blood and increases its utilization and its storage in the liver and muscle as glycogen. An excess of insulin may lower the blood glucose level to such an extent that severe hypoglycemia occurs that results in convulsions and even in death unless glucose is administered promptly. In humans, hypoglycemic convulsions may occur when the blood glucose is lowered acutely to about 20 mg/dL or less. Increased tolerance to carbohydrate is also observed in pituitary or adrenocortical insufficiency; presumably this is attributable to a decrease in the normal antagonism to insulin which results in a relative excess of that hormone.

REGULATION OF LIPID METABOLISM

The regulation of the mobilization of free fatty acids from adipose tissue has been described previously (see pp 223–227).

Regulation of Fatty Acid Synthesis (Lipogenesis)

Many animals, including humans, take their food as spaced meals and must therefore store much of the energy of their diet for use between meals. The process of lipogenesis is concerned with the conversion of glucose and intermediates such as pyruvate, lactate, and acetyl-CoA to fat, which constitutes the anabolic phase of this cycle. The nutritional state of the organism and tissues is the main factor controlling the rate of lipogenesis. Thus, the rate is high in the well-fed animal whose diet contains a high proportion of carbohydrate. It is depressed under conditions of restricted caloric intake, on a high-fat diet, or when there is a deficiency of insulin, as in diabetes mellitus. All of these conditions are associated with increased concentrations of plasma free fatty acids. There is an **inverse relationship between hepatic lipogenesis and the concentration of serum free fatty acids** (Fig 19–6). The greatest inhibition of lipogenesis occurs over the range of free fatty acids (0.3–0.8 μmol/mL of plasma) through which the plasma free fatty acids increase during transition from the fed to the starved state. Fat in the diet causes depression of lipogenesis in the liver, and when there is more than 10% of fat in the diet, there is little conversion of dietary carbohydrate to fat. Lipogenesis is higher in livers from rats consuming all their food in 2 hours. It is also higher when

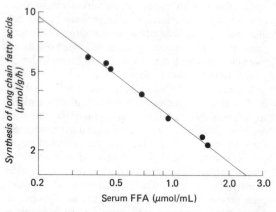

Figure 19–6. Direct inhibition of hepatic lipogenesis by free fatty acids. (Lipogenesis was determined from the incorporation of ^3H_2O into long chain fatty acids in the perfused rat liver. FFA = free fatty acids.)

sucrose is fed instead of glucose. Because of the close association between the activities of the hexose monophosphate shunt on the one hand and of the lipogenic pathway on the other, it was considered that the block in lipogenesis in fasting was due to lack of NADPH generation from the shunt pathway. However, subsequent work in which an NADPH-generating system was added to a liver homogenate from fasting rats failed to promote fatty acid synthesis.

At present it is recognized that the rate-limiting reaction in the lipogenic pathway is at the **acetyl-CoA carboxylase step** (Fig 17–4). Long chain acyl-CoA molecules inhibit acetyl-CoA carboxylase competitively with the activator citrate, an example of metabolic negative feedback inhibition by a product of a reaction sequence. Thus, if acyl-CoA accumulates because it is not esterified quickly enough, it will automatically reduce the synthesis of new fatty acid. Likewise if acyl-CoA accumulates as a result of increased lipolysis or an influx of free fatty acids into the tissue, this will also inhibit synthesis of new fatty acid.

Acyl-CoA may also inhibit the mitochondrial tricarboxylate transporter, thus preventing egress of citrate from the mitochondria into the cytosol. There is also an inverse relationship between free fatty acids and the proportion of active to inactive pyruvate dehydrogenase, which would regulate the availability of acetyl-CoA for lipogenesis. Acyl-CoA may lead to an inhibition of pyruvate dehydrogenase by inhibiting the ATP-ADP exchange transporter of the inner mitochondrial membrane, which would lead to increased intramitochondrial [ATP]/[ADP] ratios and therefore to conversion of active to inactive pyruvate dehydrogenase (Fig 19–2). Also, oxidation of fatty acids due to increased levels of free fatty acids may increase the ratio of acetyl-CoA/CoA and NADH/NAD$^+$ in mitochondria, inhibiting pyruvate dehydrogenase and thus blocking the supply of acetyl-CoA from carbohydrate via pyruvate.

Insulin stimulates lipogenesis by several possible mechanisms. It increases the transport of glucose into the cell (eg, in adipose tissue) and thereby increases the availability both of pyruvate for fatty acid synthesis and glycerol 3-phosphate for esterification of the fatty acids. Insulin converts the inactive form of pyruvate dehydrogenase and of acetyl-CoA carboxylase to the active form. Also, insulin, by its ability to depress the level of intracellular cAMP, inhibits lipolysis and thereby reduces the concentration of long chain acyl-CoA, an inhibitor of lipogenesis.

Flatt has suggested that lipogenesis from glucose in adipose tissue is an energy-releasing process and may be self-limiting because of respiratory control and availability of ADP. It is also clear that factors affecting the rate of glycolysis, which supplies acetyl-CoA for lipogenesis, must exert an overall control on the process. In ruminants, acetate—not glucose—is the starting material for lipogenesis. It follows that, in these species, many of the control mechanisms discussed above are bypassed and thus do not apply.

Various reports indicate that both the fatty acid

synthetase complex and acetyl-CoA carboxylase may be adaptive enzymes, increasing in total amount in the fed state and decreasing in fasting, feeding of fat, and diabetes. These effects on lipogenesis take several days to become fully manifested and augment the direct and immediate effect of free fatty acids (Fig 19–6).

REGULATION OF KETOGENESIS
(See Fig 18–10.)

Ketosis does not occur in vivo unless there is a concomitant rise in the level of circulating free fatty acids, severe ketosis being accompanied invariably by very high concentrations of plasma free fatty acids that arise from lipolysis of triacylglycerol in adipose tissue. In addition, numerous experiments in vitro have demonstrated that fatty acids are the precursors of ketone bodies. The liver, both in fed and in fasting conditions, has the ability to extract about 30% or more of the free fatty acids passing through it, so that at high concentrations of free fatty acids the flux passing into the liver is substantial. One of 2 fates awaits the free fatty acids upon uptake and after they are activated to acyl-CoA: They are **esterified** mainly to triacylglycerol and phospholipid or they are β-**oxidized** to acetyl-CoA. In turn, acetyl-CoA is oxidized in the citric acid cycle or used to form ketone bodies (Fig 19–7). Experiments with fasting rats have demonstrated that the magnitude of ketonemia is more directly related to the quantity of triacylglycerol present in the depots than to the quantity present in the liver, indicating that plasma free fatty acids (derived from the fat depots) are a more significant source of ketone bodies than fatty acids derived from lipolysis of liver triacylglycerol.

Among several possible factors, the capacity for esterification as an antiketogenic factor depends on the availability of precursors in the liver to supply sufficient glycerol 3-phosphate. The concentration of glycerol 3-phosphate in the livers of fasted rats is depressed when compared to that in fed animals. However, the availability of glycerol 3-phosphate does not limit esterification in fasting perfused livers, where a constant fraction is esterified, irrespective of the mass of free fatty acids taken up. It has also been found in vivo that antiketogenic effects of glycerol and dihydroxyacetone are not correlated with the levels of glycerol 3-phosphate in the liver. Thus, whether the availability of glycerol 3-phosphate in the liver is ever rate-limiting on esterification is not clear; neither is there much information on whether the in vivo activities of the enzymes involved in esterification are rate-limiting. In liver (Fig 17–16), phosphatidate phosphohydrolase appears to catalyze the rate-limiting step in esterification; this enzyme increases in activity in livers in which extra triacylglycerol synthesis is taking place. In the perfused liver, insulin increases the activity of glycerol phosphate acyltransferase, which catalyzes the first step in esterification.

Using the perfused liver, it has been shown that

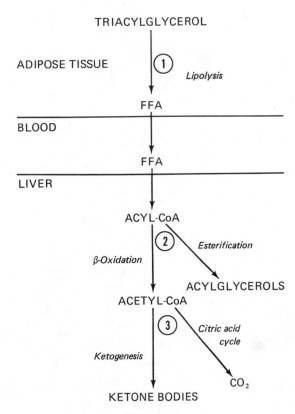

Figure 19–7. Regulation of ketogenesis. ①–③, three crucial steps in the pathway of metabolism of free fatty acids (FFA) that determine the magnitude of ketogenesis.

livers from fed rats esterify considerably more ^{14}C free fatty acids than livers from fasted rats, the balance not esterified in the livers from fasted rats being oxidized to either $^{14}CO_2$ or ^{14}C ketone bodies. These results may be explained by the fact that carnitine acyltransferase I activity in the mitochondrial membrane regulates the entry of long chain acyl groups into mitochondria prior to β-oxidation (Fig 17–2). Its activity is low in the fed state, when fatty acid oxidation is depressed, and high in fasting, when fatty acid oxidation increases. McGarry and others (1980) have shown that malonyl-CoA, the initial intermediate in fatty acid biosynthesis (Fig 17–7), which increases in concentration in the fed state, inhibits this enzyme, switching off β-oxidation. Thus, in the fed condition there is active lipogenesis and high [malonyl-CoA], which inhibits carnitine acyltransferase I (Fig 19–8). Low concentrations of free fatty acids entering the liver cell are nearly all esterified to acylglycerols and transported out of the liver in VLDL. However, as the concentration of free fatty acids increases with the onset of starvation, acetyl-CoA carboxylase is inhibited and [malonyl-CoA] decreases, releasing the inhibition of carnitine acytransferase and allowing more acyl-CoA to be oxidized. These events are reinforced in starvation by the [insulin]/[glucagon] ratio, which decreases, causing increased lipolysis in adipose tis-

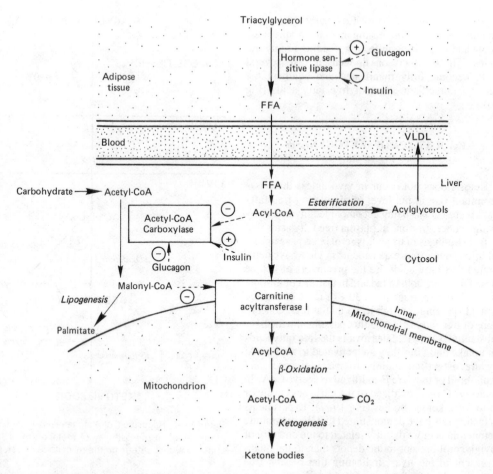

Figure 19–8. Regulation of long chain fatty acid oxidation in the liver. FFA, free fatty acids; VLDL, very low density lipoprotein. Positive (⊕) and negative (⊖) regulatory effects are represented by broken lines and substrate flow by solid lines.

sue, with release of free fatty acids, and inhibition of pyruvate kinase and acetyl-CoA carboxylase in the liver.

As the level of serum free fatty acids is raised, proportionately more free fatty acid is converted to ketone bodies and less is oxidized via the citric acid cycle to CO_2. The partition of acetyl-CoA between the ketogenic pathway and the pathway of oxidation to CO_2 is so regulated that the total free energy trapped in ATP that results from the oxidation of free fatty acids remains constant. It will be appreciated that **complete oxidation of 1 mol of palmitate involves a net production of 129 mol of ATP** via CO_2 production in the citric acid cycle (see p 201), whereas **only 33 mol of ATP are produced when acetoacetate is the end product.** Thus, ketogenesis may be regarded as a mechanism that allows the liver to oxidize large quantities of fatty acids within an apparently tightly coupled system of oxidative phosphorylation, without increasing its total energy expenditure.

Several other hypotheses have been advanced to account for the diversion of fatty acid oxidation from CO_2 formation to ketogenesis. Theoretically, a fall in

concentration of oxaloacetate, particularly within the mitochondria, could cause impairment of the citric acid cycle to metabolize acetyl-CoA. This has been considered to occur because of an increase in the [NADH]/[NAD⁺] ratio. Krebs has suggested that, since oxaloacetate is also on the main pathway of gluconeogenesis, enhanced gluconeogenesis leading to a fall in the level of oxaloacetate may be the cause of the severe forms of ketosis found in diabetes and the ketosis of cattle. Alternatively, it has been postulated that citrate synthase is inhibited, either by long chain acyl-CoA or by increased concentrations of ATP. Utter and Keech have shown that pyruvate carboxylase, which catalyzes the conversion of pyruvate to oxaloacetate, is activated by acetyl-CoA. Consequently, when there are significant amounts of acetyl-CoA, there should be sufficient oxaloacetate to initiate the condensing reaction of the citric acid cycle.

In summary, ketosis arises as a result of a deficiency in available carbohydrate. This has the following actions in fostering ketogenesis (Figs 19–7 and 19–8): ① It causes an imbalance between esterification and lipolysis in adipose tissue, with consequent release of free fatty acids into the circulation. Free fatty acids are the principal substrates for ketone body formation in the liver, and therefore all factors, metabolic or endocrine, affecting the release of free fatty acids from adipose tissue influence ketogenesis. ② Upon entry of free fatty acids into the liver, the balance between their esterification and oxidation is governed by carnitine acyltransferase I, whose activity is increased indirectly by the concentration of free fatty acids and the hormonal state of the liver. ③ As the amount of fatty acid oxidized increases, more forms ketone bodies and less forms CO_2, regulated in such a manner that the total ATP production remains constant. Ketone bodies are not oxidized significantly by the liver; they diffuse into the circulation whence they are extracted and oxidized by extrahepatic tissues preferentially to other fuels.

Ketosis in Vivo

The ketosis that occurs in starvation and fat feeding is relatively mild compared with the condition encountered in uncontrolled diabetes mellitus, pregnancy toxemia of ewes, ketosis of lactating cattle, or animals administered phlorhizin. The main reason appears to be that in the severe conditions carbohydrate is still less available to the tissues than in the mild conditions. Thus, in the milder forms of diabetes mellitus, in fat feeding, and in chronic starvation, glycogen is present in the liver in variable amounts, and free fatty acid levels are lower, which probably accounts for the less severe ketosis associated with these conditions.

In ketosis of ruminants or in phlorhizin poisoning, there is a severe drain of glucose from the blood due to excessive fetal demands, the demands of heavy lactation, or impaired reabsorption by the kidney, respectively (Fig 19–9). Extreme hypoglycemia results, coupled with negligible amounts of glycogen in the liver. Ketosis in these conditions tends to be severe. As hypoglycemia develops, the secretion of insulin diminishes, allowing not only less glucose utilization but also enhancement of lipolysis in adipose tissue.

In diabetes mellitus, the lack (or relative lack) of insulin, coupled with an increase or relative increase in glucagon concentrations, probably affects adipose tissue more than any other tissue because of its extreme sensitivity to this hormone. As a result, free fatty acids are released in quantities that give rise to plasma free fatty acid levels more than twice those in fasting normal subjects. Many changes also occur in the activity of enzymes within the liver which enhance the rate of gluconeogenesis and transfer of glucose to the blood despite high levels of circulating glucose.

this respect is the conversion of pyruvate to acetyl-CoA, as acetyl-CoA is the starting material for the synthesis of long chain fatty acids. However, the pyruvate dehydrogenase reaction is essentially nonreversible, which prevents the direct conversion of acetyl-CoA, formed from the oxidation of fatty acids, to pyruvate. There cannot be a net conversion of acetyl-CoA to oxaloacetate via the citric acid cycle since one molecule of oxaloacetate is required to condense with acetyl-CoA and only one molecule of oxaloacetate is regenerated. For similar reasons, **there cannot be a net conversion of fatty acids having an even number of carbon atoms** (which form acetyl-CoA) **to glucose or glycogen.**

Only the terminal 3-carbon portion of a fatty acid having an odd number of carbon atoms is glycogenic, as this portion of the molecule will form propionate upon oxidation. Nevertheless, it is possible for labeled carbon atoms of fatty acids to be found ultimately in glycogen after traversing the citric acid cycle: This is because oxaloacetate is an intermediate both in the citric acid cycle and in the pathway of gluconeogenesis. Many of the carbon skeletons of the nonessential amino acids can be produced from carbohydrate via the citric acid cycle and transamination. By reversal of these processes, glycogenic amino acids yield carbon skeletons that are either members or precursors of the members of the citric acid cycle. They are therefore readily converted by gluconeogenic pathways to glucose and glycogen. The ketogenic amino acids give rise to acetoacetate, which will in turn be metabolized as ketone bodies, forming acetyl-CoA in extrahepatic tissues (see Chapter 18).

For the same reasons that it is not possible for a net conversion of fatty acids to carbohydrate to occur, it is not possible for a net conversion of fatty acids to glucogenic amino acids to take place. Neither is it possible to reverse the pathways of breakdown of ketogenic amino acids, all of which fall into the category of "essential amino acids." Conversion of the carbon skeletons of glucogenic amino acids to fatty acids is possible, either by formation of pyruvate and acetyl-CoA or by reversal of nonmitochondrial reactions of the citric acid cycle from α-ketoglutarate to citrate followed by the action of ATP-citrate lyase to give acetyl-CoA (see Chapter 18). However, under most natural conditions, eg, starvation, a net breakdown of protein and amino acids is usually accompanied by a net breakdown of fat. The net conversion of amino acids to fat is therefore not a significant process except possibly in animals receiving a high-protein diet.

INTERCONVERSION OF MAJOR FOODSTUFFS
(See Fig 19–10.)

That animals may be fattened on a predominantly carbohydrate diet demonstrates the ease of conversion of carbohydrate into fat. A most significant reaction in

THE ECONOMICS OF CARBOHYDRATE & LIPID METABOLISM IN THE WHOLE BODY

Many of the details of the interplay between carbohydrate and lipid metabolism in various tissues have been described. The conversion of glucose to fat is a

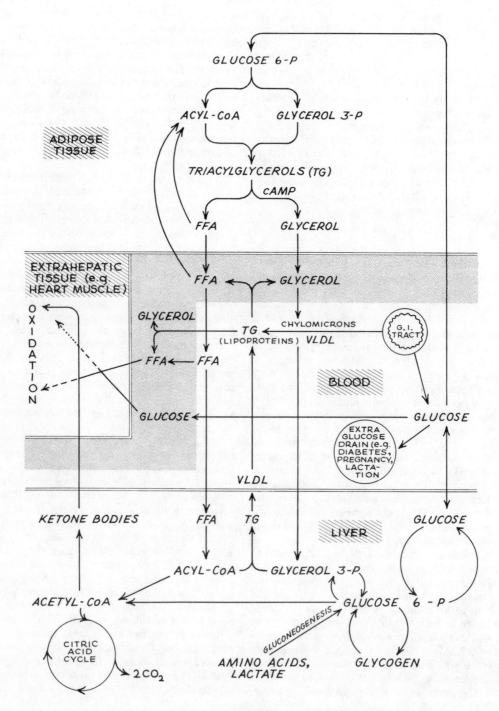

Figure 19–9. Metabolic interrelationships between adipose tissue, the liver, and extrahepatic tissues. (Stippled area, lipoprotein lipase region of capillary wall; cAMP, cyclic AMP; FFA, free fatty acids; VLDL, very low density lipoproteins.)

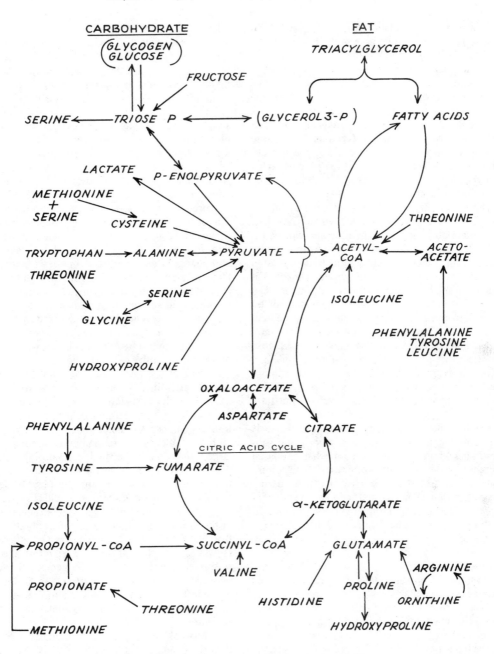

Figure 19–10. Interconversion of the major foodstuffs.

process that occurs readily under conditions of optimal nutritional intake. With the exception of glycerol, fat (as fatty acids) cannot give rise to a net formation of glucose because of the irreversible nature of the oxidative decarboxylation of pyruvate to acetyl-CoA. Certain tissues, including the central nervous system and the erythrocytes, are much more dependent upon a continual supply of glucose than others. A minimal supply of glucose is probably necessary in extrahepatic tissues to maintain the integrity of the citric acid cycle. In addition, glucose appears to be the main source of glycerol 3-phosphate in tissues devoid of glyceroki-

nase. There is a minimal and obligatory rate of glucose oxidation. Large quantities of glucose are also required for fetal nutrition and the synthesis of milk, particularly in ruminants. Certain mechanisms, in addition to gluconeogenesis, safeguard essential supplies of glucose in times of shortage by allowing other substrates to spare its oxidation.

Randle and others have demonstrated that ketone bodies and free fatty acids spare the oxidation of glucose in muscle by impairing its entry into the cell, its phosphorylation to glucose 6-phosphate, the phosphofructokinase reaction, and the oxidative decarboxylation of pyruvate. Oxidation of free fatty acids and ketone bodies causes an increase in the concentration of intracellular citrate which in turn inhibits phosphofructokinase. These observations, taken with those of Olson, who demonstrated that acetoacetate was oxidized in the perfused heart preferentially to free fatty acids, justify the conclusion that under conditions of carbohydrate shortage available **fuels are oxidized in the following order of preference:** (1) **ketone bodies** (and probably other short chain fatty acids, eg, acetate), (2) **free fatty acids,** and (3) **glucose.** This does not imply that any particular fuel is oxidized to the total exclusion of any other (Fig 19–9).

These facts help to explain the experiments of several investigators who have shown in vivo that, under certain conditions, fat mobilization can be reduced after the administration of noncarbohydrate calorigenic substrates, eg, oral administration of fat in rats or after the administration of acetate in sheep. Fat mobilization and ketogenesis in rats on all-fat diets can be reduced substantially provided the quantity of fat ingested is increased to satisfy the caloric requirement of the animal. Thus, if substrates such as free fatty acids and ketone bodies spare the oxidation of glucose in muscle, more glucose will be available, causing a reduction in output of free fatty acids from adipose tissue (either directly or via stimulation of insulin secretion) and allowing the plasma level of free fatty acids to fall. As glucose is the fuel which is "burned last," it may be appreciated how adipose tissue is sensitive to a general deficiency in calorigenic substrates in the whole body through a mechanism based specifically on the availability of glucose. The combination of the effects of free fatty acids in sparing glucose utilization in muscle and heart and the effect of the spared glucose in inhibiting free fatty acid mobilization in adipose tissue has been called the "glucose–fatty acid cycle."

Starvation

On high-carbohydrate diets, fatty acid oxidation is spared. As the animal passes from the fed to the fasting condition, glucose availability becomes less, liver glycogen being drawn upon in an attempt to maintain the blood glucose. The concentration of insulin in the blood decreases, and glucagon increases. As glucose utilization diminishes in adipose tissue and the inhibitory effect of insulin on lipolysis becomes less, fat is mobilized as free fatty acids and glycerol. The free fatty acids are esterified in other tissues, particularly the liver, and the remainder are oxidized. Glycerol joins the carbohydrate pool after activation to glycerol 3-phosphate, mainly in the liver and kidney. During this transition phase from the fully fed to the fully fasting state, endogenous glucose production (from amino acids and glycerol) does not keep pace

with its utilization and oxidation since the liver glycogen stores become depleted and blood glucose tends to fall. Thus, fat is mobilized at an ever-increasing rate, but in several hours the plasma free fatty acids and blood glucose stabilize at the fasting level (0.7–0.8 μmol/mL and 60–70 mg/dL, respectively). At this point it must be presumed that in the whole animal the supply of glucose balances the obligatory demands for glucose utilization and oxidation. This is achieved by the increased oxidation of free fatty acids and ketone bodies, sparing the nonobligatory oxidation of glucose. This fine balance is disturbed in conditions that demand more glucose or in which glucose utilization is impaired and which therefore lead to further mobilization of fat. The provision of carbohydrate by adipose tissue, in the form of **glycerol,** is an important function, for it is only this source of carbohydrate together with that provided by **gluconeogenesis from protein** that can supply the fasting organism with the glucose needed for those processes which must utilize glucose. In prolonged starvation in humans, gluconeogenesis from protein is diminished owing to reduced release of amino acids, particularly alanine, from muscle, the principal protein store. This coincides with adaptation of the brain to utilize ketone bodies in place of glucose.

A feedback mechanism for controlling free fatty acid output from adipose tissue in starvation may operate as a result of the action of ketone bodies and free fatty acids to directly stimulate the pancreas to produce insulin. Under most conditions, free fatty acids are mobilized in excess of oxidative requirements since a large proportion is esterified, even during fasting. As the liver takes up and esterifies a considerable proportion of the free fatty acid output, it plays a regulatory role in removing excess free fatty acids from the circulation. When carbohydrate supplies are adequate, most of the influx is esterified and ultimately retransported from the liver as VLDL to be utilized by other tissues. However, in the face of an increased influx of free fatty acids, an alternative route, ketogenesis, is available which enables the liver to continue to retransport much of the influx of free fatty acids in a form that is readily utilized by extrahepatic tissues under all nutritional conditions.

Most of these principles are depicted in Fig 19–9. It will be noted that there is a carbohydrate cycle involving release of glycerol from adipose tissue and its conversion in the liver to glucose, followed by its transport back to adipose tissue to complete the cycle. The other cycle, a lipid cycle, involves release of free fatty acids by adipose tissue, its transport to and esterification in the liver, and retransport as VLDL back to adipose tissue. Disturbances in carbohydrate or lipid metabolism often involve these 2 interrelated cycles where they interact in adipose tissue and in the liver.

References

Bloch K, Vance D: Control mechanisms in the synthesis of saturated fatty acids. *Annu Rev Biochem* 1977;**46**:263.

Cohen P: The regulation of protein function by multisite phosphorylation. *Trends in Biochemical Science* (Feb) 1976;**1**:38.

Czech MP: Molecular basis of insulin action. *Annu Rev Biochem* 1977;**46**:359.

Davies DD (editor): *Rate Control of Biological Processes*. Cambridge Univ Press, 1973.

Denton RM, Hughes WA: Pyruvate dehydrogenase and the hormonal regulation of fat synthesis in mammalian tissues. *Int J Biochem* 1978;**9**:545.

Denton RM, Pogson CI: *Metabolic Regulation*. Chapman and Hall, 1976.

Exton JH: Mechanisms involved in effects of catecholamines on liver carbohydrate metabolism. *Biochem Pharmacol* 1979;**28**:2237.

Hems DA: Hormonal control of glycogen-metabolizing enzymes in liver. *Biochem Soc Trans* 1978;**6**:33.

Hers HG: The control of glycogen metabolism in the liver. *Annu Rev Biochem* 1976;**45**:167.

Krebs EG, Beavo JA: Phosphorylation-dephosphorylation of enzymes. *Annu Rev Biochem* 1979;**48**:923.

Lin ECC: Glycerol utilization and its regulation in mammals. *Annu Rev Biochem* 1977;**46**:765.

Masoro EJ: Lipids and lipid metabolism. *Annu Rev Physiol* 1977;**39**:301.

McGarry JD, Foster DW: Regulation of hepatic fatty acid oxidation and ketone body production, *Annu Rev Biochem* 1980;**49**:395.

Newsholme EA, Start C: *Regulation in Metabolism*. Wiley, 1973.

Söling HD, Seufert CD (editors): *Biochemical and Clinical Aspects of Ketone Body Metabolism*. Thieme, 1978.

Söling HD, Willms B (editors): *Regulation of Gluconeogenesis*. Thieme, 1971.

20 | Biosynthesis of Amino Acids

Victor W. Rodwell, PhD

AMINO ACID METABOLISM

Amino acid metabolism includes several major topics of medical interest—protein synthesis and degradation, conversion of the carbon skeletons of amino acids to amphibolic intermediates, urea synthesis, and formation of a variety of physiologically active compounds such as serotonin (Fig 20–1).

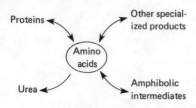

Figure 20–1. Amino acid metabolism. All indicated processes except urea formation proceed reversibly in intact cells. However, the catalysts and intermediates in biosynthetic and degradative processes generally differ.

NUTRITIONALLY ESSENTIAL & NUTRITIONALLY NONESSENTIAL AMINO ACIDS

About 20 amino acids are essential in the sense that all must be present in order for protein synthesis, and therefore life, to occur. Some life forms (plants, many bacteria) can form all 20 amino acids from amphibolic intermediates. Others, including humans and other animals, can biosynthesize only about half of those required. The remainder, which must therefore be supplied by the diet, are termed **nutritionally essential** amino acids. Those that an organism can biosynthesize are termed **nutritionally nonessential.** A given amino acid may be nutritionally essential for one form of life but nutritionally nonessential for another.

Nutritional scientists frequently refer to nutritionally essential amino acids as "essential" or "indispensable" amino acids and to nutritionally nonessential amino acids as "nonessential" or "dispensable." While in a nutritional context these terms are correct, they obscure the biologically essential nature

Table 20–1. Amino acid requirements of humans.

Nutritionally Essential	Nutritionally Nonessential
Arginine*	Alanine
Histidine*	Asparagine
Isoleucine	Aspartic acid
Leucine	Cysteine
Lysine	Glutamic acid
Methionine	Glutamine
Phenylalanine	Glycine
Threonine	Hydroxyproline†
Tryptophan	Proline
Valine	Serine
	Tyrosine

*"Nutritionally semiessential." Synthesized at rates inadequate to support growth of children.

†Not necessary for protein synthesis but formed during postsynthetic processing of collagen.

of all 20 amino acids. It might be argued that the nutritionally nonessential amino acids are more important to the cell than the nutritionally essential ones, since organisms (eg, humans) have evolved that lack the ability to manufacture the latter but not the former group.

The existence of nutritional requirements suggests that dependence on an external supply of a required intermediate can be of greater survival value than the ability to manufacture it. If a specific intermediate is present in the food, an organism that can synthesize it is reproducing and transferring to future generations genetic information of negative survival value. The survival value is negative rather than nil because ATP and nutrients are used to synthesize useless DNA. The number of enzymes required by prokaryotic cells to synthesize the nutritionally essential amino acids is large relative to the number of enzymes required to synthesize the nutritionally nonessential amino acids (Table 20–2). This suggests that there is a survival advantage in retaining the ability to manufacture "easy" amino acids while losing the ability to make "difficult" amino acids.

Table 20—2. Enzymes required for the synthesis of amino acids from amphibolic intermediates.

Number of Enzymes Required to Synthesize:			
Nutritionally Essential		**Nutritionally Nonessential**	
Arg*	7	Ala	1
His	6	Asp	1
Thr	6	Asn†	1
Met	5 (4 shared)	Glu	1
Lys	8	Gln*	1
Ile	8 (6 shared)	Pro*	3
Val	1 (7 shared)	Ser	3
Leu	3 (7 shared)	Gly‡	1
Tyr	10	Cys§	2
Phe	1 (9 shared)		14
Trp	5 (8 shared)		
	60		

*From Glu. †From Asp. ‡From Ser. §From Ser plus S^{2-}.

NUTRITIONALLY NONESSENTIAL AMINO ACIDS

NUTRITIONALLY NONESSENTIAL AMINO ACIDS FORMED FROM AMPHIBOLIC INTERMEDIATES

Alanine (All Life Forms)

Alanine is formed from pyruvate by transamination (Fig 20–2). For a detailed description of transamination see Chapters 9 and 21.

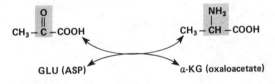

Figure 20—2. Formation of alanine by transamination of pyruvate. The amino donor may be glutamate or aspartate. The other product thus is α-ketoglutarate (α-KG) or oxaloacetate.

Glutamate (All Life Forms)

Glutamate is formed by the reaction catalyzed by L-glutamate dehydrogenase (Fig 20–3). Yeast and fungi contain 2 glutamate dehydrogenases specific for NAD^+ or $NADP^+$. Bacteria contain only an NAD^+-dependent dehydrogenase and can synthesize glutamate by other reactions. Since beef liver glutamate dehydrogenase has dual specificity for NAD^+ and for $NADP^+$, NAD^+ may function in glutamate catabolism and $NADP^+$ in glutamate biosynthesis by glutamate dehydrogenase in animals. Plants and bacteria synthesize amino acids from glucose plus ammonia. When cattle are fed diets rich in carbohydrate plus urea, rumen bacteria convert urea to ammonia, then utilize

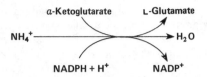

Figure 20–3. The glutamate dehydrogenase reaction. Reductive amination of α-ketoglutarate by NH_4^+ proceeds at the expense of NAD(P)H.

glutamate dehydrogenase reaction to provide the cattle with glutamate and other amino acids.

Aspartate (All Life Forms)

Aspartic acid is formed by transamination of oxaloacetate (Fig 20–2).

Glutamine (All Life Forms)

L-Glutamine and L-glutamate are of fundamental importance for amino acid biosynthesis in all forms of life. In plants, animals, and bacteria, synthesis of glutamine is catalyzed by glutamine synthetase. In this reaction, NH_4^+ aminates glutamate in a reaction requiring ATP (Fig 20–4).

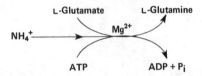

Figure 20–4. The glutamine synthetase reaction.

Asparagine

Biosynthesis of asparagine is catalyzed by asparagine synthetase (Fig 20-5).

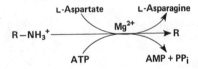

Figure 20–5. The asparagine synthetase reaction. Note similarities to and differences from the glutamine synthetase reaction (Fig 20–4). The nature of the amino donor ($R-NH_3^+$) differs depending on the life form considered.

The reaction has many similarities to the glutamine synthetase reaction (Fig 20–4). In both cases, synthesis of the amide bond requires the free acid (Asp or Glu), an amino donor, and MgATP. However, while ATP is converted to ADP + Pi in the glutamine synthetase reaction, AMP + PPi are formed in the reaction catalyzed by asparagine synthetase. In mammalian systems, the amino donor probably is glutamine, in bacteria it is ammonia, and in plants the cyano group of β-cyanoalanine. Since pyrophosphatase catalyzes hydrolysis of PP_i to $2 P_i$ (pyrophosphatases), the overall reaction:

$$\text{Asp} + \text{R—NH}_3^+ + \text{ATP} \xrightarrow{\text{Mg}^{2+}} \text{Asn} + \text{R} + \text{AMP} + 2 P_i$$

is more favored than that of glutamine synthesis by about 8 kcal.

Serine

Two pathways for serine biosynthesis coexist in mammalian tissues. In both cases the carbon skeleton is provided by D-3-phosphoglycerate, an intermediate in glycolysis (see Chapter 14). One pathway uses nonphosphorylated intermediates and the other phosphorylated intermediates (Fig 20–6).

Synthesis via phosphorylated intermediates in-volves oxidation of 3-phosphoglycerate to phospho-hydroxypyruvate, transamination to phosphoserine, and hydrolytic removal of the phosphate catalyzed by a phosphatase. For synthesis via nonphosphorylated in-termediates, phosphoglycerate is dephosphorylated to glycerate by a phosphatase, oxidized to hydroxypy-ruvate, and transaminated to L-serine. The pathway involving phosphorylated intermediates probably ac-counts for the majority of the serine synthesized by mammalian tissues, plants, and bacteria.

Glycine

Synthesis of glycine in mammalian tissues can occur in several ways. Liver cytosol contains glycine transaminases that catalyze the synthesis of glycine from glyoxylate and glutamate or alanine. Unlike most transaminase reactions, this strongly favors glycine synthesis.

Two important mammalian routes for glycine formation are from choline (Fig 20–7) and from serine via the serine hydroxymethyltransferase reaction (Fig 20–8).

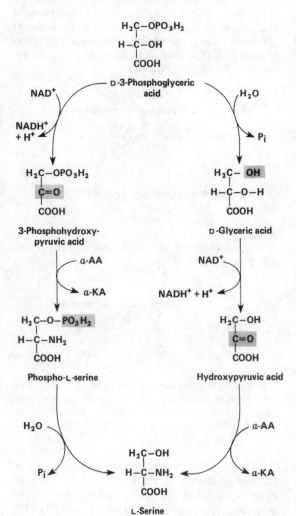

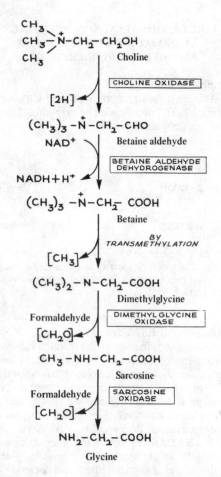

Figure 20–6. Serine biosynthesis via phosphorylated and nonphosphorylated intermediates. (α-AA = α-amino acids; α-KA = α-keto acids.)

Figure 20–7. Formation of glycine from choline.

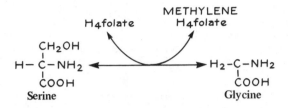

Figure 20–8. The serine hydroxymethyltransferase reaction. The reaction is freely reversible. (H₄folate = tetrahydrofolate.)

NUTRITIONALLY NONESSENTIAL AMINO ACIDS FORMED FROM OTHER NUTRITIONALLY NONESSENTIAL AMINO ACIDS

Proline

In mammals and some other life forms, proline is formed from glutamate by reversal of the reactions of proline catabolism (Fig 20–9).

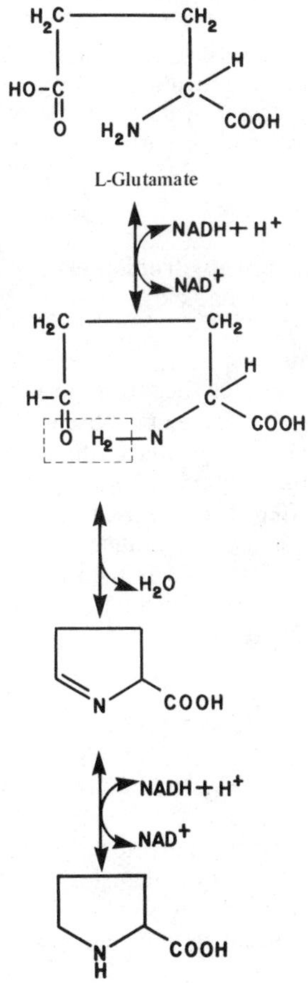

Hydroxyproline

Since proline serves as a precursor of hydroxyproline, proline and hydroxyproline belong to the glutamate family of amino acids. Although both 3- and 4-hydroxyprolines occur in mammalian tissues, little is known of the metabolic significance of 3-hydroxyproline (present in rat tail tendon and in the antibiotic telomycin). What follows refers solely to *trans*-4-hydroxyproline.

Hydroxyproline, like hydroxylysine, is almost exclusively associated with collagen, the most abundant protein of mammalian tissues. Collagen contains about one-third glycine and two-thirds proline and hydroxyproline. Hydroxyproline, which accounts for almost half of the amino acid residues of collagen, stabilizes the collagen triple helix to digestion by proteases. Unlike the hydroxyl groups of hydroxylysine, which serve as sites for attachment of galactosyl and glucosyl residues, the hydroxyl groups of collagen hydroxyproline are unsubstituted.

A unique feature of hydroxyproline and hydroxylysine metabolism is that the preformed amino acids, as they may occur in ingested food protein, are not incorporated into collagen. There is no tRNA species capable of accepting hydroxyproline or hydroxylysine and inserting them into an elongating polypeptide chain. Dietary proline is, however, a precursor of collagen hydroxyproline, and dietary lysine a precursor of collagen hydroxylysine. Hydroxylation of proline or lysine is catalyzed by prolyl hydroxylase or by lysine hydroxylase, enzymes associated with the microsomal fraction of many tissues (skin, liver, lung, heart, skeletal muscle, and granulating wounds). These enzymes are peptidyl hydroxylases, since hydroxylation only occurs subsequent to incorporation of proline or lysine into polypeptide linkage (see Chapter 33).

Both hydroxylases are mixed function oxygenases that require, in addition to substrate, molecular O_2, ascorbate, Fe^{2+}, and α-ketoglutarate. Prolyl hydroxylase has been more extensively studied, but lysyl hydroxylase appears to be an entirely analogous enzyme. For every mole of proline hydroxylated, 1 mol of α-ketoglutarate is decarboxylated to succinate. During this process, one atom of molecular O_2 is incorporated into proline and one into succinate (Fig 20–10).

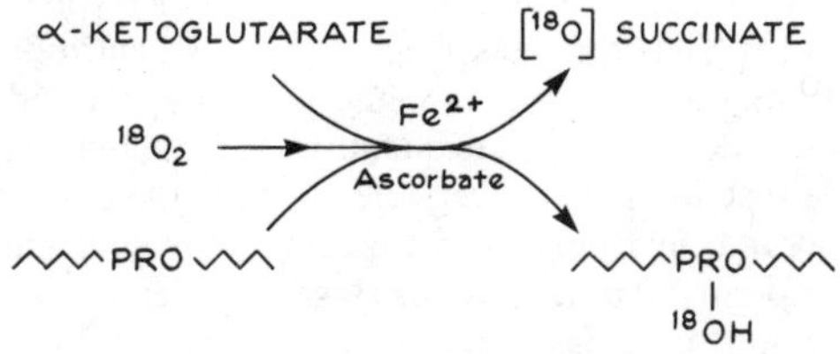

Figure 20–9. Biosynthesis of proline from glutamate by reversal of the reactions of proline catabolism.

Figure 20–10. The proline hydroxylase reaction. The substrate is a proline-rich peptide. During the course of the reaction, molecular oxygen is incorporated into both succinate and proline (shown by the use of heavy oxygen, $^{18}O_2$).

NUTRITIONALLY NONESSENTIAL AMINO ACIDS FORMED FROM NUTRITIONALLY ESSENTIAL AMINO ACIDS

Cysteine

Cysteine, while not itself nutritionally essential, is formed from methionine (nutritionally essential) and serine (nutritionally nonessential). Methionine is first converted to homocysteine via S-adenosylmethionine and S-adenosylhomocysteine (see Chapter 22). Conversion of homocysteine and serine to cysteine and homoserine is shown in Fig 20–11.

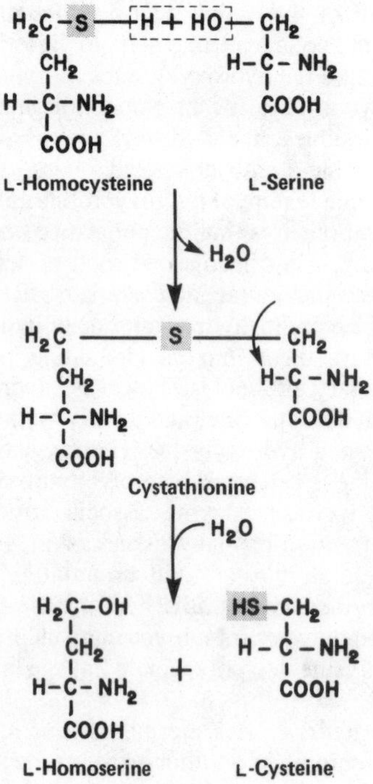

Figure 20–11. Conversion of homocysteine and serine to homoserine and cysteine. Note that while the sulfur of cysteine derives from methionine by transulfuration, the carbon skeleton is provided by serine.

Tyrosine

Tyrosine is formed from phenylalanine by the reaction catalyzed by phenylalanine hydroxylase (Fig 20–12). Thus, whereas phenylalanine is a nutritionally essential amino acid, tyrosine is not—provided the diet contains adequate quantities of phenylalanine. The reaction is not reversible, so tyrosine cannot replace the nutritional requirement for phenylalanine. The **phenylalanine hydroxylase** complex is a mixed function oxygenase present in mammalian liver but absent from other tissues. The reaction involves incorporation of one atom of molecular oxygen into the para position of phenylalanine while the other atom is reduced, forming water (Fig 20–12). The reducing power, supplied ultimately by NADPH, is immediate-

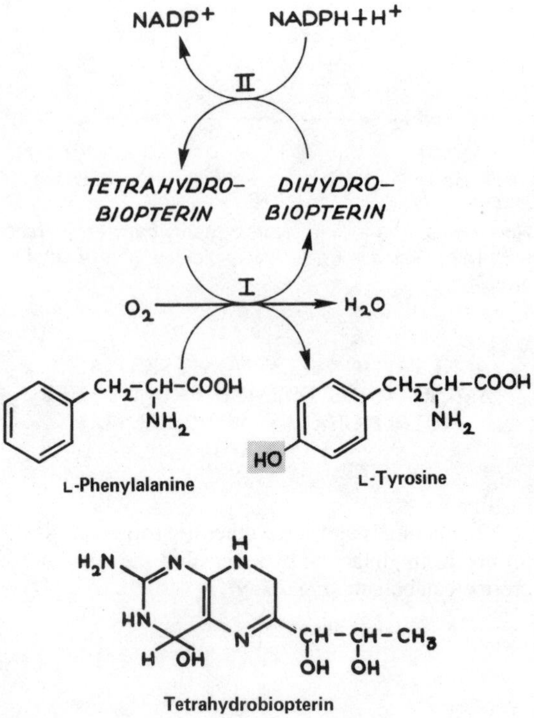

Figure 20–12. The phenylalanine hydroxylase reaction. Two distinct enzymatic activities are involved. Activity II catalyzes reduction of dihydrobiopterin by NADPH, and activity I the reduction of O_2 to H_2O and of phenylalanine to tyrosine.

ly provided as **tetrahydrobiopterin,** a pteridine resembling that in folic acid.

Hydroxylysine

5-Hydroxylysine (α,ϵ-diamino-δ-hydroxycaproate) is present in collagen but absent from most other mammalian proteins. Collagen hydroxylysine arises directly from dietary lysine, not dietary hydroxylysine. Before lysine is hydroxylated, it must first be incorporated into peptide linkage. Hydroxylation of the lysyl peptide is then catalyzed by lysyl hydroxylase, a mixed function oxidase analogous to prolyl hydroxylase.

BIOSYNTHESIS OF NUTRITIONALLY ESSENTIAL AMINO ACIDS

Biosynthesis of nutritionally essential amino acids by bacteria from glutamate, aspartate, or other amphibolic intermediates is outlined below. These reactions do not occur in mammalian tissues.

BIOSYNTHESIS OF NUTRITIONALLY ESSENTIAL AMINO ACIDS FROM GLUTAMATE

Arginine (Bacteria)

Arginine, a nutritionally essential amino acid for growing humans, can be synthesized by rats but not in quantities sufficient to permit normal growth. Microorganisms biosynthesize arginine from glutamate, via N-acetylated intermediates (Fig 20–13). One intermediate, N-acetylglutamate-γ-semialdehyde, is also a precursor of proline in bacteria. In humans and other animals, however, proline is formed from glutamate.

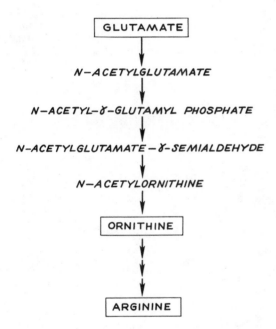

Figure 20–13. Biosynthesis of L-arginine from L-glutamate via acylated intermediates in bacteria. The reactions from glutamate to ornithine do not occur in mammalian tissues. The reactions leading from ornithine to arginine are those of the urea cycle (see Chapter 21) and are common to both bacteria and mammals.

BIOSYNTHESIS OF NUTRITIONALLY ESSENTIAL AMINO ACIDS FROM ASPARTATE

Aspartate is the precursor of a family of amino acids that includes lysine, methionine, threonine, and isoleucine (Fig 9–7). The regulatory implications of this relationship in bacteria are discussed in Chapter 9.

Methionine & Threonine (Bacteria)

Following conversion of aspartate-β-semialdehyde to homoserine, the pathways for methionine and threonine biosynthesis diverge. The interconversion of homoserine and methionine is discussed in Chapter 22.

Lysine (Bacteria)

Bacteria form lysine from aspartate-β-semialdehyde via condensation with pyruvate. The dihydropicolinate formed serves, in addition, a role in spore formation in certain spore-forming bacteria, and the diaminopimelate performs a role in bacterial cell wall synthesis.

Isoleucine

Isoleucine is considered below with other branched chain amino acids.

BIOSYNTHESIS OF NUTRITIONALLY ESSENTIAL AMINO ACIDS FROM AMPHIBOLIC INTERMEDIATES

Lysine (Bacteria & Yeast)

Lysine biosynthesis in yeast starts from α-ketoglutarate and acetyl-CoA and utilizes a series of reactions analogous to those of the citric acid cycle but catalyzed by a set of enzymes with slightly different substrate specificities.

Leucine, Valine, & Isoleucine

While leucine, valine, and isoleucine are all nutritionally essential amino acids for humans and other higher animals, mammalian tissues do contain transaminases that reversibly catalyze interconversion of all 3 amino acids with their corresponding α-keto acids (see Chapter 22). This explains the ability of the appropriate keto acids to replace their amino acids in the diet.

Histidine

Histidine, like arginine, is nutritionally semiessential. Adult humans and adult rats have been maintained in nitrogen balance for short periods in the absence of histidine. The growing animal does, however, require histidine in the diet. If studies were to be carried on for longer periods, it is probable that a requirement for histidine in adult human subjects would also be elicited.

Biosynthesis starts with 5-phosphoribosyl-1-pyrophosphate (PribPP), which condenses with ATP, forming N'-(5-phosphoribosyl)-ATP. This reaction thus closely resembles the initial reaction of purine biosynthesis.

●   ●   ●

References

Biosynthesis

Burnstein P: The biosynthesis of collagen. *Annu Rev Biochem* 1974;**43**:567.

Cardinale GJ, Udenfriend S: Prolyl hydroxylase. *Adv Enzymol* 1974;**41**:245.

Greenberg DM, Rodwell VW: Biosynthesis of amino acids and related compounds. Pages 237 and 317 in: *Metabolic Pathways*. Vol 3. Academic Press, 1969.

Meister A: *Biochemistry of the Amino Acids*, 2nd ed. Vol 2. Academic Press, 1965.

Truffa-Bachi P, Cohen GN: Some aspects of amino acid biosynthesis in microorganisms. *Annu Rev Biochem* 1968;**37**:79.

Regulation of Biosynthesis

Calvo JM, Fink GR: Regulation of biosynthetic pathways in bacteria. *Annu Rev Biochem* 1971;**40**:943.

Cohen GN: The aspartokinases and homoserine dehydrogenases of *Escherichia coli. Curr Top Cell Regul* 1969;**1**:183.

Feigelson P: Studies on the allosteric regulation of tryptophan oxygenase: Structure and function. *Adv Enzyme Regul* 1968;**7**:119.

Knox WE: The regulation of tryptophan pyrrolase activity by tryptophan. *Adv Enzyme Regul* 1966;**4**:287.

Knox WE, Greengard O: The regulation of some enzymes of nitrogen metabolism: An introduction to enzyme physiology. *Adv Enzyme Regul* 1965;**3**:247.

Schimke RT: On the roles of synthesis and degradation in regulation of enzyme levels in mammalian tissues. *Curr Top Cell Regul* 1969;**1**:77.

Schimke RT, Doyle D: Control of enzyme levels in animal tissues. *Annu Rev Biochem* 1970;**39**:929.

Tyler B: Regulation of the assimilation of nitrogen compounds. *Annu Rev Biochem* 1978;**47**:1127.

Umbarger HE: Amino acid biosynthesis and its regulation. *Annu Rev Biochem* 1978;**47**:533.

Wood WA: Allosteric L-threonine dehydrases of microorganisms. *Curr Top Cell Regul* 1969;**1**:161.

Catabolism of Amino Acid Nitrogen | 21

Victor W. Rodwell, PhD

We shall consider how nitrogen is removed from amino acids and converted to urea and the medical problems that arise when there are defects in these reactions.

OVERALL VIEW

In mammalian tissues, the α-amino groups of amino acids, derived either from the diet or from breakdown of tissue proteins, ultimately are excreted in the urine as urea. The biosynthesis of urea will be divided for discussion into 4 processes: (1) transamination, (2) oxidative deamination, (3) ammonia transport, and (4) reactions of the urea cycle. Figure 21–1 relates these areas to overall catabolism of amino acid nitrogen. Although each also plays a role in amino acid biosynthesis (see Chapter 20), what follows is here discussed from the viewpoint of amino acid catabolism. Vertebrates other than mammals share all

features of this scheme except urea synthesis. Urea, the end product of amino acid nitrogen metabolism in humans and other **ureotelic** organisms, is replaced by uric acid in **uricotelic** organisms (reptiles, birds) or by ammonia in **ammonotelic** organisms (bony fish).

TRANSAMINATION

Transamination, catalyzed by enzymes termed **transaminases** or **aminotransferases,** interconverts a pair of amino acids and a pair of keto acids. These generally are α-amino and α-keto acids (Fig 21–2).

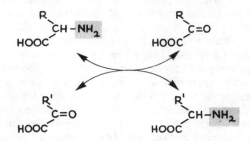

Figure 21–2. Transamination. The reaction is shown for 2 α-amino and 2 α-keto acids. Non-α-amino or carbonyl groups also participate in transamination, although this is relatively uncommon. The reaction is freely reversible with an equilibrium constant of about 1.

Pyridoxal phosphate forms an essential part of the active site of transaminases and of many other enzymes with amino acid substrates. In all pyridoxal phosphate–dependent reactions of amino acids, the initial step is formation of an enzyme-bound Schiff base intermediate (Fig 10–18).

This intermediate, stabilized by interaction with a cationic region of the active site, can be rearranged in ways that include release of a keto acid with formation of enzyme-bound pyridoxamine phosphate. The bound, amino form of the coenzyme can then form an analogous Schiff base intermediate with a keto acid. During transamination, bound coenzyme thus serves as a carrier of amino groups (Fig 21–3.)

Two transaminases, alanine-pyruvate transaminase (**alanine transaminase**) and glutamate-α-

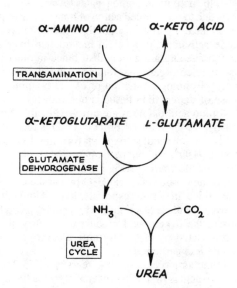

Figure 21–1. Overall flow of nitrogen in amino acid catabolism. Although the reactions shown are reversible, they are represented as being unidirectional to emphasize the direction of metabolic flow in mammalian amino acid catabolism.

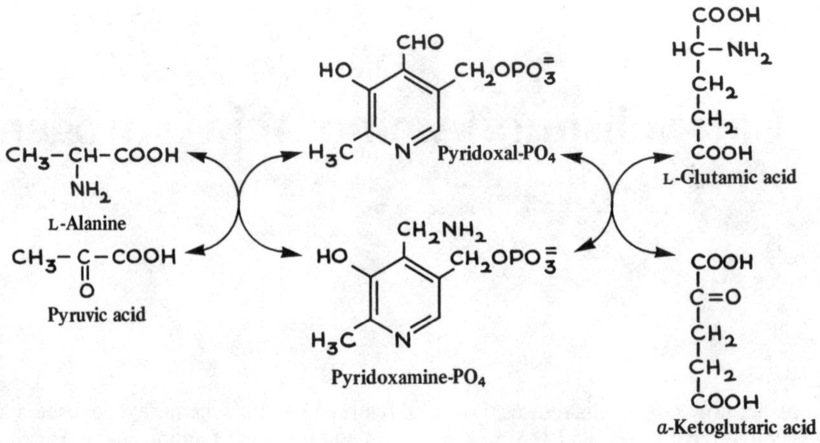

Figure 21–3. Participation of pyridoxal phosphate in transamination reactions.

ketoglutarate transaminase **(glutamate transaminase),** present in most mammalian tissues, catalyze transfer of amino groups from most amino acids to form alanine (from pyruvate) or glutamate (from α-ketoglutarate) (Fig 21–4).

Since the equilibrium constant for most transaminase reactions is close to unity, transamination is a freely reversible process. This permits transaminases to function both in amino acid catabolism and biosynthesis.

Each transaminase is specific for the specified pair of amino and keto acids as one pair of substrates but nonspecific for the other pair, which may be any of a wide variety of amino acids and their corresponding keto acids. Since alanine is also a substrate for glutamate transaminase, all of the amino nitrogen from amino acids that can undergo transamination can be concentrated in glutamate. This is important because **L-glutamate is the only amino acid in mammalian tissues which undergoes oxidative deamination** at an appreciable rate. The formation of ammonia from α-amino groups thus occurs mainly via conversion to the α-amino nitrogen of L-glutamate.

Most (but not all) amino acids are substrates for transamination. Exceptions include lysine, threonine, and the cyclic imino acids, proline and hydroxyproline. Transamination is not restricted to α-amino groups; the δ-amino group of ornithine is readily transaminated, forming glutamate γ-semialdehyde (Fig 22–3). Serum levels of transaminases are elevated in some disease states (see Chapter 8).

OXIDATIVE DEAMINATION

Oxidative conversion of many amino acids to their corresponding α-keto acids occurs in homogenates of mammalian liver and kidney tissue. Although most of the activity of homogenates toward L-α-amino acids is due to the coupled action of transaminases plus L-glutamate dehydrogenase, both L- and D-amino acid oxidase activities do occur in mammalian liver and kidney tissue and are widely distributed in other animals and microorganisms. It must be noted, however, that the physiologic function of L- and D-amino acid oxidase of mammalian tissue is not known.

Amino acid oxidases are **auto-oxidizable flavoproteins,** ie, the reduced FMN or FAD is reoxidized directly by molecular oxygen forming hydrogen peroxide (H_2O_2) without participation of cytochromes or other electron carriers (Fig 21–5). The toxic product H_2O_2 is then split to O_2 and H_2O by **catalase,** which occurs widely in tissues, especially liver. Although the amino acid oxidase reactions are reversible, if catalase is absent the α-keto acid product is nonenzymatically decarboxylated by H_2O_2, forming a carboxylic acid with one less carbon atom.

In the amino acid oxidase reactions (Fig 21–5), the amino acid is first dehydrogenated by the flavoprotein of the oxidase, forming an α-imino acid. This spontaneously adds water, then decomposes to the corresponding α-keto acid with loss of the α-imino nitrogen as ammonia.

Mammalian L-amino acid oxidase, an FMN-

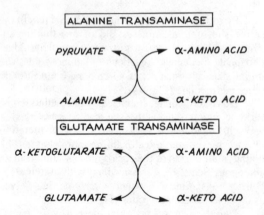

Figure 21–4. Alanine and glutamate transaminases.

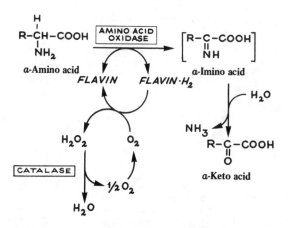

Figure 21–5. Oxidative deamination catalyzed by L-amino acid oxidase (L-α-amino acid : O_2 oxidoreductase). The α-imino acid, shown in brackets, is not a stable intermediate.

flavoprotein, is restricted to kidney and liver tissue. Its activity is quite low, and it is essentially without effect on glycine or the L-isomers of the dicarboxylic or β-hydroxy-α-amino acids. It thus is not likely that this enzyme fulfills a major role in mammalian amino acid catabolism.

Mammalian D-amino acid oxidase, an FAD-flavoprotein of broad substrate specificity, occurs in the liver and kidney tissue of most mammals. D-Asparagine and D-glutamine are not oxidized, and glycine and the D-isomers of the acidic and basic amino acids are poor substrates. The physiologic significance of this enzyme in mammals is not known.

L-GLUTAMATE DEHYDROGENASE

The amino groups of most amino acids ultimately are transferred to α-ketoglutarate by transamination, forming L-glutamate (Fig 21–1). Release of this nitrogen as ammonia is catalyzed by **L-glutamate dehydrogenase,** an enzyme of high activity widely distributed in mammalian tissues (Fig 21–6). Liver glutamate dehydrogenase is a regulated enzyme whose activity is affected by allosteric modifiers such as ATP, GTP, and NADH, which inhibit the enzyme; and

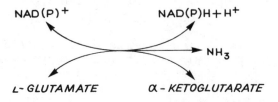

Figure 21–6. The L-glutamate dehydrogenase reaction. The designation NAD(P)$^+$ means that either NAD$^+$ or NADP$^+$ can serve as cosubstrate. The reaction is reversible, but the equilibrium constant favors glutamate formation.

ADP, which activates the enzyme. Certain hormones appear also to influence glutamate dehydrogenase activity.

Glutamate dehydrogenase uses either NAD$^+$ or NADP$^+$ as cosubstrate. The reaction is reversible and functions both in amino acid catabolism and biosynthesis. It therefore functions not only to funnel nitrogen from glutamate to urea (catabolism) but also to catalyze amination of α-ketoglutarate by free ammonia (see Chapter 20).

FORMATION OF AMMONIA

In addition to ammonia formed in the tissues, a considerable quantity is produced by intestinal bacteria from dietary protein and from urea present in fluids secreted into the gastrointestinal tract. This ammonia is absorbed from the intestine into the portal venous blood, which characteristically contains higher levels of ammonia than does systemic blood. Under normal circumstances the liver promptly removes the ammonia from the portal blood, so that blood leaving the liver (and indeed all of the peripheral blood) is virtually ammonia-free. This is essential since even minute quantities of ammonia are toxic to the central nervous system. The symptoms of **ammonia intoxication** include a peculiar flapping tremor, slurring of speech, blurring of vision, and, in severe cases, coma and death. These symptoms resemble those of the syndrome of hepatic coma which occurs when blood and, presumably, brain ammonia levels are elevated. Ammonia intoxication is assumed to be a factor in the etiology of hepatic coma. Therefore, treatment includes measures designed to reduce blood ammonia levels.

With severely impaired hepatic function or development of collateral communications between the portal and systemic veins (as may occur in cirrhosis) in the systemic blood, portal blood may bypass the liver. Ammonia may thus rise to toxic levels. Surgically produced shunting procedures (Eck fistula, or other forms of portacaval shunts) are also conducive to ammonia intoxication, particularly after ingestion of protein or after gastrointestinal hemorrhage.

The ammonia content of the blood in renal veins exceeds that in renal arteries, indicating that the kidneys produce ammonia and add it to the blood. However, the excretion into the urine of the ammonia produced by renal tubular cells constitutes a far more significant aspect of renal ammonia metabolism. Ammonia production, an important renal tubular mechanism for regulation of acid-base balance and conservation of cations, is markedly increased in metabolic acidosis and depressed in alkalosis. This ammonia is derived, not from urea, but from intracellular amino acids, particularly glutamine. Ammonia release is catalyzed by renal **glutaminase** (Fig 21–7).

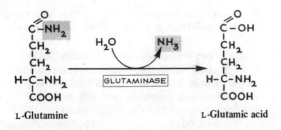

Figure 21–7. The glutaminase reaction proceeds essentially irreversibly in the direction of glutamate and NH_3 formation.

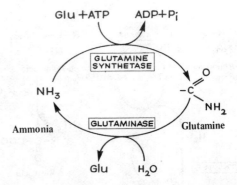

Figure 21–9. Interconversion of ammonia and of glutamine catalyzed by glutamine synthetase and glutaminase. Both reactions are strongly favored in the directions indicated by the arrows. Glutaminase thus serves solely for glutamine deamidation and glutamine synthetase solely for synthesis of glutamine from glutamate. (Glu = glutamate.)

TRANSPORT OF AMMONIA

Although ammonia may be excreted as ammonium salts—particularly in metabolic acidosis—the vast majority is excreted as urea, the principal nitrogenous component of urine. Ammonia, constantly produced in the tissues but present only in traces in peripheral blood (10–20 $\mu g/dL$), is rapidly removed from the circulation by the liver and converted to glutamate, to glutamine, or to urea. These trace levels of ammonia in blood contrast sharply with the more considerable quantities of free amino acids, particularly glutamine (Table 21–1).

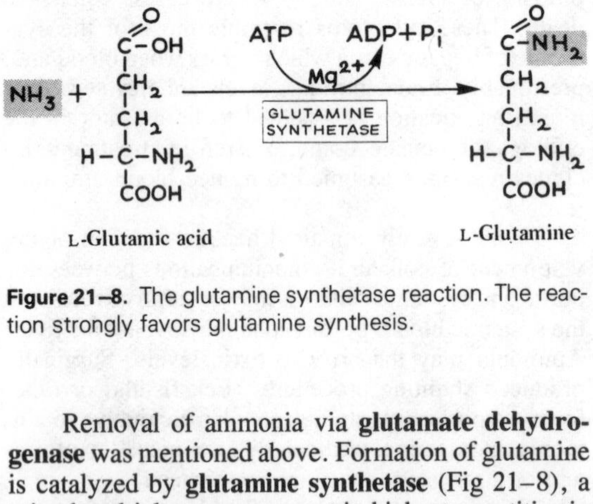

Figure 21–8. The glutamine synthetase reaction. The reaction strongly favors glutamine synthesis.

Removal of ammonia via **glutamate dehydrogenase** was mentioned above. Formation of glutamine is catalyzed by **glutamine synthetase** (Fig 21–8), a mitochondrial enzyme present in highest quantities in renal tissue. Synthesis of the amide bond of glutamine is accomplished at the expense of hydrolysis of one equivalent of ATP to ADP and P_i. The reaction is thus strongly favored in the direction of glutamine synthesis (see also Chapter 20).

Liberation of the amide nitrogen of glutamine as ammonia occurs, not by reversal of the glutamine synthetase reaction, but by hydrolytic removal of ammonia catalyzed by **glutaminase** (Fig 21–7). The glutaminase reaction, unlike the glutamine synthetase reaction, does not involve adenine nucleotides, strongly favors glutamate formation, and does not function in glutamine synthesis. Glutamine synthetase and glutaminase (Fig 21–9) thus catalyze interconversion of free ammonium ion and glutamine in a manner

reminiscent of the interconversion of glucose and glucose 6-phosphate by glucokinase and glucose-6-phosphatase (see Chapter 14). An analogous reaction is catalyzed by **L-asparaginase** of animal, plant, and microbial tissue. Asparaginase and glutaminase have both been employed as antitumor agents since certain tumors exhibit abnormally high requirements for glutamine and asparagine.

Whereas in brain the major mechanism for removal of ammonia is glutamine formation, in the liver the most important pathway is urea formation. Brain tissue can form urea, although this does not play a significant role in ammonia removal. Formation of glutamine in the brain must be preceded by synthesis of glutamate in the brain because the supply of blood glutamate is inadequate in the presence of high levels of blood ammonia. The immediate precursor is α-ketoglutarate. This would rapidly deplete citric acid cycle intermediates unless they could be replaced by CO_2 fixation with conversion of pyruvate to oxaloacetate (see Chapter 14). A significant fixation of CO_2 into amino acids does indeed occur in the brain, presumably by way of the citric acid cycle, and after infusion of ammonia more oxaloacetate is diverted to the synthesis of glutamine (rather than to aspartate) via α-ketoglutarate.

CIRCADIAN CHANGES IN PLASMA AMINO ACID LEVELS

The plasma levels of most amino acids do not remain constant throughout a 24-hour day but rather vary in a circadian rhythm about a mean value. In healthy young males fed equal meals spaced at approximately 4-hour intervals from 8 AM to 10 PM and confined to bed from 11 PM to 7 AM, amino acid levels were lowest at 2 AM and highest at 10:30 AM. Changes in physical activity had little effect on the levels or the times at which peak or nadir values occurred. However, the rhythm responds within 48 hours to an inversion of the sleeping-eating pattern. In general, plasma amino acid levels are lowest at 4 AM and rise 15–35% by noon to early afternoon. Amino acids present at the highest mean concentration (Glu, Gly, Ala, Val, Ser) change the least, whereas those present at low mean concentration (Tyr, Trp, Phe, Met, Cys, or Ile) show the most striking changes in level as a function of time of day (eg, close to 2-fold for Tyr).

Table 21–1. Mean concentrations of free amino acids in blood plasma of newborn infants and adults (expressed as mg/dL).*

Amino Acid	Newborn	Adult
Alanine	2.9	3.1
α-Amino-n-butyric acid	0.15	0.17
Arginine	0.94	1.4
Asparagine	0.6	0.6
Aspartic acid	0.11	0.22
Citrulline	0.28	0.53
Cystine	1.5	1.8
Glutamic acid	0.76	0.86
Glutamine	11.2	8.3
Glycine	2.6	1.7
Histidine	1.2	1.2
Hydroxyproline	0.42	...
Isoleucine	0.52	0.71
Leucine	0.95	1.32
Lysine	2.9	2.5
Methionine	0.44	0.32
Ornithine	1.2	0.92
Phenylalanine	1.3	0.95
Proline	2.1	2.7
Serine	1.7	1.2
Taurine	1.8	0.83
Threonine	2.6	1.9
Tryptophan	0.65	0.98
Tyrosine	1.3	0.91
Valine	1.6	2.0

*Modified from Dickinson JC & others: *Pediatrics* 1965;**36**:2.

UREA SYNTHESIS

Overall View

A moderately active man consuming about 300 g of carbohydrate, 100 g of fat, and 100 g of protein daily must excrete about 16.5 g of nitrogen daily. Ninety-five percent is eliminated by the kidneys and the remaining 5% in the stool. The **major pathway of nitrogen excretion in humans is as urea** synthesized in the liver, released into the blood, and cleared by the kidney. In humans eating an occidental diet, urea constitutes 80–90% of the nitrogen excreted.

Reactions of the Urea Cycle

The reactions and intermediates in biosynthesis of 1 mol of urea from 1 mol each of ammonia, carbon dioxide (activated with Mg^{2+} and ATP), and of the α-amino nitrogen of aspartate are shown in Fig 21–10. The overall process requires 3 mols of ATP (2 of which are converted to ADP + P_i and 1 to AMP + PP_i), and

the successive participation of 5 enzymes catalyzing the numbered reactions of Fig 21–10. Of the 6 amino acids involved in urea synthesis, one (N-acetyl-glutamate) functions as an enzyme activator rather than as an intermediate. The remaining 5—aspartate, arginine, ornithine, citrulline, and argininosuccinate—all function as carriers of atoms which ultimately become urea. Two (aspartate and arginine) occur in proteins, while the remaining 3 (ornithine, citrulline, and argininosuccinate) do not. The major metabolic role of these latter 3 amino acids in mammals is urea synthesis. Note that urea formation is in part a **cyclical process.** The ornithine used in reaction 2 is regenerated in reaction 5. There is thus no net loss or gain of ornithine, citrulline, argininosuccinate, or arginine during urea synthesis; however, ammonia, CO_2, ATP, and aspartate are consumed.

Reaction 1: Synthesis of carbamoyl phosphate. Condensation of 1 mol each of ammonia, carbon dioxide, and phosphate (derived from ATP) to form carbamoyl phosphate is catalyzed by **carbamoyl phosphate synthetase,** an enzyme present in liver **mitochondria** of all ureotelic organisms, including humans. The 2 mol of ATP hydrolyzed during this reaction provide the driving force for synthesis of 2 covalent bonds—the amide bond and the mixed carboxylic acid–phosphoric acid anhydride bond of carbamoyl phosphate. In addition to Mg^{2+}, a dicarboxylic acid, preferably N-acetylglutamate, is required. The exact role of N-acetylglutamate is not known with certainty. Its presence brings about a profound conformational change in the structure of carbamoyl phosphate synthetase which exposes certain sulfhydryl groups, conceals others, and affects the affinity of the enzyme for ATP.

In bacteria, glutamine rather than ammonia serves as a substrate for carbamoyl phosphate synthesis. A similar reaction catalyzed by carbamate kinase is also important in citrulline utilization by bacteria.

Reaction 2: Synthesis of citrulline. Transfer of a carbamoyl moiety from carbamoyl phosphate to ornithine, forming citrulline + P_i, is catalyzed by **L-ornithine transcarbamoylase** of liver mitochondria. The reaction is highly specific for ornithine, and the equilibrium strongly favors citrulline synthesis.

Reaction 3: Synthesis of argininosuccinate. In the **argininosuccinate synthetase reaction,** aspartate and citrulline are linked together via the amino group of aspartate. The reaction requires ATP, and the equilibrium strongly favors argininosuccinate.

Reaction 4: Cleavage of argininosuccinate to arginine and fumarate. Reversible cleavage of argininosuccinate to arginine plus fumarate is catalyzed by **argininosuccinase,** a cold-labile enzyme of mammalian liver and kidney tissues. Loss of activity in the cold, associated with dissociation into 2 protein components, is prevented by P_i, arginine, and argininosuccinate or by *p*-hydroxymercuribenzoate, which has no adverse effect on activity. The reaction proceeds via a *trans* elimination mechanism. The fumarate formed may be converted to oxaloacetate via the fumarase and

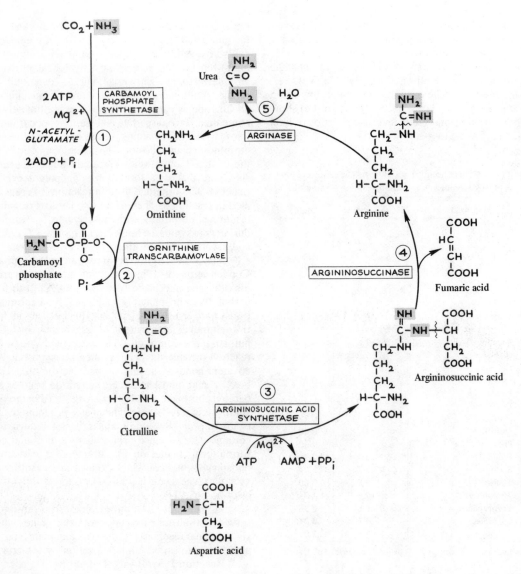

Figure 21–10. Reactions and intermediates of urea biosynthesis. The amines contributing to the formation of urea are shaded.

malate dehydrogenase reactions and then transaminated to regenerate aspartate.

Reaction 5: Cleavage of arginine to ornithine and urea. This reaction completes the urea cycle and regenerates ornithine, a substrate for reaction 2. Hydrolytic cleavage of the guanidino group of arginine is catalyzed by **arginase,** present in the livers of all ureotelic organisms. Smaller quantities of arginase also occur in renal tissue, brain, mammary gland, testicular tissue, and skin. Mammalian liver arginase is activated by Co^{2+} or Mn^{2+}. Ornithine and lysine are potent inhibitors competitive with arginine.

REGULATION OF UREA SYNTHESIS

Linkage of Glutamate Dehydrogenase With Carbamoyl Phosphate Synthetase

Carbamoyl phosphate synthetase acts with mitochondrial glutamate dehydrogenase to channel nitrogen from glutamate (and hence from all amino acids; see Fig 21–1) into carbamoyl phosphate and thus into urea. While the equilibrium constant of the glutamate dehydrogenase reaction favors glutamate rather than ammonia formation, removal of ammonia by carbamoyl phosphate synthetase and oxidation of α-ketoglutarate by citric acid cycle enzymes in the mitochondrion serve to favor glutamate catabolism. This effect is enhanced by ATP, which, in addition to being a substrate for carbamoyl phosphate synthesis, stimulates glutamate dehydrogenase activity, unidirectionally favoring ammonia formation.

METABOLIC DISORDERS OF
THE UREA CYCLE

Metabolic disorders associated with a deficiency of each of the 5 enzymes of hepatic urea synthesis (Fig 21–10) are known. The rate-limiting reactions of urea synthesis appear to be catalyzed by carbamoyl phosphate synthetase (reaction 1), ornithine transcarbamoylase (reaction 2), and arginase (reaction 5). Since the sole function of the urea cycle is to convert ammonia to the nontoxic compound urea, all disorders of urea synthesis cause ammonia intoxication. This intoxication is more severe when the metabolic block occurs at reactions 1 or 2, since some covalent linking of ammonia to carbon has already occurred if citrulline can be synthesized. Clinical symptoms common to all urea cycle disorders include vomiting in infancy, avoidance of high-protein foods, intermittent ataxia, irritability, lethargy, and mental retardation.

The clinical features and the treatment of all 5 of the disorders discussed below are similar. Significant improvement is noted on a low-protein diet, and much of the brain damage may thus be prevented. Food intake should be in frequent small meals to avoid sudden increases in blood ammonia levels. Decreasing the absorption of ammonia formed by bacterial decomposition of amino acids in the intestines by attempts at intestinal sterilization using antibiotics apparently is not of value.

Hyperammonemia Type I

One case of **carbamoyl phosphate synthetase** deficiency (reaction 1, Fig 21–10) has been reported. This probably is a familial disorder.

Hyperammonemia Type II

Numerous patients have been shown to suffer from a deficiency of **ornithine transcarbamoylase** (reaction 2, Fig 21–10). This disease is X-chromosome linked. The mothers also exhibited hyperammonemia and an aversion to high-protein foods. The only consistent clinical finding was an elevation of glutamine in blood, cerebrospinal fluid, and urine. This probably reflects enhanced synthesis of glutamine by glutamine synthetase (Fig 21–8) consequent to elevated tissue levels of ammonia.

Citrullinemia

This rare disorder (3 patients) probably is recessively inherited. Large quantities (1–2 g/d) of citrulline are excreted in the urine, and both plasma and cerebrospinal fluid citrulline levels are markedly elevated. In one patient, complete absence of **argininosuccinate synthetase** activity (reaction 3, Fig 21–10) was noted. In another, a less profound modification of this enzyme had occurred. The K_m for citrulline for the synthetase from cultured fibroblasts from this patient was 25 times normal. This suggests a mutation causing a significant but not "lethal" modification of the catalytic site of the synthetase.

Argininosuccinic Aciduria

This rare recessive inherited disease (22 cases) is characterized by elevated levels of argininosuccinic acid in the blood, cerebrospinal fluid, and urine. It frequently is associated with the occurrence of friable, tufted hair (trichorrhexis nodosa). While both early- and late-onset types are known, the disease is always manifest by age 2, and usually terminates fatally at an early age.

Argininosuccinic aciduria reflects the absence of **argininosuccinase** (reaction 4, Fig 21–10). Cultured skin fibroblasts from normal patients contain this enzyme, whereas those from patients with argininosuccinic acidemia do not. Argininosuccinase is also absent from brain, liver, kidney, and erythrocytes of patients with this disease. While the diagnosis is readily made by 2-dimensional paper chromatography of the urine, additional abnormal spots appear in urine on standing due to the tendency of argininosuccinate to form cyclic anhydrides. Confirmatory diagnosis is by measurement of erythrocyte levels of argininosuccinase. This test can be performed on cord blood for early detection. Since argininosuccinase is present in amniotic fluid cells, diagnosis by amniocentesis is also possible.

Hyperargininemia

This defect in urea synthesis (2 cases) is characterized by elevated blood and cerebrospinal fluid arginine levels, low erythrocyte levels of **arginase** (reaction 5, Fig 21–10), and a urinary amino acid pattern resembling that of lysine-cystinuria. Possibly this pattern reflects competition by arginine with lysine and cystine for reabsorption in the renal tubule. In patients, a low-protein diet resulted in lowering of plasma ammonia levels and disappearance of the urinary lysine-cystinuria pattern.

● ● ●

References

Adams E, Frank L: Metabolism of proline and the hydroxypro-lines. *Annu Rev Biochem* 1980;**49**:1005.

Fasman GD (editor): Rapid short column chromatography of amino acids related to metabolic diseases. Page 128 in: *Handbook of Biochemistry and Molecular Biology*. Vol 2. CRC Press, 1976.

Felig P: Amino acid metabolism in man. *Annu Rev Biochem* 1974;**43**:933.

Goldberg AL, Dice JF: Intracellular protein degradation in mammalian and bacterial cells. *Annu Rev Biochem* 1974; **43**:835.

Morris DR, Fillingame H: Regulation of amino acid decarboxyla-tion. *Annu Rev Biochem* 1974;**43**:303.

Nyhan WL: *Heritable Disorders of Amino Acid Metabolism: Patterns of Clinical Expression and Genetic Variation*. Wiley, 1974.

Ratner S: Enzymes of arginine and urea synthesis. *Adv Enzymol* 1973;**39**:1.

Ratner S: A long view of nitrogen metabolism. *Annu Rev Biochem* 1977;**46**:1.

Sallach HJ, Fahien LA: Nitrogen metabolism of amino acids. Page 1 in: *Metabolic Pathways*. Vol 3. Greenberg DM (editor). Academic Press, 1969.

Stanbury JB, Wyngaarden JB, Frederickson DS: *The Metabolic Basis of Inherited Disease,* 4th ed. McGraw-Hill, 1978.

Tyler B: Regulation of the assimilation of nitrogen compounds. *Annu Rev Biochem* 1978;**47**:1127.

Wurtman RJ: Time-dependent variations in amino acid metabo-lism: Mechanism of the tyrosine transaminase rhythm in rat liver. *Adv Enzyme Regul* 1968;**7**:57.

Catabolism of the Carbon Skeletons of Amino Acids | 22

Victor W. Rodwell, PhD

CONVERSION OF CARBON SKELETONS OF COMMON L-α-AMINO ACIDS TO AMPHIBOLIC INTERMEDIATES

This section deals with conversion of the carbon skeletons of common L-amino acids to amphibolic intermediates. Chapter 23 considers conversion of these carbon skeletons or of the amino acids themselves to certain specialized products.

That the carbon skeletons of the common amino acids are converted to amphibolic intermediates was evident from nutritional studies in the period 1920–1940. These data, reinforced and confirmed by studies using isotopically labeled amino acids from 1940 to 1950, supported the concept of the interconvertibility of fat, carbohydrate, and protein carbons and established that each amino acid is convertible either to carbohydrate (13 amino acids), fat (one amino acid), or both (5 amino acids) (Table 22–1). Although at the time a detailed explanation of these interconversions

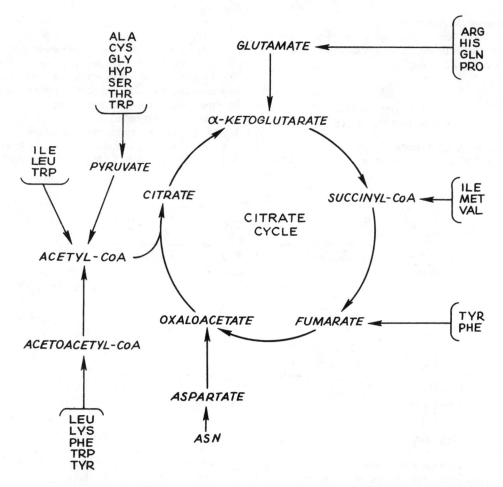

Figure 22-1. Amphibolic intermediates formed from the carbon skeleton of amino acids.

was not possible, it was established that they indeed occur. How they occur is outlined in Fig 22–1. In what follows, individual amino acids are grouped for discussion on the basis of the first amphibolic intermediates formed as end products of their catabolism.

Table 22–1. Fates of the carbon skeletons of the common L-α-amino acids.

Converted to amphibolic intermediates forming:		
Glycogen ("Glycogenic")	Fat ("Ketogenic")	Glycogen and Fat ("Glycogenic" and "Ketogenic")
Ala Hyp	Leu	Ile
Arg Met		Lys
Asp Pro		Phe
Cys Ser		Trp
Glu Thr		Tyr
Gly Val		
His		

AMINO ACIDS FORMING OXALOACETATE

Asparagine & Aspartate

All 4 carbons of asparagine and of aspartate are converted to oxaloacetate via asparaginase and a transaminase (Fig 22–2, top).

AMINO ACIDS FORMING α-KETOGLUTARATE

Glutamine & Glutamate

Catabolism of glutamine and of glutamate pro-

ceeds like that of asparagine and aspartate but with formation of α-ketoglutarate, the methylene homolog of oxaloacetate (Fig 22–2, bottom). While both glutamate and aspartate are substrates for the same transaminase, deamidation of asparagine and glutamine is catalyzed by distinct enzymes. A dual specificity glutaminase-asparaginase exists in some bacteria.

Proline

All 5 carbons of L-proline form α-ketoglutarate (Fig 22–3, left). Proline is oxidized to a dehydroproline which, on addition of water, forms glutamate γ-semialdehyde. This is then oxidized to glutamate and transaminated to α-ketoglutarate.

Arginine

While arginine and histidine also form α-ketoglutarate, one carbon and either 2 (histidine) or 3 nitrogens (arginine) must first be removed from these 6-carbon amino acids. With arginine, this requires but a single step: hydrolytic removal of the guanidino group catalyzed by arginase. The product, ornithine, then undergoes transamination of the δ-amino group, forming glutamate γ-semialdehyde, which is converted to α-ketoglutarate as described above for proline (Fig 22–3).

Histidine

For histidine, removal of the extra carbon and nitrogens requires 4 reactions (Fig 22–4). Deamination of histidine produces urocanate. Conversion of urocanate to 4-imidazolone-5-propionate, catalyzed by urocanase, involves both addition of H_2O and an internal oxidation-reduction. Although 4-imidazolone-5-propionate may undergo additional fates, conversion to α-ketoglutarate involves hydrolysis to N-formiminoglutamate followed by transfer of the

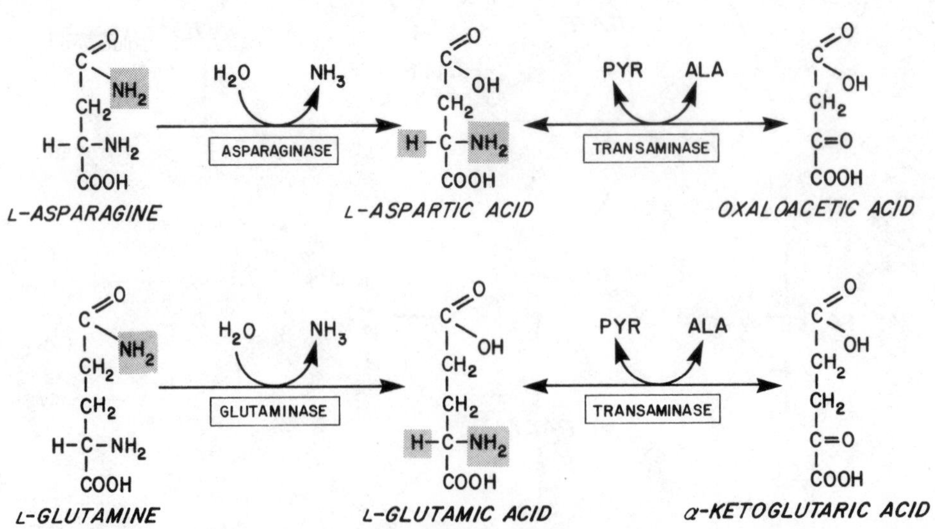

Figure 22–2. Catabolism of L-asparagine *(top)* and of L-glutamine *(bottom)* to amphibolic intermediates. PYR = pyruvic acid; ALA = L-alanine. In this and subsequent figures, shading on functional groups highlights portions of the molecules undergoing chemical change.

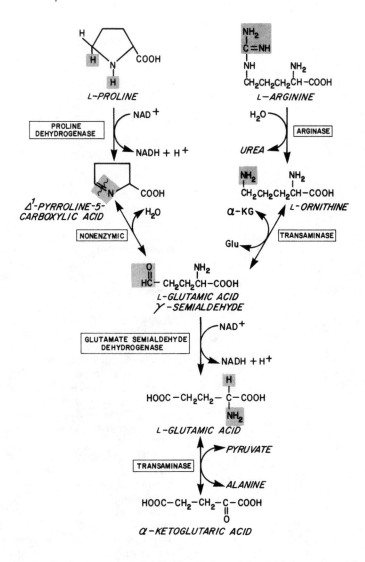

Figure 22–3. Catabolism of L-proline *(left)* and of L-arginine *(right)* to α-ketoglutarate.

formimino group on the α-carbon to tetrahydrofolate, forming N^5-formiminotetrahydrofolate. In patients with folic acid deficiency, this last reaction is partially or totally blocked and N-formiminoglutamate is excreted in the urine. This forms the basis for a test for folic acid deficiency in which N-formiminoglutamate is detected in the urine following a large dose of histidine.

AMINO ACIDS FORMING PYRUVATE

Conversion of the carbon skeletons of alanine, cysteine, cystine, glycine, threonine, and serine to pyruvate is summarized diagrammatically below. Both carbons of glycine and all 3 carbons of alanine, cysteine, and serine—but only 2 of the carbons of

threonine—form pyruvate. Pyruvate may then be converted to acetyl-CoA.

```
        L-Threonine
             ↓
          Glycine
             ↓
         L-Serine          L-Cystine
             ↓                  ↓
L-Alanine → Pyruvate ← L-Cysteine
             ↓
         Acetyl-CoA
```

Glycine

Amphibolic intermediates formed from glycine include pyruvate, CO_2, and 5,10-methylene tetrahydrofolate. Formation of pyruvate from glycine can occur by conversion to serine, catalyzed by serine

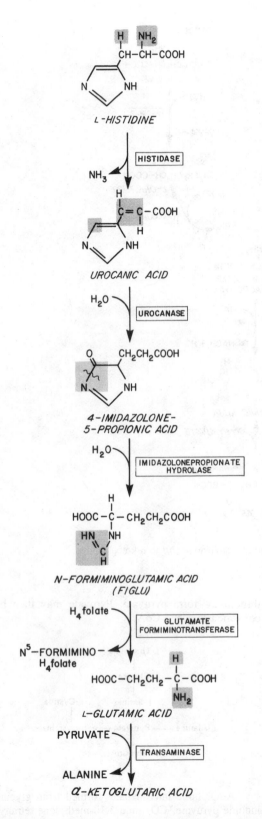

Figure 22–4. Catabolism of L-histidine to α-ketoglutarate. (H₄folate = tetrahydrofolate.)

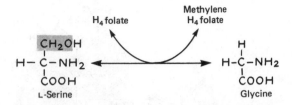

Figure 22–5. The freely reversible serine hydroxymethyl-transferase reaction. (H₄folate = tetrahydrofolate.)

hydroxymethyltransferase (Fig 22–5), followed by the serine dehydratase reaction (Fig 22–7 and see also Serine, below).

The major pathway for glycine catabolism in vertebrates probably involves conversion to CO_2 and 5,10-methylene tetrahydrofolate catalyzed by enzymes of the glycine cleavage system. This reaction sequence (Fig 22–6) resembles conversion of pyruvate to acetyl-CoA by enzymes of the pyruvate dehydrogenase complex. Both complexes comprise macromolecular aggregates in liver mitochondria. The reactions of glycine cleavage occur in liver tissue of most vertebrates, including humans, other mammals, birds, and reptiles. In uricotelic organisms, the methylene tetrahydrofolate is converted primarily to purines. In ureotelic and ammonotelic vertebrates, methylene tetrahydrofolate may be converted to serine by serine hydroxymethyltransferase (Fig 22–5) or oxidized to CO_2.

The reactions of glycine cleavage system (Fig 22–6) probably constitute the major route, not only for glycine but also for serine catabolism in humans and many other vertebrates (see also Serine, below). Liver tissue from normal human subjects readily catalyzes conversion of glycine to CO_2 with the accompanying synthesis of serine. These reactions occurred at a far slower rate in a liver biopsy specimen from a patient with hyperglycinemia. This disorder, apparently a result of a defect in the glycine cleavage system, documents the physiologic importance of this system for glycine catabolism in humans.

Alanine

Transamination of L-alanine (Fig 22–7) forms pyruvate, which may then be decarboxylated to acetyl-CoA.

Serine

Conversion of serine to pyruvate by serine dehydratase, a pyridoxal phosphate protein, involves both elimination of water and hydrolytic loss of ammonia from an imino acid intermediate (Fig 22–7). Rat and guinea pig liver is rich in serine dehydratase. Whereas in these species conversion of serine to pyruvate by serine dehydratase is of considerable physiologic significance, in humans and many other vertebrates, serine is degraded primarily to glycine and 5,10-methylene tetrahydrofolate. The initial reaction is catalyzed by serine hydroxymethyltransferase (Fig

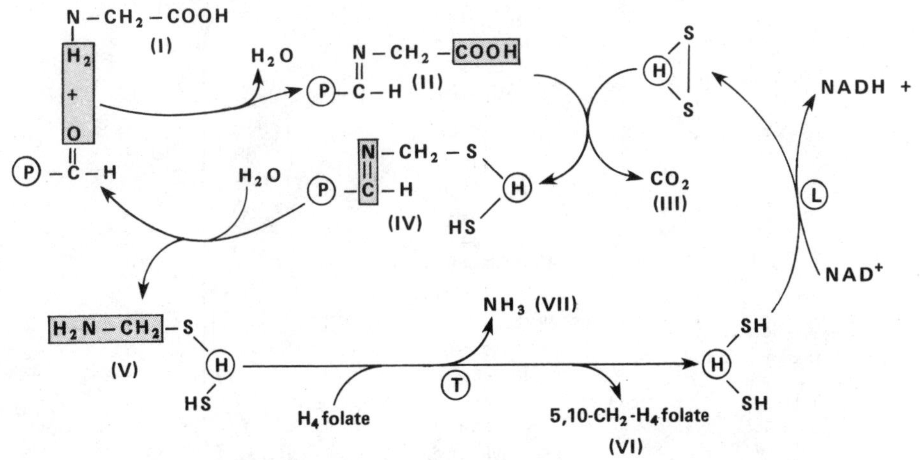

Figure 22–6. Catabolism of glycine to CO_2, NH_3, and methylene tetrahydrofolate by the glycine cleavage system of vertebrate liver. Glycine (I) combines with the P-protein, a pyridoxal phosphoprotein, to form the Schiff base (II). The disulfide form of the H-protein then combines with (II), liberating the carboxyl carbon of glycine as CO_2 (III) and forming the Schiff base–H-protein complex (IV), which decomposes to (V), re-forming the P-protein. Decomposition of (V), which requires tetrahydrofolate (H_4folate) and is catalyzed by the T-protein, forms methylene tetrahydrofolate ($5,10$-CH_2-H_4folate) (VI), NH_3 (VII), and the reduced form of the H-protein. This is oxidized to the disulfide form by NAD^+ in a reaction catalyzed by the L-protein. Although the entire sequence of reactions is reversible, unidirectional arrows are used to emphasize the direction of flow of intermediates in catabolism of glycine. (H_4folate = tetrahydrofolate.)

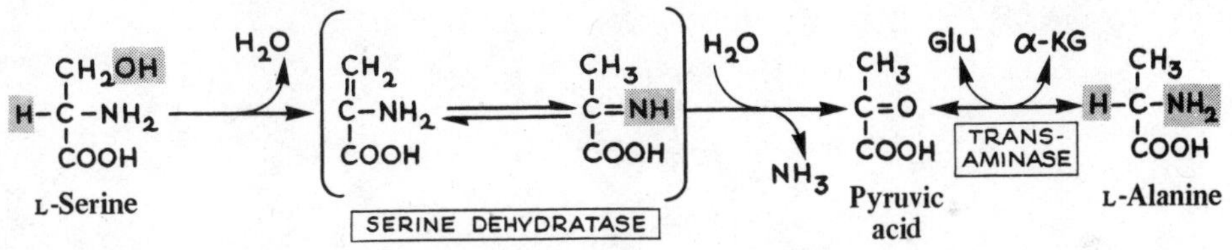

Figure 22–7. Conversion of alanine and serine to pyruvate. Both the alanine transaminase and serine dehydratase reactions require pyridoxal phosphatase as coenzyme. The serine dehydratase reaction proceeds via elimination of H_2O from serine, forming an unsaturated amino acid. This rearranges to an α-imino acid which is spontaneously hydrolyzed to pyruvate plus ammonia. There is thus no net gain or loss of water during the serine dehydratase reaction. (Glu = glutamate; α-KG = α-ketoglutarate.)

22–5). Further catabolism of serine then merges with glycine catabolism (Fig 22–6).

Cysteine & Cystine

Cystine is reduced to cysteine by an NADH-dependent oxidoreductase (Fig 22–8). Conversion of cysteine to pyruvate may then occur in any of 3 ways (Fig 22–9): (1) Via cysteine desulfhydrase, a pyridoxal phosphate–dependent reaction similar to that catalyzed by serine dehydratase (Fig 22–7). (2) By transamination and loss of H_2S. (3) By oxidation of the sulfhydryl group forming cysteine sulfinic acid, transamination, and loss of the terminal carbon's oxidized sulfur atom.

Threonine

Threonine is cleaved to acetaldehyde and glycine by **threonine aldolase.** Acetaldehyde then forms acetyl-CoA (Fig 22–10). Catabolism of glycine is discussed above.

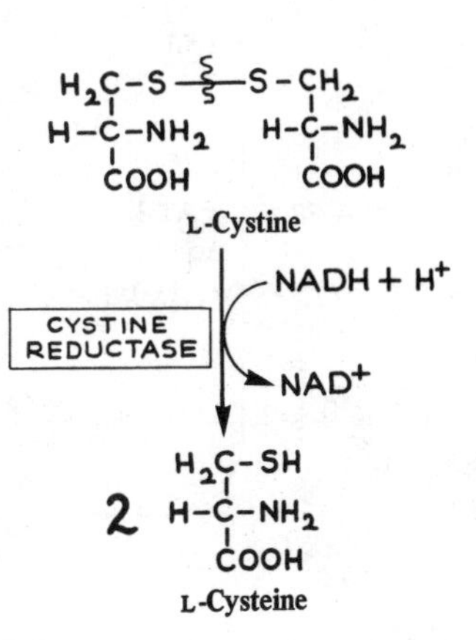

Figure 22–8. The cystine reductase reaction.

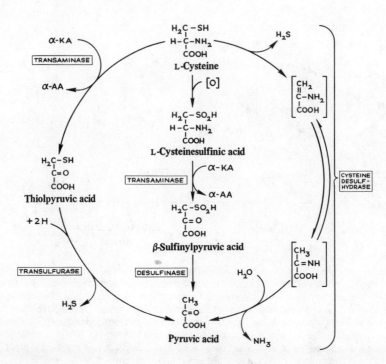

Figure 22–9. Conversion of cysteine to pyruvate. The cysteine desulfhydrase reaction is analogous to that catalyzed by serine dehydratase (Fig 22–7) except that the initial step involves loss of H_2S rather than H_2O. (α-AA = α-amino acid; α-KA = α-keto acid.)

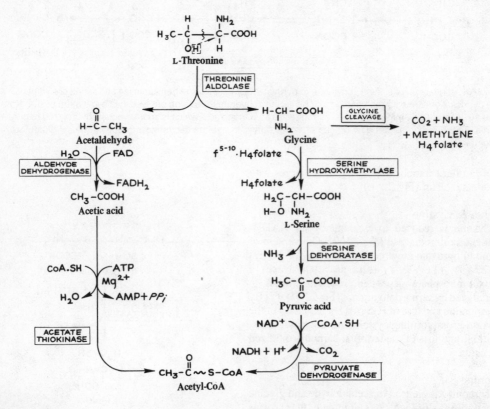

Figure 22–10. Conversion of threonine and glycine to serine, pyruvate, and acetyl-CoA. ($f^{5\cdot10}\cdot H_4$folate = formyl [5–10] tetrahydrofolic acid.)

Hydroxyproline

Three of the 5 carbons of 4-hydroxy-L-proline are converted to pyruvate (Fig 22–11). The remaining 2 form glyoxylate. A mitochondrial dehydrogenase catalyzes conversion of hydroxyproline to L-Δ^1-pyrroline-3-hydroxy-5-carboxylate. This is in nonenzymic equilibrium with γ-hydroxy-L-glutamate-γ-semialdehyde, formed by addition of water. The semialdehyde is oxidized to the corresponding carboxylic acid, erythro-γ-hydroxyglutamate, and transaminated to α-keto-γ-hydroxyglutarate. An aldol type cleavage then forms glyoxylate plus pyruvate.

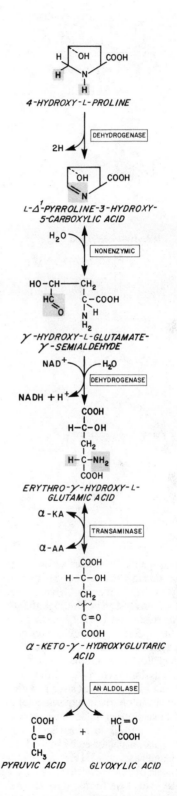

Figure 22–11. Intermediates in L-hydroxyproline catabolism in mammalian tissues. (α-KA = α-keto acid; α-AA = α-amino acid.)

AMINO ACIDS FORMING ACETYL–COENZYME A

All amino acids forming pyruvate (alanine, cysteine, cystine, glycine, serine, and threonine) are convertible to acetyl-CoA. In addition, 5 amino acids form acetyl-CoA without first forming pyruvate. These include the aromatic amino acids phenylalanine, tyrosine, and tryptophan, the basic amino acid lysine, and the neutral branched chain amino acid leucine.

Tyrosine

A. Overall Reaction Sequence: Five sequential enzymatic reactions convert tyrosine to fumarate and to acetoacetate (Fig 22–12): (1) transamination to *p*-hydroxyphenylpyruvate; (2) simultaneous oxidation and migration of the 3-carbon side chain and decarboxylation, forming homogentisate; (3) oxidation of homogentisate to maleylacetoacetate; (4) isomerization of maleylacetoacetate to fumarylacetoacetate; and (5) hydrolysis of fumarylacetoacetate to fumarate and acetoacetate. Acetoacetate may then undergo thiolytic cleavage to acetate plus acetyl-CoA.

Several intermediates of tyrosine metabolism were discovered during studies of the human genetic disease alkaptonuria. Patients with alkaptonuria excrete homogentisate in the urine, and much useful information was obtained by feeding suspected precursors of homogentisate to these patients. Early difficulties arising from the instability of several of the intermediates were resolved by the discovery that α-ketoglutarate and ascorbate are required for tyrosine oxidation by liver extracts. Subsequently, each individual enzymic reaction was studied in detail.

B. Transamination of Tyrosine: Transamination of tyrosine to *p*-hydroxyphenylpyruvate is catalyzed by **tyrosine-α-ketoglutarate transaminase,** an inducible enzyme of mammalian liver.

C. Oxidation of *p*-Hydroxyphenylpyruvate to Homogentisate: Although the reaction (Fig 22–12) appears to involve hydroxylation of *p*-hydroxyphenylpyruvate in the ortho position accompanied by oxidative loss of the carboxyl carbon, it actually involves migration of the side chain. Ring hydroxylation and side chain migration occur in a concerted manner. ***p*-Hydroxyphenylpyruvate hydroxylase** is a copper metalloprotein similar to **tyrosinase.** Although other

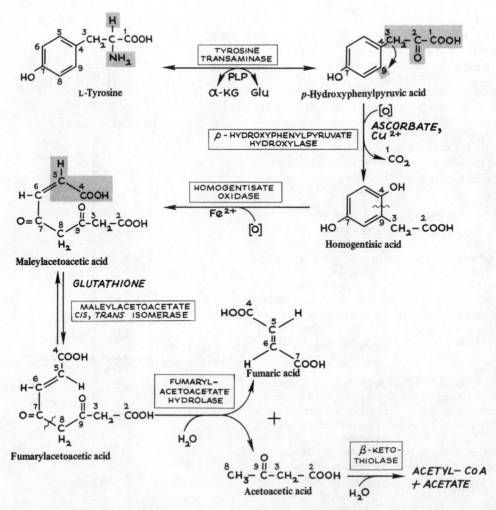

Figure 22-12. Intermediates in tyrosine catabolism. With the exception of β-ketothiolase, reactions are discussed in the text. Carbon atoms of intermediates are numbered to assist readers in determining the ultimate fate of each carbon (see also Fig 22-22). (α-KG = α-ketoglutarate; Glu = glutamate; PLP = pyridoxal phosphate.)

reducing agents can replace ascorbate as a cofactor for this reaction in vitro, scorbutic patients excrete incompletely oxidized products of tyrosine metabolism.

D. Conversion of Homogentisate to Fumarate and Acetoacetate: The benzene ring of homogentisate is ruptured, forming maleylacetoacetate in an oxidative reaction catalyzed by **homogentisate oxidase,** an iron metalloprotein of mammalian liver. Since the reaction is inhibited by α,α'-dipyridyl, a chelating agent that binds iron, treatment with α,α'-dipyridyl induces alkaptonuria in experimental animals.

Conversion of maleylacetoacetate to fumarylacetoacetate, a *cis* to *trans* isomerization about the double bond, is catalyzed by **maleylacetoacetate *cis-trans* isomerase,** an –SH enzyme of mammalian liver. Hydrolysis of fumarylacetoacetate by **fumarylacetoacetate hydrolase** forms fumarate and acetoacetate. Acetoacetate can then be converted to acetyl-CoA plus acetate by the β-ketothiolase reaction (see Chapter 17).

Phenylalanine

Phenylalanine is first converted to tyrosine by phenylalanine hydroxylase (Fig 20–19). The labeling pattern in the amphibolic products fumarate and acetoacetate (Fig 22–13) thus is identical to that for tyrosine (Fig 22–12).

Lysine

Lysine provides an exception to the rule that the first step in catabolism of an amino acid is removal of its α-amino group by transamination. In mammalian tissues, neither the α- nor ε-nitrogen atoms of L-lysine undergo transamination. Mammals convert the intact carbon skeleton of L-lysine to α-aminoadipate and α-ketoadipate (Fig 22–14). L-Lysine was formerly thought to be degraded via pipecolic acid, a cyclic imino acid. However, while liver degrades D-lysine via pipecolate, L-lysine is degraded via saccharopine (Fig 22–15), an intermediate in lysine biosynthesis by fungi.

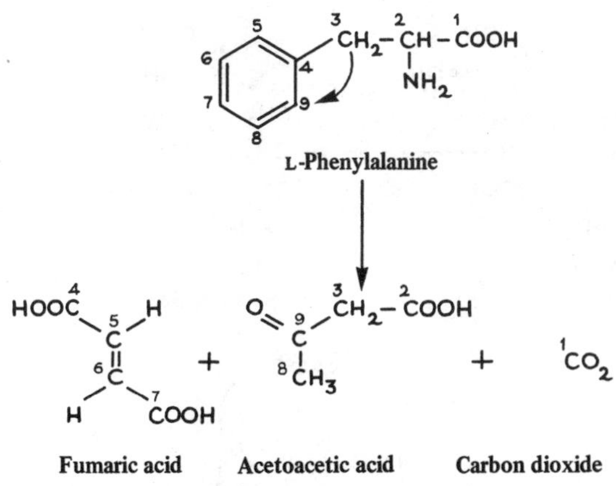

Figure 22–13. Ultimate catabolic fate of each carbon atom of phenylalanine. Pattern of isotopic labeling in the ultimate catabolites of phenylalanine (and tyrosine).

L-Lysine first condenses with α-ketoglutarate, splitting out water and forming a Schiff base. This is reduced to saccharopine by a dehydrogenase, then oxidized by a second dehydrogenase. Addition of water forms L-glutamate and L-α-aminoadipate-δ-semialdehyde. The net effect of this reaction sequence is equivalent to removal of the ϵ-nitrogen of lysine by transamination. One mole each of L-lysine and of α-ketoglutarate are converted to α-aminoadipate-δ-semialdehyde and glutamate. However, NAD^+ and NADH are specifically required as cofactors, even though no net oxidation or reduction occurs.

Further catabolism of α-aminoadipate involves transamination to α-ketoadipate, probably followed by oxidative decarboxylation to glutaryl-CoA. While lysine is both glycogenic and ketogenic, the nature of the subsequent catabolites of glutaryl-CoA in mammalian systems is not known.

Tryptophan

Tryptophan, notable for its variety of important metabolic reactions and products, was among the first amino acids shown to be nutritionally essential. *Neurospora* mutants, the bacterium *Pseudomonas*, and isolation of tryptophan metabolites from urine have proved invaluable aids in unraveling the details of tryptophan metabolism.

Although a large portion of the isotope of administered ^{14}C-L-tryptophan is incorporated into proteins, a considerable fraction appears in the urine as various catabolites. The carbon atoms both of the side chain and of the aromatic ring may be completely degraded to amphibolic intermediates via the **kynurenine-anthranilate pathway** (Fig 22–16), important both for tryptophan degradation and for conversion of tryptophan to **niacin** (Fig 9–11).

Tryptophan oxygenase (tryptophan pyrrolase) catalyzes cleavage of the indole ring with incorporation of 2 atoms of molecular oxygen, forming N-formylkynurenine. The oxygenase is an iron porphyrin metalloprotein present in the liver of mammals, amphibians, birds, and insects. Tryptophan oxygenase is inducible in liver by adrenal corticosteroids and tryptophan itself. A considerable portion of newly synthesized enzyme is in a latent form that requires activation. Tryptophan also stabilizes the oxygenase toward proteolytic degradation. Tryptophan oxygenase is feedback inhibited by nicotinic acid derivatives, including NADPH.

Hydrolytic removal of the formyl group of N-formylkynurenine is catalyzed by **kynurenine formylase** of mammalian liver. Hydrolysis in $H_2{}^{18}O_2$ incorporates one equivalent of ^{18}O into the formate formed. The enzyme catalyzes similar reactions with various arylformylamines.

The reaction catalyzed by kynurenine formylase produces **kynurenine** (Fig 22–16). This may be deaminated by transamination of the amino group of the side chain to ketoglutarate. The resulting keto derivative, 2-amino-3-hydroxybenzoyl pyruvate, loses water and spontaneous ring closure and forms **kynurenic acid.** This compound, a by-product of kynurenine, is not formed in the main pathway of tryptophan breakdown (Fig 22–16).

Further metabolism of kynurenine involves conversion to **hydroxykynurenine,** which is converted to **3-hydroxyanthranilate.** Hydroxylation requires molecular oxygen in an NADPH-dependent reaction similar to that for hydroxylation of phenylalanine (see Chapter 20).

Kynurenine and hydroxykynurenine are converted to hydroxyanthranilate by **kynureninase,** a pyridoxal phosphate enzyme. A deficiency of vitamin B_6 results in partial failure to catabolize these kynurenine derivatives, which thus reach extrahepatic tissues where they are converted to **xanthurenic acid** (Fig 22–17). This abnormal metabolite occurs in the urine of humans, monkeys, and rats when dietary vitamin B_6 is inadequate. Feeding excess tryptophan can be used to induce excretion of xanthurenic acid in vitamin B_6 deficiency.

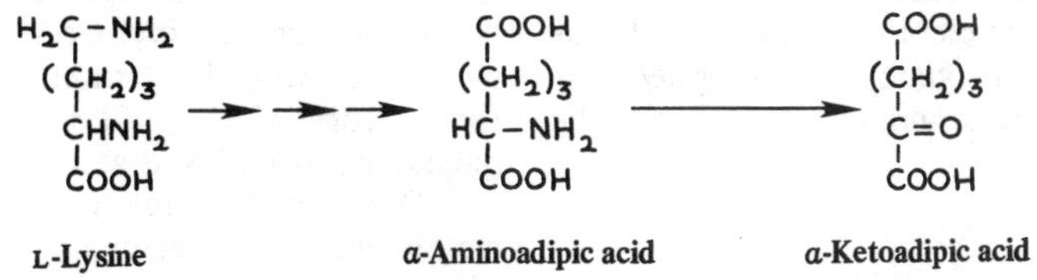

Figure 22–14. Conversion of L-lysine to α-aminoadipate and α-ketoadipate. Double arrows represent multiple reactions.

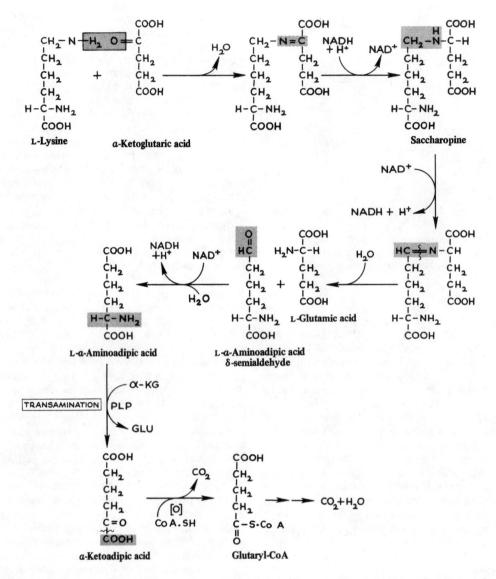

Figure 22–15. Catabolism of L-lysine. (α-KG = α-ketoglutarate; Glu = glutamate; PLP = pyridoxal phosphate.)

In many animals, conversion of tryptophan to nicotinic acid makes a supply of the vitamin in the diet unnecessary (see Chapter 10). In the rat, rabbit, dog, and pig, tryptophan can completely replace the vitamin in the diet; in humans and other animals, tryptophan increases the urinary excretion of nicotinic acid derivatives (eg, N-methylnicotinamide). In vitamin B_6 deficiency, synthesis of NAD^+ and $NADP^+$ may be impaired, a result of inadequate conversion of tryptophan to nicotinic acid for nucleotide synthesis. If an adequate supplement of nicotinic acid is supplied, nucleotide synthesis proceeds normally even in the absence of vitamin B_6.

AMINO ACIDS FORMING SUCCINYL–COENZYME A

Overall Reactions

While succinyl-CoA is the amphibolic end product for catabolism of methionine, isoleucine, and valine, only portions of the skeletons are converted (Fig 22–18). Four-fifths of the carbons of valine, three-fifths of those of methionine, and half of those of isoleucine form succinyl-CoA. The carboxyl carbons of all 3 form CO_2. The terminal 2 carbons of isoleucine form acetyl-CoA, and the S-methyl group of methionine is removed as such.

What follows relates only to conversion of methionine and isoleucine to propionyl-CoA and of valine to methylmalonyl-CoA. The reactions leading from propionyl-CoA through methylmalonyl-CoA to

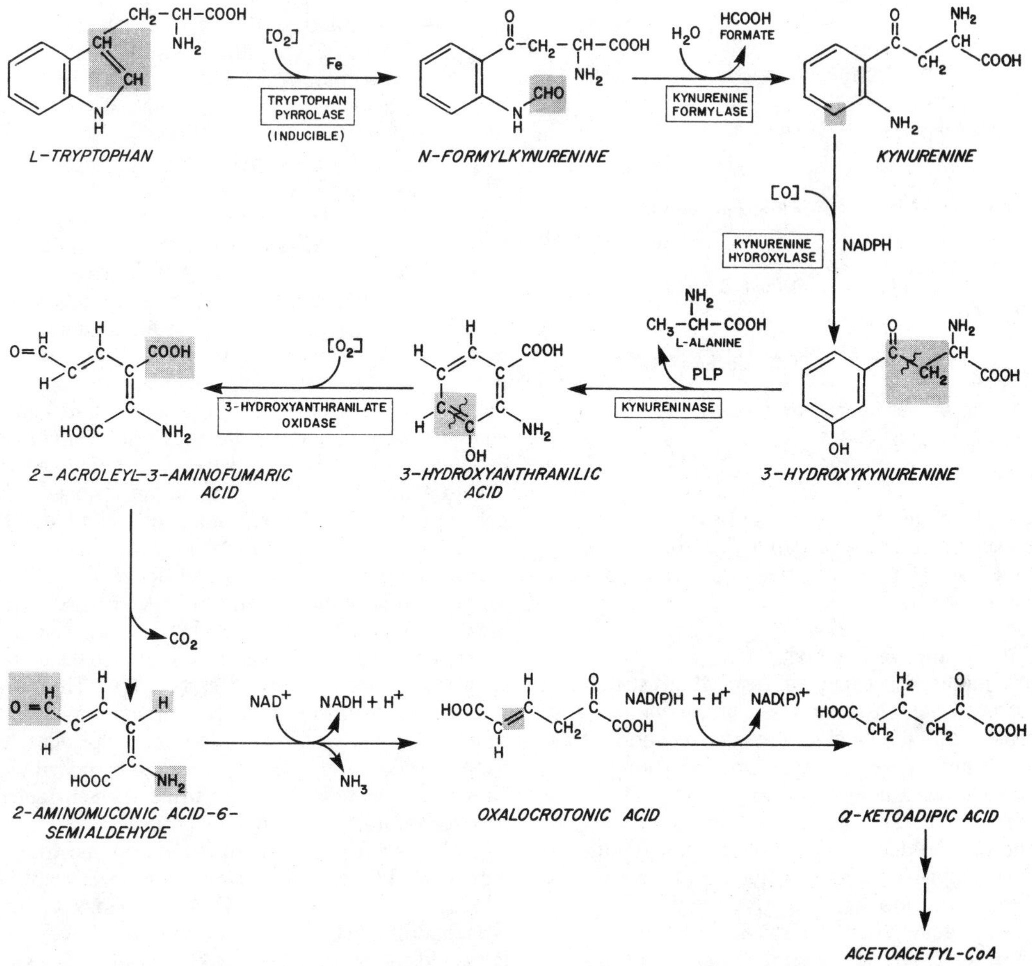

Figure 22–16. Catabolism of L-tryptophan. (PLP = pyridoxal phosphate.)

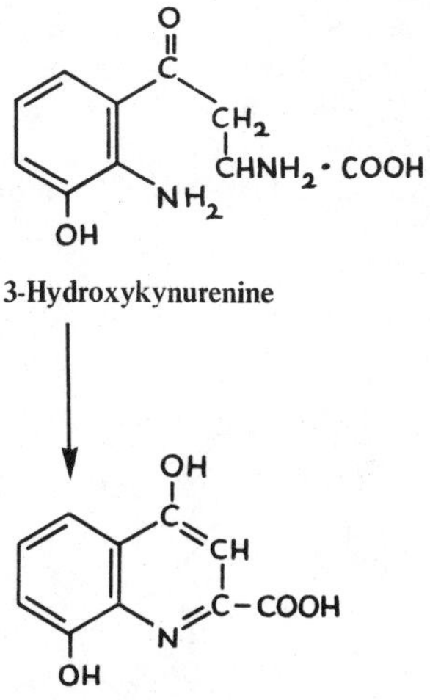

3-Hydroxykynurenine

Xanthurenic acid

Figure 22–17. Formation of xanthurenic acid in vitamin B6 deficiency. Conversion of the tryptophan metabolite 3-hydroxykynurenine to 3-hydroxyanthranilate is impaired (see Fig 22–16). A large portion is therefore converted to xanthurenic acid.

succinyl-CoA are discussed in Chapters 4 and 9 in connection with catabolism of propionate and of fatty acids containing an odd number of carbon atoms.

Methionine

L-Methionine condenses with ATP, forming S-adenosylmethionine or "active methionine" (Fig 22–19). The activated S-methyl group may transfer to various acceptor compounds.* Removal of the methyl group forms S-adenosylhomocysteine. Hydrolysis of the S–C bond yields L-homocysteine plus adenosine. Homocysteine then condenses with serine, forming cystathionine. Hydrolytic cleavage of cystathionine forms L-homoserine plus cysteine, so that the net effect is conversion of homocysteine to homoserine and of serine to cysteine. These 2 reactions are therefore also involved in biosynthesis of cysteine from serine (see Chapter 20). Homoserine is converted to α-ketobutyrate by homoserine deaminase (Fig 22–21). Conver-

*Compounds whose methyl groups derive from S-adenosylmethionine include betaines, choline, creatine, epinephrine, melatonin, sarcosine, N-methylated amino acids, nucleotides, and many plant alkaloids.

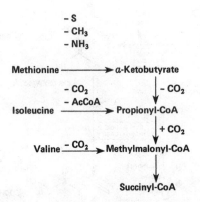

Figure 22–18. Overall catabolism of methionine, isoleucine, and valine to succinyl-CoA.

sion of α-ketobutyrate to propionyl-CoA then occurs in the usual manner for oxidative decarboxylation of α-keto acids (eg, pyruvate, α-ketoglutarate) to form acyl-CoA derivatives.

Leucine, Valine, & Isoleucine

As might be suspected from their structural similarities, catabolism of L-leucine, L-valine, and L-isoleucine initially involves the same reactions. This common pathway then diverges, and each amino acid skeleton follows a unique pathway to amphibolic intermediates (Fig 22–22). The nature of these amphibolic end products (β-hydroxy-β-methylglutaryl-CoA, succinyl-CoA, and acetyl-CoA) determines whether an amino acid is glycogenic (valine), ketogenic (leucine), or both (isoleucine). **Many of the reactions involved are analogous to reactions of straight and branched chain fatty acid catabolism.** Because of the similarities noted in Fig 22–22, it is convenient to discuss initial reactions in catabolism of all 3 amino acids together. In what follows, reaction numbers refer to reactions of Figs 22–22 through 22–25.

A. Transamination: Reversible transamination (reaction 1, Figs 22–22, 22–23, and 22–24) of all 3 branched L-α-amino acids in mammalian tissues probably involves a single transaminase. Reversibility of this reaction accounts for the ability of the corresponding α-keto acids to replace the L-α-amino acids in the diet.

B. Oxidative Decarboxylation to Acyl-CoA Thioesters: This reaction (reaction 2, Figs 22–22, 22–23, and 22–24) is analogous to oxidation of pyruvate to CO_2 and acetyl-CoA and of α-ketoglutarate to CO_2 and succinyl-CoA. Indirect evidence suggests at least 2 oxidative decarboxylases in mammals specific for only one or 2 α-keto acids. A mammalian decarboxylase catalyzes oxidative decarboxylation of α-ketoisocaproate (from leucine) and of α-keto-β-methylvalerate (from isoleucine) but not of α-ketoisovalerate (from valine). In humans, the available evidence suggests a single oxidative decarboxylase for all α-keto acids. In **maple syrup urine disease,** a rare genetic defect of infants, a metabolic block due to a nonfunctional oxidative decarboxylase prevents further catabolism of all 3 α-keto acids (Fig 22–22). These acids accumulate in the blood and urine, imparting to urine the characteristic odor for which the defect is named. The accumulation of all 3 α-keto acids suggests a single oxidative decarboxylase. The disease is associated with severe functional impairment of the central nervous system. During acute episodes, urinary excretion of the keto acids of the branched-chain amino acids increases, and the urine has a characteristic odor reminiscent of maple syrup.

C. Dehydrogenation to α,β-Unsaturated Acyl-CoA Thioesters: This reaction (reaction 3, Figs 22–22, 22–23, and 22–24) is analogous to dehydrogenation of straight chain acyl-CoA thioesters in fatty acid catabolism. It is not known whether a single enzyme catalyzes dehydrogenation of all 3 branched acyl-CoA thioesters. Indirect evidence which suggests that at least 2 enzymes are required derives from **isovaleric acidemia** wherein, following ingestion of protein-rich foods, isovalerate accumulates in the blood. An increase in other branched α-keto acids does not occur. Isovalerate is formed by deacylation of isovaleryl-CoA, the substrate for the above dehydro-

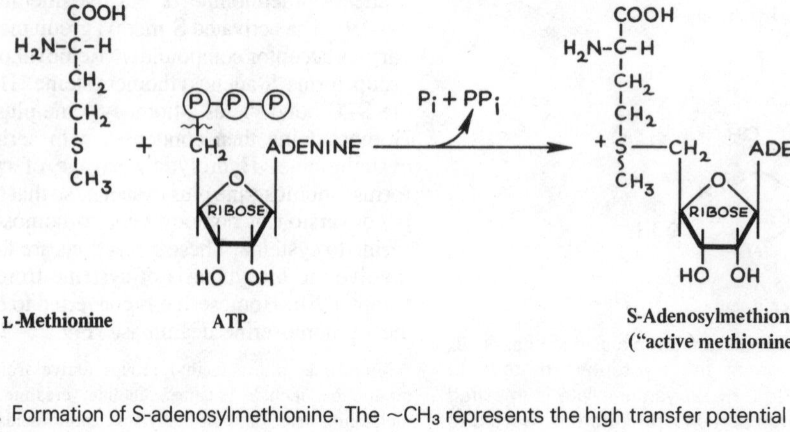

Figure 22–19. Formation of S-adenosylmethionine. The $\sim CH_3$ represents the high transfer potential of the CH_3 of "active methionine."

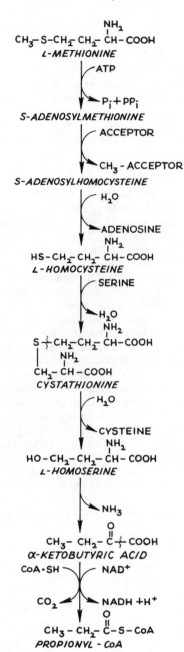

Figure 22–20. Conversion of methionine to propionyl-CoA.

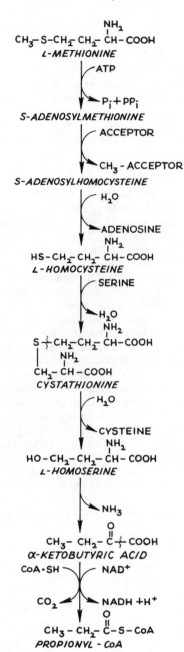

Figure at top right:

NH₂
CH₂– CH –CH–COOH
OH H
L-HOMOSERINE

↓ H₂O

[
NH₂
CH₂≡CH–CH–COOH
]

↓

[
NH₂
CH₃ CH≡C–COOH
]

↓

[
NH
CH₃– CH₂–C–COOH
]

↓ H₂O

NH₃
CH₃– CH₂– C–COOH
‖
O
α-KETOBUTYRIC ACID

Figure 22–21. Conversion of L-homoserine to α-ketobutyrate, by homoserine deaminase.

tonyl-CoA. A key observation leading to explanation of the ketogenic action of leucine was the discovery that 1 mol of CO_2 was "fixed" (ie, covalently bound) per mole of isopropyl groups (from the terminal isopropyl group of leucine) converted to acetoacetate. This CO_2 fixation (reaction 4L, Fig 22–23) requires biotinyl-CO_2, formed from enzyme-bound biotin and CO_2 at the expense of ATP. Both in bacteria and in mammalian liver, this reaction forms β-methylglutaconyl-CoA as an intermediate.

Reaction 5L: Hydration of β-methylglutaconyl-CoA. The reaction product, β-hydroxy-β-methylglutaryl-CoA, is a precursor not only of ketone bodies (reaction 6L, Fig 22–23) but also of mevalonate, and hence of cholesterol and other polyisoprenoids (see Chapter 15).

Reaction 6L: Cleavage of β-hydroxy-β-methyl-glutaryl-CoA. Cleavage of β-hydroxy-β-methylglutaryl-CoA to acetyl-CoA and acetoacetate occurs in mammalian liver, kidney, and heart mitochondria. It explains the strongly ketogenic effect of leucine, since not only is 1 mol of acetoacetate formed per mole of leucine catabolized but another ½ mol of ketone bodies may be formed indirectly from the remaining product, acetyl-CoA (see Chapter 15).

Reactions Specific to Valine Catabolism
(Fig 22–24.)
Reaction 4V: Hydration of methylacrylyl-

genase. Its formation suggests accumulation of isovaleryl-CoA, possibly due to a defective isovaleryl-CoA dehydrogenase. If a single dehydrogenase served to dehydrogenate all 3 branched acyl-CoA thioesters, accumulation of isobutyrate (from valine) and α-methylbutyrate (from isoleucine) would be anticipated following a protein-rich meal.

Reactions Specific to Leucine Catabolism
(Fig 22–23.)
Reaction 4L: Carboxylation of β-methylcro-

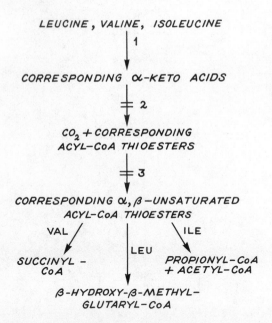

LEUCINE, VALINE, ISOLEUCINE

↓ 1

CORRESPONDING α-KETO ACIDS

⧣ 2

CO_2 + CORRESPONDING
ACYL-CoA THIOESTERS

⧣ 3

CORRESPONDING α,β-UNSATURATED
ACYL-CoA THIOESTERS

VAL ↙   ↘ ILE

LEU

SUCCINYL-CoA   PROPIONYL-CoA
                 + ACETYL-CoA

β-HYDROXY-β-METHYL-
GLUTARYL-CoA

Figure 22–22. Catabolism of the branched chain amino acids in mammals. Reactions 1–3 are common to all 3 amino acids; thereafter, the pathways diverge. Double lines intersecting arrows mark sites of metabolic blocks in 2 rare human diseases: at *2*, maple syrup urine disease, a defect in catabolism of all 3 amino acids; and at *3*, isovaleric acidemia, a defect of leucine catabolism.

CoA. This reaction, which occurs nonenzymatically at a relatively rapid rate, is catalyzed by crotonase, a hydrolase of broad specificity for L-β-hydroxyacyl-CoA thioesters having 4–9 carbon atoms.

Reaction 5V: Deacylation of β-hydroxyisobutyryl-CoA. Since the CoA thioester is not a substrate for the subsequent reaction (reaction 6V, Fig 22–24), it must first be deacylated to β-hydroxyisobutyrate (reaction 5V, Fig 22–24). This is catalyzed by a deacylase, present in many animal tissues, whose only other substrate is β-hydroxypropionyl-CoA.

Reaction 6V: Oxidation of β-hydroxyisobutyrate. Extracts of pig heart and other mammalian tissues catalyze the NAD^+-dependent oxidation of the primary alcohol group of β-hydroxyisobutyrate to an aldehyde (reaction 6V, Fig 22–24), forming methylmalonate semialdehyde. The reaction is readily reversible.

Reaction 7V: Fate of methylmalonate semialdehyde. Two fates are possible for methylmalonate semialdehyde in mammalian tissues: transamination to β-aminoisobutyrate (reaction 7V, Fig 22–24) and conversion to succinyl-CoA (reactions 8V through 10V, Fig 22–24). Transamination to α-aminoisobutyrate, a normal urinary amino acid, is catalyzed by various mammalian tissues including kidney. The second major fate involves oxidation to methylmalonate, acylation to methylmalonyl-CoA, and isomerization to succinyl-CoA (reactions 8V through 10V, Fig 22–24). Isomerization (reaction 10V, Fig 22–24) requires cobamide coenzyme and is catalyzed by methylmalonyl-CoA mutase. This reaction is important not only for valine catabolism but also for that of propionyl-CoA, a catabolite of isoleucine (Fig 22–

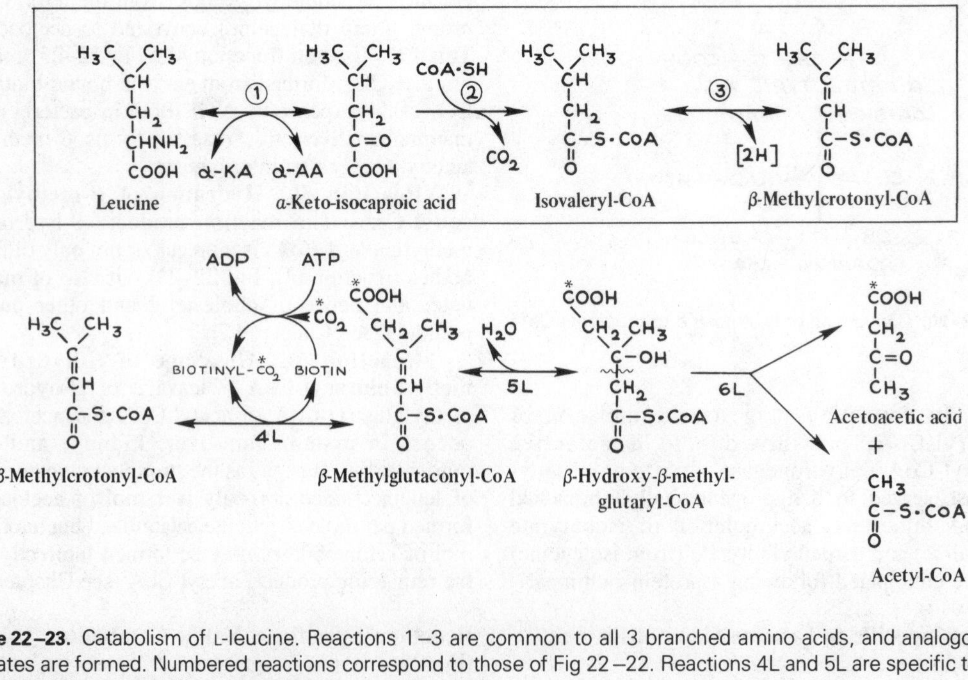

Figure 22–23. Catabolism of L-leucine. Reactions 1–3 are common to all 3 branched amino acids, and analogous intermediates are formed. Numbered reactions correspond to those of Fig 22–22. Reactions 4L and 5L are specific to leucine catabolism. (α-KA = α-keto acids; α-AA = α-amino acids.)

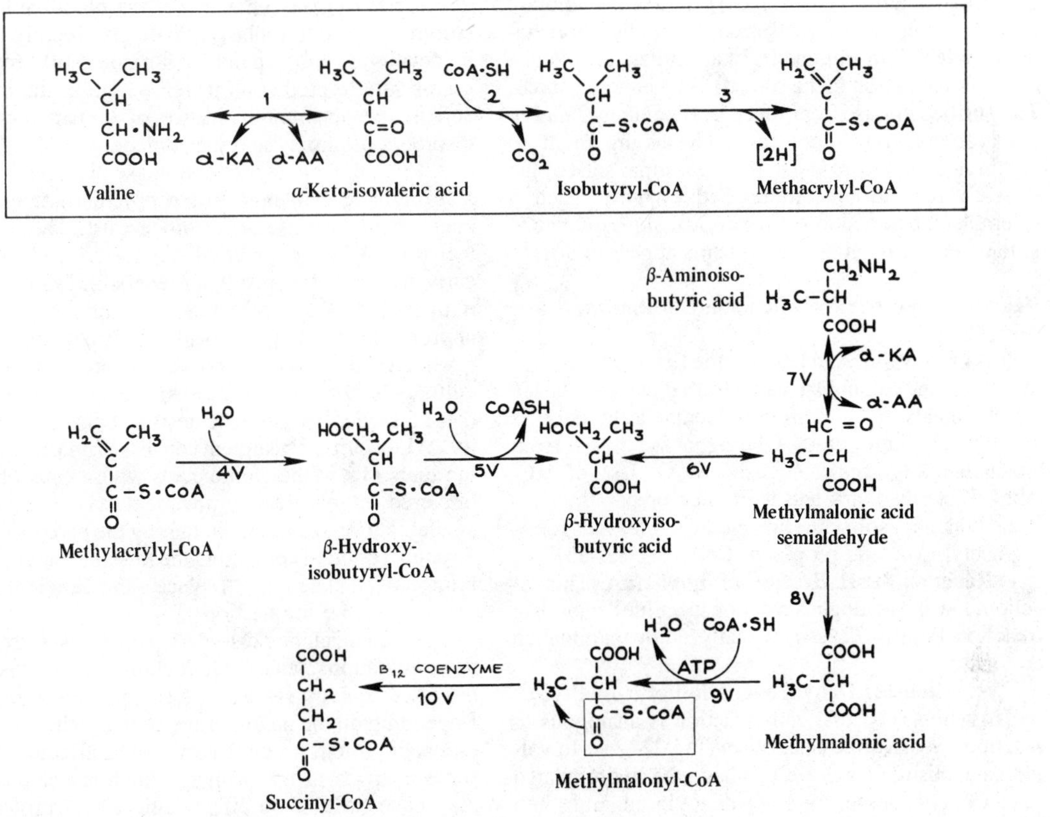

Figure 22–24. Catabolism of valine. Reactions 1–3 in the box are common to all 3 branched amino acids, and analogous intermediates are formed. The numbered reactions correspond to those of Fig 22–22. Reactions 4V through 10V are specific to valine catabolism. (α-KA = α-keto acid; α-AA = α-amino acid.)

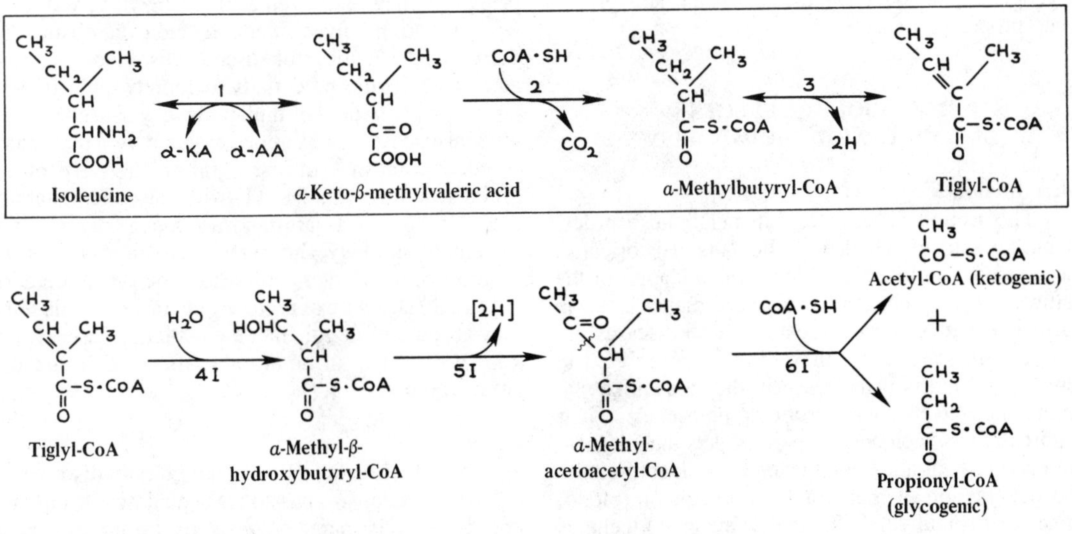

Figure 22–25. Catabolism of L-isoleucine. Reactions 1–3 in the box are common to all 3 branched amino acids, and analogous intermediates are formed. The numbered reactions correspond to those of Fig 22–22. Reactions 4I, 5I, and 6I are specific to isoleucine catabolism. (α-KA = α-keto acid; α-AA = α-amino acid.)

25). In cobalamin (vitamin B_{12}) deficiency, mutase activity is impaired. This produces a "dietary metabolic defect" in ruminants that utilize propionate (from fermentation in the rumen) as an energy source. The purified mutase from sheep liver contains 2 mol of deoxyadenosyl-B_{12} per mole. Rearrangement to succinyl-CoA occurs via an intramolecular shift of the CoA-carboxyl group. Although the overall reaction resembles isomerization of threo-β-methylaspartate to glutamate, the reaction mechanisms appear to differ.

Reactions Specific to Isoleucine Catabolism
(Fig 22–25.)

As with valine and leucine, the first data concerning isoleucine catabolism came from dietary studies in intact animals that identified isoleucine as glycogenic and weakly ketogenic. Glycogen synthesis from isoleucine was confirmed using D_2O. Use of ^{14}C-labeled intermediates and liver slice preparations revealed that the isoleucine skeleton was cleaved, forming acetyl-CoA and propionyl-CoA (Fig 22–25).

Reaction 4I: Hydration of tiglyl-CoA. This reaction, like the analogous reaction in valine catabolism (reaction 4V, Fig 22–24), is catalyzed by mammalian crotonase.

Reaction 5I: Dehydrogenation of α-methyl-β-hydroxybutyryl-CoA. This reaction is analogous to reaction 5V of valine catabolism (Fig 22–24). In valine catabolism, it will be recalled, the hydroxylated acyl-CoA thioester is first deacylated and then oxidized.

Reaction 6I: Thiolysis of α-methylaceto-acetyl-CoA. Thiolytic cleavage of the covalent bond linking carbons 2 and 3 of α-methylacetoacetyl-CoA resembles thiolysis of acetoacetyl-CoA to 2 mols of acetyl-CoA catalyzed by β-ketothiolase. The products, acetyl-CoA (ketogenic) and propionyl-CoA (glycogenic), account for the ketogenic and glycogenic properties of isoleucine.

METABOLIC DEFECTS IN AMINO ACID METABOLISM

Introduction

This section discusses certain metabolic disorders of amino acid metabolism in humans. Historically, these disorders played key roles in elucidation of the pathways by which amino acids are metabolized in normal human subjects. Most of these diseases are rare, and in some cases they have been reported in fewer than 6 individuals. As such, they are unlikely to be encountered by most practicing physicians. Their apparently low incidence in part reflects the absence, until recently, of automated technics for identification and quantitation of individual amino acids in blood, urine, and spinal fluid. Recently developed technics for screening the blood and urine of large populations for abnormal amino acids or for abnormal levels of common amino acids may lead to more frequent recognition of these disorders. Technics have also been developed to assay enzymes in the blood cells or in cultures of skin fibroblasts of patients. Technics yet to be developed will expand the horizons still further. It seems safe to predict an increase both in the number and in the apparent incidence of human metabolic disorders of amino acid metabolism.

Even though uncommon, these disorders present a formidable challenge to the psychiatrist, pediatrician, genetic counselor, or biochemist. They are detected most frequently at infancy, often are fatal at an early age, and often result in irreversible brain damage if untreated. Early detection and rapid initiation of appropriate treatment, if available, is essential. Since several of the enzymes concerned are detectable in cultures of amniotic fluid cells, prenatal diagnosis of these disorders by amniocentesis is a distinct possibility. While current treatment consists primarily of feeding diets low in the amino acids whose catabolism is impaired, more effective treatment may some day be available. For example, circulating the patient's blood through a column containing the missing enzyme in an immobilized state may "replace" the deficient or defective enzyme in question.

These metabolic disorders, which result from genetic mutations, cause production of proteins with modified primary structures (see Chapters 4 and 29). Depending on the nature of the primary change, other orders of protein structure may also be affected. While some changes in the primary structures of enzymes may have little or no effect, others may profoundly modify the 3-dimensional structure of catalytic or regulatory sites (see Chapters 5 and 6). The modified or mutant enzyme may possess altered catalytic efficiency (low V_{max} or high K_m) or altered ability to bind an allosteric regulator of its catalytic activity. Since most proteins contain over 100 amino acid residues, there are a great number of possible alterations in the primary structure of even a single enzyme, and many enzymes are involved in amino acid catabolism. Predictably, the number of discrete disorders of amino acid catabolism is potentially extremely high. In principle, a wide variety of mutations may cause the same clinical disease. For example, any mutation that causes a substantial loss of the catalytic activity of argininosuccinase (Fig 21–11) will cause the metabolic disorder known as argininosuccinic acidemia. It is extremely unlikely, however, that all cases of argininosuccinic acidemia represent the same alteration in primary structure of argininosuccinase. In this sense they are, therefore, distinct molecular diseases. Some known disorders of amino acid metabolism are discussed below.

Glycine

A. Glycinuria: Glycinuria, a rare disorder of glycine metabolism, has so far been described in only one family. It is characterized by excess urinary excretion of glycine (glycinuria) in association with a tendency to formation of oxalate renal stones, although the amount of oxalate excreted in the urine is normal. Glycinuria appears to be inherited as a dominant, possibly X-linked, trait. The plasma content of glycine is normal in the glycinuric patients that have been studied while the urinary excretion of glycine ranges from 600–1000 mg/d. Consequently, glycinuria is attributed to a defect in renal tubular transport of glycine whereby decreased reabsorption of glycine by the renal tubule permits the amino acid to escape into the urine in greatly increased amounts.

B. Primary Hyperoxaluria: Primary hyperoxaluria is a metabolic disease characterized biochemically by continuous high urinary excretion of oxalate unrelated to dietary intake of oxalate. The history of the disease is that of progressive bilateral calcium oxalate urolithiasis, nephrocalcinosis, and recurrent infection of the urinary tract. Death occurs in childhood or early adult life from renal failure or hypertension. The excess oxalate is apparently of endogenous origin, possibly from glycine, which may be deaminated to form glyoxylate, a precursor of oxalate. The metabolic defect is considered to be a disorder of glyoxylate metabolism associated with failure to convert glyoxylate to formate or to glycine by transamination. As a result, the excess glyoxylate is oxidized to oxalate. Glycine transaminase deficiency, together with some impairment of oxidation of glyoxylate to formate, may be the biochemical explanation for the inherited metabolic disease primary hyperoxaluria.

As might be expected, vitamin B_6–deficient animals (rats) excrete markedly increased quantities of oxalate because the glutamic- or alanine-glyoxylic transaminase reactions are vitamin B_6–dependent. Excretion of oxalate in B_6-deficient rats is enhanced by feeding glycine or vitamin B_6 antagonists. However, administration of vitamin B_6 has not been of benefit in clinical cases of endogenous hyperoxaluria.

Phenylalanine

Phenylketonuria is an inherited disorder of phenylalanine metabolism with a frequency of about one in 10,000 births. The disorder is biochemically attributable to absence of activity of a functional component I of phenylalanine hydroxylase (see Chapter 20). The patient is therefore unable to convert phenylalanine to tyrosine and, as a result, alternative catabolites of phenylalanine are produced (Fig 22–26); these include phenylpyruvic acid, the product of deamination of phenylalanine; phenyllactic acid, the reduction product of phenylpyruvic acid; and phenylacetic acid, produced by decarboxylation and

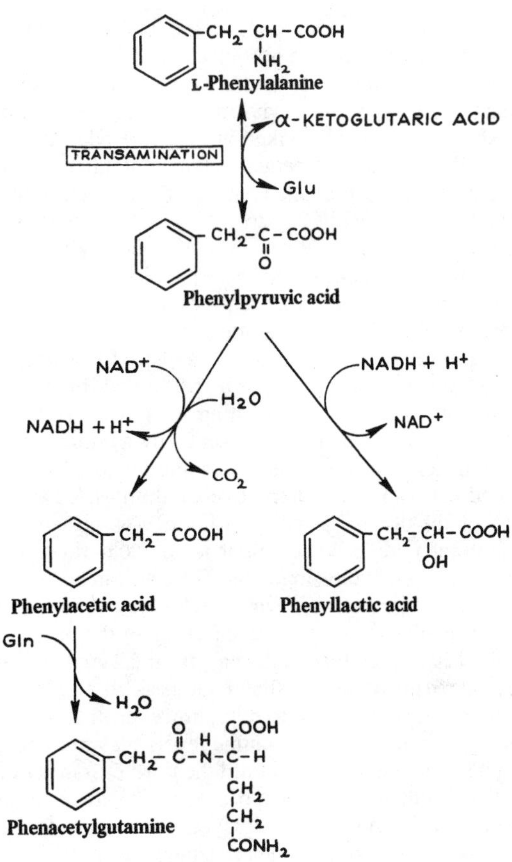

Figure 22–26. Alternative pathways of phenylalanine catabolism of particular importance in phenylketonuria. The reactions shown also occur in the liver tissue of normal individuals but are of minor significance if a functional phenylalanine hydroxylase is present. (Glu = glutamate; Gln = glutamine.)

oxidation of phenylpyruvic acid. Much of the phenylacetate is conjugated in the liver with glutamine and excreted in the urine as the conjugate, phenylacetylglutamine. Table 22–2 illustrates the chemical pattern in the blood and urine of a phenylketonuric patient. The presence in urine of the keto acid phenylpyruvate gives the disease its name—phenylketonuria.

In infants and children with this metabolic defect,

Table 22–2. Metabolites of phenylalanine accumulating in the plasma and urine of phenylketonuric patients.

Metabolite	Plasma (mg/dL)		Urine (mg/dL)	
	Normal	Phenylketonuric	Normal	Phenylketonuric
Phenylalanine	1–2	15–63	30	300–1000
Phenylpyruvate		0.3–1.8		300–2000
Phenyllactate				290–550
Phenylacetate				Increased
Phenylacetylglutamine			200–300	2400

retarded mental development occurs for unknown reasons. In the absence of a normal catabolic pathway for phenylalanine, several reactions of otherwise minor quantitative importance in normal liver assume a major catabolic role. In phenylketonurics, phenylpyruvate, phenyllactate, phenylacetate, and its glutamine conjugate phenacetylglutamine are formed and occur in the blood and urine (Fig 22–26). Although phenylpyruvate, present in the urine of most phenylketonuric patients, can be detected by a simple biochemical spot test, definitive diagnosis requires determination of elevated plasma phenylalanine levels.

Further deterioration of mental performance of phenylketonuric children can be prevented if they are maintained on a diet containing very low levels of phenylalanine. This is accompanied by a return to the normal range of blood phenylalanine levels and a reduced excretion of "alternative catabolites." Detection of the disease as early in infancy as possible is important if dietary treatment is to yield favorable results in mental development. The diet can be terminated at 6 years of age, when high concentrations of phenylalanine no longer are injurious to the brain.

Plasma phenylalanine may be measured by an automated micro method that requires as little as $20\ \mu L$ of blood. It is important to note, however, that abnormally high blood phenylalanine levels may not occur in phenylketonuric infants until the third or fourth day of life. Furthermore, false positive tests may occur in premature infants due to delayed maturation of the enzymes required for phenylalanine catabolism. A useful but less reliable screening test depends on detecting elevated urinary levels of phenylpyruvate with ferric chloride.

Administration of phenylalanine to a phenylketonuric subject should result in prolonged elevation of the level of this amino acid in the blood, ie, diminished tolerance to phenylalanine. However, abnormally low tolerance to injected phenylalanine and a high fasting level of phenylalanine are also characteristic of the parents of phenylketonurics. Evidently the recessive gene responsible for phenylketonuria can be detected biochemically in the phenotypically normal parents.

Tyrosine

Several metabolic disorders of tyrosine catabolism are characterized by excretion of tyrosine and of tyrosine catabolites in urine. Tyrosinosis, reported thus far in only one patient, is of limited clinical interest. Its significance lies in the information it provides on normal pathways of tyrosine catabolism in human liver. A range of familial disorders of tyrosine catabolism with associated cirrhosis and defective renal tubular reabsorption is reported under the descriptions of hereditary tyrosinemia, atypical tyrosinosis, genuine tyrosyluria, or tyrosinemia. While these appear to be familial disorders, the relationship between them is not clear at present. There is doubt that, despite the clinical findings, all represent true metabolic defects of tyrosine catabolism.

A. Tyrosinosis: The enzymic defect is probably the absence either of hepatic **p-hydroxyphenylpyruvate hydroxylase** or of **tyrosine transaminase** (Fig 22–12). The patient described as afflicted with tyrosinosis excreted large quantities (1.5–3 g/d) of tyrosine in the urine. On a diet rich in tyrosine, other p-hydroxyphenyl acids, including 3,4-dihydroxyphenylalanine (dopa) (see Chapter 20) and p-hydroxyphenyllactic acid, were also excreted.

B. Tyrosinemia: Over 100 cases in which plasma tyrosine levels are elevated far above normal have been reported. While these may represent a spectrum of metabolic defects, the common clinical findings include hepatosplenomegaly, nodular cirrhosis of the liver, abnormalities of tyrosine and methionine metabolism, p-hydroxyphenyllactic aciduria, multiple defects in renal tubular reabsorption, rickets, hyperphosphaturia and proteinuria, and aminoaciduria. While the enzyme defect appears to be hereditary, its exact nature is unknown. Treatment with a diet low in tyrosine and phenylalanine improves renal function and possibly also retards degenerative liver changes.

C. Alkaptonuria: This inherited metabolic disorder, noted in medical literature as early as the 16th century, was characterized in 1859. The disease is of considerable historic interest because it formed the basis for Garrod's ideas concerning heritable metabolic disorders. Its most striking clinical manifestation is the occurrence of dark urine on standing in air. Late in the disease there occur generalized pigmentation of connective tissues (ochronosis) and a form of arthritis. The metabolic defect is attributable to lack of **homogentisate oxidase** (Fig 22–12). The substrate, homogentisate, is excreted in the urine, where it is oxidized in air to a brownish-black pigment. Over 600 cases have been reported; the estimated incidence of alkaptonuria is 2–5 per million live births.

Histidine

A. Histidinemia: Histidinemia is an inherited disorder of histidine metabolism. In addition to increased levels of histidine in blood and urine, there is also increased excretion of imidazolepyruvic acid (which in a color test with ferric chloride may be mistaken for phenylpyruvic acid, so that a mistaken diagnosis of phenylketonuria could be made). Speech development may be retarded. The metabolic block in histidinemia is considered to be inadequate activity of liver histidase, which would impair conversion of histidine to urocanic acid. The alternative route of histidine metabolism, transamination to imidazolepyruvic acid, would then be favored and the excess imidazolepyruvic acid would be excreted in the urine. Imidazoleacetic acid and imidazolelactic acid, the reduction products of imidazolepyruvic acid, have also been detected in the urine of histidinemic patients.

The quantity of histidine in normal urine is relatively large. For this reason it is be more readily detected than most amino acids. A conspicuous increase in histidine excretion is a characteristic finding in normal pregnancy but does not occur in toxemic states associated with pregnancy. The normally increased excretion of histidine during pregnancy apparently does not result from a metabolic defect in histidine metabolism. The phenomenon may be explained largely on the basis of the changes in renal function characteristic of normal pregnancy as well as the pregnancy toxemias. Furthermore, the alterations in amino acid excretion during pregnancy are not confined to histidine.

B. Imidazole Aminoaciduria: Three families (5 patients) with cerebromacular degeneration have been found to have a generalized imidazole aminoaciduria. Some other members of the immediate family also exhibited a generalized imidazole aminoaciduria. The patients excreted large amounts of carnosine, anserine, histidine, and 1-methylhistidine. In normal urine, excretion of carnosine and of anserine is 2–3 mg/d and 5–7 mg/d, respectively; in these patients, 20–100 mg/d were excreted. The patients also had a greatly increased urinary content of histidine and of 1-methylhistidine. The parents and unaffected siblings had urinary biochemical abnormalities similar to those of the patients but without symptoms of neurologic and retinal disease (cerebral degeneration and blindness). The imidazoluria appears to be genetically transmitted as a dominant trait and the cerebromacular degeneration as a recessive trait. The fact that the 2 traits have been found in 3 unrelated families suggests that both traits are manifestations of the same gene. The disease resembles biochemically the findings in Hartnup's disease, a disorder of tryptophan metabolism (below), in that both diseases are characterized by defects in transport: one for the imidazoles and the other (Hartnup's disease) for the indoles.

Proline & Hydroxyproline

Defects in proline or hydroxyproline catabolism are extremely rare (2 and 3 patients, respectively). All were afflicted with severe mental retardation. Diets restricted in proline and hydroxyproline appear to be of dubious therapeutic benefit.

A. Prolinemia: This heritable disorder is characterized by elevated plasma proline levels and by the urinary excretion of large quantities of proline, hydroxyproline, and serine. Two distinct types appear to exist. Type I appears to reflect a deficiency of **proline hydroxylase;** type II, a lack of an enzyme concerned with further catabolism of Δ^1-pyrroline-5-carboxylate (Fig 22–3).

B. Hydroxyprolinemia: This rare heritable disorder probably reflects the absence of the enzyme catalyzing conversion of 4-hydroxy-L-proline to -boxylate (Fig 27–11). As such, it represents an enzyme deletion analogous to type I prolinemia. Clinical findings include severe mental retardation, elevated plasma hydroxyproline levels, and urinary excretion of abnormal quantities of hydroxyproline and hydroxyprolyl peptides.

Lysine

Two rare metabolic abnormalities of lysine catabolism are known:

A. Hyperlysinemia With Associated Hyperammonemia: Only a single case has been reported. The exact metabolic defect is not known. The hyperammonemia does not reflect a defect in any of the enzymes of urea synthesis.

B. Persistent Hyperlysinemia: In this rare disorder (7 reported cases), plasma lysine levels are significantly (but not greatly) elevated. Hyperammonemia does not occur even after a test dose of lysine. In one case, elevated plasma levels of saccharopine, a catabolite of L-lysine (Fig 22–15), were reported. No consistent mental retardation is associated with this disease.

Sulfur-Containing Amino Acids

A. Cystinuria (Cystine-Lysinuria): In this inherited metabolic disease, urinary excretion of cystine is 20–30 times normal. Excretion of lysine, arginine, and ornithine is also markedly increased. Cystinuria is considered to be due to a renal transport defect. The greatly increased excretion of lysine, arginine, and ornithine as well as cystine in urine of cystinuric patients suggests a defect in the renal reabsorptive mechanisms for these 4 amino acids. It is possible that a single reabsorptive site is involved. Thus, as far as renal mechanisms are concerned, cystinuria is not an uncomplicated defect which affects only cystine; the term "cystinuria" is therefore actually a misnomer. Cystine-lysinuria may now be the preferred descriptive term for this disease.

Because cystine is relatively insoluble, in cystinuric patients it may precipitate in the kidney tubules and form cystine calculi. This may be a major complication of the disease. Were it not for this possibility, cystinuria would be an entirely benign anomaly and probably would escape recognition in many cases.

Although cystine is the principal sulfur-containing amino acid in the urine of cystinuric patients, another sulfur-containing amino acid has also been detected in significant quantities. This is a mixed disulfide of L-cysteine and L-homocysteine (Fig 22–27). This compound is somewhat more soluble than cystine. To the extent that it may be formed at the expense of cystine, it therefore reduces the tendency to formation of cystine crystals and calculi in the urine.

There may also be an intestinal transport defect for these amino acids. A failure in concentration of cystine and lysine in cells of the jejunal mucosa obtained by biopsy of the jejunal area of the intestine of

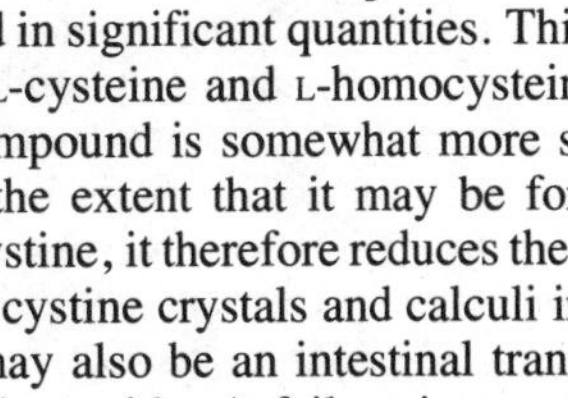

$$
\begin{array}{cc}
\mathrm{CH_2\!-\!S\!-\!S\!-\!CH_2} \\
\mathrm{\underset{\displaystyle COOH}{\overset{\displaystyle HCNH_2}{|}}} \quad \mathrm{\underset{\displaystyle \underset{\displaystyle COOH}{HCNH_2}}{\overset{\displaystyle CH_2}{|}}}
\end{array}
$$

(Cysteine)   (Homocysteine)

Figure 22–27. Mixed disulfide of cysteine and homocysteine.

cystinuric patients has been detected. In an investigation of the transport of the affected amino acids in cystinuria into kidney slices obtained by biopsy from normal and cystinuric patients, lysine and arginine transport was defective in the cystinuric tissue but cystine transport was normal. The above experiments suggest that some revision of the present concepts of the etiology of cystinuria may be required.

B. Cystinosis (Cystine Storage Disease): Cystinuria is different from cystinosis. In the latter disease, which is also inherited, cystine crystals are deposited in many tissues and organs (particularly the reticuloendothelial system) throughout the body. It is usually accompanied by a generalized aminoaciduria in which all amino acids are considerably increased in the urine. Various other renal functions are also seriously impaired, and these patients usually die at an early age with all of the manifestations of acute renal failure. On the other hand, except for the likelihood of the formation of cystine calculi, cystinuria is compatible with a normal existence.

C. Homocystinuria: The incidence of this heritable defect of methionine catabolism is estimated at one in 160,000 births. Homocystine (up to 300 mg/d), together with S-adenosylmethionine in some cases, is excreted in the urine, and plasma methionine levels are elevated. Associated clinical findings include the occurrence of thromboses, osteoporosis, dislocated lenses in the eyes, and frequently mental retardation. Two forms of the disease are known: a vitamin B_6–responsive form and a vitamin B_6–unresponsive form. Feeding a diet low in methionine and high in cystine effectively prevents pathologic changes if initiated early in life. The disease reflects impaired activity of **cystathionine synthetase** (Fig 22–19).

Branched Chain Amino Acids (Leucine, Valine, Isoleucine)

Four defects in branched chain amino acid catabolism are known. Of these, maple syrup urine disease has been most extensively studied. Over 50 cases have been reported. The incidence of the disease has been estimated as 5–10 per million live births. Hypervalinemia, intermittent branched chain ketonuria, and isovaleric acidemia have been reported in only 1, 3, and 4 children, respectively.

A. Hypervalinemia: This metabolic disease, characterized by elevated plasma levels of valine (but not of leucine or isoleucine), reflects the inability to transaminate valine to α-ketoisovalerate (reaction 1, Fig 22–24). However, transamination of leucine and isoleucine (reaction 1, Figs 22–23 and 22–25) is unimpaired. (See Table 22–3.) In the one known instance of hypervalinemia, feeding a diet low in valine prevented vomiting, improved weight gain, and reduced hyperkinesia.

B. Maple Syrup Urine Disease: As the name implies, the most striking feature of this hereditary disease is the characteristic odor of the urine, which resembles that of maple syrup or burnt sugar. In afflicted individuals, plasma and urinary levels of the

Table 22–3. Ability of leukocytes from a patient with hypervalinemia and of leukocytes from 2 normal individuals to catalyze transamination of branched chain amino acids.*

Amino Acid	Relative Rate of Transamination	
	Hypervalinemia	Control (Range)
Valine	0	70–135
Isoleucine	346	220–270
Leucine	387	140–185

*From Dancis & others: *Pediatrics* 1967;**39**:813.

branched chain amino acids leucine, isoleucine, and valine and their corresponding α-keto acids (Figs 22–23, 22–24, and 22–25) are greatly elevated (Table 22–4). For this reason, the disease has also been termed **branched chain ketonuria.** Smaller quantities of branched chain α-hydroxy acids, formed by reduction of the α-keto acids, also are present in the urine.

Although the afflicted newborn infant initially appears normal, characteristic signs of the disease are evident by the end of the first week of extrauterine life. In addition to the biochemical abnormalities described above, the infant is difficult to feed and may vomit. The patient may also exhibit lethargy. Diagnosis prior to 1 week of age is possible only by enzymic analysis. Extensive brain damage occurs in surviving children. Without treatment, death usually occurs by the end of the first year of life.

The biochemical defect is the absence or greatly reduced activity of the α-**keto acid decarboxylase** which catalyzes conversion of all 3 branched chain α-keto acids to CO_2 plus acyl-CoA thioesters (reaction 2, Figs 22–23, 22–24, and 22–25). This was established by enzymic analysis of leukocytes and of cultured skin fibroblasts from afflicted children. The mechanism of toxicity, which is probably complex, is unknown. Possible factors in toxicity include the ability of large excesses of the branched chain amino acids to impair transport of other amino acids, to alter amino acid pool sizes, and thus, possibly, to impair protein synthesis. All 3 branched chain α-keto acids also are competitive inhibitors of L-glutamate dehydrogenase activity (Fig 21–6).

Early diagnosis is very important, so that the patient can be placed on a diet in which protein is replaced by a mixture of purified amino acids from which leucine, isoleucine, and valine are omitted. When plasma levels of these amino acids fall within the normal range, they are restored to the diet in the

Table 22–4. Plasma levels of branched chain amino acids in normal individuals and in 3 patients with maple syrup urine disease.

Amino Acid	Concentration (mg/dL)			
	Normal (Range)	Maple Syrup Urine Disease, Patient		
		A	B	C
Leucine	1.5–3.0	52	14	21
Valine	2.0–3.0	24	13	14
Isoleucine	0.8–1.5	18	2.2	8.5

form of milk and other foods in amounts adequate to supply—but not to exceed—the requirements for branched chain amino acids. There is no indication when, if ever, dietary restrictions may be eased. One fatality occurred as late as age 8. In those cases where treatment was initiated in the first week of life, considerable success was achieved in mitigating the dire consequences of the disease.

C. Intermittent Branched Chain Ketonuria: This disease, a variant of maple syrup urine disease, probably reflects a less severe structural modification of the α-**keto acid decarboxylase.** The decarboxylase activity of leukocytes and of fibroblasts, while distinctly lower than that of normal individuals, is well above those characteristic of classic maple syrup urine disease. Since these individuals appear to possess an impaired but nevertheless distinct capability for catabolism of leucine, valine, and isoleucine, it is perhaps understandable that the typical symptoms of maple syrup urine disease occur later in life and only intermittently. The prognosis for successful use of dietary therapy would appear to be far more favorable in these individuals.

Taken together, maple syrup urine disease and intermittent branched chain ketonuria appear to illustrate the situation described in the introduction to this section—mutations causing different changes in the primary structure of the same enzyme. It is probable that a spectrum of activities ranging from frank disease through intermittent manifestations to normal values in fact occurs in individual subjects.

D. Isovaleric Acidemia: Relevant findings include a persistent "cheesy" odor of the breath and body fluids, vomiting, acidosis, and coma precipitated by excessive ingestion of protein, or by an episode of infectious disease. Mild mental retardation was associated with the 3 known cases. The impaired enzyme is **isovaleryl-CoA dehydrogenase** (reaction 3, Fig 22–23). Isovaleryl-CoA thus accumulates, is hydrolyzed to isovalerate, and is excreted in the urine and sweat.

Tryptophan

Hartnup's disease, a hereditary abnormality in metabolism of tryptophan, is characterized by a pellagra-like skin rash, intermittent cerebellar ataxia, and mental deterioration. The urine of patients with Hartnup's disease contains greatly increased amounts of indoleacetic acid (α-N[indole-3-acetyl]glutamine) and tryptophan.

The indole acids of human urine have been studied by paper chromatography. A total of 38 different indole acids were chromatographed. The most strikingly "abnormal" patterns of indole acid excretion were found in the urine of severely mentally retarded patients and in urine from the mentally ill. The significance of these findings has been questioned insofar as the causes of mental disease were concerned,

particularly since the urinary excretion patterns tended to revert to normal after administration of broad-spectrum antibiotics.

Defects of Propionate, Methylmalonate, & Vitamin B$_{12}$ Metabolism

Propionyl-CoA is formed from isoleucine (Fig 22–25) and methionine (Figs 22–18 and 22–20), as well as from the side chain of cholesterol and from fatty acids with odd numbers of carbon atoms. The conversion of propionyl-CoA to amphibolic intermediates involves biotin-dependent carboxylation to methylmalonyl-CoA. Methylmalonyl-CoA also is formed directly (ie, without prior formation of propionyl-CoA) from valine (Figs 22–18 and 22–24, reaction 9V). A vitamin B$_{12}$ coenzyme-dependent isomerization converts malonyl-CoA to succinyl-CoA, a citric acid cycle intermediate, which is oxidized to CO_2 and water.

Shortly after the discovery that 5'-deoxyadenosylcobalamin is a cofactor for the isomerization of methylmalonyl-CoA to succinyl-CoA, patients with acquired vitamin B$_{12}$ deficiency were observed to excrete large quantities of methylmalonate in their urine. This methylmalonic aciduria disappeared when sufficient vitamin B$_{12}$ was administered. Recently, a number of instances involving seriously ill children have been reported. In all of these cases, the patients appear to be afflicted with similar defects in propionate or methylmalonyl-CoA metabolism.

A. Propionic Acidemia: Propionyl-CoA carboxylase deficiency is characterized by high serum propionate levels and by defective catabolism of propionate by leukocytes. Treatment involves feeding a low-protein diet and measures to counteract metabolic acidosis.

B. Methylmalonic Aciduria: Two forms of methylmalonic aciduria are known. One responds to parenteral administration of physiologic doses of vitamin B$_{12}$; the other does not. A patient with this latter condition responded favorably to massive (pharmacologic) doses (1 g/d) of vitamin B$_{12}$. Cultured fibroblasts from this patient grown in media containing 25 pg of vitamin B$_{12}$ per mL oxidized ^{14}C-propionate poorly. The cultured cells contained only about 10% as much 5'-deoxyadenosylcobalamin as did control cells. When the concentration of vitamin B$_{12}$ in the medium was increased 10,000-fold, the rate of propionate oxidation and the intracellular concentration of 5'-deoxyadenosylcobalamin both approached normal. No defect in binding the coenzyme to the mutase apoenzyme was observed. The defect in the latter form of methylmalonic aciduria thus appears to be the inability to form 5'-deoxyadenosylcobalamin from normal levels of the vitamin.

The above selection of inherited diseases of amino acid catabolism is generally confined to the adequately studied diseases now known.

• • •

References

Conversion of the Carbon Skeletons of the Common Amino Acids to Amphibolic Intermediates

Felig P: Amino acid metabolism in man. *Annu Rev Biochem* 1975;**44**:933.

Greenberg DM, Rodwell VW: Carbon catabolism of amino acids. Pages 95 and 191 in: *Metabolic Pathways*. Vol 3. Greenberg DM (editor). Academic Press, 1969.

Meister A: *Biochemistry of the Amino Acids,* 2nd ed. Vol 2. Academic Press, 1965.

Metabolic Defects in Amino Acid Metabolism

Bremer HJ & others: *Amino Acid Metabolism: Clinical Chemistry and Diagnosis*. Urban & Schwarzenberg, 1981.

Frimter GW: Aminoacidurias due to disorders of metabolism. (2 parts.) *N Engl J Med* 1973;**289**:835, 895.

Morris DR, Fillingame RH: Regulation of amino acid decarboxylation. *Annu Rev Biochem* 1974;**43**:303.

Motulsky AG: Brave new world? *Science* 1974;**185**:653.

Nyhan WL (editor): *Heritable Disorders of Amino Acid Metabolism. Patterns of Clinical Expression and Genetic Variation*. Wiley, 1974.

Schwarz V: *A Clinical Companion to Biochemical Studies*. Freeman, 1978.

Shih VE: *Laboratory Techniques for the Detection of Hereditary Metabolic Disorders*. CRC Press, 1973.

Stanbury JB, Wyngaarden JB, Fredrickson DS (editors): *The Metabolic Basis of Inherited Disease,* 4th ed. McGraw-Hill, 1978.

Conversion of Amino Acids to Specialized Products | 23

Victor W. Rodwell, PhD

This chapter considers conversion of the carbon skeletons of amino acids, of amino acids of themselves, or of portions of their structures to products of biochemical interest. Since most of these products are not amino acids, the discussion merges with metabolic pathways discussed elsewhere in this book.

GLYCINE

Synthesis of Heme

The α-carbon and nitrogen atoms of glycine are used for synthesis of the porphyrin moiety of hemoglobin (see Chapter 24). The pyrrole nitrogen is derived from glycine nitrogen and an adjoining carbon from the α-carbon of glycine. The α-carbon is also the source of the methylene bridge atoms linking the pyrrole rings.

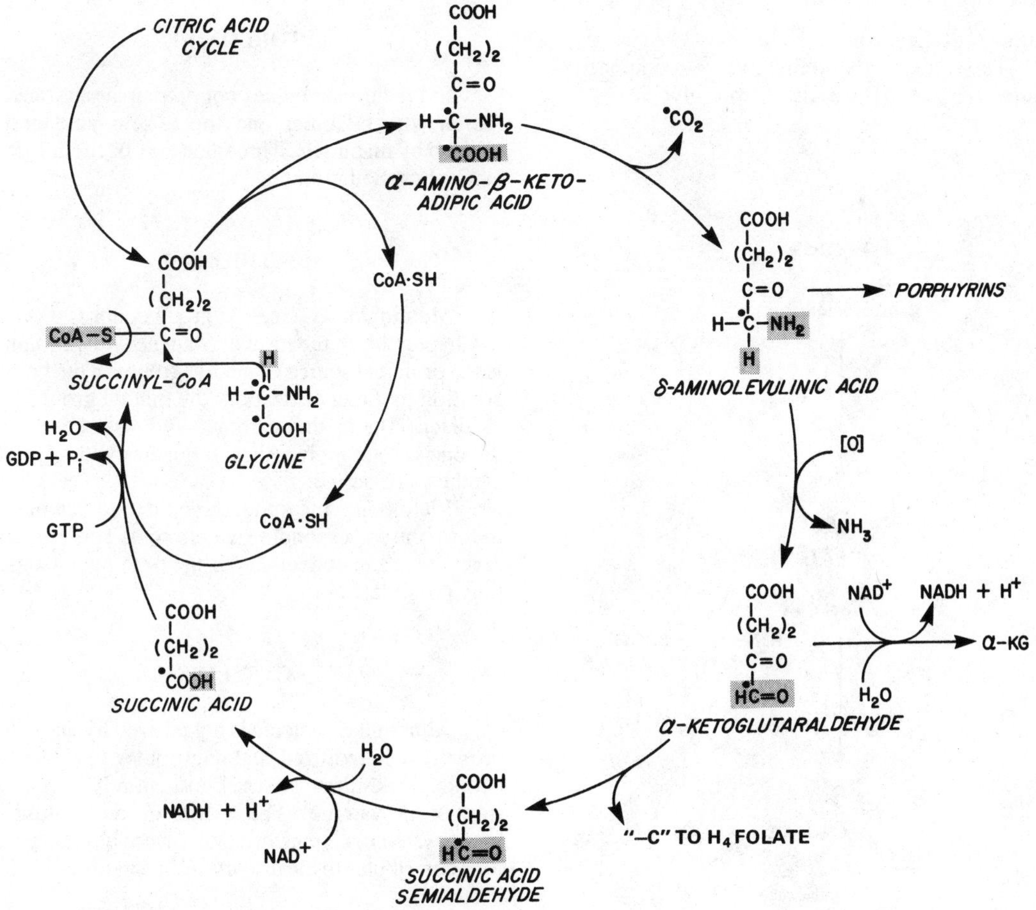

Figure 23–1. The succinate-glycine cycle.

In the **"succinate-glycine cycle"** (Fig 23–1), succinyl-CoA condenses on the α-carbon atom of glycine to form α-amino-β-ketoadipic acid. This links glycine metabolism to the citric acid cycle, which provides succinyl-CoA. α-Amino-β-ketoadipic acid is decarboxylated to δ-aminolevulinic acid, a precursor for porphyrin synthesis. Succinate and α-ketoglutarate (α-KG), which may return to the citric acid cycle, are also formed.

Synthesis of Purines

The entire glycine molecule is utilized to form positions 4, 5, and 7 of the purine skeleton. (See Chapter 26.)

Synthesis of Glutathione

Glycine is a precursor of the glycine tripeptide glutathione.

Conjugation

Glycine conjugates with cholic acid, forming glycocholic acid (see Chapter 38). With benzoic acid, it forms hippuric acid (Fig 23–2). The quantitative ability of liver to convert a measured dose of benzoic acid to hippuric acid was formerly used as a test of liver function.

Synthesis of Creatine

The sarcosine (N-methylglycine) component of creatine (Fig 23–7) is derived from glycine.

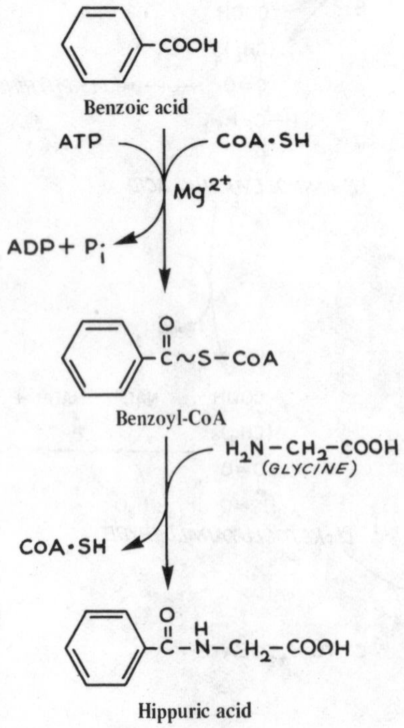

Figure 23–2. Formation of hippuric acid.

ALANINE

Alanine, together with glycine, makes up a considerable fraction of the amino nitrogen in human plasma. Both D- and L-alanine are utilized by tissues, but at differing rates. Alanine is a major component of bacterial cell walls, partly as the D-isomer: 39–50% in *Streptococcus faecalis;* 67% in *Staphylococcus aureus.*

β-Alanine is a constituent of pantothenic acid (see Chapter 9) and an end product in catabolism of the pyrimidines cytosine and uracil (see Chapter 26). In rats, β-alanine is degraded to acetate.

SERINE

Much of the serine in phosphoproteins is present as O-phosphoserine.

Serine is involved in synthesis of sphingosine. (See Chapter 17.)

Serine participates in purine and pyrimidine synthesis. The β-carbon is a source of the methyl groups of thymine (and of choline) and of the carbon in positions 2 and 8 of the purine nucleus. (See Chapters 9 and 26.)

THREONINE

Since threonine does not participate in transamination, the D-isomer and the α-keto acid are not utilized by mammals. Threonine may occur in proteins as O-phosphothreonine.

METHIONINE

Methionine as a methyl group donor is discussed in Chapter 22. In the form of S-adenosylmethionine, it is the principal source of methyl groups in the body. In addition to direct utilization, the methyl group is also oxidized. The methyl carbon may be used to produce the one-carbon moiety that conjugates with glycine in synthesis of serine.

Methionine may undergo oxidative deamination to form the corresponding α-keto acid. This reaction is reversible, and conversion of the D- to the L-isomer is thus possible.

CYSTEINE

Although D-cysteine is not utilized by animals for growth, it is oxidized and contributes to the urinary sulfate. This sulfate arises almost entirely from oxidation of L-cysteine. The sulfur of methionine (as homocysteine) is transferred to serine (Fig 20–11) and thus contributes to the urinary sulfate indirectly (ie, via cysteine).

L-Cysteine is utilized for synthesis of coenzyme A (see Chapter 9), where it serves as a precursor of the

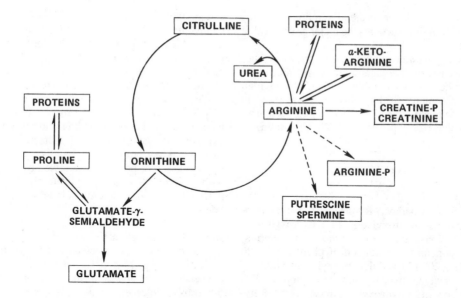

Figure 23–3. Arginine, ornithine, and proline metabolism. Reactions with solid arrows all occur in mammalian tissues. Putrescine and spermine synthesis occurs in *Escherichia coli*, a normal enteric bacterium. Arginine phosphate occurs in invertebrate muscle, where it functions as a phosphagen analogous to creatine phosphate in mammalian tissues.

thioethanolamine portion. Cysteine is also a precursor of the taurine that conjugates with bile acids, forming taurocholic acid, etc (see Chapter 38).

ARGININE

Arginine serves as a formamidine donor for creatine synthesis in primates (Fig 23–7) and for streptomycin synthesis in *Streptomyces*. Other fates include conversion to putrescine, agmatine, spermine, and spermidine by enteric bacteria (Fig 23–3) and synthesis of arginine phosphate (functionally analogous to creatine phosphate) in invertebrate muscle. Bacteria typically convert large quantities of arginine to spermine and spermidine (Fig 23–3).

HISTIDINE

Histamine is derived from histidine by decarboxylation, a reaction catalyzed in mammalian tissues by an **aromatic L-amino acid decarboxylase.** This enzyme will also catalyze decarboxylation of dopa, 5-hydroxytryptophan, phenylalanine, tyrosine, and tryptophan (see below). The decarboxylase is inhibited by α-methyl amino acids in vitro and in vivo which thus have clinical application as antihypertensive agents. In addition to the aromatic amino acid decarboxylase, a completely different enzyme, **histidine decarboxylase,** present in most cells, catalyzes decarboxylation of histidine.

Histidine compounds found in the body include **ergothioneine,** in red blood cells and liver; **carnosine,** a dipeptide of histidine and β-alanine; and **anserine,**

1-methylcarnosine. The latter 2 compounds occur in muscle (Fig 23–4).

Carnosine injected into animals has a circulatory depressant action similar to but not as potent as that of histamine.

Rabbits on vitamin E deficient diets excrete

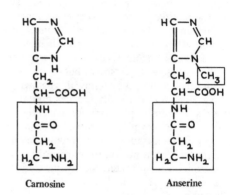

Ergothioneine

Carnosine   Anserine

Figure 23–4. Structures of compounds related to histidine. The boxes surround the components not derived from histidine.

1-methylhistidine in the urine. Excretion increases progressively until it becomes the major amino acid in the urine.

1-Methylhistidine in human urine probably is derived from anserine. Larger amounts were found in the urine after the ingestion of rabbit muscle, which is high in anserine content. 3-Methylhistidine, identified in human urine in amounts of about 50 mg/dL, is unusually low in the urine of patients with Wilson's disease.

TRYPTOPHAN

Serotonin

A secondary pathway for the metabolism of tryptophan involves hydroxylation to 5-hydroxytryptophan. Oxidation of tryptophan to the hydroxy derivative is analogous to conversion of phenylalanine to tyrosine (Fig 20–12), and liver phenylalanine hydroxylase also catalyzes hydroxylation of tryptophan. Decarboxylation of 5-hydroxytryptophan forms **5-hydroxytryptamine (serotonin)** (reaction ①, Fig 23–5), a potent vasoconstrictor and stimulator of smooth muscle contraction.

The 5-hydroxytryptophan decarboxylase that forms serotonin from hydroxytryptophan is present in the kidney (hog and guinea pig), liver, and stomach. However, the widely distributed aromatic L-amino acid decarboxylase will also catalyze decarboxylation of 5-hydroxytryptophan.

Most serotonin is metabolized by oxidative deamination to 5-hydroxyindoleacetic acid. The enzyme that catalyzes this reaction is **monoamine oxidase** (reaction ②, Fig 23–5). Inhibitors of this enzyme include iproniazid. It is hypothesized that the psychic stimultation that follows the administration of this drug is attributable to its ability to prolong the stimulating action of serotonin through inhibition of monoamine oxidase. In normal human urine, 2–8 mg of 5-hydroxyindoleacetic acid are excreted per day.

Greatly increased production of serotonin occurs in malignant **carcinoid** (argentaffinoma), a disease characterized by widespread serotonin-producing tumor cells in the argentaffin tissue of the abdominal cavity. Carcinoid has been considered an abnormality in tryptophan metabolism in which a much greater proportion of tryptophan than normal is metabolized by way of hydroxyindole. One percent of tryptophan is normally converted to serotonin, but in the carcinoid patient as much as 60% may follow this pathway. This metabolic diversion markedly reduces production of nicotinic acid from tryptophan; consequently, symptoms of pellagra as well as negative nitrogen balance may occur. Other metabolites of serotonin identified in the urine of patients with carcinoid include 5-hydroxyindoleaceturic acid (the glycine conjugate of 5-hydroxyindoleacetic acid) and N-acetylserotonin conjugated with glucuronic acid.

Melatonin

Melatonin is derived from serotonin by N-acetylation (reaction ③, Fig 23–5) followed by methylation of the 5-hydroxy group (reaction ④, Fig 23–5). Methylation is localized in pineal body tissue. In addition to methylation of N-acetylserotonin, direct methylation of serotonin (reaction ⑤, Fig 23–5) and of 5-hydroxyindoleacetic acid (reaction ⑥, Fig 23–5), the serotonin metabolite, also occurs.

Serotonin and 5-methoxytryptamine are metabolized to the corresponding acids by monoamine oxidase. Circulating melatonin is taken up by all tissues, including brain, but is rapidly metabolized by hydroxylation at position 6 followed by conjugation with sulfate (70%) and with glucuronic acid (6%). A portion is also converted to nonindolic reacting compounds.

Indole Derivatives in Urine

Tryptophan may be converted to several indole derivatives (Fig 23–5). The end products of these conversions that appear in the urine are principally 5-hydroxyindoleacetic acid, the major end product of the hydroxy tryptophan-to-serotonin pathway, and indole-3-acetic acid, from decarboxylation and oxidation of indolepyruvic acid, the keto acid of tryptophan.

Mammalian kidney and liver and bacteria from human feces decarboxylate tryptophan to tryptamine, which can then be oxidized to indole-3-acetic acid. Patients with phenylketonuria excrete increased quantities of indoleacetic acid (and indolelactic acid, formed by reduction of indolepyruvic acid).

PHENYLALANINE & TYROSINE

Melanin, the pigment of the skin and hair, is derived from tyrosine via dihydroxyphenylalanine (dopa) and its oxidation product, 3,4-dioxyphenylalanine (dopaquinone) (Fig 23–6). The hydroxylation of tyrosine to form dopa in melanocytes or pigment-forming cells is catalyzed by **tyrosinase,** a **copper-dependent** enzyme. The dopaquinone formed from dopa by the catalytic action of dopa oxidase cyclizes to form dihydroxyindole. This and intermediate indolic compounds polymerize to generate the pigment melanin. These specific reactions occur only in **melanocytes,** cells that have derived from the neural crest.

Tyrosine is also a precursor of **epinephrine** and **norepinephrine,** which are formed also in cells of neural origin. Although dopa is an intermediate in the formation of both melanin in melanocytes and norepinephrine in neuronal cells, different enzymes carry out the tyrosine hydroxylation reactions in the different cell types. **Tyrosine hydroxylase,** an enzyme that is not copper-dependent but utilizes tetrahydrobiopterin much as does phenylalanine hydroxylase, forms dopa in the neuronal and adrenal cells on the pathway to norepinephrine and epinephrine production (Fig 23–6). **Dopa decarboxylase,** a pyridoxal phosphate–dependent enzyme, forms dopamine. The latter is subjected to further hydroxylation by

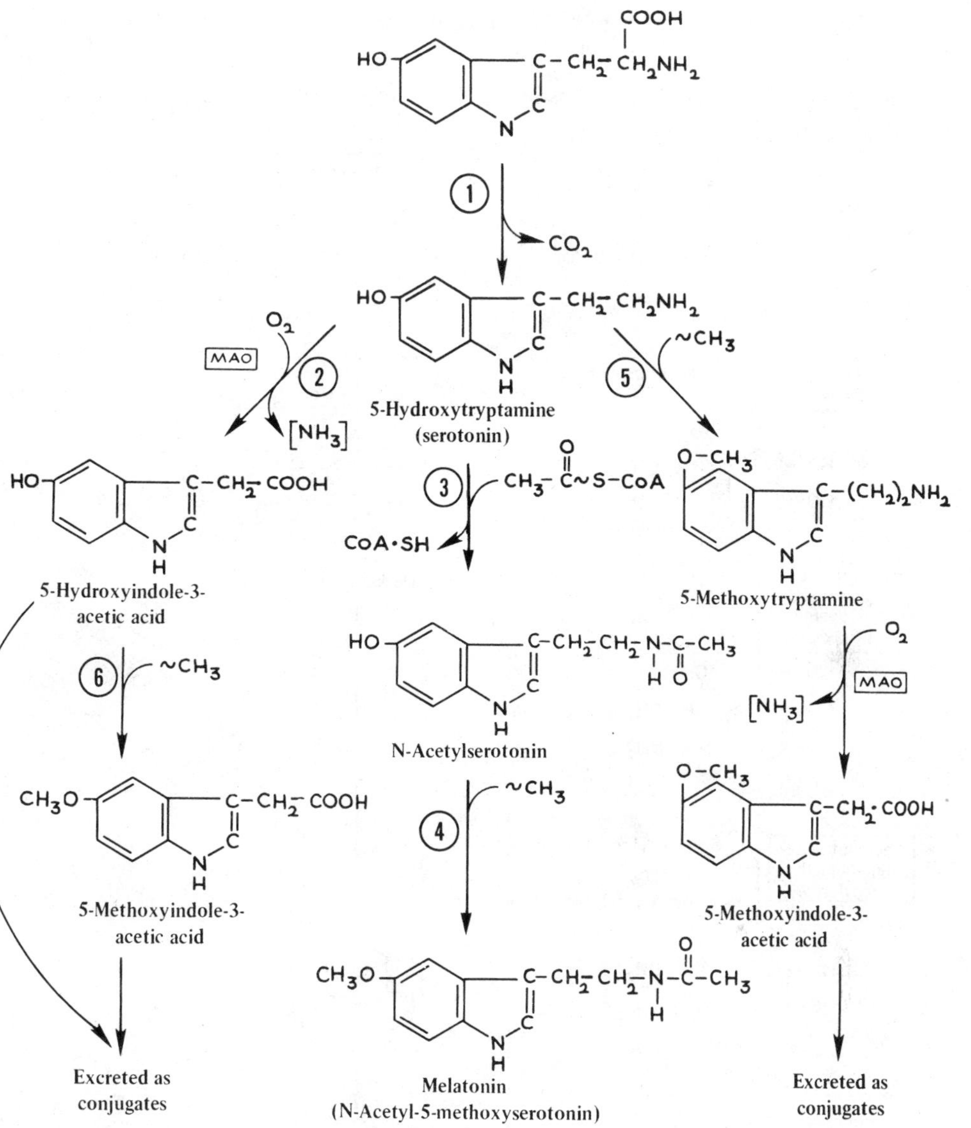

Figure 23-5. Biosynthesis and metabolism of melatonin. ([NH₃] = by transamination; MAO = monoamine oxidase.) The numbered reactions are referred to in the text.

dopamine β-oxidase, another copper-dependent enzyme that also seems to utilize vitamin C to generate norepinephrine. In the **adrenal medulla** there exists an enzyme, phenylethanolamine-N-methyltransferase, which utilizes S-adenosylmethionine to methylate the primary amine of norepinephrine to form **epinephrine** (Fig 23–6).

As discussed in Chapter 35, tyrosine is also a precursor of the thyroid hormones triiodothyronine and thyroxine.

Tyrosine is excreted in urine both free and as a sulfate, but most phenolic compounds are conjugated with sulfate when present in the urine.

METABOLISM OF
CREATINE & CREATININE

Creatine is present in muscle, brain, and blood, both as phosphocreatine and in the free state. Traces of creatine are also normally present in urine. Creatinine, the anhydride of creatine, is formed largely in muscle by irreversible nonenzymic dehydration of creatine phosphate (Fig 23–7).

The 24-hour excretion of creatinine in the urine of a given subject is remarkably constant from day to day and proportionate to muscle mass.

For synthesis of creatine, 3 amino acids — **glycine, arginine,** and **methionine**—are directly involved. The first reaction is transamidination from

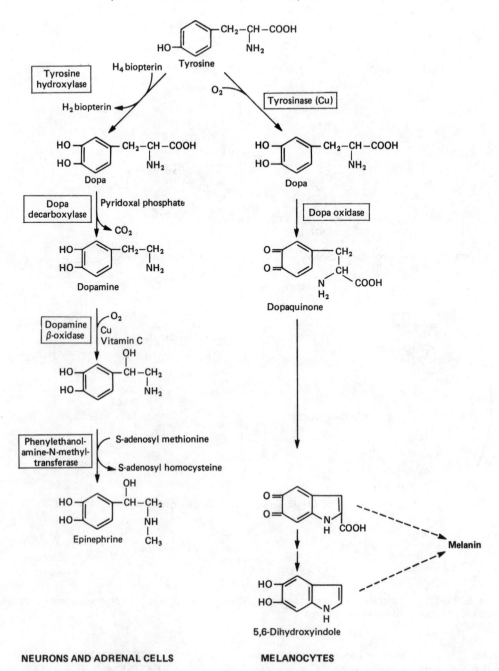

Figure 23–6. Conversion of tyrosine to epinephrine and norepinephrine in neuronal and adrenal cells and to melanin in melanocytes. Each pathway is unique to the specific cell types indicated.

arginine to glycine to form guanidoacetic acid (glycocyamine). This occurs in the kidney but not in the liver or in heart muscle. Synthesis of creatine is completed by methylation of glycocyamine by "active methionine" in the liver.

METABOLISM OF γ-AMINOBUTYRATE

Decarboxylation of glutamate produces γ-aminobutyrate (Fig 23–8). An enzyme that catalyzes its formation from glutamate by alpha decarboxylation is found in the tissues of the central nervous system, principally in the gray matter. γ-Aminobutyrate is metabolized by deamination to succinic semialdehyde. Succinic semialdehyde is then oxidized to succinate or reduced to γ-hydroxybutyrate.

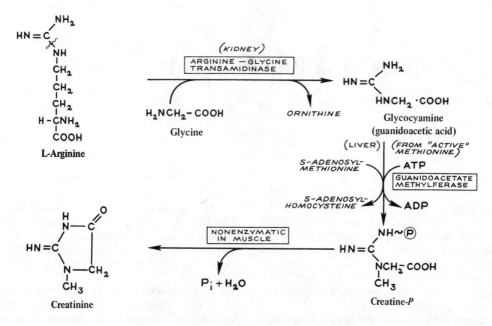

Figure 23–7. Biosynthesis of creatine and creatinine.

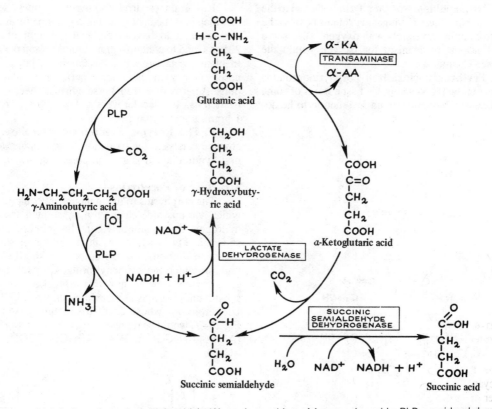

Figure 23–8. Metabolism of γ-aminobutyric acid. (α-KA = α-keto acids; α-AA = α-amino acids; PLP = pyridoxal phosphate.)

24 | Porphyrins & Bile Pigments

David W. Martin, Jr., MD

Porphyrins are cyclic compounds formed by the linkage of 4 pyrrole rings through methenyl bridges (Fig 24–1). A characteristic property of the porphyrins is the formation of complexes with metal ions bound to the nitrogen atom of the pyrrole rings. Examples are the iron porphyrins such as **heme** of hemoglobin and the magnesium-containing porphyrin **chlorophyll,** the photosynthetic pigment of plants.

In nature, the metalloporphyrins are conjugated to proteins to form many compounds important in biologic processes. These include the following:

A. Hemoglobins: Iron porphyrins attached to the protein, globin. These conjugated proteins possess the ability to combine reversibly with oxygen. They serve as the transport mechanism for oxygen within the blood (see Chapter 5).

B. Erythrocruorins: Iron porphyrinoproteins that occur in the blood and in the tissue fluids of some invertebrates. They correspond in function to hemoglobin.

C. Myoglobins: Respiratory pigments that occur in the muscle cells of vertebrates and invertebrates. An example is the myoglobin obtained from the heart muscle of the horse and crystallized by Theorell in 1934. A myoglobin molecule is similar to a subunit of hemoglobin.

D. Cytochromes: Compounds that act as electron transfer agents in oxidation-reduction reactions. An important example is **cytochrome c,** which has a molecular weight of about 13,000 and contains 1 gram-atom of iron per mole.

E. Catalases: Iron porphyrin enzymes, several of which have been obtained in crystalline form. They are assumed to have a molecular weight of about 225,000 and to contain 4 gram-atoms of iron per mole. In plants, catalase activity is minimal, but the iron porphyrin enzyme peroxidase performs similar functions. A peroxidase from horseradish has been crystallized; it has a molecular weight of 44,000 and contains 1 gram-atom of iron per mole.

F. The Enzyme Tryptophan Pyrrolase: This enzyme catalyzes the oxidation of tryptophan to formyl kynurenine. It is an iron porphyrin protein.

Structure of Porphyrins

The porphyrins found in nature are compounds in which various side-chains are substituted for the 8 hydrogen atoms numbered in the porphin nucleus shown in Fig 24–1. As a simple means of showing these substitutions, Fischer proposed a shorthand formula in which the methenyl bridges are omitted and each pyrrole ring is shown as a bracket with the 8 substituent positions numbered as shown (Fig 24–2). Uroporphyrin, whose detailed structure is shown in Fig 24–7, would be represented as shown in Fig 24–2. ($A = -CH_2COOH$; $P = -CH_2CH_2COOH$; $M = -CH_3$)

Pyrrole

Porphin
($C_{20}H_{14}N_4$)

Figure 24–1. The porphin molecule. Rings are labeled I, II, III, IV. Substituent positions on rings are labeled 1, 2, 3, 4, 5, 6, 7, 8. Methenyl bridges are labeled α, β, γ, δ.

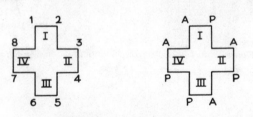

Figure 24–2. Uroporphyrin III.

The arrangement of the A and P substituents in the uroporphyrin shown in Fig 24–2 is asymmetric (in ring IV, the expected order of the acetate and propionate substituents is reversed). A porphyrin with this type of **asymmetric substitution** is classified as a type III porphyrin. A porphyrin with a completely symmetric arrangement of the substituents is classified as a type I porphyrin. Only types I and III are found in nature, and the **type III series** is by far the more abundant (Fig 24–3).

The compounds shown in Fig 24–4 are all type III porphyrins (ie, the methyl groups are asymmetrically distributed, as in type III coproporphyrin). However, they are sometimes identified as belonging to series IX because they were designated ninth in a series of isomers postulated by Hans Fischer, the pioneer worker in the field of porphyrin chemistry.

Biosynthesis of Porphyrins

Both chlorophyll, the photosynthetic pigment of plants, and heme, the iron protoporphyrin of hemoglobin in animals, are synthesized in living cells by a common pathway. The 2 starting materials are "active succinate," the **coenzyme A derivative of succinic acid,** derived from the citric acid cycle in mitochondria, and the amino acid **glycine.** Pyridoxal phosphate is also necessary in this reaction to "activate" glycine. It is probable that pyridoxal reacts with glycine to form a Schiff base, whereby the alpha carbon of glycine can be combined with the carbonyl carbon of succinate. The product of the condensation reaction between succinyl-CoA and glycine is α-amino-β-ketoadipic acid, which is rapidly decarboxylated to form δ-aminolevulinic acid (AmLev) (Fig 24–5). This step is catalyzed by the enzyme **AmLev synthetase.** This appears to be the **rate-controlling** enzyme in porphyrin biosynthesis in mammalian liver. Synthesis of aminolevulinic acid occurs in the **mitochondria.** In the cytosol, 2 molecules of AmLev are condensed by the enzyme **AmLev dehydrase** to form 2 molecules of water and one of **porphobilinogen** (Fig 24–5).

The formation of a tetrapyrrole, ie, a porphyrin, occurs by condensation of 4 monopyrroles derived from porphobilinogen (Fig 24–6). In each instance, the amino carbon (originally derived from the alpha carbon of glycine) serves as the source of the methylene (alpha, beta, gamma, delta) carbons that connect each pyrrole in the tetrapyrrole structure. Although the conversion of porphobilinogen to a porphyrin can be accomplished simply by heating under acid conditions, such as in an acid urine, this conversion is catalyzed in the tissues by specific enzymes.

It has been pointed out that only types I and III porphyrins occur in nature, and it may be assumed that the type III isomers are the more abundant since the biologically important porphyrins such as heme and the cytochromes are type III isomers.

At present, the detailed steps leading to the formation of the uroporphyrinogens from condensation of porphobilinogens remain obscure. The formation from porphobilinogen of uroporphyrinogen III, the obligatory intermediate in heme biosynthesis, is catalyzed by a complex interaction of 2 enzymes. **Uroporphyrinogen I synthetase** condenses porphobilinogen to uroporphyrinogen I in vitro (Fig 24–6). However, when a second enzyme, **uroporphyrinogen III cosynthetase,** is present, interaction between these 2 enzymes results in the formation of uroporphyrinogen III rather than the symmetric isomer uroporphyrinogen I (Fig 24–6). Under normal conditions, the uroporphyrinogen formed is almost exclusively the III isomer, but in certain of the porphyrias (discussed below) the type I isomers of porphyrinogens are also formed in excess.

Note that both of these uroporphyrinogens have the pyrrole rings connected by **methylene** bridges, which do not form a conjugated ring system. Thus, these compounds (as are all porphyrinogens) are **colorless.** However, the porphyrinogens are readily autooxidized to their respective porphyrins, as shown in Fig 24–7 for uroporphyrinogen III. These oxidations are catalyzed by light and by the porphyrins that are formed.

Uroporphyrinogen III is converted to coproporphyrinogen III by decarboxylation of all of the acetate (A) groups, which changes them to methyl (M) substituents. The reaction is catalyzed by **uroporphyrinogen decarboxylase,** which is also capable of converting uroporphyrinogen I to coproporphyrinogen I (Fig 24–8). Coproporphyrinogen III then enters the mitochondria, where it is converted to **protoporphyrinogen III** and then to **protoporphyrin III.** Several steps seem to be involved in this conversion (Fig 24–9). An enzyme, **coproporphyrinogen oxidase,** is believed to catalyze the decarboxylation and oxidation of 2 propionic side chains to form protoporphyrinogen. This enzyme is able to act only on type III coproporphyrinogen, which would explain why a type I protoporphyrin has not been identified in natural materials. The oxidation of protoporphyrinogen to protoporphyrin is believed to be catalyzed by an enzyme, **protoporphyrinogen oxidase.** In mammalian liver the reaction of conversion of coproporphyrinogen to protoporphyrin requires molecular oxygen.

Formation of Heme

The final step in heme synthesis involves the incorporation of ferrous iron into protoporphyrin in a reaction catalyzed by **heme synthetase** or **ferrochelatase** (Fig 24–4). This reaction occurs readily in the absence of enzymes, but it is noted to be much more rapid in the presence of tissue preparations, presumably because of the tissue contribution of enzymes active in catalyzing this iron chelation.

A summary of the steps in the biosynthesis of the porphyrin derivatives from porphobilinogen is given in Fig 24–10. Heme biosynthesis occurs in most mammalian tissues with the exception of mature erythrocytes, which do not contain mitochondria.

The porphyrinogens that have been described above are colorless, containing 6 extra hydrogen atoms as compared to the corresponding **colored porphyrins.** It is now apparent that these reduced porphyrins

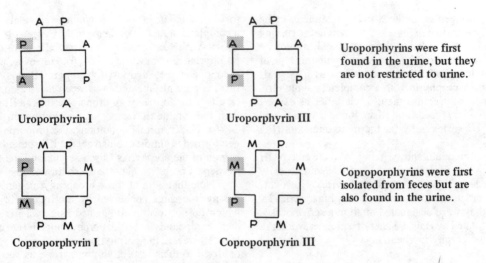

Uroporphyrins were first found in the urine, but they are not restricted to urine.

Coproporphyrins were first isolated from feces but are also found in the urine.

Figure 24–3. Uroporphyrins and coproporphyrins.

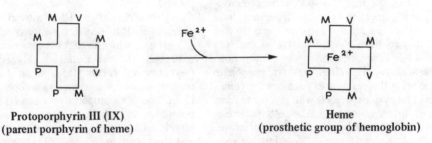

Figure 24–4. Addition of iron to protoporphyrin to form heme.

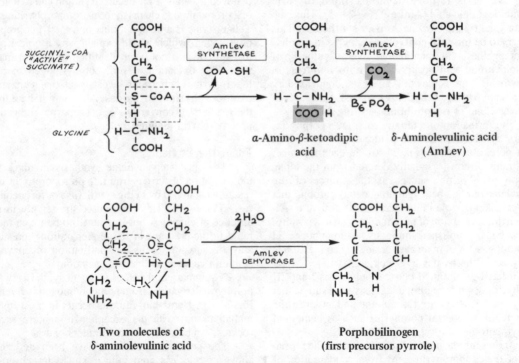

Figure 24–5. Biosynthesis of porphobilinogen. AmLev synthetase occurs in the mitochondria, whereas AmLev dehydrase is present in the cytosol.

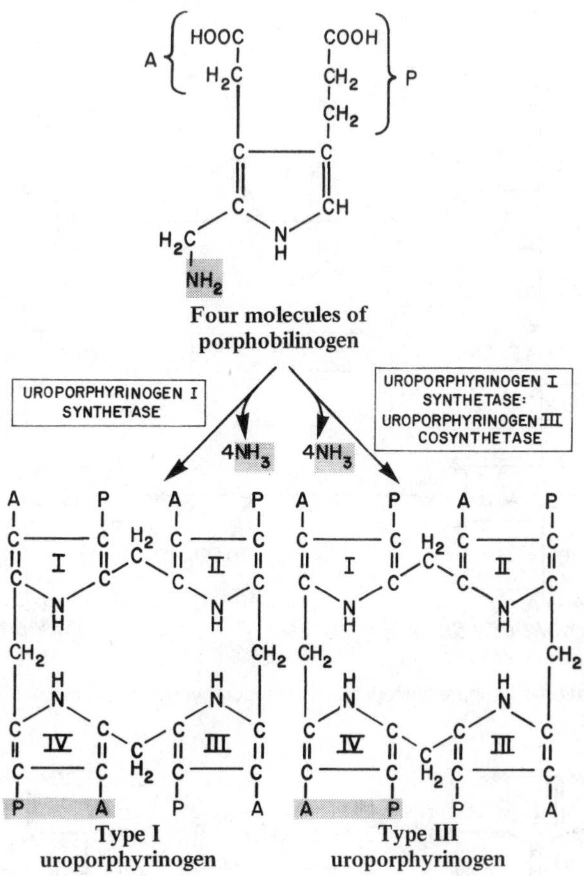

Figure 24–6. Conversion of porphobilinogen to uroporphyrinogens.

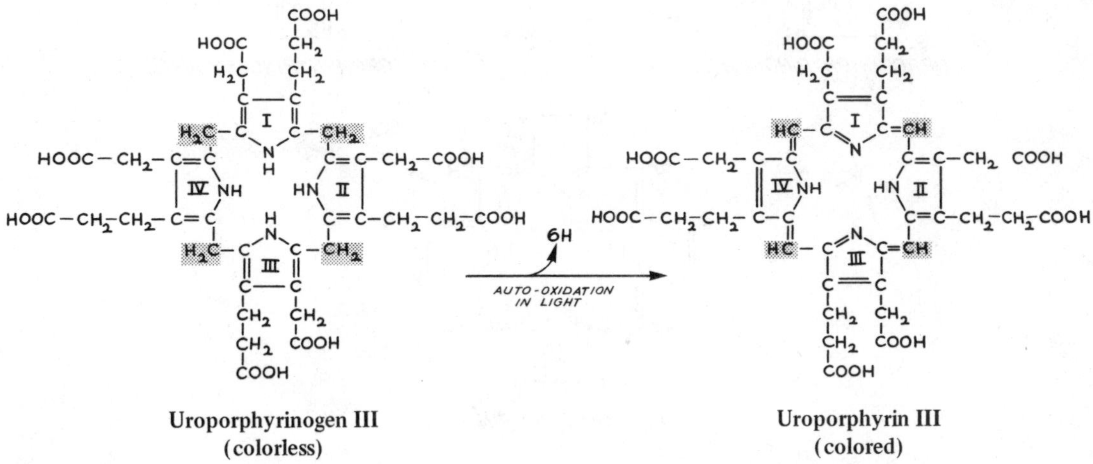

Figure 24–7. Oxidation of uroporphyrinogen to uroporphyrin. The methylene bridges between the pyrrole rings are oxidized (dehydrogenated) to methenyl bridges, generating a conjugated ring (colored) system.

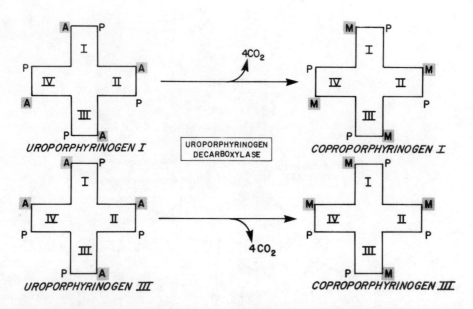

Figure 24–8. Decarboxylation of uroporphyrinogens to coproporphyrinogens in cytosol. A, acetyl; M, methyl; P, propyl.

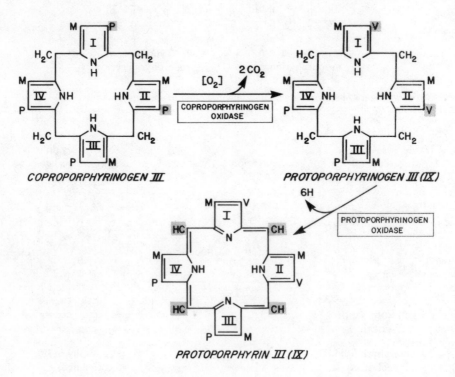

Figure 24–9. Conversion of coproporphyrinogen to protoporphyrin in mitochondria. M, methyl; P, propyl; V, vinyl.

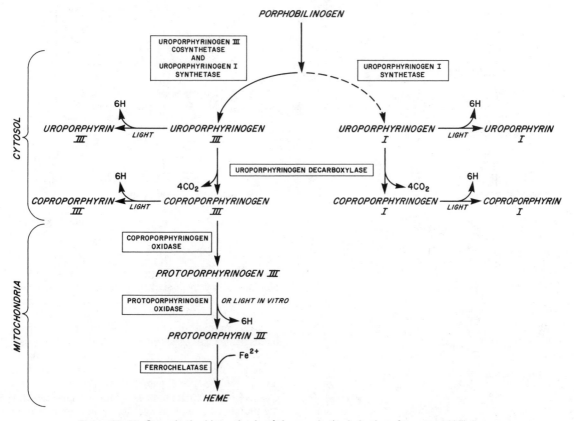

Figure 24–10. Steps in the biosynthesis of the porphyrin derivatives from porphobilinogen.

(the porphyrinogens) and not the corresponding porphyrins are the actual intermediates in the biosynthesis of protoporphyrin and of heme.

Regulation of Heme Biosynthesis

The rate-limiting reaction for the synthesis of heme occurs at the condensation of succinyl-CoA and glycine to form δ-aminolevulinic acid (AmLev) (Fig 24–5), a reaction catalyzed by the enzyme aminolevulinic acid synthetase (AmLev synthetase). The levels of AmLev synthetase activity in normal tissues capable of synthesizing heme are significantly lower than those of the other enzymes of the heme synthetic pathway. However, AmLev synthetase is a regulated enzyme. It appears that heme, probably acting through an aporepressor molecule, acts as a negative regulator of the accumulation of AmLev synthetase. This repression and derepression mechanism is depicted diagrammatically in Fig 24–11. It is possible that there is also significant feedback inhibition at this step, but the major regulatory effect of heme appears to be one in which the rate of accumulation of AmLev synthetase increases greatly in the absence of heme and is diminished in its presence.

Many compounds of diverse structures, including presently used insecticides, carcinogens, and pharmaceuticals, when administered to humans, can result in a marked increase in hepatic AmLev synthetase.

Most of these drugs are metabolized by a system in the liver that utilizes a specific hemoprotein, cytochrome P-450. During the process of metabolizing these drugs, the consumption of heme by cytochrome P-450 is greatly increased, which in turn diminishes the intracellular heme concentration. This latter event effects a derepression of AmLev synthetase with a corresponding increased rate of heme synthesis to meet the needs of the cells.

Several other factors affect the induction of AmLev synthetase in the liver. Glucose can prevent the induction of AmLev synthetase; iron in chelated form exerts a synergistic effect on the induction of hepatic AmLev synthetase; steroids play at least a permissive role in the drug-mediated derepression of AmLev synthetase in vivo. The administration of hematin in vivo can prevent the drug-mediated derepression of AmLev synthetase, as well as that of other hemoproteins in liver. In erythropoietic tissues, hypoxia increases AmLev synthetase activity without having a demonstrable effect on AmLev synthetase activity in liver.

The importance of these regulatory mechanisms is discussed below along with the diseases classified among the porphyrias.

Chemistry of Porphyrins

Because of the presence of tertiary nitrogens in

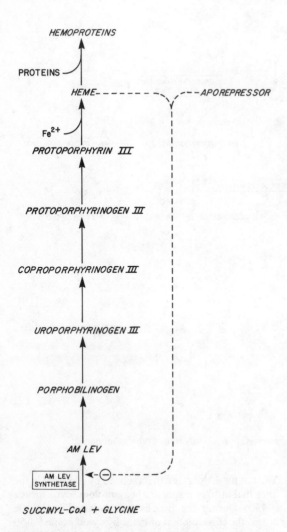

Figure 24–11. Regulation of heme synthesis at the level of AmLev synthetase by a repression-derepression mechanism mediated by heme and its hypothetical aporepressor. The dotted lines indicate the negative (–) regulation by repression.

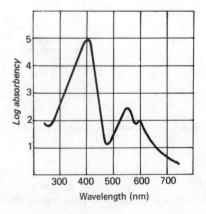

Figure 24–12. Absorption spectrum of hematoporphyrin (0.01% solution in 5% HCl).

the 2 pyrrolene rings contained in each porphyrin, these compounds act as weak bases. Those which possess a carboxyl group on one or more side chains act also as acids. Their isoelectric points range from pH 3.0 to 4.5, and within this pH range the porphyrins may easily be precipitated from an aqueous solution.

The various porphyrinogens are colorless, whereas the various **porphyrins are all colored.** In the study of porphyrins or porphyrin derivatives, the characteristic absorption spectrum that each exhibits, both in the visible and the ultraviolet regions of the spectrum, is of great value. An example is the absorption curve for a solution of porphyrin in 5% hydrochloric acid (Fig 24–12). Note the sharp absorption band near 400 nm. This is a distinguishing feature of the porphin ring and is characteristic of all porphyrins regardless of the side chains present. This band is

termed the **Soret band,** after its discoverer. Hematoporphyrin in acid solution, in addition to the Soret band, has 2 weaker absorption bands with maxima at 550 and 592 nm.

In organic solvents, porphyrins have 4 main bands in the visible spectrum as well as the Soret band. For example, a solution of protoporphyrin in an ether–acetic acid mixture exhibits absorption bands at 632.5, 576, 537, 502, and 395 nm. When porphyrins dissolved in strong mineral acids or in organic solvents are illuminated by ultraviolet light, they emit a strong red fluorescence. This **fluorescence** is so characteristic that it is frequently used to detect small amounts of free porphyrins. The double bonds in the porphyrins are responsible for the characteristic absorption and fluorescence of these compounds, and, as previously noted, the reduction (by addition of hydrogen) of the methenyl (–HC=) bridges to methylene (–CH_2–) leads to the formation of colorless compounds termed **porphyrinogens.**

When a porphyrin combines with a metal, its absorption in the visible spectrum becomes changed. This is exemplified by protoporphyrin, the iron-free precursor of heme. In alkaline solution, protoporphyrin shows several sharp absorption bands (at 645, 591, and 540 nm), whereas heme has a broad band with a plateau extending from 540 to 580 nm.

Tests for Porphyrins

The presence of coproporphyrins or of uroporphyrins is of clinical interest since these 2 types of compounds are excreted in increased amounts in the porphyrias. Coproporphyrins I and III are soluble in glacial acetic acid–ether mixtures, from which they may then be extracted by hydrochloric acid. Uroporphyrins, on the other hand, are not soluble in acetic acid–ether mixtures but are partially soluble in ethyl acetate, from which they may be extracted by hydrochloric acid. In the HCl solution, ultraviolet illumination gives a characteristic red fluorescence. A spectrophotometer may then be used to demonstrate the characteristic absorption bands.

Table 24–1. Upper limits of normal excretory values and concentrations of porphyrins and porphyrin precursors.*

	Urine (μg/24 h)	Feces (μg/g dry wt)	Erythrocytes (μg/dL cells)
AmLev	4000	–	–
Porphobilinogen	1500	–	–
Uroporphyrin	50	5	trace
Coproporphyrin	300	50	3
Protoporphyrin	–	120	80

*Modified and reproduced, with permission, from Meyer UA, Schmid R: The porphyrias. In: *The Metabolic Basis of Inherited Disease*, 4th ed. Stanbury JB, Wyngaarden JB, Fredrickson DS (editors). McGraw-Hill, 1978.

The upper limits of normal values of excretory values of porphyrins and porphyrin precursors are given in Table 24–1. In healthy subjects, the total urinary coproporphyrin averages about 67 μg/24 h; the type I isomer comprises on the average 14 μg/24 h and type III 53 μg/24 h. An alteration in the normal ratio of the excretion of types I and III coproporphyrins may be of value in detection of certain types of diseases of the liver.

During the synthesis of heme from AmLev, there is an increase in the hydrophobic qualities of the various intermediate compounds. The acetyl carboxyl groups on uroporphyrinogen are removed when it is converted to coproporphyrinogen, and 2 of the propyl groups are decarboxylated in the course of the conversion of coproporphyrinogen to protoporphyrinogen. The relative distributions in the urine and feces of the intermediates of heme biosynthesis reflect this increasing hydrophobic quality. Thus, the more polar uroporphyrinogen will be excreted to a greater extent in urine than in feces, whereas the more hydrophobic coproporphyrinogen and protoporphyrinogen will increasingly distribute themselves in the bile and ultimately the feces rather than in the aqueous urine.

THE PORPHYRIAS

The porphyrias constitute a heterogeneous group of diseases, all of which exhibit increased excretion of porphyrins or porphyrin precursors. Some forms of porphyria are inherited, whereas others are acquired. Several different classifications of the porphyrias have been proposed. It is convenient to divide the inherited porphyrias into 3 general groups—the erythropoietic porphyrias, the hepatic porphyrias, and those with both erythropoietic and hepatic abnormalities (Table 24–2). In most types of inherited porphyria, the defect is present in all tissues, but for reasons that are not clear, the metabolic abnormalities are expressed preferentially in one or another tissue type. There follows a brief description of the biochemical abnormalities characteristic of the porphyrias.

Studies of the biochemical and metabolic abnormalities characteristic of the porphyrias have provided much information about the pathogenesis of these diseases and their management. These studies have also been responsible for increased knowledge of the normal pathway for the synthesis of heme and of its regulation.

The pattern of excretion of porphyrin and porphyrin precursors is characteristic for each type of porphyria. In Fig 24–13, these patterns and their relationships to the heme synthetic pathway are depicted.

Intermittent acute porphyria (IAP) is an autosomal, dominantly inherited disease in humans that usually is not expressed before puberty. It results from an inherited partial deficiency of **uroporphyrinogen I synthetase.** Individuals with this disease are heterozygous for a defective structural gene for uroporphyrinogen I synthetase, with the result that only 50% of the normal specific catalytic activity of that enzyme is present within their cells. Patients with IAP excrete massive quantities of **porphobilinogen** and **AmLev** in the urine. Both of these compounds are **colorless,** but porphobilinogen upon exposure to light and air polymerizes slowly and spontaneously to form 2 colored compounds: porphobilin and porphyrin. These cause a **darkening of the urine upon standing** in light and air.

Table 24–2. Classification of human porphyrias.*

Condition	Mode of Inheritance	Demonstrated or Suspected Enzyme Defect	Predominant Site(s) of Metabolic Expression
Congenital erythropoietic porphyria	Autosomal recessive	Uroporphyrinogen I synthetase and/or uroporphyrinogen III cosynthetase	Erythroid cells
Hepatic porphyrias			
Intermittent acute porphyria	Autosomal dominant	Uroporphyrinogen I synthetase	Liver
Hereditary coproporphyria	Autosomal dominant	Coproporphyrinogen oxidase	Liver
Variegate porphyria	Autosomal dominant	Protoporphyrinogen oxidase	Liver
Porphyria cutanea tarda	Autosomal dominant (?)	Uroporphyrinogen decarboxylase	Liver
Toxic porphyria	Acquired	Variable	Liver
Protoporphyria	Autosomal dominant	Ferrochelatase	Erythroid cells and liver (?)

*Reproduced, with permission, from Meyer UA, Schmid R: The porphyrias. In: *The Metabolic Basis of Inherited Disease*, 4th ed. Stanbury JB, Wyngaarden JB, Fredrickson DS (editors). McGraw-Hill, 1978.

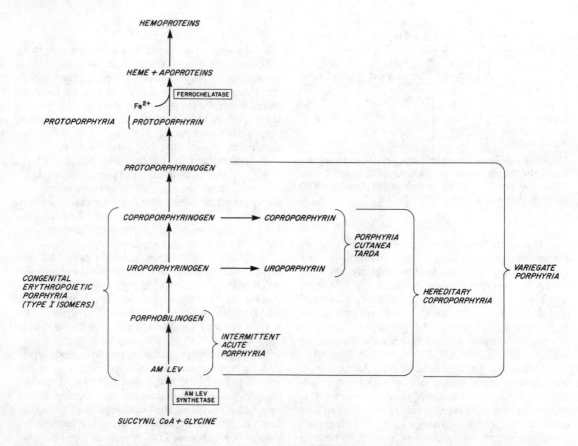

Figure 24–13. Patterns of urinary porphyrin and porphyrin precursor excretion in the porphyrias in relation to the pathway of heme biosynthesis. Intermediates of the pathway excessively excreted during the acute phase of each of the porphyrias are within the respective brackets. AM LEV, δ-aminolevulinic acid. (Modified from Kaufman K, Marver H: *N Engl J Med* 1970;**283**:954.)

Both porphobilinogen and AmLev are present in the plasma and spinal fluid of these patients, particularly during acute exacerbations. Drugs and steroid hormones that require metabolism by heme-containing proteins such as cytochrome P-450 can precipitate acute exacerbations. Apparently, because of the increased consumption of heme proteins necessitated by the metabolism of these porphyria-inducing compounds, there is a derepression of AmLev synthetase activity brought about by diminished intracellular heme concentration. The increased AmLev synthetase activity combined with the partial block in the uroporphyrinogen I synthetase results in a massive accumulation of AmLev and porphobilinogen. The acute attacks of abdominal pain, vomiting, constipation, cardiovascular abnormalities, and neuropsychiatric signs and symptoms correlate with the increased production of AmLev and porphobilinogen in these patients.

Patients with IAP do not have abnormal sensitivity to light, as do patients with other types of hepatic porphyrias. This is understandable when it is considered that these patients do not accumulate porphyrins or porphyrinogens because the inherited metabolic defect occurs in the heme synthetic pathway *prior to* the

formation of the first porphyrinogen (uroporphyrinogen).

As mentioned above, the metabolic defect in IAP occurs in cells other than hepatocytes, including erythrocytes and cultured fibroblasts, and it should be expected also in cultured amniotic fluid cells. Thus, although the enzymatic deficiency is ubiquitous, the increased AmLev synthetase activity responsible for the overproduction of AmLev and porphobilinogen is predominantly a hepatic phenomenon. This probably is because the liver is the organ in which the inducing agents are metabolized. IAP is one of the rare examples of a disease phenotype being expressed in a heterozygote in whom the known enzyme deficiency is only 50%.

As might be predicted from the proposed mechanism of regulation of AmLev synthetase by a repression-derepression system, the infusion of hematin into patients with IAP can ameliorate the induction of AmLev synthetase and, thereby, the clinical signs and symptoms.

Congenital erythropoietic porphyria is an even rarer congenital disease having an autosomal recessive mode of inheritance. The molecular nature of the defect in congenital erythropoietic porphyria is not clearly defined, but there is a definite imbalance between the relative activities of uroporphyrinogen III cosynthetase and uroporphyrinogen I synthetase. The formation of uroporphyrinogen I greatly exceeds that of uroporphyrinogen III, the normal isomer on the pathway to heme synthesis. Although the genetic defect is present in all cells, it is for an unknown reason expressed predominantly in erythropoietic tissue. Patients with congenital erythropoietic porphyria excrete large quantities of the **type I isomers** of both uroporphyrinogen and coproporphyrinogen, which in the urine are spontaneously oxidized to uroporphyrin I and coprophyrin I, both red pigments. There is reported to be a small increase in uroporphyrin III, but the ratio of the type I to type III isomer approaches 100:1. Circulating erythrocytes contain high concentrations of uroporphyrin I, although the highest concentration of this porphyrin is present in bone marrow cells and not in the hepatocytes.

Apparently because of the decreased formation of the true precursor of heme, uroporphyrinogen III, and thus a relative deficiency of heme, AmLev synthetase is induced in the erythropoietic tissues of patients with congenital erythropoietic porphyria. This induction of AmLev synthetase promotes the massive overproduction of the type I porphyrinogens. Concomitant with the increase in AmLev synthetase and overproduction of the type I porphyrinogens is an increased production and excretion of porphobilinogen and AmLev. Thus, from the biochemical abnormalities one can predict the existence of clinical symptoms comparable to those of IAP but with the addition of cutaneous photosensitivity because of the absorption spectrum of the porphyrin compounds that are formed in abnormal quantities in this disorder. These patients also exhibit a prominent increased cutaneous fragility.

Hereditary coproporphyria is an autosomal dominant disorder due to partial deficiency of **coproporphyrinogen oxidase,** the mitochondrial enzyme responsible for the conversion of coproporphyrinogen III to protophorphyrinogen IX (Fig 24–9). Coproporphyrinogen III is excreted in excessive quantities in feces, but, because of its solubility in water, it is excreted also in large quantities in urine. As is true also of uroporphyrinogen, in the presence of air and light, coproporphyrinogen is rapidly oxidized to coproporphyrin, a red pigment.

The limited capacity to produce heme in this disease—particularly under conditions of stress—will result in derepression of AmLev synthetase. This leads to the overproduction of AmLev and porphobilinogen and the other intermediates in the heme synthetic pathway proximal to the inherited block. Accordingly, patients with hereditary coproporphyria exhibit the signs and symptoms associated with the excess AmLev and porphobilinogen, such as those present in IAP, along with some photosensitivity due to the presence of excessive coproporphyrinogens and uroporphyrinogens. Again, the infusion of hematin can effect at least a partial repression of AmLev synthetase and

amelioration of the signs and symptoms secondary to overproduction of intermediates in heme synthesis.

Variegate porphyria or protocoproporphyria hereditaria is an autosomal dominant disorder in which there is a partial block in the enzymatic conversion of protoporphyrinogen to heme. Two enzymes, protoporphyrinogen oxidase and ferrochelatase, both located in the **mitochondria,** seem to be normally responsible for this conversion. Patients with variegate porphyria have only half of the normal level of **protoporphyrinogen oxidase** in their cultured skin fibroblast cells. Patients with variegate porphyria also exhibit a relative heme deficiency under stressful conditions, and the hepatic AmLev synthetase is derepressed. As discussed above, this increased activity of AmLev synthetase leads to overproduction of all of the intermediates in the heme synthetic pathway proximal to the block. Accordingly, patients with variegate porphyria excrete excessive quantities of AmLev, porphobilinogen, uroporphyrin, and coproporphyrin in their urines, and uroporphyrin, coproporphyrin, and protoporphyrin in their feces. Thus, their urines are pigmented and fluoresce, and they exhibit cutaneous photosensitivity—the latter indistinguishable from that observed in porphyria cutanea tarda, discussed below.

As with the other porphyria syndromes, the increased excretion of the accumulated intermediates of the heme pathway may be normal or only slightly elevated under nonstressful conditions but increase greatly when the demand for heme is increased—particularly in the liver, for reasons explained above. The plasma of patients frequently exhibits a remarkable red fluorescence which seems to correlate with the high concentration of coproporphyrinogen in that fluid. Erythrocyte porphyrin levels remain normal in this disease.

Porphyria cutanea tarda is probably the most common form of porphyria. It is usually associated with some form of hepatic injury, particularly alcohol or iron overload. The nature of the metabolic defect has not been well defined, but it is perhaps attributable to a partial deficiency of **uroporphyrinogen decarboxylase.** The defect appears to be transmitted as an autosomal dominant disorder, but the penetrance of the disease is variable, in most cases being dependent upon the existence of some form of hepatic injury. Predictably, the urine contains increased quantities of uroporphyrins of both type I and type III, but elevated urinary excretion of AmLev and porphobilinogen occurs only rarely. Although the urine may occasionally contain sufficient porphyrins to produce a pinkish color, upon acidification it frequently exhibits a pink fluorescence under ultraviolet light.

The liver contains large quantities of porphyrins, so that it fluoresces intensely, whereas the erythrocytes and cells of the bone marrow do not. In porphyria cutanea tarda, the major clinical manifestation is **cutaneous photosensitivity.** The lack of increased AmLev synthetase activity and corresponding lack of excess porphobilinogen and AmLev in the urines of

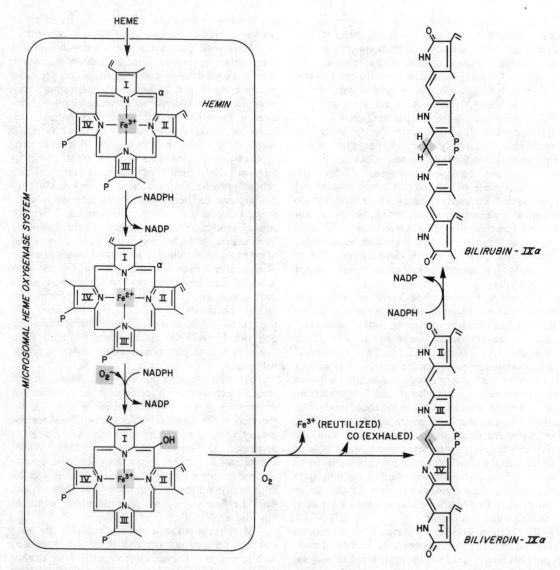

Figure 24–14. Schematic representation of the microsomal heme oxygenase system. (Modified from Schmid R, McDonough AF in: *The Porphyrins.* Dolphin D [editor]. Academic Press, 1978.)

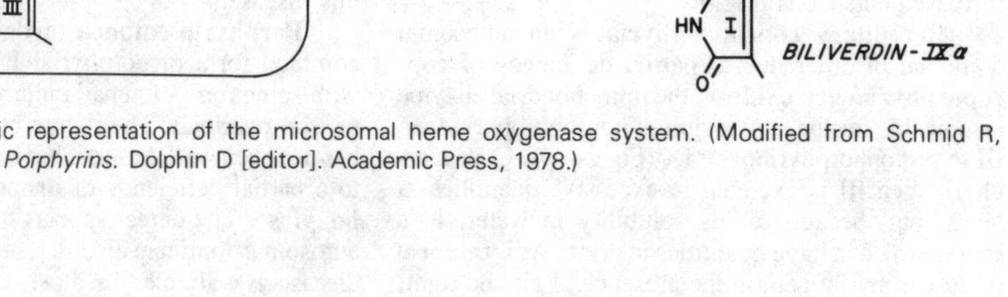

Figure 24–15. Structure of bilirubin diglucuronide (conjugated, "direct reacting" bilirubin). Glucuronic acid is attached via ester linkage to the 2 propionic acid groups to form an acylglucuronide.

these patients correlates positively with the lack of the acute manifestations typical of IAP.

Protoporphyria or erythropoietic protoporphyria appears to result from a dominantly inherited partial deficiency of **ferrochelatase** activity in the mitochondria of all tissues, and it is associated clinically with acute urticaria on exposure to sunlight. The erythrocytes, plasma, and feces contain increased quantities of protoporphyrin IX, and the reticulocytes (young erythrocytes) and skin obtained by biopsy frequently exhibit red fluorescence.

The liver probably also contributes to the overproduction of protoporphyrin IX, but there is no increased urinary excretion of porphyrin precursors or porphyrins.

Acquired porphyria can result from exposure to toxic compounds such as hexachlorobenzene, lead and other salts of heavy metals, as well as drugs such as griseofulvin and apronalide (Sedormid). Heavy metals inhibit several enzymes in the heme synthetic pathway, including AmLev dehydrase, uroporphyrinogen synthetase, and ferrochelatase.

CATABOLISM OF HEME; FORMATION OF BILE PIGMENTS

Under physiologic conditions in the human adult, $1-2 \times 10^8$ erythrocytes are destroyed per hour. Thus, in 1 day, a 70 kg human turns over approximately 6 g of hemoglobin. When hemoglobin is destroyed in the body, the protein portion, globin, may be reutilized either as such or in the form of its constituent amino acids, and the iron of heme enters the iron pool, also for reuse. However, the iron-free porphyrin portion of heme is degraded, mainly in the reticuloendothelial cells of the liver, spleen, and bone marrow.

The catabolism of heme from all of the heme proteins appears to be carried out in the microsomal fractions of the reticuloendothelial cells by a complex enzyme system called **heme oxygenase.** By the time the heme of heme proteins reaches the heme oxygenase system, the iron has usually been oxidized to the ferric form, constituting **hemin,** and may be loosely bound to albumin as methemalbumin. The heme oxygenase system is substrate-inducible. It is located in close proximity to the microsomal electron transport system. As depicted in Fig 24–14, the hemin is reduced with NADPH, and, with the aid of more NADPH, oxygen is added to the α-methenyl bridge between pyrroles I and II of the porphyrin and the ferrous iron is again oxidized to the ferric form. With the further addition of oxygen, **ferric ion** is released, **carbon monoxide** is produced, and an equimolar quantity of **biliverdin IX-α** results from the splitting of the tetrapyrrole ring. The heme itself participates in this reaction as a catalyst.

In birds and amphibia, the green biliverdin IX-α is excreted; in mammals, an enzyme called **biliverdin reductase** reduces the methenyl bridge between pyr-role III and pyrrole IV to a methylene group to produce **bilirubin IX-α,** a yellow pigment (Fig 24–14).

It is estimated that 1 g of hemoglobin yields 35 mg of bilirubin. The daily bilirubin formation in human adults is approximately 250–350 mg.

The chemical conversion of heme to bilirubin by the reticuloendothelial cells can be observed in vivo as the purple color of the heme in a hematoma is slowly converted to the yellow pigment of bilirubin.

The further metabolism of bilirubin occurs primarily in the liver. It can be divided into 3 processes: (1) uptake of bilirubin by liver parenchymal cells, (2) conjugation of bilirubin in the smooth endoplasmic reticulum, and (3) secretion of conjugated bilirubin into the bile. Each of these processes will be considered separately.

Uptake of Bilirubin by the Liver

Bilirubin is only sparingly soluble in plasma and water, but in the plasma it is protein-bound, specifically to albumin. Each molecule of albumin appears to have one high-affinity site and one low-affinity site for bilirubin. In 100 mL of plasma, approximately 25 mg of bilirubin can be **tightly bound to albumin** at its high-affinity site. Bilirubin in excess of this quantity can be bound only loosely and thus can easily be detached and diffused into tissues. A number of compounds such as antibiotics and other drugs compete with bilirubin for the high-affinity binding site on albumin. Thus, these compounds can displace bilirubin from albumin and have significant clinical effects.

In the liver, the bilirubin seems to be removed from the albumin and taken up at the sinusoidal surface of the hepatocytes by a carrier-mediated saturable system. This facilitated transport system has a very large capacity, so that even under pathologic conditions the system does not appear to be rate-limiting in the metabolism of bilirubin.

Since this facilitated transport system allows the equilibration of bilirubin across the sinusoidal membrane of the hepatocyte, the net uptake of bilirubin will be dependent upon the removal of bilirubin by subsequent metabolic pathways.

Conjugation of Bilirubin

By adding polar groups to bilirubin, the liver converts bilirubin to a water-soluble form that can subsequently be secreted into the bile. This process of **increasing the water-solubility** or polarity of bilirubin is achieved by conjugation. It is a process carried out in the smooth endoplasmic reticulum with the aid of a specific set of enzymes. Most of the bilirubin excreted in the bile of mammals is in the form of a **bilirubin diglucuronide** (Fig 24–15). The formation of the glucuronides of bilirubin is catalyzed by uridine diphosphate glucuronate glucuronyltransferase **(UDP-glucuronyltransferase),** an enzyme that exists in the smooth endoplasmic reticulum and is probably composed of more than a single entity. The reaction is depicted in Fig 24–16. It occurs chiefly in the liver but also in the kidney and the intestinal mucosa. More will

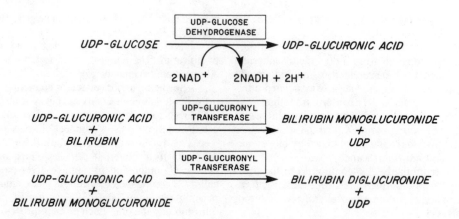

Figure 24–16. Conjugation of bilirubin with glucuronic acid. The glucuronate donor, UDP-glucuronic acid, is formed from UDP-glucose as depicted.

be said about this conjugation system in the discussion of the inherited disorders of bilirubin conjugation.

UDP-glucuronyltransferase activity can be **induced** by a number of clinically effective drugs, including phenobarbital. It has also been suggested that the synthesis of the monoglucuronide of bilirubin is catalyzed by an enzyme separate from that which adds the second glucuronide molecule to bilirubin to make bilirubin diglucuronide.

Secretion of Bilirubin Into Bile

Secretion of conjugated bilirubin into the bile occurs against a large concentration gradient and must be carried out by an active transport mechanism. The **active transport** is probably **rate-limiting** for the entire process of hepatic bilirubin metabolism. The hepatic transport of conjugated bilirubin into the bile is inducible by those same drugs that are capable of inducing the conjugation of bilirubin. Thus, the conjugation and excretion systems for bilirubin behave as a coordinated functional unit.

Under physiologic conditions, essentially all bilirubin secreted into the bile is conjugated. Only after phototherapy can significant quantities of unconjugated bilirubin be found in bile.

In the liver, there are multiple systems for secreting naturally occurring and pharmaceutical compounds into the bile after their metabolism. Some of these secreting systems are shared by the bilirubin diglucuronides, but others seem to operate independently.

Metabolism of Bilirubin in the Intestine

As the conjugated bilirubin reaches the terminal ileum and the large intestine, the glucuronides are removed by specific bacterial enzymes, and the pigment is subsequently reduced by the fecal flora to a group of colorless tetrapyrrolic compounds called urobilinogens (Fig 24–17). In the terminal ileum and large intestine, a small fraction of the urobilinogens is reabsorbed and reexcreted through the liver to constitute the **intrahepatic urobilinogen cycle.** Under abnormal conditions, particularly when excessive bile pigment is formed or liver disease interferes with this intrahepatic cycle, urobilinogen may also be excreted in the urine.

Normally, most of the **colorless urobilinogens** formed in the colon by the fecal flora are oxidized to urobilins (colored compounds) and are excreted in the feces (Fig 24–17). Darkening of feces upon standing

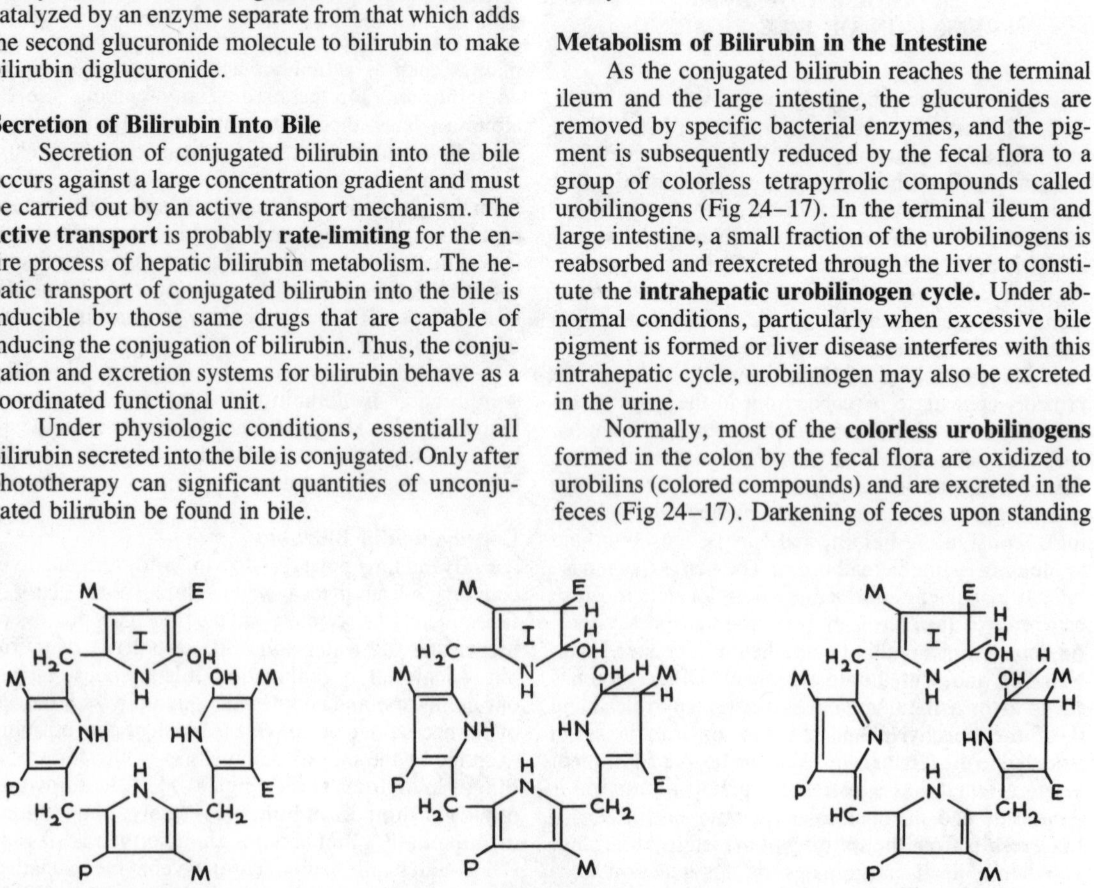

Mesobilirubinogen
($C_{33}H_{44}O_6N_4$)

Stercobilinogen
(L-urobilinogen)

Stercobilin
(L-urobilin)

Figure 24–17. Structure of some bile pigments.

in air is due to the oxidation of residual urobilinogens to urobilins.

HYPERBILIRUBINEMIA

When bilirubin in the blood exceeds 1 mg/dL (17.1 μmol/L), hyperbilirubinemia exists. Hyperbilirubinemia may be due to the production of more bilirubin than the normal liver can excrete, or it may result from the failure of a damaged liver to excrete bilirubin produced in normal amounts. In the absence of hepatic damage, obstruction to the excretory ducts of the liver—by preventing the excretion of bilirubin—will also cause hyperbilirubinemia. In all of these situations, bilirubin accumulates in the blood, and when it reaches a certain concentration, it diffuses into the tissues, which then become yellow. The condition is called **jaundice** or **icterus.**

In clinical studies of jaundice, measurement of bilirubin in the serum is of great value. A method for quantitatively assaying the bilirubin content of the serum was first devised by Van den Bergh by application of Ehrlich's test for bilirubin in urine. The Ehrlich reaction is based on the coupling of diazotized sulfanilic acid (Ehrlich's diazo reagent) and bilirubin to produce a reddish-purple azo compound. In the original procedure as described by Ehrlich, methanol was used to provide a solution in which both bilirubin and the diazo reagent were soluble. Van den Bergh inadvertently omitted the methanol on an occasion when assay of bile pigment in human bile was being attempted. To his surprise, normal development of the color occurred "directly." This form of bilirubin that would react without the addition of methanol was thus termed "direct-reacting." It was then found that this same direct reaction would also occur in serum for cases of jaundice due to obstruction. However, it was still necessary to add methanol to detect bilirubin in normal serum or that which was present in excess in serum from cases of hemolytic jaundice where no evidence of obstruction was to be found. To that form of bilirubin which could be measured only after the addition of methanol, the term "indirect-reacting" was applied.

It has now been demonstrated that the indirect bilirubin is "free" (unconjugated) bilirubin en route to the liver from the reticuloendothelial tissues where the bilirubin was originally produced by the breakdown of heme porphyrins. Since this bilirubin is not water-soluble, it requires methanol to initiate coupling with the diazo reagent. In the liver, the free bilirubin becomes conjugated with glucuronic acid, and the conjugate, bilirubin glucuronide, can then be excreted into the bile. Furthermore, conjugated bilirubin, being water-soluble, can react directly with the diazo reagent so that the "direct bilirubin" of Van den Bergh is actually a bilirubin conjugate (bilirubin glucuronide).

Depending on the type of bilirubin present in plasma, ie, unconjugated bilirubin or conjugated bilirubin, the hyperbilirubinemia may be classified as **retention** hyperbilirubinemia or **regurgitation** hyperbilirubinemia, respectively.

Only unconjugated bilirubin can cross the blood-brain barrier into the central nervous system; thus, encephalopathy due to hyperbilirubinemia (kernicterus) can occur only in connection with retention bilirubin or unconjugated hyperbilirubinemia. On the other hand, only conjugated bilirubin can appear in urine. Accordingly, **choluric jaundice** occurs only in regurgitation hyperbilirubinemia, and **acholuric jaundice** occurs only in the presence of an excess of unconjugated bilirubin.

Unconjugated Hyperbilirubinemia

Even in the event of extensive hemolysis, unconjugated hyperbilirubinemia is usually only slight (< 4 mg/dL; < 68.4 μmol/L) because of the liver's large capacity for handling bilirubin. However, if the handling of bilirubin is defective owing to either an acquired defect or an inherited abnormality, unconjugated hyperbilirubinemia may occur.

The most common cause of unconjugated hyperbilirubinemia is the transient neonatal "physiologic jaundice." This hyperbilirubinemia results from an accelerated hemolysis and an immature hepatic system for the uptake, conjugation, and secretion of bilirubin. Not only is the **UDP-glucuronyltransferase** activity reduced, but there probably is reduced synthesis of the substrate for that enzyme, UDP-glucuronic acid. Since the increased bilirubin is unconjugated, it is capable of penetrating the blood-brain barrier when its concentration in plasma exceeds that which can be tightly bound by albumin (20–25 mg/dL). This can result in a hyperbilirubinemic toxic encephalopathy or kernicterus. Because of the recognized inducibility of this bilirubin metabolizing system, phenobarbital has been administered to jaundiced neonates and is effective in this disorder. In addition, exposure to visible light (by a mechanism that is not understood) can promote the hepatic excretion of unconjugated bilirubin and convert some of the bilirubin to other derivatives that are excreted in the bile.

Crigler-Najjar Syndrome, Type I; Congenital Nonhemolytic Jaundice

Type I Crigler-Najjar syndrome is a rare autosomal recessive disorder of humans due to a primary metabolic defect in the conjugation of bilirubin. It is characterized by severe congenital jaundice due to the absence of bilirubin UDP-glucuronyltransferase activity in hepatic tissues. The disease is usually fatal within the first 15 months of life, but a few teenagers have been reported who did not develop difficulties until puberty. These children have been treated with phototherapy with some reduction in plasma bilirubin levels. Phenobarbital and other drugs that induce the bilirubin metabolizing systems in normal liver have no effect on the formation of bilirubin glucuronides in patients with type I Crigler-Najjar syndrome. Serum bilirubin usually exceeds 20 mg/dL when untreated.

Crigler-Najjar Syndrome, Type II

This rare inherited disorder seems to result from a milder defect in the bilirubin conjugating system and has a more benign course. The serum bilirubin concentrations usually do not exceed 20 mg/dL, but all of the bilirubin accumulated is of the unconjugated type. Surprisingly, the bile in these patients does contain bilirubin monoglucuronide, and it has been proposed that the genetic defect may involve the hepatic UDP-glucuronyltransferase that adds the second glucuronyl group to bilirubin monoglucuronide.

It has been demonstrated that patients with this syndrome can respond to treatment with large doses of phenobarbital. In these patients, the drug-mediated reduction of hyperbilirubinemia seems to result from induction of the entire bilirubin metabolizing system and not simply a stimulation of bilirubin conjugation.

In several instances, presumed heterozygotes for this disorder exhibited a mild unconjugated hyperbilirubinemia indistinguishable from that seen in Gilbert's disease (see below). Thus, it is possible that the autosomal recessive type II Crigler-Najjar syndrome is the homozygous state of the defect present in heterozygous form in the mild chronic hyperbilirubinemia of Gilbert.

Gilbert's Disease

Gilbert's disease is a heterogeneous group of diseases most of which are now recognized to be due to a compensated hemolysis associated with unconjugated hyperbilirubinemia. There also appears to be a defect in the hepatic clearance of bilirubin, possibly due to a defect in the uptake of bilirubin by the liver parenchymal cells. However, bilirubin UDP-glucuronyltransferase activities in the livers of those patients studied with this disease were found to be reduced.

In general, the disorders collectively termed Gilbert's disease seem to be transmitted in an autosomal dominant manner.

Toxic Hyperbilirubinemia

Unconjugated hyperbilirubinemia can result from toxin-induced liver dysfunction such as that caused by chloroform, arsphenamines, carbon tetrachloride, acetoaminophen, hepatitis virus, cirrhosis, and mushroom poisoning. Although most of these acquired disorders are due to hepatic parenchymal cell damage, there is frequently a component of obstruction of the biliary tree within the liver that results in the presence of some conjugated hyperbilirubinemia.

Conjugated Hyperbilirubinemia

Because conjugated bilirubin is water-soluble, it is detectable in the urine of most patients with conjugated hyperbilirubinemia; thus, they are frequently said to have choluric jaundice.

Chronic Idiopathic Jaundice (Dubin-Johnson Syndrome)

This autosomal recessive disorder consists of con-jugated hyperbilirubinemia in childhood or during adult life. The hyperbilirubinemia is apparently caused by a defect in the hepatic secretion of conjugated bilirubin into the bile. However, this secretory defect of conjugated compounds is not restricted to bilirubin but also involves secretion of conjugated estrogens and test compounds such as the dye sulfobromophthalein. In fact, the secretory defect of conjugated sulfobromophthalein results in its reflux into the plasma, leading to a secondary rise in the plasma concentration of this test dye, a phenomenon which is pathognomonic for Dubin-Johnson syndrome. When test compounds such as indocyanine green and rose bengal, which do not require conjugation for excretion, are used, such secondary rises in plasma concentration do not appear in these patients. Thus, the defect appears to be in the secretory process that normally deals only with conjugated compounds including conjugated bilirubins.

Another interesting but unexplained phenomenon associated with Dubin-Johnson syndrome is the abnormal distribution of coproporphyrin I and III in the urine. In patients with Dubin-Johnson syndrome, 80–90% of the coproporphyrins are of the type I isomer, in contrast to the normal situation. This abnormality includes an absolute increase in coproporphyrin I and an absolute decrease in coproporphyrin III excretion. However, there do not seem to be any abnormalities of porphyrin synthesis in Dubin-Johnson syndrome. Characteristically, in patients with Dubin-Johnson syndrome, the hepatocytes in the centrolobular area contain an abnormal pigment that has not been identified.

Biliary Tree Obstruction

Conjugated hyperbilirubinemia also results from blockage of the hepatic or common bile ducts. The bile pigment is believed to pass from the blood into the liver cells as usual but fails to be excreted. As a consequence of this, the conjugated bilirubin is absorbed into the hepatic veins and lymphatics.

The term **cholestatic jaundice** may be used to include all forms of extrahepatic obstructive jaundice in addition to some forms of parenchymal jaundice characterized by conjugated hyperbilirubinemia.

Urine Urobilinogen

Normally, there are mere traces of urobilinogen in the urine (average, 0.64 mg; maximum normal, 4 mg [in 24 hours]). In complete obstruction of the bile duct, no urobilinogen is found in the urine since bilirubin is unable to get to the intestine to form it. In this case, the presence of bilirubin in the urine without urobilinogen suggests **obstructive jaundice,** either intrahepatic or posthepatic.

In **hemolytic jaundice,** the increased production of bilirubin leads to increased production of urobilinogen, which appears in the urine in large amounts. Bilirubin is not usually found in the urine in hemolytic jaundice, so that the combination of increased urobilinogen and absence of bilirubin is suggestive of hemolytic jaundice. Increased blood destruction from

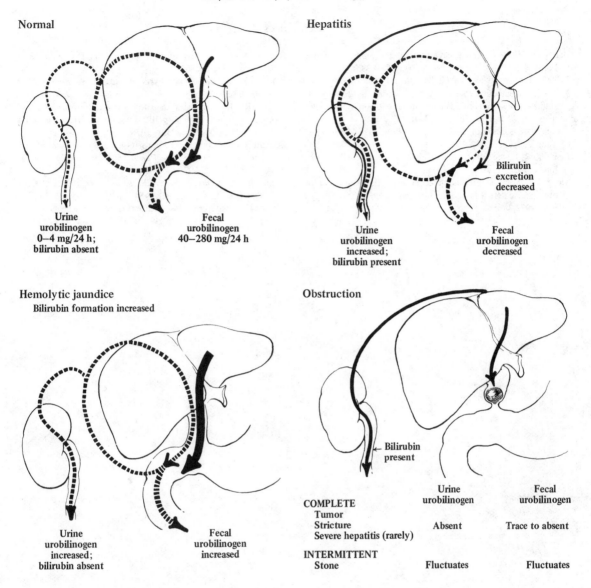

Normal

Urine
urobilinogen
0–4 mg/24 h;
bilirubin absent

Fecal
urobilinogen
40–280 mg/24 h

Hepatitis

Bilirubin
excretion
decreased

Urine
urobilinogen
increased;
bilirubin present

Fecal
urobilinogen
decreased

Hemolytic jaundice
Bilirubin formation increased

Urine
urobilinogen
increased;
bilirubin absent

Fecal
urobilinogen
increased

Obstruction

Bilirubin
present

	Urine urobilinogen	Fecal urobilinogen
COMPLETE Tumor Stricture Severe hepatitis (rarely)	Absent	Trace to absent
INTERMITTENT Stone	Fluctuates	Fluctuates

Figure 24–18. Bilirubin-urobilinogen cycle. (Solid arrows = bilirubin glucuronide; dotted arrows = urobilinogen.) (Reproduced, with permission, from Krupp MA & others: *Physician's Handbook,* 19th ed. Lange, 1979.)

any cause (eg, pernicious anemia) will, of course, also bring about an increase in urine urobilinogen. Furthermore, infection of the biliary passages may increase the urobilinogen in the absence of any reduction in liver function because of the reducing activity of the infecting bacteria.

The diagrams in Fig 24–18 summarize the events characterizing the handling of bilirubin and urobilinogen by the liver, intestine, and kidney under normal circumstances and in the presence of hemolytic jaundice, hepatitis, or jaundice associated with obstruction of the bile duct.

● ● ●

References

Battersby AR & others: Biosynthesis of the pigments of life: Formation of the macrocycle. *Nature* 1980;**285**:17.

Eales L, Grosser Y, Sears WG: The clinical biochemistry of the human hepatocutaneous porphyrias in the light of recent studies of newly identified intermediates and porphyrin derivatives. *Ann NY Acad Sci* 1975;**244**:441.

Goldberg A, Rimington C: *Diseases of Porphyrin Metabolism.* Thomas, 1962.

Lemberg R, Legge JW: *Hematin Compounds and Bile Pigments.* Interscience, 1949.

Meyer UA & others: Intermittent acute porphyria: Demonstration of a genetic defect in porphobilinogen metabolism. *N Engl J Med* 1972;**286**:1277.

Rimington C: Haem pigments and porphyrins. *Annu Rev Biochem* 1957;**26**:561.

Schmid R: Cutaneous porphyria in Turkey. *N Engl J Med* 1960;**263**:397.

Schmid R: The porphyrias. In: *The Metabolic Basis of Inherited Disease,* 4th ed. Stanbury JB, Wyngaarden JB, Fredrickson DS (editors). McGraw-Hill, 1978.

Schmid R, McDonough AF: Formation and metabolism of bile pigments in vivo. In: *The Porphyrins.* Dolphin D (editor). Academic Press, 1978.

Symposium: Porphyrin Biosynthesis and Metabolism. Ciba Foundation. Little, Brown, 1954.

Watson CJ: Gold from dross: The first century of the urobilinoids. *Ann Intern Med* 1969;**70**:839.

Nucleotides | 25

David W. Martin, Jr., MD

The nucleotides are important intracellular molecules of low molecular weight that participate in a wide variety of biochemical processes. Perhaps the best known role of the purine and pyrimidine nucleotides is to serve as the monomeric precursors of RNA and DNA. However, the **purine** ribonucleotides serve also in biologic systems as the ubiquitous high-energy source, ATP, as regulatory signals (cyclic AMP [cAMP] and cyclic GMP) in a wide variety of tissues and organisms, and as components of the widely used coenzymes FAD, NAD, and NADP and of an important methyl donor, S-adenosylmethionine.

The **pyrimidine** nucleotides, in addition to providing monomeric precursors for nucleic acids, serve as high-energy intermediates, such as UDP-glucose and UDP-galactose in carbohydrate metabolism and CDP-acylglycerol in lipid synthesis.

The various purine and pyrimidine bases that occur in the nucleotides are derived by appropriate substitution on the ring structures of the parent substances, purine or pyrimidine. Structures of these parent nitrogenous bases are shown in Fig 25–1. The positions on the rings are numbered according to the international system. Note that the direction of the numbering of the purine ring is different from that of the pyrimidine ring but that the number 5 carbon is the same in both heterocyclic compounds. Owing to their π electron clouds, both the purine and pyrimidine bases are planar molecules, the significance of which is discussed in Chapter 27.

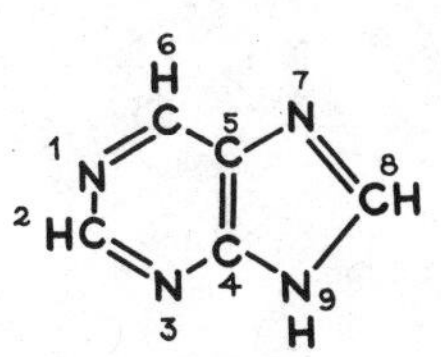

The 3 major **pyrimidine bases** found in the nucleotides of both prokaryotes and eukaryotes are **cytosine, thymine,** and **uracil** (Fig 25–2). The **purine**

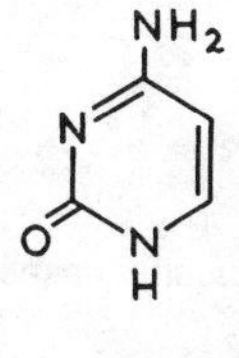

Cytosine
(2-oxy-4-aminopyrimidine)

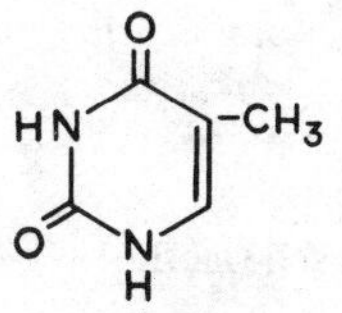

Thymine
(2,4-dioxy-5-methylpyrimidine)

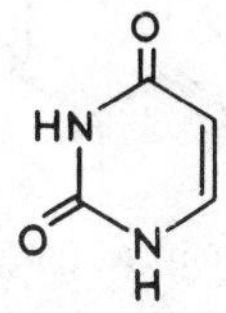

Uracil
(2,4-dioxypyrimidine)

Figure 25–2. The 3 major pyrimidine bases found in nucleotides.

bases, **adenine** and **guanine,** are the 2 major purines found in living organisms. Two other purine bases, **hypoxanthine** and **xanthine,** also occur as intermediates in the metabolism of adenine and guanine (Fig 25–3). In humans, a completely oxidized purine base, **uric acid,** is formed as the end product of purine catabolism. This compound is discussed in greater detail in Chapter 26.

Because of keto-enol tautomerism, these aromatic molecules can exist in a lactim or lactam form (Fig 25–4); the latter is by far the predominant tautomer of uracil or thymine under physiologic conditions. (The importance of the lactim versus the lactam form becomes apparent in the discussions on base pairing and mutagenesis in Chapters 28 and 29.)

In plants, a series of purine bases containing methyl substituents occurs (Fig 25–5). Many have pharmacologic properties. Examples are coffee, which contains caffeine (1,3,7-trimethylxanthine); tea, which contains theophylline (1,3-dimethylxanthine); and cocoa, which contains theobromine (3,7-dimethylxanthine). The biologic properties of these

Purine

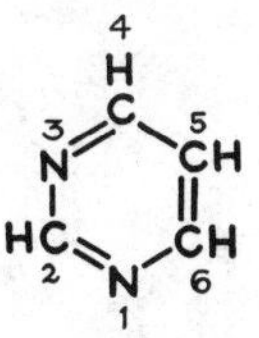

Pyrimidine

Figure 25–1. Structures of purine and pyrimidine with the positions of the elements numbered according to the international system.

Adenine
(6-aminopurine)

Guanine
(2-amino-6-oxypurine)

Hypoxanthine
(6-oxypurine)

Xanthine
(2,6-dioxypurine)

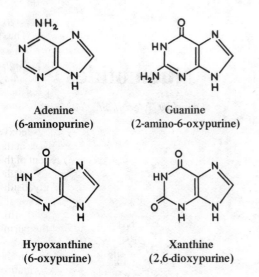

Figure 25–3. The major purine bases present in nucleotides.

Uracil (lactam) **Uracil (lactim)**

Thymine (lactam) **Thymine (lactim)**

Adenine (lactam) **Adenine (lactim)**

Guanine (lactam) **Guanine (lactim)**

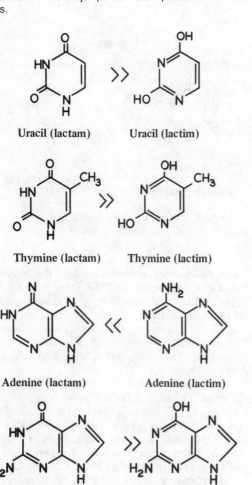

Figure 25–4. The structures of the tautomers of uracil, thymine, adenine, and guanine with the predominant forms indicated.

Caffeine
(1,3,7-trimethyl-xanthine)

Theophylline
(1,3-dimethyl-xanthine)

Theobromine
(3,7-dimethyl-xanthine)

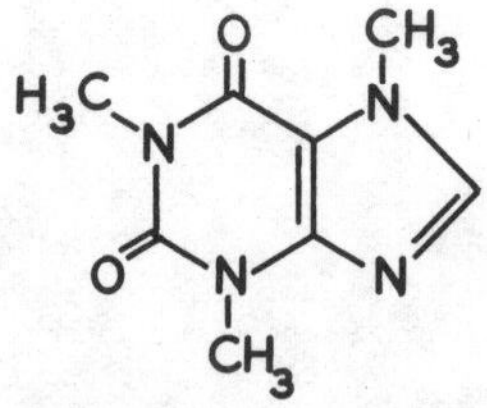

Figure 25–5. The structures of some methyl xanthines commonly occurring in foodstuffs.

compounds are described in Chapter 26 in the discussion of the metabolism of cyclic nucleotides.

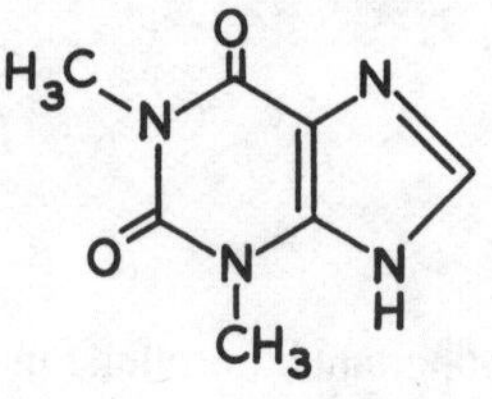

In natural materials, numerous minor (ie, unusual) bases occur in addition to the 5 major bases—adenine, guanine, cytosine, thymine, and uracil—described above. Some of these unusual substituted bases are found only in the nucleic acids of bacteria and viruses, but many are also found in the DNA and transfer RNAs of both prokaryotes and eukaryotes. Both bacterial and human DNA contain, for example, significant quantities of 5-methylcytosine; bacteriophages contain 5-hydroxymethylcytosine (Fig 25–6). More recently, several unusual bases have been discovered in the messenger RNA molecules of mammalian cells. N^6-methyladenine, N^6-dimethyladenine, and N^7-methylguanine are found in the nucleic acids of mammalian cells (Fig 25–7). A uracil modified at the N_3 position by the attachment of an (α-amino,

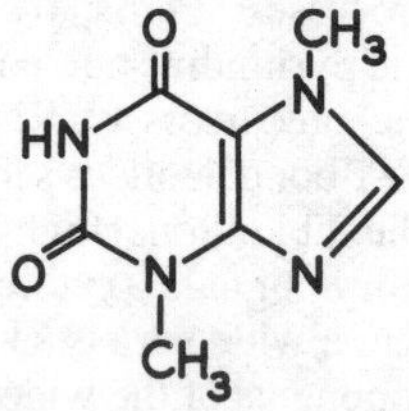

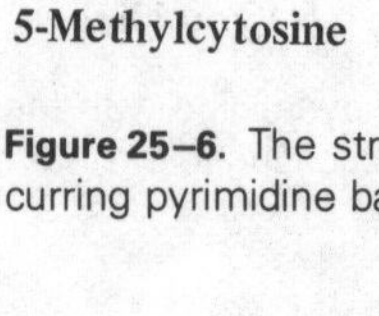

5-Methylcytosine

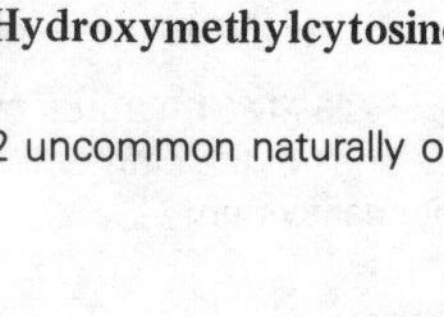

5-Hydroxymethylcytosine

Figure 25–6. The structures of 2 uncommon naturally occurring pyrimidine bases.

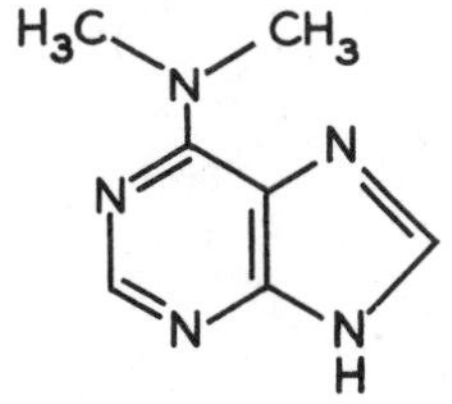

N⁶,N⁶-Dimethyladenine 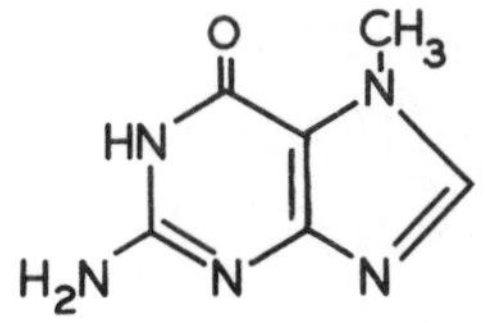   7-Methylguanine

Figure 25–7. The structures of 2 uncommon naturally occurring purine bases.

α-carboxyl)-propyl group has also been detected in bacteria. The functions of these substituted purine and pyrimidine nucleotide bases are not fully understood.

At neutral pH, guanine is the least soluble of the bases, followed in this respect by xanthine. Although uric acid as urate is relatively soluble at a neutral pH, its pK is 5.75, so that it becomes highly insoluble in a solution with a lower pH, such as urine. Guanine is not a normal constituent of human urine, but xanthine and uric acid do occur in human urine. In view of their low solubility, it is not surprising that these latter 2 purines are most likely to be found as constituents of stones formed within the urinary tract.

NUCLEOSIDES & NUCLEOTIDES

The **free** bases occurring in nature are much less abundant forms of purines and pyrimidines than are their nucleosides and nucleotides. A **nucleoside** (Fig 25–8) is composed of a purine or a pyrimidine base to

which a sugar (usually either D-ribose or 2-deoxyribose) is attached at the N₉ or N₁, respectively. Thus, the adenine ribonucleoside **adenosine** consists of adenine with D-ribose attached at the 9 position. **Guanosine** consists of guanine with D-ribose attached at the 9 position. Cytidine is cytosine with ribose attached at its N₁ position. Uridine consists of ribose attached at the N₁ position of uracil.

The 2′-deoxyribonucleosides consist of 2-deoxyribose attached to the purine or pyrimidine bases at the same positions described above. The attachment of the ribose or 2-deoxyribose to the ring structures of the purine or pyrimidine bases is through an N-glycosidic bond, which is relatively acid labile. Although, theoretically, free rotation occurs about this N-glycosidic bond of the sugar moiety and the purine or pyrimidine ring structure, steric hindrance between these 2 moieties in fact hinders free rotation. In the naturally occurring nucleosides, the **anti** conformation is strongly favored over the **syn** form (Fig 25–9). As is discussed in Chapter 27, the anti form is necessary for the proper positioning of the complementary purine and pyrimidine bases in the double-stranded form of deoxyribonucleic acid. (Because of the conventional representation of the D-ribose, in most figures of this and other chapters, the purine and pyrimidine nucleosides and nucleotides are shown in the less favored syn conformation.)

Nucleotides are nucleosides phosphorylated on one or more of the hydroxyl groups of the sugar (ribose or deoxyribose) (Fig 25–10). Thus, adenosine monophosphate (AMP or adenylate) is adenine + ribose + phosphate. 2′-Deoxyadenosine monophosphate (dAMP or deoxyadenylate) consists of adenine + 2-deoxyribose + phosphate. The only sugar com-

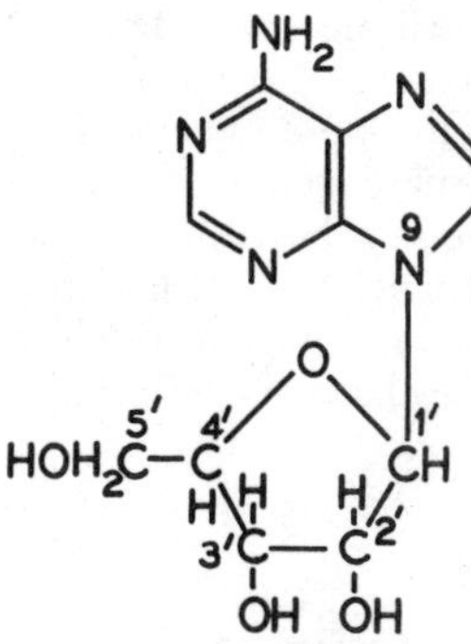

Adenosine

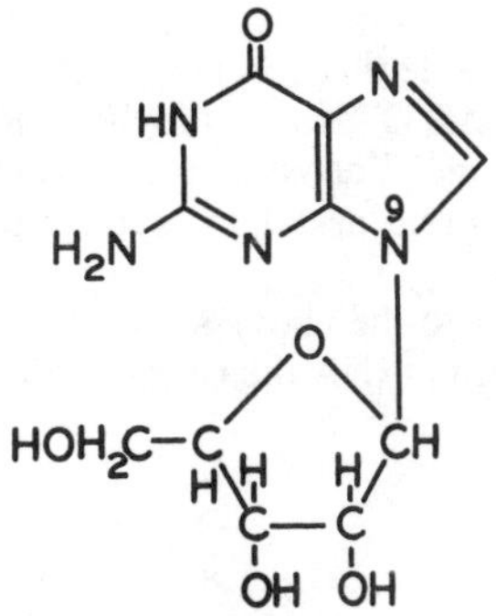

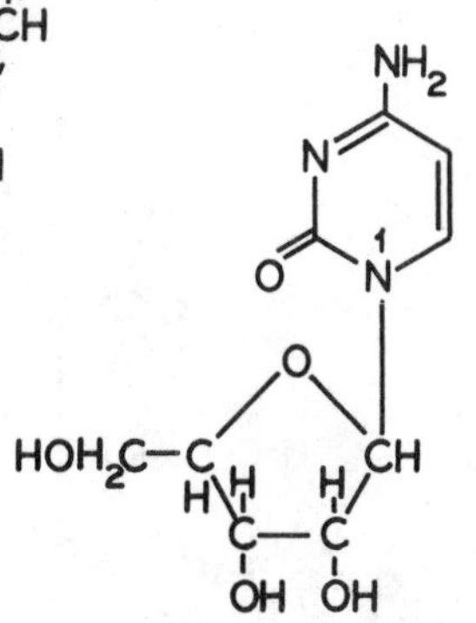

Cytidine

Guanosine

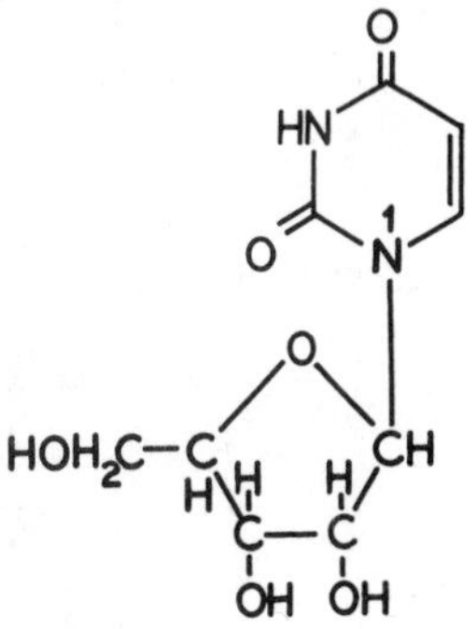

Uridine

Figure 25–8. Structures of ribonucleosides.

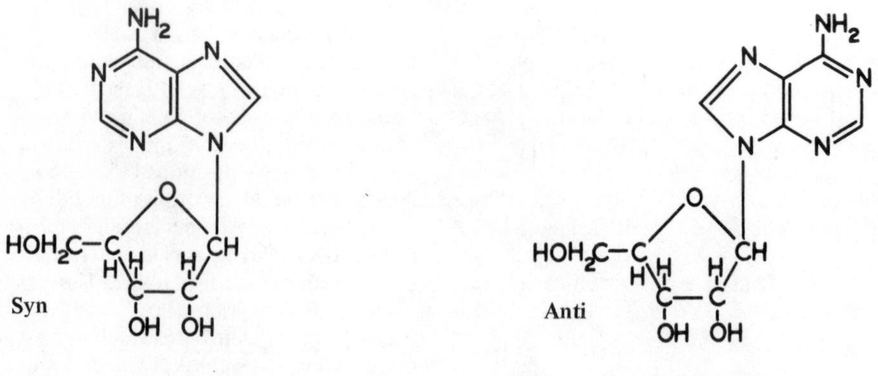

Figure 25–9. The structures of the **syn** and **anti** configurations of adenosine.

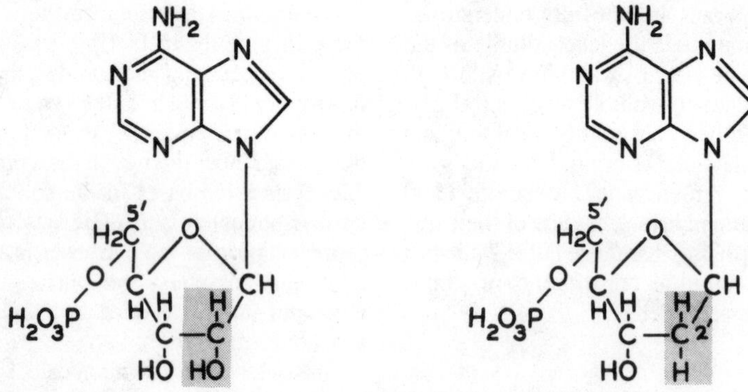

Figure 25–10. The structures of adenylic acid (AMP) *(left)* and 2'-deoxyadenylic acid (dAMP) *(right)*.

monly found attached to uracil is ribose, and that commonly found attached to thymine is 2-deoxyribose. Therefore, thymidylic acid (TMP) is thymine + 2-deoxyribose + phosphate, and uridylic acid (UMP) is uracil + ribose + phosphate (Fig 25–11). DNA is a polymer of thymidylic acid, 2'-deoxycytidylic acid, 2'-deoxyadenylic acid, and 2'deoxyguanylic acid. RNA is a polymer containing uridylate, cytidylate, adenylate, and guanylate.

There are exceptions to the above structures of nucleotides. For example, in tRNA the ribose moiety is occasionally attached to uracil at the 5 position, thus establishing a carbon-to-carbon linkage instead of the usual nitrogen-to-carbon linkage. This unusual compound is called pseudouridine (Ψ). The tRNA molecules contain another unusual nucleotide structure, ie, thymine attached to ribose monophosphate. This compound is formed subsequent to the synthesis of the tRNA by methylation of the UMP residue by S-adenosylmethionine (see below). Pseudouridylic acid (ΨMP) is similarly rearranged from uridylic acid after the tRNA molecule has been synthesized.

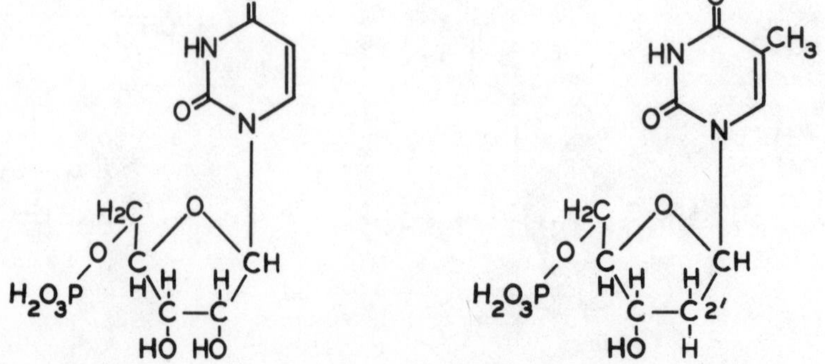

Figure 25–11. The structures of uridylic acid (UMP) *(left)* and thymidylic acid (TMP) *(right)*.

Nomenclature of Nucleosides & Nucleotides

The position of the phosphate in the nucleotide is indicated by a numeral. For example, adenosine with the phosphate attached to carbon 3 of the sugar ribose would be designated adenosine 3'-phosphate. The prime mark after the numeral is required to differentiate the numbered position on the sugar moiety from the numbered position on a purine or pyrimidine base, which would not be followed by the prime mark. A nucleotide of 2'-deoxyadenosine with the phosphate moiety attached to the carbon 5 position of the sugar would be designated 2'-deoxyadenosine-5'-phosphate. (Fig 25-12.)

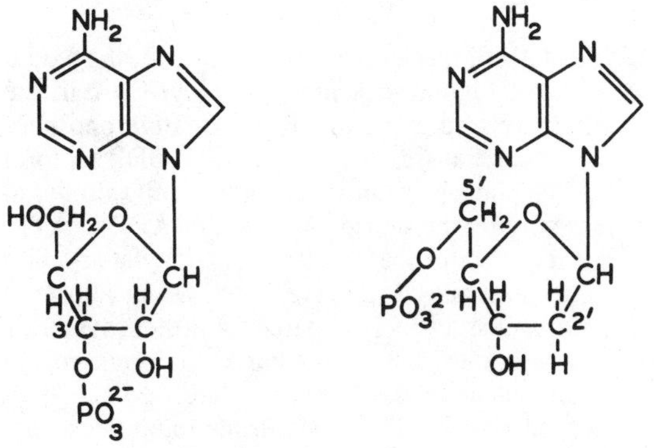

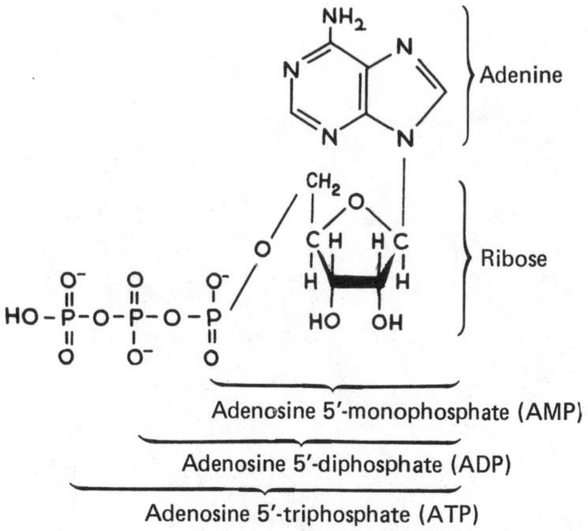

Figure 25–13. The structure of ATP and the structures of the corresponding diphosphate and monophosphate forms.

The structure of ATP is shown in Fig 25–13 along with its corresponding diphosphate and monophosphate forms. Because the phosphates are in the acid anhydride form—a low entropy situation—the phosphates are said to be high-energy ones, ie, high potential energy. The hydrolysis of 1 mol of ATP to ADP releases about 7000 cal of potential energy.

Figure 25–12. The structures of adenosine-3'-monophosphate *(left)* and 2'-deoxyadenosine-5'-monophosphate *(right).*

The abbreviations A, G, C, T, and U may be used to designate a nucleoside in accordance with the purine or pyrimidine base it contains: adenine, guanine, cytosine, thymine, or uracil, respectively. The prefix d is added if the sugar of the nucleoside is 2'-deoxyribose. When the nucleoside occurs in the free form as a mononucleotide (ie, not a component of nucleic acid polynucleotide), the abbreviation MP (monophosphate) may be added to the abbreviation designating the nucleoside. For example, guanosine containing 2'-deoxyribose would be designated dG (deoxyguanosine) and the corresponding monophosphate with the phosphate esterified to the carbon 3 of the deoxyribose moiety is designated dG-3'-MP. Generally, when the phosphate is esterified to the carbon 5 of the ribose or deoxyribose moiety, the prefixed primed number (5') is deleted. For example, guanosine 5'-monophosphate would be abbreviated GMP, while the 5'-monophosphate of 2'-deoxyguanosine would be designated dGMP. When 2 or 3 phosphates are attached to the sugar moiety in the acid anhydride form, the abbreviations DP (diphosphate) and TP (triphosphate) are added to the abbreviations for the corresponding purine or pyrimidine nucleoside. Thus, adenosine triphosphate with 3 phosphate residues attached to the 5' carbon of the adenosine would be abbreviated ATP.

NATURALLY OCCURRING NUCLEOTIDES

Free nucleotides that are not an integral part of nucleic acids are also found in tissues. Many have important functions. Some of these compounds are briefly described.

Adenosine Derivatives

Adenosine diphosphate and adenosine triphosphate are important compounds in view of their participation in oxidative phosphorylation and, in the case of ATP, as the source of high-energy phosphate for nearly every energy-requiring reaction in the cell. The ATP concentration in most living mammalian cells is nearly 1 mM. ATP is the most abundant intracellular free nucleotide.

Cyclic AMP (3',5'-adenosine monophosphate; cAMP) is an unusual but important adenosine derivative which is present in most animal cells. cAMP mediates a series of diverse extracellular signals of considerable importance to the function of the organism as a whole. cAMP is formed from ATP (Fig 25–14). The reaction is catalyzed by the enzyme **adenylate cyclase,** the activity of which is regulated by a series of complex interactions many of which involve hormone receptors. cAMP is destroyed in tissues by its conversion to AMP in a reaction catalyzed by **cAMP phosphodiesterase.** Intracellular cAMP concentrations are usually near 1 μM.

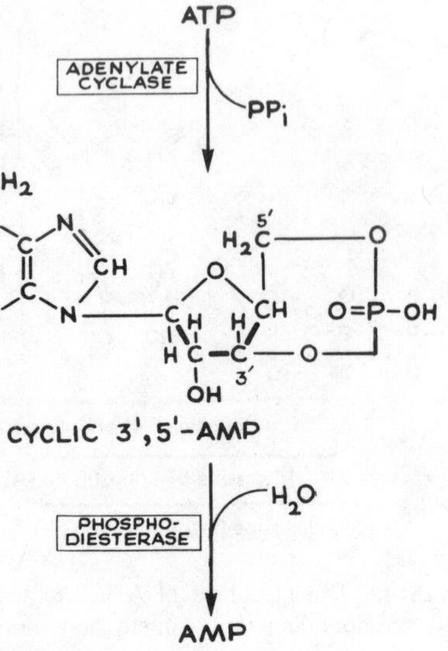

Figure 25–14. Formation of cAMP from ATP and destruction of cAMP by phosphodiesterase.

The incorporation of sulfate into ester linkages in compounds such as sulfated proteoglycans (see Chapter 32) requires the preliminary "activation" of the sulfate molecule. Sulfate is "activated" by reacting with ATP to form adenosine 3'-phosphate-5'-phosphosulfate (PAPS) in the reaction shown in Fig 25–15. The active sulfate moiety is also required as the substrate for sulfate conjugation reactions.

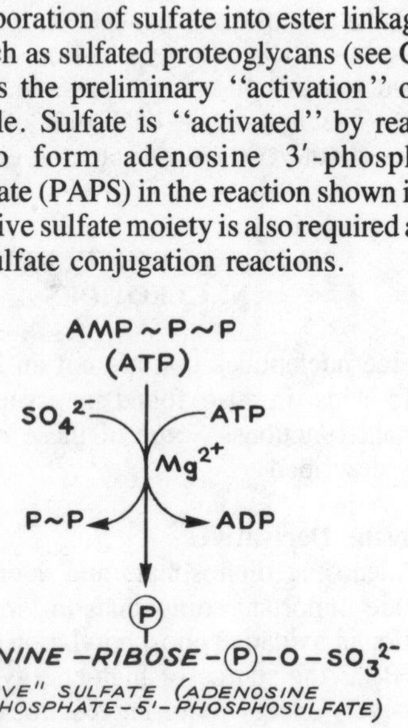

Figure 25–15. The formation of adenosine 3'-phosphate-5'-phosphosulfate.

Another important naturally occurring adenosine derivative, **S-adenosylmethionine** (Fig 25–16), serves as a form of "active" methionine. S-Adenosylmethionine serves widely as a methyl donor in many diverse methylation reactions and as a source of propylamine for the synthesis of polyamines.

Guanosine Derivatives

Guanosine nucleotides, particularly guanosine diphosphate and guanosine triphosphate, serve in several energy-requiring systems. These are analogs of

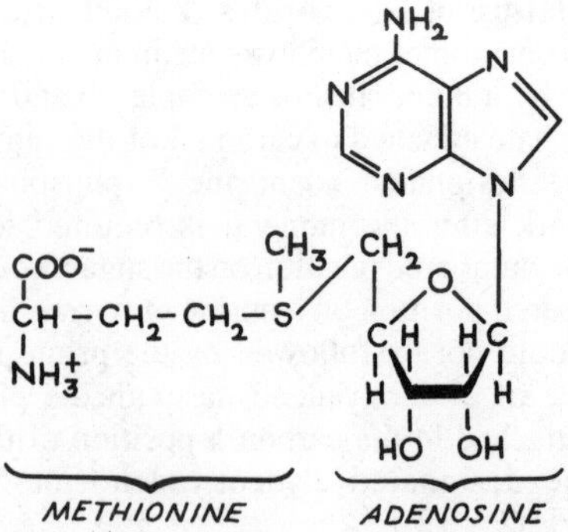

Figure 25–16. The structure of S-adenosylmethionine.

ADP and ATP, respectively. For example, the oxidation of α-ketoglutaric acid to succinyl-CoA in the tricarboxylic acid cycle involves oxidative phosphorylation with transfer of phosphate to GDP to form GTP. This phosphorylation reaction is quite similar to those involving the phosphorylation of ADP to ATP. GTP is required for the activation of adenylate cyclase by some hormones and serves both as an allosteric regulator and as an energy source for protein synthesis on polyribosomes. It therefore has an important role in the maintenance of the internal milieu.

Cyclic GMP or 3',5'-guanosine monophosphate (Fig 25–17) appears also to be an important intracellular signal of extracellular events. In at least some cases, cyclic GMP acts antagonistically to cAMP. Cyclic GMP is formed from GTP by an enzyme called **guanylate cyclase** which is similar in many ways to adenylate cyclase. Guanylate cyclase, like adenylate cyclase, appears to be regulated by a variety of effectors, including hormones. Cyclic GMP is also catabolized by a phosphodiesterase to produce its respective 5'-monophosphate.

Hypoxanthine Derivatives

Hypoxanthine ribonucleotide, usually called inosinic acid (IMP, or inosinate in the salt form), is a

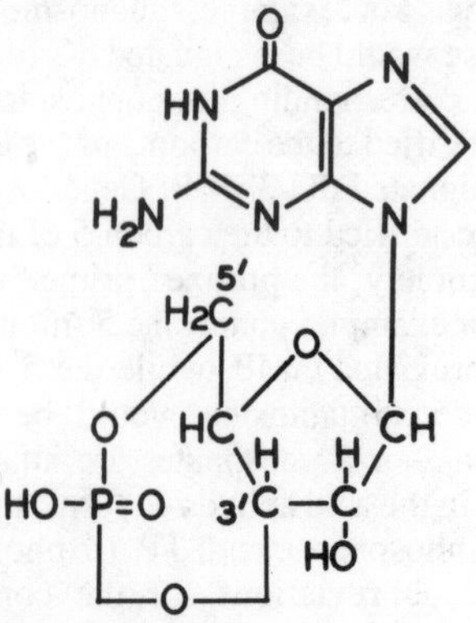

Figure 25–17. The structure of cyclic 3',5'-guanosine monophosphate (cyclic GMP).

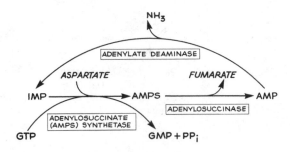

Figure 25–18. The purine nucleotide cycle.

precursor of all purine ribonucleotides synthesized de novo. Inosinate can also be formed by the deamination of AMP, a reaction which occurs particularly in muscle as part of the purine nucleotide cycle (Fig 25–18). Inosinate, derived from AMP, when reconverted to AMP results in the net production of ammonia from aspartate. Removal of the phosphate group from IMP forms the nucleoside inosine (hypoxanthine riboside), an intermediate in another cycle referred to as the purine salvage cycle (see Chapter 26).

Analogs of ADP and ATP in which the purine nucleoside derivative is inosine rather than adenosine have been found occasionally to participate in phosphorylation reactions. These compounds are inosine diphosphate (IDP) and inosine triphosphate (ITP).

Uracil Derivatives

Uridine nucleotide derivatives are important coenzymes in reactions involving the metabolism of galactose and the polymerization of sugars to form starch and the oligosaccharide moieties of glycoproteins and proteoglycans. In these reactions, the substrates are uridine diphospho- sugars. For example, uridine diphosphoglucose (UDPGlc) is the precursor of glycogen. Another uridine nucleotide coenzyme, uridine diphosphoglucuronic acid (UDPGlcUA), serves as the "active" glucuronide for conjugation reactions such as the formation of bilirubin glucuronide (see Chapter 24).

Uracil also participates in the formation of high-energy phosphate compounds analogous to ATP, GTP, or ITP. Uridine triphosphate (UTP) is utilized, for example, in the reactions involving conversion of galactose to glucose in which the UDPGlc and UDP-Gal also are formed. UTP is the precursor for the polymerization of uridine nucleotides into RNA.

Cytosine Derivatives

Cytidine (cytosine-ribose) may form the high-energy phosphate compounds cytidine diphosphate (CDP) and cytidine triphosphate (CTP); the latter serves also as the precursor for the polymerization of CMP into nucleic acids. CTP is a nucleotide required for the biosynthesis of some phosphoglycerides in animal tissue. Reactions involving ceramide and CDP-choline are responsible for the formation of sphingomyelin and other substituted sphingosines.

Cyclic nucleotide derivatives of cytidine, analogous to those of adenosine and guanosine, have been described.

Vitamin Nucleotides

The functional moieties of many vitamins are nucleotides with structures analogous to purine and pyrimidine nucleotides. Riboflavin (vitamin B_2; see Chapter 10) functions as a ribitol 5'-phosphate derivative linked to AMP by a pyrophosphate bridge (FAD). Niacin is a constituent of 2 coenzymes, nicotinamide adenine dinucleotide (NAD) and nicotinamide adenine dinucleotide phosphate (NADP). In both of these cases, nicotinamide ribose phosphate is joined to an adenosine monophosphate through a pyrophosphate linkage. Coenzyme A is pantetheine linked to adenosine 3'-phosphate through a pyrophosphate moiety. One of the biologically active derivatives of cobalamin (vitamin B_{12}) requires the attachment of a 5'-deoxyadenosyl moiety through the 5' carbon to the cobalt.

It should thus be clear that the purine and pyrimidine nucleosides and nucleotides serve many diverse functions in living organisms beyond providing the monomers of the structures of nucleic acids.

SYNTHETIC DERIVATIVES

Synthetic analogs of nucleobases, nucleosides, and nucleotides are widely used in the medical sciences and clinical medicine. In the past, most of these uses have depended upon the role of nucleotides as components of nucleic acids for cellular growth and division. For a cell to divide, its nucleic acids must be replicated, requiring that the precursors of nucleic acids—the normal purine and pyrimidine deoxyribonucleotides—be readily available. One of the most important components of the oncologist's pharmacopeia is the group of synthetic analogs of purine and pyrimidine nucleobases and nucleosides.

The pharmacologic approach has been to use an analog in which either the heterocyclic ring structure or the sugar moiety has been altered in such a way as to induce toxic effects when the analog becomes incorporated into various cellular constituents. Many of these effects result from inhibition by the drug of specific enzyme activities necessary for nucleic acid synthesis or from the incorporation of metabolites of the drug into the nucleic acids where they alter the required base pairing essential to accurate transmission of information.

The most commonly used analogs of the purine or pyrimidine rings have substituents which do not occur naturally and which alter the base pairing or the interaction of the nucleotides with specific enzymes (Fig 25–19). Examples of these would be the 5-fluoro or 5-iodo derivatives of uracil or deoxyuridine, all of which serve as thymine or thymidine analogs, respectively. Both 6-thioguanine and 6-mercaptopurine, in which naturally occurring hydroxyl groups are replaced with thiol groups at the 6 position, are widely

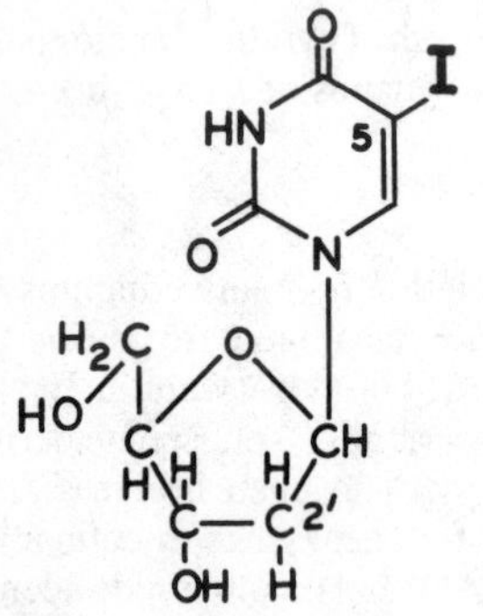

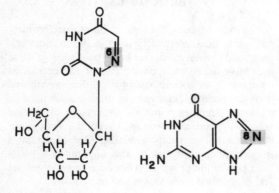

5-Iodo-2′-deoxyuridine 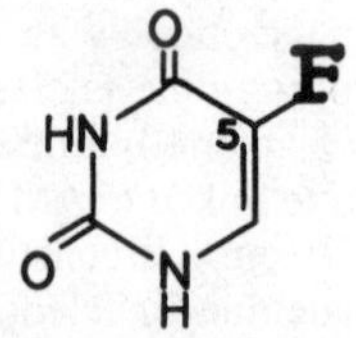   **5-Fluorouracil**

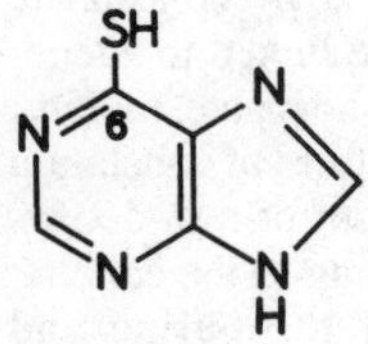

6-Mercaptopurine 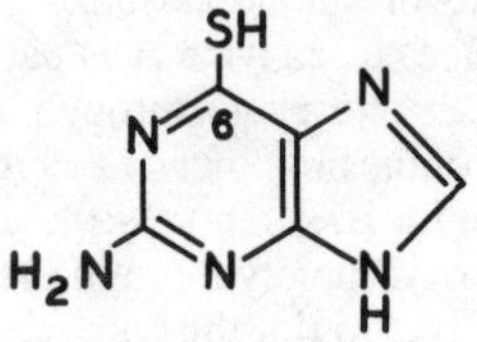   **6-Thioguanine**

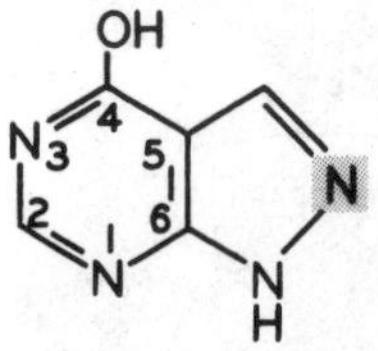

Allopurinol (lactim)

Arabinosyl cytosine

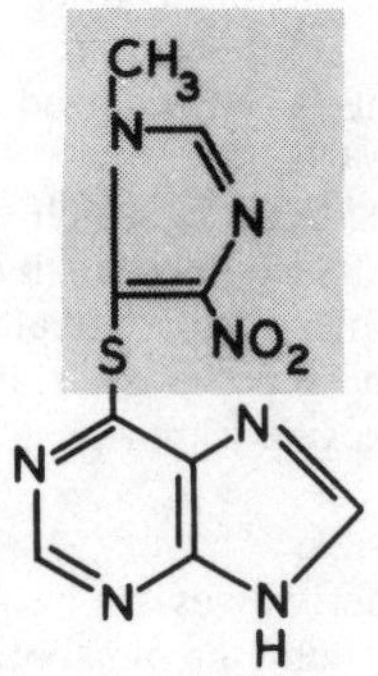

Figure 25–19. The structures of 2 synthetic pyrimidine analogs *(above)* and 2 synthetic purine analogs *(below)*.

Azathioprine

Figure 25–20. The structures of 6-azauridine *(left)* and 8-azaguanine *(right)*.

Figure 25–21. The structures of 4-hydroxypyrazolopyrimidine (allopurinol), arabinosyl cytosine (cytarabine), and azathioprine.

used clinically. The analogs in which the purine or pyrimidine ring contains extra nitrogen atoms, such as 5- or 6-azauridine or azacytidine and 8-azaguanine (Fig 25–20), also have been tested clinically.

The purine analog 4-hydroxypyrazolopyrimidine (allopurinol) is widely marketed as an inhibitor of de novo purine biosynthesis and of xanthine oxidase. It is used for the treatment of hyperuricemia and gout.

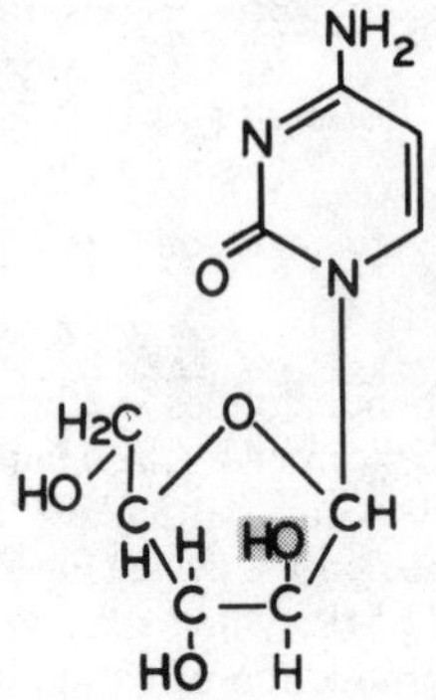

Nucleosides containing arabinose rather than ribose as the sugar moieties, notably cytarabine (arabinosyl cytosine, AraC) and vidarabine (arabinosyl adenine, AraA), are used in the chemotherapy of cancer and viral infections. (See Fig 25–21 for structures of these substances.)

Azathioprine, which is catabolized to 6-mercaptopurine, is useful in organ transplantation as a suppressor of events involved in immunologic rejection. A series of nucleoside analogs with antiviral activities has been studied for several years; one, 5-iododeoxyuridine (see above), has been demonstrated to be highly effective in the local treatment of herpetic keratitis, an infection by herpesvirus of the cornea.

• • •

References

Henderson JF, Paterson ARP: *Nucleotide Metabolism: An Introduction.* Academic Press, 1973.
Michelson AM: *The Chemistry of Nucleosides and Nucleotides.*

Academic Press, 1963.
Prusoff WH, Ward DC: Nucleoside analogs with antiviral activity. *Biochem Pharmacol* 1976;**25**:1233.

Metabolism of Purine & Pyrimidine Nucleotides | 26

David W. Martin, Jr., MD

The chemistry and, to some extent, the general roles of the purine and pyrimidine compounds have been discussed in Chapter 25. The chemistry of the nucleic acids will be described in Chapter 27. In this chapter, the metabolism of the purines and pyrimidines and their nucleosides and nucleotides will be discussed. A summary of these purine and pyrimidine derivatives is given in Table 26–1.

Digestion

Mammals and most lower vertebrates are said to be "prototrophic" for purines and pyrimidines, ie, capable of synthesizing purine and pyrimidine nucleotides de novo and thus not dependent upon exogenous sources of these important compounds. As a result, although mammals consume significant quantities of nucleic acids and nucleotides in their food, their survival is not dependent upon the absorption of these compounds or their breakdown products. Most dietary nucleic acids are ingested in the form of nucleoproteins from which the nucleic acids are liberated in the intestinal tract by the action of proteolytic enzymes. The pancreatic juice contains enzymes (nucleases) which degrade nucleic acids into nucleotides. These nucleases may be specific for the 2 major types of nucleic acids, RNA and DNA, and are appropriately termed ribonucleases and deoxyribonucleases. Intestinal enzymes—polynucleotidases or phosphoesterases—supplement the action of the pancreatic nucleases in producing mononucleotides from the nucleic acids. The mononucleotides are subsequently hydrolyzed to nucleosides by various nucleotidases and phosphatases, and the various nucleosides so produced can be either absorbed directly or further degraded by intestinal phosphorylase to the free purine or pyrimidine bases. The bases themselves may be oxidized, eg, guanine may be converted to xanthine and then to uric acid, or adenosine may be converted to inosine, to hypoxanthine, and then to uric acid (Fig 26–1). Uric acid can be absorbed across the intestinal mucosa and excreted in the urine as uric acid per se. In humans it appears that the majority of purines in ingested nucleic acids are **directly converted to uric acid** without having previously been incorporated into the nucleic acids of the ingesting organism. Free pyrimidine orally administered to rats is mostly catabolized and excreted without having entered the nucleic acids of the ingesting organism. It would thus appear that none of the free purines or pyrimidines of the diet serve as a direct precursor of tissue nucleic acids.

Somewhat different results are obtained when

Table 26–1. The naturally occurring purine and pyrimidine bases and their related nucleosides and nucleotides.

Base	Nucleoside (Base + Sugar)	Nucleotide (Base + Sugar + Phosphoric Acid)
Purines		
Adenine (6-aminopurine)	Adenosine	Adenylic acid
	Deoxyadenosine	Deoxyadenylic acid
Guanine (2-amino-6-oxypurine)	Guanosine	Guanylic acid
	Deoxyguanosine	Deoxyguanylic acid
Hypoxanthine (6-oxypurine)	Inosine (hypoxanthine riboside)	Inosinic acid (hypoxanthine ribotide)
	Deoxyinosine (hypoxanthine deoxyriboside)	Deoxyinosinic acid (hypoxanthine deoxyribotide)
Xanthine (2,6-dioxypurine)	Xanthosine	Xanthinylic acid
Pyrimidines		
Cytosine (2-oxy-4-aminopyrimidine)	Cytidine	Cytidylic acid
	Deoxycytidine	Deoxycytidylic acid
Thymine (2,4-dioxy-5-methylpyrimidine)	Thymidine (thymine deoxyriboside)	Thymidylic acid (thymine deoxyribotide)
Uracil (2,4-dioxypyrimidine)	Uridine	Uridylic acid
Uracil	Pseudouridine (5-ribosyl linkage)	Pseudouridylic acid

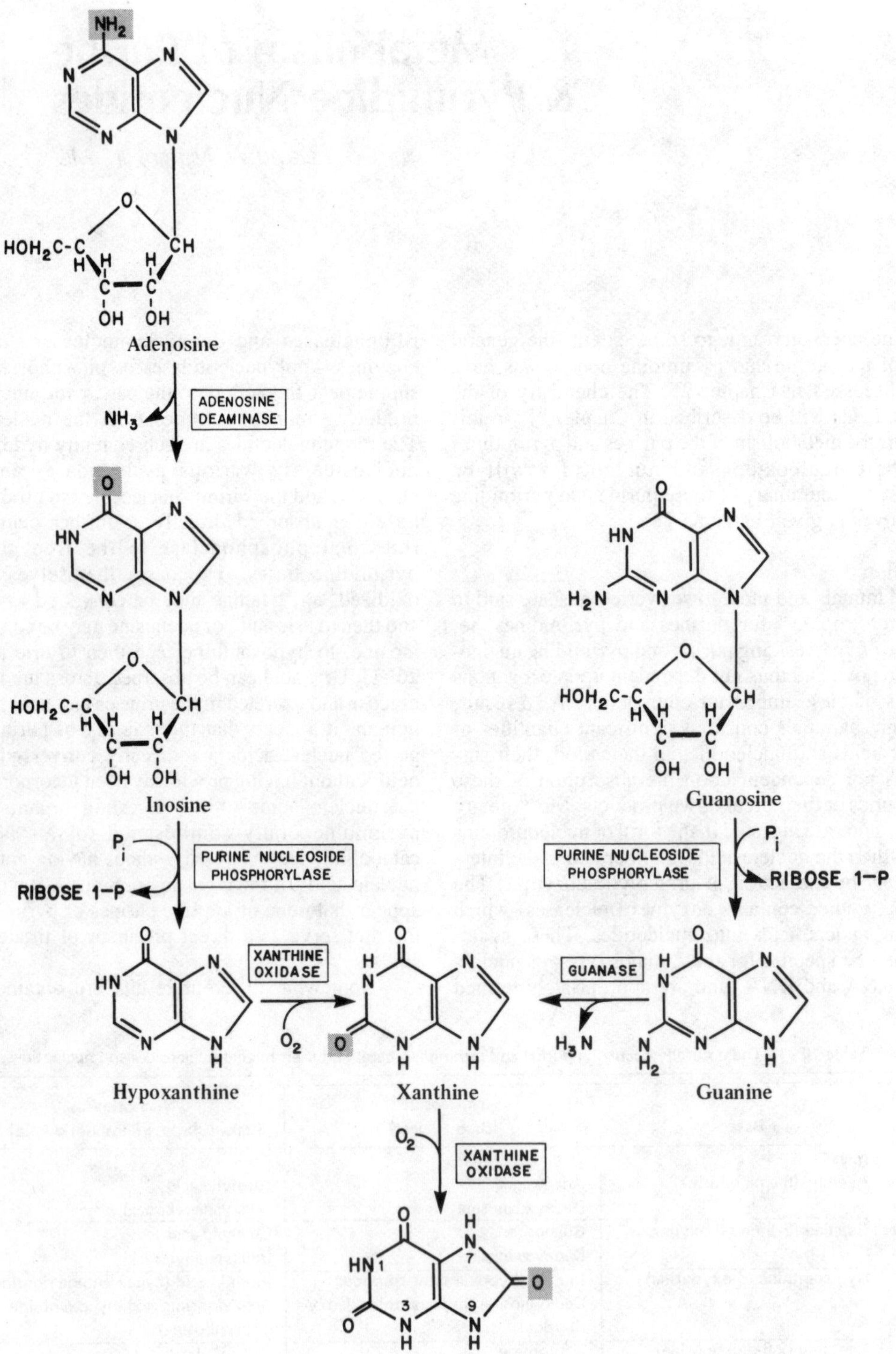

Figure 26–1. Generation of uric acid from purine nucleosides by way of the purine bases hypoxanthine, xanthine, and guanine. Purine deoxyribonucleosides are degraded by the same enzymes and pathway.

purines or pyrimidines are administered parenterally as nucleosides or nucleotides. Injected thymidine may be incorporated into DNA unaltered. This is the basis of a valuable technic for labeling newly produced DNA in a great variety of biologic materials both in vivo and in vitro. For these purposes, ^{3}H-thymidine—ie, thymidine containing tritium (^{3}H), the radioactive isotope of hydrogen—is used.

Biosynthesis of Purine Nucleotides

In humans and other mammals, purine nucleotides are synthesized to meet the needs of the organism for the monomeric precursors of nucleic acids and for those other functions described in Chapter 25. In some organisms (birds, amphibians, and reptiles), the synthesis of purine nucleotides has an additional function, which is to serve as the chemical vehicle to excrete nitrogen waste products as uric acid. Such organisms are referred to as **uricotelic,** whereas those organisms that dispose of nitrogenous waste products in the form of urea, as humans do, are referred to as **ureotelic.** Because the uricotelic organisms must dispose of their nitrogenous wastes in the form of uric acid, they synthesize purine nucleotides at a relatively greater rate than do ureotelic organisms. However, the steps involved in de novo purine nucleotide synthesis in mammals (ureotelic) are analogous to those in birds (uricotelic).

Information on the sources of the various atoms of the purine base obtained by tracer studies in birds, rats, and humans is presented in Fig 26–2.

The biosynthetic pathway for the synthesis of purine nucleotides is shown in Fig 26–3. In order to understand the regulation of de novo purine nucleotide synthesis, the first step (reaction 1, Fig 26–3) in the synthesis of purine nucleotides must be regarded as the formation of 1-pyrophosphorylribosyl-5-phosphate (PPriboseP). Although the conversion of ribose 5-phosphate of ATP to AMP + PPriboseP (Fig 26–4) is not uniquely committed to the synthesis of purine

nucleotides, it appears from a regulatory aspect to be a most important process. As discussed in the latter part of this chapter, PPriboseP also serves as a precursor of the pyrimidine nucleotides and is required for the synthesis of NAD and NADP, 2 cofactors derived from niacin (see Chapter 9).

PPriboseP then reacts (reaction 2, Fig 26–3) with glutamine in a reaction catalyzed by the enzyme **phosphoribosylpyrophosphate amidotransferase** to form 5-phosphoribosylamine accompanied by the displacement of pyrophosphate and the formation of glutamic acid. Although other mechanisms have been proposed for the synthesis of 5-phosphoribosylamine in mammalian tissues, genetic experiments confirm that the physiologically important reaction is that catalyzed by the amidotransferase. The 5-phosphoribosylamine so formed then reacts (reaction 3, Fig 26–3) with glycine to produce glycinamide ribosylphosphate (glycinamide ribotide [GAR]). The amido group from glutamine contributes the 9 N of the eventual purine ring while the glycine contributes carbons 4 and 5 and the 7 N. The enzyme catalyzing reaction 3 is designated **glycinamide kinosynthetase** since it requires ATP and generates ADP and phosphate in that reaction.

The N_7 of glycinamide ribosylphosphate is then formylated (reaction 4, Fig 26–3), which requires N^5,N^{10}-methenyltetrahydrofolate (see Chapter 9) and the enzyme **glycinamide ribosylphosphate formyltransferase** to transfer the C_1 moiety which becomes the C_8 of the purine base. In reaction 5, again with glutamine as the amide donor, amidation occurs at the C_4 of the formylglycinamide ribosylphosphate, catalyzed by **formylglycinamidine ribosylphosphate synthetase,** which requires ATP in addition to glutamine. The amide N becomes position 3 in the purine.

The closure of the imidazole ring is catalyzed by the enzyme **aminoimidazole ribosylphosphate synthetase,** which also requires ATP and which forms aminoimidazole ribosylphosphate. The synthesis progresses (reaction 7) to aminoimidazole carboxylate ribosyl phosphate by addition to the precursor compound of a carbonyl group, the source of which is respiratory CO_2. The utilization of CO_2, as in other CO_2 fixation reactions, apparently requires biotin; the precursor substance, aminoimidazole ribosylphosphate, has been found to accumulate in biotin-deficient animals. The source of the nitrogen in the 1 position is the α-amino group of aspartate (reaction 8), the remaining portion of which is indicated as the succinyl moiety of aminoimidazole succinylcarboxamide ribosylphosphate, abbreviated as SAICAR. In reaction 9, the succinyl group of SAICAR is split off as fumaric acid. Aminoimidazole carboxamide ribosylphosphate, which remains, is then formylated (reaction 10) by N^{10}-formyltetrahydrofolate ($f^{10} \cdot H_4$folate) to form amidoimidazole carboxamide ribosylphosphate in a reaction catalyzed by the appropriate **formyl transferase.** The newly added carbon, which, like the C_8 of the purine base, is derived from the C_1 pool via the

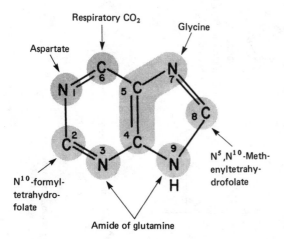

Figure 26–2. The sources of the nitrogen and carbon atoms of the purine ring.

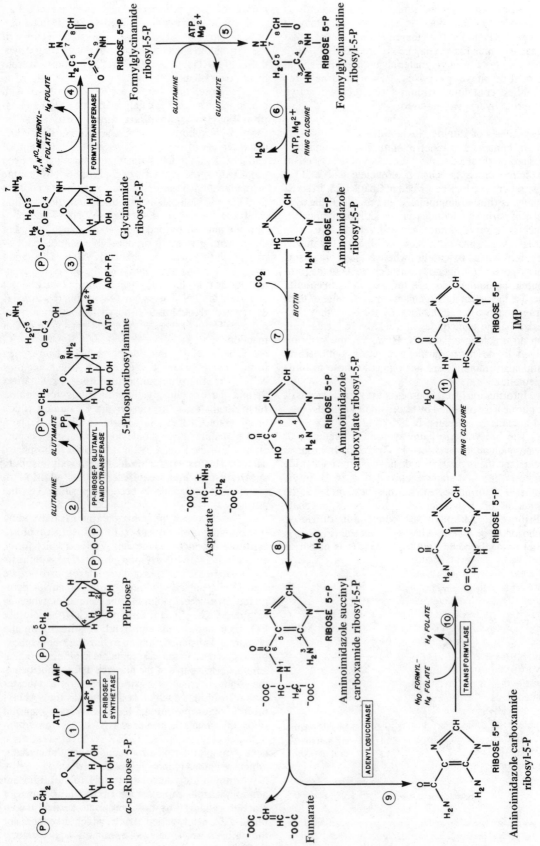

Figure 26–3. The pathway of de novo purine biosynthesis from ribose 5-phosphate and ATP. (See text for explanation.)

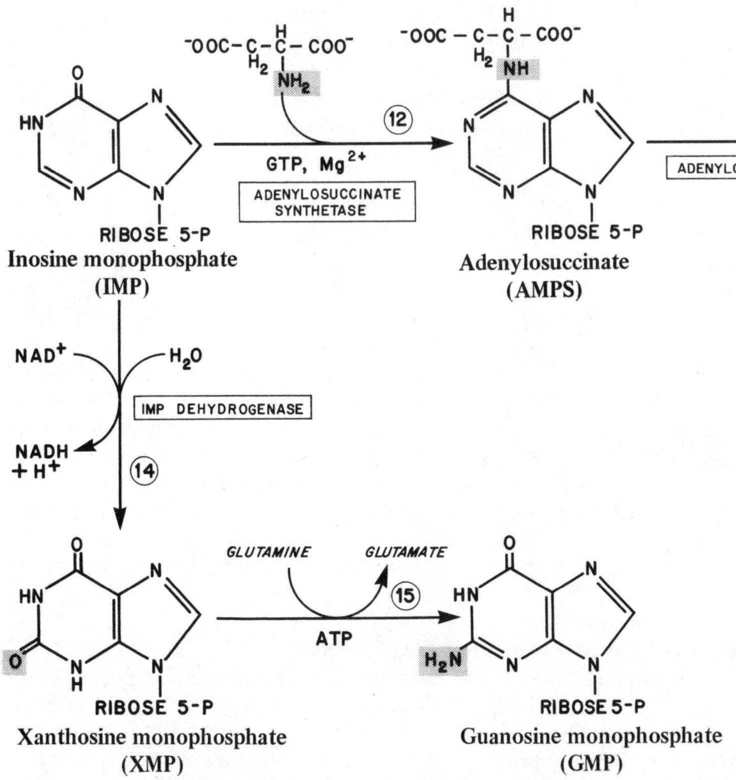

Figure 26–4. The conversions of IMP to AMP and GMP. (See text for explanation.)

tetrahydrofolate carrier, will be C_2 of the purine nucleus. Ring closure now occurs (reaction 11) via **IMP cyclohydrolase,** and the first purine nucleotide, **inosinic acid (inosine monophosphate, IMP),** is thus formed.

The importance of folate metabolism (see Chapter 9) in the de novo synthesis of purine nucleotides should be evident. Two one-carbon moieties are added to the purine ring at positions 8 and 2 by $N^5,-N^{10}$-methenyltetrahydrofolate and N^{10}-formyltetrahydrofolate, respectively. The latter is derived from the former. The N^5,N^{10}-methenyltetrahydrofolate is derived from the NADP-dependent dehydrogenation of N^5,N^{10}-methylenetetrahydrofolate. The N^5,N^{10}-methylenetetrahydrofolate can donate a one-carbon moiety to numerous acceptors, but once N^5,N^{10}-methenyltetrahydrofolate is formed, the one-carbon group is committed to transfer only into purines, whence it is donated either directly or after conversion to N^{10}-formyltetrahydrofolate. Thus, any inhibition of the formation of these tetrahydrofolate compounds will have a detrimental effect upon the de novo synthesis of purines.

As is clear from the scheme in Fig 26–4, adenine nucleotides (reactions 12 and 13) and guanine nucleotides (reactions 14 and 15) are derived from **inosine monophosphate** (IMP) by amination and by oxidation and amination, respectively. The amination of IMP is accomplished through the formation of an intermediate

compound in which aspartic acid is attached to inosinic acid to form adenylosuccinate. This reaction is similar to that of a preceding reaction (reaction 9) in which the nitrogen at position 1 of the purine nucleus was added by way of α nitrogen of aspartic acid. The formation of adenylosuccinate is catalyzed by **adenylosuccinate synthetase,** and it requires GTP, which provides a potential regulatory mechanism. The splitting off, as fumaric acid, of the remaining portion of aspartic acid from adenylosuccinate produces the final product, adenylic acid (adenosine monophosphate, AMP). Cleavage of fumaric acid from adenylosuccinate is catalyzed by the enzyme **adenylosuccinase,** which is also responsible for the cleavage of fumarate from the succinyl of aminoimidazole succinyl carboxamide ribosylphosphate (reaction 9).

Also in 2 steps, IMP is converted to guanosine monophosphate (GMP). The first reaction in this sequence (reaction 14) is an oxidation utilizing NAD as cofactor and water to form xanthosine monophosphate (XMP). XMP is aminated by the amido group of glutamine in a reaction which requires ATP, somewhat analogous to the requirement of GTP for the conversion of IMP to AMP.

Several antimetabolites that are glutamine analogs are effective inhibitors of various steps in purine biosynthesis. **Azaserine** (O-diazoacetyl-L-serine) is an antagonist to glutamine, particularly at reaction 5. **Diazonorleucine** ([6-diazo-5-oxo]-L-norleu-

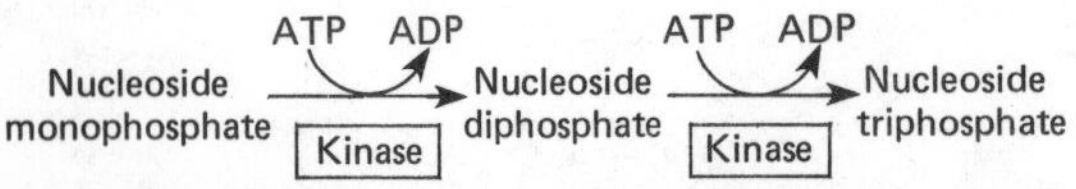

Figure 26-5. The reactions responsible for the conversion of nucleoside monophosphates to nucleoside diphosphates and nucleoside triphosphates.

cine) blocks reaction 2 in purine synthesis, and **6-mercaptopurine,** among its other actions, inhibits reactions 13 and 14 in the synthesis of AMP and GMP, respectively. Mycophenolic acid inhibits reaction 14.

The conversions of AMP and GMP to their respective nucleoside diphosphates and nucleoside triphosphates occur in 2 successive steps (Fig 26–5). The successive transfers of the high-energy phosphate groups from ATP are catalyzed by **nucleoside monophosphate kinase** and **nucleoside diphosphate kinase,** respectively. The enzyme which phosphorylates adenylate is also called **myokinase** (see Chapter 33).

The synthesis of the purine and pyrimidine deoxyribonucleotides occurs by **direct reduction at the 2′ carbon** in the ribose moiety of the corresponding nucleotide (see below) rather than by the synthesis of the entire nucleotide utilizing a 2′-deoxy analog of PPriboseP. The reduction at the 2′ carbon occurs only after the purine and pyrimidine nucleotides have been converted to their respective nucleoside diphosphates. In prokaryotic organisms, cobalamin (vitamin B_{12}) is required for this reductive process, although it is not required for the same reaction in humans. The reduction of ribonucleoside diphosphates to deoxyribonucleoside diphosphates is a complex reaction in mammals. The reaction (Fig 26–6) is catalyzed by **ribonucleotide reductase** and requires **thioredoxin** (a protein cofactor), **thioredoxin reductase** (a flavoprotein), and NADPH as a cofactor. The immediate electron donor to the nucleotide is the reduced form of thioredoxin that has accepted electrons from NADPH.

The reversible oxidation-reduction of thioredoxin is catalyzed by **thioredoxin reductase.** The reduction of the ribonucleoside diphosphate by reduced thioredoxin is catalyzed by ribonucleotide reductase. This complex enzyme system is present in cells only when they are actively synthesizing DNA and dividing.

Not all tissues in the human body are capable of de novo synthesis of purine nucleotides. The erythrocytes and polymorphonuclear leukocytes are incapable of synthesizing 5-phosphoribosylamine and therefore are dependent upon exogenous purines for the formation of purine nucleotides. Peripheral lymphocytes do possess some ability to synthesize purines de novo. Mammalian brain appears to have a reduced content of PPriboseP amidotransferase; indeed, it has been suggested that the human brain is dependent upon exogenous purines for the formation of purine nucleotides. The mammalian liver is a major site of purine nucleotide synthesis and provides purines in the form of bases or nucleosides to be salvaged and utilized by those tissues incapable of synthesizing purines de novo.

Purine Salvage Pathways

The salvage of these preformed purine compounds can occur by 2 general mechanisms. The quantitatively more important mechanism is the **phosphoribosylation of the free purine bases** by specific enzymes requiring PPriboseP as the ribose phosphate donor. The second general mechanism is the **phosphorylation of purine nucleosides** on their 5′-hydroxyl groups.

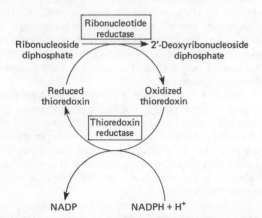

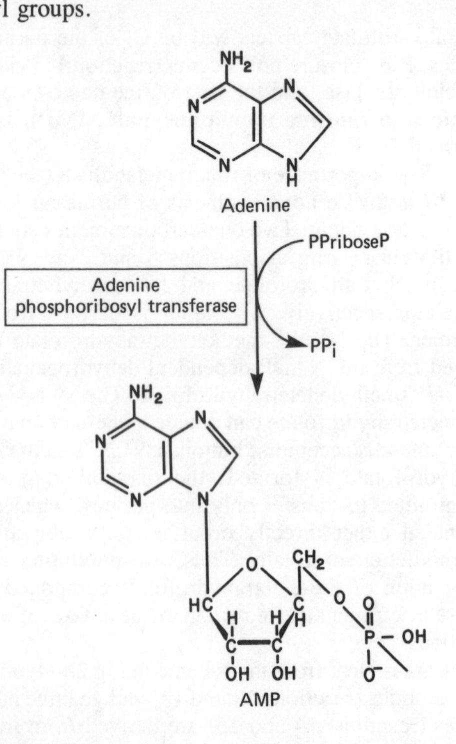

Figure 26-6. The reactions involved in the reduction of ribonucleoside diphosphates to 2′ deoxyribonucleoside diphosphates.

Figure 26-7. Phosphoribosylation of adenine catalyzed by adenine phosphoribosyl transferase.

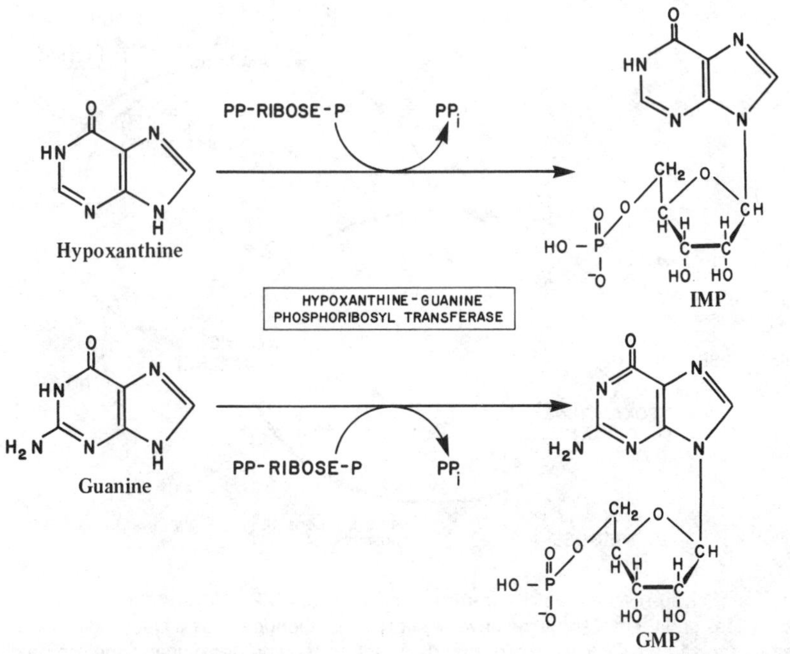

Figure 26–8. Phosphoribosylation of hypoxanthine and guanine to form IMP and GMP, respectively. The reactions are catalyzed by the enzyme hypoxanthine-guanine phosphoribosyl transferase.

There are 2 enzymes in human tissues that can phosphoribosylate purine bases. One enzyme (Fig 26–7) is capable of phosphoribosylating adenine with PPriboseP to generate AMP: **adenine phosphoribosyl transferase.** The second (Fig 26–8) is capable of phosphoribosylating hypoxanthine and guanine with PPriboseP to yield IMP and GMP, respectively: **hypoxanthine-guanine phosphoribosyl transferase.** As will be discussed below, the latter pathway (the salvage of hypoxanthine and guanine to IMP and GMP) is more active than the formation of AMP from adenine.

The salvage of purine ribonucleosides to purine ribonucleotides is carried out in humans by **adenosine kinase** only (Fig 26–9). This enzyme demonstrates no ability to phosphorylate guanosine, inosine, or their 2′-deoxy derivatives to their respective ribonucleo-

tides. Deoxycytidine kinase can phosphorylate 2′-deoxyadenosine and 2′-deoxyguanosine to deoxy AMP and deoxy GMP, respectively.

However, there is more to the purine salvage pathways. In humans, there is a cycle (Fig 26–10) in which IMP and GMP as well as their respective deoxyribonucleotides are converted to their respective nucleosides (inosine, deoxyinosine, guanosine, and deoxyguanosine) by a **purine 5′-nucleotidase.** These purine ribonucleosides and 2′-deoxynucleosides are converted to hypoxanthine or guanine by **purine nucleoside phosphorylase,** producing ribose 1-phosphate or 2′-deoxyribose 1-phosphate as phosphorolysis products. The hypoxanthine and guanine can then again be phosphoribosylated by PPriboseP to IMP and GMP to complete the cycle. The functions of this purine salvage cycle are unknown, but it is clear

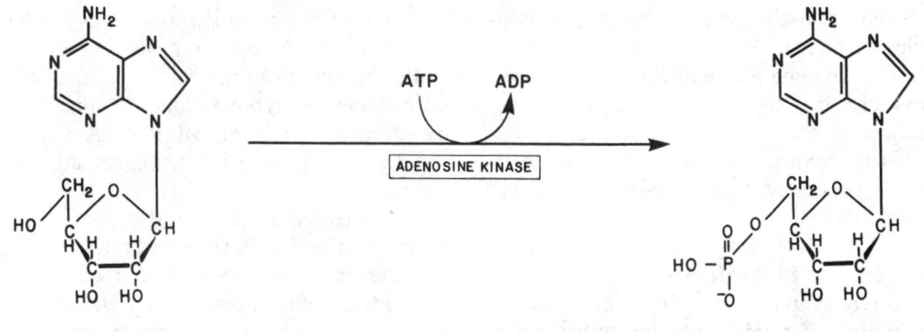

Figure 26–9. Phosphorylation of adenosine to AMP by adenosine kinase.

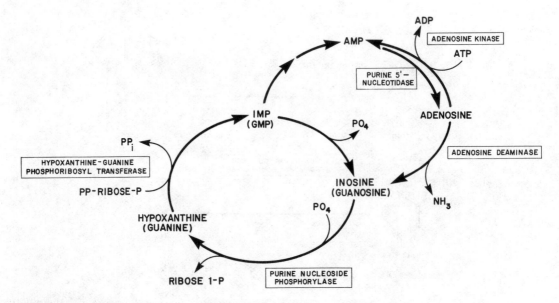

Figure 26–10. The purine salvage cycles involving the interconversion of AMP, IMP, and—to a lesser extent—GMP to their respective ribonucleosides and their eventual reconversion to purine ribonucleotides. Deoxyadenosine, deoxyinosine, and deoxyguanosine share the same pathways except that deoxyadenosine and deoxyguanosine can be directly phosphorylated to deoxy AMP and deoxy GMP, respectively.

that, in the human organism as a whole, the consumption of PPriboseP by this salvage cycle is greater than the consumption of PPriboseP for the synthesis of purine nucleotides de novo.

There is a lateral pathway of this cycle which involves the conversion of IMP to AMP (reactions 12 and 13, Fig 26–4), with the subsequent conversion of AMP to adenosine. The latter is probably catalyzed by the same purine 5'-nucleotidase that hydrolyzes IMP to inosine. The adenosine so produced is then either salvaged directly back to AMP via **adenosine kinase** or is converted to inosine by the enzyme **adenosine deaminase.** Quantitatively, the function of this inosine loop is less important than the previously described cycle. Qualitatively, the action of adenosine deaminase is an important process, particularly for the immune system, as described in the discussion of inherited disorders of purine metabolism.

The salvage of the free purine adenine by adenine phosphoribosyl transferase seems to prevent the xanthine oxidase–mediated oxidation of adenine to 2,8-dihydroxyadenine. Dihydroxyadenine is a highly insoluble product which appears as kidney stones in patients devoid of adenine phosphoribosyl transferase activity. The source of free adenine for such a salvage process is not known with certainty, although it probably derives from the hydrolysis of 5'-methylthioadenosine, a by-product of the synthesis of polyamines from S-adenosylmethionine.

Regulation of Purine Biosynthesis

The de novo synthesis of IMP consumes the equivalent of 6 high-energy phosphodiester bonds (by ATP hydrolysis) along with the other required precursors, glycine, glutamine, methenyltetrahydrofolate, and aspartate. Thus, it is important for the conservation of energy and nutrients that the cell economically regulate its rate of de novo purine biosynthesis. The single most important regulator of de novo purine biosynthesis is the intracellular concentration of PPriboseP. As with so many other intracellular compounds, the regulation of PPriboseP concentration is dependent upon its rate of synthesis versus its rate of utilization or degradation. The rate of synthesis of PPriboseP is dependent upon (1) the availability of its substrates, particularly ribose 5-phosphate, which is more likely to be limiting than is ATP; and (2) the catalytic activity of PPriboseP synthetase, which is dependent upon the intracellular phosphate concentration as well as the concentrations of the purine and pyrimidine ribonucleotides acting as allosteric regulators (Fig 26–11). The rate of utilization of PPriboseP is dependent to a large extent on its consumption by the salvage pathway that phosphoribosylates hypoxanthine and guanine to their respective ribonucleotides. To a lesser extent, utilization is dependent upon the rate of de novo purine synthesis. This conclusion stems from the observation that, in males with inherited deficiencies of hypoxanthine-guanine phosphoribosyl transferase, the levels of PPriboseP in their erythrocytes and cultured fibroblasts are elevated severalfold.

The first enzyme uniquely committed to de novo purine synthesis, PPriboseP amidotransferase, demonstrates in vitro a sensitivity to feedback inhibition by purine nucleotides, particularly adenosine monophosphate and guanosine monophosphate. These feedback inhibitors of the amidotransferase are competitive with

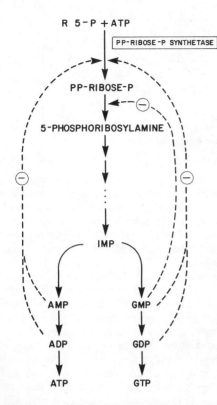

Figure 26–11. A regulatory scheme for the control of the rate of de novo purine synthesis. Solid lines represent chemical flow and dotted lines represent feedback inhibition by end products of the pathway.

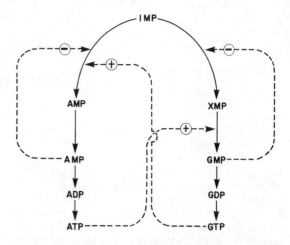

Figure 26–12. The regulation of the interconversion of IMP to adenosine nucleotides and guanosine nucleotides. Solid lines represent chemical flow and dotted lines represent both positive $\oplus$ and negative $\ominus$ feedback regulation.

Catabolism of Purines

In humans, the ultimate catabolite (end product) of purines is uric acid. Reasoning from observations made in humans with inherited enzyme deficiencies, it appears that over 99% of the uric acid is derived from substrates of purine nucleoside phosphorylase, a component of the purine salvage pathway described above. The purine products of purine nucleoside phosphorylase, guanine and hypoxanthine, are converted to

the substrate PPriboseP, and thus, again, PPriboseP plays a major role in the regulation of de novo purine synthesis. Numerous indirect experiments suggest that the regulation of de novo purine synthesis by amidotransferase is physiologically less important than that by PPriboseP synthetase.

The conversion of IMP to GMP or to AMP is regulated by 2 mechanisms (Fig 26–12). AMP feedback regulates its own synthesis at the level of adenylosuccinate synthetase, GMP by feedback inhibition of IMP dehydrogenase. Furthermore, the conversion of IMP to adenylosuccinate en route to AMP requires the presence of GTP. The conversion of xanthinylate to GMP requires the presence of ATP. Thus, there is significant cross-regulation between the divergent pathways in the metabolism of IMP. This regulation prevents the synthesis of one purine nucleotide when there is a deficiency of the other. Hypoxanthine-guanine phosphoribosyl transferase, which converts hypoxanthine and guanine to IMP and GMP, respectively, is quite sensitive to product inhibition by these same nucleotides.

The reduction of ribonucleoside diphosphates to deoxyribonucleoside diphosphates is subject to complex regulation (Fig 26–13). This process of regulation, which is depicted in Fig 26–13, provides for the proper balancing of deoxyribonucleotides for the synthesis of DNA.

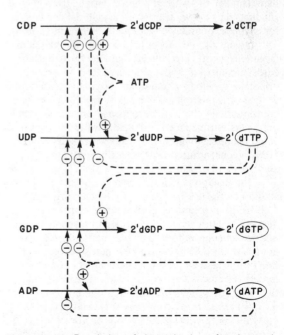

Figure 26–13. Regulation of the reduction of purine and pyrimidine ribonucleotides to their respective 2' deoxyribonucleotides. Solid lines represent chemical flow and dotted lines represent negative $\ominus$ or positive $\oplus$ feedback regulation.

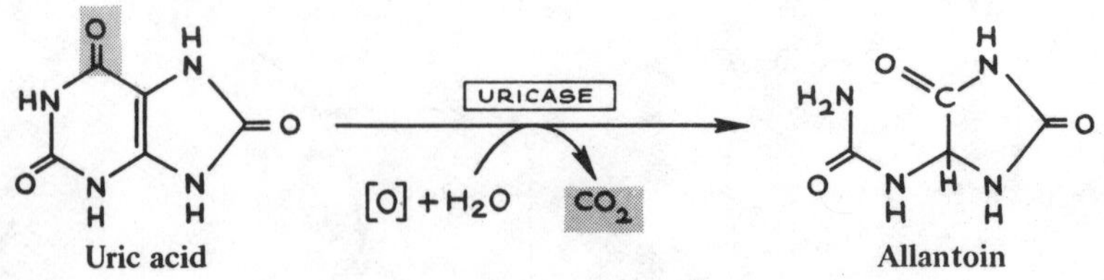

Figure 26–14. Conversion of uric acid to allantoin.

uric acid by way of xanthine in reactions catalyzed by the enzymes **guanase** and **xanthine oxidase,** respectively (Fig 26–1). Xanthine oxidase is very active in liver, small intestine, and kidney, and in its absence no uric acid is formed. As described above, some uric acid may be produced from nucleic acids by the bacterial flora of the intestinal tract, whence it is absorbed and directly excreted. This pathway seems to be a minor contributor to the urinary uric acid of persons on a normal diet.

As discussed below under the disorders of purine metabolism, the activity of xanthine oxidase is an important site for pharmacologic intervention in patients with hyperuricemia and gout. In lower primates and other mammals, the enzyme **uricase** is responsible for the hydrolysis of uric acid to allantoin (Fig 26–14), a highly water-soluble end product of purine catabolism in those animals. Amphibians, birds, and reptiles do not possess uricase activity. These animals excrete uric acid and guanine as the end products of both purine metabolism and nitrogen (protein) metabolism. (In fact, the word guanine is derived from guano [*huanu,* dung], a white crystalline material deposited, for example, on many coastal rocks by marine birds.)

Organisms that form uric acid as the major nitrogenous waste product are said to be **uricotelic.** Birds, amphibians, and reptiles seem to have evolved a uricotelic system to regain water of hydration from uric acid after it precipitates out, as it will at rather low concentrations. If they were to use urea as the end product of nitrogen metabolism, the water of hydration could not be regained since urea is water-soluble up to 10M, a concentration far higher than any kidney can attain.

The metabolism of uric acid in humans has been studied by the use of isotopically labeled uric acid as well as its precursors, glycine and formate. Single doses of N^{15} uric acid were injected intravenously into normal human subjects and patients suffering from gout, a disease characterized by increased accumulation of uric acid and sodium urate. The dilution of the injected labeled isotope was used to calculate the quantity of total uric acid equilibrating with body water, a quantity referred to as the **miscible urate pool.** The mass of the rapidly miscible pool of uric acid in 25 normal male adult subjects averaged 1200 mg with a range of 866–1578 mg. In 3 normal female subjects the pool ranged from 541 to 687 mg. In gouty subjects the miscible urate pool was much larger, generally ranging from 2000 to 4000 mg in patients without

tophi, ie, deposits of sodium urate in soft tissues. However, in severe tophaceous gout the pool was as high as 31,000 mg. The turnover of the miscible pool of total uric acid in normal persons is approximately 600 mg/24 h. Isotope studies have demonstrated that 18–20% of the lost uric acid is not excreted in the urine but is degraded to CO_2 and ammonia and excreted in the feces, where it can be further metabolized by intestinal flora. It is known that some uric acid is excreted in the bile and thus is subject to degradation by intestinal flora. However, in humans, the breakdown of uric acid to CO_2 and NH_3 is independent of intestinal bacteria.

The handling of sodium urate, a salt of uric acid, by the mammalian kidney has been the subject of many studies. It appears from recent studies that sodium urate is freely filtered by the mammalian glomerulus, is extensively reabsorbed and partially secreted in the proximal tubule, is further secreted in the loop of Henle, and perhaps is again partially reabsorbed in the distal convoluted tubule. The net excretion of total uric acid in normal men is 400–600 mg/24 h. Many pharmacologic and naturally occurring compounds influence the renal absorption and secretion of sodium urate. Aspirin in high doses competitively inhibits urate excretion as well as reabsorption.

Biosynthesis of Pyrimidines

The pyrimidine nucleotides possess a heterocyclic ring structure that occurs also in the purine nucleus. These nucleotides have chemical and physiologic properties similar to those of purine nucleotides. Although the pyrimidine nucleus is simpler and its synthetic pathway briefer than that of the purine structure, the 2 share several common precursors. **PPriboseP, glutamine, CO_2,** and **aspartate** are required for the synthesis of all pyrimidine and purine nucleotides. For the thymidine nucleotides and for all purine nucleotides, **tetrahydrofolate** derivatives are also necessary. There is one striking difference between the synthesis of pyrimidine nucleotides and that of purine nucleotides, namely, that the synthesis of the purine nucleotides commences with ribose phosphate as an integral part of the earliest precursor molecule, whereas the pyrimidine base is formed and **attachment of the ribose phosphate moiety delayed until the later steps** of the pathway.

The synthesis of the pyrimidine ring commences with the formation of **carbamoyl phosphate** from glutamine, ATP, and CO_2 in a reaction catalyzed by the carbamoyl phosphate synthetase located in the

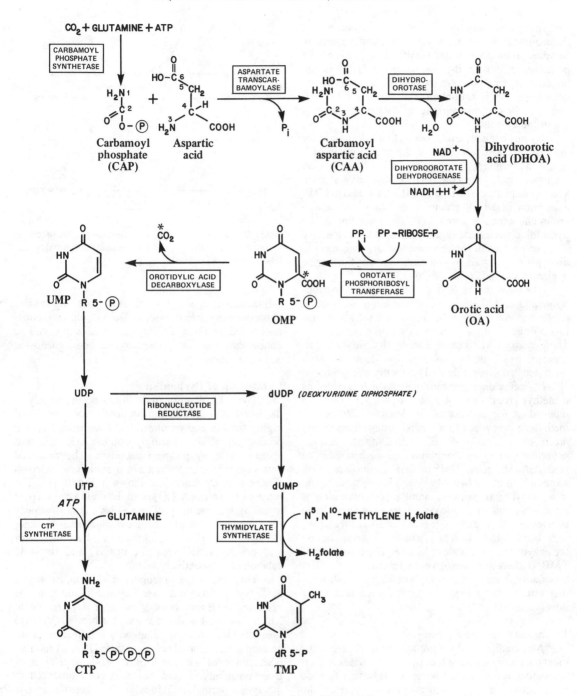

Figure 26–15. The biosynthetic pathway for pyrimidine nucleotides.

cytosol of the cell (Fig 26–15). In contrast, the carbamoyl phosphate synthetase enzyme responsible for the early steps in urea synthesis resides in the mitochondria. The first step uniquely committed to the biosynthesis of pyrimidines is the formation of carbamoyl aspartate by the condensation of carbamoyl phosphate and aspartate, a reaction catalyzed by the enzyme **aspartate transcarbamoylase.** A ring structure can then be formed from carbamoyl aspartate by loss of H_2O catalyzed by the enzyme **dihydroorotase.**

In a subsequent dehydrogenation step catalyzed by **dihydroorotate dehydrogenase** and utilizing NAD as a cofactor, **orotic acid** is formed. The next step is that in which a ribose phosphate moiety is added to orotic acid to form **orotidylate (orotidine monophosphate, OMP).** This reaction is catalyzed by **orotate phosphoribosyl transferase,** an enzyme analogous to the hypoxanthine-guanine phosphoribosyl transferase and the adenine phosphoribosyl transferase involved in the phosphoribosylation of preformed purine rings. The first true pyrimidine ribonucleotide is formed by the decarboxylation of orotidylate to form **uridylate (uridine monophosphate, UMP).** Thus, only at the penultimate step in the formation of UMP is the heterocyclic ring phosphoribosylated. Dihydroorotate dehydrogenase is **mitochondrial;** all the other enzymes in the de novo pyrimidine nucleotide pathway are in the **cytosol.**

By mechanisms analogous to those described for the further phosphorylation of the purine nucleoside monophosphates, the pyrimidine nucleoside monophosphates are converted to their diphosphate and triphosphate derivatives. UTP is aminated to CTP, a reaction in which glutamine provides the amino group and which requires ATP. The reduction of the pyrimidine nucleoside diphosphates to the respective $2'$-deoxynucleoside diphosphates occurs by a mechanism also analogous to that described for the purine nucleotides (Figs 26–6 and 26–13).

The formation of **thymidylate (thymidine monophosphate, TMP)** is the one reaction in pyrimidine nucleotide biosynthesis that requires a **tetrahydrofolate** donor of a single carbon compound. The $2'$-deoxy UMP is methylated by **thymidylate synthetase,** which utilizes as a methyl donor N^5,N^{10}-methylenetetrahydrofolate. The methylene group of N^5,N^{10}-methylenetetrahydrofolate, which is added as a methyl group to the C_5 of deoxy-UMP, must be reduced in the process of its donation. While the methylene is reduced to a methyl group, the tetrahydrofolate carrier is oxidized to dihydrofolate, and the net redox state of the reaction is thus unchanged. The methylation of deoxy-UMP to TMP results in an overall reduction of the hydroxymethyl group from serine to a methyl group with the simultaneous oxidation of tetrahydrofolate to dihydrofolate. In order to continue to use the folate carrier, the cell must reduce dihydrofolate to tetrahydrofolate, a reaction carried out by the enzyme dihydrofolate reductase. The formation of TMP is therefore sensitive to inhibitors of dihydrofolate reductase. An example of such an inhibitor is methotrexate (amethopterin), a widely used anticancer drug.

Pyrimidine Salvage Pathways

Mammalian cells do not appear to possess efficient means of salvaging **free** pyrimidine bases to their respective pyrimidine nucleotides. However, they do have active salvage pathways for converting the pyrimidine **nucleosides** uridine, cytidine, and thymidine to their respective nucleotides (Fig 26–16). The enzyme required for de novo primidine biosynthesis, **orotate phosphoribosyl transferase,** is capable of salvaging orotic acid to OMP, but in a strict sense orotic acid is not considered a complete pyrimidine base. The orotate phosphoribosyl transferase cannot use normal pyrimidine bases as substrates, although it is capable of converting allopurinol (4-hydroxypyrazolopyrimidine) to a nucleotide in which the ribosyl phosphate is attached to the N_1 of the pyrimidine ring of that drug. The anticancer drug

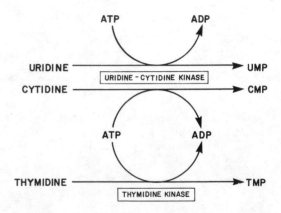

Figure 26–16. The pyrimidine nucleoside kinase reactions responsible for formation of the respective pyrimidine nucleoside monophosphates.

5-fluorouracil is also phosphoribosylated by orotate phosphoribosyl transferase. $2'$-Deoxycytidine is phosphorylated by a distinct enzyme called deoxycytidine kinase that can also phosphorylate deoxyguanosine and deoxyadenosine.

Catabolism of Pyrimidines

The catabolism of pyrimidines occurs mainly in the liver. It results in the production of a series of highly soluble end products. This contrasts with the production of the sparingly soluble uric acid and sodium urate by purine catabolism. The proposed pathways for the degradation of pyrimidines, based on fragmentary evidence, are shown in Fig 26–17. The release of respiratory CO_2 from the ureido carbon (C_2) of the pyrimidine nucleus represents a major pathway for the catabolism of uracil, cytosine, and thymine. β-Alanine and β-aminoisobutyric acid are the major end products of cytosine, uracil, and thymine catabolism, respectively.

Thymine is the precursor of β-aminoisobutyric acid, both in laboratory animals and in humans. The excretion of β-aminoisobutyric acid is increased in leukemia as well as after the body has been subjected to x-irradiation. This is undoubtedly a reflection of increased destruction of cells and their DNA. A familial occurrence of an abnormally high excretion of β-aminoisobutyric acid has also been observed in otherwise normal individuals. This genetic trait is traceable to a recessively expressed gene. High excretors result only when the trait is homozygous. It is of interest that approximately 25% of tested persons of Chinese or Japanese ancestry consistently excreted large amounts of β-aminoisobutyric acid. Although little is known about the mechanisms whereby β-aminoisobutyric acid is degraded in humans, an enzyme which catalyzes the reversible transamination reaction has been identified in pig kidney. The β-aminoisobutyric acid is converted to methylmalonic semialdehyde and thence to propionic acid, which in turn proceeds to succinate.

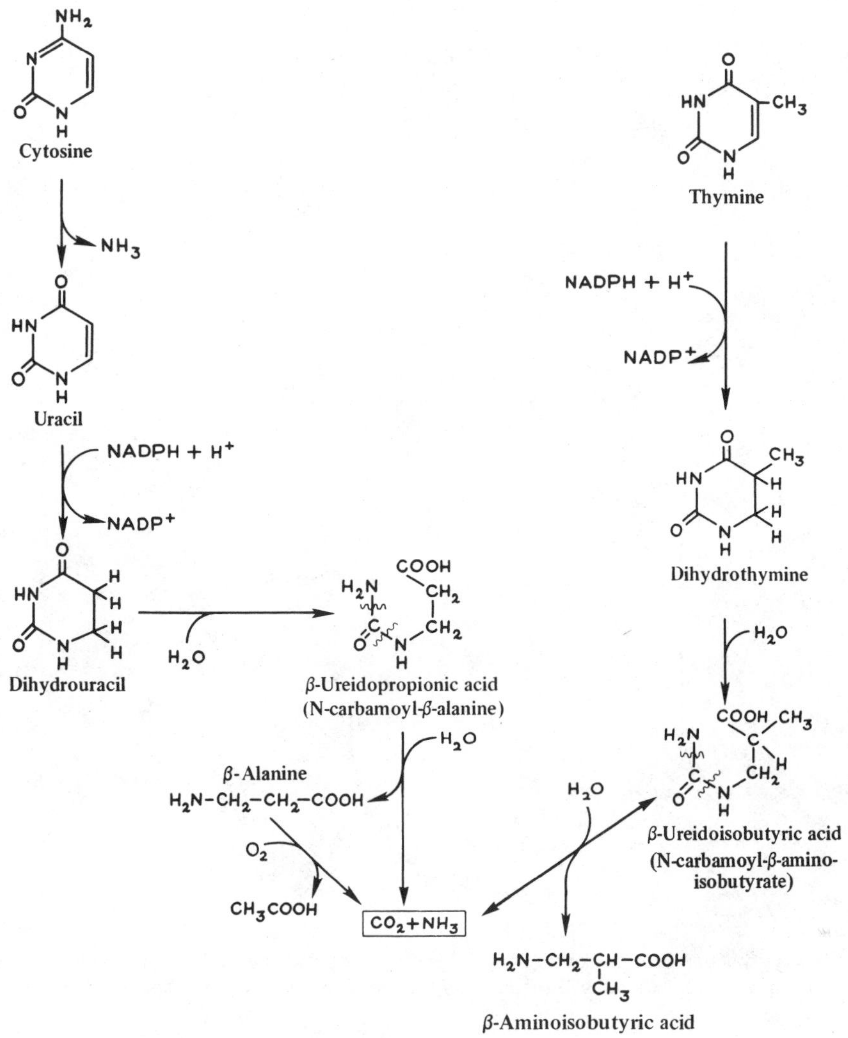

Figure 26–17. Catabolism of pyrimidines.

It should be noted that the initial steps in the degradation of pyrimidine nucleotides, including the removal of the sugar phosphate moiety by hydrolysis of the N-glycosidic bond, are similar to reversing the latter part of the synthetic pathway. For pseudouridine, which is formed in situ in tRNA by a rearrangement reaction, there is no mechanism to catalyze the hydrolysis or phosphorolysis of this unusual nucleoside to its respective pyrimidine base, uracil. Consequently, pseudouridine is excreted unchanged in the urine of normal persons.

Regulation of Pyrimidine Biosynthesis

The pathway of pyrimidine nucleotide biosynthesis is regulated by 2 general mechanisms. The first 2 enzymes in the pathway are sensitive to **allosteric regulation,** while the first 3 enzymes are regulated by an apparently coordinate **repression and derepression,** as are the last 2 enzymes of the pathway. **Car-**bamoyl phosphate synthetase is inhibited by UTP and purine nucleotides but activated by PPriboseP (Fig 26–18). **Aspartate transcarbamoylase** is particularly sensitive to inhibition by CTP. The allosteric properties of the aspartate transcarbamoylase in microorganisms have been the subject of extensive and now classic studies in allostery.

It has been estimated from isotope incorporation studies that on a molar basis the rate of pyrimidine biosynthesis parallels that of purine biosynthesis, demonstrating a coordinate control of purine and pyrimidine nucleotide synthesis. It should be noted that PPriboseP synthetase, an enzyme which forms a necessary precursor for both purine nucleotide and pyrimidine nucleotide biosynthesis, is subject to feedback inhibition by both purine and pyrimidine nucleotides. Furthermore, carbamoyl phosphate synthetase is sensitive to feedback inhibition by both purine and pyrimidine nucleotides and activation by PPriboseP.

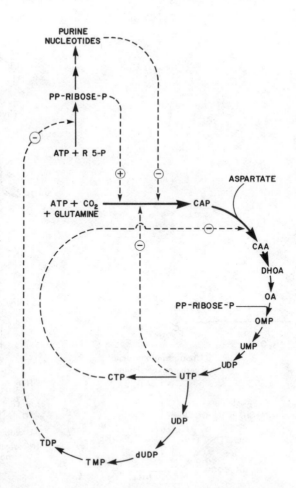

Figure 26–18. Regulatory scheme for the control of pyrimidine nucleotide synthesis. Solid lines represent chemical flow and broken lines represent positive and negative feedback regulation. The abbreviations used are defined in Figure 26–15.

Table 26–2. Inherited disorders of purine metabolism and their associated enzyme abnormalities.

Clinical Disorder	Defective Enzyme	Nature of the Defect	Characteristics of Clinical Disorder	Inheritance Pattern
Gout	PPriboseP synthetase	Superactive (increased V_{max})	Purine overproduction and overexcretion	X-linked recessive
Gout	PPriboseP synthetase	Resistance to feedback inhibition	Purine overproduction and overexcretion	X-linked recessive
Gout	PPriboseP synthetase	Low K_m for ribose 5-phosphate	Purine overproduction and overexcretion	Probably X-linked recessive
Gout	HGPRTase*	Partial deficiency	Purine overproduction and overexcretion	X-linked recessive
Lesch-Nyhan syndrome	HGPRTase*	Complete deficiency	Purine overproduction and overexcretion; cerebral palsy and self-mutilation.	X-linked recessive
Immune deficiency	Adenosine deaminase	Severe deficiency	Combined (T cell and B cell) immunodeficiency, deoxyadenosinuria	Autosomal recessive
Immune deficiency	Purine nucleoside phosphorylase	Severe deficiency	T cell deficiency, inosinuria, deoxyinosinuria, guanosinuria, deoxyguanosinuria, hypouricemia	Autosomal recessive
Renal lithiasis	Adenine phosphoribosyl transferase	Complete deficiency	2,8-Dihydroxyadenine renal lithiasis	Autosomal recessive
Xanthinuria	Xanthine oxidase	Complete deficiency	Xanthine renal lithiasis, hypouricemia	Autosomal recessive

*HGPRTase = hypoxanthine-guanine phosphoribosyl transferase.

Thus, there are several sites at which there is significant cross-regulation between purine and pyrimidine nucleotide synthesis.

CLINICAL DISORDERS OF PURINE METABOLISM
(See Table 26–2.)

Hyperuricemia & Gout

The predominant form of uric acid is determined by the pH of its milieu (eg, blood, urine, cerebrospinal fluid). The **pK of the N^9 proton is 5.75,** and the pK of the N^1 proton is 10.3. Thus, under physiologic conditions—ie, at the usual pH of physiologic fluids—only uric acid and its monosodium salt, sodium urate, are found. In a fluid where the pH is less than 5.75, the predominant molecular species will be uric acid. In a fluid at pH 5.75, the concentration of sodium urate will equal that of uric acid. At a pH greater than 5.75, sodium urate will predominate in the solution.

The miscible urate pool in the body is reflected by the sodium urate concentration in the serum. When this level exceeds the solubility of sodium urate in serum, a circumstance referred to as **hyperuricemia,** the serum becomes supersaturated and crystals of sodium urate may precipitate. The solubility of sodium urate in serum at 37 C is 7 mg/dL. There is currently no convincing evidence that under physiologic conditions sodium urate is bound by serum proteins. Crystals of sodium urate that precipitate out of solution can collect and deposit in soft tissues, particularly in or about joints. These urate deposits are referred to as **tophi.** Accumulation of sodium urate crystals in the tissues, including phagocytosis of the crystals by polymorphonuclear leukocytes in joint spaces, can lead to an acute inflammatory reaction called **acute gouty arthritis.** The chronic inflammatory changes induced by the deposition of sodium urate tophi can generate **chronic gouty arthritis,** resulting in joint destruction.

In water, uric acid—the protonated form of urate—is only one-seventeenth as soluble as sodium urate. An aqueous solution becomes saturated with uric acid when its concentration is greater than 80 mg/dL. Because the pH of urine of normal persons generally is below the pK of uric acid (ie, 5.75), the predominant form of urate in urine is as uric acid, the highly insoluble form. Uric acid becomes the predominant form once the urine is acidified to a pH of less than 5.75, a process which occurs in the distal tubule and collecting ducts of the kidney. If crystals of this end product of purine catabolism are formed in the urinary system, they will be sodium urate at any site proximal to the site of acidification of urine; at any site distal to the acidification, uric acid crystals will be formed. Therefore, most stones of the urinary collecting system are uric acid. The precipitation of uric acid stones can be prevented to a considerable extent by alkalinization of the urine to ensure that sodium urate, the more soluble form, will predominate.

Table 26–3. Classification of patients with hyperuricemia.

I. Normal excretion of urate; renal disorder responsible for elevated serum urate.
II. Excessive excretion of urate because of overproduction.
A. Secondary to other diseases, eg, malignancy, psoriasis.
B. Known enzyme defects responsible for overproduction.
1. PPriboseP synthetase abnormalities.
2. Hypoxanthine-guanine phosphoribosyl transferase deficiencies.
3. Glucose-6-phosphatase deficiencies.
C. Unrecognized defects.

The needle-shaped sodium urate crystals are intensely **negatively birefringent** (optically anisotropic); thus, when viewed through a polarizing microscope, they can be distinguished from other types of crystals. If the synovial or joint fluid of a patient shows polymorphonuclear leukocytes containing crystals whose color is yellow when viewed with their long axis parallel to the plane of polarized light and blue when perpendicular to the plane of light, then sodium urate crystals are present. The diagnosis is gout. It should be noted, however, that calcium pyrophosphate crystals, which are found in synovial fluid, are positively birefringent and can be responsible for a syndrome referred to as "pseudogout."

The classification of the disorders of purine metabolism includes those exhibiting **hyperuricemia,** those exhibiting **hypouricemia,** and the immunodeficiency diseases. As shown in Table 26–3, individuals with hyperuricemia can be divided into 2 groups: those with normal urate excretion rates and those excreting excessive quantities of total urates.

Among those individuals with hyperuricemia and no other associated disease, the majority excrete urates at a normal rate; a renal disorder is responsible for the hyperuricemia. This renal disorder is somewhat analogous to an elevated threshold wherein excretion of the normal amount of urate formed daily requires that the level of serum urate be elevated to "flow over the dam," so to speak.

Lesch-Nyhan Syndrome & Von Gierke's Disease

Some individuals with urate overexcretion (greater than 600 mg of uric acid per 24 hours) can be categorized as having secondary hyperuricemia. They have other disease processes such as malignancies or psoriasis that lead to enhanced tissue destruction.

Finally, there are persons with identifiable enzyme defects, including abnormalities of PPriboseP synthetase (feedback resistant and enhanced enzyme activities), the HGPRTase (hypoxanthine-guanine phosphoribosyl transferase) deficiencies (both the complete [Lesch-Nyhan syndrome] and incomplete deficiencies), and **glucose-6-phosphatase deficiency** (von Gierke's disease). There exists also a group of patients exhibiting idiopathic overproduction hyperuricemia, which will certainly be regarded as a heterogeneous group of diseases once the molecular bases for their metabolic defects are recognized.

Table 26–4. Inherited disorders of pyrimidine metabolism and their associated enzyme abnormalities.

Clinical Disorder	Defective Enzyme	Nature of the Defect	Characteristics of Clinical Disorder	Inheritance Pattern
β-Aminoisobutyric aciduria	Transaminase	Deficiency	No symptoms; frequent in Orientals.	Autosomal recessive
Orotic aciduria, type I	Orotate phosphoribosyl-transferase and orotidylate decarboxylase	Deficiencies	Orotic acid crystalluria, failure to thrive, and megaloblastic anemia. (?) Immune deficiency. Remission with oral uridine.	Autosomal recessive
Orotic aciduria, type II	Orotidylate decarboxylase	Deficiency	Orotidinuria and orotic aciduria, megaloblastic anemia. Remission with oral uridine.	Autosomal recessive
Orotic aciduria	Ornithine transcarbamoylase	Deficiency	Protein intolerance, hepatic encephalopathy, and mild orotic aciduria.	X-linked recessive

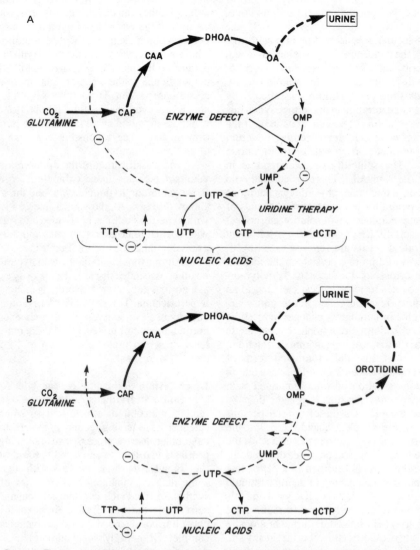

Figure 26–19. *Panel A:* The enzyme defect and consequences of orotic aciduria type I, in which both orotate phosphoribosyl transferase and orotidylic decarboxylase are deficient. *Panel B:* The defect and consequences of orotic aciduria type II, in which orotidylic decarboxylase is deficient. The dotted lines in which a negative sign is inserted represent feedback inhibition that exists under normal conditions. In type I orotic aciduria, orotic acid is spilled in the urine, whereas in type II both orotic acid and orotidine appear in the urine. The abbreviations used are defined in Fig 26–15. (Redrawn and reproduced, with permission, from Smith LH Jr: Pyrimidine metabolism in man. *N Engl J Med* 1973;**288**:764.)

The **Lesch-Nyhan syndrome** (complete HGPRTase deficiency) is an inherited X-linked recessive disorder characterized by cerebral palsy with choreoathetosis and spasticity, a bizarre syndrome of self-mutilation, and severe overproduction hyperuricemia. There is usually an associated uric acid lithiasis. The mothers of these children, who are heterozygous and mosaic for the HGPRTase deficiency, frequently exhibit overproduction hyperuricemia but without any neurologic manifestations. There also exist male patients with partial deficiencies of HGPRTase attributable to a different mutation of the same gene. These males have severe overproduction hyperuricemia but usually are without significant neurologic signs and symptoms.

Purine overproduction by patients deficient in hypoxanthine-guanine phosphoribosyl transferase is related to the increased intracellular concentrations of PPriboseP. Increased PPriboseP levels seem to result from the sparing of PPriboseP by the deficient salvage pathway. The biochemical basis for the neurologic disorder in Lesch-Nyhan syndrome is unknown.

The basis of purine overproduction and hyperuricemia in von Gierke's disease is purportedly secondary to the enhanced activity of the hexose monophosphate shunt and thus enhanced generation of ribose 5-phosphate, from which PPriboseP is synthesized. However, patients with glucose-6-phosphatase deficiency also have chronic lactic acidosis and thus have elevated renal thresholds for secretion of urate contributing to the accumulation of total body urates.

All of the known enzyme defects (except the glucose-6-phosphatase deficiency, which has not been tested) are associated with increased intracellular concentrations of PPriboseP, and the theoretic basis for the purine overproduction in the glucose-6-phosphatase deficiency is probably similarly caused. Thus, it seems likely that many more disorders of overproduction hyperuricemia will eventually be discovered to be associated with increased accumulation of intracellular PPriboseP.

Other Purine Disorders

Hypouricemia is due either to enhanced excretion or to decreased production of urate and uric acid. Dalmatian dogs, although possessing uricase activity, as do all dogs, are not capable of reabsorbing completely the filtered uric acid in their kidneys. They excrete urate and uric acid in amounts that are excessive in respect to their serum urate levels. A similar defect has been discovered in a human with hypouricemia.

Deficiency of the enzyme xanthine oxidase, either due to an inherited genetic defect or because of severe liver damage, results in hypouricemia and increased excretion of the oxypurines, hypoxanthine and xanthine. In severe xanthine oxidase deficiencies, patients frequently exhibit **xanthinuria** and xanthine lithiasis.

A deficiency of the enzyme purine nucleoside phosphorylase is associated with hypouricemia because individuals lacking this enzyme are not capable of producing hypoxanthine and guanine from inosine and guanosine, respectively. As a result, excessive quantities of purine nucleosides are excreted in their urine. Two of the purine nucleosides excreted in significant quantities, guanosine and deoxyguanosine, have limited solubility and can therefore result in renal lithiasis.

Two immunodeficiency diseases associated with deficiencies of purine metabolizing enzymes have been described in recent years. **Adenosine deaminase deficiency** is associated with a severe combined immunodeficiency disease in which both thymus-derived lymphocytes (T cells) and bone marrow–derived lymphocytes (B cells) are sparse and dysfunctional. **Purine nucleoside phosphorylase deficiency** is associated with a severe thymus-derived lymphocyte deficiency with apparently normal B cell function, a much milder form of immunodeficiency. Both of these immunodeficiency diseases are inherited as autosomal recessive disorders. The molecular bases for the immune dysfunctions seem to involve the intracellular accumulation of the triphosphates of the deoxyribonucleoside substrates, deoxyguanosine and deoxyadenosine, of purine nucleoside phosphorylase and adenosine deaminase, respectively. These deoxynucleoside triphosphates, deoxy GTP and deoxy ATP, are capable of allosterically inhibiting ribonucleotide reductase and thereby depleting cells, such as T cells, of the precursors of DNA synthesis, particularly deoxy CTP.

Purine deficiency states are rare in humans. These are limited to circumstances attributable primarily to deficiencies of folic acid and perhaps of vitamin B_{12} when the latter results in a secondary deficiency of folate derivatives (see Chapter 10).

CLINICAL DISORDERS OF PYRIMIDINE METABOLISM
(See Table 26–4.)

As described above, the end products of pyrimidine metabolism, unlike those of purine metabolism, are **highly water-soluble compounds** such as CO_2, ammonia, β-alanine, and propionate. Thus, in circumstances where pyrimidine overproduction occurs, clinically detectable abnormalities are rarely evident. In cases of hyperuricemia associated with severe PPriboseP overproduction, there is concomitant overproduction of pyrimidine nucleotides with increased excretion of compounds such as β-alanine. Because of the requirement for N^5,N^{10}-methylenetetrahydrofolate for thymidylate synthesis, disorders of folate and vitamin B_{12} metabolism result in deficiencies of TMP (in the case of vitamin B_{12} deficiency, by an indirect mechanism).

β-Aminoisobutyric aciduria is an autosomal, recessively inherited disorder prevalent among the Oriental races. It is not associated with any pathologic state. It has been discussed above in connection with pyrimidine catabolism.

As described earlier, pseudouridine appears in normal urine. When increased nucleic acid turnover occurs in patients with leukemia or lymphoma, there is a markedly increased urinary excretion of pseudouridine. This compound is highly soluble and by itself produces no disease.

Two types of **hereditary orotic aciduria** have been reported. The more common type (type I), although still rare, is that in which both orotate phosphoribosyl transferase and orotidylate (OMP) decarboxylase are missing in all cell types tested (Fig 26–19). The patients are pyrimidine auxotrophs. They are readily treated with uridine. As infants, these patients fail to thrive and exhibit megaloblastic anemias and orange crystalluria (orotic acid). Unless treated with a source of pyrimidine nucleosides, they succumb to infections. The second type of hereditary orotic aciduria (type II) is due to a deficiency only of OMP decarboxylase (Fig 26–19). In patients with type I orotic aciduria, orotic acid is the major abnormal excretory product. In the one patient with type II, orotidine is the major excretory product, although some orotic acid is also excreted. In the erythrocytes of patients with type I orotic aciduria, the specific catalytic activities of aspartate transcarbamoylase and dihydroorotase were found to be greatly increased but returned to normal upon treatment of the patient with oral uridine. These observations suggest that one or more end products of the pathway are normally responsible for the maintenance of these enzyme activities at a regulated level. In a deficient state when the cells are deprived of the end products of this pathway, there is a derepression, probably a coordinate one, of at least those 2 enzymes.

The enzymology of the de novo pyrimidine pathway has suggested that there is a common protein molecule shared by carbamoyl phosphate synthetase, aspartate transcarbamoylase, and dihydroorotase, and another shared by orotate phosphoribosyl transferase and OMP decarboxylase.

Increased excretion of orotic acid, uracil, and uridine has been described in patients deficient in ornithine transcarbamoylase, a liver mitochondrial enzyme responsible for an early step in urea and arginine biosynthesis. In these patients there is apparently mitochondrial carbamoyl phosphate accumulation in response to the enzyme block. The mitochondrial carbamoyl phosphate diffuses into the cytosol to be utilized as a substrate for de novo pyrimidine nucleotide synthesis. The excess production of orotic acid is then manifested as orotic aciduria, which usually occurs in a mild degree and appears without crystal formation but increases upon the ingestion of foodstuffs such as meat that contain large amounts of nitrogen.

At least 2 drugs, one of which is widely used clinically, can result in orotic aciduria. Allopurinol, 4-hydroxypyrazolopyrimidine, a purine analog that directly inhibits xanthine oxidase, can be phosphoribosylated by orotate phosphoribosyl transferase, thereby competitively inhibiting the phosphoribosylation of orotic acid. Furthermore, the unusual nucleotide formed inhibits orotidylate decarboxylase, producing orotic aciduria and orotidinuria. In humans, at least, the pyrimidine pathway appears to readjust itself to this inhibition so that the organism is only transiently starved for pyrimidine nucleotides during the early stages of treatment.

6-Azauridine, after conversion to 6-azauridylate, is a competitive inhibitor of OMP decarboxylase, inducing high rates of excretion of orotic acid and orotidine as a result.

In specific liver mitochondrial failure, such as in Reye's syndrome, there is a secondary orotic aciduria. It is probably secondary to the inability of the mitochondria to utilize carbamoyl phosphate, which then, as in the inherited deficiency of ornithine transcarbamoylase, causes overproduction of orotic acid and a resultant orotic aciduria.

• • •

References

Henderson JF: *Regulation of Purine Biosynthesis.* Monograph No. 170. American Chemical Society, 1972.

Henderson JF, Paterson ARP: *Nucleotide Metabolism: An Introduction.* Academic Press, 1973.

Jones M: Pyrimidine nucleotide biosynthesis in animal cells. *Annu Rev Biochem* 1980;**49**:253.

Kempe TD & others: Stable mutants of mammalian cells that overproduce the first three enzymes of pyrimidine nucleotide biosynthesis. *Cell* 1976;**9**:541.

Martin DW Jr, Gelfand EW: Biochemistry of diseases of immunodevelopment. *Annu Rev Biochem* 1981;**50**:845.

Smith LH Jr: Pyrimidine metabolism in man. *N Engl J Med* 1973;**288**:764.

Stanbury JB, Wyngaarden JB, Fredrickson DS (editors): *The Metabolic Basis of Inherited Disease,* 4th ed. McGraw-Hill, 1978.

Thelander L, Reichard P: Reduction of ribonucleotides. *Annu Rev Biochem* 1979;**48**:133.

Wyngaarden JB, Kelley WN: *Gout and Hyperuricemia.* Grune & Stratton, 1976.

Nucleic Acids & Chromatin | 27

David W. Martin, Jr., MD

By any assessment of the major discoveries in science by the fourth quarter of the 20th century, it appears certain that the discovery that genetic information is coded along the length of a polymeric molecule composed of only 4 types of monomeric units will be regarded as a major scientific achievement of this century. This polymeric molecule, **DNA, is the chemical basis of heredity.** The demonstration that DNA contained the genetic information was first made in 1944 in a series of experiments by Avery, MacLeod, and McCarty, who showed that the genetic determination of the character (type) of the capsule of a specific pneumococcus could be transmitted to another of a distinctly different capsular type by introducing purified DNA from the former coccus into the latter. These authors referred to the agent (DNA) accomplishing the change as "transforming factor." (Fig 27–1.) Subsequently, this type of genetic manipulation has become commonplace in bacteriologic and genetic laboratories. Similar experiments have been performed utilizing cultured mammalian cells as recipients and isolated DNA and chromosomes as the donors of genetic information.

Chemical Nature of DNA

The chemical nature of the monomeric units of DNA—**deoxyadenylate, deoxyguanylate, deoxycytidylate,** and **thymidylate**—is described in Chapter 25. These monomeric units constituting a single strand of DNA are held in polymeric form by 3′,5′-phosphodiester bridges as depicted in Fig 27–2. The informational content of DNA resides in the sequence in which these monomers—purine and pyrimidine deoxyribonucleotides—are ordered. The polymer as depicted possesses a polarity; one end has a 5′-hydroxyl or phosphate terminus while the other has a 3′-phosphate or hydroxyl moiety. The importance of this polarity will become evident. Since the genetic information resides in the order of the monomeric units within the polymers, there must exist a mechanism of reproducing or replicating this specific information with a high degree of fidelity. That requirement, together with x-ray diffraction data from the DNA molecule and the observation of Chargaff that in DNA molecules the concentration of deoxyadenosine (A) nucleotides equals that of thymidine (T) nucleotides (A = T), while the concentration of deoxyguanosine (G) nucleo-

tides equals that of deoxycytidine (C) nucleotides (G = C), led Watson, Crick, and Wilkins to propose in the early 1950s a model of a double-stranded DNA molecule. The model of the currently accepted B form of DNA is depicted in Fig 27–3. The 2 strands of this double-stranded molecule are held together by **hydrogen bonds** between the purine and pyrimidine bases of the respective linear molecules. The pairings between the purine and pyrimidine nucleotides on the opposite strands are very specific and are dependent upon hydrogen bonding of **A with T,** and **G with C.** (Fig 27–4.)

Because of the restrictions imposed by the phosphodiester bond, the favored **anti** configuration of the glycosidic bond, and the predominant tautomers of the 4 bases (A, G, T, and C) in the polymer, A can pair only with T, and G only with C, as depicted in Fig 27–4. This base-pairing restriction explains the earlier observation that in a double-stranded DNA molecule the content of A equals that of T and the content of G equals that of C. The 2 strands of the double helical molecule, each of which possesses a polarity, are **antiparallel,** ie, one strand runs in the 5′ to 3′ direction and the other in the 3′ to 5′ direction. This is analogous to 2 parallel streets, each running one way but carrying traffic in opposite directions. In the double-stranded DNA molecules, since the information resides in the sequence of nucleotides on one strand, the opposite strand might be considered "antisense," ie, the complement of the "sense" strand.

As noted in the above base pairings, 3 hydrogen bonds hold the deoxyguanosine nucleotide to the deoxycytidine nucleotide whereas the other pair, the A-T pair, is held together by 2 hydrogen bonds. Thus, the G-C bond is stronger by approximately 50%, and the higher the G-C content of a DNA molecule, the greater is its buoyant density. The B form has a pitch of 3.4 nm per turn. Within a single turn 10 base pairs exist, each planar base being stacked to resemble 2 winding stacks of coins side by side. The 2 stacks are held together by hydrogen bonding at each level between the 2 coins of opposite stacks and by 2 ribbons wound in a right-hand turn about the 2 stacks and representing the phosphodiester backbone.

This double-stranded structure in solution can be melted by increasing temperature or decreasing salt concentration. Not only do the 2 stacks of bases pull

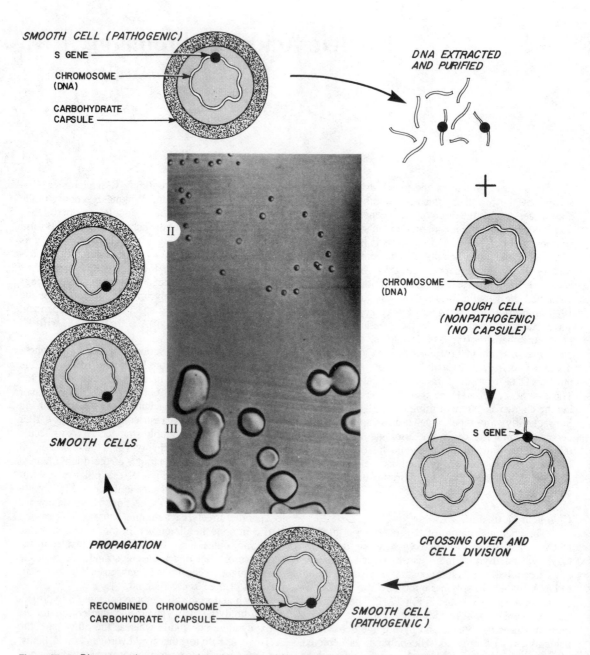

Figure 27–1. Diagrammatic representation of the Avery-MacLeod-McCarty experiment demonstrating that genetic information is contained in DNA. Pathogenic pneumococci with a capsule of carbohydrate resulting in the formation of smooth colonies were extracted, and the DNA containing the S gene was purified. The purified DNA was added to nonpathogenic, nonencapsulated pneumococci, which form rough colonies. The recipient nonencapsulated pneumococci were allowed to absorb and interact with the DNA and divide. Some of the resulting daughter pneumococci had acquired the ability (via the S gene) to form a carbohydrate capsule, smooth colonies, and thus pathogenicity. The photograph in the center (× 3.5) demonstrates smooth (pathogenic) type III and rough (nonpathogenic) type II colonies of these pneumococci. (Redrawn and reproduced, with permission, from Avery OT, MacLeod CM, McCarty M: *J Exp Med* 1944;**79**:137.)

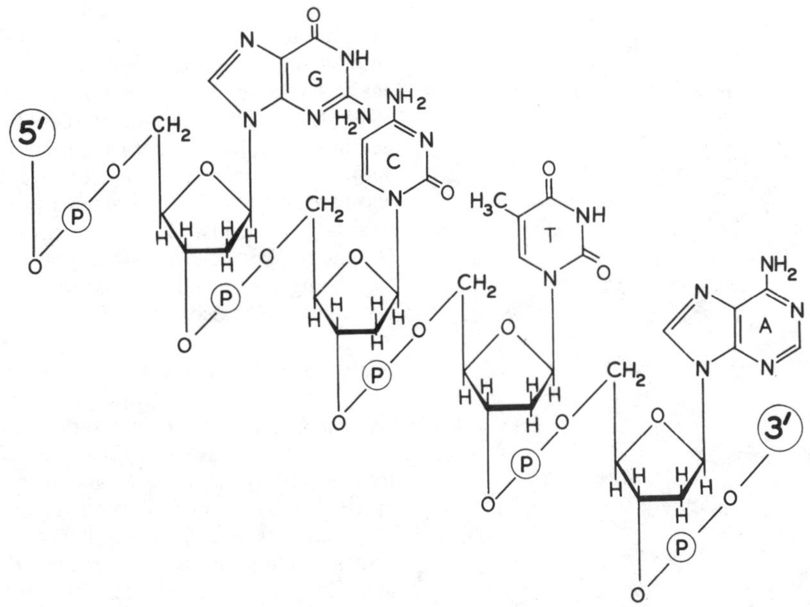

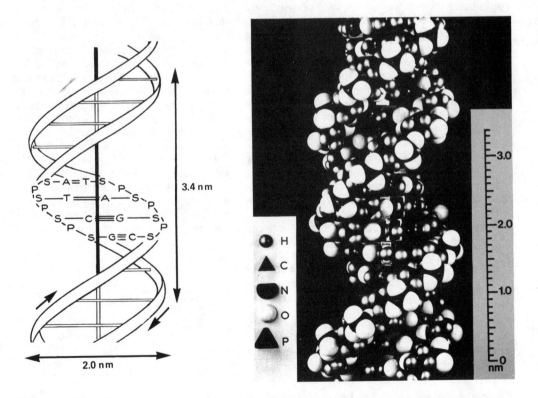

Figure 27–2. A segment of a structure of DNA molecule in which the purine and pyrimidine bases adenine (A), thymine (T), cytosine (C), and guanine (G) are held together by a phosphodiester backbone between 2'-deoxyribosyl moieties attached to the nucleobases by an N--glycosidic bond. Note that the backbone has a polarity (ie, a direction).

Figure 27–3. The Watson and Crick model of the double helical structure of DNA. *Left:* Diagrammatic representation of structure (modified). A = adenine, C = cytosine, G = guanine, T = thymine, P = phosphate, S = sugar (deoxyribose). *Right:* Space-filling model of DNA structure. (Photograph from James D. Watson, *Molecular Biology of the Gene,* 3rd ed. Copyright © 1976, 1970, 1965, by W.A. Benjamin, Inc, Menlo Park, California.)

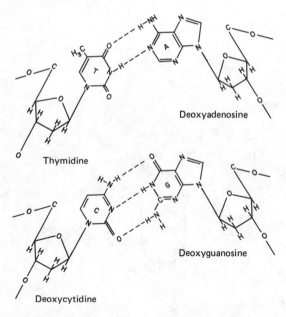

Deoxyadenosine

Thymidine

Deoxyguanosine

Deoxycytidine

Figure 27–4. Base-pairing between the favored tautomers of deoxyadenosine and thymidine and between those of deoxycytidine and deoxyguanosine, as proposed by Watson and Crick. The broken lines represent hydrogen bonds. (The phosphodiester bridges are not shown.)

apart, but the bases themselves unstack while still connected in the polymer by the phosphodiester backbone. Concomitant with this **denaturation** of the DNA molecule is an increase in the optical absorbency of the purine and pyrimidine bases—a phenomenon referred to as **hyperchromicity** of denaturation. Because of the stacking of the bases and the hydrogen bonding between the stacks, the double-stranded DNA molecule exhibits properties of a fiber and in solution is a viscous material that loses its viscosity upon denaturation.

Careful examination of the model depicted in Fig 27–3 reveals a **major groove** and a **minor groove** winding along the molecule parallel to the phosphodiester backbones. In these grooves, specific proteins interact with DNA molecules.

In some organisms such as bacteria, bacteriophages, and many DNA-containing animal viruses, the 2 ends of the DNA molecules are joined to create a closed circle with no terminus. This of course does not destroy the polarity of the molecules, but it eliminates all free 3′ and 5′ hydroxyl and phosphoryl groups.

Chromatin

Chromatin is the chromosomal material extracted from nuclei of cells of eukaryotic organisms.* Chromatin consists of very long double-stranded **DNA**

molecules and a nearly equal mass of rather small basic proteins termed **histones** as well as a smaller amount of **nonhistone proteins** (most of which are acidic and larger than histones) and a small quantity of **RNA.** Electron microscopic studies of chromatin have demonstrated dense spherical particles called **nucleosomes** which are approximately 12.5 nm in diameter and connected by DNA filaments (Fig 27–5). When one (H1) of the histone components is removed from chromatin, the nucleosomes are not so closely packed, suggesting that histone H1 is involved in the superpacking of nucleosomes in nuclei.

Histones & Nucleosomes

The H1 (lysine-rich) histones are somewhat heterogeneous, consisting of a series of closely related basic proteins. Among the histones, H1 histones are the least tightly bound to chromatin and are, therefore, easily removed with a salt solution, after which chromatin becomes soluble. The isolated core nucleosomes contain 4 classes of histones: H2A, H2B, H3, and H4 (Table 27–1). The structures of slightly lysine-rich histones—H2A and H2B—appear to have been significantly conserved between species, while the structures of arginine-rich histones—H3 and H4—have been highly conserved between species. This severe conservation implies that the function of histones is identical in all eukaryotes and that the entire molecule is involved quite specifically in carrying out this function. The C-terminal two-thirds of the molecules have amino acid compositions typical of globular proteins, and their N-terminal thirds contain the basic amino acids. These 4 core histones are subject to 5 types of **covalent modifications:** acetylation, methylation, phosphorylation, ADP-ribosylation, and covalent linkage (H2A only) to the nuclear protein, ubiquitin. When removed from chromatin, the histones interact with each other in very specific ways. **H3 and H4 aggregate to form a tetramer** containing 2 molecules of each (H3$_2$-H4$_2$), while **H2A and H2B form dimers** (H2A-H2B) and higher oligomeric complexes (H2A-H2B)$_n$. The tetrameric H3-H4 does not associate with the H2A-H2B dimer or oligomer, and H1 does not associate directly with any of the other histones.

Table 27–1. Histone nomenclature.

	Original Schemes		New Scheme
Lysine-rich	fl	Ib	H1
	(f2c)	(V)	(H5)
Slightly lysine-rich	f2a2	IIb1	H2A
	f2b	IIb2	H2B
Arginine-rich	f3	III	H3
	f2al	IV	H4

*So far as possible, the remaining discussion of this chapter and of Chapters 28, 29, and 30 will pertain to mammalian organisms, which are, of course, among the higher eukaryotes. At times it will be necessary to refer to observations made in prokaryotic organisms such as bacteria and viruses, but when such occurs it

will be acknowledged as being information that must be extrapolated to mammalian organisms. The division of the material presented in this chapter and in Chapters 28 and 29 is somewhat arbitrary and should not be taken to mean that the processes described are not fully integrated and interdependent.

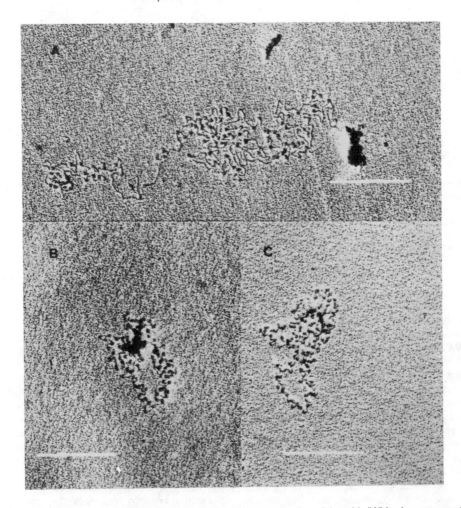

Figure 27–5. Electron micrograph of nucleosomes attached by strands of nucleic acid. (White bar represents 2.5 μm.) (Reproduced, with permission, from Oudet P, Gross-Bellard M, Chambon P: *Cell* 1975;4:281.)

However, it was found by Roger Kornberg and Jean Thomas that when the ($H3_2$-$H4_2$) tetramer and (H2A-H2B) dimers were mixed with purified, double-stranded DNA, the same x-ray diffraction pattern was formed as that observed in freshly isolated chromatin. Electron microscopic studies confirmed the existence of a self-assimilating **nucleosome** structure. Furthermore, the reconstitution of nucleosomes from DNA and histones H2A, H2B, H3, and H4 was independent of the organismal or cellular origin of the various components. The histone H1 and the nonhistone proteins are not necessary for the reconstitution of the nucleosome core.

In the nucleosome, the DNA is supercoiled in a left-handed helix over the surface of the disk-shaped histone octamer consisting of one H3-H4 tetramer ($H3_2$-$H4_2$) and two H2A-H2B dimers. The $H3_2$-$H4_2$ itself can confer nucleosomelike properties on DNA and thus has a central role in the formation of the nucleosome. The $H3_2$-$H4_2$ can protect approximately 80 base pairs of DNA in the central turn of the nucleosome from attack by nucleases. The addition of two H2A-H2B dimers stabilizes the primary particle and binds firmly 2 additional half-turns of DNA previously bound only loosely to the $H3_2$-$H4_2$. Thus, **1.75 superhelical turns of DNA** are wrapped around the surface of the histone octamer, **protecting 146 base pairs of DNA** and forming the **nucleosome core** (Fig 27–6). As the DNA wraps around the surface of the histone octamer to form the nucleosome, it comes in contact with the histones in the order:

H2A—H2B—H4—H3—H3—H4—H2B—H2A

Histone H1 binds to the DNA, where it enters and leaves the nucleosome core to seal a **2-turn, 166 base pair DNA superhelix** generating the **nucleosome** (Fig 27–6).

The assembly of nucleosomes is probably mediated by the anionic nuclear protein **nucleoplasmin.** Histones, which are strongly cationic, can bind nonspecifically to the strongly anionic DNA by forming salt bridges. Clearly, such a nonspecific interaction of histones and DNA would be detrimental to nucleo-

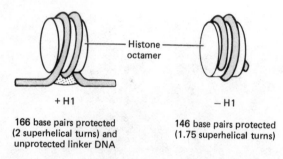

+ H1

166 base pairs protected
(2 superhelical turns) and
unprotected linker DNA

− H1

146 base pairs protected
(1.75 superhelical turns)

Figure 27–6. Model for the structure of the nucleosome (left) and nucleosome core (right), in which DNA is wrapped around the surface of a flat protein cylinder consisting of 2 each of histones H2A, H2B, H3, and H4. (Reproduced, with permission, from Laskey RA, Earnshaw WC: Nucleosome assembly. *Nature* 1980;286:763.)

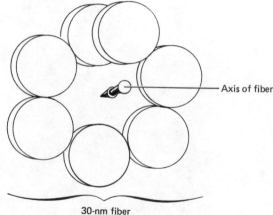

— Axis of fiber

30-nm fiber

Figure 27–8. Proposed structure of the 30-nm chromatin fiber consisting of superhelixes of 10-nm fibrils of nucleosomes. The axis of the 30-nm fiber is perpendicular to the plane of the page.

some formation and chromatin function. Nucleoplasmin is an anionic pentameric protein that binds neither to DNA nor to chromatin, but it can interact reversibly and stoichiometrically with one histone octamer in such a way that the histones no longer adhere nonspecifically to negatively charged surfaces such as DNA. It seems that nucleoplasmin thereby maintains in the nucleus an ionic environment conducive to the specific interaction of histones and DNA and assembly nucleosomes. As the nucleosome is assembled, nucleoplasmin must be released from the histones. DNA topoisomerase I, a nicking-closing enzyme discussed below, may be involved in similar nucleosome assembly functions.

The super-packing of nucleosomes in nuclei is seemingly dependent upon the interaction of the H1 histones with the double-stranded DNA connecting the nucleosomes. The topology of the interaction of the double-stranded DNA with the H1 histones to form the internucleosome spacer regions is not well delineated. It is clear that the association of H1 with double-stranded DNA is not dependent upon the sequence of nucleotides in the DNA molecule.

Electron microscopy of chromatin reveals 2 higher orders of structure—the 10-nm fibril and the 25- to 30-nm chromatin fiber—beyond that of the nucleosome itself. The disklike nucleosome structure has an 11-nm diameter and a height of 5.5 nm. The **10-nm fibril** seems to consist of nucleosomes arranged with their edges touching and their flat faces parallel with the fibril axis (Fig 27–7). The 10-nm fibril is probably further supercoiled with 6–7 nucleosomes

per turn to form the **30-nm chromatin fiber** (Fig 27–8). Each turn of the supercoil would be relatively flat, and the faces of the nucleosomes of successive turns would be nearly parallel to each other. H1 histones appear to stabilize the 30-nm fiber, but their position and that of the variable length spacer DNA are not clear. It is probable that nucleosomes can form a variety of packed structures. In order to form a mitotic chromosome, the 30-nm fiber must be compacted in length another 100-fold (see below). Undoubtedly, many of the chemical modifications of histones in chromatin are involved with the formation of the higher orders of structure and with the changing interrelationships between histones and DNA during replication and transcription.

Interestingly, some of the major nonhistone proteins in chromatin that have been identified include myosin, actin, tubulin, and tropomyosin. Their functions at this site are unknown, but they are involved in cytokinesis. In sperm, many of the basic histone proteins are replaced with other basic proteins such as protamines, which serve to increase even further the density of nucleic acid packing.

At metaphase, mammalian **chromosomes** possess a 2-fold symmetry, with identical **sister chromatids** connected at a **centromere,** the relative position of which is characteristic for a given chromosome (Fig 27–9). Each sister chromatid probably contains one double-stranded DNA molecule. During interphase, the packing of the DNA molecule is less dense than it is in the condensed chromosome during the metaphase.

The human haploid genome consists of 3.5×10^9 base pairs or pairs of nucleotides extending over 1.7×10^7 nucleosomes. Thus, each of the 23 chromosomes in the human haploid genome would contain on the average 1.5×10^6 nucleotides in one double-stranded DNA molecule. The length of each DNA molecule

Fibril
axis

5.5 nm

10-nm
Fibril

Figure 27–7. Proposed structure of the 10-nm fibril of chromatin made up of disk-shaped nucleosomes. The positions of the H1 histone-spacer regions are undefined.

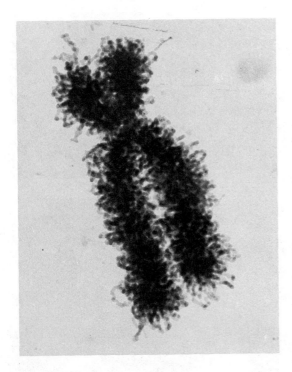

Figure 27-9. Human chromosome 12. × 27,850. (Reproduced, with permission, from DuPraw EJ: *DNA and Chromosomes.* Holt, Rinehart, & Winston, 1970.)

Table 27-2. The packing ratios of each of the orders of DNA structure.

Chromatin Form	Packing Ratio
Bare double-helix DNA	≡ 1.0
~ 2 turns of DNA on nucleosome	2.5
10-nm fibril of nucleosomes	5
25- to 30-nm chromatin fiber of superhelical nucleosomes	30
Condensed metaphase chromosome of loops	8000

must be **compressed about 8000-fold** to generate the structure of a condensed metaphase chromosome. The 25- to 30-nm chromatin fiber is folded into a series of **looped domains,** each 20–80 thousand base pairs in length, in the interphase chromosome. The packing ratios of each of the orders of DNA structure are summarized in Table 27–2. Each looped domain of chromatin may correspond to a separate genetic function containing both the coding and noncoding regions of a gene (see Chapter 28).

The packaging of nucleoproteins within chromatids is not random, as evidenced by the characteristic patterns observed when chromatids are stained with specific dyes such as quinacrine or Giemsa's stain (Fig 27–10).

From individual to individual within a single species, the pattern of staining (banding) of the entire

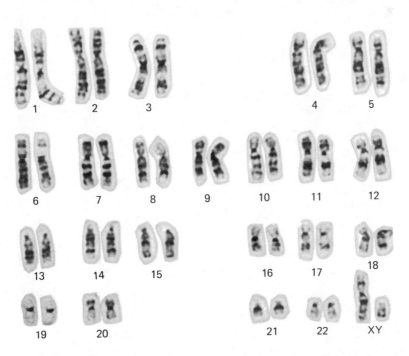

Figure 27-10. A human karyotype (of a man with a normal 46 XY constitution), in which the chromosomes have been stained by the Giemsa method and aligned according to the Paris Convention. (Courtesy of Helen Lawce and Dr Felix Conte, Department of Pediatrics, University of California School of Medicine, San Francisco.)

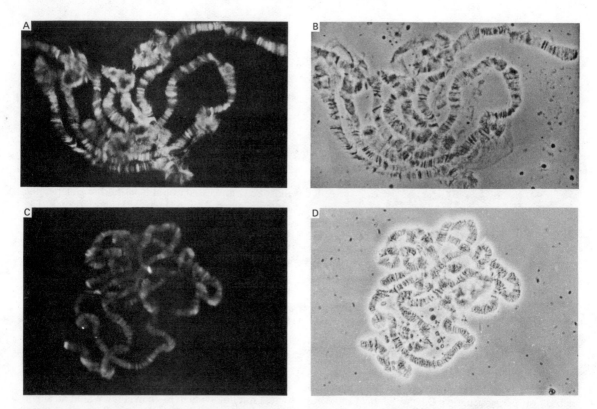

Figure 27–11. Localization of chromosomal proteins by immunofluorescence. Polytene chromosomes of *Drosophila melanogaster* salivary glands were treated with the serum of a rabbit immunized against a chromosomal protein. The locations of that protein were then visualized by means of a fluorescent antibody against rabbit antibodies. *(A)* Histone H1, shown to be generally distributed throughout the chromosomes in the same pattern as in *(B)* phase contrast density. *(C)* Nonhistone protein D1, widely distributed but highly concentrated in region 81F, also shown in *(D)* phase contrast. (Courtesy of CR Alfageme, GT Rudkin, & LH Cohen. The Institute for Cancer Research, Fox Chase, Philadelphia.)

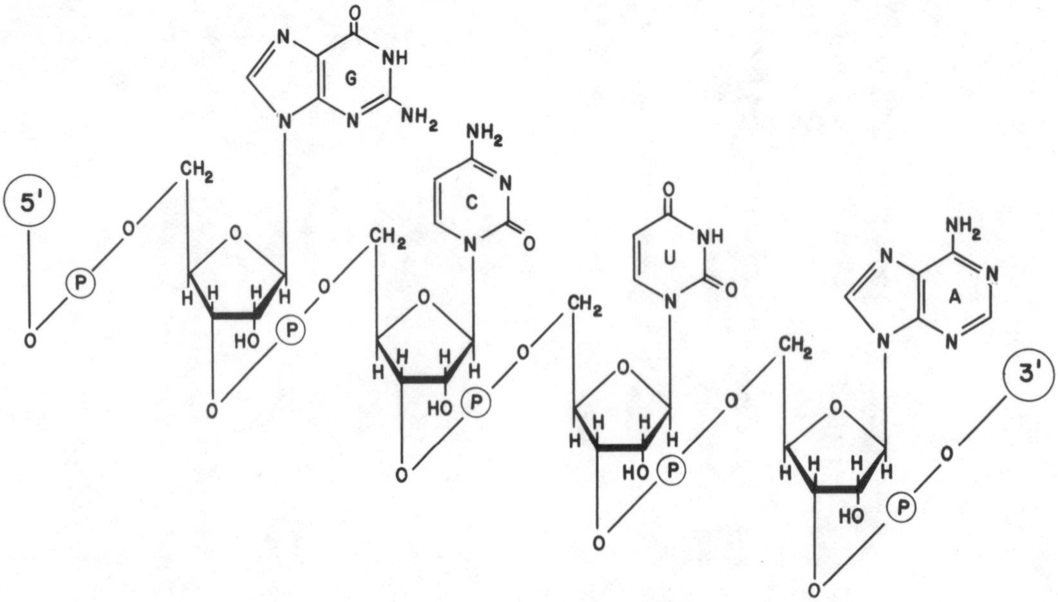

Figure 27–12. A segment of a ribonucleic acid (RNA) molecule in which the purine and pyrimidine bases —adenine (A), uracil (U), cytosine (C), and guanine (G)—are held together by phosphodiester bonds between ribosyl moieties attached to the nucleobases by N glycosidic bonds. Note that the polymer has a polarity.

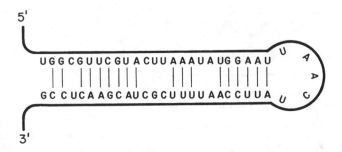

5'

UGGCGUUCGU A CUU AAAU AU GG A AU
| | | | | | | | | | | | | | | | | | | |
GC CUC A AGC AUCGCU UUU AAC CUU A

U A
A
A
U C

3'

Figure 27–13. Diagrammatic representation of the secondary structure of an RNA molecule in which a "hairpin" has been formed and is dependent upon the intramolecular base pairing.

chromosome complement is highly reproducible; nonetheless, it differs significantly from other species, even those closely related. Thus, the packaging of the nucleoproteins in chromosomes of higher eukaryotes must in some way be dependent upon the nucleotide sequences in the DNA molecules.

Using fluorescent antibodies against specific nuclear proteins, Cohen has been able to provide some resolution to the association of these proteins with DNA in the giant chromosomes of *Drosophila* (Fig 27–11).

Chemical Nature of Ribonucleic Acid (RNA)

Ribonucleic acid is a polymer of purine and pyrimidine ribonucleotides linked together by 3',5'-phosphodiester bridges analogous to those in DNA (Fig 27–12). Although sharing many features with DNA, RNA possesses several specific differences:

(1) As indicated by its name, the sugar moiety in RNA to which the phosphates and purine and pyrimidine bases are attached is **ribose** rather than the 2'-deoxyribose of DNA.

(2) Although RNA contains the ribonucleotides of adenine, guanine, and cytosine, it does not possess thymine except in the rare case mentioned below. Instead of thymine, RNA contains the ribonucleotide of **uracil.** Thus, the pyrimidine components of RNA differ from those of DNA.

(3) RNA exists natively as a **single-stranded** molecule rather than as a double-stranded helical molecule, as does DNA. However, given the proper

complementary base sequence with opposite polarity, the single strand of RNA, as demonstrated in Fig 27–13, is capable of folding back on itself like a hairpin and thus acquiring double-stranded characteristics.

(4) Since the RNA molecule is single-stranded and complementary to only one of the 2 strands of a gene, its guanine content does *not* necessarily equal its cytosine content, nor does its adenine content necessarily equal its uracil content.

(5) RNA can be **hydrolyzed by alkali** to 2',3' cyclic diesters of the mononucleotides. A necessary intermediate in this hydrolysis is the 2',3',5'-triester, an intermediate which cannot be formed in alkali-treated DNA because of the absence of a 2'-hydroxyl group. The alkali lability of RNA is useful both diagnostically and analytically.

Information within the single strand of RNA is contained in its sequence ("primary structure") of purine and pyrimidine nucleotides within the polymer. The sequence is complementary to the "sense" strand of the gene from which it was transcribed. Because of this complementarity, an RNA molecule will hybridize with its template DNA strand, the strand which is thus necessarily referred to as being the "sense" strand; it will not hybridize with the "antisense" strand of the DNA of its gene. The sequence of the RNA molecule (except for U replacing T) is the same as that of the "antisense" strand of the gene (Fig 27–14).

Small quantities of double-stranded RNA other

DNA STRANDS:

ANTISENSE → 5'-T GG A AT T G T G AG C G G AT A AC A AT T T C AC AC A G G AA A C A G C T AT G A C C AT G-3'
SENSE ——→ 3'-A CC T T A AC A C T C G C C T A T T G T T A A A G T G T G T C C T T T G T C G A T A C T G G T A C-5'

RNA   5'   pA U U G U G AG C G G AU A AC A AU U U C A C AC A G G AA A C A G C U AU G A C C AU G   3'
TRANSCRIPT

Figure 27–14. The relationship between the sequences of an RNA transcript and its gene, in which the sense and antisense strands are shown with their polarities. The RNA transcript with a 5' to 3' polarity is complementary to the sense strand with its 3' to 5' polarity. Note that the sequence in the RNA transcript and its polarity is the same as that in the antisense strand, except that the U of the transcript replaces the T of the gene.

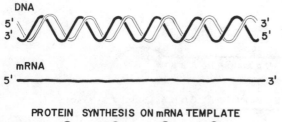

PROTEIN SYNTHESIS ON mRNA TEMPLATE

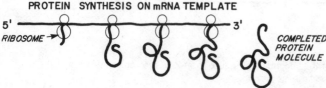

Figure 27–15. The expression of genetic information in DNA into the form of an mRNA transcript. This is subsequently translated by ribosomes into a specific protein molecule.

than transfer RNA have been detected in and isolated from mammalian organisms, including humans. Double-stranded RNA may have some physiologic function such as serving as an inducer of **interferon,** an antiviral protein which most animal cells are capable of generating as a defense mechanism.

Structural Organization of RNA

In all prokaryotic and eukaryotic organisms, 3 main classes of RNA molecules exist: **messenger RNA (mRNA), transfer RNA (tRNA),** and **ribosomal RNA (rRNA).** Each class differs from the others by size, function, and general stability.

The **messenger RNA (mRNA)** class is the most heterogeneous in size and stability. All of the members of the class function as messengers conveying the information in a gene to the protein-synthesizing machinery, where each serves as a template on which a specific sequence of amino acids is polymerized to form a specific protein molecule, the ultimate gene product (Fig 27–15).

The messenger RNAs are single-stranded and complementary to the sense strand of their respective structural genes. The RNA molecules, particularly in mammals, have some unique chemical characteristics. The 5' terminus of mRNA is "capped" by a 7-methyl-

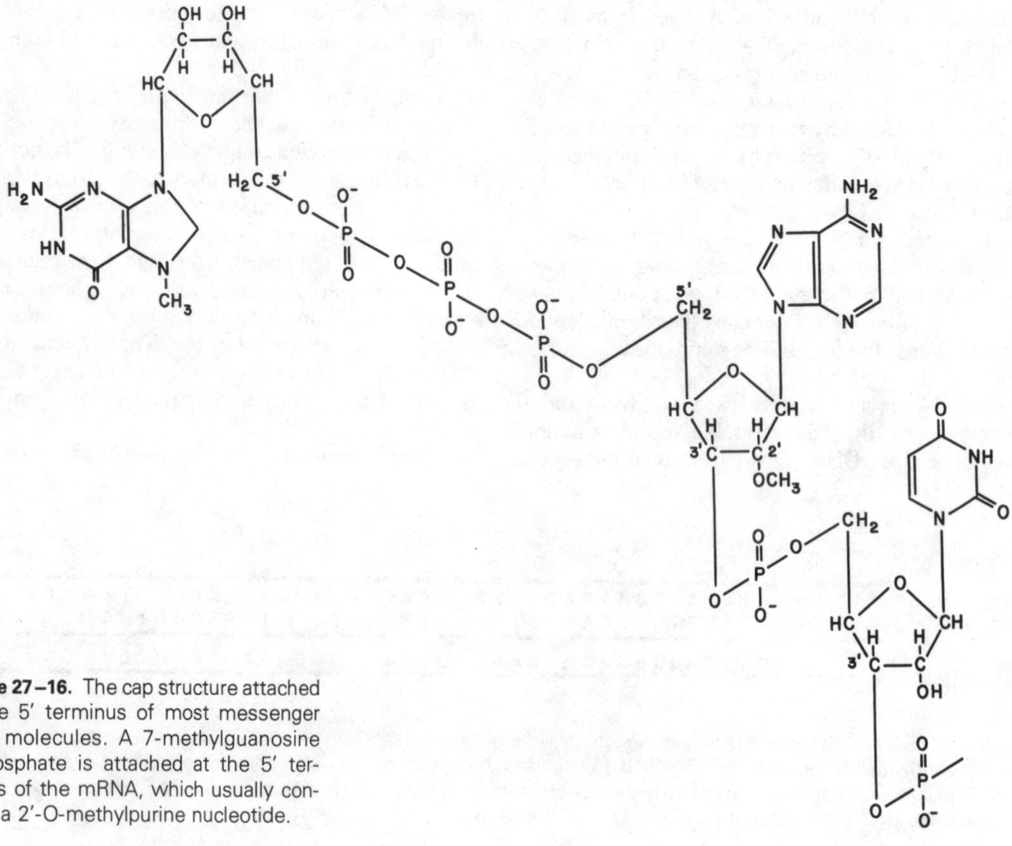

Figure 27–16. The cap structure attached to the 5' terminus of most messenger RNA molecules. A 7-methylguanosine triphosphate is attached at the 5' terminus of the mRNA, which usually contains a 2'-O-methylpurine nucleotide.

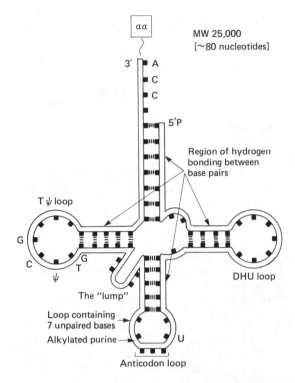

Figure 27–17. A typical aminoacyl tRNA in which the amino acid ($\alpha\alpha$) is attached to the 3' ACC terminus. The anticodon, TψC, and DHU loops are indicated, as are the positions of the intramolecular hydrogen bonding between these base pairs. (From James D. Watson, *Molecular Biology of the Gene,* 3rd ed. Copyright © 1976, 1970, 1965, by W.A. Benjamin, Inc, Menlo Park, California.)

molecules. These nuclear RNA molecules are very heterogeneous in size and are quite large. The **heterogeneous nuclear RNA (hnRNA)** molecules may exceed 10^7 daltons, whereas the mRNA molecules are generally smaller than 2×10^6 daltons. As is discussed in Chapter 28, the hnRNA molecules are processed to generate the mRNA molecules which then enter the cytoplasm to serve as templates for protein synthesis.

The **transfer RNA (tRNA)** molecules consist of approximately 75 nucleotides and thus have a molecular weight of 25,000. They also are generated by nuclear processing of a precursor molecule (see Chapter 28). The tRNA molecules serve as adaptors for the translation of the information in the sequence of nucleotides of the mRNA into specific amino acids. There are at least 20 tRNA molecules in every cell, at least one corresponding to each of the 20 amino acids required for protein synthesis. Although each specific tRNA differs from the others in its sequence of nucleotides, the tRNA molecules as a class have many features in common. The primary structure—ie, the nucleotide sequence—of all tRNA molecules allows extensive folding and intrastrand complementarity to generate a significant secondary structure which can appear like a cloverleaf (Fig 27–17). X-ray diffraction studies have allowed the formulation of a schematic diagram illustrating the folding of the phenylalanine-accepting tRNA from yeast (Fig 27–18).

The features that all tRNA molecules have in common include an **ACC sequence** at the 3' termini. It

guanosine triphosphate that is linked to an adjacent 2'-O-methyl ribonucleoside at its 5'-hydroxyl through the 3 phosphates (Fig 27–16). The mRNA molecules frequently contain internal 6-methyladenylates and other 2'-O-ribose methylated nucleotides. Although the function of this capping of mRNAs is not completely understood, the cap is probably involved in the recognition of mRNA by the translating machinery. The protein-synthesizing machinery begins translating the mRNA into proteins at the 5' or capped terminus. The other end of most mRNA molecules, the 3'-hydroxyl terminus, has attached a polymer of adenylate residues 20–250 nucleotides in length. The specific function of the **poly(A) "tail"** at the 3'-hydroxyl terminus of mRNAs is not understood, but it has been suggested that it maintains the intracellular stability of the specific mRNA. The mRNAs for the histones do not contain poly(A).

In mammalian cells, including cells of humans, the mRNA molecules present in the cytoplasm are not the RNA products immediately synthesized from the DNA template but must be formed by processing from a precursor molecule before entering the cytoplasm. Thus in mammalian nuclei, the immediate products of gene transcription constitute a fourth class of RNA

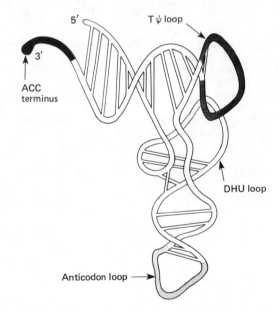

Figure 27–18. The 3-dimensional structure of a tRNA molecule as determined by x-ray crystallography. The specified amino acid is attached at the ACC 3' terminus. The TψC loop, the dihydrouracil (DHU) loop, and the anticodon loop are indicated. (Redrawn and reproduced, with permission, from Stryer L: *Biochemistry.* Freeman, 1975. Copyright © 1975. [Based on a drawing by Dr Sung-Han Kim.])

is through an ester bond to the 3′-hydroxyl group of the adenosyl moiety that the carboxyl groups of amino acids are attached. The **anticodon loop** at the end of a base-paired stem recognizes the triplet nucleotide or codon (discussed in Chapter 29) of the template mRNA. In nearly all tRNA molecules there is a loop containing the nucleotides of ribothymine and pseudouridine and another loop containing the minor base dihydrouracil. (See also Chapter 29.)

Although tRNAs are quite stable in prokaryotes, they are somewhat less stable in eukaryotes. The opposite is true for mRNAs, which are quite unstable in prokaryotes but generally stable in eukaryotic organisms.

Ribosomal RNA

A ribosome is a cytoplasmic nucleoprotein structure that acts as the machinery for the synthesis of proteins from the mRNA templates. On the ribosomes, the mRNA and tRNA molecules interact to translate into a specific protein molecule information transcribed from the gene. Ribosomal particles are very complex, having been self-assembled from at least 4 distinct RNA molecules and nearly 100 specific protein molecules (Table 27–3).

The mammalian ribosome contains 2 major nucleoprotein subunits, a larger one of 2.7 megadaltons (60S) and a smaller subunit of 1.3 megadaltons (40S). The **60S subunit** contains a **5S ribosomal RNA**

Table 27–3. RNA components of mammalian ribosomes.

Subunit Size (Svedberg Units)	Subunit MW	RNA Size (Svedberg Units)	MW RNA
60S (>50 polypeptides)	2.7 × 10⁶	5S	35,000
		5.8S	45,000
		28S	1.5 × 10⁶
40S (>30 polypeptides)	1.3 × 10⁶	18S	750,000

(rRNA), a **5.8S rRNA** (formerly 7S rRNA), and a **28S rRNA;** there are also probably more than 50 specific polypeptides. The smaller or **40S subunit** contains a single **18S rRNA** and approximately 30 polypeptide chains. All of the ribosomal RNA molecules except the 5S rRNA are processed from a single 45S precursor RNA molecule in the nucleolus (see Chapter 29). The 5S rRNA apparently has its own precursor that is independently transcribed. The highly methylated ribosomal RNA molecules are packaged in the nucleolus with the specific ribosomal proteins. In the cytoplasm, the ribosomes remain quite stable and capable of many translations. The functions of the ribosomal RNA molecules in the ribosomal particle are not fully understood, but they are necessary for ribosomal assembly and seem to provide a specific sequence to which the mRNA molecule can bind in order to be translated.

●   ●   ●

References

Bauer WR & others: Supercoiled DNA. *Sci Am* (July) 1980;**243**:118.

Brawerman G: Eukaryotic messenger RNA. *Annu Rev Biochem* 1974;**43**:621.

Klug A & others: A low resolution structure for the histone core of the nucleosome. *Nature* 1980;**287**:509.

Kornberg R: Structure of chromatin. *Annu Rev Biochem* 1977;**46**:931.

Laskey RA, Earnshaw WC: Nucleosome Assembly. *Nature* 1980;**286**:763.

McGhee JD, Felsenfeld G: Nucleosome structure. *Annu Rev Biochem* 1980;**49**:1115.

Oudet P, Gross-Bellard M, Chambon P: Electron microscopic and biochemical evidence that chromatin structure is a repeating unit. *Cell* 1975;**4**:281.

Rich A, Raj Bhandary UL: Transfer RNA: Molecular structure, sequence and properties. *Annu Rev Biochem* 1976;**45**:805.

Watson JD: *The Double Helix.* Atheneum, 1968.

Watson JD, Crick FHC: Molecular structure of nucleic acids. *Nature* 1953;**171**:737.

Weisbrod S, Weintraub H: HMG proteins in chromatin. *Proc Nat Acad Sci USA* 1979;**76**:635.

Nucleic Acid Replication, Transcription, & Processing | 28

David W. Martin, Jr., MD

THE NATURE OF DNA

As described in Chapter 27, DNA is a very long polymer of purine and pyrimidine deoxyribonucleotide monomers bound one to another by phosphodiester bridges. In nature, DNA exists as a double-stranded molecule, the strands being held together by the hydrophobic or Van der Waals forces between stacked planar purine and pyrimidine bases and by hydrogen bonding between the purine and pyrimidine bases of the 2 strands. The 2 strands have **polarity** and extend in opposite directions, ie, each is **antiparallel** as it runs in the double-stranded DNA molecule. For each purine of pyrimidine base in one strand there exists in the other strand a related pyrimidine or purine base whose specificity is determined by the base-pairing rules set forth in Chapter 27. The most favored tautomers and the anti configuration of the N-glycosidic bond of each nucleotide restrict the binding in the DNA double helix to adenine (A) paired with thymine (T) and guanine (G) paired with cytosine (C). Genetic information is contained in the primary structure, ie, the sequence of mononucleotides of the DNA molecule. For each gene in the DNA molecule there is a "sense" strand and its complementary "antisense" strand.

This complementarity of the Watson and Crick double-stranded model of DNA strongly suggests that replication of the DNA molecule occurs in a semiconservative manner. Thus, when each strand of the double-stranded DNA molecule separates from its complement during replication, **each can then serve as a template** on which a new complementary strand can be synthesized (Fig 28–1). The 2 newly formed double-stranded DNA molecules, each containing one strand (but complementary rather than identical) from the parent double-stranded DNA molecule, can then be sorted between the 2 daughter cells (Fig 28–2). Each daughter cell will contain DNA molecules with information identical to that which the parent possessed; yet in each daughter cell the DNA molecule of the parent cell has been only semiconserved.

The **semiconservative** nature of DNA replication in the bacterium *Escherichia coli* was unequivocally demonstrated by Meselson and Stahl in a now classic experiment using the heavy isotope of nitrogen and centrifugal equilibrium technics. This classic experi-

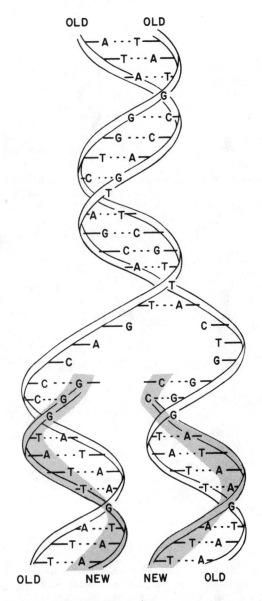

Figure 28–1. The double-stranded structure of DNA and the template function of each old strand on which a new complementary strand is synthesized. (From James D. Watson, *Molecular Biology of the Gene,* 3rd ed. Copyright © 1976, 1970, 1965, by W.A. Benjamin, Inc. Menlo Park, California.)

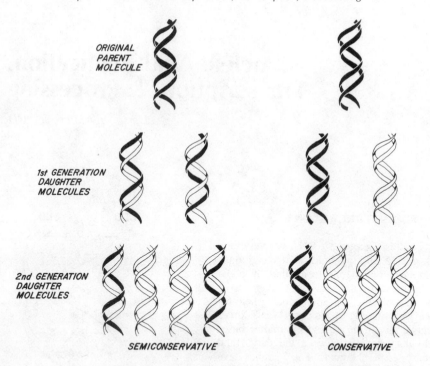

Figure 28–2. The expected distributions of parental DNA strands during semiconservative and conservative replication. The parental strands are solid and the newly synthesized strands are open. (Redrawn and reproduced, with permission, from Lehninger AL: *Biochemistry,* 2nd ed. Worth, 1975.)

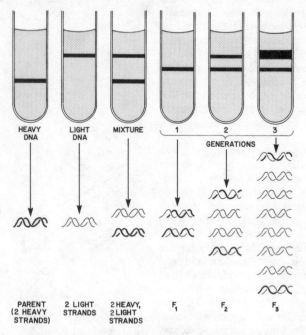

Figure 28–3. Schematic representation of the results of the Meselson-Stahl experiment demonstrating semiconservative replication of bacterial DNA. The tubes in which the equilibrium centrifugation conditions have been established are represented at the top and contain the bands of DNA with the indicated densities. In the lower part of the figure are represented the parent DNA strands containing the heavy isotope of nitrogen (^{15}N) and the strands isolated from daughter cells grown in the presence of the naturally occurring light isotope of nitrogen (^{14}N). The appearance of a band of DNA with an intermediate density and its persistence through 3 generations with the subsequent appearance of totally light DNA confirms the semiconservative nature of DNA replication in prokaryotes. (Redrawn and reproduced, with permission, from Lehninger AL: *Biochemistry,* 2nd ed. Worth, 1975.)

ment is depicted in Fig 28–3. The DNA of *E coli* is chemically identical to that of humans, although the sequences of nucleotides are, of course, different, and the human cell contains about 1000 times more DNA per cell than does the bacterium. Furthermore, the chemistry of replication of DNA in prokaryotes such as *E coli* appears to be identical to that in eukaryotes, including humans, even though the enzymes carrying out the reactions of DNA synthesis and replication are different. Thus, any observations on the chemical nature or chemical reactions of nucleic acids of prokaryotes are very likely applicable to eukaryotic organisms. Indeed, the Meselson and Stahl type of experiment has now been performed in mammalian cells and has yielded results comparable to those obtained with *E coli*.

GENETIC ORGANIZATION OF THE MAMMALIAN GENOME

The **diploid** genome of each human cell consists of 7×10^9 base pairs of DNA, subdivided into 23 pairs of chromosomes. The entire diploid genome contains sufficient DNA to code for nearly 3 million pairs of genes. However, studies of mutation rates and of the complexities of the genomes of higher organisms strongly suggest that humans have only about 20–50 thousand essential proteins. This implies that most of the DNA is noncoding, ie, its information is never translated into an amino acid sequence of a protein molecule. Two recent observations with widespread biologic implications provide insight into the relationship between coding and noncoding DNA. The earlier observation, mentioned in Chapter 27, is that of the large hnRNA transcribed from the DNA, only a **small fraction** ever makes it to the cytoplasm to yield mRNA; the largest portion of the transcribed material is degraded in the nucleus. The second (more recent) observation has been that the **coding regions of DNA,** the transcripts of which ultimately appear in the cytoplasm as single mRNA molecules, **are interrupted in the genome by large intervening sequences of noncoding DNA.** Accordingly, the primary transcripts of DNA—hnRNA—contain noncoding intervening sequences of RNA that must be removed in a process that also joins together the appropriate coding segments to form the mature mRNA. Most coding sequences for a single mRNA are interrupted in the genome and thus in the primary transcript by at least one—in many cases nearly 20—noncoding intervening sequences **(introns).** In most cases the **introns** are much longer than the continuous coding regions **(exons).** These observations account for the discrepancy between the coding capacity of the human genome and the actual number of coding regions (structural genes).

The function of the intervening sequences or introns is not clear. They may serve to separate functional domains (exons) of coding information in a form that permits genetic rearrangement by recombination to occur more rapidly than if all coding regions for a given genetic function were contiguous. Such an enhanced rate of genetic rearrangement of functional domains might allow more rapid evolution of biologic function.

DNA SYNTHESIS & REPLICATION

The primary function of DNA is understood to be the provision of progeny with the genetic information possessed by the parent. Thus, the replication of DNA must be complete and carried out with **high fidelity to maintain genetic stability** within the organism and the species. The process of DNA replication is complex and involves many cellular functions and several verification procedures to ensure fidelity in replication. The first enzymologic observations on DNA replication were made in *E coli* by Arthur Kornberg, who described in that organism the existence of an enzyme now called DNA polymerase I. This enzyme has multiple catalytic activities, a complex structure, and a requirement for the triphosphates of the 4 deoxyribonucleosides of adenine, guanine, cytosine, and thymine. The polymerization reaction catalyzed by DNA polymerase I of *E coli* has served as a prototype for all DNA polymerases of both prokaryotes and eukaryotes, even though it is now recognized that the major role of this polymerase is to ensure fidelity and to repair rather than to replicate DNA.

The initiation of DNA synthesis (Fig 28–4) is surprisingly complex and occurs after the de novo formation of a **short link of RNA,** about 10 nucleotides in length, to which, at its 3′-hydroxyl end, is attached the first deoxyribonucleotide. This process involves the **nucleophilic attack by the 3′-hydroxyl group of the RNA initiator to the alpha phosphate of the deoxynucleoside triphosphate** with the splitting off of pyrophosphate. The 3′-hydroxyl group of the recently attached deoxyribonucleoside monophosphate is then free to carry out a nucleophilic attack on the next entering deoxyribonucleoside triphosphate, again at its alpha phosphate moiety, with the splitting off of pyrophosphate. Of course, the selection of the proper deoxyribonucleotide whose terminal 3′-hydroxyl group is to be attacked is dependent upon **proper pairing with the other (template) strand** of the DNA molecule according to the rules proposed originally by Watson and Crick (Fig 28–5). When an adenine deoxyribonucleoside monophosphoryl moiety is in the template position, a thymidine triphosphate will enter and its alpha phosphate will be attacked by the 3′-hydroxyl group of the deoxyribonucleoside monophosphoryl most recently added to the polymer. By this stepwise process, the template dictates which deoxyribonucleoside triphosphate is complementary and by hydrogen bonding holds it in place while the 3′-hydroxyl group of the growing strand attacks and incorporates the new nucleotide into the polymer. These fragments of DNA attached to an RNA initiator component were discovered by Okazaki and are therefore referred to as **Okazaki pieces** (Fig 28–6). In

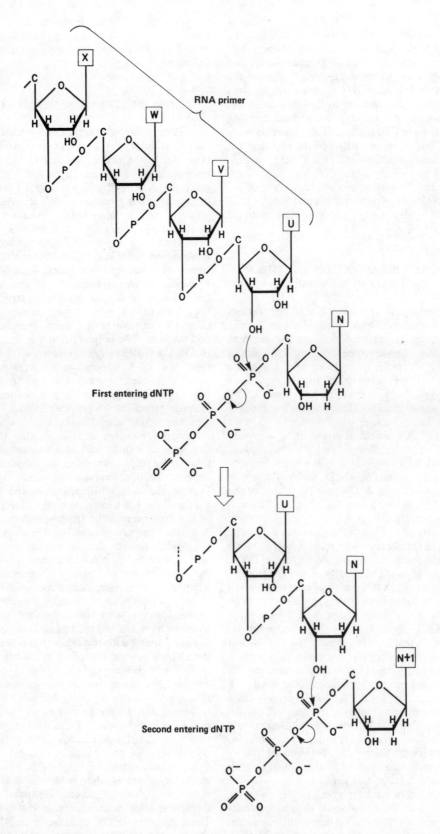

Figure 28–4. The initiation of DNA synthesis upon a primer of RNA and the subsequent attachment of the second deoxyribonucleoside triphosphate.

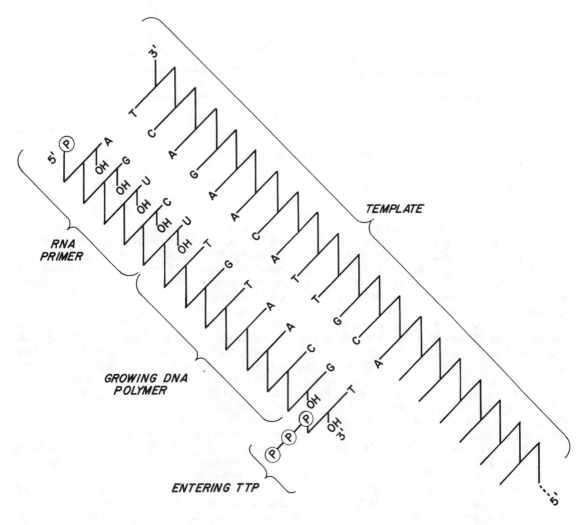

Figure 28–5. The synthesis of DNA on an RNA primer demonstrating the template function of the complementary strand of parental DNA.

mammals, after many Okazaki pieces are generated, the replication complex begins to remove the RNA primers, to fill in the gaps left by their removal with the proper base-paired deoxynucleotide, and then to seal the fragments of newly synthesized DNA by enzymes referred to as **DNA ligases.**

As has already been noted, DNA molecules are double-stranded and the 2 strands are antiparallel, ie, running in opposite directions. The replication of DNA in prokaryotes and eukaryotes occurs on **both strands simultaneously.** However, an enzyme capable of polymerizing DNA in the 3′ to 5′ direction does not

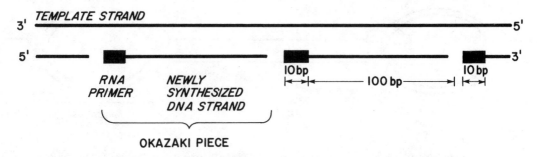

Figure 28–6. The discontinuous polymerization of deoxyribonucleotides and formation of Okazaki pieces.

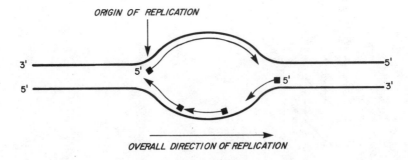

Figure 28–7. The process of semidiscontinuous, simultaneous replication of both strands of double-stranded DNA.

exist in any organism, so that both of the newly replicated DNA strands cannot grow in the same direction simultaneously. Nevertheless, the same enzyme appears to replicate both strands at the same time. The single enzyme replicates **one strand ("leading strand") in a continuous manner in the 5′ to 3′ direction,** with the same overall forward direction. It replicates the **other strand ("lagging strand") discontinuously** by "turning its back," as it were, in the overall direction of replication, while polymerizing the nucleotides in short spurts of 150–250 nucleotides again in the 5′ to 3′ direction, but at the same time it faces toward the back end of the preceding RNA primer rather than toward the unreplicated portion. This process of semidiscontinuous DNA synthesis is shown diagrammatically in Fig 28–7.

In the mammalian nuclear genome, all of the RNA primers are eventually removed as part of the replication process, whereas after replication of the mitochondrial genome the small piece of RNA remains as an integral part of the closed circular DNA structure.

In mammalian cells, there is one class of DNA polymerase enzymes, called maxi (large) polymerase or **polymerase alpha,** responsible for chromosome replication. One polymerase alpha molecule is capable of polymerizing about 100 nucleotides per second, a rate 10-fold less than the rate of polymerization of deoxynucleotides by the bacterial DNA polymerase. This reduced rate almost certainly results from the

interference by nucleosomes that do remain attached to DNA during its replication, perhaps all remaining attached to one of the 2 daughter strands. Newly synthesized core histones in the octameric form would then attach to the other daughter strands as the replication fork progresses.

A lower molecular weight polymerase, mini polymerase or **polymerase beta,** is also present in mammalian nuclei but is not responsible for the usual DNA replication. It may function in DNA repair (see below). Mitochondrial DNA polymerase, **polymerase gamma,** is responsible for replication of the mitochondrial genome, another DNA molecule that exists in circular form.

To replicate the entire mammalian genome in 9 hours, the average period required for formation of a tetraploid genome from a diploid genome in a replicating cell, there are on the chromosomes **multiple origins** of DNA replication that occur in clusters of up to 100 of these replication units. It has been suggested that the portions of DNA between nucleosomes serve as the template sites for the Okazaki pieces. Replication occurs in **both directions** up and down the chromosome and on both strands simultaneously. This replication process generates "replication bubbles" (Fig 28–8).

During the replication of the double-stranded helix of DNA, there must be a separation of the 2 strands to allow each to serve as a template by hy-

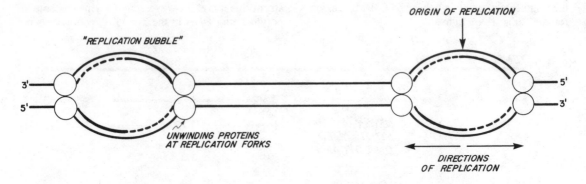

Figure 28–8. The generation of "replication bubbles" during the process of DNA synthesis. The bidirectional replication and the proposed positions of unwinding proteins at the replication forks are depicted.

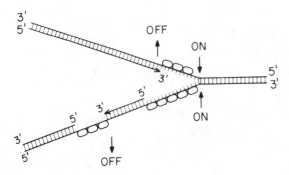

Figure 28–9. Hypothetical scheme for single-strand binding protein action at a replicating fork. The protein is recycled after binding single-stranded regions of the template and facilitating replication. (Courtesy of Professor B Alberts.)

drogen bonding its nucleotide bases to the incoming deoxynucleoside triphosphate. The separation of the DNA double helix is promoted by specific protein molecules that **stabilize the single-stranded structure** as the replication fork progresses. These stabilizing proteins bind stoichiometrically to the single

strands without interfering with the abilities of the nucleobases to serve as templates (Fig 28–9). In addition to separating the 2 strands of the double helix, there must be an **unwinding** of the molecule (once every 10 nucleotide pairs) to allow the rewinding of the newly formed semiconserved DNA replicas. Given the time during which DNA replication must occur in prokaryotes, it can be calculated that the molecule must unwind at approximately 400,000 turns per second, which is clearly an impossible feat. Thus, there must be multiple ''swivels'' interspersed in the DNA molecules of all organisms. The swivel function is provided by a specific enzyme that introduces **"nicks" in one strand of the unwinding double helix,** thereby allowing the unwinding process to proceed. The nicks are quickly resealed without requiring energy input due to the formation of a high-energy covalent bond between the nicked phosphodiester backbone and the nicking-sealing enzyme. This process is depicted diagrammatically in Fig 28–10 and there compared to the ATP-dependent resealing carried out by the DNA ligases. The nicking-resealing enzyme is called **DNA topoisomerase** and is also capable of unwinding supercoiled DNA. Supercoiled

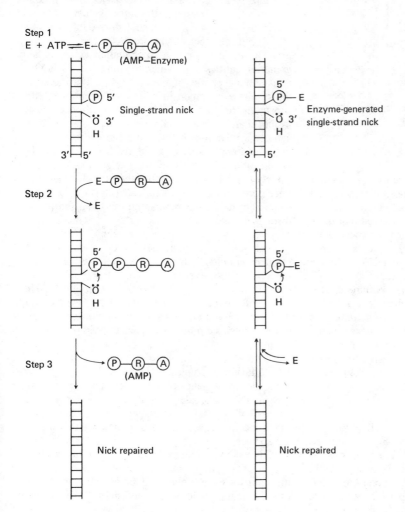

Figure 28–10 (at left). Comparison of 2 types of nick-sealing reactions on DNA. The series of reactions at far left is catalyzed by DNA ligase; that at near left by DNA topoisomerase I. (Slightly modified and reproduced, with permission, from Lehninger AL: *Biochemistry,* 2nd ed. Worth, 1975.)

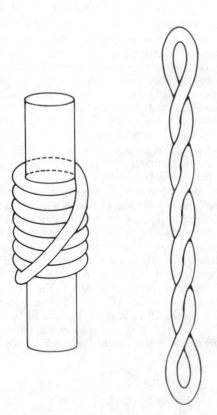

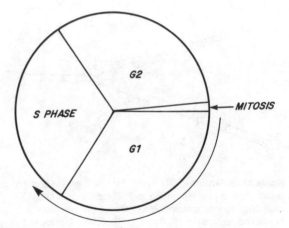

Figure 28–12. Mammalian cell cycle. The DNA synthetic phase (S phase) is separated from mitosis by gap 1 (G₁) and gap 2 (G₂). (Arrow indicates direction of cell progression.)

Figure 28–11. Supercoiling of DNA. A left-handed toroidal (selenoidal) supercoil, at left, will convert to a right-handed interwound supercoil, at right, when the cylindric core is removed. Such a transition is analogous to that which occurs when nucleosomes are disrupted by the high salt extraction of histones from chromatin.

DNA is a higher ordered structure occurring in circular (or extraordinarily long) DNA molecules wrapped around a core, as depicted in Fig 28–11.

In recent years it has been discovered that there exists in many animal virus particles (retroviruses) a class of enzymes capable of synthesizing a single-stranded and then a double-stranded DNA molecule from a single-stranded RNA template. This polymerase, RNA-dependent DNA polymerase or **"reverse transcriptase"** first synthesizes a DNA-RNA hybrid molecule utilizing the RNA genome as a template. A specific enzyme, RNase H, degrades the RNA strand, and the remaining DNA strand in turn serves as a template to form a double-stranded DNA molecule containing the information originally present in the RNA genome of the animal virus.

Regulation of DNA Synthesis

In animal cells, including human cells, the replication of the DNA genome occurs only at specified times during the life span of the cell. These periods are referred to as synthetic or S phases. They are usually temporally separated from the mitotic phase by non-synthetic periods referred to as gap 1 (G₁) and gap 2

(G₂), occurring before and after the S phase, respectively (Fig 28–12). The cell regulates its DNA synthesis grossly by allowing it to occur only at specific times and mostly in cells preparing to divide by a mitotic process. The regulation of the entry of a cell into an S phase involves cyclic purine nucleotides and probably dCTP, but the mechanisms are unknown.

During the S phase, mammalian cells contain greater quantities of polymerase alpha than during the nonsynthetic phases of the cell cycle. Furthermore, those enzymes responsible for the formation of the substrates for DNA synthesis, ie, deoxyribonucleoside triphosphates, are also increased in activity, and their activity will diminish following the synthetic phase until the reappearance of the signal for renewed DNA synthesis. During S phase, the nuclear DNA is **completely replicated once and only once.** It seems that once chromatin has been replicated, it is marked so as to prevent its further replication until it again passes through mitosis. It has been suggested that methylation may serve as such a covalent marker.

In general, a given pair of chromosomes will replicate simultaneously and within a fixed portion of the S phase upon every replication. On a chromosome, clusters of replication units replicate coordinately. The nature of the signals that regulate DNA synthesis at these levels is unknown, but the regulation does appear to be an intrinsic property of each individual chromosome.

Degradation & Repair of DNA

The maintenance of the integrity of the information in DNA molecules is of utmost importance to the survival of a particular organism as well as to survival of the species. Thus, it might be concluded that surviving species must have evolved mechanisms for repairing DNA damage incurred as a result of either replication errors or environmental insults. That such repair mechanisms have evolved can be corroborated by the estimate that replication and environmentally induced errors result in an average of about 6 nucleotide changes per year in the human germ line. Presumably, at least that number of nucleotide changes or mutations must occur per year in the somatic cells as well.

As described in Chapter 27, the major responsibility for the fidelity of replication resides in the specific pairing of nucleotide bases. Proper pairing is dependent upon the presence of the favored tautomers of the purine and pyrimidine nucleotides, but the equilibrium wherein one tautomer is more stable than another is only about 10^4 or 10^5 in favor of that with the greater stability. Although this is not sufficiently favorable to ensure the high fidelity that is necessary, the favoring of the preferred tautomers, and thus of the proper base pairing, could be assured by monitoring the base pairing twice. Such double monitoring does indeed appear to occur in both bacterial and mammalian systems: once at the time of insertion of the deoxyribonucleoside triphosphates, and later by a follow-up mechanism which removes all improper bases that may occur in the newly formed strand. This double monitoring does not permit errors of mispairing due to the presence of the unfavored tautomers to occur more frequently than once every 10^8–10^{10} base pairs. The molecule responsible for this monitoring mechanism is the $3' \rightarrow 5'$ exonuclease activity of DNA polymerase in *E coli,* but mammalian DNA polymerases do not clearly possess such a nuclease "editing" function.

Damage to DNA by environmental, physical, and chemical agents may be classified into 4 types (Table 28–1). The damaged regions of DNA may be **repaired, replaced** by recombination, or **retained** leading to mutations (and cancer) and, potentially, cell death. The first 2 of these processes exploit the redundancy of information inherent in the double helical DNA structure. The defective region in one strand can be returned to its original form by relying on the complementary information stored in the unaffected strand.

The key to all of the repair or recombinational processes is the initial **recognition of the defect** and

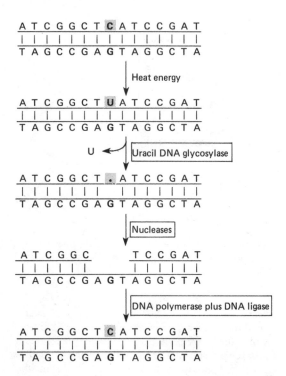

Figure 28–13. The enzyme uracil DNA glycosylase removes the uracil created by spontaneous deamination of cytosine in the DNA. (Courtesy of Professor B Alberts.)

either repairing it during the recognition step or marking it for future attention. The **depurination** of DNA, which happens spontaneously owing to the thermal lability of the purine N-glycosidic bond, occurs at a rate of 5–10 thousand/cell/d at 37 C. Specific enzymes recognize a depurinated site and replace the appropriate purine directly, without interruption of the phosphodiester backbone.

Both cytosine and adenine bases in DNA spontaneously **deaminate** to form uracil and hypoxanthine, respectively. Since neither uracil nor hypoxanthine normally exists in DNA, it is not surprising that specific N-glycosylases can recognize these abnormal bases and remove the base itself from the DNA. This removal marks the site of the defect and allows an apurinic or apyrimidinic endonuclease to incise the appropriate backbone near the defect. Subsequently, the sequential actions of an exonuclease, a repair DNA polymerase, and a ligase return the DNA to its original state (Fig 28–13). This series of events is called **excision-repair.** By a similar series of steps involving initially the recognition of the defect, alkylated bases and base analogs can be removed from DNA and the DNA returned to its original informational content.

The repair of insertions or deletions of nucleotides normally occurs by recombinational mechanisms either with or without replication.

Ultraviolet light induces the formation of pyrimidine-pyrimidine dimers, predominantly the dimerization of 2 juxtaposed thymines in the same

---

Table 28–1. Types of damage to DNA.

I. **Single-base alteration**
   A. Depurination
   B. Deamination of cytosine to uracil
   C. Deamination of adenine to hypoxanthine
   D. Alkylation of base
   E. Insertion or deletion of nucleotide
   F. Base-analog incorporation

II. **Two-base alteration**
   A. UV light–induced thymine-thymine dimer
   B. Bifunctional alkylating agent cross-linkage

III. **Chain breaks**
   A. Ionizing radiation
   B. Radioactive disintegration of backbone element

IV. **Cross-linkage**
   A. Between bases in same or opposite strands
   B. Between DNA and protein molecules (eg, histones)

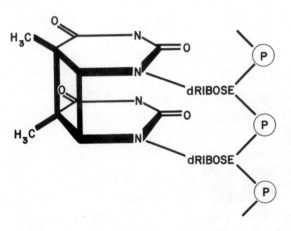

Figure 28–14. A thymine–thymine dimer formed via a cyclobutane moiety between juxtaposed thymine residues of DNA.

strand (Fig 28–14). There are apparently 2 mechanisms for removing or repairing these thymine-thymine dimers. One is excision-repair analogous to that described above. The second mechanism involves visible light photoactivation of a specific enzyme that directly reverses the dimer formation in situ.

Single-strand breaks induced by ionizing radiation can be repaired by direct ligation or by recombination. The mechanisms responsible for the repair of cross-linkages between bases on opposite strands of the DNA double helix or between the DNA and protein molecules are poorly understood.

In general, damage caused by ionizing radiation and by alkylation of bases is repaired in short patches of excision and resynthesis. Ultraviolet light damage and strand cross-linkages are repaired by long patches of excision and resynthesis. In mammalian cells, repair replication can be observed as **unscheduled DNA synthesis,** ie, incorporation of DNA precursors (radioactive thymidine) into DNA when a cell is not in S phase.

Associated with the increased excision-repair activity in response to DNA damaging agents, mammalian cells exhibit increased activity of the enzyme **poly(ADP-ribose) polymerase.** This enzyme uses the coenzyme NAD^+ to ADP-ribosylate chromatin proteins. It adds mostly mono(ADP-ribose), but to some extent homopolymeric chains of ADP-ribose are added. It is not evident what function poly(ADP-ribose) polymerase or its product, $(ADP-ribose)_n$, has in the excision-repair process. There is a temporal relationship between the increased repair activity and the increased specific enzyme. Furthermore, inhibition of the enzyme by specific inhibitors prevents the rejoining of broken DNA strands. The increased activity of poly(ADP-ribose) polymerase appears to be a response to DNA fragmentation in the nucleus. This fragmentation might be induced primarily by physical agents such as x-ray, or secondarily by the incision mechanism responding to other chemical or physical

agents such as ultraviolet light or alkylating agents. The activity of the polymerase is sufficiently great to cause a depletion of intracellular NAD^+ following environmentally induced DNA damage.

Xeroderma pigmentosum is an autosomal recessive genetic disease. The clinical syndrome includes marked sensitivity to sunlight (ultraviolet) with subsequent formation of multiple skin cancers and premature death. The inherited defect seems to involve the repair of damaged DNA. Cells cultured from patients with xeroderma pigmentosum exhibit low activity for the photoactivated thymine dimer cleavage process. However, the involved DNA repair processes in this disease are quite complex; there are at least 7 genetic complementation groups. The major abnormality in xeroderma pigmentosum may be defective preparation of the chromatin for the various repair processes.

In cells from most if not all complementation groups of xeroderma pigmentosum, there is an abnormal temporal or quantitative response of the poly(ADP-ribose) polymerase to ultraviolet light exposure. It seems that the abnormal response in at least one complementation group is due to the inability to incise the DNA strand at the site of damage since the addition of deoxyribonuclease to permeabilized defective cells is followed by a normal or nearly normal increase in poly(ADP-ribose) polymerase activity.

In patients with **ataxia-telangiectasia,** an autosomal recessive disease in humans resulting in the development of cerebellar ataxia and lymphoreticular neoplasms, there appears to exist an increased sensitivity to damage by x-ray. Patients with **Fanconi's anemia,** an autosomal recessive anemia characterized also by an increased frequency of cancer and by chromosomal instability, probably have defective repair of cross-linking damage. All 3 of these clinical syndromes are associated with increased frequency of cancer. It is likely that other human diseases resulting from disordered DNA repair capabilities will be found in the future.

ALTERATION & REARRANGEMENT OF GENETIC MATERIAL

An alteration in the sequence of purine and pyrimidine bases in a gene due to a change, a removal, or an insertion of one or more bases results in an altered gene product that in most instances ultimately is a protein. Such alteration in the genetic material results in a **mutation,** the consequences of which are discussed in detail in Chapter 29.

Prokaryotic and eukaryotic organisms are capable of exchanging genetic information between similar chromosomes. The exchange or **recombination** event occurs primarily during meiosis in mammalian cells and requires alignment of homologous chromosomes, an alignment which almost always occurs with great exactness. A process of crossing-over occurs as shown in Fig 28–15. This results in a reciprocal exchange of

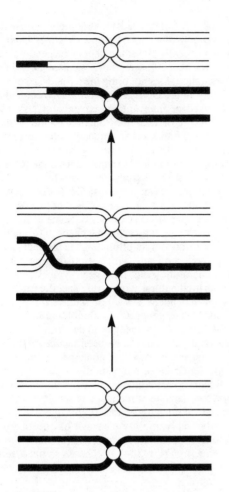

Figure 28–15. The process of crossing-over between homologous chromosomes to generate recombinant chromosomes.

genetic information between homologous chromosomes. If the homologous chromosomes possess different alleles of the same genes, the crossover may produce noticeable and heritable genetic linkage differences. In the rare case where the alignment of homologous chromosomes is not exact, the crossing-over or recombination event may result in nonreciprocal exchange of information. One chromosome may receive less genetic material and thus a deletion, while the other partner of the chromosome pair receives more genetic material and thus an insertion (Fig 28–16). Unequal crossing-over does occur (though rarely) in humans, as evidenced by the existence of hemoglobins designated Lepore and anti-Lepore.

Some bacterial viruses, ie, bacteriophage, are capable of recombining with the DNA of a bacterial host in such a way that the genetic information of the bacteriophage is incorporated in a linear fashion into the genetic information of the host. This integration, which is a form of recombination, occurs by the mechanism shown in Fig 28–17. The backbone of the circular bacteriophage genome is broken, as is that of the DNA molecule of the host; the appropriate ends are resealed with the proper polarity. The bacteriophage DNA is figuratively straightened out as it is integrated into the bacterial DNA molecule—frequently a closed circle as well. The site at which the bacteriophage genome integrates or recombines with the bacterial genome is chosen by one of 2 mechanisms. If the bacteriophage contains a DNA sequence **homologous** to a sequence in the host DNA molecule, then a recombination event analogous to that occurring between homologous chromosomes can occur. However, many bacteriophages synthesize proteins that bind specific sites on bacterial chromosomes with a nonhomologous site specifically of the bacteriophage DNA molecule.

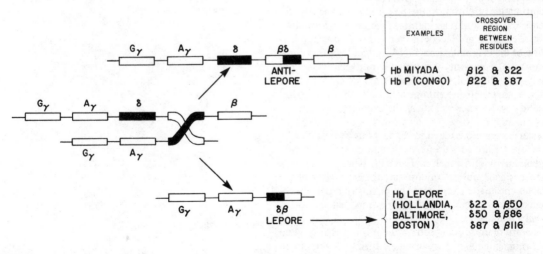

Figure 28–16. The process of unequal crossover in the region of the mammalian genome that harbors the structural genes for hemoglobin and the generation of the unequal recombinant products hemoglobin delta-beta Lepore and beta-delta anti-Lepore. The examples given show the locations of the crossover regions between amino acid residues. (Redrawn and reproduced, with permission, from Clegg JB, Weatherall DJ: β° Thalassemia: Time for a reappraisal? *Lancet* 1974;2:133.)

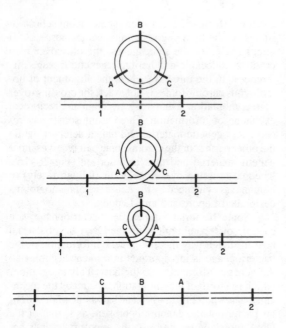

Figure 28–17. The integration of a circular genome (with genes A, B, and C) into the DNA molecule of a host (with genes 1 and 2) and the consequent ordering of the genes.

Integration occurs at the site and is said to be **"site-specific."**

Many animal viruses, particularly the oncogenic viruses—either directly or, in the case of RNA viruses, their DNA transcripts—can be integrated into chromosomes of the mammalian cell. The integration of the animal virus into the animal genome is not "site-specific."

In diploid eukaryotic organisms such as humans, after cells progress through the S phase they contain a tetraploid content of DNA. This is in the form of sister chromatids of chromosome pairs. Each of these sister chromatids contains identical genetic information since each is a product of the semiconservative replication of the original parent DNA molecule of that chromosome. Crossing-over occurs between these genetically identical sister chromatids. Of course, these **sister chromatid exchanges** (Fig 28–18) have no genetic consequence so long as the exchange is the result of an equal crossover. However, the frequency of sister chromatid exchanges appears to be an index of the frequency of genetic exchange events occurring generally within a mammalian cell. It seems that cells that are incapable of minimizing the frequency of the sister chromatid exchanges (by unknown repair mechanisms) are susceptible to other events that are potentially mutagenic.

In mammalian cells, some interesting gene rearrangements occur normally during development and differentiation. For example, in mice the V_L and C_L genes for a single immunoglobulin molecule (see Chapters 30 and 39) are separated in the germ line DNA by a long, unknown stretch of DNA. In the DNA of a differentiated immunoglobulin-producing (plasma) cell, the same V_L and C_L genes have been moved physically closer together in the genome. However, even then, this rearrangement of DNA during differentiation does not bring the V_L and C_L genes into contiguity in the DNA. Instead, the DNA contains an interspersed or interruption sequence of about 1200 base pairs at or near the junction of the V and C regions. The interspersed sequence is transcribed into RNA along with the V_L and C_L genes, and the interspersed information is removed from the RNA during its nuclear processing (see below).

With the advancement of DNA chemistry and enzymology in recent years, it has been possible to synthesize specific genes in vitro. Some of these synthetic genes can express their genetic information in vivo in the form of an ultimate gene product—a specific protein molecule which itself has normal function. Some of the genes have been synthesized, utilizing a purified naturally occurring specific mRNA and an RNA-dependent DNA polymerase (reverse transcriptase) that generates a double-stranded DNA (cDNA) gene complementary to the mRNA molecule. Other synthetic genes have been synthesized chemically using the information contained within the nucleotide sequence of the naturally occurring gene.

Recently, great interest has been shown in a series of enzymes capable of recognizing specific symmetric sequences of nucleotides in a DNA molecule and subsequently catalyzing the cleavage of phosphodiester backbone at specific symmetric sites within the specific sequences (Fig 28–19). These enzymes, termed **restriction endonucleases,** are isolated from bacteria,

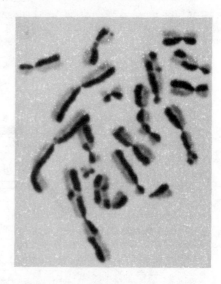

Figure 28–18. Sister chromatid exchanges between human chromosomes. These are detectable by Giemsa staining of the chromosomes of cells replicated for 2 cycles in the presence of bromodeoxyuridine. (Courtesy of Dr Sheldon Wolff and Judy Bodycote, Laboratory of Radiobiology and Department of Anatomy, University of California School of Medicine, San Francisco.)

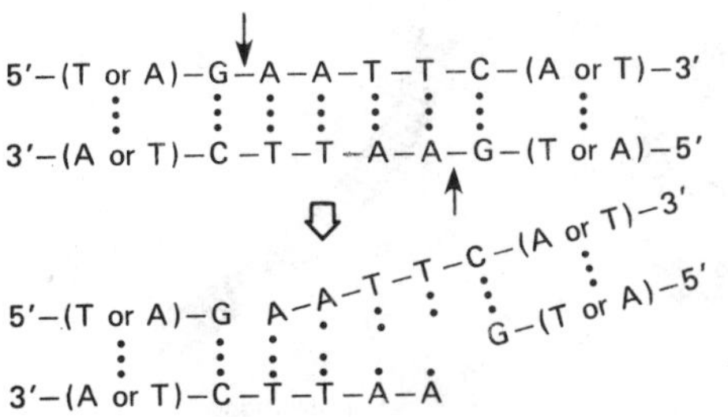

Figure 28–19. The sequence-specific symmetric cleavage of a double-stranded DNA molecule by EcoRI restriction endonuclease. The interstrand H bonds are depicted by the dots. Cohesive ("sticky") ends are generated by the symmetric staggered cleavage.

in which they play a defensive role to destroy DNA from foreign organisms. The restriction endonucleases (Table 28–2) have provided scientists with the means of physically mapping DNA molecules and recombining DNA molecules from different sources to create new genetic sequences. These latter exercises are referred to as **recombinant DNA experiments.** Quite recently, they have received much attention both in the lay press and in the scientific literature.

Some bacteria harbor circular DNA molecules that replicate autonomously in the bacterial protoplasm. Such an autonomous DNA molecule is called a **plasmid.** Plasmids may carry genetic information to confer **resistance to antibiotics** on the host bacterium. Using **recombinant DNA technology,** a specific segment of DNA can be integrated in vitro into a plasmid (Fig 28–20). In this manner, a bacterial culture can be utilized for the autonomous replication of the recombinant plasmid including the new segment of DNA. With similar approaches, it is possible to use recombinant plasmids to introduce specific nonbacterial genes into bacteria that can then act as factories for the production of the specific protein molecules coded for by the introduced gene. By such technics, some protein hormones have been produced in experimental quantities. Restriction endonucleases can also be used to clip out specifically the sequence originally inserted into the plasmid and thus to obtain milligram quantities of specific DNA sequences. Such technology would appear to provide great potential medical and agricultural benefits to society.

DNA Sequencing

The segments of specific DNA molecules obtained by recombinant DNA technology can be ana-

Table 28–2. Substrate specificities of some restriction endonucleases.[*]

Enzyme	Sequence	Number of Cleavage Sites			Microorganism
		λ	Ad2	SV40	
Hap II	CCGG	>50	>50	1	*Haemophilus aphrophilus*
Bsu I	GGCC	>50	>50	18	*Bacillus subtilis* strain X5
Alu I	AGCT	>50	>50	32	*Arthrobacter luteus*
Eco RII	CCTGG	>35	>35	16	*Escherichia coli* R245
Eco RII	CCAGG	>35	>35	16	*Escherichia coli* R245
Hind III	AAGCTT	6	11	6	*Haemophilus influenzae* R_d
Hinc II	GTPyPuAC	34	>20	7	*Haemophilus influenzae* R_c
Hpa I	GTTAAC	11	6	5	*Haemophilus parainfluenzae*
Eco RI	GAATTC	5	5	1	*Escherichia coli* RY13
Bam HI	GGATTC	5	3	1	*Bacillus amyloliquefaciens* H
Bal I	CGGCCG	15	17	0	*Brevibacterium albidum*
Hae II	PuGCGCPy	>30	>30	1	*Haemophilus aegyptius*
Hha I	GCGC	>50	>50	2	*Haemophilus haemolyticus*
Mbo I	GATC	>50	>50	6	*Moraxella bovis*
Sma I	CCCGGG	3	12	0	*Serratia marcescens* Sb_b
Bgl II	AGATCT	5	10	0	*Bacillus globiggi*
Hinf I	GANTC	>50	>50	10	*Haemophilus influenzae* R_f
Taq I	TCGA	?	?	?	*Thermus aquaticus* YTI

[*]Arrows indicate the site of cleavage and sequence specificity of the endonucleases. The number of cleavage sites refers to the genomes of lambda bacteriophage (λ), adenovirus 2 (Ad2), and simian virus 40 (SV40).

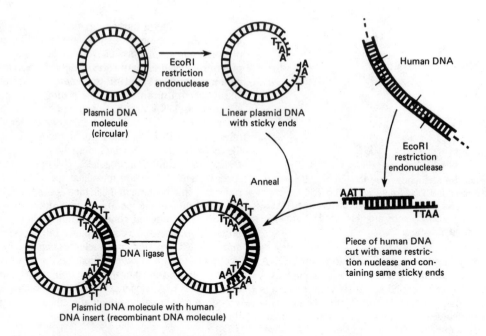

Figure 28–20. Use of restriction nucleases to make new recombinant DNA molecules. When inserted back into a bacterial cell, the **plasmid DNA replicates not only itself but also the new DNA insert.** Since recombining the sticky ends, as indicated, regenerates the same DNA sequence recognized by the original restriction enzyme (Fig 28–17), the cloned DNA insert **can be cleanly cut back out of the recombinant plasmid circle with this nuclease.** If a mixture of all of the DNA pieces created by treatment of total human DNA with a single restriction nuclease is used as the source of the human DNA here, a million or so different types of recombinant DNA molecules can be obtained, each pure in its own bacterial clone. (Modified and reproduced, with permission, from Cohen SN: The manipulation of genes. *Sci Am* [July] 1975;**233:**24.)

lyzed for their nucleotide sequence (Fig 28–21). The method depends upon having a large number of identical DNA molecules. This requirement can be satisfied by recombinant DNA technology and the stringent sequence specificity of the restriction endonucleases. The method shown is that of Maxam and Gilbert and employs chemical methods to cleave the DNA molecules where they contain the specific nucleobases. A second method (Sanger's) employs specific nucleotide analogs that terminate DNA strand synthesis at specific nucleobases as the strand is synthesized on purified template nucleic acid.

BIOLOGIC FUNCTION OF RIBONUCLEIC ACID (RNA)

As is the case with DNA, RNA contains information by way of its specific sequence of polymerized purine and pyrimidine ribonucleotides. However, the structure of RNA is somewhat different from that of DNA. RNA contains the same purine bases—adenine and guanine—present in DNA, but only one of the pyrimidine bases—cytosine—is the same as that in DNA. Thymine, present in DNA, has been replaced in RNA by uracil, whose structure, while similar to that of thymine, differs by lacking the 5-methyl substituent (see Chapter 25). As described in Chapter 27, RNA normally exists as a single-stranded molecule but is

capable of folding back on itself to form hairpinlike loops with double-stranded portions of the single molecule. The information in RNA, contained within the specific sequence of nucleotides, is in nearly all circumstances derived from a DNA molecule and dictated by base-pairing rules similar to those responsible for the double-stranded helix of DNA. The only difference in the base-pairing scheme dictating the sequence of the RNA nucleotides is that adenine of DNA pairs with a uracil while the complementary RNA molecule is being synthesized.

Although all naturally-occurring RNA molecules contain information in their sequences, some of these molecules never have any of their informational content translated into the specific amino acid sequence of a protein molecule. Those cytoplasmic RNA molecules, which serve as templates for protein synthesis, are designated as mRNA. Many other cytoplasmic RNA molecules have structural roles wherein they contribute to the formation of ribosomes (the organellar machinery for protein synthesis) or serve as adapter molecules (tRNA) for the translation of RNA information into specific sequences of polymerized amino acids. Most of the RNA synthesized from DNA templates in eukaryotic cells, including mammalian cells, is **degraded within the nucleus,** and it never serves as either a structural or an informational entity within the cellular cytoplasm. As discussed below under RNA processing, these portions of RNA

Step 1

Isolate the population ($\sim 10^{12}$) of identical DNA molecules. (Identical molecules will, of course, have identical termini, nucleotide sequence, and length.) DNA molecular cloning and restriction endonuclease digestion clearly provide the most effective means for obtaining the molecules.

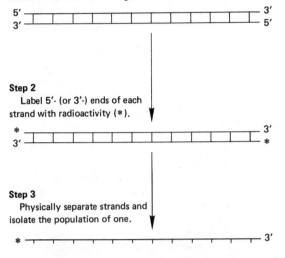

Step 2

Label 5'- (or 3'-) ends of each strand with radioactivity (*).

Step 3

Physically separate strands and isolate the population of one.

Step 4

Divide into 4 tubes. To each tube is added a different specific chemical reagent that will destroy specifically one or 2 of the 4 nucleobases (A, T, C, G) at the sites where they occur in the DNA strand and thereby break the strand at that site. The destruction must be controlled so that it is incomplete and only some of the strands are broken at each of the sites where a given base exists.

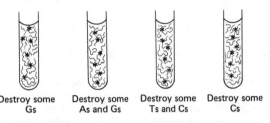

Destroy some Gs Destroy some As and Gs Destroy some Ts and Cs Destroy some Cs

This will generate in each tube a mixture of radioactively labeled strand-fragments (and many unlabeled fragments) of different lengths. The lengths of the labeled fragments will reflect the number of nucleotides between the labeled (*) end and the specific nucleobases (which were destroyed) where they appear in the single-stranded molecule.

Step 5

The components of each mixture of strand-fragments are then separated by size (length) using polyacrylamide gel slab electrophoresis. The shorter fragments move more rapidly than the longer fragments. The slab gel is autoradiographed, and the bands of the labeled strand-fragment components of each mixture produce an image on the x-ray film.

Sequence of original strand:
$* - A - G - T - C - T - T - G - G - A - G - C - T - 3'$

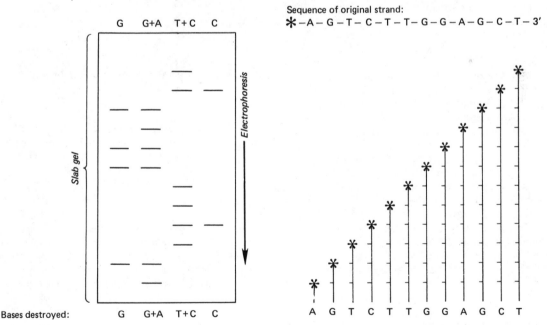

The ladderlike arrays represent from bottom to top all of the successively longer fragments of the original DNA strand. Knowing which specific one or 2 nucleobases were chemically destroyed to produce each mixture of fragments, one can determine the sequence of nucleotides from the labeled end toward the unlabeled end by reading up the gel. The base-pairing rules of Watson and Crick (A–T, G–C) dictate the sequence of the other (complementary) strand.

Figure 28–21. Sequencing of DNA by the method devised by Maxam and Gilbert.

molecules nonetheless are thought to play some regulatory roles.

Most RNA molecules transcribed in the cell nucleus appear to have at least portions that are involved in protein synthesis, but there are in cultured human cells small RNA species not directly involved in protein synthesis but which may have roles in RNA processing and the cellular architecture. These relatively small molecules vary in size from 90 to about 300 nucleotides.

The genetic material for some animal and plant viruses is RNA rather than DNA. Although some RNA viruses do not ever have their information transcribed into a DNA molecule, many animal RNA viruses—specifically the retroviruses—are transcribed by an **RNA-dependent DNA polymerase** to produce a double-stranded DNA copy of their RNA genome. In many cases the resulting double-stranded DNA transcript is integrated into the host genome and subsequently serves as a template for gene expression and from which new viral RNA genomes can be transcribed.

RNA METABOLISM

RNA Synthesis

The process of synthesizing RNA from a DNA template has been characterized best in prokaryotes. Although in mammalian cells the regulation of RNA synthesis and the processing of the RNA transcripts is different from that in prokaryotes, the process of RNA synthesis per se is quite similar in these 2 classes of organisms. Therefore, the description of RNA synthesis in prokaryotes will be applicable to eukaryotes even though the enzymes involved and the regulatory signals are different. The sequence of ribonucleotides in an RNA molecule is complementary to the sequence of deoxyribonucleotides in one strand of the DNA template molecule (Fig 28–22). The strand that is transcribed into an RNA molecule is referred to as the **sense strand** of the DNA. The other DNA strand is frequently referred to as the **antisense strand** of that gene. In the case of a double-stranded DNA molecule containing many genes, the sense strand for each gene will not necessarily be the same strand of the DNA double helix (Fig 28–23). Thus, a given strand of a double-stranded DNA molecule will serve as the sense strand for some genes and the antisense strand of other genes.

GENE A
GENE B
GENE C
GENE D
3'
5'
5'
3'
SENSE STRANDS

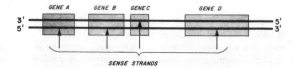

Figure 28–23. Sense strands of the linked genes. These are not necessarily the same strand of the DNA double helix.

DNA-dependent RNA polymerase is responsible for the polymerization of ribonucleotides into a sequence complementary to the sense strand of the gene (Fig 28–24). The enzyme attaches at a specific site, the **promoter,** toward the 3′ end of the sense strand of the gene to be transcribed. The DNA-dependent RNA polymerase of the bacterium *E coli* exists as a core molecule composed of 4 subunits; 2 of these are identical to each other (the α subunits), and 2 are similar to each other but not identical (the β subunit and the β' subunit). The core RNA polymerase utilizes a specific protein factor (the sigma [σ] factor) which assists the core enzyme to attach more tightly to the specific deoxynucleotide sequence of the promoter region (Fig 28–25). This holoenzyme (core polymerase + σ factor), in the presence of all 4 ribonucleoside triphosphates (ATP, GTP, CTP, UTP), commences movement along the sense strand toward its 5′ terminus. The

PPP-5'-PURINE
RNA
RNA
POLYMERASE CORE
SENSE STRAND
3'
5'
5'
3'
ANTISENSE STRAND

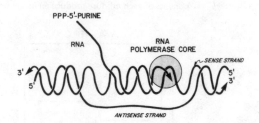

Figure 28–24. The RNA polymerase–catalyzed polymerization of ribonucleotides into an RNA sequence complementary to the sense strand of the gene. (From James D. Watson, *Molecular Biology of the Gene,* 3rd ed. Copyright © 1976, 1970, 1965, by W.A. Benjamin, Inc, Menlo Park, California.)

enzyme polymerizes the ribonucleotides in a specific sequence that is dictated by the template (sense) strand and interpreted by the base-pairing rules. Pyrophosphate is released in the polymerization reaction. In both prokaryotes and eukaryotes, a purine ribonu-

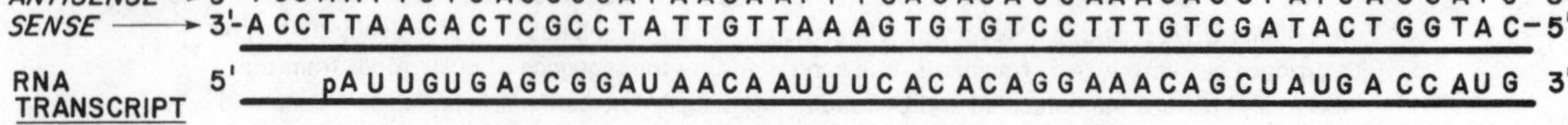

DNA STRANDS:
ANTISENSE → 5'-TGGAATTGTGAGCGGATAACAATTTCACACAGGAAACAGCTATGACCATG-3'
SENSE → 3'-ACCTTAACACTCGCCTATTGTTAAAGTGTGTCCTTTGTCGATACTGGTAC-5'
RNA TRANSCRIPT 5' pAUUGUGAGCGGAUAACAAUUUCACACAGGAAACAGCUAUGACCAUG 3'

Figure 28–22. The relationship between the sense strand and antisense strand in the DNA molecule and the RNA molecule complementary to the sense strand.

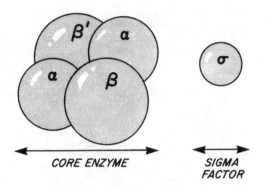

Figure 28–25. A diagrammatic representation of the sub-unit structure of DNA-dependent RNA polymerase and the sigma factor. (From James D. Watson, *Molecular Biology of the Gene,* 3rd ed. Copyright © 1976, 1970, 1965, by W.A. Benjamin, Inc, Menlo Park, California.)

cleotide is the first to be polymerized into the RNA molecule.

The process of RNA synthesis, depicted in Fig 28–26, involves first the binding of the holo RNA polymerase molecule to the template at the promoter site. Initiation of formation of the RNA molecule at its 5' end then follows with the release of the σ factor, while the elongation of the RNA molecule from the 5' to its 3' end continues antiparallel to its template.

Termination of the synthesis of the RNA molecule is signaled by a specific sequence in the sense strand of the DNA molecule, a signal that is recognized by a termination protein, the rho (ρ) factor. Following termination of synthesis of the RNA molecule, the core enzyme separates from the DNA template. With the assistance of another σ factor, the core enzyme then recognizes a promoter at which the synthesis of a new RNA molecule commences. More than one RNA polymerase molecule may transcribe the same sense strand of a gene simultaneously, but the process is phased and spaced in such a way that at any one moment each is transcribing a different portion of the DNA sequence. RNA synthesis is shown in an electron micrograph (Fig 28–27). The antibiotic **rifampin** (rifampicin) inhibits the binding of prokaryotic DNA-dependent RNA polymerase to promoter sites of genes.

The regulation of transcription in prokaryotes is described in somewhat more detail in Chapter 30.

Mammalian cells possess several DNA-dependent RNA polymerases, the properties of which are described in Table 28–3. Each of these DNA-dependent RNA polymerases seems to be responsible for the transcription of different sets of genes. The subunit structures of mammalian polymerases have been described, but the functions of each of the subunits are not yet understood. Certainly, many must have regulatory functions, such as serving to assist the

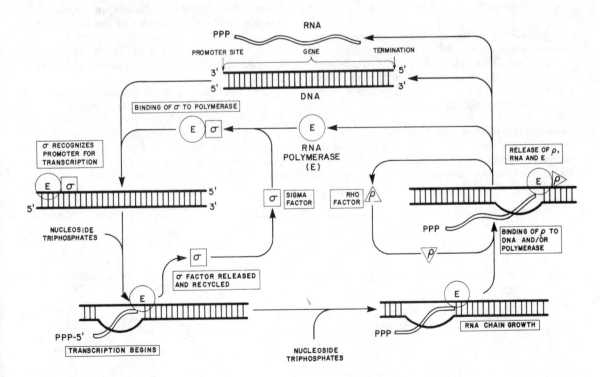

Figure 28–26. The process of RNA synthesis. It begins at the upper left-hand portion of the figure with the binding of sigma to polymerase to form a complex that recognizes the promoter for transcription. The process is completed as the RNA transcriptase is released from the gene, and all of the catalytic components are free to recycle. (From James D. Watson, *Molecular Biology of the Gene,* 3rd ed. Copyright © 1976, 1970, 1965, by W.A. Benjamin, Inc, Menlo Park, California.)

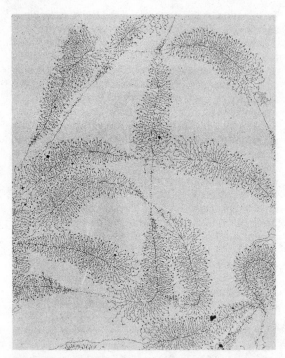

Figure 28–27. Electron photomicrograph of multiple copies of ribosomal RNA genes being transcribed in an amphibian cell. × 6000. (Reproduced, with permission, from Miller OL Jr, Beatty BR: Portrait of a gene. *J Cell Physiol* 1969; **74** [Suppl 1]:225.)

Table 28–3. Nomenclature and localization of animal DNA-dependent RNA polymerases.

Class of Enzyme	Sensitivity to α-Amanitin	Products	Principal Localization
I (A)	Insensitive	rRNA	Nucleolar
II (B)	Sensitive to low concentration (10^{-8} to 10^{-9} M)	hnRNA (mRNA)	Nucleoplasmic
III (C)	Sensitive to high concentration	tRNA and 5S RNA	Nucleoplasmic

core polymerase in the recognition of specific sequences like promoters and termination signals.

One toxin from the mushroom *Amanita phalloides,* α-amanitin, is a specific inhibitor of the eukaryotic nucleoplasmic DNA-dependent RNA polymerase (RNA polymerase II).

Transcriptional Signals in Mammalian DNA

The DNA sequence analysis of specific eukaryotic genes obtained by DNA recombinant technology has allowed the recognition of a number of signal sequences important in gene transcription. The mammalian DNA-dependent RNA polymerase II, which is responsible for the generation of the mRNA precursor molecules, appears to recognize a specific AT-rich region (a promoter) about 25 base pairs upstream from the point (start point) at which it commences transcribing the gene. This region, frequently referred to as the **Hogness box,** has the consensus sequence of **TATAAAAG** and bears remarkable homology to the functionally related **Pribnow box** (TATAATG) located about 10 base pairs upstream from prokaryotic mRNA start points. It is clear that the RNA polymerase II binds to DNA in the region of the TATA box and then commences transcription of the sense strand about 32 nucleotides downstream at a T, which is surrounded by purines (Fig 28–28). The 5′ termini of the primary RNA transcript and the mature cytoplasmic mRNA are identical. Thus, the **start point of transcription corresponds to the 5′ nucleotide of the mRNA.** The primary transcript is promptly capped by 7-methylguanosine-triphosphate (Fig 27–15), a cap that persists and eventually appears on the mature cytoplasmic mRNA.

The RNA polymerase II continues to transcribe the sense strand of the gene until it generates a sequence of 5′-AAUAAA. Approximately 20 nucleotides thereafter, it terminates polymerization, having completed the primary transcript. The poly(A) tail is rapidly added to the 3′ terminus of the primary transcript in the nucleus, as described below.

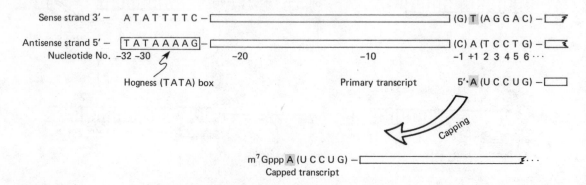

Figure 28–28. The DNA-dependent RNA polymerase II binds to the complement of the TATA box and commences transcription of the **sense strand** about 32 nucleotides downstream at a T that is surrounded by purines. The primary transcript is rapidly capped at the first nucleotide (5′-purine).

DNA-dependent RNA polymerase III, which transcribes the tRNA genes and the 5S ribosomal RNA genes, seems to recognize a promoter that is internal to the gene to be expressed, rather than upstream of the transcription starting point.

Little is known about the finer points of regulation of gene transcription such as that occurring in development, in differentiation, and in response to hormonal influences. However, it is clear that in eukaryotes a smaller proportion of C residues in active or recently active genes contain 5-methyl substituents (m⁵C; see Fig 25–6) than is the case in inactive regions of the genome. In addition, in chromatin the active genes are more susceptible to digestion by deoxyribonuclease I in vitro than are inactive regions. This latter difference is not understood at the molecular level but likely involves nucleosome rearrangement that is necessary for transcription.

Processing of RNA Molecules

In prokaryotic organisms, most RNA molecules transcribed from the sense strand of a gene begin to serve as translation templates even before their transcription has been completed. Thus, they are subjected to little modification and processing prior to carrying out their intended function in protein synthesis. The exception is the tRNA molecules, which are transcribed in units considerably longer than the ultimate tRNA molecule. In fact, many of the transcription units contain more than one tRNA molecule. Thus, in prokaryotes the processing of these tRNA precursor molecules is required for the generation of the ultimate functional molecules, the specific tRNAs.

The process is somewhat different in eukaryotic cells, particularly mammalian cells. Nearly all RNA molecules undergo extensive processing between the time they are synthesized and the time at which they serve their ultimate function, whether it be as mRNA or as a structural molecule. In many cases the processing occurs within the nucleus as well as after transportation from the nucleus to the cytoplasm. The processing includes **nucleolytic and ligation reactions, terminal additions** of nucleotides, and **nucleoside modifications.**

As a result of advances in technics for mapping DNA molecules by restriction endonucleases and DNA sequencing, it is now apparent that interspersed within the amino acid–coding portions of many genes are long sequences of deoxynucleotides that do not contribute to the genetic information ultimately translated into the amino sequence of a protein molecule. These **intervening sequences** exist within most but not all genes of higher eukaryotes (Fig 28–29). The RNA transcripts of the structural genes contain the transcripts of the interspersed sequences. However, the interspersed RNA sequences are cleaved out of the transcript, and the remaining portions of the transcript are appropriately spliced together in the nucleus before the resulting mRNA molecule appears in the cytoplasm for translation (Fig 28–29).

The precise mechanisms whereby the introns are removed from the primary transcript in the nucleus, the exons are ligated to form the mRNA molecule, and the mRNA molecule is transported to the cytoplasm are not known. However, again based on DNA recombinant technology, it has been possible at least to propose

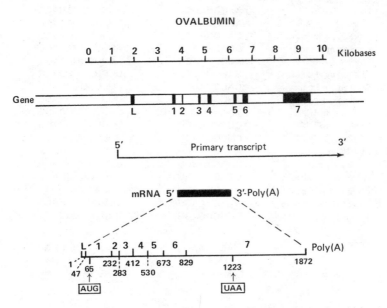

Figure 28–29. The arrangement of noncoding intervening sequences within the gene for chicken ovalbumin. Those informational segments eventually appearing in the mature mRNA are numbered and shown solid. The primary transcript commences upstream of the untranslated L exon and extends beyond the untranslated region of exon 7. The expanded depiction of the mature mRNA includes the corresponding numbers of the exons along the top and the numbers of nucleotides along the bottom. The positions of the start (AUG) and stop (UAA) codons are indicated.

mechanisms consistent with the observations. Although the sequences of nucleotides in the introns of the various eukaryotic transcripts, and even those within a single transcript, are very heterogeneous, there is a consensus sequence at each of the 2 exon-intron (splice) junctions (Fig 28–30). This **consensus sequence at the splice junction** is not sufficiently unique to allow a specific nuclease to cleave only at exon-intron junctions. Thus, it is likely that some other recognition process is involved. Interestingly, the very **abundant small nuclear RNA, U1 RNA,** possesses a ribonucleotide sequence with **complementarity to the consensus sequence across the potential splice sites** (Fig 28–31). Specific ribonuclease molecules in pro-

Gene	5′ Exon |◄——— Intron ———►| Exon 3′	
Rat insulin	CAGGUAUGU	... CUAUCUUCCAGG
Rat insulin	AAGGUAAGC	... CUCCCUGGCAGU
Rat insulin	CAGGUAUGU	... CUAUCUUCCAGG
γ1 Chain (newborn mouse)		... UUUUCUUGUAGC
	UUGGUGAGA	UCUCUCCACAGU
γ1 Chain (newborn mouse)	CAGGUAAGU	... UUCAUCCUUAGU
γ1 Chain (newborn mouse)	AAGGUGAGA	... CCCACCCACAGG
		UUUUCUUGUAGC
γ1 Chain (mouse myeloma)	UUGAGAGGA	... UCUCUCCACAGU
	CAGGUAAGU	UUCAUCCUUAGU
γ2 Chain (mouse myeloma)	AAGGUGAGA	... CUCACUCACAGG
γ1 Chain (mouse myeloma)	CAGGUCAGC	... CCUGUUUGCAGG
	CAGGUCAGC	UCUGUUUGCAGG
γ1 Chain (mouse myeloma)	UAGGUGAGU	... UCAUCCUGCGGC
	AACGUAAGU	UCCUUCCUCAGU
γ2 Chain	AACGUAAGU	... UCCUUCCUCAGG
λ1 Chain	AACCUAAGU	... UCCUUCCUCAGG
κ Chain	AACGUAAGU	... UCCUUCCUCAGG
κ Chain	AACGUAAGU	... UCCUUCCUCAGG
κ Chain	AAGGUUAAA	... UCCACUCCUAGG
κ Chain	CAGGUUGGU	... UCCCUUUUUAGG
κ Chain	AGGGUGAGU	... UAUUCCCACAGC
κ Chain	CAGGUUGGU	... CAUUUUCUCAGG
Mouse β-globin	AGGGUGAGU	... UUUUCCUACAGC
Rabbit β-globin		... UCCUCCCACAGC
Rabbit β-globin		... CUUCUCCGCAGC
Human β-globin	AAGGUAGGC	... GUUUGCUCUAGA
Human δ-globin	AAGGUGAGC	... UUCAAUUACAGG
Chicken ovalbumin	CAGGUACAG	... UUUCUAUUCAGU
Chicken ovalbumin	CCAGUAAGU	... UUGCUUUACAGG
Chicken ovalbumin	AUGGUAAGG	... CAUUCUUAAAGG
Chicken ovalbumin	GAGGUAUAU	... UGGUUCUCCAGC
Chicken ovalbumin	CAGGUAUGG	... UUUCCUUGCAGC
Chicken ovalbumin	AAGGUACCU	... UUUUAUUUCAGG
SV40 late mRNAs	AAGGUUCGU	... UUUUAUUUCAGG
SV40 late mRNAs	CUGGUAAGU	... UUUUAUUUCAGG
SV40 late mRNAs	CUGGUAAGU	... UUUACUUCUAGG
SV40 early mRNAs	AAGGUAAAU	... GUGUAUUUUAGA
SV40 early mRNAs	GAGGUAUUU	... GUGUAUUUUAGA
Polyoma late mRNAs	CAAGUAAGU	... UAUUUCCCUAGG
Polyoma late mRNAs	CAAGUAAGU	... UUUAAUUCUAGG
Polyoma late mRNAs	CAAGUAAGU	... UCUAUUUUAAGA
Silk fibroin	CAGGUGAGU	... UUUUGUUUCAGU
Consensus	^A_CAGGUAAGU	UYUYYYU CAGG

5′ Exon \|◄——— Intron ———►\| Exon 3′

Figure 28–30. Sequences at splice junctions. The 36 "donor" (5′ end) sequences and 37 "acceptor" (3′ end) sequences represent 43 possible splicing events (each event is depicted on a separate line). Underlined sequences are redundant (either because they are identical to a homologous region or because they represent an alternative splice involving the same region) and were not included in the tabulation. (Slightly modified and reproduced, with permission, from Lerner MR & others: Are snRNPs involved in splicing? *Nature* 1980;**283**:220.)

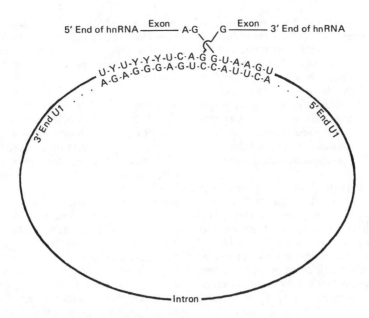

Figure 28–31. Proposed mechanism for establishing the splice site for intron removal from the hnRNA. The U1 RNA molecule is complementary to the portion of the intron across the splice site.

karyotes are known to contain RNA molecules necessary for their specific action. The U1 RNA molecules are also found associated with specific protein molecules in eukaryotic nuclei and may function in conjunction with specific nucleases and ligases to provide the necessary recognition function for specific enzymes to carry out the specific splicing process.

Interestingly, patients with lupus erythematosus, an autoimmune disease, have antibodies to some of these specific nuclear nucleoprotein molecules containing U1 and related RNA. The relationship to the autoimmune disease per se is unknown.

It seems that the mystery of the relationship between hnRNA and the mature mRNA in eukaryotic cells is solved. The hnRNA molecules are the primary transcripts plus their early processed products, which, after the addition of caps and poly(A) tails and removal of the portion corresponding to the introns, are transported to the cytoplasm as mature mRNA molecules.

The processing of hnRNA molecules is a potential site for regulation of gene expression. In fact, it seems that in a model of early undifferentiated embryonic cells—cultured embryonal carcinoma cells—the nuclear machinery is incapable of removing introns from the primary transcript of SV40 virus DNA. Accordingly, the genes on the SV40 genome are not expressed in the undifferentiated embryonal carcinoma cells. As those cells "differentiate" in vitro, they acquire the capacity to remove introns from primary transcripts and the SV40 genes are expressed.

One form of β-thalassemia, a disease in which the beta-globin gene of hemoglobin is severely underexpressed, appears to result from a nucleotide change at an exon-intron junction, precluding removal of the intron and therefore leading to diminished or absent synthesis of the β chain. It is also evident from other studies that primary transcripts of genes lacking introns are likely not ever to appear in the cytosol as mature mRNA molecules.

The function of the **capped structure** on hnRNA molecules is presumed to be related to the function of the same on mRNA molecules, where it appears to be necessary for the initiation of **messenger translation.** The function of the poly(A) tail present on about 20% of the hnRNA molecules is also unknown, but clearly it does not serve as a qualitative signal responsible for the selection of those hnRNA molecules to be processed and transported to the cytoplasm. Many mRNA molecules do not contain poly(A). Many poly(A)-tailed RNA molecules receive their tails in the cytoplasm after transport from the nucleus.

Messenger RNA (mRNA)

As mentioned above, most but not all mammalian mRNA molecules contain a capped structure at their 5'-phosphate terminus and a poly(A) tail at the 3' terminus. The cap structures are added in the nucleus prior to transport of the mRNA molecule to the cytoplasm. The poly(A) tails (when present) appear to be added either in the nucleus or in the cytoplasm. The secondary methylations of mRNA molecules, those on the 2'-hydroxy groups and the N_6 of adenylate residues, occur after the mRNA molecule has appeared in the cytoplasm. The function of the cap structures presumably is to assist in recognition of the proper site on the template mRNA at which to commence protein synthesis.

The function of the poly(A) tail is unknown. In any event, the presence or absence of the poly(A) tail does not determine whether a precursor molecule in the nucleus appears in the cytoplasm because all poly(A)-tailed hnRNA molecules do not contribute to cytoplasmic mRNA, nor do all cytoplasmic mRNA molecules contain poly(A) tails. Cytoplasmic processes in mammalian cells can both add and remove adenylate residues from the poly(A) tails, but this processing does not appear to influence the stability of the mRNA or its function in a homologous system. Ovalbumin mRNA, after the removal of its poly(A) tail, is translated less efficiently in both rabbit reticulocyte and wheat germ protein–synthesizing systems in vitro.

The turnover of poly(A)-containing mRNA in cultured mammalian cells is a first-order process with a half-time approximately equal to the doubling time of the cell culture. The kinetics of the degradation of histone mRNA which does not contain a poly(A) tail appears to be a zero-order process in which there is an age-dependent decay with a lifetime of approximately 6 hours. It is not clear whether this difference is related to the presence or absence of poly(A) or to some intrinsic property of these mRNA molecules.

The size of the cytoplasmic mRNA molecules after the poly(A) tail is removed is still considerably greater than the size required to code for the specific protein for which it is template. A summary of the required sizes and actual sizes of different mRNAs is given in Table 28–4. The extra nucleotides occur in untranslated regions both 5′ and 3′ to the coding region.

Transfer RNA Molecules (tRNA)

The tRNA molecules, as described in Chapters 27 and 29, serve as adapter molecules for the translation of mRNA into protein sequences. The tRNAs contain many peculiar bases; some are simply methylated derivatives and some possess rearranged glycosidic bonds. The tRNA molecules are transcribed in both prokaryotes and eukaryotes as large precursors which are then subjected to **nucleolytic processing** and reduced in size by a specific class of ribonucleases, **ribonuclease P.** In addition, the genes of some tRNA molecules contain—very near the portion corresponding to the anticodon loop—**intervening sequences** of about 18 nucleotides. These intervening sequences in the tRNA genes are transcribed. Thus, the processing of the precursor transcripts of many tRNA molecules must include removal of the 18-ribonucleotide intervening piece and proper splicing of the anticodon region to generate an active adaptor molecule for protein

Table 28–4. Lengths of isolated messenger RNAs.*†

Cell	Protein	Coding Length	mRNA Length	Poly(A) Length
Rabbit red blood cell	Globin	430	550 610 650	40
Mouse red blood cell	Globin			40, 60, 100
Duck red blood cell	Globin			100
Mouse myeloma	Light Ig	660	1200 1250 1300	 200
Mouse myeloma	Heavy Ig	1350	1800	150–200
Chick oviduct	Ovalbumin	1164	1670 2640	Not known
Calf lens	α A2-Crystallin	520	1460	200
Calf lens	δ-Crystallin	1260	2000	Not known
Bombyx mori silk gland	Fibroin	14,000	16,000	100
Lytechinus pictus (sea urchin)	Histone f2al	310	370–400	None
HeLa‡	Molecules: 50% total 25% total 25% total	 < 1000 1000–2000 > 2000	 < 1400 1400–3000 > 3000	 150–200 150–200 150–200
	Mass: 50% total 50% total	 < 2100 > 2100	 < 2200 > 2200	 150–200 150–200

*Reproduced, with permission, from Lewin B: Units of transcription and translation: Sequence components of heterogeneous nuclear RNA and messenger RNA. *Cell* 1975;4:480.

†Coding lengths are the number of nucleotides required to specify each protein, estimated from its number of amino acids or molecular weight. The lengths of the mRNAs are those determined experimentally; where more than one value is shown, each represents an independent determination. The length of poly(A) on a messenger is not constant but declines with age; thus, the apparent length depends on whether it is determined by steady state or by pulse labeling, which explains the variation in measured globin mRNA poly(A) lengths. "Not known" indicates that poly(A) is present but that its length has not been determined.

‡The distribution of HeLa protein and messenger sizes is only approximate; an estimate of the number of molecules in each size class suggests a median coding length in mRNA of about 1200 nucleotides (1400 less the poly[A] content), and an estimate of the mass of protein or mRNA in each size class suggests a number average molecular weight for the coding length of 2000 (ie, 2200 less the poly[A] content).

synthesis. Some tRNA precursors in prokaryotes contain the sequence for 2 different tRNA molecules. The modification of the tRNA molecules includes nucleotide **alkylations** and arrangements required for normal function, the proper **folding** to generate a partial double-stranded character, and the **attachment of the characteristic C·C·A terminus** at the 3' end of the molecule. This C·C·A terminus is the point of attachment for the specific amino acid that is to enter into the polymerization reaction of protein synthesis. The methylation of mammalian tRNA precursors probably occurs in the nucleus, whereas the cleavage and C·C·A attachment are cytoplasmic functions since the termini turn over more rapidly than do the tRNA molecules themselves. Enzymes within the cytoplasm of mammalian cells are required for the attachment of amino acids to the C·C·A residues. The tRNA molecules are more stable in growing eukaryotic cells than in resting cells. In the growing cells, the half-time is approximately 60 hours.

Ribosomal RNA (rRNA)

In mammalian cells, the 2 major rRNA molecules and one minor rRNA molecule are transcribed from a single large precursor molecule (Fig 28–32). The precursor is subsequently processed in the nucleolus to provide the ribosome subunits for the cytoplasm. The rRNA genes are located in the nucleoli of mammalian cells. Thousands of copies of these genes are present in every cell. The rRNA genes are transcribed as units, each of which contains, from 5' to 3', an 18S, a 5.8S (formerly 7S), and a 28S ribosomal RNA. The transcript is a 45S molecule which is highly methylated in the nucleolus. In the **45S precursor,** the eventual 28S segment contains 65 ribose-methyl groups and 5 base-methyl groups. Only those portions of the precursor that eventually become rRNA molecules are methylated. The 45S precursor is nucleolytically processed. Nearly half of the original is discarded as ''degradation products'' as shown in Fig 28–32. During the processing of rRNA, further methylation occurs, and eventually in the nucleoli the 28S chains

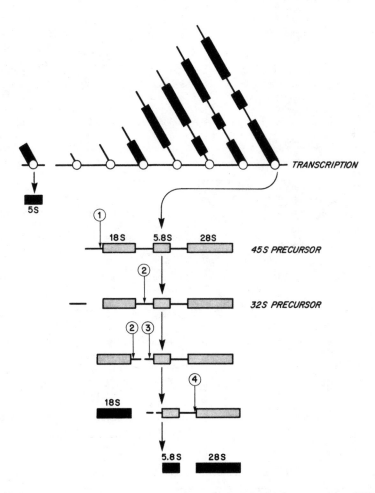

Figure 28–32. Diagrammatic representation of the processing of ribosomal RNA from precursor RNA molecules. (Reproduced, with permission, from Perry RP: *Annu Rev Biochem* 1976;45:611.)

self-assemble with ribosomal proteins newly synthesized in the cytoplasm to form the larger 60S subunit. The smaller (40S) ribosomal subunits may not be formed in the nucleoli from the 18S rRNA molecule. The 5.8S rRNA molecule also formed from the 45S precursor RNA in the nucleolus becomes an integral part of the smaller ribosomal subunit.

Both of the 2 major rRNA species present in the cytoplasm are stable in growing cells but unstable in resting cells. In resting cells the 28S rRNA exhibits even greater instability than does the 18S rRNA.

INHIBITORS OF DNA & RNA SYNTHESIS

Many antibiotics and nucleotide analogs inhibit the synthesis of DNA and RNA. These are used both experimentally (in research) and clinically in the management of malignant diseases. A list of some of these inhibitors is shown in Table 28–5 with some indication of their mechanisms and effects.

Table 28–5. Inhibitors of DNA and RNA synthesis.*

Type of Inhibition	Inhibitor	Mechanism	Inhibition or Effect
Template binding Noncovalent	Actinomycin D	Binds to and intercalates between dG-dC pairs	RNA and DNA chain elongation
	Anthracyclines (eg, nogalamycin)	Binds and intercalates alternating A-T sequence	RNA and DNA chain elongation
	Acridine dyes (eg, acriflavine)	Intercalates	Frame shift mutation; RNA chain initiation
	Ethidium bromide	Intercalates	DNA replication and mutagenesis
	Kanchanomycin	Strong Mg^{2+} complex with template	*E coli* DNA polymerase I
	8-Aminoquinolines		*E coli* and *M luteus* DNA polymerase I; RNA polymerase only partially.
Covalent	Mitomycin (reduced) Bleomycin, phleomycin Anthramycin	Cross-links Chain breaks	DNA replication DNA replication DNA and RNA synthesis
Nucleotide analogs Chain terminator	Dideoxynucleoside triphosphates	Incorporated into DNA	DNA chain growth and $3' \rightarrow 5'$ degradation
	Arabinosyl nucleoside triphosphates	Incorporated into DNA	DNA chain growth and $3' \rightarrow 5'$ degradation; bacterial and animal cells.
	Cordycepin triphosphate (3'-deoxy ATP)	Incorporated into DNA and RNA	DNA and RNA chain growth
	3'-Amino ATP	Incorporated into DNA and RNA	DNA chain growth
Defective DNA	dUTP	Incorporated into DNA	Template degraded
	5-Hydroxyuridine or 5-amino-uridine	Incorporated into RNA	RNA and DNA synthesis
	5-Bromouridine	Incorporated into DNA; triphosphate inhibits ribonucleotide reductase	Mutagenic, causes replication errors
	Tubericidin "ATP," formycin "ATP"	Incorporated into RNA and DNA	RNA and DNA synthesis and functions
Enzyme binding	Hydroxyphenylhydrazino-uracil	Ternary complex with template and enzyme	*B subtilis* polymerase III; reversed by dGTP.
	Hydroxyphenylhydrazinoiso-cytosine	Ternary complex with template and enzyme	*B subtilis* polymerase III; reversed by dATP.
Enzyme binding	Rifampicin, streptovaricin	β-Subunit of bacterial RNA polymerase	RNA initiation
	Streptolydigin	β-Subunit of bacterial RNA polymerase	RNA chain growth
	α-Amanitin		Mammalian nuclear RNA polymerase
	Kanchanomycin		*E coli* RNA polymerase
Unknown mechanism	Edeine		DNA replication in bacteria
	Nalidixic acid		DNA replication in bacteria

*Reproduced, with permission, from Kornberg A: *DNA Synthesis.* Freeman, 1974.

NUCLEASES

Enzymes capable of degrading nucleic acids have been recognized for many years. These can be classified in several ways. Those which exhibit specificity for deoxyribonucleic acid are referred to as **deoxyribonucleases.** Those which specifically hydrolyze ribonucleic acids are **ribonucleases.** Within both of these classes are enzymes capable of cleaving internal phosphodiester bonds to produce a 3'-hydroxyl and a 5'-phosphoryl or a 5'-hydroxyl and a 3'-phosphoryl terminus. These are referred to as **endonucleases.** Some are capable of hydrolyzing both strands of a **double-stranded** molecule, whereas others can only cleave **single strands** of nucleic acids. Some nucleases can hydrolyze only unpaired single strands, while others are capable of hydrolyzing single strands participating in the formation of a double-stranded molecule. There exist classes of endonucleases which recognize specific sequences in DNA; the majority of these are the **restriction endonucleases,** which have in recent years become an important tool in molecular genetics and medical sciences.

A list of some currently recognized restriction endonucleases is presented in Table 28–2.

Some nucleases are capable of hydrolyzing a nucleotide only when it is present at a terminus of a molecule; these are referred to as **exonucleases.** Exonucleases may act in one direction (3' → 5' or 5' → 3') only. In bacteria, a 3' → 5' exonuclease is an integral part of the DNA replication machinery and there serves to edit the most recently added deoxynucleotide for a base-pairing error.

• • •

References

Abelson HT & others: Changes in RNA in relation to growth of the fibroblast: The lifetime of mRNA, rRNA, and tRNA in resting and growing cells. *Cell* 1974;**1**:161.

Berger NA & others: Defective poly(adenosine diphosphoribose) synthesis in xeroderma pigmentosum. *Biochemistry* 1980;**2**:289.

Chambon P: Eukaryotic nuclear RNA polymerases. *Annu Rev Biochem* 1975;**44**:613.

Cordin J & others: Promoter sequences of eukaryotic protein-coding genes. *Science* 1980;**209**;1406.

Crick F: Split genes and RNA splicing. *Science* 1979;**204**:264.

Demple B, Linn S: Dna N-glycosylases and UV repair. *Nature* 1980;**287**:203.

DePamphilis ML, Wassarman PM: Replication of eukaryotic chromosomes: A close-up of the replication fork. *Annu Rev Biochem* 1980;**49**:627.

Efstratiadis A & others: Enzymatic in vitro synthesis of globin genes. *Cell* 1976;**7**:279.

Fritsch EF & others: Molecular cloning and characterization of the human beta-like globin gene cluster. *Cell* 1980;**19**:959.

Gilbert W, Villa-Komaroff L: Useful proteins from recombinant bacteria. *Sci Am* (April) 1980;**242**:74

Hamkalo B, Miller OL Jr: Electron microscopy of genetic activity. *Annu Rev Biochem* 1973;**42**:379.

Hanawalt PC & others: DNA repair in bacteria and mammalian cells. *Annu Rev Biochem* 1979;**48**:783.

Kantor JA & others: Beta thalassemia: Mutations which affect processing of the beta-globin mRNA precursor. *Cell* 1980;**21**:149.

Kornberg A: *DNA Replication.* Freeman, 1980.

Lerner MR & others: Are snRNPs involved in splicing? *Nature* 1980;**283**:220.

Maxam AM: Sequencing the DNA of recombinant chromosomes. *Fed Proc* 1980;**39**:2830.

Nathans D, Smith HO: Restriction endonucleases in the analysis and restructuring of DNA molecules. *Annu Rev Biochem* 1975;**44**:273.

Ogawa T, Okazaki T: Discontinuous DNA replication. *Annu Rev Biochem* 1980;**49**:421.

Perry RP: Processing of RNA. *Annu Rev Biochem* 1976;**45**:605.

Radding CM: Molecular mechanisms in genetic recombination. *Annu Rev Genetics* 1973;**7**:87.

Razin A, Riggs AD: DNA methylation and gene function. *Science* 1980;**210**:604.

Rich A, RajBhandary UL: Transfer RNA: Molecular structure, sequence, and properties. *Annu Rev Biochem* 1976;**45**:805.

Rogers J, Wall R: A mechanism for RNA splicing. *Proc Natl Acad Sci USA* 1980;**77**:1877.

Tidghman SM & others: Intervening sequence of DNA identified in the structural portion of a mouse β-globin gene. *Proc Natl Acad Sci USA* 1978;**75**:725.

Ziff EB: Transcription and RNA processing by the DNA tumour viruses. *Nature* 1980;**287**:491.

29 | Protein Synthesis & the Genetic Code

David W. Martin, Jr., MD

As previously described, the genetic information within the nucleotide sequence of DNA is transcribed in the nucleus into the specific nucleotide sequence of an RNA molecule. The sequence of nucleotides in the RNA transcript is complementary to the nucleotide sequence of the "sense" strand of its gene in accordance with the base-pairing rules. In higher eukaryotic cells, this transcript, heterogeneous nuclear RNA (hnRNA), is processed in the nucleus, and the appropriately spliced portion appears subsequently in the cytoplasm as messenger RNA (mRNA).

In a series of elegant experiments by Charles Yanofsky, it has been shown that in prokaryotes there is a linear correspondence between the gene and its polypeptide product or protein. Using the technics of genetic mapping and protein sequencing, Yanofsky demonstrated that the order of mutants on the genetic map of tryptophan synthetase in *Escherichia coli* was the same as the order of the corresponding changes in the amino acid sequence of the tryptophan synthetase enzyme molecule (Fig 29–1).

The cell must possess the machinery necessary to translate information from the nucleotide sequence of an mRNA into the sequence of amino acids of the corresponding specific protein. This process, termed **translation,** was not understood for many years, until the relatively recent clarification of our understanding of the process of translation and the deciphering of the genetic code, which is undoubtedly a major accomplishment of modern biology. It was realized early that mRNA molecules in themselves have no affinity for amino acids and, therefore, that the translation of the information in the mRNA nucleotide sequence into the amino acid sequence of a protein requires an intermediate, adapter molecule. This adapter molecule must recognize a specific nucleotide sequence on the one hand as well as a specific amino acid on the other. With such an adapter molecule, the cell can direct a specific amino acid into the proper sequential position of a protein as dictated by the nucleotide sequence of the specific mRNA. In fact, the functional groups of the amino acids do not themselves actually come into contact with the mRNA template.

In the nucleotide sequence of the mRNA molecule, code words exist for each amino acid. This is referred to as the **genetic code.** The adapter molecules that translate the code words into the amino acid sequence of a protein are the **transfer RNA (tRNA)** molecules. The **ribosome** is the cellular component on which these various functional entities interact to assemble the protein molecule. Many of these subcellular units (ribosomes) can aggregate to translate

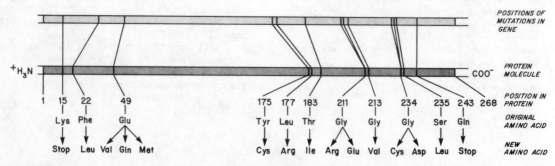

Figure 29–1. A diagram of the colinearity of the gene (Trp A) for the tryptophan synthetase A protein with the protein molecule itself. The positions of the mutations in the Trp A gene are indicated in the top bar, and the position of the corresponding altered amino acid determined by sequence analyses of the mutant protein molecule is shown in the lower bar. The numbers represent the number of the altered amino acid starting at the amino terminus of the protein molecule. Shown below the numbers of the altered amino acid residues are the original amino acids at those positions in the normal protein molecule. Below the normal amino acids are those occurring in the protein as the result of a mutation in the gene at the corresponding positions. (From Stryer L: *Biochemistry.* Freeman, 1975. Copyright © 1975. Redrawn, with permission, from Yanofsky C: Gene structure and protein structure. *Sci Am* [May] 1967;**216**:89.)

simultaneously a single mRNA molecule and, in so doing, form a **polyribosome.** In the cell, there are factories in which polyribosomes are gathered together for the formation of different classes of protein molecules. The **rough endoplasmic reticulum** is such a factory of polyribosomes attached to membrane structures that provides for the synthesis of integral membrane proteins and proteins to be exported. Polyribosomal structures also exist free in the cytoplasm, where they synthesize proteins that remain within the cell.

Twenty different amino acids are required for the synthesis of proteins, and thus there must be at least 20 distinct code words that comprise the genetic code. Since there are only 4 different nucleotides in mRNA, each code word must consist of more than a single purine or pyrimidine nucleotide. Code words consisting of 2 nucleotides each could provide for only 16 (4 × 4) specific code words, whereas code words of 3 nucleotides could provide 64 (4 × 4 × 4) specific code words.

As a result of the initial observations of Matthaei and Nirenberg, it is now known that each code word, termed a **codon,** consists of a sequence of 3 nucleotides, ie, it is a triplet code. With 4 distinct bases in an mRNA molecule, in a triplet code there can be 64 triplets to provide for 20 amino acids. The deciphering of the genetic code (Table 29–1) was carried out largely in the laboratory of Marshall Nirenberg. It depended heavily on the chemical synthesis of nucleotide polymers, particularly triplets, by Khorana.

Three codons do not code for specific amino acids; these have been termed **nonsense codons.** At least 2 of these so-called nonsense codons are utilized in the cell as signals to terminate the polymerization of amino acids where a protein molecule is to end. The remaining 61 codons code for 20 amino acids. Thus there must be "degeneracy" in the genetic code. An examination of the genetic code in Table 29–1 reveals that the 64 possible codons may be arranged in **16 families,** a family of codons being those that have the **same first 2 bases.** In Table 29–1, each family occupies a single column between the horizontal lines. For example, the codons CCN, where N can be U, C, A, or G, define a family located in Table 29–1 in the second column of the second box from the top. In some families, all 4 codons code for the same amino acid, as do the members of the CC family described immediately above. These are referred to as **unmixed families.** Eight of the 16 families of codons are unmixed (Table 29–1). Those families of codons that code for more than one amino acid are said to be **mixed** families. In 6 of the mixed families, codons with pyrimidines (U or C) at the third position code for one amino acid, while members with purines (A or G) at the third position code for another amino acid or chain termination signal (Table 29–1). The 2 remaining families—the UG family and the AU family—do not exhibit either pattern and are unique. Some rather startling recent observations concerning the functions of these unique families of codons in mitochondria are discussed below. Thus, in general, the third nucleotide in a codon is less important than the other 2 in determining the specific amino acid to be incorporated, and this accounts for most of the **degeneracy** of the code. However, for any specific codon only a single amino acid is indicated; the genetic code is **unambiguous,** ie, given a specific codon, only a single amino acid is indicated. The distinction between ambiguity and degeneracy is an important concept to be emphasized.

The unambiguous but degenerate code can be described in molecular terms. The recognition of specific codons in the mRNA by the tRNA adapter molecules is dependent upon their **anticodon region** and the base-pairing rules. Each tRNA molecule contains a specific sequence, complementary to a codon, which is termed its anticodon. For a given codon in the mRNA, only a single species of tRNA molecule possesses the proper anticodon. Since each tRNA molecule can be charged with only one specific amino acid, each codon therefore specifies only one amino acid. However, some tRNA molecules can utilize the anticodon to recognize more than one codon. As can be seen from the example of unmixed families, the nucleotide in the anticodon that recognizes the third (3'-) base of the codon could be less discriminating (mixed families) or nondiscriminating (unmixed families) and still manage to insert the proper amino acid when called for. This reduced stringency between the third base of the codon and the complementary nucleotide in the anticodon is referred to as **wobble.** Therefore, given a specific codon, only a specific amino acid will

Table 29–1. The genetic code (codon assignments in messenger RNA).*

First Nucleotide	Second Nucleotide				Third Nucleotide
	U	C	A	G	
U	Phe	Ser	Tyr	Cys	U
	Phe	Ser	Tyr	Cys	C
	Leu	Ser	CT	CT†	A
	Leu	Ser	CT	Trp	G
C	Leu	Pro	His	Arg	U
	Leu	Pro	His	Arg	C
	Leu	Pro	Gln	Arg	A
	Leu	Pro	Gln	Arg	G
A	Ile	Thr	Asn	Ser	U
	Ile	Thr	Asn	Ser	C
	Ile†	Thr	Lys	Arg†	A
	Met (CI)	Thr	Lys	Arg†	G
G	Val	Ala	Asp	Gly	U
	Val	Ala	Asp	Gly	C
	Val	Ala	Glu	Gly	A
	Val	Ala	Glu	Gly	G

*The terms first, second, and third nucleotide refer to the individual nucleotides of a triplet codon. U = uridine nucleotide; C = cytosine nucleotide; A = adenine nucleotide; G = guanine nucleotide; CI = chain initiator codon; CT = chain terminator codon. (Abbreviations of amino acids are explained in Chapter 3.)

†In mammalian mitochondria, AUA codes for Met, UGA for Trp, and AGA and AGG serve as chain terminators.

be incorporated—although, given a specific amino acid, more than one codon may call for it.

As discussed below, the reading of the genetic code during the process of protein synthesis does not involve any overlap of codons. Furthermore, once the reading is commenced at a specific codon, there is **no punctuation** between codons, and the message is read in a continuing sequence of nucleotide triplets until a nonsense codon is reached.

Until recently, the genetic code (Table 29–1) was thought to be universal. It has now been shown that the set of tRNA molecules in mitochondria from lower and higher eukaryotes, including humans, reads 4 codons differently from the tRNA molecules in the cytoplasm of even the same cells. As noted in Table 29–1, the codon AUA is read as Met, and UGA codes for Trp in mammalian mitochondria. These 2 codons reside in the 2 codon families noted to be unique: the UG family and the AU family. Apparently, in order to minimize the number of tRNA molecules necessary to translate the genetic code, mitochondria have managed to convert the UG family and the AU family to simple mixed types. In addition, the codons AGA and AGG are read as stop or chain terminator codons rather than as Arg. As a result, mitochondria require only 22 tRNA molecules to read their genetic code, whereas the cytoplasmic translation system possesses a full complement of 31 tRNA species. These exceptions noted, **the genetic code is universal.** The frequency of use of each amino acid codon in 4 different mammalian proteins is given in Table 29–2.

Transfer RNA Function

There exists at least one transfer RNA (tRNA) for each of the 20 amino acids. All of the tRNA molecules have extraordinarily similar functions and extraordinarily similar 3-dimensional structures. The adapter function of the tRNA molecules requires the charging of each specific tRNA with its specific amino acid. Since there is no affinity of nucleic acids for specific functional groups of amino acids, this recognition must be carried out by a protein molecule capable of recognizing both a specific tRNA molecule and a specific amino acid. At least 20 specific enzymes are required for these specific recognition functions and for the proper attachment of the 20 amino acids to specific tRNA molecules. The process of recognition and attachment (charging) is carried out in 2 steps by one enzyme for each of the 20 amino acids. These enzymes are termed **aminoacyl-tRNA synthetases.** They form an activated intermediate of aminoacyl-AMP-enzyme complex as depicted in Fig 29–2. The specific aminoacyl-AMP-enzyme complex then recognizes a specific tRNA to which it attaches the aminoacyl moiety at the 3′-hydroxyl adenosine terminus (Fig 29–3). The amino acid remains attached to its specific tRNA in an ester linkage until it is polymerized at a specific position in the fabrication of a polypeptide precursor of a protein molecule.

The common features of tRNA molecules are diagrammatically represented in Fig 29–4. The 3′-hydroxyl terminus possesses an A•C•C sequence which,

Table 29–2. Codon usage in α- and β-globin, immunoglobulin and insulin mRNAs.*

1			U: α	β	Im	Ins		C: α	β	Im	Ins			A: α	β	Im	Ins		G: α	β	Im	Ins	3
U	Phe	UUU	0	3	1	1	UCU	3	3	1	0	Tyr	UAU	2	1	2	0	UGU	0	1	1	2	U
	Phe	UUC	8	5	7	2	UCC (Ser)	4	3	6	2		UAC	1	2	5	3	Cys UGC	1	0	1	4	C
	Leu	UUA	0	0	0	0	UCA	0	0	4	0	Term	UAA	1	0	0	0	Term UGA	0	1	0	1	A
	Leu	UUG	1	0	2	1	UCG	0	0	0	0		UAG	0	0	0	0	Trp UGG	1	2	1	1	G
C	Leu	CUU	0	0	0	2	CCU	1	3	1	2	His	CAU	1	4	1	0	CGU	1	0	0	4	U
	Leu	CUC	2	2	1	3	CCC (Pro)	5	0	4	2		CAC	10	5	2	2	Arg CGC	0	0	0	0	C
	Leu	CUA	0	0	1	0	CCA	0	1	5	1	Gln	CAA	0	0	2	3	CGA	0	0	1	0	A
	Leu	CUG	14	16	0	8	CCG	1	0	0	2		CAG	1	4	2	5	CGG	1	0	2	1	G
A	Ile	AUU	0	1	2	1	ACU	2	2	5	0	Asn	AAU	1	4	3	0	AGU	1	4	1	0	U
	Ile	AUC	3	0	2	1	ACC (Thr)	10	2	10	2		AAC	3	4	8	3	Ser AGC	3	0	5	1	C
	Ile	AUA	0	0	1	0	ACA	0	0	3	1	Lys	AAA	2	3	6	1	AGA	0	0	0	0	A
	Met	AUG	1	1	1	0	ACG	0	0	2	0		AAG	10	9	10	2	Arg AGG	1	3	1	0	G
G	Val	GUU	0	4	0	1	GCU	1	7	2	3	Asp	GAU	0	1	3	2	GGU	1	4	1	3	U
	Val	GUC	0	2	3	2	GCC (Ala)	10	6	3	3		GAC	7	3	2	1	Gly GGC	8	6	2	2	C
	Val	GUA	0	0	2	0	GCA	0	1	2	1	Glu	GAA	3	4	1	2	GGA	0	0	1	1	A
	Val	GUG	10	12	2	5	GCG	2	1	0	0		GAG	4	6	1	7	GGG	0	1	0	2	G

*Reproduced, with permission, from Heindell HC & others: The primary sequence of rabbit α-globin mRNA. *Cell* 1978;15:43.

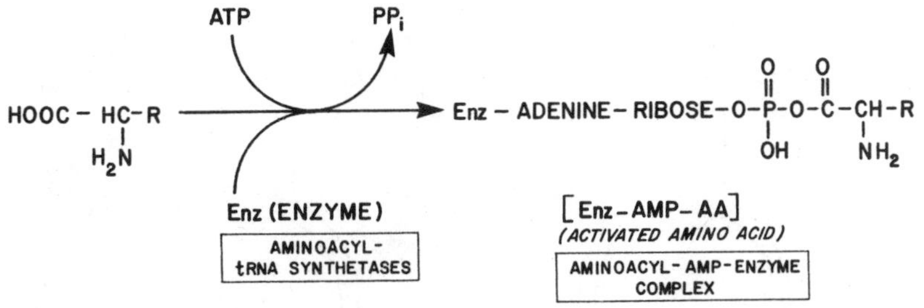

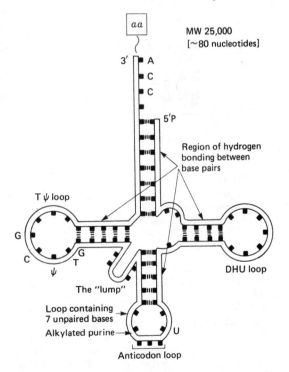

Figure at top showing:

ATP → PP$_i$

$$HOOC - \underset{\underset{H_2N}{|}}{HC} - R \longrightarrow Enz - ADENINE - RIBOSE - O - \overset{\overset{O}{\|}}{\underset{\underset{OH}{|}}{P}} - O - \overset{\overset{O}{\|}}{C} - \underset{\underset{NH_2}{|}}{CH} - R$$

Enz (ENZYME)

AMINOACYL-
tRNA SYNTHETASES

[Enz – AMP – AA]
(ACTIVATED AMINO ACID)

AMINOACYL- AMP- ENZYME
COMPLEX

Figure 29–2. Activation of amino acids by the formation of an enzyme-AMP–amino acid complex. The formation of the complex is catalyzed by the specific aminoacyl–tRNA synthetase itself.

as described in Chapter 28, is continually turning over in the cell cytoplasm. **At the 3′-hydroxyl adenosyl terminus, the specific amino acid is attached through an ester bond.** The thymidine-pseudouridine-cytidine (T•ψ•C) loop is involved in the binding of the aminoacyl-tRNA to the ribosomal surface at the site of protein synthesis. There exists an extra arm (the lump) that is variable among the different species of tRNA molecules. The loop containing dihydrouracil (DHU loop) is one of the sites important for the proper recognition of a given tRNA species by its proper charging enzyme or aminoacyl-tRNA synthetase.

The anticodon loop exists at a pole of the tRNA molecule quite distant from the pole to which the aminoacyl moiety is attached. The **anticodon loop** of tRNA molecules consists of 7 nucleotides. The sequence read from the 3′ to 5′ direction in that anticodon loop consists of a variable base•modified purine•X•Y•Z•pyrimidine•pyrimidine-5′. Note that this direction of reading the anticodon is 3′ to 5′, whereas the genetic code in Table 29–1 is read 5′ to 3′, since the codon and the anticodon loop of the mRNA and tRNA molecules, respectively, are **antiparallel** in their complementarity.

Fig 27–17 is a schematic diagram of the 3-dimensional structure of yeast phenylalanine tRNA as deduced from x-ray crystallographic studies.

The degeneracy of the genetic code resides mostly in the last nucleotide of the codon triplet, suggesting that the base pairing between this last nucleotide and the corresponding nucleotide of the anticodon is not strict. This phenomenon is referred to as

wobble; the pairing of the codon and anticodon can "wobble" at this specific nucleotide-to-nucleotide pairing site. This is depicted in Fig 29–5, in which the 2 anticodons for arginine, A•G•A and A•G•G, can bind to the same codon having a uracil at its 5′ end. Similarly, 3 codons for glycine, G•G•U, G•G•C, and G•G•A, are shown base-pairing with one anticodon, C•C•I. I is an inosine nucleotide, another of the peculiar bases appearing in tRNA molecules.

The codon recognition by a tRNA molecule does not depend upon the amino acid that is attached at its 3′-hydroxyl terminus. This has been ingeniously dem-

Figure 29–4. A typical aminoacyl-tRNA in which the amino acid is attached to the 3′ A•C•C terminus. The anticodon, T ψ C, and DHU loops are indicated, as are the positions of the intramolecular hydrogen bonding between base pairs. (From James D. Watson, *Molecular Biology of the Gene,* 3rd ed. Copyright © 1976, 1970, 1965, by W.A. Benjamin, Inc, Menlo Park, California.)

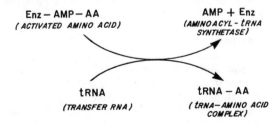

Enz – AMP – AA
(ACTIVATED AMINO ACID)

AMP + Enz
(AMINOACYL- tRNA SYNTHETASE)

tRNA
(TRANSFER RNA)

tRNA – AA
(tRNA–AMINO ACID COMPLEX)

Figure 29–3. Formation of the aminoacyl-tRNA from the activated amino acid and the appropriate tRNA. During the formation of the aminoacyl-tRNA complex, AMP and the aminoacyl–tRNA synthetase enzyme are released.

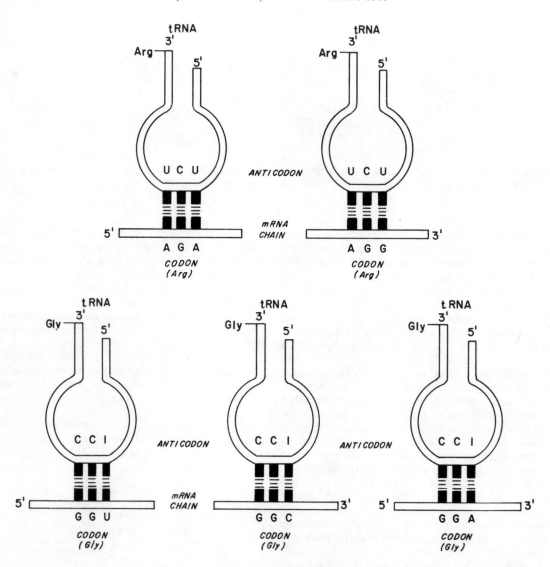

Figure 29–5. A diagrammatic representation of the binding of arginyl-tRNA and glycyl-tRNA to their respective codons of the mRNA chain. Note the antiparallel relationship of the tRNA and mRNAs and the "wobble" or lack of stringency of the base pairing between the nucleotide at the 5' terminus of the anticodon loop and that at the 3' terminus of the codon. I represents inosinate in phosphodiester linkage. (From James D. Watson, *Molecular Biology of the Gene,* 3rd ed. Copyright © 1976, 1970, 1965, by W.A. Benjamin, Inc, Menlo Park, California.)

onstrated by charging a tRNA specific for cysteine (tRNA$_{cys}$) with radioactively labeled cysteine. By chemical means, the cysteinyl residue was then altered to generate a tRNA molecule specific for cysteine but charged instead with alanine. The chemical transformation of the cysteinyl to the alanyl moiety did not alter the anticodon portion of the cysteine-specific tRNA molecule. When this alanyl-tRNA$_{cys}$ was used in the translation of a hemoglobin mRNA, a radioactive alanine was incorporated at what was normally a cysteine site in the hemoglobin protein molecule. The experiment demonstrated that the aminoacyl derivative of an aminoacyl-tRNA molecule does not play a role in the codon recognition. As already noted, the

aminoacyl moiety never comes in contact with the template mRNA containing the codons.

Mutations

A mutation is a change in the nucleotide sequence of a gene. Although the initial change may not occur in the sense strand of the double-stranded DNA molecule for that gene, after replication, daughter DNA molecules with mutations in the sense strand will segregate and appear in the population of organisms. Single base changes may be **transitions** or **transversions.** In the former, a given pyrimidine is changed to the other pyrimidine or a given purine is changed to the other purine. Transversions are changes from a purine

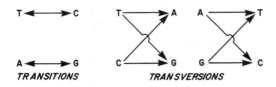

Figure 29–6. Diagrammatic representation of transition mutations and transversion mutations.

to either of the 2 pyrimidines or the change of a pyrimidine into either of the 2 purines, as shown in Fig 29–6.

If the nucleotide sequence of the gene containing the mutation is transcribed into an mRNA molecule, then the mRNA molecule will possess a complementary base change at this corresponding locus.

Single base changes in the mRNA molecules may have one of several effects when translated into protein:

(1) There may be **no detectable effect** because of the degeneracy of the code. This would be more likely if the changed base in the mRNA molecule were to fall on the third nucleotide of a codon. The translation of a codon is least sensitive to a change at the third position.

(2) A **missense** effect will occur when a different amino acid is incorporated at the corresponding site in the protein molecule. This mistaken amino acid or missense, depending upon its location in the specific protein, might be **acceptable, partially acceptable,** or **unacceptable** to the function of that protein molecule. From a careful examination of the genetic code, one can conclude that most single-base changes would result in the replacement of one amino acid by another with rather similar functional groups. This is an effective mechanism to avoid drastic change in the

physical properties of a protein molecule. If an acceptable missense effect occurs, the resulting protein molecule may not be distinguishable from the normal one. A partially acceptable missense will result in a protein molecule with partial but abnormal function. If an unacceptable missense effect occurs, then the protein molecule will not be capable of functioning in its assigned role.

(3) A **nonsense** codon may appear that would then result in the **premature termination** of amino acid incorporation into a peptide chain and the production of only a fragment of the intended protein molecule. The probability is high that a prematurely terminated protein molecule would not function in its assigned role.

Much information is available on the amino acid sequences of the normal and abnormal human hemoglobins (see Chapter 5). The hemoglobin molecule can be used to demonstrate the effects of single-base changes in the hemoglobin structural gene. The **lack of effect** of a single-base change would be demonstrable only by sequencing the nucleotides in the messenger RNA molecules or structural genes for hemoglobin from a large number of humans with normal hemoglobin molecules. However, it can be deduced that the codon for valine at position 67 of the β chain of hemoglobin is not identical in all persons possessing the normal β chain of hemoglobin. Hemoglobin Milwaukee has at position 67 a glutamic acid; hemoglobin Bristol contains aspartic acid at position 67. In order to account for the amino acid change by the change of a single nucleotide residue in the codon for amino acid 67, one must infer that the precursor of hemoglobin Bristol possessed a G•U•U or G•U•C codon prior to a later change to G•A•U or G•A•C, both codons for aspartic acid (Fig 29–7). However, the precursor of

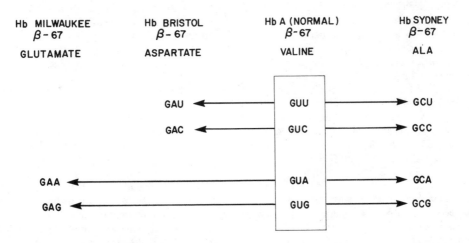

Figure 29–7. The normal valine at position 67 of the β chain of hemoglobin A can be coded for by one of the 4 codons shown in the box. In abnormal hemoglobin Milwaukee, the amino acid at position 67 of the β chain contains glutamate, coded for by G•A•A or G•A•G, either one of which could have resulted from a single-step transversion from the valine codons G•U•A or G•U•G. Similarly, the alanine present at position 67 of the β chain of hemoglobin Sydney could have resulted from a single-step transition from any one of the 4 valine codons. However, the aspartate residue at position 67 of hemoglobin Bristol could have resulted from a single-step transversion only from the G•U•U or G•U•C valine codons.

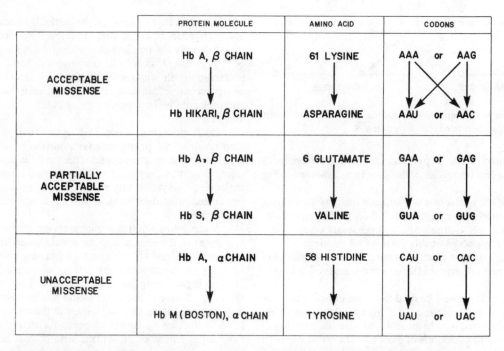

	PROTEIN MOLECULE	AMINO ACID	CODONS
ACCEPTABLE MISSENSE	Hb A, β CHAIN ↓ Hb HIKARI, β CHAIN	61 LYSINE ↓ ASPARAGINE	AAA or AAG ↓ (crossed) ↓ AAU or AAC
PARTIALLY ACCEPTABLE MISSENSE	Hb A, β CHAIN ↓ Hb S, β CHAIN	6 GLUTAMATE ↓ VALINE	GAA or GAG ↓ ↓ GUA or GUG
UNACCEPTABLE MISSENSE	Hb A, α CHAIN ↓ Hb M (BOSTON), α CHAIN	58 HISTIDINE ↓ TYROSINE	CAU or CAC ↓ ↓ UAU or UAC

Figure 29–8. Examples of 3 types of missense mutations resulting in abnormal hemoglobin chains. The amino acid alterations and possible alterations in the respective codons are indicated. The hemoglobin Hakari β chain mutation has apparently normal physiologic properties but is electrophoretically altered. Hemoglobin S has a β chain mutation and partial function; hemoglobin S combines oxygen but precipitates when deoxygenated. Hemoglobin M Boston, an α chain mutation, permits the oxidation of the heme ferrous iron to the ferric state and thus will not bind oxygen at all.

hemoglobin Milwaukee would have to possess at position 67 a codon G•U•A or G•U•G in order that a single nucleotide change could provide for the appearance of the glutamic acid codons G•A•A or G•A•G. Hemoglobin Sydney, which contains an alanine at position 67, could have arisen by the change of a single nucleotide in any of the 4 codons for valine (G•U•U, G•U•C, G•U•A, or G•U•G) to the alanine codons (G•C•U, G•C•C, G•C•A, or G•C•G, respectively).

An example of an **acceptable missense** mutation (Fig 29–8, top) in the structural gene for the β chain of hemoglobin could be detected by the presence of an electrophoretically altered hemoglobin in the red cells of an apparently healthy individual. Hemoglobin Hikari has been found in at least 2 families of Japanese people. This hemoglobin has asparagine substituted for lysine at the 61 position in the β chain. The corresponding transversion might be either A•A•A or A•A•G changed to either A•A•U or A•A•C. The replacement of the specific lysine with asparagine apparently does not alter the normal function of the β chain in these individuals.

A **partially acceptable missense** mutation (Fig 29–8, center) is best exemplified by **hemoglobin S,** sickle hemoglobin, in which the normal amino acid in position 6 of the β chain, glutamic acid, has been replaced by valine. The corresponding single nucleotide change within the codon would be G•A•A or G•A•G of glutamic acid to G•U•A or G•U•G of valine.

Clearly, this missense mutation hinders normal function and results in sickle cell anemia when the mutant gene is present in the homozygous state. The glutamate-to-valine change may be considered to be partially acceptable because hemoglobin S does bind and release oxygen, although abnormally.

An **unacceptable missense** mutation (Fig 29–8, bottom) in a hemoglobin gene generates a nonfunctioning hemoglobin molecule. For example, the hemoglobin M mutations generate molecules that allow the Fe^{2+} of the heme moiety to be oxidized to Fe^{3+} producing methemoglobin. Methemoglobin cannot transport oxygen. (See Chapter 5.)

Frame shift mutations, as a result of the deletion or insertion of nucleotides in the gene, generate altered nucleotide sequences of mRNA molecules. The deletion of a single nucleotide from the sense strand of a gene would result in an altered reading frame in the mRNA. The machinery translating the mRNA would not recognize that a base was missing since there is no punctuation in the reading of codons. A severe alteration in the sequence of polymerized amino acids, as depicted in Fig 29–9, would result. Altering the reading frame would result in a garbled translation of the mRNA distal to the single nucleotide deletion. Not only would the sequence of amino acids distal to this deletion be garbled, but the reading of the message might also result in the appearance of a nonsense codon and thus the production of a polypeptide prematurely

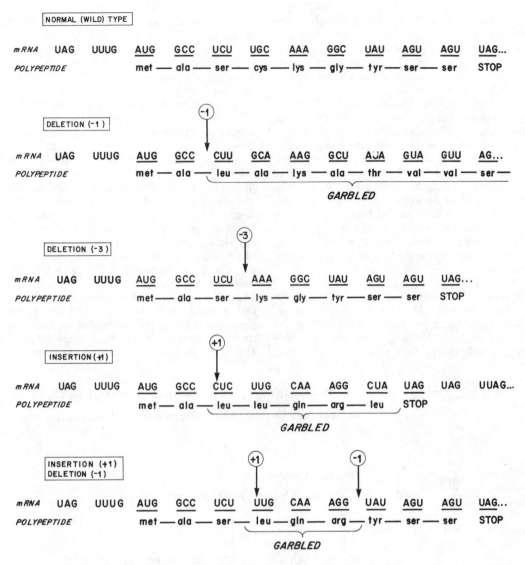

Figure 29–9. Demonstration of the effects of deletions and insertions in a gene on the sequence of the mRNA transcript and of the polypeptide chain translated therefrom. The arrows indicate the sites of deletions or insertions, and the numbers in the circles indicate the number of nucleotide residues deleted or inserted.

terminated and garbled near its carboxyl terminus.

If 3 nucleotides or a multiple of 3 were deleted from a gene, the corresponding messenger when translated would provide a protein from which is missing the corresponding number of amino acids. Because the reading frame is a triplet, the reading phase would not be disturbed for those codons distal to the deletion. If, however, deletion of one or 2 nucleotides occurs just prior to or within the normal termination codon (nonsense codon), the reading of the normal termination signal would then be disturbed. Such a deletion might result in reading through a termination signal until another nonsense codon was encountered. Excellent examples of this phenomenon are described in discussions of hemoglobinopathies.

Insertions of one or 2 or nonmultiples of 3 nu-

cleotides into a gene will result in an mRNA in which the reading frame will be distorted upon translation, and the same effects that occur with deletions would be reflected in the mRNA translation. This may be **garbled amino acid sequences** distal to the insertion, and the generation of a **nonsense codon** at or distal to the insertion, or perhaps **reading through** the normal termination codon. Following a deletion in a gene, an insertion (or vice versa) can reestablish the proper reading frame. The corresponding mRNA, when translated, would contain a garbled amino acid sequence between the insertion and deletion. Beyond the reestablishment of the reading frame, the amino acid sequence would be correct. One can imagine that different combinations of deletions, of insertions, or of deletions and insertions would result in formation of a protein wherein a portion is abnormal, but this portion is surrounded by the normal amino acid sequences. Such phenomena have been demonstrated convincingly in the bacteriophage T4, a finding which contributed significantly to establishment of evidence that the reading frame is a triplet.

The hemoglobinopathies again provide excellent examples of the effects of frame shift mutations. Generally speaking, fragments of normal proteins resulting from premature termination or proteins containing significant portions that are garbled are rapidly degraded in the cell by normal protein monitoring processes of the organism. Unfortunately, examples are not currently available of hemoglobins demonstrating significant fractions that are garbled distal to deletions or insertions. However, one form of $\beta°$-thalassemia is due to the appearance of a nonsense codon at the position corresponding to the number 17 amino acid of the β chain.

Hemoglobin Wayne results from a frame shift mutation at position 138 of the structural gene for the hemoglobin α chain. As shown in Fig 29–10, an adenosine nucleotide has been deleted so that the codon for amino acid 139 has been changed from A•A•A to A•A•U. The distal reading frame has been

altered so that the normal termination signal, U•A•A, is read through but is out of phase. This results in the addition of 5 amino acids to the terminally garbled 3 amino acids of the protein. The reading is terminated when the new termination signal, U•A•G, appears in the out-of-phase reading.

Also shown in Fig 29–10 are 2 other mutants in the gene for the α chain of hemoglobin that result in an **altered termination signal.** In hemoglobin Icaria the normal termination signal U•A•A has been altered by a single base change to A•A•A in the mRNA, allowing the peptide-synthesizing machinery to read through this normal termination signal. Similarly, the first nucleotide of the normal termination signal U•A•A has been changed to a C in the message for hemoglobin Constant Spring. This mutation results in the addition of a similar abnormal peptide at the carboxy terminus of the α chain of the hemoglobin molecule.

Fig 29–11 summarizes the **chain termination mutants** which affect the codon U•A•A at position 142 of the α chain of the hemoglobin molecule. Note that all but 2 of the predicted mutations have been observed. Note also that, because of the degeneracy of the termination signal, 2 of the nucleotide changes (to U•G•A or to U•A•G) would not be detectable by

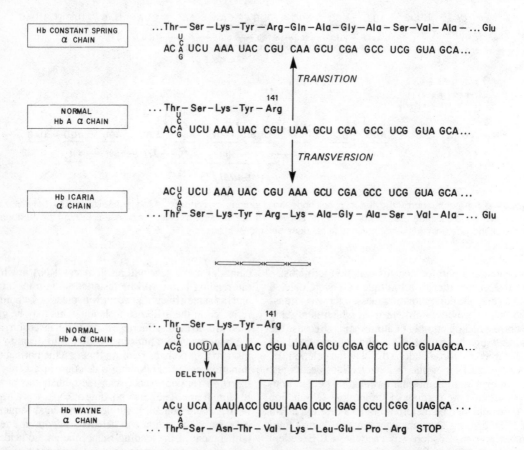

Figure 29–10. The demonstration of the effects of transitions or a deletion in the end of the hemoglobin α chain gene. Three abnormal hemoglobin molecules can result. The vertical lines in the lower portion represent the reading frame in the mRNA for hemoglobin Wayne and its origin.

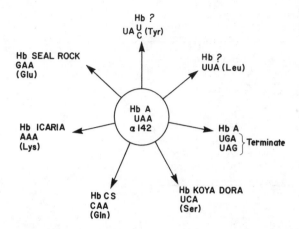

Figure 29–11. The results of all possible alterations of the normal termination signal (U·A·A) at position 142 of the mRNA for the α chain of hemoglobin A. Hemoglobin CS represents hemoglobin Constant Spring, and the hemoglobins with tyrosine or leucine at position 142 have yet to be discovered. (Redrawn and reproduced, with permission, from Weatherall DJ: Molecular pathology of the thalassemia disorders. *West J Med* 1976;124:388.)

examination of the hemoglobin molecule.

The above discussion of the altered protein products of gene mutations is based on the presence of normally functioning tRNA molecules. However, in prokaryotic and lower eukaryotic organisms, **abnormally functioning tRNA molecules** have been discovered that are themselves the results of mutations. Some of these abnormal tRNA molecules are capable of suppressing the effects of mutations in distant structural genes. These **suppressor tRNA molecules,** usually as the result of alterations in their anticodon regions, are capable of suppressing missense mutations, nonsense mutations, and frame shift mutations. However, since the suppressor tRNA molecules are not capable of distinguishing between a normal codon and one resulting from a gene mutation, their presence in a cell usually results in decreased viability. For instance, the nonsense suppressor tRNA molecules can suppress the normal termination signals to allow a read-through when this is not desirable. Frame shift suppressor tRNA molecules may read a normal codon plus a component of a juxtaposed codon to provide a frame shift, also when it is not desirable. Suppressor tRNA molecules have not been found in mammalian cells.

Protein Synthesis

The general structural characteristics of ribosomes and their self-assembly process have been discussed in Chapter 28. These particulate entities serve as the machinery on which the mRNA nucleotide sequence is translated into the sequence of amino acids of the specified protein. The translation of the mRNA commences near its 5' terminus with the formation of the corresponding amino terminus of the protein

molecule. The message is read toward its 3' terminus, concluding with the formation of the carboxy terminus of the protein. As described in Chapter 28, the transcription of a gene into the corresponding mRNA or its precursor first forms the 5' terminus of the RNA molecule. In prokaryotes this allows for the beginning of mRNA translation before the transcription of the gene is completed. In eukaryotic organisms, the process of transcription is a nuclear one; mRNA translation occurs in the cytoplasm. This precludes simultaneous transcription and translation in eukaryotic organisms and makes possible the processing necessary to generate mature mRNA from the primary transcript—hnRNA.

THE PROCESS OF PROTEIN SYNTHESIS

The process of protein synthesis, like that of gene transcription, can be described in 3 phases: initiation, elongation, and termination.

Initiation of Protein Synthesis
(See Fig 29–12.)

The 5' termini of most mRNA molecules in eukaryotes are "capped" as described in Chapter 28. This methyl-guanosyl triphosphate cap seems necessary for the binding of many mRNA molecules to the 40S ribosomal subunit. The first codon to be translated, usually A·U·G, is indented from the capped 5' terminus. As the result of intramolecular base pairing, the 5' portions of mRNA molecules have a secondary structure (folding) upon which the 40S ribosomal subunit depends for proper recognition of the first codon to be translated. The 18S ribosomal RNA (rRNA) of the 40S ribosomal subunit binds to a region of the mRNA that precedes the first translated codon. This binding of the mRNA to the 40S ribosomal subunit requires the presence of a protein factor, initiation factor 3 (IF-3).

The aminoacyl-tRNA called for by the first codon then interacts with GTP and initiation factor 2 (IF-2) to form a complex. This complex in the presence of initiation factor 1 (IF-1) attaches the anticodon of the tRNA to the first codon of the message to form an initiation complex with the 40S ribosomal subunit. Upon release of the initiation factors (IF-1, IF-2, and IF-3), the 60S ribosomal subunit attaches and the GTP is hydrolyzed. The formation of the 80S ribosome is thus complete.

The complete ribosome contains 2 sites for tRNA molecules. The peptidyl or **P site** contains the peptidyl-tRNA attached to its codon on the mRNA. The aminoacyl or **A site** contains the aminoacyl-tRNA attached to its respective codon on the mRNA. With the formation of the initiation complex for the first codon, the aminoacyl-tRNA molecule enters at what will become the P site, leaving the A site free. Thus, the reading frame is defined by attachment of the tRNA to the first codon to be translated in the mRNA. The recognition of this specific initiating codon is appar-

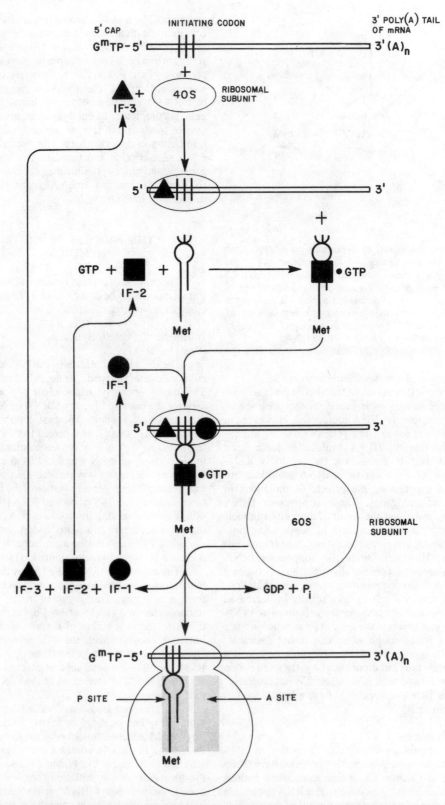

Figure 29–12. Diagrammatic representation of the initiation of protein synthesis on the mRNA template containing a 5′ cap and 3′ poly(A) terminus. IF-1, IF-2, and IF-3 represent initiaion factor 1, initiation factor 2, and initiation factor 3, respectively; and the hairpinlike structure with Met at one end represents the methionyl tRNA. The P site and the A site represent the peptidyl-tRNA and aminoacyl-tRNA binding sites of the ribosome, respectively.

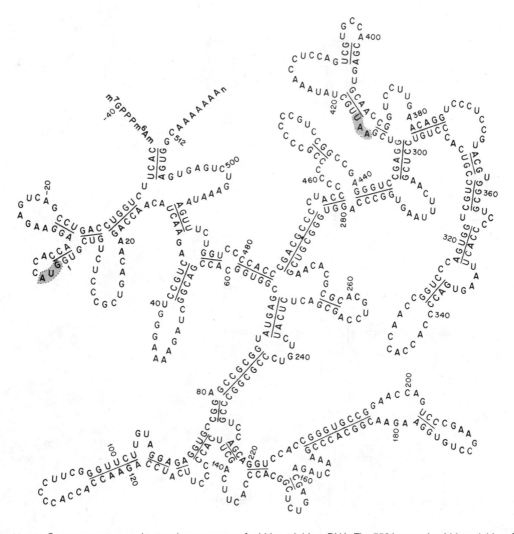

Figure 29–13. Computer-generated secondary structure of rabbit α-globin mRNA. The 552 base-pair rabbit α-globin mRNA sequence is depicted in the most stable base-pairing arrangement generated by a computer program. The nucleotides (A, G, C, U) are numbered starting at the first nucleotide following the initiation codon. The initiation and the termination codons are shaded. The m represents methylation. Base-paired regions are indicated by the solid lines drawn parallel to the stem regions. (Reproduced, with permission, from Heindell HC & others: The primary sequence of rabbit α-globin mRNA. *Cell* 1978;**15**:43.)

ently dependent upon the secondary structure of the mRNA molecule (Fig 29–13) and a specific sequence of nucleotides complementary to the a segment of the 40S ribosomal RNA.

In prokaryotes, a specific aminoacyl-tRNA is involved in the initiation of synthesis of most, if not all, protein molecules. N-Formylmethionyl-tRNA initiates most proteins in prokaryotes. Although methionine is the N-terminal amino acid in many eukaryotic proteins, the methionyl-tRNA is not formylated in eukaryotes. In prokaryotes, the N-formylation of the methionyl on the tRNA seems to deceive the P site of the ribosome by appearing to be a peptide bond. There exists also in prokaryotes an enzyme capable of removing the N-terminal formyl moiety or N-terminal methionyl residue (or both) from proteins,

in many cases even before the complete protein molecule has been formed.

Elongation

In the complete 80S ribosome formed during the process of initiation, the A site is free. The binding of the proper aminoacyl-tRNA in the A site requires proper codon recognition. Elongation factor 1 (EF-1) forms a complex with GTP and the entering aminoacyl-tRNA (Fig 29–14). This complex then allows the aminoacyl-tRNA to enter the A site with the release of EF-1·GDP and phosphate. As shown in Fig 29-14, EF-1·GDP then recycles to EF-1·GTP with the aid of other soluble protein factors and GTP.

The α amino group of the new aminoacyl-tRNA in the A site carries out a nucleophilic attack on the

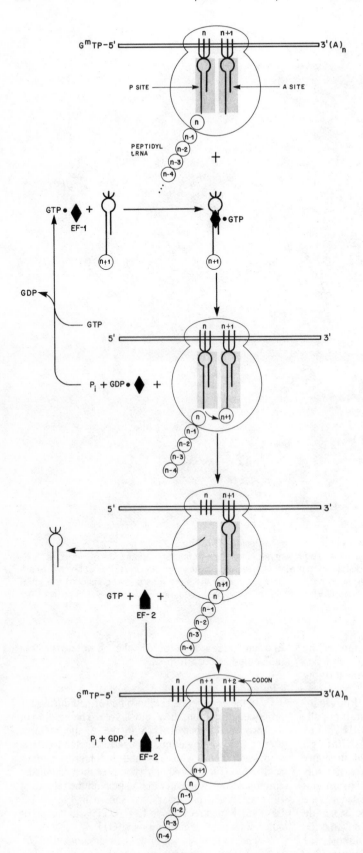

Figure 29–14. Diagrammatic representation of the peptide elongation process of protein synthesis. The small circles labeled n-1, n, n+1, etc represent the amino acid residues of the newly formed protein molecule. EF-1 and EF-2 represent elongation factors 1 and 2, respectively. The peptidyl-tRNA and aminoacyl-tRNA sites on the ribosome are represented by P site and A site, respectively.

esterified carboxyl group of the peptidyl-tRNA occupying the P site. This reaction is catalyzed by a protein component, **peptidyl transferase,** of the 60S ribosomal subunit. Because the amino acid on the aminoacyl-tRNA is already "activated," no further energy source is required for this reaction. The reaction results in attachment of the growing peptide chain to the tRNA in the A site.

Upon removal of the peptidyl moiety from the tRNA in the P site, the discharged tRNA quickly vacates the P site. Elongation factor 2 (EF-2) and GTP are responsible for the **translocation** of the newly formed peptidyl-tRNA at the A site into the vacated P site. The GTP required for EF-2 is hydrolyzed to GDP and phosphate during the translocation process. The translocation of the newly formed peptidyl-tRNA and its corresponding codon into the P site then frees the A site for another cycle of aminoacyl-tRNA codon recognition and elongation.

The energy requirements for the formation of one peptide bond include the equivalent of the hydrolysis of 2 ATP molecules to ADP and 2 GTP molecules to GDP. The charging of the tRNA molecule with the aminoacyl moiety requires the hydrolysis of an ATP to an AMP, equivalent to the hydrolysis of 2 ATPs to 2 ADPs and phosphates. The entry of the aminoacyl-tRNA into the A site results in the hydrolysis of one GTP to GDP. The translocation of the newly formed peptidyl-tRNA in the A site into the P site by EF-2 similarly results in the hydrolysis of GTP to GDP and phosphate.

Termination

After multiple cycles of elongation culminating in polymerization of the specific amino acids into a protein molecule, the nonsense or terminating codon of mRNA appears in the A site. There is no tRNA with an anticodon to recognize such a termination signal. **Releasing factors** are capable of recognizing that a termination signal resides in the A site (Fig 29–15). The releasing factor, in conjunction with GTP and the peptidyl transferase, promotes the hydrolysis of the bond between the peptide and the tRNA occupying the P site. This hydrolysis releases the protein and the tRNA from the P site. Upon hydrolysis and release, the **80S ribosome dissociates** into its 40S and 60S subunits, which are then recycled.

The releasing factors are proteins—one of which (releasing factor 1) hydrolyzes the peptide bond when a U·A·A or U·A·G codon occupies the A site. The other, releasing factor 2, hydrolyzes the peptidyl-tRNA bond when either the U·A·A or the U·G·A codon occupies the A site.

Many ribosomes can translate the same mRNA molecule simultaneously. Because of their relatively large size, the ribosome particles cannot attach to an mRNA any closer than 80 nucleotides apart. Multiple ribosomes on the same mRNA molecule form a **polyribosome** or "polysome." In an unrestricted system, the number of ribosomes attached to an mRNA and thus the size of polyribosomes correlates positively with the length of the mRNA molecule. The mass of the mRNA molecule is, of course, quite small compared to the mass of even a single ribosome.

A single ribosome is capable of translating in 10 seconds about 400 codons into a protein with a molecular weight of approximately 40,000.

Polyribosomes actively synthesizing proteins can exist as free particles in the cellular cytoplasm or may be attached to sheets of membranous cytoplasmic material referred to as endoplasmic reticulum. The attachment of the particulate polyribosomes to the endoplasmic reticulum is responsible for their "rough" appearance as seen by electron microscopy. The proteins synthesized by the attached polyribosomes are extruded into the cisternal space between the sheets of rough endoplasmic reticulum and are exported from there. Some of the protein products of the rough endoplasmic reticulum are packaged by the Golgi apparatus into zymogen particles for eventual exportation. (See Chapter 31.) The polyribosomal particles free in the cytosol are responsible for the synthesis of proteins required for intracellular functions.

Protein Processing

Some animal viruses, notably poliovirus (an RNA virus), synthesize long polycistronic proteins from one long mRNA molecule. These protein molecules are subsequently cleaved at specific sites to provide the several specific proteins required for viral function. In animal cells, many proteins are modified following their synthesis from the mRNA template. Insulin, a low-molecular-weight protein having 2 polypeptide chains with interchain and intrachain disulfide bridges, is synthesized as a proinsulin molecule. The single polypeptide proinsulin folds to allow the disulfide bridges to form, and then a specific protease clips out a segment at the head of the hairpin (Fig 35–11). These posttranslational modifications are responsible for generation of the functional insulin molecule.

Many other peptide hormones are synthesized as **prohormones** that require modification before attaining biologic activity. Many of the posttranslational modifications involve the removal of N-terminal amino acid residues by specific aminopeptidases. Collagen, an abundant protein in the extracellular spaces of higher eukaryotes, is synthesized as procollagen. Three procollagen molecules, frequently not identical in sequence, align themselves in a way dependent upon the existence of specific amino terminal peptides. Specific enzymes then carry out hydroxylations and oxidations of specific amino acid residues within the procollagen molecules to provide cross-links for greater stability. Amino terminal peptides are cleaved off the molecule to form the final product, a strong, insoluble collagen molecule. (See Chapter 33.)

Inhibitors of Protein Synthesis

Many clinically effective antibiotics act by specifically inhibiting protein synthesis in prokaryotic organisms. Most of these inhibitors interact specifically

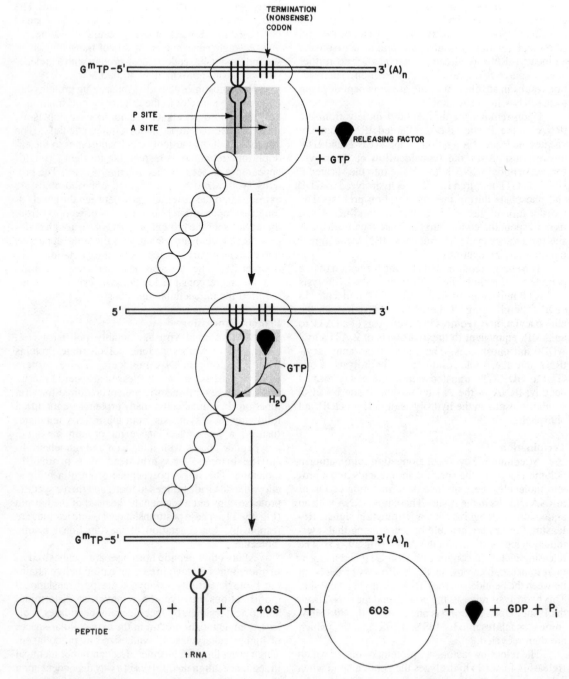

Figure 29–15. Diagrammatic representation of the termination process of protein synthesis. The peptidyl-tRNA and aminoacyl-tRNA sites are indicated as P site and A site, respectively. The hydrolysis of the peptidyl-tRNA complex is shown by the entry of H_2O.

with the proteins of prokaryotic ribosomes. A number of the effective antibiotics do not interact with the specific proteins of eukaryotic ribosomal particles and are thus not toxic to eukaryotes.

Puromycin, the structure of which is shown in Fig 29–16, is a structural analog of tyrosinyl-tRNA. Puromycin is incorporated via the A site on the ribo-

some into the carboxyl terminal position of a peptide but causes the premature release of the polypeptide. Puromycin, as a tyrosinyl-tRNA analog, effectively inhibits protein synthesis in both prokaryotes and eukaryotes.

Diphtheria toxin, an exotoxin of *Corynebacterium diphtheriae* infected with a specific lysogenic

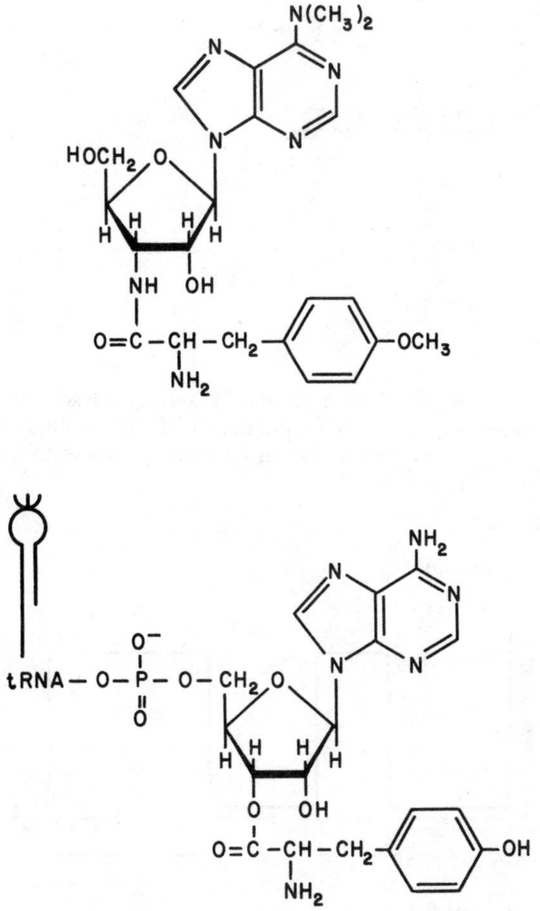

Table 29–3. Antibiotic inhibitors of translation.

	Eukaryotes (Cytoplasm)	Eukaryotes (Mitochondria)	Prokaryotes
Initiation			
Aurintricarboxylic acid	–	–	+
Elongation			
Amicetin	?	?	+
Anisomycin	–	?	+
Chloramphenicol	–	+	+
Cycloheximide	+	–	–
Fusidic acid	?	?	+
Lincocin	–	?	+
Puromycin	+	+	+
Sparsomycin	+	+	+
Tetracyclines	–	+	+
Termination			
Anisomycin	?	?	*
Amicetin	?	?	+
Erythromycin	–	+	+
Lincocin	?	?	*
Sparsomycin	+	+	+
Streptomycin	+	±	+

+ = inhibition; – = no inhibition; * = stimulation; ? = unknown.

phage, catalyzes the ADP ribosylation of EF-2 in mammalian cells. This modification inactivates EF-2 and thereby specifically inhibits mammalian protein synthesis. Many organisms such as mice are resistant to diphtheria toxin. This resistance is due to inability of diphtheria toxin to cross the cell membrane rather than to insensitivity of mouse EF-2 to diphtheria toxin–catalyzed ADP ribosylation by NAD.

Table 29–3 summarizes the effects of some antibiotics on the 3 phases of protein synthesis.

Figure 29–16. The comparative structures of the antibiotic puromycin and the 3' terminal portion of tyrosyl-tRNA.

•   •   •

References

Barrell BG & others: Different pattern of codon recognition by mammalian mitochondrial tRNAs. *Proc Nat Acad Sci USA* 1980;**77**:3164.

Drake JW, Baltz RH: The biochemistry of mutagenesis. *Annu Rev Biochem* 1976;**45**:11.

Forget BG: Molecular genetics of human hemoglobin synthesis. *Ann Intern Med* 1979;**91**:605.

Haselkorn R, Rothman-Denes LB: Protein synthesis. *Annu Rev Biochem* 1973;**42**:397.

Roth JR: Frameshift mutations. *Annu Rev Genet* 1974;**8**:319.

Schafritz DA & others: Evidence for the role of M^{7}G$^{5'}$-phosphate group in recognition of eukaryotic mRNA by inhibition factor

IF-M$_3$. *Nature* 1976;**261**:291.

Schlessinger D: Genetic and antibiotic modification of protein synthesis. *Annu Rev Genet* 1974;**8**:135.

Weatherall D: Molecular pathology of the thalassemia disorders. *West J Med* 1976;**124**:388.

Weatherall D, Clegg J: Recent developments in the molecular genetics of human hemoglobin. *Cell* 1979;**16**:487.

Weissbach G, Ochoa S: Soluble factors required for eukaryotic protein synthesis. *Annu Rev Biochem* 1976;**45**:191.

Wool I: The structure and function of eukaryotic ribosomes. *Annu Rev Biochem* 1979;**48**:719.

30 | Regulation of Gene Expression

David W. Martin, Jr., MD

The genetic information present in each somatic cell of a metazoan organism is practically identical. The exceptions are found in those few cells that have amplified or rearranged genes in order to carry out specialized cellular functions. The expression of the genetic information must be regulated during ontogeny and differentiation of the organism and its cellular components. Furthermore, in order for the organism to adapt to its environment and to conserve energy and nutrients, the expression of genetic information must be responsive to extrinsic signals. As organisms have evolved, more sophisticated regulatory mechanisms have appeared to provide the organism and its cells with the responsiveness necessary for survival in its complex environment. Mammalian cells possess only about 1000 times more genetic information than does the bacterium *Escherichia coli;* however, much of this additional genetic information is involved in the regulation of gene expression.

In simple terms, there are only 2 types of gene regulation: **positive regulation** and **negative regulation** (Table 30–1). When the expression of genetic information is quantitatively **increased** by the presence of a specific regulatory molecule, regulation is said to be **positive;** whereas when the expression of genetic information is **diminished** by the presence of a specific regulatory molecule, regulation is said to be **negative.** The molecule mediating the negative regulation is said to be a negative regulator; that mediating positive regulation is a positive regulator. However, a **double negative** has the effect of acting as a **positive.** Thus, an effector which inhibits the function of a negative regulator will appear to bring about a positive regulation. In many regulated systems that appear to be induced, they are, in fact, derepressed at the molecular level. (See Chapter 9 for a description of these terms.)

In biologic organisms, there are 3 types of temporal responses to a regulatory signal. These 3 responses are depicted diagrammatically in Fig 30–1 as rate of gene expression in temporal response to an inducing signal.

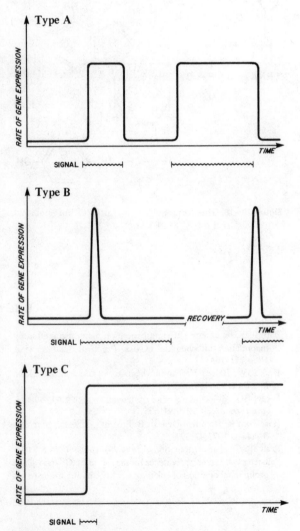

Figure 30–1. Diagrammatic representations of the responses of the rate of expression of a gene to specific regulatory signals such as a hormone.

Table 30–1. Effects of positive and negative regulation on gene expression.

	Rate of Gene Expression	
	Negative Regulation	**Positive Regulation**
Regulator present	Decreased	Increased
Regulator absent	Increased	Decreased

A **type A response** is characterized by an increased rate of gene expression that is **dependent** upon the continued presence of the inducing signal. When the inducing signal is removed, the rate of gene expression diminishes to its basal level, but the rate repeatedly increases in response to the reappearance of the specific signal. This type of response is commonly observed in many higher organisms after exposures to inducers such as steroid hormones (see Chapter 34).

A **type B response** exhibits an increased rate of gene expression that is **transient** even in the continued presence of the regulatory signal. After the regulatory signal has terminated and the cell has been allowed to recover, a second transient response to a subsequent regulatory signal may be observed. This type of response may commonly occur during development of an organism when only the transient appearance of a specific gene product is required although the signal persists.

The **type C response** pattern exhibits, in response to the regulatory signal, an increased rate of gene expression that persists **indefinitely** even after the termination of the signal. The signal acts as a trigger in this pattern. The response is typical of a differentiative process. Once the gene expression is initiated in the cell, it cannot be terminated even in the daughter cells; it is therefore an irreversible and inherited alteration. The methylation of DNA bases may well be responsible for this effect.

Models for the Study of the Regulation of Gene Expression

In the last 20 years, with the understanding of how information flows from the gene through a messenger RNA to a specific protein molecule, there has developed sophisticated knowledge of the regulation of gene expression in prokaryotic cells. Most of the detailed knowledge about molecular mechanisms has been limited until recent years to prokaryotic and lower eukaryotic systems. This was due to the more advanced genetic analyses first available in the primitive organisms but yet to be obtained for mammalian cells or organisms. In this chapter, much of the discussion will center on prokaryotic systems. The impressive genetic studies will not be described, but rather what may be termed the physiology of gene expression will be discussed. However, nearly all of the conclusions about this physiology have been derived from genetic studies.

Before the physiology can be explained, a few specialized genetic terms must be defined for prokaryotic systems. A glossary is provided following Chapter 31.

The **cistron** is the smallest unit of genetic expression. As described in Chapter 9, some enzymes and other protein molecules are composed of 2 or more nonidentical subunits. Thus, the so-called "one gene, one enzyme" concept is now known not to be necessarily valid. The cistron is the genetic unit coding for the structure of the subunit of a protein molecule, acting as it does as the smallest unit of genetic expression. Thus, the one gene, one enzyme idea might more accurately be regarded as a **one cistron, one subunit concept.**

An **inducible gene** is one the expression of which increases in response to an **inducer,** a specific regulatory signal.

The expression of some genes is **constitutive,** meaning that they are expressed at a reasonably high rate in the absence of any specific regulatory signal. As the result of mutation, some inducible gene products become constitutively expressed. A mutation resulting in constitutive expression of what was formerly an inducible gene is called a constitutive mutation.

The Lac Operon

François Jacob and Jacques Monod in 1961 described their **operon** model in what is now regarded as a classic paper. Their hypothesis was to a large extent based on observations on the regulation of lactose metabolism by the intestinal bacterium *E coli*. The molecular mechanisms responsible for the regulation of the genes involved in the metabolism of lactose are among the best understood in any organism. β-Galactosidase hydrolyzes the β-galactoside lactose to galactose and glucose (Fig 30–2). The structural (Z) gene

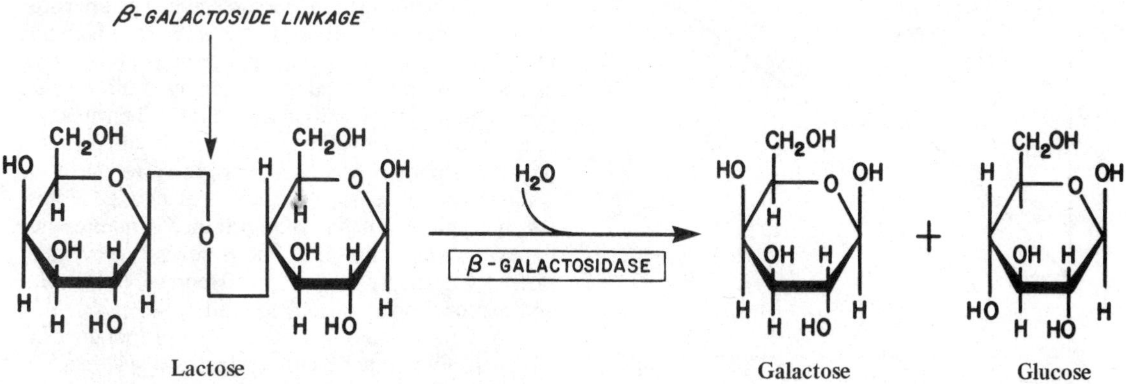

Figure 30–2. The hydrolysis by the enzyme β-galactosidase of lactose to galactose and glucose.

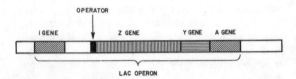

Figure 30–3. The positional relationships of the structural and regulatory genes of the lac operon.

for β-galactosidase is clustered with the genes responsible for the permeation of galactose into the cell (Y) and for galactoside acetylase (A), whose function is not understood. The structural genes for these 3 enzymes are physically associated with regulatory genes to constitute the **lac operon** as depicted in Fig 30–3. This genetic arrangement of the structural genes and their regulatory genes allows for the **coordinate expression** of the 3 enzymes concerned with lactose metabolism.

When *E coli* is presented with lactose or some specific lactose analogs, the expression of the activities of β-galactosidase, galactoside permease, and galactoside acetylase is increased 10-fold to 100-fold. This is a type A response, as seen in Fig 30–1. Upon removal of the signal, ie, the inducer, the rate of synthesis of these 3 enzymes declines. Since there is no significant degradation of these enzymes in bacteria, the level of β-galactosidase as well as those of the other 2 enzymes will remain the same unless they are diluted out by cell division.

When *E coli* is exposed to both lactose and glucose as sources of carbon, the organisms first metabolize the glucose and then temporarily cease growing until the genes of the lac operon become induced to provide the ability to metabolize lactose. This type of growth in the presence of 2 carbon sources such as glucose and lactose is biphasic; it is termed **diauxie** (Fig 30–4).

Although lactose is present from the beginning of the bacterial growth phase, the cell does not commence

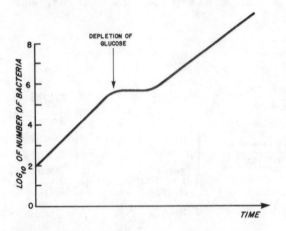

Figure 30–4. The diauxic growth of *Escherichia coli* on a mixture of glucose and lactose.

to induce those enzymes necessary for catabolism of lactose until the glucose has been exhausted. This phenomenon was first thought to be attributable to the repression of the lactose operon by some catabolite of glucose; hence it was termed **catabolite repression.** It is now known that "catabolite repression" is in fact mediated by a **catabolite gene activator protein (CAP)** and **cyclic AMP (cAMP).** The expression of many inducible enzyme systems or operons in *E coli* and other prokaryotes is sensitive to catabolite repression, as discussed below.

The physiology of the induction of the lac operon is well understood at the molecular level, and it will now be described (Fig 30–5).

The expression of the normal **i gene** of the lac operon is constitutive; it is expressed at a constant rate, resulting in the formation of the subunits of the **lac repressor.** Four identical subunits of MW 38,000 assemble into a lac repressor molecule. The repressor protein molecule, the product of the i gene, has a high affinity (K_d about 10^{-13}M) for the operator locus. The operator locus is a region of double-stranded DNA 27 base pairs long with a 2-fold rotational symmetry (indicated by solid lines about the dotted axis) in a region that is 21 base pairs long, as shown below:

$$5'-\overline{\text{AATTGTGAGC}} \; \text{G} \; \overline{\text{GAT}} \; \overline{\text{AACAATT}}$$
$$3'-\underline{\text{TTAACACTCG}} \; \text{C} \; \underline{\text{CTA}} \underline{\text{TTGTTAA}}$$

The minimum effective size of an operator for lac repressor binding is 17 base pairs (boldface letters in above sequence). At any one time, only 2 subunits of the repressors appear to bind to the operator, and within the 17 base pair region at least one base of each base pair is involved in the lac repressor recognition and binding. Thus, the binding occurs in both the **major** and, to some extent, **minor grooves** of the double helical DNA of the operator. The amino acid residues in positions 1–52 of the repressor subunits seem to recognize DNA nonspecifically, whereas the amino acid residues in positions 53–58 of the repressor specifically bind to the 17 base pair region, a region about 6–7 nm long. The amino acid residues in positions 74 and 75 are particularly involved in the binding of the inducer to the repressor molecule. The **operator locus** is between the **promoter site,** at which the DNA-dependent RNA polymerase attaches to commence transcription, and the beginning of the **Z gene,** the structural gene for β-galactosidase. When attached to the operator locus, the repressor molecule prevents the transcription of the operator locus as well as of the distal structural genes, Z, Y, and A. Thus, the repressor molecule is a **negative regulator;** in its presence the expression of the Z, Y, and A genes is prevented. There are normally present 20–40 repressor molecules and one or 2 operator loci per cell.

A lactose analog that is capable of inducing the lac operon while not itself serving as a substrate for β-galactosidase is called a **gratuitous inducer.** The addition of lactose or of a gratuitous inducer to bacteria growing on a limited carbon source (such as succinate)

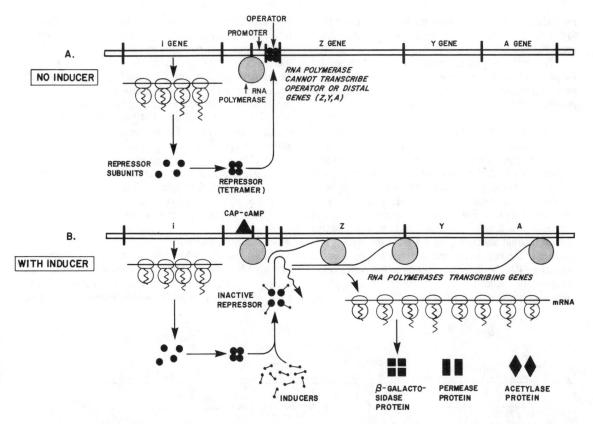

Figure 30–5. The mechanism of repression and derepression of the lactose operon. When no inducer is present *(A)*, the i gene products that are synthesized constitutively form a repressor molecule which binds at the operator locus to prevent the binding of RNA polymerase at the promoter locus and thus to prevent the subsequent transcription of the Z, Y, and A structural genes. When inducer is present, the constitutively expressed i gene forms repressor molecules that are inactivated by the inducer and cannot bind to the operator locus. In the presence of cAMP and its binding protein (CAP), the RNA polymerase can transcribe the structural genes Z, Y, and A, and the polycistronic mRNA molecule formed can be translated into the corresponding protein molecules β-galactosidase, permease, and acetylase, allowing for the catabolism of lactose.

results in the prompt induction of β-galactosidase, permease, and acetylase. Small amounts of the gratuitous inducer or of lactose are able to enter the cell even in the absence of permease. The repressor molecules, both those attached to the operator loci and those free in the cytosol, have an affinity for the inducer. The binding of the inducer to a repressor molecule attached to the operator locus will cause the repressor to be detached. If DNA-dependent RNA polymerase has already attached to the sense strand at the promoter site, transcription will commence. The polymerase generates a polycistronic mRNA, the 5′ terminus of which is complementary to the sense strand of the operator. In such a manner, an inducer derepresses the lac operon and allows the transcription of the structural genes for galactosidase, galactoside permease, and galactoside acetylase. The translation of the polycistronic mRNA can occur even before the transcription is completed. The derepression of the lac operon allows the cell to synthesize the enzymes necessary to catabolize lactose as an energy source. In order for the RNA polymerase to attach at the promoter

site, there must also be present the catabolite gene activation protein (CAP) to which cAMP is attached. By an independent mechanism, the bacterium accumulates cAMP only when it is starved for a source of carbon. In the presence of glucose or of glycerol in concentrations sufficient for growth, the bacteria will lack sufficient cAMP to bind to CAP. Thus, in the presence of glucose or glycerol, cAMP-saturated CAP is lacking, so that the DNA-dependent RNA polymerase cannot commence the transcription of the lac operon. In the presence of the CAP-cAMP complex on the promoter site, transcription then occurs. Thus, the CAP-cAMP regulator is acting as a **positive regulator** because its presence is required for gene expression. This phenomenon accounts for the diauxic growth of *E coli* on glucose and lactose.

When the i gene has been mutated so that its product, the lac repressor, is not capable of binding to DNA, the organism will exhibit **constitutive expression** of the lac operon. An organism with an i gene mutation that prevents the binding of an inducer to the repressor will remain repressed even in the presence of the inducer molecule because the inducer cannot bind to the repressor at the operator locus in order to derepress the operon.

Bacteria harboring mutations in their operator locus such that the operator sequence will not bind a normal repressor molecule are constitutive for the expression of the lac operon genes.

The Arabinose Operon

The structural genes of the arabinose operon in *E coli* are responsible for the formation of 3 enzymes required to metabolize arabinose. AraD, AraA, and AraB code for the enzymes L-ribulose-5-phosphate-4-epimerase, L-arabinose isomerase, and L-ribulokinase, respectively. (Fig 30–6.) The protein product of the AraC gene acts as a regulator and exists in 2 active conformational states. In the **P1** state the AraC gene product is the **repressor** and in the **P2** state it is the **activator.** P1, the repressor, binds to the AraO gene, the operator locus, to prevent the expression of the arabinose operon. The presence of L-arabinose, the

first substrate for the pathway, changes the conformation of P1, the repressor, to P2, the activator. P2 binds to the I gene, also a regulatory site, and there promotes the expression of the arabinose gene. Thus, **P1 is a negative regulator and P2 a positive regulator,** and both are products of the **same gene,** AraC. The arabinose operon is also subject to catabolite repression. As expected, CAP-cAMP must bind at the controlling site in order for the structural genes of the arabinose operon to be expressed. Similarly, another regulatory nucleotide, guanosine tetraphosphate (ppGpp), stimulates the expression of the arabinose operon in a cell-free system. The mechanism of interaction of this latter regulatory nucleotide and the CAP-cAMP binding site is as yet unknown.

The Histidine Operon

Salmonella typhimurium is capable of synthesizing histidine from ATP and PPriboseP when this α-amino acid is not present in the environment. However, when it is present in the environment, histidine

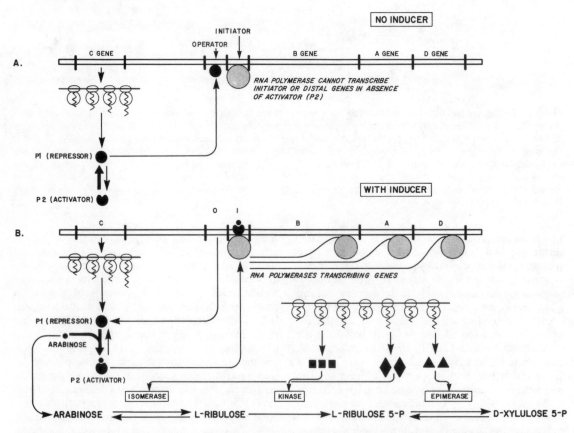

Figure 30–6. Diagrammatic representation of the repression *(A)* and induction *(B)* of the arabinose operon. When no inducer is present *(A),* the C gene product—the repressor (P1)—binds at the operator locus, and the initiator locus lacks the activator (P2). Both conditions prevent the transcription of the distal B, A, and D genes by RNA polymerase. When inducer (arabinose) is present *(B),* arabinose binds the C gene product—the P1 repressor—to form an activator (P2) molecule that can bind at the initiator site. The conversion of the P1 repressor to a P2 activator molecule not only shifts the equilibrium of the P1 repressor off the operator locus, but the presence of the P2 activator on the initiator locus allows the RNA polymerase to transcribe the distal structural genes B, A, and D. A messenger RNA transcribed from these genes can then be translated into the corresponding enzymes ribulokinase, isomerase, and polymerase, thus allowing the catabolism of arabinose.

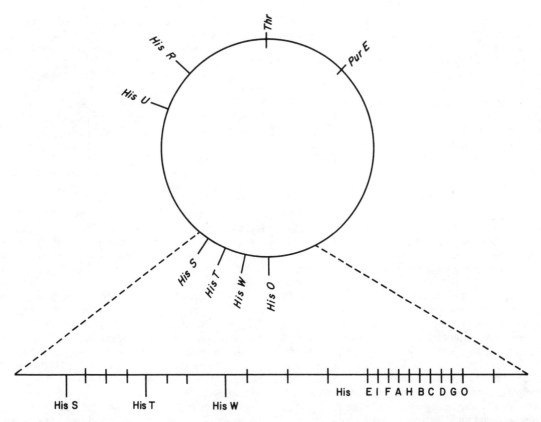

Figure 30–7. The genetic map of *Salmonella typhimurium* in which the His genes are represented and their relationship to threonine (Thr) and Pur E loci shown. (The portion of the *Salmonella* genome that contains most of the His genes has been expanded in a linear form in the lower portion of the diagram.) (Redrawn and reproduced, with permission, from Brenner M, Ames BN: The histidine operon and its regulation. Chap 11 in: *Metabolic Regulation.* Vogel HJ [editor]. Vol 5 in: *Metabolic Pathways,* 3rd ed. Greenberg DM [editor]. Academic Press, 1971.)

prevents the formation of those enzymes responsible for the de novo synthesis of histidine. Coding for the 10 enzymes required for the de novo synthesis of histidine is provided by 10 structural genes, all of which are genetically linked as the **histidine (His) operon.** The linkage map is shown in Fig 30–7.

In Table 30–2, the products of the 10 structural genes are identified by the name of the enzyme. All 10 enzymes of the pathway are **coordinately expressed.**

Table 30–2. Relationship of His genes to histidine pathway enzymes.

His Gene	Enzyme
G	Phosphoribosyl-ATP synthetase
D	Dehydrogenase
C	Aminotransferase
B	Dehydratase
B	Phosphatase
H	Amidotransferase
A	Isomerase
F	Cyclase
I	Phosphoribosyl-AMP hydrolase
E	Phosphoribosyl-ATP pyrophosphohydrolase
S	Histidyl-tRNA synthetase

There are in *S typhimurium* 6 gene mutations in 6 different genes that can cause constitutive expression of the His operon. The **His O** gene is the operator, and mutants in this region have an altered operator-promotor function. The **His S** gene codes for the histidinyl tRNA synthetase; **His R** gene is the structural gene for histidine tRNA. The **His W** gene codes for the tRNA maturation enzyme; and the **His T** gene codes for a protein which is responsible for the modification of 2 uridine residues to form pseudouridine in the His tRNA. The function of the **His U** gene is unknown. From the characterization of these genes, which, when altered, cause constitutive expression of the His operon, Ames and his colleagues have concluded that the histidinyl tRNA is involved directly or indirectly in the regulation of the expression of the His operon.

It has also been demonstrated that the first enzyme of the histidine de novo synthetic pathway (N-1,5′-phosphoribosyl-ATP:pyrophosphate phosphoribosyl transferase) (the product of the His G gene) specifically blocks the transcription of the histidine operon in vitro. It is not evident whether the histidinyl tRNA interacts with the His G gene product to regulate in a negative manner the expression of the 10 structural genes of that operon.

Regulation of Immunoglobulin Gene Expression

Some of the most interesting and perplexing questions raised by biologists in recent decades concern the genetic and molecular basis of antibody diversity (see Chapter 39). In addition, advances in immunology have made it apparent that as cells of the humoral immunity system differentiate, they produce antibodies with the same specificity but different effector functions. Within the last several years, with the aid of DNA recombinant technology, many laboratories have contributed greatly to the understanding of the genetic basis of antibody diversity and regulation of the expression of immunoglobulin genes during development and differentiation. Currently, the regulation of gene expression in mammals is probably best understood in the immunoglobulin system.

As described in Chapter 28, the coding segments responsible for the generation of specific protein molecules are frequently not contiguous in the mammalian genome. The coding segments for the variable and the constant domains of the immunoglobulin (antibody) light chain were the first recognized to be separated in the genome. As described in more detail in Chapter 39, immunoglobulin molecules are composed of 2 types of polypeptide chains, light (L) and heavy (H) chains (Fig 39–4). The L and H chains are each divided into N-terminal variable (V) and carboxy-terminal constant (C) regions. The V regions are responsible for the recognition of antigens (foreign molecules) and the constant regions for effector functions that determine how the antibody molecule will dispense with the antigen.

There are 3 unlinked families of genes responsible for immunoglobulin molecule structure. Two families are responsible for the light chains (λ and κ chains) and one family for heavy chains.

Each **light chain** is encoded by 3 distinct segments, the variable (V_L), the joining (J_L), and the constant (C_L) elements. The mammalian haploid genome contains over 500 V_L segments, five or six J_L segments, and perhaps ten or twenty C_L segments. During the differentiation of a lymphoid B cell, a V_L segment is brought from a distant site on the same chromosome to a position closer to the region of the genome containing the J_L and C_L segments. This **DNA rearrangement** then allows the V_L, J_L, and C_L segments to be transcribed as a single mRNA precursor and subsequently processed to generate the mRNA for a specific antibody light chain. By rearrangement of the various V_L, J_L, and C_L segments in the genome, the immunity system can generate an immensely diverse library of antigen-specific immunoglobulin molecules.

This DNA rearrangement is referred to as **V-J joining** of the light chain.

The **heavy chain** is encoded by 4 gene segments: the V_H, the D (diversity), the J_H, and the C_H DNA segments. The variable region of the heavy chain is generated by joining the V_H with a D and a J_H segment. The resulting V_H-D-J_H DNA region is in turn linked to a C_H gene, of which there are 8. These C_H genes (C_μ,

C_δ, $C_\gamma 3$, $C_\gamma 1$, $C_\gamma 2b$, $C_\gamma 2a$, C_α, and C_ϵ) determine the immunoglobulin class or subclass—IgM, IgG, IgG, etc—of the immunoglobulin molecule (see Chapter 39).

During its differentiation, a B cell that secretes antibody to a **specific antigen** will secrete antibodies of different classes having the same antigen specificity but different biologic roles. The different classes of immunoglobulins contain the same light chains and V_H regions but different C_H regions. Thus, a single B cell and its clonal derivatives can undergo "class switching." Class switching is the result of a second type of **DNA rearrangement** occurring during differentiation of the immunity system.

Developmentally and temporally, the **V-J joining** for light chain expression and the **V-D-J joining** for the heavy chain expression **precede the class switching DNA rearrangement.**

V-J Joining

In the undifferentiated cell (eg, germ line cell), the κ-J gene (J_κ) is closely linked to the C_κ gene, but the gene segment for the κ-variable region (V_κ) is quite distant on the same chromosome. In a lymphoid cell destined to make antibodies, one of the 100 or more V_κ gene segments (coding for amino acids 1–95 of the L chain) join to one of any of the four J_κ gene segments (amino acids 96–107) by a process that apparently involves deletion of the DNA originally separating the V_κ and J_κ genes. This results in formation of a V_κ region gene that encodes all 107 amino acids as an uninterrupted nucleotide sequence. The J_κ gene segment is sufficiently close to the C_κ gene so that the intervening sequence can be eliminated from the primary transcript during nuclear RNA processing (see Chapter 28).

Both the V_κ-J_κ and the similar V_λ-J_λ gene rearrangements seem to involve 2 short conserved sequences that exist in the direction **3′ to the V segment** and **5′ to the J segment,** close to the point of recombination. The 2 conserved sequences 3′ to the V segment are the heptamer CACAGTG and the nonamer ACAAAAACC. These 2 conserved sequences 3′ to the V segments are separated by 11 or 12 nonconserved bases in V_κ and by 22 or 23 bases in the V_λ segments.

The conserved sequences 5′ to the J_L segments are the heptamer CACTGTG and the nonamer GGTTTTTGT. In the J_κ segments, these 2 conserved sequences are separated by 21–24 bases and in the V_κ segments by 12 bases. There are 2 striking features of these conserved sequences. First, the conserved **sequences of the J_L segments are inverse complements of the conserved sequences in the V_L segments.** Second, the **length** of the nonconserved sequence separating the heptamers and the nonamers is highly conserved. Accordingly, the conserved sequences can be arranged as shown in Fig 30–8 to juxtapose the 2 segments that must be recombined in the differentiated B cell. Interestingly, the conserved lengths of spacers separating the conserved sequences are close to one or to 2 complete turns of a DNA double

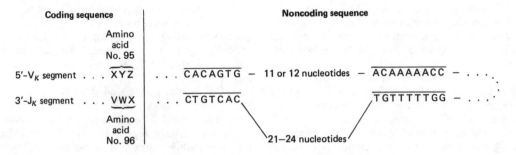

Figure 30–8. A possible arrangement of the conserved heptamers and nonamers in the noncoding, flanking regions of the V_κ and J_κ segments. Such an arrangement allows the coding regions of the genes to be juxtaposed for potential DNA rearrangement necessary to generate the gene for the V_L portion of the L chain.

helix. It has been proposed that 2 different but closely related **joining proteins** recognize the one- and 2-turn separated sequences, form a complex with these sequences to catalyze the recombining or splicing of the DNA, and generate the rearranged variable region sequence.

The variable region of the heavy chain involves three DNA segments, V_H, D, and J_H, which must be joined in a process involving two DNA rearrangements, since all 3 segments are separated. However, the J_H segments are found near the C_μ gene in the germ line genome. Remarkably, the conserved heptamer and nonamer sequences described for the light chain regions are found similarly placed in the noncoding regions 3′ to the V_H segment and 5′ to the J_H segment. In both of these positions, the conserved heptamer and nonamer sequences are interrupted by 22 or 23 nucleotides. The D segment, which is interspersed between the V_H and J_H segments in the rearranged genes, is flanked at both its 5′ and 3′ ends by the same conserved heptamer and nonamer sequences. However, the

members of each of these sets of heptamers and nonamers are interrupted by 12 nucleotides. As depicted in Fig 30–9, this permits an arrangement of the V_H, D, and J_H segments analogous to that of the V_H-J_H segments shown in Fig 30–8. This might allow for the same joining proteins to recognize the one- and 2-turn spaced sequences for both the light and heavy chain VJ DNA rearrangements.

Class Switching

During the ontogeny of an immunoglobulin-secreting B cell and its clonal derivatives, including the terminally differentiated plasma cell, the sequence of immunoglobulin production and secretion commences with IgM and subsequently switches to IgA or IgG, etc. In the germ line genome, the J_H segments are next to the C_μ genes; thus, once the V_H-D-J_H rearrangement has occurred, no further DNA rearrangement is necessary to allow transcription of an mRNA precursor for a μ chain. However, as differentiation proceeds and immunoglobulin production

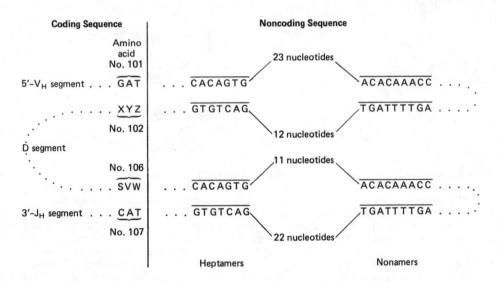

Figure 30–9. A possible arrangement of the conserved heptamers and nonamers in the noncoding, flanking regions of the V_H, D, and J_H segments. Such an arrangement allows the coding regions of the genes to be juxtaposed for potential DNA rearrangement necessary to generate the gene for the V_H portion of the H chain. Note the similarity to Fig 30–8.

switches from IgM to IgA, the V-D-J region of the parent B cell must be rearranged with a C_α gene to permit the transcription of an mRNA precursor for an alpha chain containing the same antigen-specific variable region.

The physical order of the 8 closely linked C_H genes is C_μ, C_δ, $C_\gamma 3$, $C_\gamma 1$, $C_\gamma 2b$, $C_\gamma 2a$, C_α, and C_ϵ. The **temporal order of the class switching is unidirectional** within this physical order, from left to right. In most cases studied to date, rearrangement of the C_H genes seems to involve deletion of those C_H genes 5' to (left of) the C_H gene joined to the V-D-J region.

An example of the recombination or rearrangement events leading to the complete $\gamma 2b$ gene is shown in Fig 30–10. The sequence first involves rearrangement of the V-D-J segments and subsequently the appropriate deletion or rearrangement of the C_H genes. The C region gene sequences coincide with the domains in the hinge region described in Chapter 39. The intervening sequences or introns that are transcribed and appear in the primary transcript are removed by RNA splicing events described in Chapter 28.

The switch sites appear to be different for different class switches but probably involve conserved sequences occurring in the appropriate flanking regions of the genes to be rearranged, analogous to those described above for V_L-J_L joining and V_H-D-J_H joining.

The information encoded in the genome can clearly be increased by this combinatorial joining of gene segments. This mechanism would not only increase the variable region diversity but would also effectively allow rearranged (useful or advantageous) information to be retained and perpetuated as a cell line alters its effector function during differentiation.

This seemingly complex DNA rearrangement during development and differentiation could be rather simply regulated by the appropriate induction and repression of specific joining proteins that recognize the highly conserved sequences flanking the coding sequences to be rearranged.

Different mRNAs From a Single Gene

As described above, the first immunoglobulin synthesized by differentiating B cells is IgM. How-

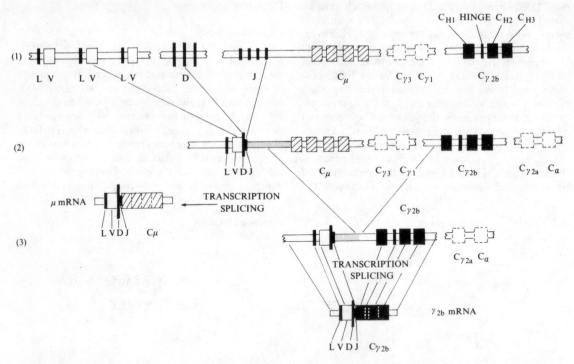

Figure 30–10. Recombination events leading to a complete γ2b gene. (1) The germ line DNA before rearrangement. There is a cluster of at least 50 genes (each with a short leader sequence L) coding for part of the variable (V) vegion, a cluster of D gene segments coding for most of the third hypervariable region, and some distance away there are four J segments that complete the V region coding sequence. The J segments lie about 8000 bases from the C_μ gene that lies at the start of a cluster containing all the C region genes. The C region gene sequences are interrupted by noncoding sequences to give a series of exons that coincide with the domains and the hinge region in the C region amino acid sequence. (2) In the first translocation event, one of each of the V, D, and J segments are recombined to give a complete μ chain transcription unit. The transcript is a copy of the gene as shown, but the noncoding sequences (introns) are removed by splicing events that lead to a continuous coding sequence in the μ mRNA. (3) A second translocation event, the heavy chain switch, deletes the C_μ, $C_\gamma 3$ and $C_\gamma 1$ gene segments and places the VDJ segment and part of the J-C_μ intron near the $C_\gamma 2b$ gene. Following transcription, the introns are removed by splicing, leading to a continuous coding sequence in the γ2b mRNA. (Reproduced, with permission, from Molgaard HV: Assembly of immunoglobulin heavy chain genes. *Nature* 1980;**286**:659.)

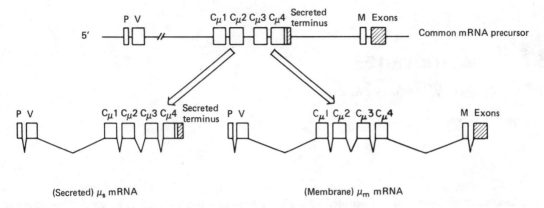

Figure 30–11. Splicing patterns deduced for μ_m and μ_s mRNAs. The μ_m and μ_s mRNAs are identical 5' to $C_\mu 4$. Raised boxes indicate exons. 3' Untranslated sequences are crosshatched. P refers to the signal peptide exon and V to the rearranged V_H exon. Bent lines indicate RNA splicing between exons. (Reproduced, with permission, from Early & others: Two mRNAs can be produced from a single immunoglobulin μ gene by alternative RNA processing pathways. *Cell* 1980;**20**:318.)

ever, the IgM of the earliest B cell is not extruded all the way through the membrane to be secreted. Instead, the C-terminal region of the μ chain remains trapped in the membrane as an integral protein (see Chapter 31). The μ chain of **secreted IgM** is referred to as μ_s, and the μ chain of the **membrane-associated IgM** is called μ_m. The μ_s and μ_m chains of the same B cell or B cell lineage contain identical amino acid sequences up to the very C-terminal region of the $C_\mu 4$ domain (Fig 39–4). The μ_s chain has a 20-amino-acid **hydrophilic** C-terminal segment after the $C_\mu 4$ domain, while the μ_m chain has a C-terminal segment containing 38 **hydrophobic** amino acids followed by -Lys-Val-Lys. This hydrophobic amino acid sequence can thus embed itself in the membrane bilayer up to the charged Lys residues (see Chapter 31). Accordingly, μ_s and μ_m must be translated from different mRNA molecules.

These different mRNA molecules have been isolated and their nucleotide sequence determined indirectly by DNA sequencing. The μ_m mRNA consists of 2700 bases and the μ_s mRNA 2400 bases. By isolating and sequencing the genomic region coding for these μ mRNA molecules, it has been possible to demonstrate

that they are both derived from a **common mRNA precursor** molecule as a result of **alternative RNA processing** pathways in the nucleus. Figure 30–11 depicts the 2 splicing patterns deduced for the μ_m and μ_s mRNA molecules transcribed from a single μ gene.

The last 187 nucleotides of the μ_s **mRNA** are transcribed directly from DNA contiguous with the 3' end of the $C_\mu 4$ domain. The μ_m **mRNA** does not contain these 187 nucleotides but instead contains 392 nucleotides transcribed from 2 exons located nearly 2000 base pairs 3' to the $C_\mu 4$ sequence. Thus, as depicted in Fig 30–11, 2 extra RNA splicing events must occur to provide the μ_m RNA containing the two M exons and not the nucleotide sequence corresponding to the secreted terminus. Again, from sequence data, it is clear that both splice sites satisfy the GT/AG rule (see Chapter 28) and exhibit complementarity to the U1 sequence described in Chapter 28.

Thus, it should be clear that during differentiation, RNA processing may be regulated to provide from the same gene the expression of protein molecules with subtly different but functionally important amino acid sequence differences.

● ● ●

References

Brenner M, Ames BN: The histidine operon and its regulation. *Metabolic Pathways* 1971;**5**:350.

Englesberg E, Wilcox G: Regulation: Positive control. *Annu Rev Genet* 1974;**8**:219.

Goldberg AL, St. John AC: Intracellular protein degradation in mammalian and bacterial cells. *Annu Rev Biochem* 1976;**45**:747.

Herskowitz I: Control of gene expression in bacteriophage

lambda. *Annu Rev Genet* 1973;**7**:289.

Jacob F, Monod J: Genetic regulatory mechanisms in protein synthesis. *J Mol Biol* 1961;**3**:318.

Seidman JG & others: Immunoglobulin V/J recombination is accompanied by deletion of joining site and variable region segments. *Proc Natl Acad Sci USA* 1980;**77**:6022.

Wu R, Bahl CP, Narang SA: Lactose operator-repressor interaction. *Curr Top Cell Regul* 1978;**13**:137.

31 | Membranes

David W. Martin, Jr., MD

Membranes are 2-dimensional oriented viscous solutions surrounding all living cells. By forming closed compartments around the cellular protoplasm, membranes separate one cell from another, thus permitting cellular individuality and differentiation. By separating the cell from its environment, membranes provide the main distinction between inside and outside. **Membranes act as barriers, with selective permeabilities** to material and information and thereby maintain the difference between inside and outside. The selective permeabilities are provided by **gates** and **pumps** as well as by specific **receptors** for enzymes, substrates, and signals such as hormones. Membranes also provide sites of energy transduction, such as in photosynthesis and oxidative phosphorylation.

Most membranes are composed predominantly of **lipids** and **proteins** but also contain **carbohydrates.** Different membranes have different ratios of proteins to lipids (Fig 31–1) that are dependent upon their specific functions. Membranes are asymmetric sheet-like enclosed structures with an inside and an outside. These sheetlike structures are noncovalent assemblies that are **thermodynamically stable but metabolically active.** Specific protein molecules are anchored in the membrane, where they carry out specific functions of the cell and the organism.

LIPID COMPOSITION

The lipid elements of membrane composition are **phospholipids, glycolipids,** and **sterols**—cholesterol in mammalian membranes.

Phospholipids

Of the 2 major phospholipid groups present in membranes, **phosphoglycerides** are the more common and consist of a glycerol backbone to which is attached 2 fatty acids in ester linkage and a **phosphorylated** alcohol (Fig 31–2). The fatty acid constituents are usually even-numbered carbon molecules, most commonly 14 or 16 carbons. They are unbranched and

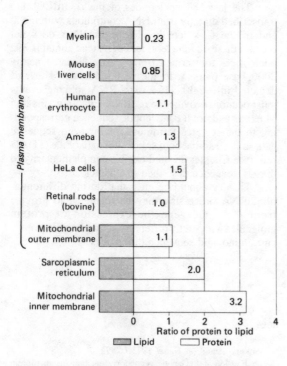

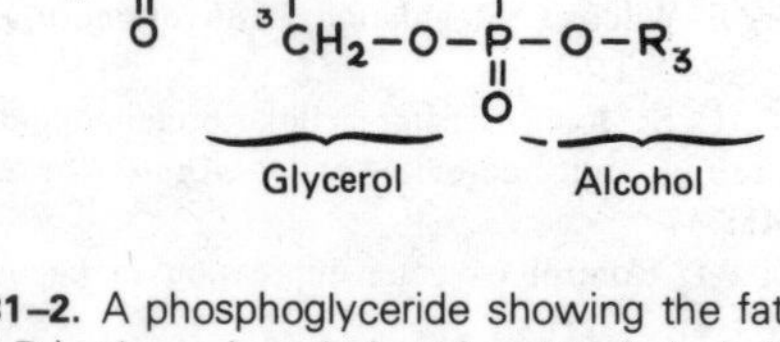

Figure 31–1. Proteins equal or exceed the quantity of lipid in nearly all membranes. The outstanding exception is myelin, thought to act as an insulator of the neuron—a function that would be incompatible with a high proportion of active (protein) molecules. (Reproduced, with permission, from Singer SJ: Architecture and topography of biologic membranes. Chapter 4 in *Cell Membranes: Biochemistry, Cell Biology & Pathology.* Weissmann G, Claiborne R [editors]. HP Publishing Co., 1975.)

Figure 31–2. A phosphoglyceride showing the fatty acids (R_1 and R_2), glycerol, and phosphorylated alcohol components. In phosphatidic acid, R_3 is hydrogen.

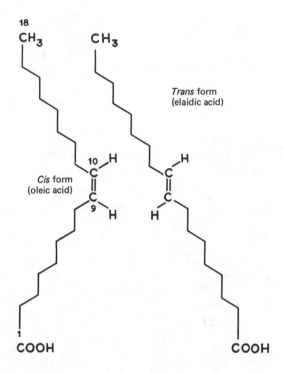

18
CH₃   CH₃

Trans form
(elaidic acid)

Cis form
(oleic acid)

10 H   H
   C   C

   C   C
9 H   H

COOH   COOH

Figure 31–3. Geometric isomerism of oleic (left) and elaidic (right) acids.

primary hydroxyl group of sphingosine is esterified to phosphorylcholine (Fig 31–5).

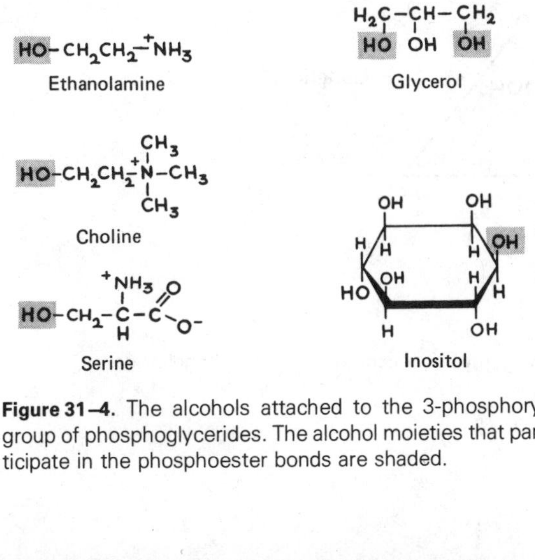

Glycolipids

The glycolipids, as the name implies, are sugar-containing lipids such as cerebrosides and gangliosides and are also derived from sphingosine. The cerebrosides and gangliosides differ from sphingomyelin by the nature of the moiety attached to the primary hydroxyl group of sphingosine. In sphingomyelin, a phosphorylcholine is attached to the alcoholic group. A **cerebroside** contains a single hexose moiety, glucose or galactose, at that site (Fig 31–5). A **ganglioside** contains a branched chain of up to 7 sugars attached to the primary alcohol moiety of sphingosine.

Sterols

The most common sterol in membranes is **cholesterol,** which exists almost exclusively in the plasma membranes of mammalian cells but can also be found in lesser quantity in mitochondria, Golgi complex, and nuclear membranes. Cholesterol is generally more abundant toward the outside of the plasma membrane.

All major lipids in membranes are **amphipathic** and are remarkably similar molecules, as can be seen from their space-filling models (Fig 31–6). An amphipathic molecule is one that contains both **hydrophobic** and **hydrophilic regions.** If the hydrophobic region were separated from the rest of the molecule, it would be insoluble in water but soluble in oil. Conversely, if the hydrophobic region were separated from the rest of the molecule, it would be insoluble in oil but soluble in water. The amphipathic membrane lipids have a polar head group and nonpolar tails; this can be represented as shown in Fig 31–7. **Detergents** are amphipathic molecules that have importance in biochemistry and in the household. The molecular structure of the detergent is not unlike that of a phospholipid.

can be saturated or unsaturated. The unsaturated fatty acid is almost exclusively of the *cis* configuration (Fig 31–3). The simplest phosphoglyceride is phosphatidate, which is a diacyl glycerol 3-phosphate, a key intermediate in the formation of all other phospholipids (see Chapter 16). In other phospholipids, the 3-phosphate is esterified to an alcohol such as ethanolamine, choline, serine, glycerol, or inositol (Fig 31–4).

The second class of phospholipids are the **sphingomyelins,** which contain a sphingosine backbone rather than glycerol. A fatty acid is attached by an amide linkage to the amino group of sphingosine. The

ORGANIZATION OF MEMBRANE LIPIDS

The amphipathic character of phospholipids suggests that the 2 regions of the molecule have incompatible solubilities; however, in a solvent such as water, phospholipids organize themselves into a form that thermodynamically satisfies both ends. A **micelle,** depicted in Fig 31–8, is a favored structure in which the hydrophobic regions are shielded from water while the hydrophilic polar groups are "happily" immersed in the aqueous environment. The stability of this structure is based on the fact that significant **free energy** is required to transfer a nonpolar molecule from a nonpolar medium to water. For example, 2.6 kcal of free energy are required to transfer 1 mol of methane from a nonpolar medium to an aqueous one. At the other end, much energy is required to transfer a polar moiety from water to a nonpolar medium. As an example, 6 kcal of free energy are required to transfer zwitterionic glycine

HO–CH₂CH₂–⁺NH₃
Ethanolamine

H₂C–CH–CH₂
HO OH OH
Glycerol

CH₃
HO–CH₂CH₂–⁺N–CH₃
CH₃
Choline

⁺NH₃ O
HO–CH₂–C–C–O⁻
H
Serine

OH   OH
H   H   OH
H
HO   OH   H
H   H
H   OH
Inositol

Figure 31–4. The alcohols attached to the 3-phosphoryl group of phosphoglycerides. The alcohol moieties that participate in the phosphoester bonds are shaded.

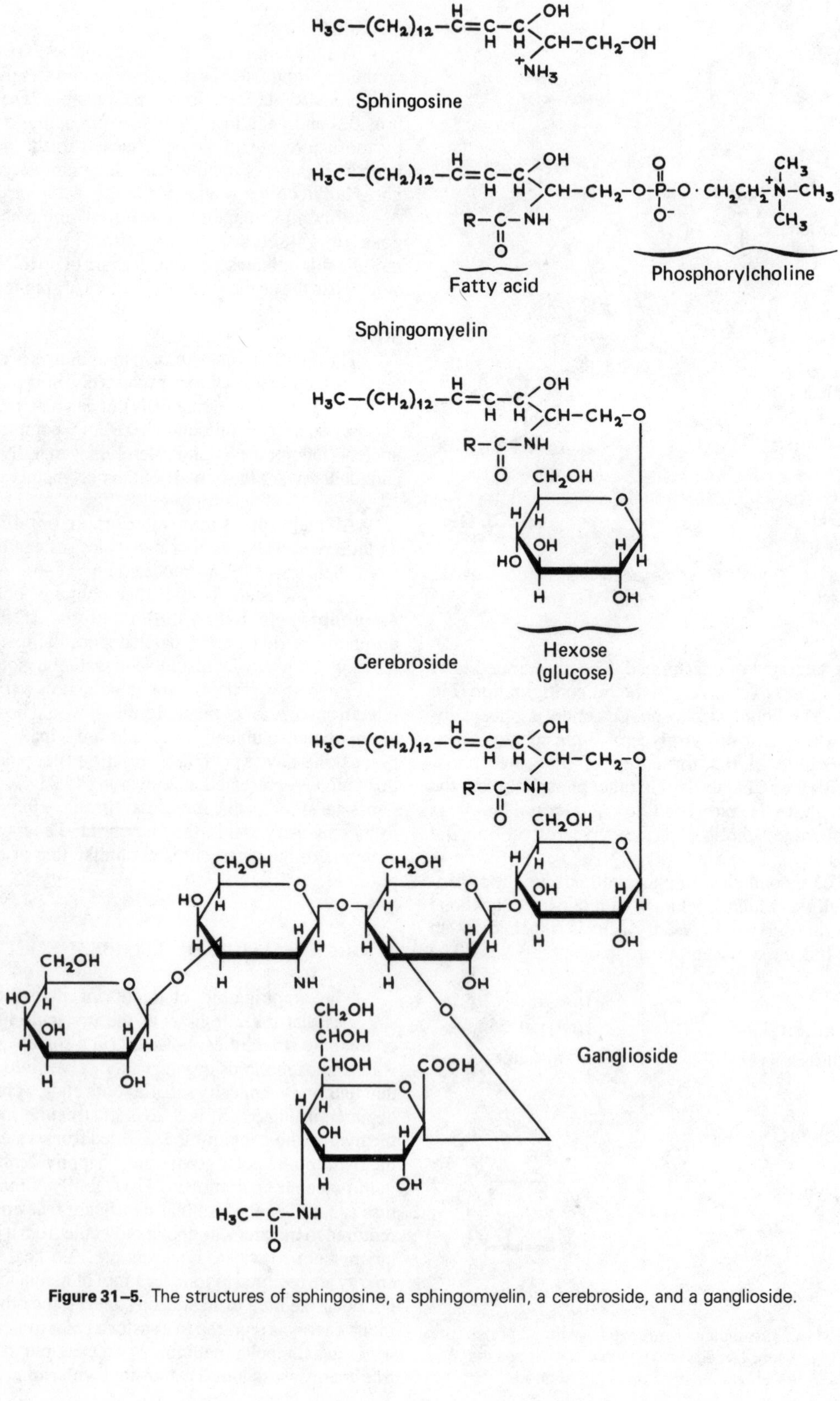

Figure 31–5. The structures of sphingosine, a sphingomyelin, a cerebroside, and a ganglioside.

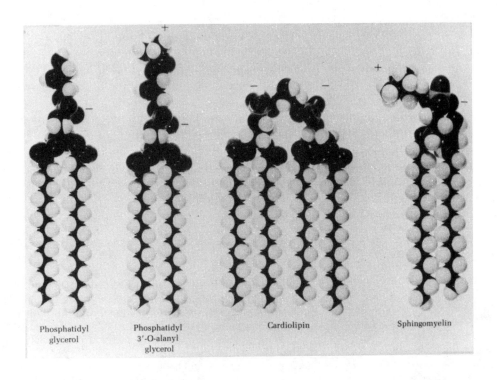

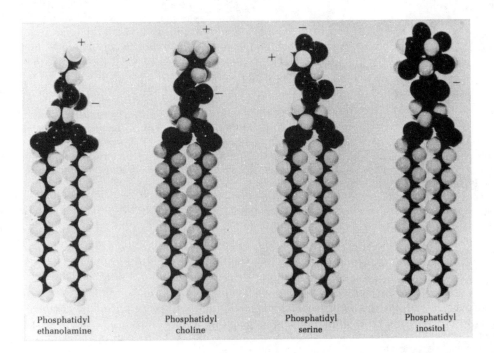

Figure 31–6. Space-filling models of the major phosphoglycerides. For convenience, all the fatty acid components are shown as palmitic acid. Sphingomyelin, although it is not a phosphoglyceride, is included to show its structural similarity. The electrical charges shown assume pH = 7.0. (Reproduced, with permission, from Lehninger AL: *Biochemistry,* 1st ed. Worth, 1970.)

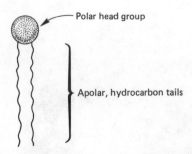

Figure 31–7. Diagrammatic representation of a phospholipid or other membrane lipid. The polar head group is hydrophilic, and the hydrocarbon tails are hydrophobic or lipophilic.

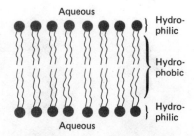

Figure 31–9. Diagram of a section of a bilayer membrane formed from phospholipid molecules. (Reproduced, with permission, from Stryer L: *Biochemistry,* 2nd ed. Freeman, 1981.)

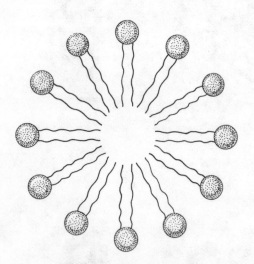

Figure 31–8. Cross section of a micelle. The polar head groups are bathed in water, whereas the hydrophobic hydrocarbon tails are surrounded by other hydrocarbons and thereby protected from water. Micelles are spherical structures.

from water to acetone. Thus, the micelle provides a minimal energy configuration and accordingly is **thermodynamically stable.** Compared to the above-described hydrophobic and hydrophilic interactions, hydrogen bonding and salt or electrostatic bonds are of only secondary importance to the micelle structure.

As recognized 55 years ago by Gorter and Grendel, a bimolecular layer or **bilayer** can also satisfy the thermodynamic requirements of amphipathic molecules in an aqueous environment. A bilayer exists as a sheet in which the hydrophobic regions of the phospholipids are protected from the aqueous environment, while the hydrophilic regions are immersed in water (Fig 31–9). Only the ends or edges of the bilayer sheet are exposed to an unfavorable environment, but even those exposed edges can be eliminated by folding the sheet back upon itself to form an **enclosed vesicle with no edges.** The closed bilayer provides the essential functions of membranes. It is im-

permeable to most water-soluble molecules, since they would be insoluble in the hydrophobic core of the bilayer. Gases such as oxygen, CO_2, and nitrogen, which are small molecules and exhibit little interaction with solvents, readily diffuse through the hydrophobic regions of the membrane. Organic nonelectrolyte molecules exhibit diffusion rates that are dependent upon their oil-water partition coefficients (Fig 31–10)—the greater the lipid solubility of a molecule, the greater will be its diffusion rate across the membrane. This bimolecular structure also allows for the interaction of amphipathic proteins with the membrane.

In biologic membranes, there is **inside-outside (transverse) asymmetry of the phospholipids.** The choline-containing phospholipids are located mainly in the outer molecular layer; the aminophospholipids are preferentially in the inner layer. Sphingomyelin and cholesterol are generally present in larger amounts on the outside than on the inside. Obviously, if this asymmetry is to exist at all, there must be **limited transverse mobility** (flip-flop) of the membrane phospholipids. In fact, phospholipids in synthetic bilayers exhibit an extraordinarily slow rate of flip-flop; the half-life of the asymmetry can be measured in days or weeks. However, when certain membrane proteins such as the erythrocyte protein glycophorin are inserted artifically into synthetic bilayers, the fre-

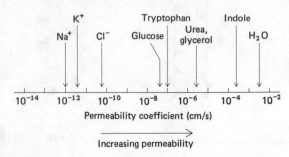

Figure 31–10. Permeability coefficients of some ions and molecules in lipid bilayer membranes. (Reproduced, with permission, from Stryer L: *Biochemistry,* 2nd ed. Freeman, 1981.)

quency of phospholipid flip-flop may increase as much as 100-fold.

Even the enzymes involved in the synthesis of phospholipids and triglycerides are located on the cytoplasmic side of microsomal membrane vesicles, contributing a transverse asymmetry to the membrane.

MEMBRANE PROTEINS

The membrane phospholipids act as a **solvent** for the membrane proteins, creating an environment for the protein function. Of the 20 amino acids contributing to protein primary structure, the functional groups attached to the alpha carbon are strongly hydrophobic in 6, weakly hydrophobic in a few, and hydrophilic in the remainder. As described in Chapter 4, the α-helical structure of proteins minimizes the hydrophilic character of the peptide bonds themselves. Thus, **proteins can be amphipathic** and form an integral part of the membrane by having hydrophilic regions protruding at the inside and outside faces of the membrane but connected by a hydrophobic region traversing the hydrophobic core of the bilayer. In fact, membrane proteins do contain substantial hydrophobic amino acids and α-helical content.

Different proteins provide different functions in membranes; there is no such thing as a typical membrane structure.

The asymmetry of membranes can be partially attributed to the **asymmetric distribution of proteins** within the membranes. An inside-outside asymmetry is provided also by the outside location of the carbohydrates attached to membrane proteins. In addition, specific enzymes are located exclusively on the outside or exclusively on the inside of membranes, as in the mitochondria and plasma membranes.

There are **regional asymmetries** in membranes. Some, such as the villous borders of mucosal cells, are almost macroscopically visible. Others, such as the gap junctions, tight junctions, and synapses, occupy much smaller regions of the membrane and generate local asymmetries.

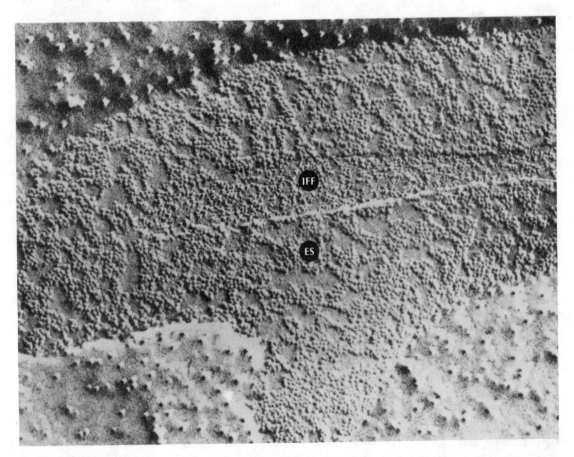

Figure 31–11. Electron micrograph of freeze-etched erythrocyte membrane (left) shows "bumps" on both exterior surface (ES) and inner fracture face (IFF). ES bumps are ferritin-labeled agglutinin attached to protein-bound sugars; the "bumps" on the IFF are globules of protein within the membrane. Close examination reveals the pattern of "bumps" is apparently continuous across the 2 regions, suggesting that the 2 proteins are actually one. (Reproduced, with permission, from Marchesi VT: The structure and orientation of a membrane protein. Chapter 5 in *Cell Membranes: Biochemistry, Cell Biology & Pathology.* Weissman G, Claiborne R [editors]. HP Publishing Co., 1975.)

Integral & Peripheral Membrane Proteins

Most membrane proteins are integral components of the membrane, and in fact all of those that have been adequately studied span the entire 5- to 10-nm transverse distance of the bilayer. These **integral proteins** are usually globular in shape and are themselves amphipathic. They consist of 2 hydrophilic ends separated by an intervening hydrophobic region that traverses the hydrophobic core of the bilayer.

Freeze-fracture etching technics have visually demonstrated the existence of integral membrane proteins traversing the hydrophobic core of the membrane bilayer (Fig 31–11).

Nonionic detergents dissolve or bind to integral proteins, usually without concomitant loss of function, since the hydrophilic ends of the proteins are not bound by the detergent. However, ionic detergents interact with both the hydrophilic ends and the hydrophobic portion of integral proteins and inactivate their function as they do non-membrane associated, water-soluble proteins.

Integral proteins are asymmetrically distributed across the membrane bilayer (Fig 31–12). If a membrane containing an asymmetrically distributed integral protein is dissolved in detergent and the detergent is then slowly removed, the phospholipids and the integral proteins will self-assemble, but the latter will lose their specific inside-outside orientation in the membrane. Thus, at least some proteins must be given their asymmetric orientation in the membrane at the time of its insertion in the lipid bilayer. The hydrophilic external region of an amphipathic protein, which is clearly synthesized inside of the cell, must traverse the hydrophobic core of the membrane and eventually be found external to the membrane. The molecular mechanisms of membrane assembly are discussed below.

Peripheral proteins do not interact directly with the phospholipids in the bilayer but are instead **weakly bound** to the hydrophilic regions of **specific integral proteins.** For example, ankyrin, a peripheral protein, is bound to the integral protein "band III" of erythrocyte membrane. Spectrin, a cytoskeletal structure within the erythrocyte, is in turn bound to ankyrin and thereby plays an important role in the maintenance of the biconclave shape of the erythrocyte. The **immunoglobulin molecules** on the plasma membranes of lymphocytes are integral membrane proteins and can be released by the shedding of small fragments of the membrane. Many **hormone receptor molecules** are integral proteins, and the specific polypeptide hormones that bind to these receptor molecules may therefore be considered peripheral proteins. Peripheral proteins may even organize the distribution of the integral proteins within the plane of the bilayer.

THE FLUID MOSAIC MODEL OF MEMBRANE STRUCTURE

Functional membranes are 2-dimensional solutions of globular integral proteins dispersed in a fluid phospholipid matrix. This **fluid mosaic model** of membrane structure was proposed in 1972 by Singer

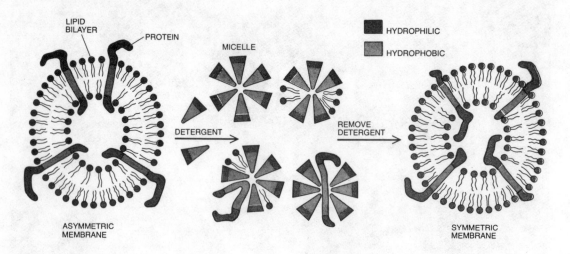

Figure 31–12. Self-assembly of a membrane preserves its basic structure but not its asymmetry. A membrane can be disrupted by a high concentration of a detergent, which is an amphipathic molecule that forms the small droplets called micelles. The detergent dissolves the components of the membrane by enveloping the hydrophobic portions of both lipids and proteins in micelles, where they are protected from contact with water. If the detergent is then removed, the lipids spontaneously form a new bilayer, incorporating the integral proteins in it. The proteins, however, generally assume random orientations. Experiments such as this one have shown that all membranes in the cell cannot be self-assembled; instead, at least some integral proteins must be inserted in a membrane that already exists and has a defined sidedness. (Reproduced, with permission, from Lodish HF, Rothman JE: The assembly of cell membranes. Sci Am [Jan] 1979;**240**:43.)

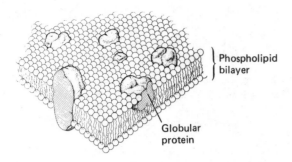

Figure 31–13. Fluid mosaic model: Schematic 3-dimensional cross section.

and Nicholson (Fig 31–13). At that time, the most compelling evidence suggesting the model was the rapid redistribution of species-specific integral proteins in the interspecies hybrid cell formed by the artificially induced fusion of their membranes (Fig 31–14). It has subsequently been demonstrated that phospholipids also undergo rapid redistribution in the plane of the membrane. This diffusion within the plane of the membrane, referred to as **translational diffusion,** can be quite rapid for a phospholipid. In fact, within the plane of the membrane, one molecule of

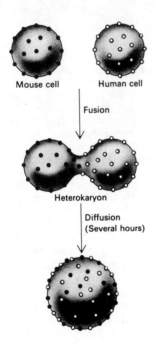

Figure 31–14. The fusion of a mouse cell and a human cell, followed by diffusion of membrane components in the plane of the plasma membrane. The open and closed circles are completely intermingled after several hours. (Reproduced, with permission, from Stryer L: *Biochemistry,* 2nd ed. Freeman, 1981.)

phospholipid can move several micrometers per second.

The **phase changes** and thus the **fluidity** of membranes are highly dependent upon the lipid composition of the membrane. In a lipid bilayer, the hydrophobic chains of the fatty acids can be highly aligned or ordered to provide a rather stiff structure. As the temperature is increased, the hydrophobic side chains will undergo a transition from the ordered state to a disordered one, taking on a more liquidlike or fluid arrangement. The temperature at which the structure undergoes the transition of **ordered to disordered** is called the **transition temperature.** The longer and more saturated fatty acid chains exhibit higher transition temperatures—ie, higher temperatures are required to increase the fluidity of the structure. Unsaturated bonds that exist in the *cis* configuration tend to increase the fluidity of a bilayer by decreasing the **compactness of the side chain packing.**

Cholesterol acts as a moderator molecule in membranes, producing **intermediate states of fluidity.** If the acyl side chains exist in a disordered phase, cholesterol will have a condensing effect; if the acyl side chains are ordered or in a crystalline phase, cholesterol will add disorder. At high cholesterol-phospholipid ratios, transition temperatures are abolished altogether.

The fluidity of a membrane has significant effects on its functions. As membrane fluidity increases, so does its permeability to water and other small hydrophilic molecules. The lateral mobility of integral proteins increases as the fluidity of the membrane increases. If an integral protein involved in some given function has its active site residing exclusively in its hydrophilic regions, there probably will be little effect of changing lipid fluidity on the protein's activity. However, if the protein is involved in a transport function in which transport components span the membrane, lipid phase effects may significantly alter the transport rate.

A state of fluidity and thus translational mobility in a membrane may be confined to certain regions of membranes under certain conditions. For example, protein-protein interaction may take place within the plane of the membrane such that the **integral proteins form a rigid matrix**—in contrast to the more usual situation, where the lipid acts as the matrix. Such regions of rigid protein matrix can exist side by side in the same membrane with the usual lipid matrix. **Gap junctions, tight junctions,** and **bacteriorhodopsin-containing regions** of the purple membranes of halobacteria are clear examples of such side-by-side coexistence of different matrices.

Some of the protein-protein interactions taking place within the plane of the membrane may be mediated by **interconnecting peripheral proteins,** such as cross-linking antibodies or lectins that are known to **patch** or **cap** on membrane surfaces. Thus, peripheral proteins, by their specific attachments, may restrict the mobility of integral proteins within the membrane.

MEMBRANE ASSEMBLY

As mentioned above, the enzymes responsible for the synthesis of phospholipids reside on the cytoplasmic aspects of the vesicles of endoplasmic reticulum. As phospholipids are synthesized at that site, they probably self-assemble into the thermodynamically stable bimolecular layers, thereby expanding the sheet of the vesicle. The lipid vesicles originating as endoplasmic reticulum seem to migrate to the Golgi apparatus, which in turn eventually fuses with the plasma membrane. Both the Golgi complex and the endoplasmic reticulum vesicles exhibit transverse asymmetries of both lipid and protein, and these asymmetries are maintained during fusion with the plasma membrane. **The inside of the vesicle after fusion becomes the outside of the plasma membrane,** and the cytoplasmic side of the vesicles remains the cytoplasmic side of the membrane (Fig 31–15). Since the transverse asymmetry of the membranes already exists in the vesicles of the endoplasmic reticulum well before they are fused to the plasma membrane, the major problem of the membrane assembly becomes how the integral proteins are to be **inserted** asymmetrically into the lipid bilayer of the endoplasmic reticulum.

Integral and secreted proteins frequently are synthesized with an **N-terminal leader sequence** of 15–30 mostly hydrophobic amino acids. Rarely, the hydrophobic ''leader sequence'' may be internal. The N-terminal leader sequence is usually removed from the protein during or after its integration into the membrane, producing the mature membrane or secreted protein (see Chapter 32).

There is strong evidence that the leader sequence is involved in the process of protein insertion. Mutant proteins containing altered leader sequences in which a hydrophobic amino acid is replaced by a hydrophilic one are not inserted into membranes. Nonmembrane proteins to which a leader sequence is attached by genetic engineering will be inserted into membranes or even secreted.

Two models have been proposed to describe the integration of proteins into membrane: the signal hypothesis and the membrane trigger hypothesis. The **signal hypothesis** proposes that the protein is inserted into the membrane simultaneously with the translation of its mRNA on polyribosomes, so-called cotranslational insertion. The leader sequence is thought to cause the protein and the ribosome on which it is being synthesized to bind to a specific protein transport channel (receptor) in the endoplasmic reticulum membrane. The process of elongation of the remaining portion of the protein molecule drives the protein chain across the lipid bilayer as the ribosomes remain attached to the endoplasmic reticulum. Thus, the **rough** (or ribosome-studded) **endoplasmic reticulum** is formed. Ribosomes remain attached to the endoplasmic reticulum during synthesis of the membrane protein but are released and dissociated into their respective subunits as the protein is completed (Fig 31–16). The leader sequence is cleaved off and carbohydrate

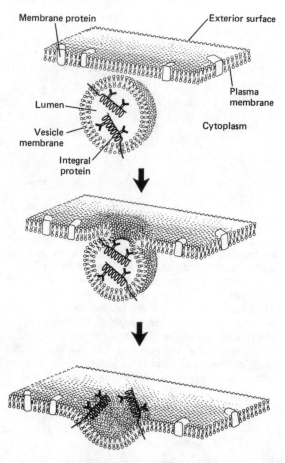

Figure 31–15. Fusion of a vesicle with the plasma membrane preserves the orientation of any integral proteins embedded in the vesicle bilayer. Initially, the N-terminal of the protein faces the lumen, or inner cavity, of such a vesicle. After fusion, the N-terminal is on the exterior surface of the plasma membrane. That the orientation of the protein has not been reversed can be perceived by noting that the other end of the molecule, the C-terminal, is always immersed in the cytoplasm. The lumen of a vesicle and the outside of the cell are topologically equivalent. (Redrawn and modified, with permission, from Lodish HF, Rothman JE: The assembly of cell membranes. *Sci Am* [Jan] 1979;**240**:43.)

attached as the early synthesized portion of the protein enters the interior of the endoplasmic reticulum vesicle.

Integral membrane proteins do not completely cross the membrane, probably prevented from doing so by a hydrophilic C-terminal region. However, secreted proteins completely traverse the membrane bilayer and are discharged into the lumen of the endoplasmic reticulum. By the time they reach the interior of that vesicle, carbohydrate moieties have already been attached (see Chapter 32). Subsequently, the secretory proteins are found in the lumen of the Golgi apparatus, where their carbohydrate attachments are modified prior to their entering granular or secretory

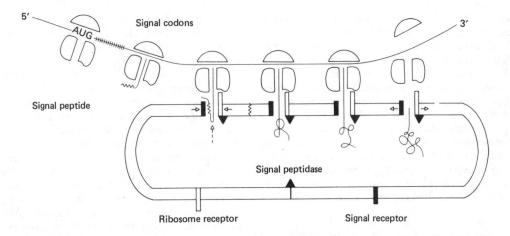

5' Signal codons 3'
AUG

Signal peptide

Signal peptidase

Ribosome receptor Signal receptor

Figure 31–16. Diagram of the signal hypothesis for the transport of secreted proteins across the endoplasmic reticulum membrane. The ribosomes synthesizing a protein move along the messenger RNA specifying the amino acid sequence of the protein. (The messenger is represented by the line between 5' and 3'.) The codon AUG marks the start of the message for the protein; the hatched lines that follow AUG represent the codons for the signal sequence. As the protein grows out from the larger ribosomal subunit, the signal sequence is exposed and binds to its receptor (represented by the solid bar) on the endoplasmic reticulum membrane. There is also a receptor (open bar) for the ribosome itself. The interaction of the ribosome and growing peptide chain with the endoplasmic reticulum membrane results in the opening of a pore through which the protein is transported to the interior space of the endoplasmic reticulum. During transport, the signal sequence of most proteins is removed by an enzyme called the signal peptidase. The completed protein is eventually released by the ribosome, which then separates into its 2 components, the large and small ribosomal subunits. The protein ends up inside the endoplasmic reticulum. (Reproduced, with permission, from: Newly made proteins zip through the cell. *Science* 1980;**207**:164. Copyright 1980 by the American Association for the Advancement of Science.)

vesicles, which ultimately fuse with the plasma membrane.

Some proteins traverse one membrane and subsequently become anchored in a second juxtaposition membrane, such as the mitochondrial inner membrane.

The **membrane trigger hypothesis** minimizes the role of catalysis in membrane assembly and emphasizes the role of the leader sequence in altering the **folding pathway** of the protein itself. The leader sequence is said to promote an alternative folding of the usually hydrophobic integral protein, so that it can remain soluble in the aqueous environment of the cytoplasm where it is synthesized. The membrane lipid bilayer is said to **trigger the refolding** of the protein into a conformation that favors its insertion into that particular bilayer. Thus, the protein is triggered to self-assemble into the membrane in a manner that establishes the necessary transverse asymmetry. Once the protein is inserted or integrated, the leader is cleaved off. The trigger hypothesis does not require specific ribosome membrane interactions, but this still does not mean that protein synthesis on membranes cannot occur.

The major characteristics of the signal hypothesis and the trigger hypothesis are compared in Table 31–1.

It is clear that the signal mechanism and the trigger mechanism must both exist even in the same cell. Some membrane proteins and secreted proteins are synthesized on membrane-bound polysomes, while

Table 31–1. A comparison of two models for membrane assembly.*

Stage of Synthesis	Signal Hypothesis	Membrane Trigger Hypothesis
Site of initiation	Soluble polysomes	Soluble polysomes
Role of the leader peptide	Recognized by the protein transport channel	To alter the folding pathway
Association of the new protein with membrane	When leader peptide is complete *Place:* protein transport channel	During or after protein synthesis *Place:* receptor protein or lipid portions of the bilayer
Specific ribosome associations	With the protein transport channel	None
Catalysis for assembly	A specific pore	The effect of the leader peptide on conformation
Driving force for assembly	Polypeptide chain elongation	Protein-protein and protein-lipid associations: self-assembly
Removal of leader peptide	During polypeptide extrusion	During or after polypeptide assembly into bilayer
Final orientation	C-terminus in, N-terminus out	Specified by the primary sequence

*Modified and reproduced, with permission, from Wickner W: The assembly of proteins into biological membranes: The membrane trigger hypothesis. *Annu Rev Biochem* 1979;**48**:23.

others are formed on free cytoplasmic polysomes. Some proteins will not enter the so-called assembly pathway to be secreted or inserted unless they interact with the membrane bilayer early in the process of their own synthesis on ribosomes. Some proteins can self-assemble or integrate in an oriented fashion into membranes after their synthesis is completed but still require the presence of a normal leader sequence. Some single-peptide chains or proteins such as bacteriorhodopsin can span a membrane back and forth several times, a phenomenon not easily attributed to the signal hypothesis. Finally, some integral proteins are oriented so that their C-terminal region is exterior while their N-terminal region is interior.

TRANSPORT ACROSS MEMBRANES

The plasma membrane of cells acts as a selectively permeable interface between the cell and its environment, distinguishing inside from outside. Two major questions are then raised: How do molecules in the environment traverse the membrane to enter the cell, and how is the selectivity effected? Three major mechanisms are responsible for satisfying the above requirements: **diffusion, active transport,** and **endocytosis.**

Diffusion

As described above, some solutes such as gases can enter the cell by diffusing down an electrochemical gradient across the membrane without requiring metabolic energy. The rate of simple diffusion of a solute across the membrane will not be limited and will be proportionate to the solubility of that solute in the hydrophobic core of the membrane bilayer. The fluidity of a membrane can significantly affect the diffusion of solutes, and even solvents such as water, through the membrane. The rate of diffusion is inversely proportionate to the number of hydrogen bonds that must be broken in order for a solute in the external aqueous phase to become partitioned into the hydrophobic bilayer. Electrolytes diffuse across membranes slowly for the above reason, and the greater their charge density, the slower the diffusion rate. In natural membranes, as opposed to synthetic membrane bilayers, there appear to be transmembrane channels or porelike structures generating ion-conductive pathways. The membranes of nerve cells contain well-studied ion channels that are responsible for the action potentials generated in the membrane. Some microbial peptides provide ion channels, or **ionophores,** that function as ion shuttles for the movement of ions across membranes. These ionophores contain hydrophilic centers that bind specific ions and are surrounded by peripheral hydrophobic regions, allowing them to dissolve effectively in the membrane and diffuse transversely therein (Fig 31–17). **Metabolic uncouplers** such as dinitrophenol similarly provide shuttles for **protons** across membranes, thereby collapsing proton gradients necessary for the generation of ATP, as described in the chemosmotic theory of Mitchell (see Chapter 12).

Some specific solutes diffuse down electrochemical gradients across membranes more rapidly than might be expected from their size, charge, or partition coefficients. Their diffusion is said to be **facilitated** and exhibits properties distinct from those of simple diffusion. The rate of diffusion can be **saturated,** ie, the number of sites involved in diffusion of the specific solutes appears to be finite. Many of the facilitated diffusion systems are stereospecific, and, like the simple diffusion process, **no metabolic energy is required.**

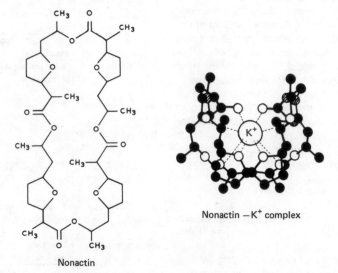

Nonactin

Nonactin $-K^+$ complex

Figure 31–17. The ionophore nonactin and its complex with K^+. (Reproduced, with permission, from Finean JB, Coleman R, Michell RH: *Membranes and Their Cellular Functions.* Wiley, 1974.)

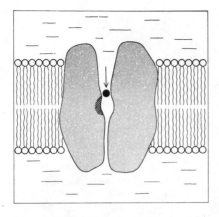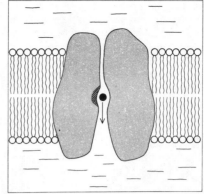

Figure 31–18. Active transport of molecule through membrane protein channel is visualized 2-dimensionally. Molecule impinges (top) on active site (shaded) of protein, following which some energy-yielding enzyme reaction triggers shift in subunit configuration (bottom) that "squeezes" the molecule through the membrane. (Reproduced, with permission, from Singer SJ: Architecture and topography of biologic membranes. Chapter 4 in: *Cell Membranes: Biochemistry, Cell Biology & Pathology.* Weissman G, Claiborne R [editors]. HP Publishing Co., 1975.)

From the above, it should be clear that the inside/outside asymmetry of membrane proteins is stable, and transverse mobility of proteins in the membrane is rare. Therefore, transverse mobility of specific carrier proteins is not likely to account for facilitated diffusion processes except those described above for microbial ionophores.

Fixed pore mechanisms involving a protein-lined pore that changes conformation upon binding specific ligands may account for the translocation of specific molecules across membranes (Fig 31–18). Peripheral and integral membrane proteins may function jointly to provide a facilitated diffusion system. The peripheral protein may provide specificity by its stereospecific binding of the ligand, while the integral protein provides the transmembrane pore (Fig 31–19).

Active Transport

The process of active transport differs from diffusion by requiring a continuous supply of **energy** and transporting molecules **unidirectionally,** frequently **against an electrochemical gradient.** In fact, only by transporting against an electrochemical gradient can a gradient be maintained. The maintenance of electrochemical gradients in biologic systems is so important that it consumes perhaps **30–40% of the total energy input** in a resting human.

In general, living cells maintain a low intracellular Na^+ concentration and a high intracellular K^+ concentration, along with a net **negative electric potential inside.** An integral part of the pump that maintains these gradients is an **ATPase** that is activated by Na^+ and K^+. The ATPase is an integral membrane

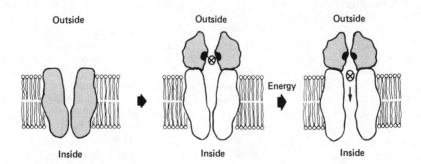

Figure 31–19. A schematic mechanism for the translocation event in active transport, where a peripheral binding protein is obligatorily involved. It is proposed that there are present in the membrane subunit aggregates of specific integral proteins that span the membrane, forming a water-filled pore. This pore (left) is initially closed to the diffusion of molecules other than water. A binding protein with an active binding site for ligand X (shaded) attaches specifically to the exposed surface of the integral protein (center), the pore remaining closed. Some energy-yielding step results in a quaternary rearrangement of the subunits of this structure (right), opening the pore and releasing X to the other side of the membrane. (Modified and reproduced, with permission, from Singer SJ: The molecular organization of membranes. *Annu Rev Biochem* 1974;**43**:805.)

protein and requires phospholipids for activity. The ATPase catalytic activity interacts with both ATP and Na$^+$ on the **cytoplasmic side** of the membrane, but the K$^+$ binding site is located on the **extracellular** side of the membrane. From the extracellular side of the membrane only, **ouabain** (digitalis) inhibits the ATPase that is catalytically active only on the cytoplasmic side of the membrane. Inhibition of ATPase by ouabain can be antagonized by extracellular K$^+$.

Nerve Impulse Transmission

The membrane forming the surface of neuronal cells maintains asymmetry of the inside/outside voltage (electric potential), as described above, and is "excitable." When appropriately stimulated by a chemical signal mediated by a specific membrane receptor (see signal transmission, below), gateways in the membrane can be opened to allow the rapid influx of Na$^+$ followed by the efflux of K$^+$, so that the **voltage difference rapidly collapses.** However, as a result of the ion pumps in the membrane, the gradient is quickly restored.

When large areas of the membrane are "depolarized" in this manner, the electrochemical disturbance can propagate in wavelike form down the membrane, generating a nerve impulse. An electrical insulator surrounding most of the nerve will greatly speed up the propagation of the wave (signal) by allowing ions to flow in and out of the membrane only where the membrane is free of the insulation. **Myelin** sheets, formed by Schwann cells, wrap around nerve fibers and provide just such an insulation. Myelin is the membrane of the Schwann cell and, of course, includes phospholipids, cholesterol, proteins, and cerebrosides. There are relatively few integral and peripheral proteins associated with the myelin membrane structure; those present appear to hold together higher orders of membrane bilayers to form the hydrophobic structure that is impermeable to ions and water.

INTERCELLULAR CONTACT & COMMUNICATION

In a metazoan organism, there exist many areas of intercellular contact. This necessitates contact between the plasma membranes of the individual cells. Cells have developed specialized regions on their membranes for intercellular communication in close proximity. **Gap junctions** mediate and regulate the passage of ions and small molecules through a narrow **hydrophilic pore** connecting the cytoplasms of adjacent cells. These pores are composed of subunits called "connexons" that have been studied by x-ray crystallography. As shown in Fig 31–20, connexons consist of 6 protein subunits that span the membrane and connect with the analogous structures on the adjacent cells. Each subunit is apparently rigid, and, in response to specific chemical stimuli, the subunits rearrange themselves relative to one another (see Hemoglobin, Fig 5–9) to provide a tangential central

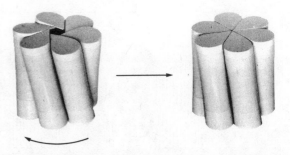

Figure 31–20. Simple model of the connexon, depicting the transition from the "open" to the "closed" configuration. It is proposed that the closure on the cytoplasmic face (uppermost) is achieved by the subunits sliding against each other, decreasing their inclination and hence rotating, in a clockwise sense, at the base. The darker shading on the side of the model indicates the portion that would be embedded in the membrane. The radial displacement of each subunit at the cytoplasmic end would be about 0.6 nm, given the observed inclination change of 5 degrees distributed over its 7.5-nm length. (Reproduced, with permission, from Unwin PNT, Zampighi G: Structure of the junction between communicating cells. *Nature* 1980;**283**:545.)

opening about 2 nm in diameter. It is through this central opening that ions and small molecules can pass from one cytoplasm to another in a regulated fashion.

Signal Transmission

Specific biochemical signals such as neurotransmitters, hormones, and immunoglobulins bind to specific receptors (integral proteins) exposed to the outside of cellular membranes and transmit information through these membranes to the cytoplasm. The β-adrenergic receptor, which stereospecifically binds catecholamines, is asymmetrically located on the outer aspect of plasma membranes of target cells, such as the erythrocytes. The binding of the catecholamine on the outside stimulates the catalytic activity of adenylate cyclase, asymmetrically located on the inside of the membrane. Adenylate cyclase generates cAMP from ATP (see Chapter 25). Thus, the information that a specific catecholamine is present on the outside is transmitted to the inside of the cell, where a second messenger, cAMP, takes up the role of further conveying the information.

When the catecholamine binds to the beta receptor, the latter, by conformational change, activates **phospholipid methyltransferase I,** an integral enzyme oriented toward the cytoplasmic side of the membrane. This enzyme generates phosphatidyl-N-monomethylethanolamine from phosphatidylethanolamine (Fig 31–21). The phosphatidyl-N-monomethylethanolamine flip-flops toward the outside of the membrane and is further methylated to phosphatidyl-N-dimethylethanolamine and subsequently to phosphatidylcholine by the integral enzyme **phospholipid methyltransferase II,** located toward the outside of the membrane. The increased local concentration of phosphatidylcholine enhances the local

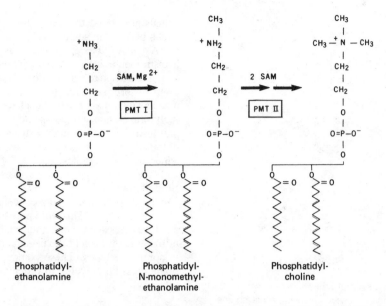

Figure 31–21. The enzymatic conversion of phosphatidylethanolamine to phosphatidylcholine. (PMT I, phospholipid methyltransferase I; PMT II, phospholipid methyltransferase II; SAM, S-adenosyl-L-methionine.) (Reproduced, with permission, from Hirata F, Axelrod J: Phospholipid methylation and biological signal transmission. *Science* 1980;**209**:1082. Copyright 1980 by the American Association for the Advancement of Science.)

membrane fluidity. The enhanced fluidity seems to allow the occupied beta receptor to interact with the GTP-dependent coupling factor and adenylate cyclase to activate the latter on the **cytoplasmic** aspect of the membrane (Fig 31–22). Furthermore, the increased fluidity **exposes** more preexisting beta receptor molecules to the outside membrane surface.

Phospholipid methylation may serve as an initial common pathway for the transduction of many receptor-mediated biologic signals through membranes. In some systems, the increased fluidity due to phospholipid methylation may allow the rapid influx of calcium, which can bind to **calmodulin** and activate specific enzymes, including phospholipases. From phosphatidyl choline, the phospholipases can in turn generate free fatty acids, including **arachidonic acid,** an immediate precursor of **prostaglandins.** The latter are known to be involved in signal transmission in several transmembrane, hormonally responsive systems.

Endocytosis

Endocytosis is a transport process that allows cells to internalize extracellular material and involves the formation of endocytotic vesicles during that process. **Endocytotic vesicles** are generated when segments of the plasma membrane invaginate, enclosing a volume of extracellular fluid, and then pinch off as the fusion of plasma membranes seals the neck of the vesicle and the original site of invagination (Fig 31–23). Subsequent fusion of the endocytotic vesicles with other membrane structures accomplishes the

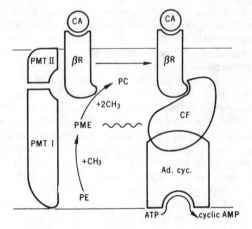

Figure 31–22. Phospholipid methylation and β-adrenergic receptor coupling. When catecholamine (CA) binds to β-adrenergic receptor (βR), it stimulates phospholipid methyltransferase I (PMT I) and phospholipid methyltransferase II (PMT II). This increases the methylation of phosphatidylethanolamine (PE) to phosphatidyl-N-monomethylethanolamine (PME) and to phosphatidylcholine (PC). As the phospholipids are methylated, they flip-flop and increase fluidity (~). This facilitates the lateral mobility of the β-adrenergic receptor to interact with the guanylnucleotide coupling factor (CF) and adenylate cyclase (Ad. cyc.) to generate cyclic AMP. (Reproduced, with permission, from Hirata F, Axelrod J: Phospholipid methylation and biological signal transmission. *Science* 1980;**209**:1082. Copyright 1980 by the American Association for the Advancement of Science.)

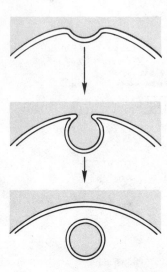

Figure 31–23. Formation of an endocytotic vesicle by the process of invagination at the cell plasma membrane.

transport of its contents to other cellular compartments or even back to the cell exterior.

There are 2 general types of endocytosis. **Phagocytosis** (not discussed here) occurs only in specialized phagocytic cells such as macrophages and granulocytes present in blood. **Pinocytosis** is a property of all cells and leads to the cellular uptake of fluid and fluid contents. There are 2 types. **Adsorptive pinocytosis** is a receptor-mediated, selective process primarily responsible for the uptake of macromolecules for which there is a finite number of binding sites on the plasma membrane. These high-affinity receptors permit pinocytosis to **concentrate ligands** from the medium and to minimize the uptake of fluid or soluble unbound macromolecules. The vesicles formed in the process of adsorptive pinocytosis are derived from invaginations (pits) that are coated on the cytoplasmic side with a filamentous material. In many systems, **clathrin** is the filamentous material and is probably a peripheral membrane protein.

For example, the LDL molecule and its receptor (Chapter 18) are internalized via coated pits containing the LDL receptor. These endocytotic vesicles containing LDL and its receptor fuse to lysosomes in the cell. The receptor is released and recycled, but LDL apoprotein is degraded and the cholesteryl esters metabolized. Synthesis of the LDL receptor is regulated by secondary or tertiary consequences of pinocytosis, ie, by metabolites of LDL. Disorders of the LDL receptor and its internalization are discussed in Chapter 18.

Other macromolecules, including several hormones, are subject to adsorptive pinocytosis and form **receptosomes,** vesicles that avoid lysosomes and deliver their contents to other intracellular sites, such as the Golgi system.

Adsorptive pinocytosis of extracellular glycoproteins requires that the glycoproteins carry specific **carbohydrate recognition signals.** These recognition signals are bound by membrane receptor molecules, which play a role analogous to that of the LDL receptor. A galactosyl receptor on the surface of hepatocytes is instrumental in the adsorptive pinocytosis of asialoglycoproteins in the circulation. Acid hydrolases taken up by adsorptive pinocytosis in fibroblasts are recognized by their mannose 6-phosphate moieties. Interestingly, the mannose 6-phosphate moiety also seems to play an important role in the **intracellular segregation** of the acid hydrolases to the lysosomes of the cells in which they are synthesized.

The other type of pinocytosis is a nonselective fluid phase process in which the uptake of a solute is simply proportionate to its concentration in the surrounding medium. This **fluid phase pinocytosis** forms small vesicles and is an extraordinarily active process, utilizing up to 50% of the plasma membrane per hour in some cell types. These components of the membrane must be recycled in order to maintain cellular integrity.

DISORDERS OF MEMBRANES

The abnormality of adsorptive pinocytosis in autosomal dominant **familial hypercholesterolemia** has been described in Chapter 18.

Multiple sclerosis is a somewhat confusing neurologic disorder in which nervous tissue is demyelinated by an unknown process. The demyelinization removes the neuronal insulation described above and profoundly decreases the velocity of nerve impulse transmission.

Pseudohypoparathyroidism is an inherited disorder in which there is defective signaling across the plasma membranes of several types of target cells. In the affected target cells, the parathormone signal is normally mediated by activation of adenylate cyclase, as described above for the β-adrenergic system. In pseudohypoparathyroidism, there is in the membrane a defective coupling protein that prevents transmission of the extracellular hormone signal to the adenylate cyclase. It is not yet clear whether the defect involves abnormal phospholipid methylation reactions or whether the abnormality occurs after the increased fluidity brought about by binding of parathormone to the specific receptor molecules.

I cell disease is a rare autosomal recessive disorder apparently due to inability of the patient's fibroblasts to attach the mannose 6-phosphate signal to the acid hydrolases synthesized in various cell types. Accordingly, the acid hydrolases do not segregate normally to the primary lysosomes but are instead secreted into the extracellular space, leaving the intracellular lysosomes deficient in these important hydrolases. Thus, the lysosomes accumulate excessive debris and thereby generate intracellular cytoplasmic inclusions (I). These abnormal secreted hydrolases are not subject to adsorptive pinocytosis by the patient's or even by normal fibroblasts, since they lack the necessary mannose 6-phosphate recognition signal.

•   •   •

References

Bedouelle H & others: Mutations which alter the function of the signal sequence of the maltose binding protein of *Escherichia coli*. *Nature* 1980;**285**:78.

Blobel G & others: Translocation of proteins across membranes: The signal hypothesis and beyond. *Symp Soc Exp Biol* 1979;**33**:9.

Davis BD, Tai P-C: The mechanism of protein secretion across membranes. *Nature* 1980;**283**:433.

Goldstein JL, Anderson RGW, Brown MS: Coated pits, coated vesicles and receptor-mediated endocytosis. *Nature* 1979;**279**:679.

Hirata F, Axelrod J: Phospholipid methylation and biological signal transmission. *Science* 1980;**209**:1082.

Lodish HF, Rothman JE: The assembly of cell membranes. *Sci Am* (Jan) 1979;**240**:43.

Morell P, Norton WT: Myelin. *Sci Am* (May) 1980;**242**:88.

Op den Kamp JAF: Lipid asymmetry in membranes. *Annu Rev Biochem* 1979;**48**:47.

Singer SJ, Nicolson GL: The fluid mosaic model of the structure of cell membranes. *Science* 1972;**175**:720.

Sly WS: Saccharide traffic signals in receptor-mediated endocytosis and transport of acid hydrolase. Page 433 in: *Structure and Function of the Gangliosides*. Svennerholm L & others (editors). Plenum Press, 1980.

Wickner W: Assembly of proteins into membranes. *Science* 1980;**210**:861.

Willingham MC, Pastan I: The receptosome: An intermediate organelle of receptor-mediated endocytosis in cultured fibroblasts. *Cell* 1980;**21**:67.

Unwin PNT, Zampighi G: Structure of the junction between communicating cells. *Nature* 1980;**283**:545.

GLOSSARY FOR CHAPTERS 27–31*

Amber mutation: A mutation in which a polypeptide chain is terminated prematurely; results from an alteration in a codon such that the codon becomes UAG, which signals chain termination.

Anticodon: The triplet of nucleotides in a tRNA molecule that associates by complementary base pairing with the codon in the mRNA during translation.

Antiparallel: Describes molecules that are parallel but point in opposite directions (the strands of DNA are antiparallel).

Antisense: Strand of DNA that has the same sequence as mRNA.

AUG: See initiation codon.

Blunt end: DNA end with no unpaired bases.

Cap: The structure found at the 5' end of many eukaryotic mRNAs. It consists of 7'-methyl-guanosine-pppX, where X is the first nucleotide encoded in the DNA. It is not present in prokaryotic mRNAs; it is added posttranscriptionally near the TATA (Hogness) box.

CAP: Not to be confused with cap. CAP is catabolite gene activator protein (sometimes CRP or CGA); it participates in the initiation of transcription in prokaryotes.

Capsid: The protein coat of a virion or virus particle.

C$_H$: Constant portion of the immunoglobulin heavy chain.

Cistron: A DNA fragment or portion that specifies or codes for a particular polypeptide.

Class switch: A switch in the expression of a B lymphocyte from one antibody class to another.

Codon: A group of 3 nucleotides that codes for an amino acid.

Cohesive termini (cohesive ends): DNA molecules with single-stranded ends that show complementarity, making it possible, for example, to join end to end with introduced fragments.

Complementary DNA (cDNA): DNA that is complementary to messenger RNA; used for cloning or as a specific and sensitive probe in hybridization studies.

Consensus sequence: An average sequence, each nucleotide of which is the most frequent at that position in a set of examples; used for RNA splice sites and other sites.

Cross hybridization: Hybridization of a probe to imperfectly matching (less than 100% complementarity) molecules.

Crossing-over: Exchange of genetic material between chromosomes that pair during meiosis (homologous chromosomes).

Cut: A double-strand scission in the duplex polynucleotide—in distinction to the single-strand "nick."

Episome: A circular gene fragment.

Exon: Portion of DNA that codes for the final mRNA.

Exon shuffle: The alternative RNA processing patterns that lead to expression of different combinations of exons from the same gene.

Fc: An antibody (immunoglobulin) fragment from C$_H$ that is crystallizable.

Fc receptor: The receptor for the Fc fragment.

Gap: A double-stranded DNA is said to be gapped when one strand is missing over a short region.

Gene library: Random collection of cloned fragments in a vector that ideally includes all the genetic information of that species, eg, chicken, human. Sometimes called shotgun collection.

Gene splicing: See splicing.

Genome: All the genes of an organism or individual.

Genomic blotting: See Southern blotting.

Grünstein-Hogness assay: Colony hybridization procedure for identification of plasmid clones. (Colonies are transferred to a filter and hybridized with a probe.)

H chain: Heavy chain of immunoglobulin molecule; see V$_H$ and C$_H$.

Heteroduplex: A DNA molecule the 2 strands of which come from different individuals, so that there may be some base pairs of blocks of base pairs that do not match.

Hinge: Short flexible amino acid sequence of an immunoglobulin protein, permitting one portion to move relative to the other. When present, the hinge separates the antigen-combining site from the Fc portion of the molecule.

Hogness box (TATA box): The hypothesized eukaryotic RNA polymerase II promoter, analogous to the Pribnow box.

IF-1: Initiation factor 1 (also IF-2, IF-3) for protein synthesis.

Immunoglobulin class: For example, in the mouse there are 8 classes of immunoglobulins (Ig): IgM (μ chain); IgD (δ chain); four IgGs (γ chains); IgA (α chain); and IgE (ϵ chain). The class is determined by the constant region of the heavy chain. Class is associated with generic properties of the antibody, cellular and tissue localization, complement binding, and other factors. Class is independent of the variable region and of the light chain.

Initiation codon: (AUG; sometimes GUG) Codes for the first amino acid in protein sequences, which is formylmethionine. fMet is often removed posttranslationally.

Integration and excision: Integration: a recombination in which a genetic element is inserted; excision: reverse of integration.

Intervening sequence: A portion of a gene that is transcribed but does not appear in the final mRNA transcript.

Intron: Intervening sequence in DNA.

Inversion: The alteration of a DNA molecule made by removing a fragment, reversing its orientation, and pulling it back into place.

Inverted repeat in DNA: See palindrome.

Lac operon: An operon in *Escherichia coli* that codes for 3 genes involved in the metabolism of lactose.

Ligase, DNA ligase: Catalyzes the formation of a phosphodiester bond at the site of a single-strand break in duplex DNA. (RNA can also act as a substrate to some extent.)

mRNA: Messenger RNA.

Nick: A single-strand scission of the DNA (can be made with deoxyribonuclease and ethidium bromide).

Nonsense mutation: A mutation that results in the termination of a polypeptide chain, eg, ochre and amber.

Nucleotide replacement site: Position in a codon where a point mutation has occurred.

Ochre mutation: A mutation in which a polypeptide chain is terminated prematurely; results from an alteration in the codon such that the codon becomes UGA, which signals chain termination.

Operator: A region of DNA that interacts with a repressor protein to control the expression of an adjacent gene or group of genes.

Operon: A gene unit consisting of one or more genes that specify a polypeptide and an "operator" that regulates the transcription of the structural gene. (The regulator and the coding genes are adjacent on the DNA molecule.)

Palindrome: A self-complementary nucleic acid sequence, ie, a sequence identical to its complementary strand (both read in the same 5' to 3' direction). Perfect palindromes (eg, GAATTC) frequently occur as sites of recognition for restriction enzymes. Less perfect palindromes (eg,

*Excerpted and reprinted, with permission, from *Science* 1980;**209**:1435. Copyright 1980 by the American Association for the Advancement of Science.

TACCTCTGGCGTGATA) frequently occur in binding sites for other proteins, such as repressors. Interrupted palindromes (eg, an inverted repeat such as GGTTXXXAACC) afford the possibility in single-stranded nucleic acids for the loop stem (hairpin) structure as in tRNA.

Plasmid: Extrachromosomal, autonomously replicating, circular DNA segment.

Polyadenylylation: Nontranscriptive addition of poly(A) (polyadenylate) to the 3′ end of eukaryotic RNA.

Polymerase: Enzyme that catalyzes the assembly of nucleotides into RNA and of deoxynucleotides into DNA.

Pribnow box: TATAATG; consensus sequence near the RNA start point of prokaryotic promoters.

Promoter: A DNA sequence at which RNA polymerase binds and then initiates transcription.

Pseudogene: A sequence that looks like a gene but does not function as one; it appears to have no phenotype and could be the vestigial remains of a gene.

Reading: One-way linear process by which nucleotide sequences are decoded, eg, by protein-synthesizing systems.

Readthrough: The transcription of a region beyond a normal termination sequence, due to occasional failure of RNA polymerase to recognize the termination signal.

Regulatory gene: A gene whose product is involved in the regulation of another gene, such as a repressor gene.

Regulatory sequence: A DNA sequence involved in regulating the expression of the gene (eg, promoters, operators).

Repressor: The protein that binds to a regulatory sequence (operator) adjacent to a gene and which, when bound, blocks transcription of the gene.

Restriction endonuclease: Site-specific endodeoxyribonuclease; cleavage is sequence-specific; both strands are cleaved, usually have been isolated from bacteria. There are many, eg, Eco RI; Bam I, Hind III.

R loop: Three-stranded structure in which an RNA-DNA hybrid displaces the other strand of DNA, leaving a DNA loop with characteristic appearance in the electron microscope.

RNA splicing: See splicing.

SD sequence: Shine-Dalgarno or ribosome recognition sequence, begins 3–11 nucleotides upstream from the AUG in mRNA. It is complementary to the 3′ end of 16S ribosomal RNA.

Sequence ladder: Bands in gel corresponding to DNA sequence.

Shotgunning: See gene library.

Silent site mutation, silent mutation: Mutation in a codon or sequence that does not cause an amino acid change.

Southern blot technic: Method of transferring DNA fragments that have been separated by gel electrophoresis (agarose) to a nitrocellulose filter such that the relative positions of the DNA fragments are maintained. The DNA is usually visualized by hybridization with a ^{32}P-labeled DNA or RNA probe.

Spheroplast: A bacterial cell whose wall is partially, or nearly completely, removed, so that the cell assumes a spherical shape.

Splicing: 1. Gene splicing: manipulations the object of which is to attach one DNA molecule to another. 2. RNA splicing: Removal of introns from mRNA precursors.

Split gene: One that is not continuous but has been interrupted; interrupted gene.

Start codon: See initiation codon.

Start point: (RNA technology) First nucleotide of a transcript.

Sticky ends: See cohesive termini.

Structural gene: A gene that determines the primary structure (ie, the amino acid sequences) of a polypeptide. (See operon; regulatory gene.)

Suppressor gene: A gene that can reverse the effect of a specific type of mutation in other genes.

Suppressor mutation: A mutation that totally or partially restores a function lost by a primary mutation and is located at a genetic site different from the primary mutation.

Termination codon: A codon that specifies the termination of translation.

Termination sequence: A DNA sequence at the end of a transcriptional unit that signals the end of transcription.

Transcription: Formation of the RNA from the DNA template.

Transduction: The transfer of genetic material from one cell to another by means of a viral vector. (For bacteria, the vector is bacteriophage.)

Transfection: Infection of a cell with isolated DNA or RNA from a virus or viral vector.

Transformation: The introduction of an exogenous DNA preparation (transforming agent) into a cell.

Translation: The process in which the genetic code contained in the nucleotide sequences of mRNA directs the order of amino acids in the formation of peptide.

Transposable element: A segment or fragment of DNA that can move from one position in the genome to another.

Transversion: A mutation caused by the substitution of a pyrimidine for a purine or vice versa.

tRNA: Transfer RNA.

tRNA gene: Region of DNA that is transcribed to produce tRNA.

tRNA suppressor: A mutation in a tRNA gene that alters its anticodon to a sequence that is complementary to a termination codon. This allows the suppression of amino acid chain termination (nonsense mutation).

V$_H$: Variable portion of immunoglobulin heavy chain.

Vector: An agent consisting of a DNA molecule known to autonomously replicate in a cell to which another DNA segment may be attached experimentally, so as to bring about the replication of the attached segment.

32 | Glycoproteins, Proteoglycans, & Glycosaminoglycans

David W. Martin, Jr., MD

The descriptions of the biochemistry of glycoproteins, proteoglycans, and glycosaminoglycans are included in one chapter because these 3 types of molecules have several features in common, including aspects of their structure, synthesis, degradation, and even function. The 3 classes of molecules can be clearly defined, although in the past some confusion has existed because of overlapping terminology. **Glycoproteins** differ from other proteins in having oligosaccharide chains covalently attached to their polypeptide backbones. **Proteoglycans** are also proteins to which oligosaccharide chains are covalently attached to the polypeptide backbone, but the oligosaccharides differ chemically from those attached to glycoproteins (Fig 32–1). The oligosaccharide chains of proteoglycans consist of repeating disaccharide units that contain (1) glucosamine or galactosamine, (2) a uronic acid (except for keratan sulfate), and (3) covalently attached sulfate loops (except for hyaluronic acid). **Glycosaminoglycans** are oligosaccharide structures that have been removed from the protein backbone of their proteoglycan precursor. The structures, synthesis, degradation, and functions of each of these classes of molecules will be discussed in turn. All 3 classes of molecules exist mostly in the **extracellular space** but are synthesized intracellularly in close association with the intracellular membrane systems of the endoplasmic reticulum and Golgi complex (see Chapter 31). The oligosaccharide moieties appear to be important for both directing the export of these molecules and providing some specifically extracellular functional advantage, perhaps stability or localization.

Glycoprotein: Protein
                                  |
                          Oligosaccharide

Proteoglycan: Protein
                                |
Oligosaccharide (uronic acid and/or SO$_4$)
                                ↓➤Protein

Glycosaminoglycan: Oligosaccharide (uronic acid and/or SO$_4$)

Figure 32–1. Similarities and relationships between glycoproteins, proteoglycans, and glycosaminoglycans.

GLYCOPROTEINS

Glycoproteins range in molecular weight from 15,000 to over 1 million, usually contain 15 or fewer sugar units per covalently attached oligosaccharide chain, and may have carbohydrate contents ranging from 1 to 85% by weight. Glycoproteins are present in most organisms, including plants, bacteria, fungi, viruses, and animals, and have several functions. As explained in Chapter 31, most membrane proteins and secreted proteins are glycoproteins. Table 32–1 sets forth a partial list of functions of different glycoproteins.

Table 32–1. Some functions served by glycoproteins.

Structural molecules
Cell walls
Collagen, elastin
Fibrins
Bone matrix
Lubricants and protective agents
Mucins
Mucous secretions
Transport molecules for
Vitamins
Lipids
Minerals and trace elements
Immunologic molecules
Immunoglobins
Histocompatibility antigens
Complement
Interferon
Hormones
Chorionic gonadotropin
Thyrotropin (TSH)
Enzymes
Proteases
Nucleases
Glycosidases
Hydrolases
Clotting factors
Cell attachment/recognition sites
Cell-cell
Virus-cell
Bacterium-cell
Hormone receptors
Antifreeze in antarctic fishes
Lectins

Structures of Oligosaccharides Attached to Glycoproteins

Nine different sugar residues are found in the oligosaccharide chains attached to the glycoproteins. Glucose (Glc) is found only in collagen, but galactose (Gal) and mannose (Man) are more common and widely distributed. The 2 most frequently found hexoses are N-acetylgalactosamine (GalNAc) and N-acetylglucosamine (GlcNAc). Fucose (Fuc), which is 6-deoxygalactose, is a common constituent. Two pentoses, arabinose (Ara) and xylose (Xyl), are found, and the ninth are the sialic acids (Sial), of which N-acetylneuraminic acid (Nana) is an example (see Chapter 13). In general, the N-acetylhexosamines are at the end of the oligosaccharide chains most proximal to the protein. The fucose and Nana residues are more distal in the chain, frequently at terminal sites.

The oligosaccharide chains are attached to the polypeptide backbone of glycoproteins at one of 5 amino acid residues: **asparagine** (Asn), **serine** (Ser), **threonine** (Thr), **hydroxylysine** (Hyl), or **hydroxyproline** (Hyp). There are 2 types of chemical bonds that provide the attachment sites, O-glycosidic links and N-glycosidic links.

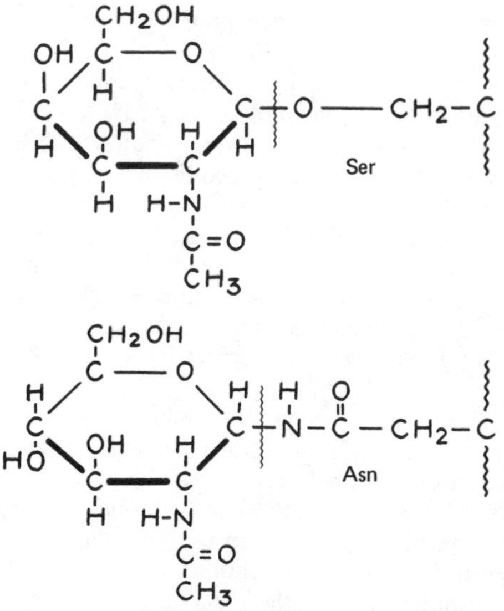

Figure 32–2. Linkage of N-acetylgalactosamine to serine and linkage of N-acetylglucosamine to asparagine.

O-Glycosidic Links

Most of the O-glycosidic links occur through the free alcohol groups of Ser or Thr residues of the polypeptide (Fig 32–2), in a tripeptide sequence of Asn-Y-Ser(Thr), where Y is an amino acid other than aspartate. This specific tripeptide sequence is very common in proteins, but every such sequence is not glycosylated. The decision to glycosylate such Ser or

Thr residues also is based on the protein conformation surrounding that tripeptide as it emerges through the endoplasmic reticulum (see Chapter 31).

The most common sugar residue attached directly to the Ser or Thr residue is GalNAc. About 6 different types of oligosaccharide structures can be found attached to this GalNAc-Ser(Thr) linkage. As shown in Table 32–2, many mucins, blood group substances,

Table 32–2. Glycopeptides linked through N-acetylgalactosamine to the hydroxyl group of serine and threonine.[*]

	Structure	Glycoprotein
A	Nana $\xrightarrow{a2,6}$ GalNAc $\longrightarrow$ Ser(Thr)	Submaxillary mucins
B	Gal $\xrightarrow{\beta1,3}$ GalNAc $\longrightarrow$ Ser(Thr)	"Antifreeze" glycoprotein of antarctic fish; human IgA1; β subunit HCG; cartilage keratin sulfate; epiglycanin of TA$_3$-HA cells; lymphocyte, RBC, and milk fat globule membranes
C	Gal $\xrightarrow{\beta1,3}$ GalNAc $\longrightarrow$ Ser(Thr) $\uparrow a2,3$ Nana	Bovine kininogen; epiglycanin of TA$_3$-HA cells; B$_{16}$ melanoma cells
D	Gal $\xrightarrow{\beta1,3}$ GalNAc $\longrightarrow$ Ser(Thr) $\uparrow a2,3 \qquad \uparrow a2,6$ Nana $\qquad$ Nana	Fetuin; human RBC membrane sialoglycoprotein; bovine kininogen; rat brain
E	Gal $\xrightarrow{\beta1,3(4)}$ GlcNAc $\xrightarrow{1,2(4,6)}$ Gal $\xrightarrow{\beta1,3(4)}$ GalNAc $\longrightarrow$ Ser(Thr) $\uparrow a2,3$ Nana	Epiglycanin
F	Gal $\xrightarrow{1,3}$ GlcNAc $\xrightarrow{1,3}$ Gal $\xrightarrow{1,3}$ GalNAc $\longrightarrow$ Ser(Thr) $\uparrow 1,6$ GlcNAc $\uparrow 1,4$ Gal	Human gastric mucin; core region of human and hog blood group substances

[*]Slightly modified and reproduced, with permission, from Lennarz WJ: *The Biochemistry of Glycoproteins and Proteoglycans.* Plenum Press, 1980.

and other common glycopeptides possess a Gal or Nana as the next residue attached to the GalNAc. The initiation and extension of these types of oligosaccharide chains of glycoproteins occur by the stepwise donation of sugar residues from pyrimidine or purine nucleotide sugars, as discussed below.

The O-glycosidic linkage to Ser or Thr may occur through sugars other than GalNAc. In yeast and fungi, Man-Ser(Thr) linkages are found, and human urine contains Fuc-Thr remnants of glycoproteins, providing evidence for their existence. As discussed below, Xyl-Ser(Thr) linkages are common in the proteoglycans.

Oligosaccharides may be linked to proteins via O-glycosidic bonds to Hyl or Hyp, which are amino acid residues uniquely found in **collagens** and some fibrous proteins of plants. Gal is frequently the lead sugar attached directly to the Hyl, and that linkage is common in basement membranes. As for other O-glycosidic linkages, the sugar moiety is donated by an "activated" nucleotide sugar.

N-Glycosidic Linkage to Polypeptide Chains

The N-glycosidic linkage of oligosaccharides to proteins occurs exclusively through a GlcNAc-Asn bond (Fig 32–2) and consists of a core region with the structure Man-β-1,4-GlcNAc-β-1,4-GlcNAc-Asn. The sequence GlcNAc-β-1,4-GlcNAc-β-Asn is referred to as the **di-N-acetylchitobiose** sequence. The

oligosaccharide chains attached to glycoproteins by way of this N-glycosidic core region are of 2 types: the high-mannose (simple) type and the complex type. A single protein can contain oligosaccharide chains of both high-mannose and complex types as well as the types employing O-glycosidic linkages described above.

The **high-mannose chains** contain only Man and GlcNAc residues, and all are remarkably similar in structure, as shown in Fig 32–3. Note that these high-mannose structures contain the same β-mannosyl-di-N-acetylchitobiose core structure and exhibit the same branching pattern of their outer α-Man residues. The outer chain **branch** is confined to the Man linked to the C$_6$ of the core β-Man residue.

Although all high-mannose oligosaccharides are synthesized from nucleotide sugars, there exists an important **lipid-linked precursor oligosaccharide** that is transferred en bloc from a lipid carrier to the Asn of the protein. The formation and function of the lipid-linked carrier is described below. The synthesis of the high-mannose glycoproteins occurs at the endoplasmic reticulum, as briefly described in Chapter 31 and in more detail below.

The **complex N-linked oligosaccharides** also contain the β-Man-di-N-acetylchitobiose core structure but consist also of a variable number of **outer chains** containing Sial, Gal, and Fuc residues linked to the core. Usually, 2 α-Man residues are attached di-

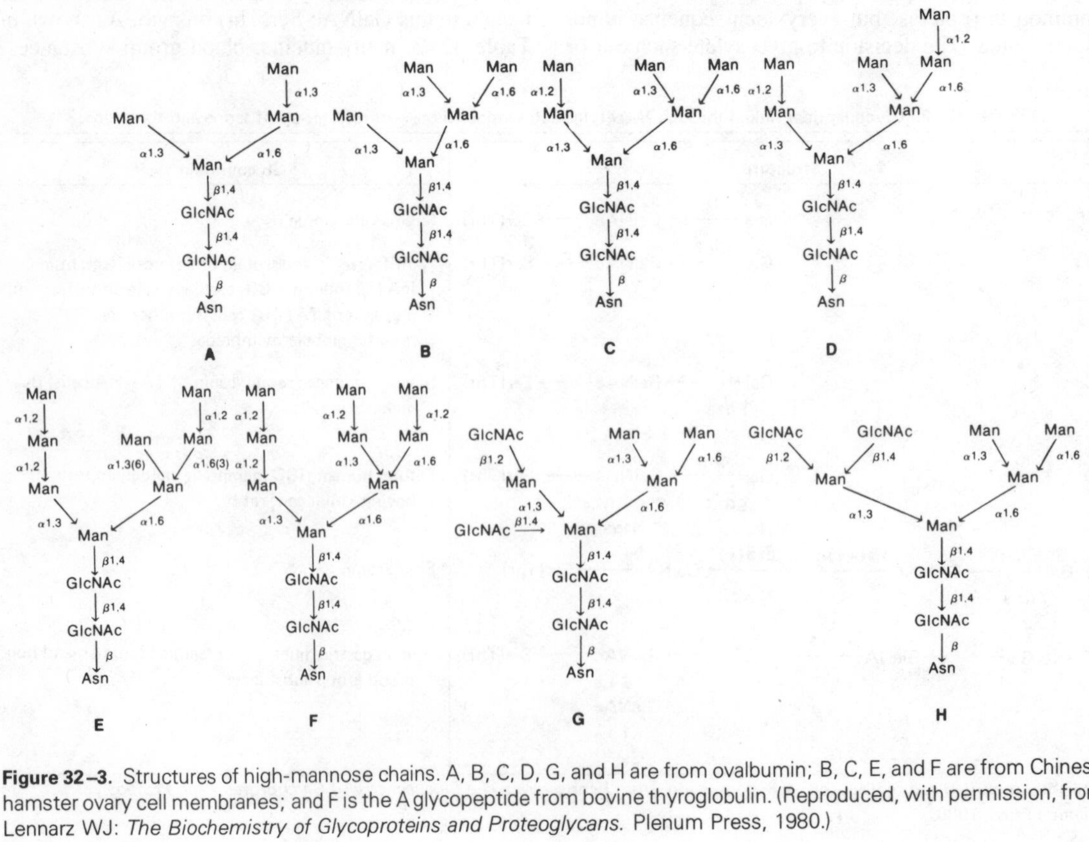

Figure 32–3. Structures of high-mannose chains. A, B, C, D, G, and H are from ovalbumin; B, C, E, and F are from Chinese hamster ovary cell membranes; and F is the A glycopeptide from bovine thyroglobulin. (Reproduced, with permission, from Lennarz WJ: *The Biochemistry of Glycoproteins and Proteoglycans.* Plenum Press, 1980.)

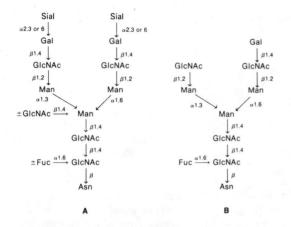

A   **B**

Figure 32–4. Structures of glycopeptides with complex N-linked oligosaccharides. *A* is a composite structure characteristic of many glycopeptides as described in the text, and *B* is from human IgG. (Reproduced, with permission, from Lennarz WJ: *The Biochemistry of Glycoproteins and Proteoglycans.* Plenum Press, 1980.)

rectly to the β-Man-N-acetylchitobiose structure (Fig 32–4). The outer chains most often consist of Sial-Gal-GlcNAc.

Complex N-linked oligosaccharide structures are found **only in higher animals,** whereas the high-mannose type are common in primitive organisms. Synthesis of the complex oligosaccharides occurs by way of the same lipid-linked precursor oligosaccharide that participates in synthesis of the high-mannose oligosaccharide. Thus, the **core regions** of both the high-mannose oligosaccharides and the complex oligosaccharides are **identical.** Clearly, the lipid-linked process used for the synthesis of the high-mannose oligosaccharides in ancestral organisms has been employed for the generation of the recently evolved complex oligosaccharide structures.

Lipid-Linked Oligosaccharide Precursor

Polyisoprenol compounds, occurring as free alcohols, exist in both bacteria and eukaryotic tissues. They participate in the synthesis of bacterial cell walls and of the glycoproteins and proteoglycans in eukaryotic tissues. The polyisoprenol primarily used in eukaryotic tissues is **dolichol,** which is, next to rubber,

the longest naturally occurring hydrocarbon made up of a single repeating unit. A space-filling model is illustrated in Fig 32–5. This very hydrophobic molecule extends approximately 10 nm, significantly greater than the width of the membrane bilayer where it is commonly found.

Glc-NAc-pyrophosphoryl-dolichyl (GlcNAc-P-P-Dol) is the key glycosyl lipid that acts as **acceptor** for other glycosyl units in the oligosaccharide-lipid assembly mechanism. It is also found in the membranes of a wide variety of tissues. This primary precursor is synthesized from UDP-Glc-NAc and dolichol phosphate in the following reaction:

$$\text{Dol-P} + \text{UDP-GlcNAc} \rightarrow \text{Dol-P-P-GlcNAc} + \text{UMP}$$

Retinol, the alcoholic form of vitamin A, is also a hydrophobic polyisoprenoid compound widely distributed in animal tissues (see Chapter 11). Retinol is capable of stimulating glycoprotein synthesis. Beta-Man-P-retinol and Gal-P-retinol appear to act as intermediates in glycoprotein synthesis, seemingly as a substitute for dolichol phosphosugar.

On the GlcNAc-P-P-Dol primer is built an oligosaccharide structure like the high-mannose type present in glycoproteins. The synthesis occurs as depicted in Fig 32–6. The penultimate GlcNAc is donated by UDP-GlcNAc to form a second beta-linked GlcNAc. The mannose is next added in a beta- linkage

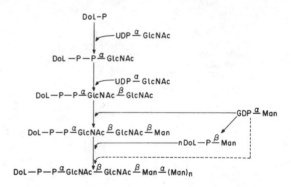

Figure 32–6. Pathway for assembly of oligosaccharide–dolichol. (Reproduced, with permission, from Lennarz WJ: *The Biochemistry of Glycoproteins and Proteoglycans.* Plenum Press, 1980.)

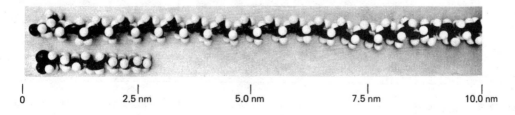

0	2.5 nm	5.0 nm	7.5 nm 10.0 nm

Figure 32–5. Molecular model of dolichol. In fully extended form it is 10 nm in length. Oleic acid (2.5 nm) is shown for comparison. (Reproduced, with permission, from Lennarz WJ: *The Biochemistry of Glycoproteins and Proteoglycans.* Plenum Press, 1980.)

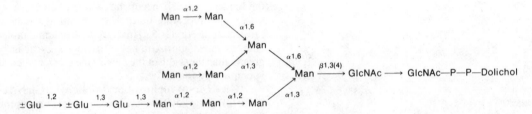

Figure 32–7. Proposed structure of the lipid-linked oligosaccharide precursor in glycoprotein synthesis. (Reproduced, with permission, from Lennarz WJ: *The Biochemistry of Glycoproteins and Proteoglycans.* Plenum Press, 1980.)

from GDP-α-Man in a reaction that involves an inversion of the glycosidic bond from alpha to beta. The subsequent Man moieties that become linked in the alpha configuration are donated by another dolichol derivative, Man-P-Dol. The Man-P-Dol is formed in the following reaction:

$$\text{Dol-P} + \text{GDP-}\alpha\text{-Man} \rightarrow \text{Dol-P-}\beta\text{-Man} + \text{GDP}$$

It seems that some of the lipid-linked oligosaccharide precursors contain Glc residues donated by Glc-P-Dol, which have been generated similarly from UDP-Glc and P-Dol. In this way are generated the lipid-linked oligosaccharide precursors, with a structure taking the general form depicted in Fig 32–7.

The high-mannose oligosaccharide moiety linked to pyrophosphoryldolichol is then transferred en bloc to form an N-glycosidic bond with the Asn moiety of a protein molecule emerging through the endoplasmic reticulum membrane (see Chapter 31). The reaction is catalyzed by an "oligosaccharide transferase," a membrane-associated enzyme. The transferase will recognize and transfer any glycolipid with the general structure R-(GlcNAc)$_2$-P-P-Dol. The recipient proteins in the endoplasmic reticulum have molecular weights ranging from 15,000 to 145,000 and include both secreted and integral membrane proteins. The intracellular soluble proteins are rarely if ever glycosylated. This transfer reaction is depicted in Fig 32–8.

The other product of the oligosaccharide transferase reaction is dolichol pyrophosphate, which is subsequently converted to dolichol phosphate. The

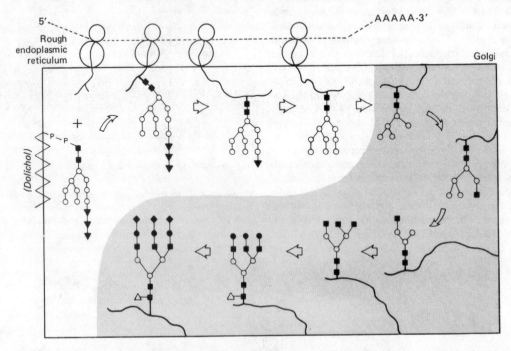

Figure 32–8. Proposed sequence for the processing of peptide-bound N-linked oligosaccharide chains: ■, *N*-acetylglucosamine residues; ○, mannose residues; ▼, glucose residues; ●, galactose residues; ◆, sialic acid residues; and △, fucose residues. The wavy line represents the polypeptide chain; the broken line is the mRNA. The processes within the shaded area occur in the Golgi complex. (Modified and reproduced, with permission, from Lennarz WJ: *The Biochemistry of Glycoproteins and Proteoglycans.* Plenum Press, 1980.)

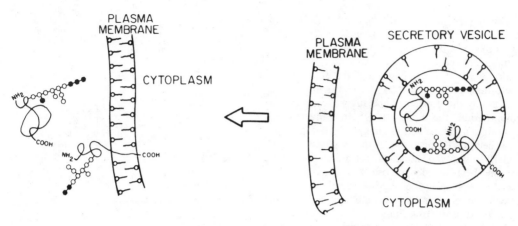

Figure 32–9. Depiction of the fusion of a secretory vesicle with the plasma membrane. The process provides integral plasma membrane glycoproteins and secretes luminal proteins to the extracellular space. (Reproduced, with permission, from Lennarz WJ: *The Biochemistry of Glycoproteins and Proteoglycans.* Plenum Press, 1980.)

dolichol phosphate can serve again as an acceptor for the synthesis of a lipid-linked oligosaccharide precursor.

The generation of the oligosaccharide dolichol precursor and the transfer of its oligosaccharide moiety occurs in the rough endoplasmic reticulum. At that site, glycosylated integral membrane proteins remain within the endoplasmic reticulum membrane structure, while secretory proteins that have been glycosylated are extruded into the lumen of the endoplasmic reticulum. These glycosylated proteins, which contain the high-mannose oligosaccharide moieties, migrate to the Golgi complex, perhaps by lateral diffusion within the plane of the membrane. In the Golgi complex, the oligosaccharide moieties of these glycoproteins may be further modified to form complex oligosaccharides described above. This modification process involves glycosidase and glycosyl transferase enzymes and will be described in detail below. Vesicles are formed from the Golgi complex and then fuse with a plasma membrane, as depicted in Fig 32–9. Luminal glycoproteins are secreted into the surrounding medium, while integral membrane proteins in secretory vesicles become integral components of the plasma membranes. Vesicles of similar structures deliver integral proteins to the internal membrane structures and provide glycoproteins to the lumens of internal membrane structures such as lysosomes.

Synthesis of Dolichol

The isoprenol structure of dolichol is derived from mevalonate by the condensation of isopentenyl pyrophosphate and dimethylallyl pyrophosphate to form farnesyl pyrophosphate (see Chapter 18). The transfarnesyl pyrophosphate then acts as an acceptor of more isoprene units from isoprenyl pyrophosphate, eventually to form dolichol phosphate. As mentioned above, dolichol phosphate can also be regenerated from dolichol pyrophosphate, a by-product of the oligosaccharide transferase reaction in the endoplasmic reticulum.

There are a number of inhibitors of the synthesis of oligopyrophosphoryl dolichol. The 2-deoxysugars such as 2-deoxyglucose, the fluorodeoxysugars, and the amino sugars can all inhibit formation of oligosaccharide moieties by mechanisms that are not clearly defined. The antibiotic **bacitracin** in bacteria blocks the dephosphorylation of undecaprenol pyrophosphate to form the necessary undecaprenol phosphate. In animal pancreas microsomes, bacitracin blocks the synthesis of GlcNAc-P-P-Dol.

Tunicamycin, an antibiotic from *Streptomyces,* also blocks the synthesis of GlcNAc-P-P-Dol from Dol-P and UDP-GlcNAc. Both of these antibiotics— particularly the latter—are useful in the study of the functional roles of glycoproteins. The regulation of dolichol phosphate synthesis appears to occur both at the level of synthesis of mevalonic acid and at the level of regeneration of dolichol phosphate from dolichol pyrophosphate.

The Synthesis of Complex Carbohydrates of Glycoproteins

The discovery of the mechanism of glycogen synthetase established the role of nucleotides in the synthesis of complex carbohydrate molecules, such as starch and glycogen. The nucleotide sugars are formed from nucleoside triphosphates and sugar 1-phosphates in the following reaction:

$$NTP + \text{P-1-Sugar} \rightarrow \text{NDP-Sugar} + PP_i$$

The reaction is catalyzed by cytoplasmic enzymes. The sugar nucleotides formed by these reactions include the following:

UDP-α-Glc
UDP-α-Gal
UDP-α-GlcNAc
UDP-α-GalNAc
GDP-α-Man
GDP-β-Fuc

The nucleotide of sialic acid, CMP-Sial, is formed from CTP by sialyltransferases located in the Golgi complex and in the nucleoplasm.

In animal cells, the sugars are linked to the nucleotides by the alpha- linkage, with the exception of the beta- linkage of L-fucose to GDP. As mentioned above, during the transfer of the sugar moiety to the oligosaccharide, the alpha- bridges are inverted to beta- bridges and vice versa. Thus, GDP-α-Man provides a beta-linked mannose in the oligosaccharide. The GDP-α-Man can, however, form Man-β-P-Dol. When this beta-linked mannose is transferred from dolichol phosphate to the oligosaccharide, a second inversion occurs, thereby generating the alpha-Man bridges found in oligosaccharides.

A series of specific glycosyltransferase enzymes catalyze the transfer of the sugar moieties to generate the complex glycoproteins that have the general structure (Glc)$_x$(Man-α)$_y$Man-β-1,4-GlcNAc-β-1,4-GlcNAc-Asn. These glycosyltransferases generally require divalent **manganese.** The order of addition is dictated by the substrate specificities of the glycosyltransferase enzymes. As depicted in Fig 32–8, by the time the high-mannose oligosaccharide-polypeptide has reached the Golgi complex, it may have had its sugar moieties trimmed such that only 5 mannosyl residues remain attached to the di-N-acetylchitobiose core.

A Golgi-localized enzyme, UDPGlcNAc transferase I, can then donate a GlcNAc to a linear or branched α-Man moiety to form GlcNAc-β-1,2-Man linkages. A second transferase, UDPGlcNAc transferase II, will donate its GlcNAc moiety **only to a branched structure** to which one GlcNAc has already been attached, such as by the transferase I enzyme. As depicted in Fig 32–8, the attachment of the first GlcNAc moiety seems to be followed by further trimming of the α-mannosyl residues from the oligosaccharide by membrane-associated mannosidases.

Fucosal transferases can then act on the products of GlcNAc transferase I or transferase II but must have at least one GlcNAc residue on the Man$_3$GlcNAc$_2$Asn core. The galactosyltransferase enzymes are also located on the Golgi complex and attach a galactosyl residue usually to the end of a chain or occasionally penultimate to a sialic acid residue. The galactosyl residues are usually linked to GlcNAc by beta-1,4-linkages but occasionally by beta-1,6- linkages.

The galactosyltransferase enzyme is unique; in the presence of manganese and glucose or GlcNAc, it binds tightly to α-lactalbumin, present in colostrum and milk, and becomes the lactose synthetase A enzyme per se.

At least 4 different sialyltransferase enzymes can be found in the Golgi complex and utilize CMP-sialic acid as donor for the sialation of protein-linked oligosaccharides. The Sial residues are always found linked to a subterminal Gal moiety at a nonreducing terminus in alpha-linkage, usually 2,3- or 2,6-.

This elongation process generating the complex type oligosaccharides of glycoproteins occurs exclu-

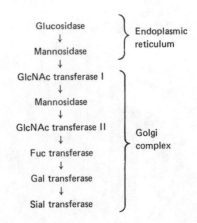

Figure 32–10. Order in which the specific glycosyltransferase enzymes act to form the specific complex type oligosaccharide structures of glycoproteins. The parentheses denote that either enzyme can act first. The locations of the enzymes are indicated.

sively in the Golgi complex. Each linkage appears to be carried out by a specific glycosyltransferase; thus, there seems to be a **"one linkage, one glycosyltransferase"** synthetic arrangement. The specific sequence in which the glycosyltransferases act is generalized in Fig 32–10. The ordered generation of the oligosaccharide and its location are depicted in Fig 32–8.

BLOOD GROUP ANTIGENS

The blood group antigens are oligosaccharides of specific medical interest. Their structures and syntheses will be described in detail. In 1900, **Landsteiner** described the **ABO blood groups.** Today, there are more than 20 blood group systems expressing more than 160 distinct antigens. The most commonly studied blood groups are those of the ABH(O) and the Lewis (Le) systems. These erythrocyte antigens are linked to specific membrane proteins by O-glycosidic bonds in which GalNAc is the most proximal sugar residue. The specific oligosaccharides forming these antigens occur in 3 forms: (1) as glycosphingolipids and glycoproteins on the surfaces of erythrocytes and other cells, (2) as oligosaccharides in milk and urine, and (3) as oligosaccharides attached to mucins secreted in the gastrointestinal, genitourinary, and respiratory tracts.

There are 4 independent gene systems related to the expressions of these oligosaccharide antigens (Table 32–3).

The H Locus

The **H locus** codes for a fucosyltransferase that attaches a fucose residue in alpha-1,2- linkage to a Gal residue, itself attached in either beta-1,4- or beta-1,3-

Table 32–3. The 4 independent gene systems responsible for the expressions of the ABH(O) and Lewis (Le) blood group antigens.

Genetic Locus	Alleles
H	H, h
Secretor	Se, se
ABO	A, B, O
Lewis	Le, le

linkage to an oligosaccharide. The fucosyltransferase catalyzes

$$GDP \; \beta\text{-Fuc} + Gal\text{-}\beta\text{-R} \rightarrow Fuc\text{-}\alpha\text{-}1,2\text{-Gal-}\beta\text{-R} + GDP$$

The product, Fuc-α-1,2-Gal-β-R, is a **precursor** for the formation of both the A and B oligosaccharide antigens. The h allele of the H locus codes for an inactive fucosyltransferase; therefore, individuals with the **hh genotype cannot generate this necessary precursor** of the A and B antigens. Accordingly, hh genotypic persons will be type O even though they may possess genes for the active A or active B glycosyltransferases described below.

The Secretor Locus

The **secretor locus** controls the appearance of the H-specific Fuc transferase in some secretory organs, such as the exocrine glands, but *not* in the erythrocytes. Accordingly—for example—individuals with the Hh or HH genotype and an Se allele will generate the A and B antigen **precursor** in the exocrine glands that form saliva. Those individuals who are SeSe or Sese and possess an H allele will be secretors of the A or B antigens (or both) when the A- or B-specific transferases are present (Table 32–4). Individuals who are sese genotype will **not secrete A or B** antigens, but if they possess an H allele and A or B alleles, their **erythrocytes will express** the A, B, or both antigens.

Table 32–4. A, B antigen expression.

	Genotypes		Phenotypes	
		Secretor		
ABO Locus	H Locus	Locus	Erythrocytes	Secretions
OO	Any	Any	O	O
A and/or B	HH or Hh	SeSe or Sese	A and/or B	A and/or B
A and/or B	HH or Hh	sese	A and/or B	O
A and/or B	hh	Any	O	O

The ABO Locus

The ABO locus codes for 2 specific transferases that act to transfer specific Gal moieties to the Fuc-α-1,2-Gal-β-R precursor oligosaccharide formed by the action of the H allele–coded fucosyltransferase. The

A-specific transferase carries out the following reaction:

$$UDP\text{-}\alpha\text{-}\textbf{GalNAc} + Fuc\text{-}\alpha\text{-}1,2\text{-Gal-}\beta\text{-R} \rightarrow$$
$$GalNAc\text{-}\alpha\text{-}1,3\text{-}(Fuc\text{-}\alpha\text{-}1,2)Gal\text{-}\beta\text{-R} + UDP$$

The B allele-specific transferase catalyzes the reaction

$$UDP\text{-}\alpha\text{-}\textbf{Gal} + Fuc\text{-}\alpha\text{-}1,2\text{-Gal-}\beta\text{-R} \rightarrow$$
$$Gal\text{-}\alpha\text{-}1,3\text{-}(Fuc\text{-}\alpha\text{-}1,2)Gal\text{-}\beta\text{-R} + UDP$$

Accordingly, persons possessing an A allele will attach a **GalNAc moiety to the precursor generated by the H allele** transferase, and individuals possessing a B allele will transfer a **Gal moiety to the same precursor** (Fig 32–11). Individuals possessing both an A allele and a B allele will generate both oligosaccharides, ie, one with a GalNAc and another with a Gal moiety on the nonreducing terminus. Individuals lacking both A and B alleles (OO homozygotes) will not attach either GalNAc or Gal to the precursor. The anti-A antiserum originally described by Landsteiner recognizes the specific oligosaccharide with the GalNAc nonreducing terminus. The anti-B antiserum recognizes the closely related oligosaccharide with the Gal nonreducing terminus. When neither GalNAc nor Gal is at the reducing terminus of this oligosaccharide, it will not be recognized by either anti-A or anti-B antisera, and the blood group antigen is said to be **type O**. It can be seen that individuals with the hh genotype and thus incapable of attaching the Fuc moiety to the appropriate Gal-β-R oligosaccharide would be incapable of expressing the A or the B antigen determinant

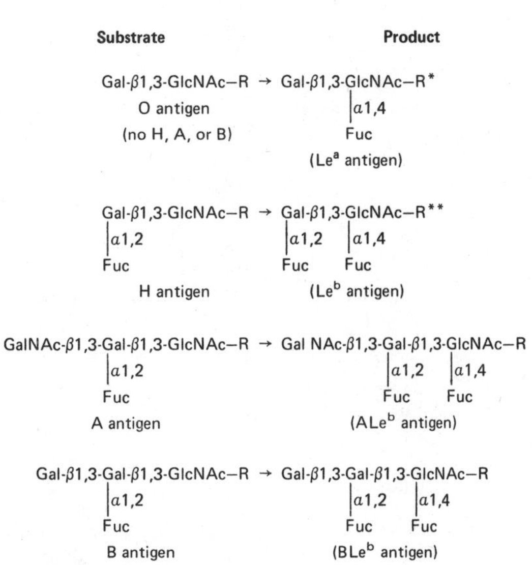

Substrate	Product

Gal-β1,3-GlcNAc—R → Gal-β1,3-GlcNAc—R*
  O antigen |α1,4
  (no H, A, or B)   Fuc
                               (Le^a antigen)

Gal-β1,3-GlcNAc—R → Gal-β1,3-GlcNAc—R**
  |α1,2 |α1,2 |α1,4
  Fuc   Fuc   Fuc
  H antigen   (Le^b antigen)

GalNAc-β1,3-Gal-β1,3-GlcNAc—R → Gal NAc-β1,3-Gal-β1,3-GlcNAc—R
  |α1,2 |α1,2 |α1,4
  Fuc   Fuc   Fuc
  A antigen   (ALe^b antigen)

Gal-β1,3-Gal-β1,3-GlcNAc—R → Gal-β1,3-Gal-β1,3-GlcNAc—R
  |α1,2 |α1,2 |α1,4
  Fuc   Fuc   Fuc
  B antigen   (BLe^b antigen)

*Not substrate for H transferase.
**Not substrate for A or B transferase.

Figure 32–11. The A and B antigens and substrate specificity of the Lewis-dependent α-1,4-fucosyltransferase.

and thus also would be considered to be of the O type blood group.

The Lewis Locus

The Le gene of the Lewis locus codes for an α-1,4-fucosyltransferase activity, which has a rather strict oligosaccharide substrate specificity. The Lewis-dependent transferase will attach in alpha-1,4-linkage, a Fuc moiety to a GlcNAc residue that already has attached to it a β-Gal in a 1,3- linkage (Fig 32–11). Note that this Lewis fucosyltransferase will not utilize as a substrate a GlcNAc oligosaccharide that contains a β-Gal in a 1,4- linkage; it is that 4-moiety of the GlcNAc to which it must attach its own Fuc moiety. The Lewis-dependent fucosyltransferase is not specific about what is *not* attached to the Gal-1,3-β group. Thus, if the H transferase has already put on a Fuc-1,2-α moiety, or even if the A-dependent transferase or B-dependent transferase has attached GalNAc or Gal moieties, respectively, the Lewis transferase will still attach a Fuc in an alpha-1,4- linkage to that same GalNAc residue (Fig 32–11).

When no H allele is present (hh), the product of the Lewis α-1,4-fucosyltransferase is referred to as the Lea antigen (Figs 32–11 and 32–12). When present, the H-dependent α-1,2-fucosyltransferase cannot act on the Lea antigen, because of the prior attachment of the α-Fuc in 1,4- linkage to the penultimate GlcNAc residue. Thus, the Lea antigen cannot have A or B antigenicity even when the A or B transferases are also present.

When both the H allele and the Le allele fucosyltransferases have acted on the Gal-1,3-R oligosaccharide, the product is referred to as the Leb antigen (Figs 32–11 and 32–12). The Leb structure can in addition have A antigenicity or B antigenicity, since the Lewis α-1,4-fucosyltransferase can act on both the A oligosaccharide and the B oligosaccharide. However, if the Lewis fucosyl alpha-1,4- moiety is attached to the H antigen before the A or B transferases have attached their sugar moieties, the A and B transferases will not be able to utilize that oligosaccharide containing the 2 juxtaposed α-Fuc residues (Fig 32–12). The Leb antigen may also exist without A antigenicity or B antigenicity on the same molecule when (1) neither the A transferase nor the B transferase exists (OO genotype) or (2) when the Lewis α-1,4-fucosyltransferase acts on its substrate prior to the action of the A transferase or B transferase on the same molecule (Fig 32–12).

The le allele codes for an inactive Lewis transferase, and thus neither Lea nor Leb antigens will be formed in a person with lele genotype (Fig 32–12).

PROTEOGLYCANS

The proteoglycans and the glycoproteins are molecules consisting of proteins to which oligosaccharide or polysaccharide chains are covalently attached. The distinction between proteoglycans and glycoproteins is based on the chemical nature of the

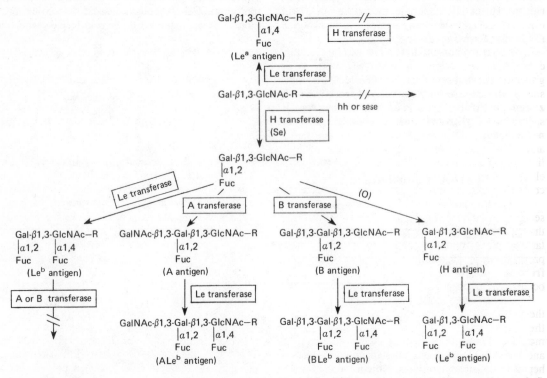

Figure 32–12. Pathways generating the antigenic oligosaccharides of the ABO-Lewis system. An interrupted arrow indicates a blocked pathway due to an inactive glycosyltransferase (hh, sese) or inappropriate substrate.

attached polysaccharides. In proteoglycans, each polysaccharide consists of **repeating disaccharide units in which D-glucosamine or D-galactosamine is always present.** Each disaccharide unit in the proteoglycan polysaccharides (with the exception of keratan sulfate) contains a uronic acid, **glucuronic acid (GlcUA)** or its 5-epimer, **L-iduronic acid (IdUA).** With the exception of hyaluronic acid, all polysaccharides of proteoglycans contain **sulfate groups** either as O-esters or N-sulfate (in heparin and heparan sulfate).

The linkage of the proteoglycan polysaccharides to their polypeptide chain is one of 3 types.

(1) An O-glycosidic bond between the Xyl and Ser, a bond that is **unique to proteoglycans.**

(2) An O-glycosidic bond between GalNAc and Ser(Thr), present in keratan sulfate II.

(3) An N-glycosylamine bond between GlcNAc and the amide nitrogen of Asn.

The formation of the polysaccharide chains occurs in pathways quite similar to those responsible for the attachment and growth of the oligosaccharide chains of glycoproteins. A UDP-Xyl transferase attaches the Xyl of the nucleotide sugar to Ser to form the Xyl-Ser O-glycosidic bond. The formation of the O-glycosidic bond between GalNAc and Ser (or Thr) probably occurs by a similar UDP-GalNAc transferase. The N-glycosidic bond between GlcNAc and the amide nitrogen of Asn almost certainly involves the lipid-linked polysaccharide, dolichol-P-P polysaccharide, which, as discussed above, is responsible for the transfer of a preformed oligo- or polysaccharide in the formation of glycoproteins. However, the details of this reaction in the synthesis of proteoglycans have not been established.

The chain elongation process involves the nucleotidyl sugars acting as donors. The reactions are governed primarily by the substrate specifities of the specific glycosyltransferases. Again, the **"one enzyme, one linkage"** relationship seems to hold. The specificity of these reactions is dependent upon the nucleotide sugar donor, the acceptor oligosaccharide, and the anomeric configuration and position of the linkage. The enzyme systems involved in this chain elongation are capable of high-fidelity reproduction of complex polysaccharides.

The termination of polysaccharide chain growth seems to result from (1) capping effects of **sialation** by the specific sialyl transferases; (2) **sulfation,** particularly at the 4- positions of the sugars, and (3) the progression of the particular polysaccharide **away from the site** in the membrane where the catalysis occurs.

After formation of the polysaccharide chain, there occur numerous chemical **modifications,** such as the introduction of sulfate groups onto GalNAc moieties of chondroitin sulfate and dermatan sulfate and the epimerization of GlcUA to IdUA residues in heparin and heparan sulfates.

An important aspect of the metabolism of proteoglycans is their **degradation.** Inherited defects in the degradation of the polysaccharide chains of proteoglycans lead to the group of diseases known as **mucopolysaccharidoses** and **mucolipidoses,** discussed below and in Chapter 13. These catabolic defects have allowed the study of specific degradation enzymes and their substrates. There exists a battery of exoglycosidases that act in a stepwise manner to remove the sulfate moieties and glycosyl groups. In addition, there are normally present endoglycosidases with different specificities. For example, **hyaluronidase** is a widely distributed enzyme that cleaves N-acetylhexosamine linkages in hyaluronic acid and chondroitin sulfates.

There are **7 types of polysaccharides** (glycosaminoglycans) found covalently attached to the proteins of proteoglycans. Six of them are structurally related and contain **alternating uronic acid and hexosamine residues** in repeating disaccharide units. All except hyaluronic acid contain **sulfated sugars.** The 7 types of polysaccharides can be distinguished by their **monomer composition,** their **glycosidic linkage,** and the amount and location of their **sulfate substituents.**

All of the glycosaminoglycans are **polyanions,** since they have acidic sulfate or carboxyl groups of uronic acids present throughout their structures. Many of their functions result from this particular characteristic.

The structures of the 7 glycosaminoglycans of the proteoglycan molecules are summarized in Fig 32–13.

Hyaluronic Acid

Hyaluronic acid consists of an unbranched chain of repeating disaccharide units containing GlcUA and GlcNAc. There is no firm evidence that hyaluronic acid is linked to a protein molecule, as are other connective tissue polysaccharides, but it is probably synthesized as a proteoglycan, as are the other glycosaminoglycans. Hyaluronic acid is present in bacteria and widely distributed among various animal organisms and tissues, including synovial fluid, the vitreous body of the eye, and loose connective tissue.

Chondroitin Sulfates

Chondroitin sulfates are proteoglycans that are a very prominent component of cartilage. The polysaccharide is linked to protein by the Xyl-Ser O-glycosidic bond. The structure of the chondroitin sulfates is summarized in Fig 32–13. The repeating disaccharide unit is very similar to that of hyaluronic acid, except that the hexosamine is GalNAc rather than GlcNAc. However, in both the chondroitin sulfates and hyaluronic acid, the uronic acid is GlcUA, and the bond positions and anomeric configurations are the same. In the chondroitin sulfates, the GalNAc carries a sulfate substituent in the 4 or 6 position. As a rule, both 4- and 6-sulfate substituents are present in the same molecule but not on the same monosaccharide residue. There is on the average about one sulfate substituent per disaccharide unit. Each chain of polysaccharide consists of about 40 repeating disaccharide units and thus has a molecular weight of about 20,000. Many

Hyaluronic acid: $\xrightarrow{\beta1,4}$ GlcUA $\xrightarrow{\beta1,3}$ GlcNAc $\xrightarrow{\beta1,4}$ GlcUA $\xrightarrow{\beta1,3}$ GlcNAc $\xrightarrow{\beta1,4}$

Chondroitin sulfates: $\xrightarrow{\beta1,4}$ GlcUA $\xrightarrow{\beta1,3}$ GalNAc $\xrightarrow{\beta1,4}$ GlcUA $\xrightarrow{\beta1,3}$ Gal $\xrightarrow{\beta1,3}$ Gal $\xrightarrow{\beta1,4}$ Xyl $\xrightarrow{\beta}$ Ser
　　　　　　　　　　　|
　　　　　　　4- or 6-sulfate

Keratan sulfates:

$\xrightarrow{\beta1,4}$ GlcNAc $\xrightarrow{\beta1,3}$ Gal $\xrightarrow{\beta1,4}$ GlcNAc $\xrightarrow{\beta1,3}$ Gal $\overset{(GlcNAc,Man)}{\cdots}$ GlcNAc $\xrightarrow{\beta}$ Asn (keratan sulfate I)
　　　　　　　　　　|　　　　　　　|
　　　　　　6-sulfate　　6-sulfate　　$\overset{1,6}{\cdots}$ GalNAc $\xrightarrow{\alpha}$ Thr(Ser) (keratan sulfate II)
　　　　　　　　　　　　　　　　　　|
　　　　　　　　　　　　　　　　Gal-Nana

Heparin and heparan sulfate:

　　　　　　　　　　　6-sulfate
　　　　　　　　　　　　|
$\xrightarrow{\alpha1,4}$ IdUA $\xrightarrow{\alpha1,4}$ GlcN $\xrightarrow{\alpha1,4}$ GlcUA $\xrightarrow{\beta1,4}$ GlcNAc $\xrightarrow{\alpha1,4}$ GlcUA $\xrightarrow{\beta1,3}$ Gal $\xrightarrow{\beta1,3}$ Gal $\xrightarrow{\beta1,4}$ Xyl $\xrightarrow{\beta}$ Ser
　　　|　　　　　|
2-sulfate　　SO_3^- or Ac

Dermatan sulfate: $\xrightarrow{\beta1,4}$ IdUA $\xrightarrow{\alpha1,3}$ GalNAc $\xrightarrow{\beta1,4}$ GlcUA $\xrightarrow{\beta1,3}$ GalNAc $\xrightarrow{\beta1,4}$ GlcUA $\xrightarrow{\beta1,3}$ Gal $\xrightarrow{\beta1,3}$ Gal $\xrightarrow{\beta1,4}$ Xyl $\xrightarrow{\beta}$ Ser
　　　　|　　　　　|
2-sulfate　　4-sulfate

Figure 32–13. Summary of structures of proteoglycans and glycosaminoglycans. (GlcUA, D-glucuronic acid; IdUA, L-iduronic acid; GlcN, D-glucosamine; GalN, D-galactosamine; Ac, N-acetyl; Gal, D-galactose; Xyl, D-xylose; Ser, L-serine; Thr, L-threonine; Asn, L-asparagine; Man, D-mannose; Nana, N-acetylneuraminic acid.) The summary structures are qualitative representations only and do not reflect, for example, the uronic acid composition of hybrid polysaccharides such as heparin and dermatan sulfate, which contain both L-iduronic and D-glucuronic acid. Neither should it be assumed that the much smaller proportion of these residues are sulfated in dermatan sulfate. (Slightly modified and reproduced, with permission, from Lennarz WJ: *The Biochemistry of Glycoproteins and Proteoglycans.* Plenum Press, 1980.)

such chains are attached to a single protein molecule, generating high-molecular-weight proteoglycans. For instance, the molecular weight of nasal cartilage chondroitin sulfate is approximately 2.5×10^6.

The chondroitin sulfates associate tightly with hyaluronic acid with the aid of 2 **"link proteins"** to generate very large aggregates in connective tissue. These aggregates can be observed in the electron microscope (Fig 32–14) and are diagrammatically presented in Fig 32–15.

The link proteins are strongly hydrophobic and interact both with hyaluronic acid and the proteoglycan.

The chondroitin sulfates contain 6 types of intersaccharide linkages and thus are synthesized by 6 different glycosyltransferase enzymes, one for each type of linkage. In addition, there are 2 types of sulfate esters, one on the 4- and another on the 6- position. Two sulfotransferases carry out these esterifications. The sulfate-containing substrate for these sulfotransferases is 3-phosphoadenyl 5'-phosphosulfate (PAPS).

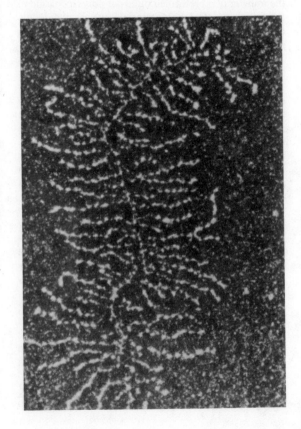

Figure 32–14 (at right). Darkfield electron micrograph of a proteoglycan aggregate of intermediate size in which the proteoglycan subunits and filamentous backbone are particularly well extended. (Reproduced, with permission, from Rosenberg L, Hellman W, Kleinschmidt AK: Electron microscopic studies of proteoglycan aggregates from bovine articular cartilage. *J Biol Chem* 1975;**250**:1877.)

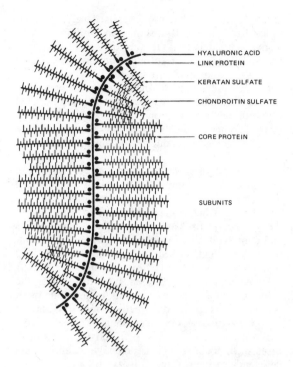

HYALURONIC ACID

LINK PROTEIN

KERATAN SULFATE

CHONDROITIN SULFATE

CORE PROTEIN

SUBUNITS

Figure 32–15. Schematic representation of proteoglycan aggregate. (Reproduced, with permission, from Lennarz WJ: *The Biochemistry of Glycoproteins and Proteoglycans.* Plenum Press, 1980.)

Keratan Sulfate I and Keratan Sulfate II

As shown in Fig 32–13, the keratan sulfates consist of repeating Gal-GlcNAc disaccharide units and contain sulfates on the 6- position of GlcNAc residues and occasionally on the Gal 6- position. The polysaccharide of keratan sulfate I is attached to its polypeptide chain by a **GlcNAc-Asn** bond. It is abundant in the cornea.

Keratan sulfate II is a skeletal proteoglycan present along with chondroitin sulfate, attached to hyaluronic acid in loose connective tissue. Its polysaccharide chains are attached to its polypeptide chain by a **GalNAc-Thr(Ser)** linkage.

Heparin

Heparin is a classic proteoglycan in which several polysaccharide chains are linked to a common protein core. However, heparin is found stored in granules of mast cells and thus occurs **intracellularly.** Heparin has several other unique structural and functional features, including some that are of medical importance. Fig 32–16 illustrates some characteristic features of the heparin structure. The repeating disaccharide unit contains **glucosamine** (GlcN) and a uronic acid. Most of the amino groups of the GlcN residues are **N-sulfated,** but a few are **acetylated.** The GlcN also carries a C_6 sulfate ester.

Approximately 90% of the uronic acid residues are IdUA; only 10% are GlcUA. Initially, all of the uronic acids are GlcUA, but, as described below, a 5-epimerase converts approximately 90% of the GlcUA residues to IdUA residues after the polysaccharide is formed. The IdUA residues are frequently sulfated at the 2- position.

The protein molecule of the heparin proteoglycan is unique, consisting exclusively of **serine and glycine** residues. Approximately two-thirds of the serine residues contain polysaccharide chains, usually with molecular weights of 5000–15,000 but occasionally as high as 100,000.

The polysaccharide chains of the heparin proteoglycans undergo a specific sequence of modification after the polymerization. This sequence of modifications occurs in the following way:

(1) The primary product is not sulfated but fully N-acetylated and thus is a polymer of (GlcUA-GlcNAc)$_n$.

(2) Approximately 50% of the GlcNAc residues are N-deacetylated.

(3) The free amino groups of the GlcN are sulfated; subsequently, there is further deacetylation of about half of the remaining GlcNAc residues.

(4) The N-sulfated polymer then becomes a substrate for the 5-epimerase that converts approximately 90% of the GlcUA residues to IdUA.

(5) The recently formed IdUA residues are then O-sulfated on their C_2 positions.

(6) The modification is then completed by O-sulfation of the C_6 positions of GlcN units.

Heparan Sulfate

Heparan sulfate is present throughout cell surfaces as a proteoglycan and is **extracellular.** The polypeptide backbone of the heparan sulfate proteo-

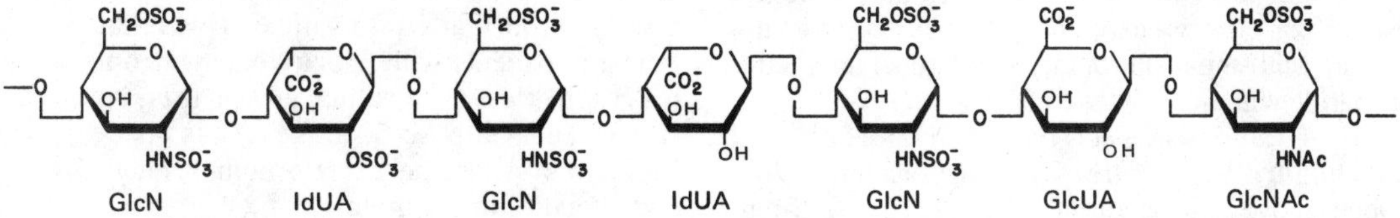

CH$_2$OSO$_3^-$ CO$_2^-$ CH$_2$OSO$_3^-$ CO$_2^-$ CH$_2$OSO$_3^-$ CO$_2^-$ CH$_2$OSO$_3^-$

OH   OH   OH   OH   OH   OH   OH

HNSO$_3^-$ OSO$_3^-$ HNSO$_3^-$ OH   HNSO$_3^-$ OH   HNAc

GlcN   IdUA   GlcN   IdUA   GlcN   GlcUA   GlcNAc

Figure 32–16. Structure of heparin. The polymer section illustrates structural features typical of heparin; however, the sequence of variously substituted repeating disaccharide units has been arbitrarily selected. In addition, non-O-sulfated or 3-O-sulfated glucosamine residues may also occur. (Modified, redrawn, and reproduced, with permission, from Lindahl U & others: Structure and biosynthesis of heparin-like polysaccharides. *Fed Proc* 1977;**36**:19.)

glycan has a typical amino acid complement, unlike that for heparin. In the process of modification of its polysaccharide chains, there is less deacetylation of the GlcNAc residues, and thus it contains fewer N-sulfates. Because the 5-epimerase (as described above for the modification of heparin) requires the N-sulfate substituents on its substrate, heparan sulfate contains a lower content of IdUA but more GlcUA than does heparin. Accordingly, GlcUA is the predominant uronic acid in heparan sulfate, while IdUA is the predominant uronic acid in heparin.

Dermatan Sulfate

Dermatan sulfate is a proteoglycan widely distributed in animal tissues. Structurally, it resembles both chondroitin sulfates and heparan sulfates. Its structure is similar to that of chondroitin sulfate except that in place of a GlcUA in beta-1,3- linkage to Gal-NAc, dermatan sulfate contains an **IdUA** and an **alpha**-1,3- linkage to GlcNAc. Formation of the IdUA occurs, as in heparin and heparan sulfate, by the 5-epimerization of GlcUA. As in the formation of heparin, the epimerization reaction is coupled tightly to the sulfation of hexosamine. Thus, the dermatan sulfate contains 2 types of repeating disaccharide units: IdUA-GlcNAc and GlcUA-GlcNAc.

DEGRADATION OF THE POLYSACCHARIDE MOIETIES OF GLYCOPROTEINS & PROTEOGLYCANS

Our understanding of the degradative pathways for glycoproteins, proteoglycans, and glycosaminoglycans has been greatly aided by discoveries of the specific enzyme deficiencies of inborn errors of human metabolism. Two groups of diseases whose study has contributed greatly are the mucopolysaccharidoses and the mucolipidoses. (For many years, what we now call proteoglycans were called mucopolysaccharides.) Table 32–5 lists the biochemical defects in the mucopolysaccharidoses, mucolipidoses, and related disorders.

Degradation of the polysaccharide chains is carried out by **endoglycosidases, exoglycosidases,** and **sulfatases.** In each case, the enzymes exhibit substrate specificities that allow one to deduce which of the polysaccharide chains will be subject to degradation by the particular glycosidase or sulfatase.

Hyaluronidase is a widely distributed endoglycosidase that cleaves hexosaminidic linkages. From hyaluronic acid, the hyaluronidase will generate a tetrasaccharide with the structure (GlcUA-β-1,3-GlcNAc-β-1,4)$_2$. Hyaluronidase acts on both **hyaluronic acid** and **chondroitin sulfate.** The tetrasaccharide described above can be further degraded by a β-glucuronidase and β-N-acetylhexosaminidase.

β-Glucuronidase is an exoglycosidase that removes both GlcUA and IdUA from nonreducing termini of tetrasaccharides or larger polysaccharides. In general, the disaccharides are poor substrates for β-

glucuronidase. β-Glucuronidase, itself a glycoprotein, is localized in both **lysosomes** and **microsomes** of many mammalian cells. Its substrates include **dermatan sulfate, heparan sulfate, chondroitin sulfate,** and **hyaluronic acid.** In inherited β-glucuronidase deficiency in humans, dermatan sulfate, heparan sulfate, and chondroitin sulfate compounds are excreted in the urine, but hyaluronic acid is not. Apparently there are other degradative pathways that can degrade the tetrasaccharide produced from hyaluronic acid by hyaluronidase.

β-D-Acetylhexosaminidase is an exoglycosidase present in many mammalian tissues. It cleaves from the nonreducing termini of polysaccharides GlcNAc and GalNAc when in beta- linkage. The substrates for the β-D-acetylhexosaminidase include **gangliosides** and **chondroitin sulfates, hyaluronic acid, dermatan sulfates,** and **keratan sulfates** I and II. There are 2 isozymes of β-D-acetylhexosaminidase. The **A isozyme** consists of 2 different types of subunits, the alpha subunit and the beta subunit ($\alpha\beta$)n, while the **B isozyme** consists of only beta subunits ($\beta\beta$)n. In **Tay-Sachs disease,** the alpha subunit is defective, and thus only the A isozyme is inactive. In **Sandoff disease,** the beta subunit is defective, resulting in a deficiency of both A and B isozyme.

β-Galactosidases exist in several forms in animal tissues. Both chondroitin sulfate and keratan sulfate contain β-galactosides and thus are substrates for the **acid galactosidases.** In the deficiency of acid β-galactosidase, both keratan sulfate and glycoprotein fragments accumulate, along with the G_{M1} gangliosides.

α-L-Iduronidase is a lysosomal hydrolase that removes IdUA from the nonreducing terminus of polysaccharide chains. This enzyme is deficient in **Hurler's syndrome.**

Mammalian tissues contain heparin and heparan sulfate–specific endoglycosidases, particularly an endoglucuronidase that exists in liver, intestinal mucosa, platelets, and lysosomes.

A large series of specific **sulfatases** exist for the removal of the sulfate substituents. There are 3 arylsulfatases: A, B, and C. **Arylsulfatase A** degrades the Gal-3-sulfate from ceramides. **Arylsulfatase B** removes the 4-sulfate from chondroitin sulfate and dermatan sulfate. However, patients with inherited deficiency of 4-sulfatase (**Maroteaux-Lamy syndrome**) spill only dermatan sulfate in urine. Distinct from arylsulfatases A and B is an enzyme that cleaves the 6-sulfate from GalNAc-6-sulfate. This sulfatase is deficient in patients with **Morquio's syndrome.** It normally will cleave the sulfate groups from both Gal-6-sulfate and GalNAc-6-sulfate. Thus, patients with Morquio's syndrome excrete both keratan 6-sulfate and chondroitin 6-sulfate.

A deficiency of **N-acetylglucosamine-6-sulfatase** has been observed in mucopolysaccharidosis A. This enzyme can utilize as a substrate GlcNAc-6-sulfate and Glc-6-sulfate.

Iduronate sulfatase is a specific exoenzyme that

Table 32–5. Biochemical defects in mucopolysaccharisoses, mucolipidoses and related disorders, and diagnostic tests.[*]

Name	Alternate Designation	Enzymatic Defect	Material for Enzyme Assay	Abnormal ^{35}S-Mucopolysaccharide Level in Fibroblasts	Urinary Metabolites
Mucopolysaccharidoses					
Hurler, Scheie, Hurler/Scheie	MPS I	α-L-Iduronidase	Fibroblasts, leukocytes, tissues, amniotic fluid cells	+	DS, HS
Hunter	MPS II	Iduronate sulfatase	Serum, fibroblasts, leukocytes, tissues, amniotic fluid cells, amniotic fluid	+	DS, HS
Sanfilippo A	MPS III A	HS N-sulfatase (sulfamidase)	Fibroblasts, leukocytes, tissues, amniotic fluid cells	±	HS (±)
Sanfilippo B	MPS III B	α-N-acetylglucosaminidase	Serum, fibroblasts, leukocytes, tissues, amniotic fluid cells	+	HS
Sanfilippo C	MPS III C	Acetyltransferase	Fibroblasts	+	HS
Morquio	MPS IV	N-Acetylgalactosamine 6-sulfatase	Fibroblasts	—	KS
Morquiolike	None	β-Galactosidase	Fibroblasts	—	KS
Maroteaux-Lamy	MPS VI	N-Acetylgalactosamine 4-sulfatase (arylsulfatase B)	Fibroblasts, leukocytes, tissues, amniotic fluid cells	+	DS
β-Glucuronidase deficiency	MPS VII	β-Glucuronidase	Serum, fibroblasts, leukocytes, amniotic fluid cells	+	DS, HS (±)
Unnamed disorder	MPS VIII	N-Acetylglucosamine 6-sulfatase	Fibroblasts	+	HS, KS
Mucolipidoses and related disorders					
Sialidosis	ML I	Sialidase (neuraminidase)	Fibroblasts, leukocytes	—	GF
I-cell disease	ML II	UDP-N-Acetylglucosamine: glycoprotein N-acetylglucosaminylphosphotransferase (acid hydrolases thus lack phosphomannosyl residue)	Serum, fibroblasts, amniotic fluid cells	+	GF
Pseudo Hurler polydystrophy	ML III	As for ML II but deficiency is incomplete	Serum, fibroblasts, amniotic fluid cells	±	GF
Multiple sulfatase deficiency	None	Arylsulfatase A and other sulfatases	Serum, fibroblasts, leukocytes, tissues, amniotic fluid cells	+	DS, Hs
Mannosidosis	None	α-Mannosidase	Serum, fibroblasts, leukocytes, amniotic fluid cells	—	GF
Fucosidosis	None	α-L-Fucosidase	Serum, fibroblasts, leukocytes, amniotic fluid cells	—	GF

MPS = mucopolysaccharidosis; ML = mucolipidosis; DS = dermatan sulfate; KS = keratan sulfate; HS = heparan sulfate; GF = glycoprotein fragments.

[*]Reproduced, with permission, from DiNatale P, Neufeld EF: The biochemical diagnosis of mucopolysaccharidoses, mucolipidosis and related disorders. In: *Perspectives in Inherited Metabolic Diseases.* Vol 2. Barra B & others (editors). Editones Ermes (Milan), 1979.

will cleave the C_2 sulfate from an IdUA residue at the nonreducing end of heparin, heparan sulfate, and dermatan sulfate. This enzyme is present normally in serum, lymphocytes, fibroblasts, and amniotic fluid. The inherited deficiency of iduronate sulfatase causes **Hunter's syndrome.**

A specific α-**N-acetylglucosaminidase** can remove the specific alpha-linked GlcNAc residues present in heparin and heparan sulfate. The enzyme is normally present in fibroblasts but is missing in **Sanfilippo B syndrome.**

Heparin sulfamidase (heparan-N-sulfatase) is present in spleen, lung, and ileum. This enzyme is capable of removing a sulfate from GlcN-sulfates at a nonreducing terminus of heparin and heparan sulfate. It is deficient in **Sanfilippo A syndrome.** When the sulfates are removed, an α-glucosamine (GlcN), a free

amino group, remains. This GlcN is not a substrate for the α-N-acetylglucosaminidase described above. The enzyme α-glucosamine:N-acetyltransferase **reacetylates** the free amino group of GlcN at a nonreducing terminus, using acetyl-CoA as the acetyl donor, and thereby renders its product susceptible to the action of the above-described α-N-acetylglucosaminidase. The acetyltransferase activity is absent in **Sanfilippo C syndrome.**

Functional Aspects of Glycosaminoglycans & Proteoglycans

The binding between glycosaminoglycans and other extracellular macromolecules contributes significantly to the structural organization of connective tissue matrix. Glycosaminoglycans can interact with extracellular macromolecules, plasma proteins, cell surface components, and intracellular macromolecules.

The binding of glycosaminoglycans is generally **electrostatic** in character because of their remarkable polyanionic nature. However, some binding interactions are more specific. Generally, the glycosaminoglycans containing IdUA, such as dermatan sulfate and heparan sulfate, bind proteins with greater affinities than do those containing GlcUA as their only uronic acid constituent.

Interactions With Extracellular Macromolecules

All glycosaminoglycans except those that lack sulfate groups (hyaluronate) or carboxyl groups (keratan sulfates) bind electrostatically to collagen at neutral pH. The presence of IdUA promotes tighter binding, and the proteoglycans interact more strongly than the corresponding glycosaminoglycans. Between 2 and 5 polysaccharide chains bind to each collagen monomer. The soluble collagens (types I, II, and III) all bind chondroitin sulfate proteoglycan.

Chondroitin sulfate and heparan sulfate bind specifically to elastin.

As mentioned above, chondroitin sulfate and keratan sulfate chains in their respective proteoglycans aggregate with the aid of link proteins with hyaluronic acid. As many as 100 proteoglycan molecules may bind to one hyaluronate molecule.

Interactions With Plasma Proteins

The intima of the arterial wall contains hyaluronate and chondroitin sulfate, dermatan sulfate, and heparan sulfate proteoglycans. Of these proteoglycans, **dermatan sulfate binds plasma lipoproteins.** In addition, dermatan sulfate appears to be the major glycosaminoglycan **synthesized by arterial smooth muscle cells.** As these smooth muscle cells are those that proliferate at the atherosclerotic lesion in arterial vessels, dermatan sulfate may play a significant role in development of the atherosclerotic plaque.

Heparin, although synthesized and stored in mast cells, is always in close proximity to blood vessels. Heparin, with its high negative charge density (due to the IdUA and sulfate residues), interacts strongly with several plasma components. Heparin specifically binds clotting factors IX and XI. More important in the **anticoagulant activity** of heparin is its interaction with a plasma alpha₂ glycoprotein called **antithrombin III**. The 1:1 stoichiometric binding of heparin to antithrombin III greatly accelerates the ability of the latter to inactivate serine proteases, particularly thrombin (see Chapter 39). The binding of heparin to Lys residues in antithrombin III appears to induce a conformational change that favors the binding of antithrombin III to the serine proteases. Such a scheme is diagrammatically depicted in Fig 32–17.

Commercially available heparin contains 2 components—a high-affinity heparin and a low-affinity heparin—both of which seem to bind to the same site of antithrombin III molecules. However, high-affinity heparin has an anticoagulant activity

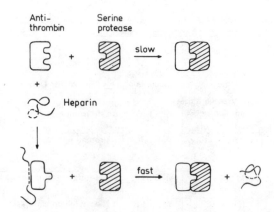

Figure 32–17. Schematic representation of inactivation by antithrombin of serine proteases (eg, thrombin) participating in the coagulation mechanism. Heparin is believed to accelerate the inactivation by binding to antithrombin, thereby inducing a conformational change in the antithrombin molecule that facilitates its interaction with thrombin. (Binding of heparin to thrombin as well cannot be excluded.) The interaction requires a specific binding site (– – –) in the polysaccharide chain. (Reproduced, with permission, from Lindahl U, Höök M: Glycosaminoglycans and their binding to biological macromolecules. *Annu Rev Biochem* 1978; **47**:385. Copyright by Annual Reviews, Inc.)

about 10 times higher than that of low-affinity material, and its binding constant is similarly greater. The N-desulfation or modification of the IdUA residues of heparin reduces its anticoagulant activity.

Heparan sulfate, the structure of which resembles that of heparin, is also capable of accelerating the action of antithrombin III, but it is much less potent than heparin.

Heparin can bind specifically to **lipoprotein lipase** present in capillary walls and cause a release of that triglyceride-degrading enzyme into the circulation. Similarly, hepatic lipase binds heparin and is released into the circulation, but it binds heparin with a lower affinity than does the lipoprotein lipase. Lipoprotein lipase, unlike antithrombin III, will bind partially N-desulfated heparin.

Glycosaminoglycans & Cell Surface Molecules

Heparin is capable of associating with many cell types, including blood platelets, arterial endothelial cells, and liver cells. Chondroitin sulfate, dermatan sulfate, and heparan sulfate bind to independent sites on surfaces of cells such as fibroblasts. At those sites, the glycosaminoglycans and proteoglycans are taken up by fibroblasts and degraded.

Hyaluronate is deposited by cells as they grow on the plastic substrata of culture dishes. In addition, hyaluronate appears to be involved in the cell-cell adhesion processes so important during the growth and development of metazoan organisms.

Some proteoglycans appear to serve as **receptors** and **carriers** for macromolecules, including the lipoproteins, lipases, and, as described above, antithrombin. Proteoglycans seem to be involved in the regulation of cell growth, the mediation of cell-cell communication, and the shielding of cell surface receptors.

Glycosaminoglycans & Intracellular Macromolecules

In addition to interacting with the enzymes involved in their biosynthesis and degradation, proteoglycans and their glycosaminoglycan components have effects on protein synthesis and intranuclear functions. Heparin particularly seems to have an effect on chromatin structure and can activate DNA polymerase activities in vitro. It is not clear how physiologic these actions are. Glycosaminoglycans are found in significant quantities in nuclei from different cell types, and in fact there is some suggestion that heparan sulfate has some role in the embryonic development of sea urchins.

Various lysosomal acid hydrolase activities can be affected in negative or positive ways by chondroitin sulfates, dermatan sulfates, and heparin. The acid hydrolases in lysosomes may be naturally complexed with glycosaminoglycans to provide a protected and inactive form.

Numerous storage or secretory granules such as the chromaffin granules in adrenal medulla, the prolactin secretory granules in the pituitary gland, and the basophilic granules in mast cells contain sulfated glycosaminoglycans. The glycosaminoglycan-peptide complexes that occur in these granules may play a role in the release of biogenic amines.

● ● ●

References

DiNatale P, Neufeld EF: The biochemical diagnosis of mucopolysaccharidoses, mucolipidosis and related disorders. In: *Perspectives in Inherited Metabolic Diseases*. Vol 2. Barra B & others (editors). Editiones Ermes (Milan), 1979.

Jaques LB: Heparin: An old drug with a new paradigm. *Science* 1979;**206**:528.

Lennarz WJ: *The Biochemistry of Glycoproteins and Proteoglycans*. Plenum Press, 1980.

Lindahl U, Höök M: Glycosaminoglycans and their binding to biological macromolecules. *Annu Rev Biochem* 1978;**47**:385.

Poole AR & others: Proteoglycans from bovine nasal cartilage; immunochemical studies of link protein. *J Biol Chem* 1980;**255**:9295.

Reitman ML & others: Fibroblasts from patients with I-cell disease and pseudo-Hurler polydystrophy are deficient in uridine 5'-diphosphate-N-acetylglucosamine:glycoprotein N-acetylglucosaminylphosphotransferase activity. *J Clin Invest* 1981;**67**:1574.

Wedgwood JF, Strominger JL: Enzymatic activities in cultured human lymphocytes that dephosphorylate dolichyl pyrophosphate and dolichyl phosphate. *J Biol Chem* 1980;**255**:1120.

33 | Contractile & Structural Proteins

David W. Martin, Jr., MD

Protein molecules in biologic systems may serve primary functions other than catalysis. The regulatory, signal transmission, and recognition functions of protein molecules have been described in earlier chapters. Protein molecules also provide important transducing and structural functions to biologic systems. Some of these latter roles, which are dependent upon the fibrous nature of specific protein molecules, are reviewed in this chapter.

Muscle Structure

Striated muscle is composed of fibrils surrounded by an electrically excitable membrane, the **sarcolemma.** When an individual muscle fiber is examined microscopically, it will be found to consist of a bundle of many myofibrils arranged in parallel; these are embedded in a type of intracellular fluid termed the **sarcoplasm.** Within this fluid is contained glycogen, the high-energy compounds ATP and phosphocreatine, and the enzymes of glycolysis.

The **sarcomere** is the functional unit of muscle. It is repeated along the axis of a fibril at distances of 1500–2300 nm (Fig 33–1). When the myofibril is examined by electron microscopy, alternating dark and light bands (A bands and I bands) can be observed. The central region of the A band (the H zone) appears less dense than the rest of the band. The I band is bisected by a very dense and narrow Z line. These structural details are illustrated in Fig 33–2.

MUSCLE

Muscle is the major biochemical transducer (machine) that converts potential (chemical) energy into kinetic (mechanical) energy. Muscle is the largest

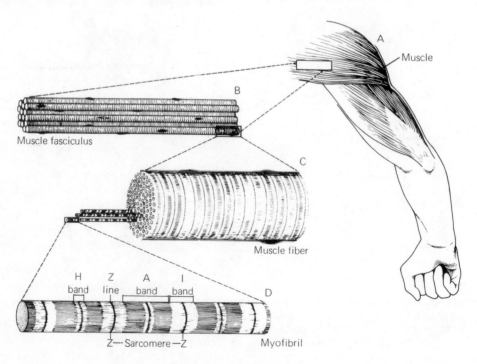

Figure 33–1. The structure of voluntary muscle. (Drawing by Sylvia Colard Keene. Reproduced, with permission, from Bloom W, Fawcett DW: *A Textbook of Histology,* 10th ed. Saunders, 1975.)

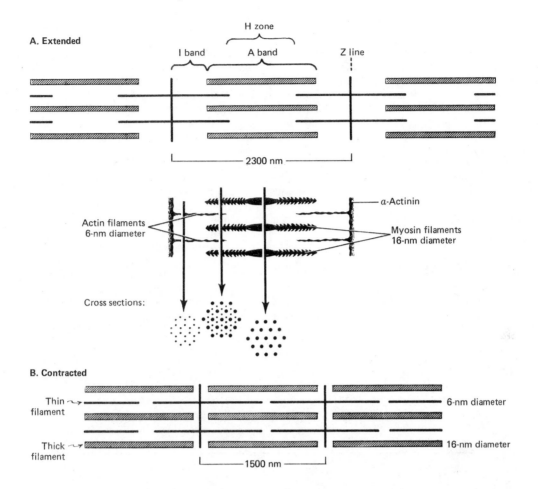

Figure 33–2. Arrangement of filaments in striated muscle. *A:* Extended. *B:* Contracted.

single tissue in the human body, comprising somewhat less than 25% of body mass at birth, more than 40% of body mass in the young adult, and somewhat less than 30% in the aged adult.

An effective **chemical-mechanical transducer** must meet several requirements: (1) There must exist a constant supply of chemical energy. In vertebrate muscle, ATP and creatine phosphate are the forms of chemical energy. (2) There must be a means of regulating the mechanical activity—ie, the speed, duration, and force of contraction in the case of muscle. (3) The machine must be connected to an operator, a requirement met in biologic systems by the nervous system. (4) If it is to be used more than once, there must be a way of returning the machine to its original state.

Muscle is only a pulling machine, not a pushing machine. Therefore, a given muscle must be antagonized by another group of muscles or another force such as gravity or elastic recoil.

In vertebrate organisms, the above requirements and the specific needs of the organisms are met by the existence of 3 types of muscles: skeletal muscle, cardiac muscle, and smooth muscle. Both **skeletal** and **cardiac muscle** appear **striated** upon microscopic ob-

servation; **smooth muscle** is **nonstriated.** Although skeletal muscle is under **voluntary** nervous control, the control of both cardiac and smooth muscle is **involuntary.**

When **cross sections** of a myofibril are examined in an electron micrograph, it appears that each myofibril is constructed of 2 types of longitudinal filaments. One type (the thick filament), confined to the A band, contains chiefly the protein **myosin.** These filaments are about 16 nm in diameter and arranged in cross section as a hexagonal array (Fig 33–2). The other filament (thick filament) lies in the I band and extends also into the A band but not into the H zone of the A band (Fig 33–2). The thin filaments are about 6 nm in diameter. They contain the proteins **actin, tropomyosin,** and **troponin.** In the A band, the thick filaments are arranged around the thin (myosin) filament as a secondary hexagonal array. Thus, as shown in Fig 33–2, each thin filament lies symmetrically between 3 thick filaments, and each thick filament is surrounded symmetrically by 6 thin filaments.

The thick and thin filaments interact via crossbridges that emerge at intervals of 14 nm along the thick filaments. As depicted in Fig 33–2, the cross-bridges or "arrowheads" on the thick filaments have opposite polarities at the 2 ends of the filaments. The 2 poles of the filaments are separated by a 150-nm segment (the M band) that is free of projections.

When muscle contracts, there is no change in the lengths of the thick filaments or of the thin filaments, but the **H zone and the I bands shorten.** Thus, the **arrays of interdigitating filaments must slide past one another during muscle contraction.** The **cross-bridges generate and sustain the tension.** The tension developed during muscle contraction is proportionate to the filament overlap and thereby the number of cross-bridges. Each cross-bridge head is connected to the thick filament via a flexible fibrous segment that can bend outward from the thick filament to accommodate the interfilament spacing.

The Proteins of Muscle

The mass of a fresh muscle fibril is made up of 75% water and more than 20% protein. The 2 major muscle proteins are actin and myosin.

Monomeric (globular) actin (G-actin) is a 43,000-MW globular protein that comprises 25% of

muscle protein by weight. At physiologic ionic strength and in the presence of magnesium, G-actin **polymerizes** noncovalently to form an insoluble double helical filament called F-actin (Fig 33–3). The **F-actin** fiber is 6–7 nm thick and has a pitch or repeating structure every 35.5 nm. Neither G- nor F-actin exhibits any catalytic activity.

In striated muscle, there are 4 other proteins that are minor in terms of their mass contribution but important in terms of their function. **Tropomyosin** is a fibrous molecule that consists of 2 chains, alpha and beta, that attach to the F-actin in the groove between the 2 polymers (Fig 33–3). **Tropomyosin is present in all muscle** and musclelike structures. The **troponin** system is unique to **striated muscle** and consists of 3 separate proteins. **Troponin T (TpT)** binds to tropomyosin as well as the other 2 troponin components (Fig 33–3). **Troponin I (TpI)** inhibits the F-actin myosin interaction and also binds to the other components of troponin. **Troponin C (TpC)** is a calcium-binding protein that has a primary and secondary structure as well as a function quite analogous to that of the calcium-dependent regulator (CDR) pro-

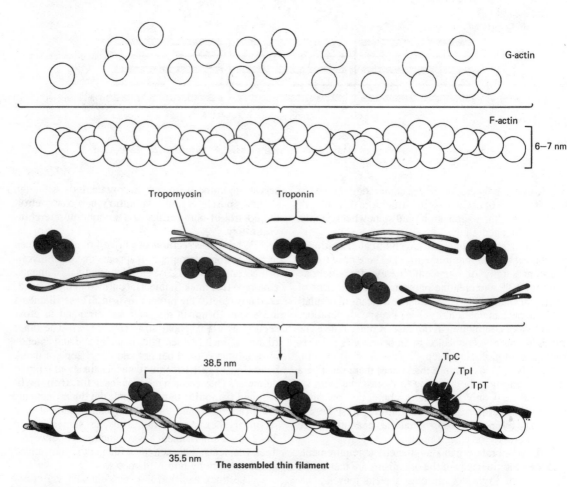

Figure 33–3. Schematic representation of the thin filament, showing the spatial configuration of the 3 major protein components—actin, tropomyosin, and troponin.

tein widely spread in nature and recently named **cal-modulin.** Four molecules of calcium ion are bound per molecule of troponin C or calmodulin, and both protein molecules have a molecular weight of 17,000. The thin filament of striated muscle consists of F-actin, tropomyosin, and the 3 components of troponin: TpC, TpI, and TpT (Fig 33–3). The repeat distance of the tropomyosin and troponin system is 38.5 nm.

Myosin contributes 55% of muscle protein by weight and forms the thick filaments. Myosin is an asymmetric hexamer with a molecular weight of 460,000. The myosin has a **fibrous portion** consisting of 2 intertwined helices, each with a **globular head** portion attached at one end (Fig 33–4). The **hexamer** consists of one pair of heavy chains (MW 200,000) and 2 pairs of light chains (MW 15,000–27,000). Skeletal muscle myosin exhibits **ATP-hydrolyzing (ATPase) activity** and binds to F-actin, an insoluble molecule.

Much has been learned from studies of the partial digestion products of myosin. When myosin is digested with trypsin, 2 myosin fragments (meromyosins) are generated. Light meromyosin (LMM) consists of aggregated, insoluble α-helical fibers (Fig 33–5). LMM exhibits no ATPase activity and will not bind to F-actin.

Heavy meromyosin (HMM) is a 340,000-MW soluble protein that has both a fibrous portion and a globular portion (Fig 33–5). HMM exhibits **ATPase activity** and **binds to F-actin.** The digestion of HMM with papain generates 2 subfragments, S-1 and S-2.

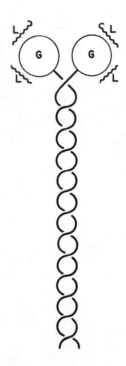

Figure 33–4. Diagram of a myosin molecule showing the 2 intertwined α-helices (fibrous portion), the globular region (G), and the light chains (L).

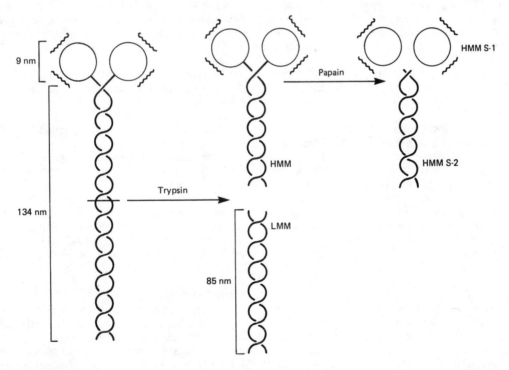

Figure 33–5. Enzymatic cleavage of myosin. HMM = heavy meromyosin; LMM = light meromyosin. S-1 = subfragment 1; S-2 = subfragment 2.

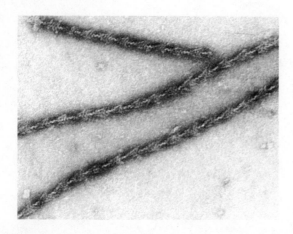

Figure 33–6. The decoration of actin filaments with the S-1 fragments of myosin to form "arrowheads." (Courtesy of Professor James Spudich, Stanford University.)

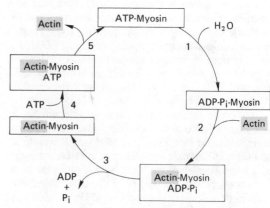

Figure 33–7. The hydrolysis of ATP drives the cyclic association and dissociation of actin and myosin in 5 reactions described in the text. (Modified from Stryer L: *Biochemistry,* 2nd ed. Freeman, 1981.)

The S-2 is fibrous in character, exhibits no ATPase activity, and does not bind to F-actin.

S-1 has a molecular weight of 115,000, exhibits **ATPase activity,** and in the absence of ATP will **bind to and "decorate" actin with arrowheads** (Fig 33–6). Although both S-1 and HMM exhibit ATPase activity, that **catalytic activity is accelerated 100- to 200-fold by the addition of F-actin.** As discussed below, F-actin greatly enhances the rate at which myosin ATPase releases its products, ADP and P_i. Thus, although F-actin does not affect the hydrolysis step per se, its ability to **promote the release of the ATPase products** greatly accelerates the overall rate of catalysis.

α-**Actinin** is a protein molecule found in the Z line to which the ends of the F-actin molecules of the thin filaments attach (Fig 33–2).

The Molecular Function of Muscle

The question of how the structure and function of muscle are related can be rephrased in biochemical terms: **How can ATP hydrolysis produce macroscopic movement?** It should be apparent from the above discussion that muscle contraction consists of the **cyclic attachment and detachment of the globular head portion of myosin to the F-actin filament.** The attachment is followed by a change in the actin-myosin interaction, so that the actin filaments and the myosin filaments slide past one another. The energy is supplied by ATP, which is hydrolyzed. ATP hydrolysis by the myosin ATPase is greatly accelerated by the binding of the myosin head to F-actin. The biochemical cycle of muscle contraction consists of 5 steps (Fig 33–7): (1) The myosin head alone can hydrolyze ATP to ADP + P_i, but it cannot release the products of this hydrolysis. Thus, the hydrolysis of ATP by the myosin head alone is stoichiometric rather than catalytic. (2) The myosin head containing ADP and P_i can bind to

F-actin, an interaction that (3) promotes the release of ADP and P_i from the actin-myosin complex. (4) A new ATP molecule binds to the myosin–F-actin complex, **changing the conformation** of the myosin molecule at the junction of its head and neck and thereby changing the angle of the myosin-actin attachment sites. This causes a **sliding** (a contraction of 10–15 nm) of the thick and thin filaments past each other and results in (5) the release of the myosin head from the F-actin. This last step is **relaxation,** a process clearly **dependent upon the binding of ATP** to the actin-myosin complex. The ATP is again hydrolyzed by the myosin head but without releasing ADP + P_i—to continue the cycle.

It should be clear that **ATP dissociates the myosin head from the thin filament and powers the contraction.**

The Regulation of Muscle Contraction & Relaxation

The contraction of muscles from all sources occurs by the general mechanism described immediately above. Muscles from different organisms and from different cells and tissues within the same organism may have different molecular mechanisms responsible for the regulation of their contraction and relaxation. In all systems, **Ca^{2+} plays a key regulatory role.** There are 2 general mechanisms of regulation of muscle contraction: actin-based and myosin-based.

Actin-Based Regulation

Actin-based regulation of muscle occurs in vertebrate skeletal and cardiac muscles, both **striated.** In the general mechanism described above, the only potentially limiting factor in the cycle of muscle contraction might be ATP, not a seemingly ideal regulatory molecule, since it is required as the immediate energy source for contraction. The skeletal muscle system is inhibited at rest and is deinhibited to activate contraction. The **inhibitor of striated muscle is the troponin system,** which is bound to tropomyosin and F-actin in the thin filament (Fig 33–3). In striated muscle, there is no control of contraction (or ATPase as a biochemical indicator of contraction) unless the tropomyosin-troponin systems are present along with the actin and myosin filaments. As described above, tropomyosin lies along the groove of F-actin, and the 3 components of troponin—TpT, TpI, and TpC—are bound to the F-actin-tropomyosin complex. TpI prevents binding of the myosin head to its F-actin attachment site either by altering the conformation of F-actin via the tropomyosin molecules or by simply rolling tropomyosin into a position that directly blocks the sites on F-actin to which the myosin heads attach. Either way prevents the acceleration of the myosin ATPase that is mediated by binding of the myosin head to F-actin. Hence, the TpI system blocks the contraction cycle at step 2 of Fig 33–7. This accounts for the inhibited state of relaxed striated muscle.

The excitation of muscle contraction is mediated by Ca^{2+}. In resting muscle sarcoplasm, the concentration of Ca^{2+} is 10^{-7}–10^{-8}M. Calcium is sequestered in the sarcoplasmic reticulum, a network of fine membranous sacs, by an active transport system utilizing a Ca^{2+} binding protein called calsequestrin. The sarcomere is surrounded by an **excitable membrane** that has transverse (T) channels closely associated with the sarcoplasmic reticulum. When the sarcomere membrane is excited, such as by the occupation of an acetylcholine receptor by acetylcholine, Ca^{2+} **is rapidly released** into the sarcoplasm from the sarcoplasmic reticulum. The Ca^{2+} concentration in sarcoplasm rapidly rises to 10^{-5}M. The Ca^{2+} binding sites on TpC in the thin filament are quickly occupied by Ca^{2+}. The $TpC·4Ca^{2+}$ interacts with TpI and TpT to alter their interaction with tropomyosin. Accordingly, tropomyosin simply moves out of the way or alters the F-actin conformation so that the myosin head ADP-Pi can interact with F-actin to start the contraction cycle.

Relaxation occurs when (1) sarcoplasm Ca^{2+} falls below 10^{-7}M owing to its resequestration in the sarcoplasmic reticulum by an energy-dependent Ca^{2+} pump; (2) $TpC·4Ca^{2+}$ loses its Ca^{2+}; (3) troponin, via its interaction with tropomyosin, inhibits further myosin head–F-actin interaction; and (4) in the presence of ATP, the myosin head detaches from the F-actin to induce relaxation. Thus, Ca^{2+} **controls muscle contraction by an allosteric mechanism** mediated by TpC, TpI, TpT, tropomyosin, and F-actin.

The loss of ATP in the sarcoplasm has 2 major effects: (1) The Ca^{2+} pump in the sarcoplasmic reticulum ceases to maintain the low sarcoplasm Ca^{2+} concentration. Thus, the interaction of the myosin heads with F-actin is promoted. (2) The ATP-dependent detachment of myosin heads from F-actin cannot occur, and "rigor mortis" sets in.

Muscle contraction is not an all-or-none phenomenon, as anyone who can turn these pages will recognize. Muscle contraction is a delicate dynamic balance of the attachment and detachment of myosin heads to F-actin. The system is subject to fine regulation via the nervous system.

Myosin-Based Regulation of Contraction

As described above, all muscles contain actin, myosin, and tropomyosin, but **only vertebrate striated muscles contain the troponin system.** Thus, the mechanisms of regulating contraction must differ in various contractile systems.

Smooth muscles have molecular structures very similar to those in striated muscle, but the sarcomeres are not aligned in such a way as to generate the striated appearance. Smooth muscles contain α-actinin and tropomyosin molecules, as do skeletal muscles. They do not have the troponin system, and the light chains of smooth muscle myosin molecules differ from those of striated muscle myosin. However, like striated muscle, **smooth muscle contraction is regulated by** Ca^{2+}.

When smooth muscle myosin is bound to F-actin in the absence of other muscle proteins such as tropomyosin, there is no detectable ATPase activity. This absence of ATPase is quite unlike the situation described for striated muscle myosin and F-actin, which has abundant ATPase activity. Smooth muscle myosin contains a light chain (p-light chain) that prevents the binding of the myosin molecule to F-actin. The p-light chain must be phosphorylated before it allows F-actin to activate ATPase. The **phosphorylation of p-light chain commences the attachment-detachment contraction cycle of smooth muscle.**

In smooth muscle sarcoplasm, there exists a cAMP-independent **myosin light chain kinase. The myosin light chain kinase activity is calcium-dependent.** The Ca^{2+} activation of myosin light chain kinase requires binding of calmodulin·$4Ca^{2+}$ to its 105,000-MW kinase subunit (Fig 33–8). The calmodulin·$4Ca^{2+}$-activated light chain kinase phosphorylates the p-light chain, which then ceases to inhibit the myosin–F-actin interaction. The contraction cycle then begins (Fig 33–8).

Relaxation of smooth muscle occurs when (1) sarcoplasm Ca^{2+} falls below 10^{-7}M. The Ca^{2+} dissociates from calmodulin, which in turn dissociates from the myosin light chain kinase, (2) inactivating the kinase. (3) No new phosphates are attached to the p-light chain, and light chain protein phosphatase, which is continually active and calcium-independent, removes the existing phosphates from the p-light chain. (4) Dephosphorylated myosin p-light chain then inhibits the binding of myosin heads to F-actin and the ATPase activity. (5) The myosin head detaches from the F-actin in the presence of ATP, but it cannot reattach because of the presence of dephosphorylated p-light chain; hence, relaxation occurs.

Table 33–1 summarizes and compares the regulation of actin-myosin interactions (activation of myosin ATPase) in striated and smooth muscles.

The myosin light chain kinase is not directly af-

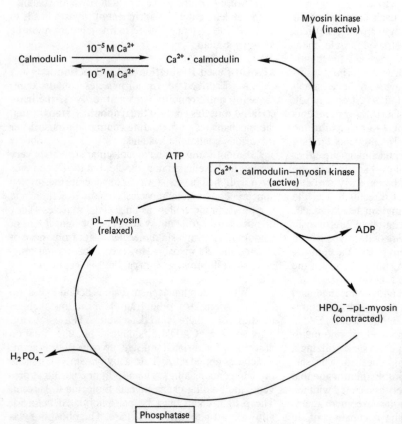

Figure 33–8. Regulation of smooth muscle contraction by Ca^{2+} (Adapted from Adelstein RS, Eisenberg R: Regulation and kinetics of actin-myosin ATP interaction. *Annu Rev Biochem* 1980; 49:921.)

fected or activated by cAMP. However, the usual cAMP-activated protein kinase (see Chapter 34) can phosphorylate the myosin light chain kinase (*not* the p-light chain itself). The phosphorylated myosin light chain kinase exhibits a significantly lower affinity for calmodulin·Ca^{2+} and thus is less sensitive to activation. Accordingly, an increase in cAMP dampens the contraction response of smooth muscle to a given elevation of sarcoplasm Ca^{2+}. This molecular mechanism can explain the relaxing effect of β-adrenergic stimulation on smooth muscle.

Striated muscle from mollusks such as the scallop

Table 33–1. Actin-myosin interactions in striated and smooth muscle.

	Striated Muscle	Smooth Muscle (and Nonmuscle Cells)
Proteins of muscle filaments	Actin Myosin (hexamer) Tropomyosin Troponin (TpI, TpT, TpC)	Actin Myosin (hexamer)* Tropomyosin
Spontaneous interaction of F-actin and myosin *alone* (spontaneous activation of myosin ATPase by F-actin)	Yes	No
Inhibitor of F-actin-myosin interaction (inhibitor of F-actin-dependent activation of ATPase)	Troponin system (TpI)	Unphosphorylated myosin p-light chain
Contraction activated by	Ca^{2+}	Ca^{2+}
Direct effect of Ca^{2+}	$4Ca^{2+}$ bind to TpC	$4Ca^{2+}$ bind to calmodulin
Effect of protein-bound Ca^{2+}	TpC · $4Ca^{2+}$ antagonizes TpI inhibition of F-actin-myosin interaction (allows F-actin activation of ATPase).	Calmodulin · $4Ca^{2+}$ activates myosin light chain kinase which phosphorylates myosin p-light chain. The phosphorylated p-light chain no longer inhibits F-actin-myosin interaction (allows F-actin activation of ATPase).

*Light chains of myosin are different in striated and smooth muscles.

exhibits a myosin-based regulation of contraction. Like myosin and F-actin from smooth muscle, that from scallops also exhibits no ATPase, an effect of the inhibitory properties of the "regulatory" light chain of scallop myosin. The inhibition of scallop actin-myosin interaction is relieved when Ca^{2+} binds directly to a specific site on the myosin molecule. This regulation does not require covalent modification of myosin or the addition of a separate protein such as calmodulin or TpC to be Ca^{2+}-dependent.

Phosphorylation of Muscle Proteins

As described above, the phosphorylation of the light chain of smooth muscle myosin alleviates its inhibitory effect on the actin-myosin interaction and thereby commences the contraction cycle. Thus, phosphorylation is required for the actin-myosin interaction of smooth muscle.

One of the pairs of light chains of skeletal muscle myosin can also be phosphorylated, but this has no effect on the actin-activated ATPase of myosin, as it does on smooth muscle myosin. It has been proposed that the phosphate on the myosin light chains may form a chelate with the Ca^{2+} bound to the tropomyosin-TpC-actin complex, leading to an increased rate of formation of cross-bridges between the myosin heads and actin.

Some recent evidence suggests that phosphorylation of myosin heavy chains is a prerequisite for their assembly into the thick filaments in skeletal muscle, smooth muscle, and nonmuscle cells (see below).

The TpI of cardiac muscle can be phosphorylated in vitro by cAMP-dependent protein kinase. There is a rough correlation between the phosphorylation of TpI and the increased contraction of cardiac muscle induced by catecholamines. This mechanism may account for the inotropic effects (increased contractility) of the β-adrenergic compounds on the heart.

Muscle Metabolism

The ATP required as the constant energy source for the contraction-relaxation cycle of muscle can be generated by glycolysis, oxidative phosphorylation, creatine phosphate, or two ADP molecules. The ATP stores in skeletal muscle are short-lived during contraction, providing energy probably for less than 1 second of contraction.

Phosphagens such as creatine phosphate prevent the rapid depletion of ATP by providing a readily available high-energy phosphate, which is all that is necessary to reform ATP from ADP. Creatine phosphate is formed from ATP and creatine at times when the muscle is relaxed and ATP demands are not so great. The enzyme catalyzing the phosphorylation of creatine is creatine phosphokinase (CPK), a muscle-specific enzyme with clinical utility in the detection of acute or chronic disorders of muscle.

Skeletal muscle sarcoplasm contains significant **glycogen** stores. The release of glucose from glycogen is dependent upon a specific muscle phosphorylase enzyme (see Chapter 15). This enzyme is missing in a specific disorder of muscle (McArdle's disease), a form of glycogen storage disease.

ATP is also available from oxidative phosphorylation in muscle tissue, a process dependent upon a constant oxygen supply. Muscles that have high oxygen demands as a result of sustained contraction (such as to maintain posture) have the ability to store oxygen in **myoglobin** (see Chapter 5). Because of the heme moiety to which oxygen is bound in myoglobin, muscles containing myoglobin are red, as compared to white skeletal muscle. Table 33–2 compares some of the properties of fast or white skeletal muscle with slow or red skeletal muscle.

Table 33–2. Characteristics of fast and slow skeletal muscle.

	Fast Skeletal Muscle	Slow Skeletal Muscle
Myosin ATPase	High	Low
Energy utilization	High	Low
Color	White	Red
Myoglobin	No	Yes
contraction		
Rate	Fast	Slow
Duration	Short	Prolonged

Myoadenylate kinase, an enzyme present in muscle, catalyzes the formation of one ATP molecule and one AMP from two ADP molecules. This reaction is shown in Fig 33–9 coupled with the hydrolysis of ATP by myosin ATPase during muscle contraction. The relationships between these various sources of ATP and its consumption during muscle contraction are also depicted.

In humans, skeletal muscle protein is the major nonfat source of stored energy. This explains the very large losses of muscle mass, particularly in adults, resulting from prolonged caloric undernutrition.

The study of tissue protein breakdown in vivo is difficult because amino acids released during intracellular breakdown of proteins can be extensively reutilized for protein synthesis within the cell, or the amino acids may be transported to other organs where they enter anabolic pathways. However, actin and myosin are methylated following synthesis of their peptide bonds, producing **3-methylhistidine** (3-MeHis). During intracellular breakdown of actin and myosin, 3-MeHis is released and excreted into the urine. When labeled material was administered to rats and humans, it was found that the urinary output of the methylated amino acid provides a reliable index of the rate of myofibrillar protein breakdown in the musculature of rats or human subjects. The fractional rate of muscle protein breakdown is not significantly different in the elderly as compared with young adults, but since muscle mass is less in the elderly, this tissue contributes less to the whole body protein breakdown that occurs with aging in humans.

As noted above, skeletal muscle is the major reserve of protein in the body. In addition, this tissue is

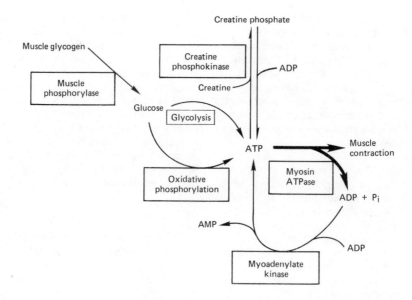

Figure 33–9. The multiple sources of ATP in muscle.

highly active in the degradation of certain amino acids as well as in the synthesis of others. In mammals, muscle appears to be the primary site of catabolism of the branched chain amino acids. It oxidizes leucine to CO_2 and converts the carbon skeletons of aspartate, asparagine, glutamate, isoleucine, and valine into intermediates of the tricarboxylic acid cycle. The capacity of muscles to degrade branched chain amino acids increases 3- to 5-fold during fasting and in diabetes.

Muscle also synthesizes and releases large amounts of alanine and glutamine. These compounds are synthesized utilizing amino groups that are generated in the breakdown of branched chain amino acids, and the amino nitrogen is then transferred to α-ketoglutarate and to pyruvate by transamination. Glycolysis from exogenous glucose is the source of almost all of the pyruvate for synthesis of alanine. These reactions constitute the so-called ''glucose-alanine cycle,'' wherein alanine from muscle is utilized in hepatic gluconeogenesis while at the same time bringing amino groups to the liver for removal as urea.

The carbon skeletons of the amino acids that are degraded in muscle and enter the tricarboxylic acid cycle in muscle are converted mostly to glutamine and to pyruvate, which itself is further oxidized or converted to lactate. It thus appears that in fasting or the postabsorptive state, muscle releases most amino acids coming from net protein breakdown except for isoleucine, valine, glutamate, aspartate, and asparagine, which are used to contribute to the formation of glutamine, which itself is released for use by other tissues.

For many years, it has been observed that working muscle releases ammonia. It is now known that the immediate source of ammonia in skeletal muscle is AMP, which is deaminated to IMP, catalyzed by ade-

nylate deaminase. IMP may be converted back to AMP by reactions utilizing aspartate and catalyzed by adenylosuccinate synthetase and adenylosuccinase (see Chapter 26).

CELL MOTILITY & THE CYTOSKELETON

It is apparent that nonmuscle cells perform mechanical work, including self-propulsion, morphogenesis, cleavage, endocytosis, exocytosis, intracellular transport, and changing cell shape. These cellular functions are carried out by an extensive intracellular network of filamentous structures constituting the **cytoskeleton.** As will be shown, the cell cytoplasm is not a structural sac of fluid, as once thought. Essentially all eukaryotic cells contain 3 types of filamentous structures: **actin filaments** (7–9.5 nm in diameter), **microtubules** (25 nm), and **intermediate filaments** (10–12 nm). Each of these types of filaments can be distinguished biochemically and electron microscopically by special technics.

Nonmuscle Actin

The G-actin protein isolated from nonmuscle cells has a molecular weight of about 43,000 and contains, as does muscle actin (α-actin), N-methylhistidyl residues. In the presence of magnesium and potassium chloride, this actin will spontaneously polymerize to form the double helical **F-actin filaments** like those seen in muscle. There are at least 2 types of actin in nonmuscle cells: β-actin and γ-actin. Both types can coexist in the same cell and probably even copolymerize in the same filament. In the cellular cytoplasm, actin forms **microfilaments** of 7–9.5 nm that frequently exist as bundles of tangled-

Microfilaments are also tightly packed in a meshwork pattern underlying the leading edge or "ruffle" of a motile cell (Fig 33–11). Actin microfilaments are found in all cellular microprojections such as filopodia and microvilli. For instance, the microvilli of intestinal mucosal cells contain 20–30 actin mi-

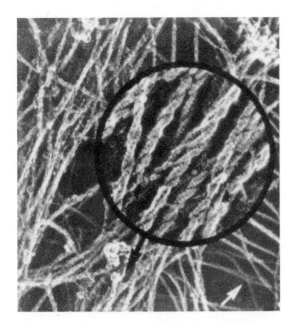

Figure 33–10. Replica of a freeze-dried cytoskeleton that was exposed to the myosin subfragment 1 (S-1) before quick-freezing. Nearly all the filaments in the lengthwise bundles, and many of the intervening filaments, have been thickened and converted into ropelike double helices (see *inset*). However, some of the filaments that travel by themselves, in between the bundles, remain totally undecorated (arrow); these are presumably intermediate filaments. × 70,000; *inset,* × 200,000. (Reproduced, with permission, from Heuser JE, Kirschner MW: Filament organization revealed in platinum replicas of freeze-dried cytoskeletons. *J Cell Biol* 1980;**86**:212.)

appearing meshwork. The bundles of microfilaments are prominent just underlying the plasma membrane of resting cells and are there referred to as **stress fibers.** These stress fibers will decorate with the S-1 portion of myosin to reveal their double helical character (Fig 33–10). The stress fibers disappear as cell motility increases or upon the malignant transformation of the cell by chemicals or oncogenic viruses.

Figure 33–11 (at right). Three moderately high-powered views of ruffles or lamellipodia from fibroblasts that were fixed while whole (in *A*), were extracted with Triton before fixation (in *B*), or extracted with Triton after fixation (in *C*). In *A*, the plasma membrane is intact, and no internal structure can be seen. In *B*, the plasma membrane has been removed and an underlying web of "kinky" filaments revealed. In other experiments, these filaments decorate with S-1, but they are much more concentrated and much more extensively interdigitated than actin in other regions of the cell. In *C*, the plasma membrane has again been removed, but only after the cell was fixed with aldehyde. The delicate meshwork of underlying filaments appears coarser after the chemical fixation. (*A,* × 140,000; *B* and *C,* × 115,000.) (Reproduced, with permission, from Heuser JE, Kirschner MW: Filament organization revealed in platinum replicas of freeze-dried cytoskeletons. *J Cell Biol* 1980;**86**:212.)

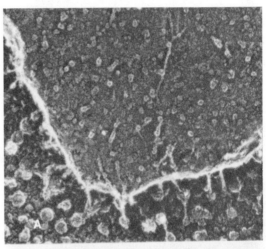
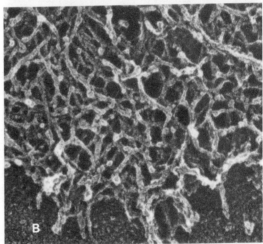
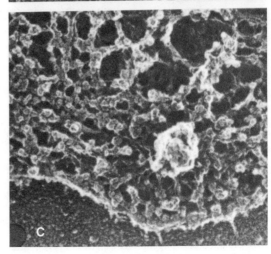

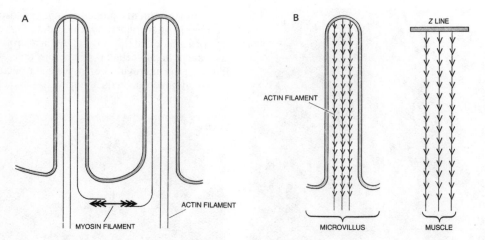

Figure 33–12. Microvilli are tiny cytoplasmic protrusions that extend out from the epithelial cells lining the small intestine, greatly increasing the surface for the absorption of nutrients. Microvilli contain both actin and myosin filaments and are known to contract much like muscle cells, and so they provide a convincing example of nonmuscle movement mediated by sliding filaments of actin and myosin. As is shown in *A,* bundles of actin filaments project upward inside each microvillus; the myosin filaments are localized at the base of the microvilli. In *B* the orientation of the actin filaments was determined by treating the microvilli with isolated head fragments from muscle myosin, termed heavy meromyosin; these fragments retain the ability to bind to actin filaments. When the head fragments are applied to muscle cells, they form "arrowhead" complexes with the actin filaments that point in the direction of the filaments. When heavy meromyosin was added to microvilli, the head fragments formed arrowhead complexes with the actin filaments that pointed downward from the attachment sites in the tips of the microvilli. The actin filaments within the microvilli are therefore analogous to the actin filament arrays of muscle cells. (Reproduced, with permission, from Lazarides E, Revel JP: The molecular basis of cell movement. *Sci Am* [May] 1979;**240**:100.)

crofilaments arranged longitudinally within the microvilli as diagrammed in Fig 33–12. These microfilaments will decorate with myosin S-1, demonstrating a uniform polarity (Fig 33–12). At the base of the microvilli, myosin filaments exist and are capable of pulling together the actin filaments projecting into the microvilli. The contraction process does not involve any change of length of actin or myosin and thus must occur, as in muscle, by the sliding filament mechanism of Huxley. As in smooth muscle, the activation of the actin-myosin interaction and thereby contraction is mediated by phosphorylation of the myosin light chain.

Actin and myosin are also both found between the spindle poles and the chromosomes and along the cleavage furrow of mitotic telophase.

Actin microfilaments are associated with other musclelike proteins in nonmuscle cells. α-**Actinin** is present at the plasma membrane sites to which microfilaments attach, such as the tips of microvilli. The geodesic domes—cytoskeletal scaffolding surrounding the nuclei of eukaryotic cells—consist of actin, α-actinin, and tropomyosin. α-Actinin is also found along actin microfilaments themselves.

As described above, **myosin** is found in association with actin microfilaments at the bases of microvilli. Myosin is also found along the actin fibers but as filaments thinner and shorter than in muscle. They seem to play a role in maintenance of the filamentous character of actin.

Tropomyosin, as mentioned above, participates

in the formation of the geodomes surrounding nuclei. Tropomyosin along actin microfilaments seems to serve a structural rather than a motility function.

The regulation of nonmuscle actin function seems to depend upon several specialized proteins. **Profilin** prevents the polymerization of G-actin even in the presence of the proper concentrations of magnesium and potassium chloride. **Filamin** promotes the formation of an actin microfilament meshwork. **Tropomyosin** promotes the formation of bundles of actin stress fibers. α-**Actinin** promotes the attachment of actin microfilaments to membranes, substratum, and other cell organelles. **Cytochalasin** is a naturally occurring peptide that breaks microfilaments and prevents their polymerization. It is frequently used as a diagnostic test for the existence or function of microfilaments.

The actual motility of cells appears to be led by the **ruffle membrane** or lamellipodium that contains fingerlike projections called filopodia. The ruffle attaches at its tip to the substratum via the filopodia, and the cell then seems to pull in its rear margins. The ruffle releases and folds back over the top of the cell as new filopodia attach to the substratum (Fig 33–13).

Microtubules

Microtubules are an integral component of the cellular cytoskeleton. They consist of cytoplasmic tubes 25 nm in diameter and of indefinite length. Microtubules are necessary for the formation and function of the **mitotic spindle** and thus are present in all eukaryotic cells. Microtubules carry out a number of

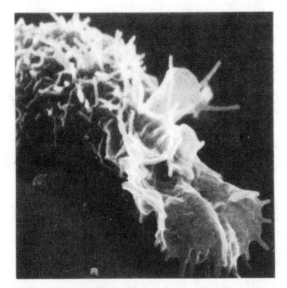

Figure 33–13. Individual cells in tissue culture are depicted. The delicate feathery structure at the bottom right is a "ruffle," or lamellipodium, which marks the leading edge of the cell. A cell is shown from an oblique angle as it moves across the substrate, extending its ruffle to form new adhesions. (Reproduced, with permission, from Lazarides E, Revel JP: The molecular basis of cell movement. *Sci Am* [May] 1979;**240:**100.)

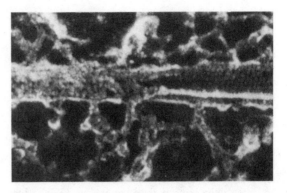

Figure 33–14. High magnification of a microtubule that was fractured and deep etched after quick-freezing. The left half of the field illustrates the outer surface of the microtubule, which displays longitudinal bands of bumps spaced 5.5 nm apart, which may represent the microtubule's protofilaments. To the right, the microtubule is fractured open to reveal its inner luminal walls, which display characteristic oblique striations separated by 4.0 nm. The reticulum surrounding the microtubule is thought to be unpolymerized tubulin and microtubule-associated proteins. (Reproduced, with permission, from Heuser JE, Kirschner MW: Filament organization revealed in platinum replicas of freeze-dried cytoskeletons. *J Cell Biol* 1980;**86:**212.)

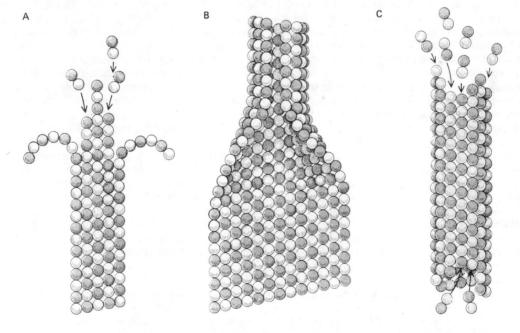

Figure 33–15. Assembly of microtubules in the laboratory begins with 2 protein molecules, α-tubulin and β-tubulin, which are globular molecules (probably more ovoid than these highly schematic spheres). The tubulins form dimers, or double molecules. If the dimers are present in a high enough concentration, they associate to form various intermediate structures, including double rings, spirals, and stacked rings; the equilibrium is biased in favor of either the isolated dimers or the intermediate structures, depending on the conditions. The next steps are not well established. It seems that the rings or spirals open up to form strands, called protofilaments, of linearly associated dimers, which assemble side by side in a sheet *(A);* sometimes the ends of protofilaments curve. When a sheet is wide enough, it forms a tube, perhaps by curling up *(B).* Once a short tube has formed *(C),* it is lengthened by the addition of dimers preferentially at one end. (Reproduced, with permission, from Dustin P: Microtubules. *Sci Am* [Aug] 1980;**243:**67.)

other cellular functions. They are responsible for the intracellular movement of endocytotic and exocytotic vesicles. They form the major structural component of **cilia and flagella.** Microtubules are a major protein component of **axons and dendrites,** where they maintain the structure and participate in the axoplasmic flow of material along these neuronal processes.

Microtubules are cylinders of 13 longitudinally arranged **protofilaments,** each consisting of dimers of α-**tubulin** and β-**tubulin** (Fig 33–14). α-Tubulin (MW 53,000) and β-tubulin (MW 55,000) are closely related protein molecules. The tubulin dimers assemble into protofilaments and subsequently into sheets and then cylinders, as depicted in Fig 33–15. The assembly of tubulin into microtubules requires two **GTP** molecules per tubulin dimer. Two proteins termed high-molecular-weight (HMW) protein and Tau promote the formation of microtubules but are not required for assembly. Calmodulin and phosphorylation may both play roles in microtubule assembly.

A number of particularly important alkaloids can prevent microtubule assembly. These include colchicine and its derivative demecolcine (used for treatment of acute gouty arthritis), vinblastine (a *Vinca* alkaloid used for treating cancer), and griseofulvin (an antifungal agent).

Microtubules "grow" with a polarity from specific sites (centrioles) within cells. On each chromatid of a chromosome (see Chapter 27) there exists a kinetochore that serves as a point of origin for microtubular growth. Many abnormalities of chromosomal segregation result from abnormal structure or function of kinetochores. The centrosome, which is at the center of the mitotic poles, also nucleates microtubular formation. The movement of chromosomes during anaphase of mitosis is dependent upon microtubules, but the molecular mechanism has not been delineated.

At the base of all eukaryotic flagella and cilia is a structure called the **basal body;** it is identical to the centriole and acts as a nucleation center for the formation of the 9-doublet array of microtubules in the flagella and cilia.

Intermediate Filaments

Recent studies have confirmed the existence of an intracellular fibrous system of filaments 10–12 nm in diameter and distinct from microfilaments and microtubules. There are 5 major classes of these filaments that exhibit diameters **intermediate** in size between actin microfilaments and microtubules. Each intermediate filament consists of biochemically and immunologically distinct subunits. Table 33–3 summarizes some properties and distributions of intermediate filaments.

COLLAGEN

Collagen, the major macromolecule of connective tissues, is the most common protein in the animal world. It provides an extracellular framework for all metazoan animals and exists in virtually every animal tissue. There are at least **5 distinct types** of collagen in mammalian tissues; thus, they exist as a family of molecules sharing many properties. The most definitive property of collagen molecules is their **triple helix,** a coiled coil of 3 polypeptide subunits. Each polypeptide subunit or alpha chain is twisted into a **left-handed helix of 3 residues per turn.** Three of these left-handed helices are then wound to a right-handed superhelix to form a stiff rodlike molecule 1.4 nm in diameter and about 300 nm long. These triple helical molecules—unique to collagen—are then associated bilaterally and longitudinally into fibrils (Fig 33–16). The arrangement of collagen fibrils involves longitudinal staggering slightly less than one-quarter the length of the triple helix. Between the end of one triple helix and the beginning of the next is a gap that may provide a site for deposition of hydroxyapatite crystals in bone formation. Collagen fibrils range from 10 to 100 nm in diameter and are visible by microscopy as banded structures in the extracellular matrix of connective tissues.

The other striking characteristic of the collagen molecule is that **glycine constitutes every third residue** in the triple helical portion of each alpha chain. Glycine is the only amino acid small enough to exist in the limited space available down the central core of the triple helical molecule; thus, the central core of the triple helical molecule consists of glycine residues provided by each of the 3 alpha subunits. This repeating structure can be represented by $(Gly-X-Y)_n$, where X and Y are amino acids other than glycine.

Table 33–3. Classes of intermediate filaments and their distributions.

Proteins	MW (Thousands)	Diameter (nm)	Distributions
Keratin (tonofilaments)	40–65 (6–7 major proteins)	8	Epithelial cells (never cells of mesenchymal origin).
Desmin	50–55	10	Muscle (Z lines).
Vimentin	52	10	Mesenchymal and nonmesenchymal cells, eg, muscle, glial cells, epithelial cells.
Neurofilament	200 150 70	10	Neurons.
Glial filament	51	10	Glial cells.

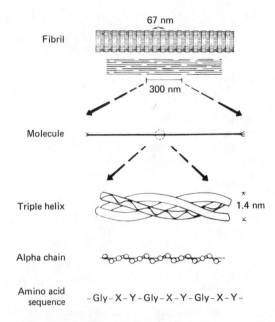

Fibril

67 nm

300 nm

Molecule

Triple helix

1.4 nm

Alpha chain

Amino acid sequence

$- Gly - X - Y - Gly - X - Y - Gly - X - Y -$

Figure 33–16. Molecular features of collagen structure from primary sequence up to the fibril. (Slightly modified and reproduced, with permission, from Eyre DR: Collagen: Molecular diversity in the body's protein scaffold. *Science* 1980;**207**:1315. Copyright 1980 by the American Association for the Advancement of Science.)

In mammalian collagen, about 100 of the X positions are **proline** and 100 of the Y positions are **4-hydroxyproline.** These rigid imino acids limit rotation of the polypeptide backbone and thus increase the stability of the triple helix. The hydroxyproline resi-

dues contribute additional stability to the collagen triple helix by forming more intramolecular hydrogen bonds mediated through extra water molecules. Collagen also contains 3-hydroxyproline in some X positions and **5-hydroxylysine in Y positions. The collagen triple helix is stabilized by multiple interchain cross-links** between lysyl and hydroxylysyl residues. The chemical nature of these cross-links is described below. Mature collagen is a glycoprotein containing saccharides attached in O-glycosidic linkage to the hydroxylysine residues.

A summary of the vertebrate collagens, their tissue distributions, and distinctive features is presented in Table 33–4.

The Synthesis of Collagen

Collagen is an extracellular protein but is synthesized as an intracellular precursor molecule that undergoes posttranslational modification before becoming a mature collagen fibril. Like all secreted proteins, the precursor of collagen is processed as it passes through the endoplasmic reticulum and Golgi complex prior to appearing extracellularly (Chapters 31 and 32). The earliest collagen precursor is a **preprocollagen** that contains a leader or signal sequence of approximately 100 amino acids at its amino terminus. Preprocollagen is generated by ribosomes attached to the endoplasmic reticulum. As the signal sequence penetrates into the vesicular space of the endoplasmic reticulum, the leader sequence is cleaved off and the amino-terminal end of **procollagen** continues to protrude into the endoplasmic reticular space. At this site, **prolyl 4-hydroxylase** and **lysyl hydroxylase** act on proline or lysine residues, respectively, in the Y position of the $(Gly-X-Y)_n$ peptide. A prolyl 3-hydroxylase acts on

Table 33–4. Genetically distinct vertebrate collagens. At least 5 different molecules containing 7 genetically distinct α chains are present in higher animals.[*]

Type	Molecular Formula	Native Polymer	Tissue Distribution	Distinctive Features
I	$[\alpha1(I)]_2\alpha2$	Fibril	Skin, tendon, bone, dentin, fascia; widespread.	Low content of hydroxylysine; few sites of hydroxylysine glycosylation; broad fibrils.
II	$[\alpha1(II)]_3$	Fibril	Cartilage, nucleus pulposus, notochord, vitreous body.	High content of hydroxylysine; heavily glycosylated; usually thinner fibrils than type I.
III	$[\alpha1(III)]_3$	Fibril	Skin, uterus, blood vessels; "reticulin" fibers generally.	High content of hydroxyproline; low content of hydroxylysine; few sites of hydroxylysine glycosylation; interchain disulfides between cysteines at the carboxyl end of the helix; long carboxyl telopeptide.
IV	$[\alpha1(IV)]_3$ (tentative, under dispute)	Basement lamina	Kidney glomeruli, lens capsule; Descemet's membrane; basement laminae of all epithelial and endothelial cells?	Very high content of hydroxylysine; almost fully glycosylated; relatively rich in 3-hydroxyproline; low alanine content; retains procollagen extension pieces.
V	$\alpha A(\alpha B)_2$ or $(\alpha A)_3$ and $(\alpha B)_3$	Unknown	Widespread in small amounts; basement lamina of smooth and striated muscle cells? exoskeleton of fibroblasts and other mesenchymal cells?	High content of hydroxylysine; heavily glycosylated; low alanine content: fails to form native fibrils in vitro.

[*]Reproduced, with permission, from Eyre DR: Collagen: Molecular diversity in the body's protein scaffold. *Science* 1980;**207**:1315. Copyright 1980 by the American Association for the Advancement of Science.

Table 33–5. Order and location of processing the collagen precursor (containing repeating structure [Gly-X-Y]$_n$).

Intracellular (endoplasmic reticulum)

  (1) Cleavage of signal peptide.

  (2) 4-Hydroxylation of Y-prolyl residues.

  (3) 3-Hydroxylation of X-prolyl, where Y = 4-hydroxyprolyl residue.

  (4) 5-Hydroxylation of Y-lysyl residues.

  (5) Glycosylation of hydroxylysyl residues.

  (6) Formation of intrachain and interchain S–S bonds.

  (7) Formation of triple helix procollagen.

Extracellular

  (1) Cleavage of NH$_2$-terminal propeptide (MW 20,000).

  (2) Cleavage of COOH-terminal propeptide (MW 30–35,000).

  (3) Formation of immature collagen fibrils.

  (4) Oxidation of lysyl, hydroxylysyl, glycosylated hydroxylysyl residue to aldehydes.

  (5) Cross-linking of chains and helical molecules of fibrils via Schiff bases and aldol condensations.

prolyl residues in the X position immediately preceding a 4-hydroxyproline in the Y position.

The procollagen molecule contains at its amino terminus a 20,000-MW peptide and at its carboxy terminus a 30- to 35-thousand-MW peptide, neither of which is present in mature collagen. Both of these propeptides contain **cysteine** residues. While the amino-terminal propeptide collagen forms only intrachain disulfide bonds, the carboxy-terminal peptides form both intrachain and interchain disulfide bonds. Following the formation of these disulfide bonds, the procollagen molecules assemble as the triple helix.

After formation of the triple helix, further hydroxylation of prolyl and lysyl residues *cannot* occur. The glycosyltransferase activities that attach glucose or galactose to hydroxylysine residues also require that the procollagen alpha chains be nonhelical.

Following this intracellular processing, the glycosylated procollagen molecule reaches the outside of the cell by way of the Golgi complex. Extracellular **procollagen aminoprotease** and **procollagen carboxyprotease** remove the amino-terminal and carboxy-terminal propeptides, respectively. The newly formed collagen molecules have approximately 1000 amino acids and spontaneously assemble into **collagen fibrils** that are indistinguishable from the mature fibrils found in tissues.

These fibrils, however, do not have the tensile strength of mature collagen fibrils until they are **cross-linked by a series of covalent bonds.** The extracellular copper-containing enzyme lysyl oxidase oxidatively deaminates the ϵ-amino groups of certain lysyl and hydroxylysyl residues of collagen, yielding reactive aldehydes. The aldehydes can form Schiff bases with ϵ-amino groups of other lysines or hydroxylysines or even glycosylated hydroxylysines. These Schiff bases are chemically rearranged and provide stable covalent cross-links such as new peptide bonds or secondary amine bridges. The aldehyde component derived from a hydroxylysine forms a more stable cross-link than does the aldehyde derived from a lysyl residue. Aldol bridges also provide intramolecular cross-links.

The intracellular and extracellular processing of the collagen precursor molecule is summarized in Table 33–5.

Inherited Defects of Collagen & Its Assembly

Patients with type VI Ehlers-Danlos syndrome have an inherited deficiency of lysyl hydroxylase. This disease is characterized by frequent abnormalities of the eye, severe scoliosis (abnormal vertebral column curvature), and hyperextensibility of the skin and joints. The cross-linking of hydroxylysine-deficient collagen is less stable than collagen containing adequate hydroxylysine.

A group of X-linked diseases is associated with a deficiency of lysyl oxidase activity. These include type V Ehlers-Danlos syndrome and some forms of cutis laxa. The absence of lysyl oxidase activity prevents normal cross-linking of collagen. The same lysyl oxidases participate in the cross-linking of elastin, another important connective tissue protein. Lysyl oxidase is a copper-requiring enzyme; copper deficiency, such as seen in Menkes' kinky hair syndrome, is thus associated with severe arteriovascular and skeletal changes.

Type VII Ehlers-Danlos syndrome involves a mutation in the primary structure of procollagen such that it does not serve as a substrate for the procollagen aminoprotease. The patients have hip dislocations, increased skin elasticity, and short stature.

Type IV Ehlers-Danlos syndrome is associated with a decreased rate of synthesis of type III collagen. The molecular nature of the defect is not delineated.

•   •   •

References

Adelstein RS, Eisenberg R: Regulation and kinetics of actin-myosin ATP interaction. *Annu Rev Biochem* 1980;**49:**921.

Adelstein RS & others: Phosphorylation of muscle contractile proteins. *Fed Proc* 1980;**39:**1544.

Barany M, Barany K: Phosphorylation of the myofibrillar proteins. *Annu Rev Physiol* 1980;**42:**275.

Bornstein P, Sage H: Structurally distinct collagen types. *Annu Rev Biochem* 1980;**49:**957.

Clark M, Spudich JA: Nonmuscle contractile proteins: The role of actin and myosin in cell motility and shape determination. *Annu Rev Biochem* 1977;**46:**797.

Dustin P: Microtubules. *Sci Am* (Aug) 1980;**243:**67.

Eyre DR: Collagen: Molecular diversity in the body's protein scaffold. *Science* 1980;**207:**1315.

Heuser JE, Kirschner MW: Filament organization revealed in platinum replicas of freeze-dried cytoskeletons. *J Cell Biol* 1980;**86:**212.

Lazarides E: Intermediate filaments as mechanical integrators of cellular space. *Nature* 1980;**283:**249.

Lazarides E, Revel JP: The molecular basis of cell movement. *Sci Am* (May) 1979;**240:**100.

Murray JM, Weber A: The cooperative action of muscle proteins. *Sci Am* (Feb) 1974;**230:**59.

Prockop DJ & others: The biosynthesis of collagen and its disorders. *N Engl J Med* 1979;**301:**13.

34 | General Characteristics of Hormones

Gerold M. Grodsky, PhD

Hormones are synthesized in a variety of **duct-less glands** and secreted into the blood for transmission to various "target tissues." At these sites they affect diverse metabolic processes. Hormones are usually required in very small amounts and are not consumed as part of their action.

Since hormones are secreted into the blood prior to use, circulating levels can give some indication of endocrine gland activity and target organ exposure. Because of the small amounts of hormones required, blood levels can be extremely low. For example, circulating levels of protein hormones range from 10^{-10} to 10^{-12}M, and the circulating levels of thyroid and steroid hormones are from 10^{-6} to 10^{-9}M.

The hormones include proteins often with molecular weights of 30,000 or less, small polypeptides, single amino acid derivatives, and steroids.

The action of a hormone at a target organ is regulated by 5 factors: (1) rate of synthesis and secretion of the stored hormone from the endocrine gland of origin; (2) in some cases, specific transport systems in the plasma; (3) sometimes, conversion to a more active form in the target tissue; (4) hormone-specific receptors in target cell cytosol or plasma membranes that differ from tissue to tissue; and (5) ultimate degradation of the hormone, usually by the liver or kidneys. Variation in any of these factors can result in a change in the amount or activity of a hormone at a given tissue site.

It is characteristic of the endocrine system that a balanced state of feedback regulation is normally maintained among the various glands. This is particularly notable with respect to releasing substances from the hypothalamus, which regulate synthesis and secretion of anterior pituitary hormones. The pituitary hormones in turn regulate activity of various target endocrine glands (Fig 34–1; also see pp 504–506). Characteristically, elevated hormone levels result in both direct and indirect feedback inhibition of their production by the originating gland.

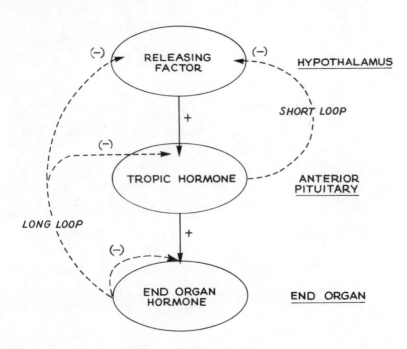

Figure 34–1. General feedback control of endocrine systems involving the hypothalamus, anterior pituitary, and end organ.

General Mechanisms of Action of Hormones

A. Induction of Enzyme Synthesis at the Nuclear Level: Hydrophobic hormones such as thyroxine and the steroids circulate bound to specific protein transporters in plasma. Their total concentration in the plasma, therefore, changes slowly over hours or days depending on the equilibrium between the free and bound forms. These hormones act to stimulate the accumulation of specific RNA molecules in target cells and thereby increase the synthesis of specific protein molecules, frequently an enzyme or group of enzymes catalyzing a specific metabolic pathway.

Steroid hormones initially act by binding to a specific high-affinity receptor protein in the cytosol (Fig 34–2). The complex that is formed (often involving structural transformation of the receptor protein) is then transported to the nucleus of the cell wherein it interacts with the chromatin. This interaction in turn influences the accumulation of specific messenger RNA (mRNA) molecules that will act as a template directing the synthesis of specific proteins. In addition, steroid hormones may nonspecifically increase general synthesis of messenger, transfer, and ribosomal RNAs by specifically increasing an RNA polymerase required for general RNA synthesis. Changes in metabolism are produced by this indirect route. It is to be noted that a direct chemical reaction of the hormone with DNA or RNA is not likely. Instead, it is postulated that the hormone must first combine with a specific receptor protein, and it is this combination that acts on chromatin. It is probable that chromatin proteins may influence hormonal activity by modifying the ability of the receptor complex to bind to DNA. This action of certain chromatin proteins could account for the specific binding of preformed receptor complexes to the chromatin of the hormone's target cells, whereas chromatin from other cells has less affinity.

Thyroid hormones act similarly to increase RNA and enzyme synthesis but may do so by directly binding to specific receptor proteins in the nucleus.

Hormones acting as described above may do so by regulating gene expression. Experimentally, isotopically labeled hormones are found to be localized in the nucleus. Other evidence of nuclear action is the frequent demonstration of increased RNA synthesis as measured by incorporation of labeled precursors into the nuclear RNA. Finally, the increase of activity of an enzyme after hormone administration can often be blocked by the administration of inhibitors of RNA synthesis such as dactinomycin, indicating that the hormonal action on enzyme activity was dependent upon concomitant RNA synthesis. Hormone action leading to a change in the rate of RNA and enzyme synthesis with a consequent effect on cellular metabolism may require hours or even days of exposure to the hormone before the effect may be detectable. Similarly, the effect of these hormones can persist long after their circulatory level has declined, since the induced enzymes may degrade slowly.

B. Stimulation of Enzyme Synthesis at the Ribosomal Level: Hormones may stimulate the rate of translation of information carried by the messenger RNA on the ribosomes to form protein. Ribosomes from a growth hormone–treated animal, for example, have a modified capacity to synthesize protein in the presence of normal mRNA levels.

C. Hormone Action at the Membrane Level: Many protein hormones (eg, insulin) and the catecholamines cause rapid secondary metabolic changes in their target tissue but have little effect on metabolic activity of membrane-free preparations. Usually these hormones can effectively activate different membrane enzyme systems by direct binding to specific integral membrane proteins (receptors). (See Chapter 31.)

Receptor levels themselves are highly sensitive to environmental and metabolic changes. For example, administration of insulin within hours causes a decrease in the synthesis and number of membrane insulin receptors ("down regulation"). In other states, the affinity of the receptor for the hormone may be affected. Thus, an inverse feedback regulation between hormone and receptor may be a general endocrinologic phenomenon. Indeed, changes in receptor activity may be as important as hormone levels in determining overall hormonal effectiveness. Examples of the mechanisms involved in the coupling between receptor binding and biologic action are described in Chapter 31.

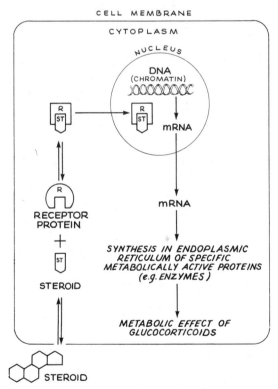

Figure 34–2. Steps in glucocorticoid action. St = steroid; R = specific glucocorticoid receptor; the dissimilar shapes of R are intended to represent different conformations of this protein. (Redrawn, with permission, from Baxter & Forsham [1972].)

D. Hormonal Action Related to Level of Cyclic Nucleotides: (Fig 34–3.) Cyclic AMP (cyclic 3',5'-AMP, cAMP) is a nucleotide that plays a unique role in the action of many hormones. Its level may be increased or decreased by hormonal action; the effect varies, depending on the tissue. Thus, glucagon may cause large increases of cAMP in the liver but comparatively small increases in muscle. In contrast, epinephrine produces a greater increase of cAMP in muscle than in liver. Insulin can decrease hepatic cAMP in opposition to the increase caused by glucagon. The hormones probably act at specific receptor sites in the different cell membranes that in turn activate the adenylate cyclase (the enzyme responsible for the synthesis of cAMP from ATP). (See Chapter 31.) It is probable that receptors for different hormones in a cell membrane activate a common adenylate cyclase.

Most of the varied effects of cAMP appear to reflect its general ability to activate a large variety of protein kinase enzymes that in turn phorphorylate (activating or inactivating) target enzymes. Thus, cAMP activation of glycogen phosphorylase is the result of a specific activation of the hepatic protein kinases, which results ultimately in the conversion of inactive dephosphophosphorylase to active phosphorylase (see pp 170–172). In adipose tissue, cAMP may activate lipolysis by a similar stimulation of protein kinase that causes increased lipase activity. cAMP can increase also the activity of protein kinases that phosphorylate nuclear histones and possibly other nuclear proteins. Thus, changing levels of cAMP may influence the function of regulators in the nucleus and explain how some hormones regulate gene expression. In the absence of cAMP, a protein kinase regulatory (inhibiting) subunit is bound to the kinase catalytic subunit. When cAMP binds to the regulatory subunit, the latter

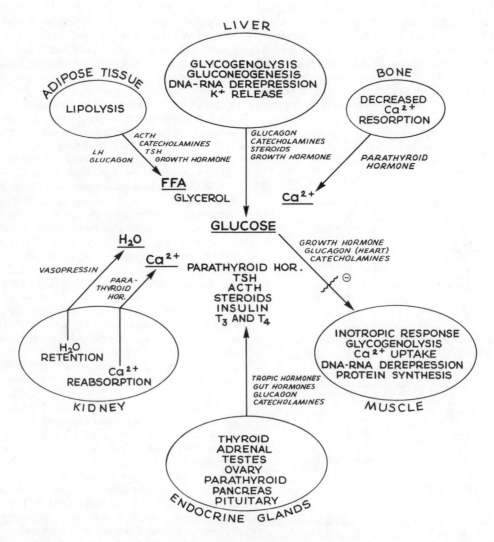

Figure 34–3. Tissue processes increased by cyclic AMP (cAMP) and the hormones that generate it. Insulin and some prostaglandins often decrease cAMP and reverse the mechanisms in tissues. (LH = luteinizing hormone; TSH = thyrotropin.)

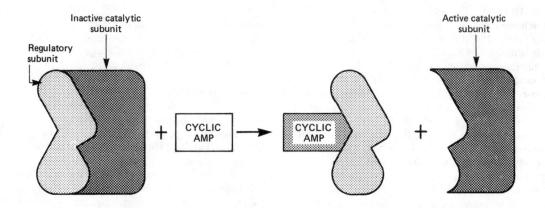

Figure 34–4. Activation of protein kinase by cyclic AMP (cAMP).

disassociates from, and thereby liberates, the active kinase (Fig 34–4).

Tissue levels of cAMP (approximately 10^{-7}M) can be influenced not only by hormones but also by nicotinic acid, imidazole, and methyl xanthines acting on its synthesis and degradation. However, the effects of these agents can vary with concentration or type of tissue and may not always relate to cAMP metabolism.

Though originally discovered as an endocrinologic phenomenon, cAMP is now recognized as a ubiquitous nucleotide that may be as important as ATP or AMP in controlling enzymatic reactions. A rise in cAMP is usually associated with beta-adrenergic reactions, and levels can be influenced by most metabolic changes caused by stress or diet.

Increased cAMP in cells can diffuse to extracellular fluid. Hormones that increase hepatic (glucagon) or renal (parathyroid hormone) cAMP bring about an increased level of the cyclic nucleotide in blood and urine, respectively. Although this may be useful for diagnostic purposes, extracellular cAMP has little or no biologic activity in mammals.

Cyclic GMP (guanosine-3′,5′-monophosphate, cGMP) is also found in most tissues. The exact role of this nucleotide is unknown, but tissue levels often rise and fall inversely to cAMP.

Role of Calcium in Hormone Action & Secretion

The action of most protein hormones is inhibited in the absence of calcium even though ability to increase or decrease cAMP is comparatively unimpaired. Thus, calcium may be a more terminal signal for hormonal secretion and action than cAMP (see section on parathyroid hormone in Chapter 35).

Rasmussen (1978) has suggested that calcium in a cytosolic compartment is the important signal (Fig 34–5). The source of this calcium may be the extracellular fluid, or it may arise from mobilization of intracellular, tissue-bound calcium. Protein hormones increase the uptake of extracellular calcium, whereas cAMP primarily mobilizes tissue-bound calcium.

Hormones that also activate adenylate cyclase have a dual action, increasing cytosol calcium derived from both sources mentioned above. This observation would explain why cAMP can mimic the actions of many hormones but (usually) with different kinetic characteristics. It also casts cAMP in the role of a modulator of hormone action instead of as the final signal. Intracellular calcium is now believed to act by binding to a ubiquitous 17,000-dalton heat labile, acidic protein, **calmodulin** which has a 45% structural homology with muscle troponin-C. Calmodulin has 4 binding sites for calcium and a calcium affinity in the range of cytosolic calcium levels (10^{-7}M). It is distributed throughout the cells and, in particular, is found associated with cellular membranes and many enzymes. Thus, calcium binding to calmodulin can result in conformational changes leading to rapid changes in enzymatic and membrane activity. This peptide has been implicated in calcium activation of hormone secretion; adenylate cyclase (and, at high

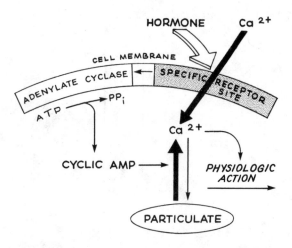

Figure 34–5. Interrelationships between hormone action, cyclic AMP, and calcium ion.

concentration, phosphodiesterase); phosphorylation of protein kinase, myosin kinases, and membranes; ATPases; microtubule depolymerization; and calcium transport. The activation of protein kinases by calcium-calmodulin explains how many hormones may duplicate the effects of cAMP via protein phosphorylation without acting on or changing levels of cAMP.

The secretion of almost all hormones stored in granules requires calcium. Stimulators often increase uptake of calcium whether or not they increase cAMP. As above, cAMP can partially modulate the action of primary stimulators by mobilizing intracellular bound calcium.

Many hormones increase calcium uptake by depolarizing the cell. In addition, hormone secretion is usually enhanced by increased K^+ or by stimulators that produce depolarization. For example, glucose depolarizes the B cell as part of its mechanism for stimulating insulin secretion.

All of the mechanisms described above may be involved in the action of a given hormone and may vary in significance when the action of a hormone is studied in different tissues. For example, insulin has a major and rapid effect on membrane transport in adipose and muscle tissue, but its hepatic action is to suppress enzyme phosphorylation and to modify enzyme synthesis at the nuclear level. Finally, all of the mechanisms are intimately related. An effect on transport would thus permit the entrance of substances that could act as enzyme activators or, at the nuclear level, as repressors or derepressors of RNA synthesis. Similarly, a direct effect on one enzyme system could

modify the availability of substrates or products for other pathways or for activation or inactivation at the nuclear or membrane level. Because of the interdependency of these mechanisms, the primary action of a given hormone is not easily established.

Assay of Hormones

A. Biologic Assays: Biologic assays, in which an aspect of hormonal activity is measured in vitro or in vivo, remain important since they measure levels of functional activity. However, these assays often lack precision and sensitivity and are usually not specific.

B. Chemical Assays: These are often used in conjunction with isotope dilution and employ classic isolation and purification technics, including gas and column chromatography, electrophoresis, and differential solvent extraction. They provide a measure of the absolute quantity of a given hormone but can be burdensome and, in the case of protein hormones, are generally not applicable.

C. Radiodisplacement Chemical Assays: These have been widely adopted in recent years for both protein and nonprotein hormones. They are based on the competition for a specific binding protein of radiolabeled hormones with unlabeled hormone (Fig 34–6). The binding protein may be a specific antibody, membrane receptor, or serum transport protein. Unlabeled hormone, present as either a standard or an unknown, competitively displaces the labeled hormone, resulting in an increase in radioactivity in the unbound fraction. Although many methods are available, they differ primarily in the technics used to separate the bound and free hormone fractions.

Traces of radiolabeled hormone (●) incubated with excess antisera or specific binding protein (○). Little radioactivity remains in free fraction.

Addition of unlabeled hormone (sample or standard) (○) increased radioactivity in supernatant.

Figure 34–6. Principle of immunochemical assay for measuring hormone in biologic fluids. The amount of radioactivity in the supernatant is a direct function of the amount of hormone in the specimen.

Radiodisplacement methods are more sensitive than most bioassays since they permit detection of hormones in concentrations less than 1 ng/mL. Some radiodisplacement methods are highly specific and relatively convenient. One defect of these assays is that they can measure degradation fragments or precursors of the hormone that retain some binding activity but can vary in their biologic activity. When possible, both chemical and biologic assays should be performed on identical samples.

• • •

References

Abramowitz V, Iyengar R, Birnbaumer L: Guanyl nucleotide regulation of hormonally-responsive adenyl cyclases. *Mol Cell Endocrinol* 1979;**16:**129.

Baxter JD, Forsham PH: Tissue effects of glucocorticoids. *Am J Med* 1972;**53:**573.

Catt KJ & others: Basic concepts of the mechanism of action of peptide hormones. *Biol Reprod* 1976;**14:**1.

Cuatrecasas P, Hollenberg MD: Membrane receptors and hormone action. *Adv Protein Chem* 1976;**30:**251.

Hall R, Gomez-Pan A: Hypothalamic regulatory hormones and their clinical applications. *Adv Clin Chem* 1976;**18:**173.

Means AR, Dedman JR: Calmodulin: An intracellular calcium receptor. *Nature* 1980;**285:**73.

Posner BI: Polypeptide hormone receptors: Characteristics and applications. *Can J Physiol Pharmacol* 1975;**53:**689.

Rasmussen H: Calcium and cyclic nucleotides as universal second messengers. *Cell Tissue Interactions* 1978;**32:**243.

35 | Chemistry & Functions of the Hormones: I. Thyroid, Pancreas, Adrenal, & Gastrointestinal Tract

Gerold M. Grodsky, PhD

THE THYROID

The thyroid gland consists of 2 lobes, one on each side of the trachea, with a connecting portion making the entire gland more or less H-shaped in appearance. In the adult, the gland weighs about 25–30 g. Although there is some evidence of extrathyroidal production of thyroidlike hormones, the thyroid gland is the primary source of their production.

Function

Thyroid hormone is particularly important as a regulator of differentiation during development. A closely related function is that of a catalyst for the oxidative reactions and regulation of metabolic rates in the body. Increased thyroid hormone is associated with increased oxygen consumption, body temperature, pulse, systolic blood pressure, mental and physical vigor, irritability, lipolysis, and weight loss. Cholesterol levels are decreased in blood.

Although a number of effects of thyroid hormone on specific metabolic reactions have been demonstrated, a unifying concept of the mechanism by which it produces acceleration of metabolism is not yet apparent. This is in part due to the different effects noted when the hormone is studied at physiologic levels or at unphysiologically high doses.

Thyroid hormones act relatively slowly, suggesting that their primary, if not exclusive, action is on protein synthesis in the target cell as described (see Chapter 34, p 463). In contrast to the steroids, thyroid hormones bind directly to proteins associated with chromatin in the nucleus without intermediate binding to any cytosol receptor. The nuclear binding proteins are acidic and nonhistone in nature and are bound to nuclear DNA where they serve as specific receptors for thyroid hormone (Fig 35–1). Increased mRNA and protein synthesis result and may account for the general anabolic effect of thyroid hormone. However, the increased protein synthesis is specific; for instance, in pituitary tumor cells only 0.5% of detectable proteins were influenced by the addition of thyroid hormones. RNA polymerases, ribosomal RNA, and tRNA are also increased, suggesting that thyroid hormone may increase gene expression at the transcriptional level. Protein synthesis in mitochondria is also increased and may account for some of the known hormonal effects

on respiration. A specific action to increase both mRNA coding for growth hormone and growth hormone production may explain part of thyroid hormone's anabolic effects in the intact animal. The hormone also increases hyaluronidase synthesis in tadpoles, which has been related to increased differentiation.

At high concentrations of thyroid hormone, negative nitrogen balance is observed and protein synthesis is depressed. Thyroid hormone uncouples oxidative phosphorylation and increases swelling in the mitochondria. Such an action results in the production of heat rather than the storage of energy as ATP. However, these effects are observed only with very

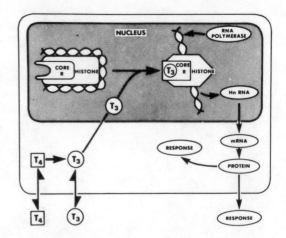

Figure 35–1. Working model for the mechanism of thyroid hormone action in a responsive cell. Thyroid hormones enter the cell by as yet unknown mechanisms and may be metabolized as is shown for the conversion of T_4 to the biologically active T_3. After association of T_3 with the "holo" receptor ("core" receptor plus histones), there is a structural change in chromatin that influences the transcription of specific genes. Subsequent to transcription, processing of precursor forms of RNA may occur, yielding the mature mRNA. Translation of the mRNA results in the synthesis of proteins whose effects may be expressed intracellularly or extracellularly (eg, growth hormone). (Reproduced, with permission, from Baxter JD & others: Thyroid hormone receptors and responses. *Recent Prog Horm Res* 1979;35:97.)

high concentrations of the hormone and may not reflect its effect in the small physiologic doses characteristic of the intact organism. Thyroxine can increase the ATPase associated with ion pumps. Thus, a primary action of the hormone may be to increase ATP utiliza-

tion, the resulting ATP depletion being responsible for the observed increase in oxygen uptake. Thyroid hormone also potentiates the action of glucagon and catecholamines. This may be explained by its ability to increase cAMP via inhibition of phosphodiesterase.

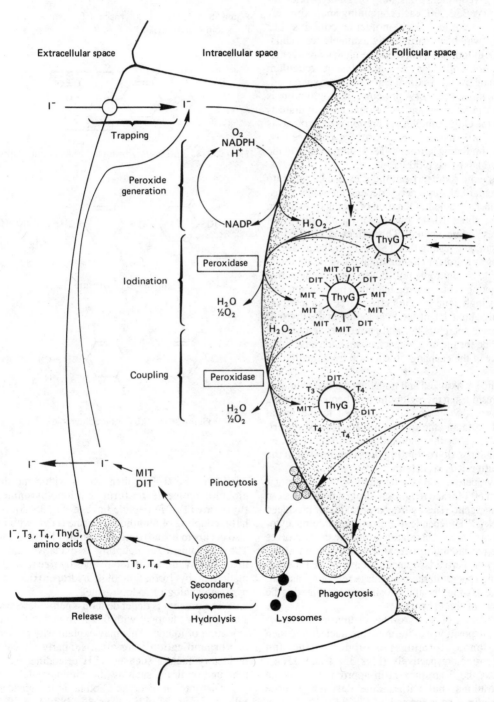

Figure 35–2. Model of iodine metabolism in the thyroid follicle. A follicular cell is shown facing the follicular lumen (stippled area) and the extracellular space (lower part). The sequence of events shown has been documented for the most part. However, the possibility of active iodide transport at the apex of the cell or of intracellular iodination and the relative roles of pinocytosis versus phagocytosis and of diffusion versus secretion of thyroid hormones remain controversial. (ThyG, thyroglobulin; MIT, monoiodotyrosine; DIT, diiodotyrosine.)

Synthesis & Chemistry of Thyroid Hormones

Lobules of the thyroid gland consist of follicles that are a single layer of epithelial cells surrounding a cavity, or follicle lumen. The primary percursor for thyroid hormone is **iodothyroglobulin.** Thyroglobulin is a 19S glycoprotein consisting of 2 polypeptide dimers of MW 330,000, each containing approximately 10% carbohydrate. Each molecule contains 115 tyrosines, which are particularly available for iodination. The uniodinated polypeptide chains are synthesized in the follicular cell endoplasmic reticulum where some of the proximal carbohydrates are added. As with most secretory proteins, thyroglobulin is packaged in vesicles and additional carbohydrate is added at the Golgi complex. Secretion is by exocytosis into the follicular lumen, a process enhanced by thyroid-stimulating hormone (TSH, thyrotropin) of the pituitary gland (see p 509).

Inorganic iodide* from the diet is taken up into the follicular cells by energy-dependent active transport against a gradient. Of a total of 50 mg of iodine in the body, about 10–15 mg are in the thyroid. TSH stimulates iodide uptake. This effect is blocked by puromycin, suggesting that TSH acts to synthesize an iodotransport protein. Iodide uptake can be inhibited by cyanide or dinitrophenol. It also requires an active sodium pump, uptake being inhibited by ouabain. Despite this high concentration effect, free iodide represents only about 1% of the total iodine in the thyroid. Thiocyanate, perchlorate, and pertechnetate compete with iodide for the uptake mechanism and cause rapid discharge of the exchangeable iodide from the thyroid gland.

Iodide is oxidized and transferred to the abundant tyrosyl residues in thyroglobulin by a heme-containing peroxidase, thyroperoxidase, attached to the apical cell surface facing the follicle lumen. Isotope experiments show that this iodination is rapid and occurs extracellularly; **thyroglobulin thus is iodinated in the lumen after it is secreted.**

Thyroperoxidase is a tetramer with a molecular weight of 60,000 and requires hydrogen peroxide as an oxidizing agent. The hydrogen peroxide is produced by an NADPH-dependent enzyme resembling cytochrome c reductase. Oxidation of iodide thus involves both the production of peroxide and oxidation of the iodide by the peroxidase enzyme. Free iodide is not the iodinating species in the peroxidase reaction; instead, free radicals of iodine and tyrosine are combined at the active site of the enzyme.

Iodination of the tyrosines in thyroglobulin occurs first in position 3 of the aromatic nucleus and then at position 5, forming monoiodotyrosine and diiodotyrosine, respectively (Figs 35–3 and 35–4). Normally, the 2 are present in approximately equal concentrations, but with iodine deficiency more monoiodotyrosine is formed.

It is assumed that coupling of 2 molecules of

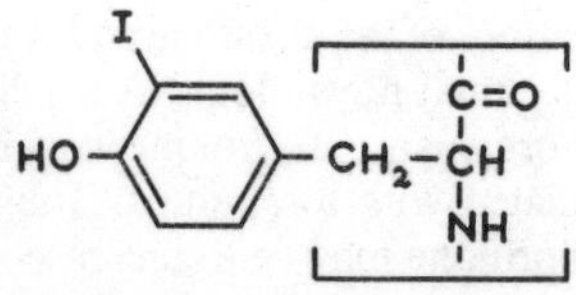

Figure 35–3. 3-Monoiodotyrosine (ITyr) (shown in peptide linkage in thyroglobulin).

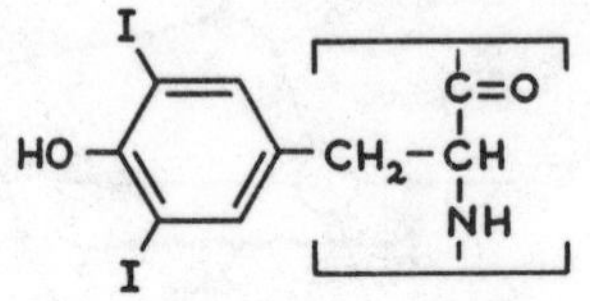

Figure 35–4. 3,5-Diiodotyrosine (I$_2$Tyr) (in peptide linkage).

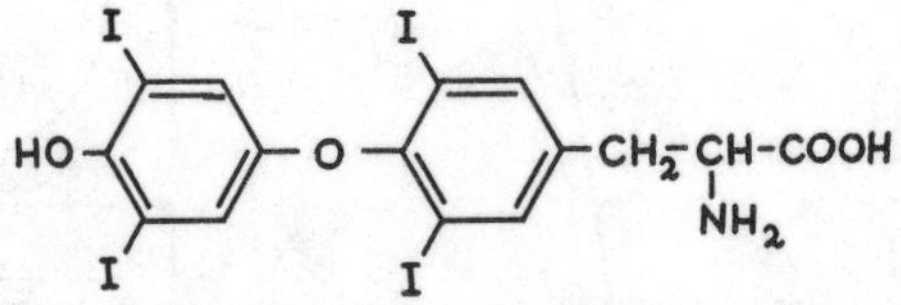

Figure 35–5. Thyroxine (T$_4$).

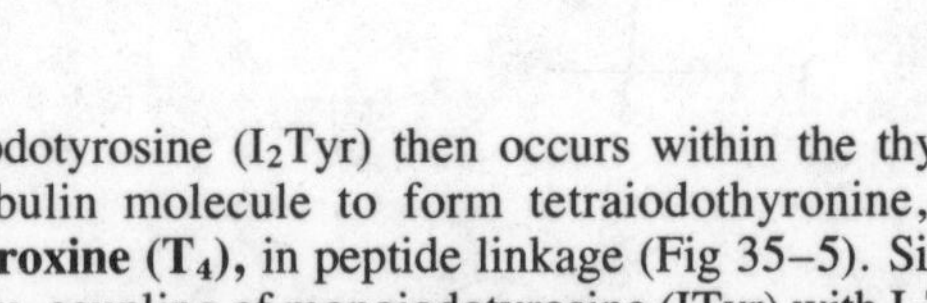

Figure 35–6. 3,5,3'-Triiodothyronine (T$_3$).

diiodotyrosine (I$_2$Tyr) then occurs within the thyroglobulin molecule to form tetraiodothyronine, or **thyroxine (T$_4$),** in peptide linkage (Fig 35–5). Similarly, coupling of monoiodotyrosine (ITyr) with I$_2$Tyr also occurs to form **triiodothyronine (T$_3$)** (Fig 35–6). The mechanism for coupling is oxidative and may involve activation of iodotyrosines by free radical formation or by formation of a hydroperoxide of the pyruvate analog of iodotyrosine.

The process is dependent on a peroxidase system similar to or identical with that involved in the initial oxidation of iodide. This may explain why both steps of "organification" are often similarly affected by regulatory factors such as TSH or iodine itself, or inhibited by drugs such as phenylthiouracil.

Distribution of organic iodine in the gland is as follows: I$_2$Tyr, 24–42%; ITyr, 17–28%: T$_4$, 35%; T$_3$, 5–8%. Approximately 20% of the thyroglobulin tyrosine residues are iodinated.

On stimulation (eg, by thyrotropin), thyroglobulin-containing colloid is taken up by the follicular

*In this chapter, iodine is used generically and includes all forms of the element. Iodide refers only to the ionic form, I⁻.

cells via the process of endocytosis (Fig 35–2). The resulting secretory droplets combine transiently with lysosomes, the latter providing the proteolytic enzymes that break down thyroglobulin. Proteolysis of thyroglobulin may be facilitated by a disulfide cleavage step using a glutathione-catalyzed transhydrogenase similar to that which reduces insulin in the liver. Thyroxine and triiodothyronine generated by the breakdown of iodothyroglobulin are then released from the gland by a secretion process involving microtubules and microfilaments. The hydrolysis of thyroglobulin also liberates ITyr and I_2Tyr. If these iodinated amino acids were lost from the gland, considerable amounts of iodide would be biologically unavailable for the synthesis of active hormone. However, particulate thyroidal deiodinase (or dehalogenase) enzymes rapidly remove the iodine and permit its reutilization for the synthesis of new hormone (Fig 35–2). Approximately one-third of the total iodine in the thyroid is recycled in this manner. Both pituitary thyrotropin and exposure to a cold environment stimulate thyroglobulin endocytosis, breakdown, and the release of active hormone. Thyroglobulin breakdown is directly inhibited by iodide. Intact thyroglobulin can enter the circulation during surgical manipulation or irradiation of the thyroid gland.

The accumulation of inorganic iodide and its conversion to iodothyroglobulin in the thyroid are completed over about a 48-hour period, but radioactively labeled protein-bound iodine does not appear in the plasma for several days after the original administration of radioactive iodine.

Within the plasma, T_4 and T_3 are transported almost entirely in association with 2 proteins, the so-called thyroxine-binding proteins, which act as specific carrier agents for the hormones. A glycoprotein (MW 50,000) that migrates electrophoretically in a region between the alpha$_1$ and alpha$_2$ globulins is designated **thyroxine-binding globulin** and is the major transporter. Another protein, **thyroxine-binding prealbumin,** is detectable electrophoretically just ahead of the albumin fraction. When large amounts of T_4 and T_3 are present and the binding capacities of these specific carrier proteins are exceeded, the hormones bind to serum albumin. Approximately 0.05% of the circulating thyroxine is in the free, unbound state. "Free" T_3 **and** T_4 are the metabolically active hormones in the plasma. However, bound and free hormone are in rapid equilibration. Thus, bound hormone serves as a ready reservoir to provide hormone to the target tissues in the event of transient decreases in function of the thyroid gland. The macromolecular binding proteins are particularly important to prevent rapid clearance and degradation of circulating T_3 and T_4 by the kidney.

T_4 and T_3 can be dissociated from their binding proteins by competing anions such as phenytoin, salicylates, or dinitrophenol. Because it is more loosely bound by the serum proteins, T_3 disappears from the blood 20 times more rapidly than T_4 (halftime of T_4 is 6–7 days).

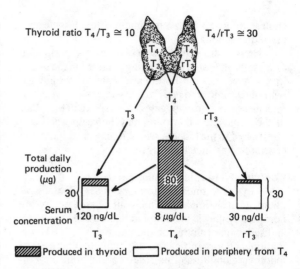

Figure 35–7. Quantitative outline of thyroidal secretion and peripheral conversions of thyroxine (T_4) and thyroidal and peripheral production of triiodothyronine (T_3) and reverse triiodothyronine (rT_3). The approximate serum concentrations of T_3 and rT_3 derived from thyroidal and peripheral production are also shown. (Reproduced, with permission, from Schimmel M, Utiger RD: Thyroidal and peripheral production of thyroid hormones. *Ann Intern Med* 1977; 87:760.)

T_3 is 3–5 times more biologically active than T_4 and is the major active form of the thyroid hormone since it has a much higher affinity for the thyroid hormone receptor protein in the nucleus (Fig 35–1). Approximately 80% of circulating T_4 is converted in peripheral tissue, particularly the liver and kidneys, to T_3 and to reverse T_3 (3,5′,3′-triiodothyronine). This accounts for more than two-thirds of the T_3 produced in the body and almost all of the reverse T_3 (Fig 35–7).

Since T_4 is the precursor for both active T_3 and less active reverse T_3, intimate control of peripheral thyroid hormone activity can be regulated by the specific deiodination that occurs. Conversion of T_4 to T_3 is increased by phenytoin and is decreased in aging individuals. Reverse T_3 is high at birth, during total starvation in adults, and after propylthiouracil or glucocorticoid administration.

In contrast to the steroids, thyroid hormones may bind directly to specific receptor proteins in the acid nuclear chromatin; receptors in the cytosol are less effective as regulators. Although the exact chemical mechanism of action of T_3 and T_4 is not known, iodine is required at the 3,5 position, suggesting that binding of T_3 and T_4 to tissue receptors involves this portion of the molecule.

Both T_4 and T_3 are metabolized in the peripheral tissues by deamination and decarboxylation to **tetraiodothyroacetic acid** or **triiodothyroacetic acid.** These metabolites are about one-fourth as active on a weight basis as their hormonal precursors, although their onset of action may be more rapid. Both substances have been used as agents to decrease serum cholesterol levels with a minimum of the less desired thyroxine actions.

Deiodination may also occur in the peripheral tissues, the liberated iodide being excreted in the urine. In the liver, thyroid hormone is rapidly conjugated with glucuronic acid and, to a lesser extent, with sulfate; these inactive conjugates are excreted in bile. Part of the conjugated thyroxine may be reabsorbed and transported to the kidney, where it may be deiodinated or excreted as intact conjugate.

Control of Thyroid Hormone Release

Thyroid-stimulating hormone (TSH) from the pituitary gland stimulates almost all phases of thyroid hormone synthesis including iodide uptake, synthesis and secretion of thyroglobulin into colloid, H_2O_2 formation and organification of iodine, synthesis of iodothyroglobulin and its reabsorption from the colloid, and final secretion of thyroid hormones. Since all of these phenomena are interdependent, the specific sites of TSH action are unknown. TSH acts in part by increasing thyroidal cAMP and altering intracellular calcium distribution. This results in rapid effects such as increased organification of iodine with concomitant iodothyroglobulin synthesis and increase of both the required secretion into and reabsorption from the colloid necessary for increased T_4 and T_3 secretion. This increased secretion explains why an early effect of TSH is depletion of thyroid iodine. TSH also increases the slower process of thyroglobulin peptide synthesis. An increased synthesis of iodide carrier protein(s) is probably responsible for the observed late but dramatic increase in glandular uptake of iodine in response to TSH.

Exposure to cold causes a release of thyroid hormone, but this is probably mediated through TSH release by the pituitary. TSH, in turn, is regulated by the hypothalamic tripeptide **(thyrotropin-releasing hormone, TRH)** (Fig 36–6).

Thyroxine is a feedback inhibitor of its own secretion. This inhibitory effect occurs at the pituitary by inhibition of TSH secretion; it may be due to a direct action of thyroxine (or triiodothyronine) that decreases the pituitary sensitivity to thyroxine-releasing hormone. There is some evidence that thyroxine can, to a lesser extent, also inhibit the secretion of thyroxine-releasing hormone at the hypothalamic level.

The controlling effect of thyroxine on TSH release in the pituitary is blocked by substances inhibiting protein synthesis, whereas the effect of thyroxine-releasing hormone is not. Thus, the 2 agents operate by different mechanisms.

Iodine itself is an important autoregulator in thyroid gland function. Decreased iodide (or, more likely, decreased organified iodine) rapidly increases subsequent iodide uptake as well as breakdown of thyroglobulin to T_4. Catecholamines can also directly stimulate thyroid hormone secretion.

Antithyroid drugs (Fig 35–8). Certain compounds act as antithyroid agents, inhibiting the production of thyroxine both at the organification and at the

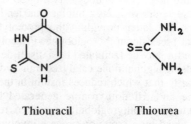

Thiouracil   Thiourea

Figure 35–8. Antithyroid drugs.

coupling steps. Examples of these antithyroid drugs are the goitrogens—thiouracil, propylthiouracil, methylthiouracil, carbimazole, thiourea, and methimazole (Tapazole, 1-methyl-2-mercaptoimidazole). Thiouracil is relatively toxic; the other compounds less so.

Abnormalities of Thyroid Function

A. Hypothyroid States: A deficiency of thyroid hormone produces a number of clinical states depending upon the degree of the deficiency and the age at which it occurs.

Though comparatively rare, congenital defects in iodine uptake, organification, coupling, deiodination, and hormone secretion have all been described.

1. Cretinism, characterized by mental retardation and impaired growth, results from the incomplete development or congenital absence of the thyroid gland.

2. Childhood hypothyroidism (juvenile myxedema) appears later in life than cretinism and is less severe.

3. Myxedema is caused by hypothyroidism in the adult. The basal metabolic rate and body temperature are lowered, and there is undue sensitivity to cold. Anemia and slowing of physical and mental reactions are also present.

4. Hashimoto's disease is a form of hypothyroidism in which all aspects of thyroid function may be impaired. This has now been established as an autoimmune disease in which the thyroid has been subjected to attack by the immunity system.

5. Simple (endemic or colloid) goiter is a deficiency disease caused by an inadequate supply of iodine in the diet. The decreased production of thyroid hormone causes overstimulation of the gland because of increased pituitary TSH production incident to the lack of the "braking" effect of thyroid hormone. Simple goiter is common where the soil and water are low in iodine. The use of iodized salt has done much to reduce its incidence.

B. Hyperthyroid States: Toxic goiter differs from simple goiter in that enlargement of the gland is accompanied by the secretion of excessive amounts of thyroid hormone. The term "toxic" does not refer to the secretion of the gland but to the toxic symptoms incident to the hyperthyroidism. Symptoms include nervousness, fatigability, loss of weight, increased body temperature with excessive sweating, and an increase in the heart rate.

The most common form of hyperthyroidism is **exophthalmic goiter.** A characteristic protrusion of the eyeballs (exophthalmos) usually accompanies hyperthyroidism.

One form of toxic goiter (Graves' disease) is characterized by the presence of a thyroid-stimulating protein factor that is immunologically different from thyroid-stimulating hormone (thyrotropin) of the pituitary. Qualitatively, it duplicates most actions of thyrotropin, but its maximal thyroid-stimulating effect occurs many hours after that of thyrotropin. For these reasons, it has been designated **long-acting thyroid stimulator (LATS).** Long-acting thyroid stimulator is an antibody developed as an autoimmune phenomenon against thyroid protein. Transplacental transfer of long-acting thyroid stimulator antibody from mother to fetus may be responsible for neonatal thyrotoxicosis.

A substance called **LATS protector** (long-acting thyroid stimulator protector), which in vitro can prevent inactivation of LATS by thyroid tissue fractions, has also been detected in the serum of hyperthyroid patients. It can directly stimulate the thyroid gland. LATS protector, like LATS, is an antibody directed against some constituents of the tissues of the thyroid gland. Both LATS and LATS protector are referred to as thyroid-stimulating antibody.

Hyperthyroidism can be treated by thyroid removal by surgery, or by radioactive iodine (^{131}I). It is also treated by antithyroid drugs (goitrogens) that prevent the gland from incorporating inorganic iodide into the organic forms, or by agents such as thiocyanate or perchlorate that compete with iodide for the uptake mechanism.

Calcitonin

Though now believed to be a hormone elucidated primarily by the C cells of the thyroid gland, calcitonin's metabolic actions and historical interest relate closely with parathyroid hormone. It is therefore discussed in the following section.

THE PARATHYROIDS

The parathyroid glands are 4 small glands so closely associated with the thyroid that they remained unrecognized for some time and were often removed during thyroidectomy. In humans, the parathyroids are reddish or yellowish-brown egg-shaped bodies; the 4 glands together weigh about 0.05–0.3 g.

Chemistry

The active parathyroid hormone (PTH) is a linear polypeptide consisting of 84 amino acids. The amino acid sequence of this polypeptide is shown in Fig 35–9. Parathyroid hormones from different species differ only slightly; bovine and porcine hormone are identical except for 7 amino acids. Studies of the

synthetic PTH polypeptide indicate that the essential requirements for the physiologic actions of this hormone on both skeletal and renal tissues are contained within the 1–29 or possibly the 1–34 N-terminal amino acids.

PTH is initially synthesized in the chief cells as a **preprohormone** consisting of 31 extra amino acids (mostly hydrophobic) attached to the N terminus (Fig 35–9). The initiating amino acid, as in most preproteins, is methionine. Preproparathyroid hormone is

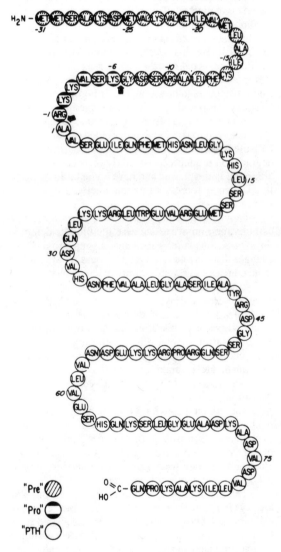

Figure 35–9. Primary structure of preproparathyroid hormone (PreProPTH). Arrows indicate sites of specific peptide bond cleavages that occur in the cell and result in the sequential conversion of preproparathyroid hormone to proparathyroid hormone (cleavage at glycyl-lysyl bond at positions −7 and −6) and conversion of proparathyroid hormone to parathyroid hormone (cleavage at arginyl-alanyl bond at positions −1 and +1). (Reproduced, with permission, from Habener JF, Potts JT Jr: Biosynthesis of parathyroid hormone. [First of two parts.] *N Engl J Med* 1978;**299**:582.)

converted in minutes to the **prohormone** that contains a residual hexapeptide on the N terminus of PTH.

Regulation of Parathyroid Hormone Secretion & Degradation

In contrast to many protein hormones, only small amounts of parathyroid hormone are stored in the human gland; relatively few storage granules are present. Consequently, it is synthesized and secreted continuously.

Secretion of parathyroid hormone is subject to control by a negative feedback mechanism relating to the levels of ionized calcium in the plasma; parathyroid hormone concentrations are decreased abruptly by administration of calcium ion and rise when circulating ionized calcium is lowered. Calcium loss associated with chronic renal disease and rickets also results in increased circulating parathyroid hormone. Although calcium appears to be an important homeostatic regulator of parathyroid secretion, a change in the amount of phosphate has no effect on hormone release.

The secreted hormone is degraded rapidly; it has a half-life of about 18 minutes. Circulating precursor or degradation products (particularly ones of MW 7000) are found in the plasma and have some biologic activity. They may represent important active forms of the hormone.

Parathyroid extracts have been assayed biologically by their ability to increase the blood calcium in dogs or in rats after subcutaneous injection. Other changes that may be observed in bioassays are rapidly induced rises in excretion of urinary phosphate and of $3',5'$-cAMP. Bioassay in vitro is based on activation of renal adenylate cyclase and increase in cAMP in fetal rat skull or renal tissue. Radioimmunoassay for PTH is used routinely for measuring levels of the hormone in the circulation. However, circulating breakdown products of variable biologic and immunologic activity can impair the accuracy of this assay.

Action

The primary function of the parathyroid glands, mediated by their secretion of parathyroid hormone, is to maintain the concentration of ionized calcium in the plasma within the narrow range characteristic of this electrolyte despite wide variations in calcium intake, excretion, and deposition in bone.

The major sites of action of PTH are bone and kidney. In bone, the hormone causes rapid release of calcium and phosphorus, which is associated with bone resorption by the osteocytes. This effect is similar to that produced by $1\alpha,25$-dihydroxycholecalciferol, an active form of vitamin D (see Chapter 11). Both the vitamin D derivative and PTH act synergistically although their mechanisms of action differ. PTH acts via cAMP.

In the kidney, PTH increases phosphate excretion but increases calcium reabsorption. The overall effects of high PTH are to increase plasma calcium and decrease plasma phosphate. In renal tubules, PTH increases the rate of conversion of 25-hydroxycholecal-

ciferol to 1,25-dihydroxycholecalciferol (see Chapter 11).

There is also evidence that parathyroid hormone increases the rate of absorption of calcium from the intestine, an effect which is, however, comparatively minor and likely secondary to its increasing the production of 1,25-dihydroxycholecalciferol in the kidney.

The actions of the PTH on bone and kidney are independent processes, as indicated by the fact that the hormone effectively mobilizes bone calcium in nephrectomized animals as well as from bone tissue incubated in vitro.

PTH may act to stimulate protein synthesis in the osteoclasts, which, in turn, effect resorption of bone. This idea is supported by the observation that inhibition of RNA synthesis (and thus, indirectly, protein

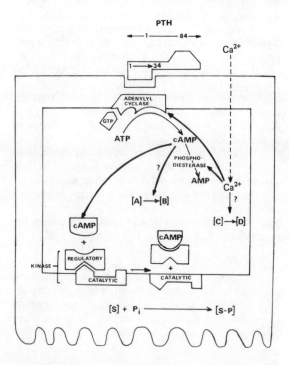

Figure 35–10. Hypothetical scheme of parathyroid hormone (PTH) action on its target cell (renal cell). The active NH_2-terminal portion of the PTH molecule binds to the specific membrane receptor and stimulates adenylyl cyclase (whose activity can be influenced by nucleotide, eg, GTP, interaction), resulting in cAMP accumulation. Concomitantly, calcium (Ca^{2+}) influx is enhanced by the hormone. Cyclic AMP may activate a kinase (presumably on the luminal surface of the renal cell) to phosphorylate a protein [S] participating in solute transport. Other intracellular reactions ([A] → [B]) may be mediated as well. The cytosol calcium levels may, in turn, influence net cAMP concentrations by effects on the activity of the cyclase and the esterase and may perhaps independently alter intracellular enzyme sequences ([C] → [D]) involved in hormonal action. (Reproduced, with permission, from Goltzman D: Biochemical mode of action of parathyroid hormone. In: *Endocrinology.* Vol 2. DeGroot LJ [editor]. Grune & Stratton, 1979.)

synthesis) by dactinomycin blocks the activity of the hormone in vivo. However, the rapid acute effect of PTH on bone resorption is not inhibited by dactinomycin, indicating that at least part of the activity is independent of RNA synthesis and possibly of protein synthesis as well.

A primary action of PTH is to stimulate the uptake of extracellular calcium. In turn, the increased calcium in the cytosol may trigger the metabolic events in bone and in kidney, including bone resorption and tubular reabsorption of calcium (Figs 34–5 and 35–10). cAMP also increases the bone resorption but does so by increasing calcium via mobilization of intracellular membrane-bound calcium. PTH activates adenylate cyclase in both bone and kidney, the latter action being reflected by a rise in urinary cAMP. Therefore, the hormone has a dual action to increase cytosol calcium. In the absence of calcium, PTH still increases cAMP but no longer stimulates bone resorption or osteoblastic activity. Thus, a major requirement for the parathyroid activation of calcium mobilization may be, paradoxically, to increase uptake of ionized calcium into the cells. Circulating phosphate ion can reverse the action of PTH, presumably by influencing phosphate-calcium transport at the level of both mitochondria and cell membranes.

Calcitonin (Thyrocalcitonin)

Calcitonin or **thyrocalcitonin** is a calcium-lowering hormone originating from the C cells of the thyroid gland. The release of calcitonin is stimulated by high levels of ionized calcium in the serum.

Calcitonin is directly effective on bone, where it results in metabolic effects opposite to those of parathyroid hormone though it does not act by the same mechanisms. It acts on circulating calcium levels faster than does parathyroid hormone, but the effects in general are less and shorter in duration. Indeed, the half-time of calcitonin is 4–12 minutes, or about half that of PTH. Calcitonin may therefore be specifically involved in maintaining the constancy of calcium ion in the plasma only when minor changes are involved. In the kidney, calcitonin, in contrast to PTH, increases calcium excretion and inhibits synthesis of 1,25-dihydroxycholecalciferol; however, it does not do so by affecting cAMP levels. By inhibiting the resorption of the organic phase of bone, calcitonin decreases the excretion of urinary hydroxyproline. Young animals are 50–100 times more sensitive to this hormone than adults.

In most species, including humans, calcitonin is a peptide of MW 3600 (32 amino acids). In contrast to parathyroid hormone, the complete structure of calcitonin is required for biologic activity, although large variations in the amino acid composition occur among different species.

Medullary thyroid carcinoma is a disorder of the C cells that results in abnormally high production of calcitonin.

Abnormalities of Parathyroid Function

A. Hypoparathyroidism: This is usually the re-sult of surgical removal of the parathyroids, as by accidental damage during thyroid surgery. If hypoparathyroidism begins early in childhood, there may be stunting of growth, defective tooth development, and mental retardation.

Serum calcium is low, serum phosphate is elevated, urinary calcium is low to absent, and urinary phosphate is low in the absence of renal failure.

B. Hyperparathyroidism: An increase in parathyroid hormone production is usually due to a tumor of the gland (parathyroid adenoma). Some extraparathyroid tumors associated with hyperparathyroidism contain biologically active material immunologically indistinguishable from parathyroid hormone. In primary hyperparathyroidism, serum calcium is high and serum phosphate low. Urine calcium is increased as well as urine phosphate (tubular reabsorption of phosphate decreased). In chronic renal disease, with secondary hyperactivity of the parathyroid, serum calcium is low. Urinary calcium and phosphate are both low, and there is resistance to the action of vitamin D, in the presence of uremia and acidosis. Associated with the bone abnormalities, serum alkaline phosphatase is often elevated.

As a result of the increased renal cAMP levels, hyperparathyroidism is one of the few conditions in which cAMP is markedly elevated in urine.

THE PANCREAS

The endocrine function of the pancreas is localized in the islets of Langerhans, clumps of cells that make up 1% of pancreatic tissue. Two hormones that affect carbohydrate metabolism are produced by the islet tissue: **insulin by the B cells,** and **glucagon by the A cells.** Other islet cells store and secrete somatostatin and pancreatic polypeptide hormone.

INSULIN

Insulin plays an important role in metabolism, causing increased carbohydrate metabolism, glycogen storage, fatty acid synthesis, amino acid uptake, and protein synthesis. It is thus an important anabolic hormone that acts on a variety of tissues including liver, fat, and muscle.

Chemistry

The structure of porcine insulin is shown in Fig 35–11. In all species, the molecule consists of 2 chains connected by disulfide bridges. A third intradisulfide bridge also occurs on the A chain. Breaking the disulfide bonds with alkali or reducing agents inactivates insulin.

The structures of a number of insulins obtained from various animal sources have been elucidated. That of pork pancreas is the most similar to human

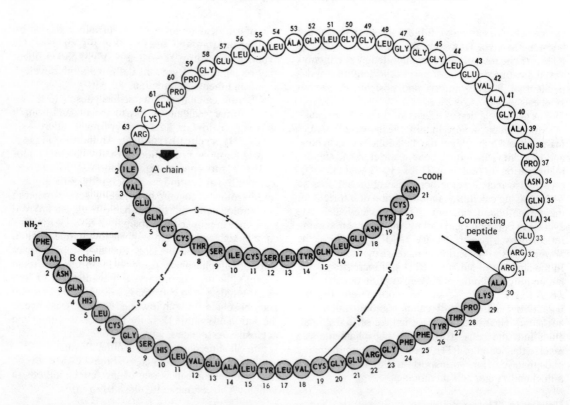

Figure 35–11. Structure of porcine proinsulin. Shaded area is the insulin portion of the molecule. (Modified and reproduced, with permission, from Chance RE, Ellis RM, Bromer WW: Porcine proinsulin: Characterization and amino acid sequence. *Science* 1968;161:166.)

insulin. The 2 insulins differ only in the terminal amino acid (number 30) of the B chain, which is alanine in porcine insulin and threonine in human insulin.

Insulins from the pig, whale, and dog are structurally identical. Those from the sheep, horse, and cow differ from porcine insulin only in 3 amino acids under the disulfide bridge in the A chain. Other species may differ in as much as 29 out of the 51 amino acids. Two structurally different insulins have been isolated from a single rat pancreas, differing by a single amino acid (lysine or methionine) in the A chain. Despite the wide variation in primary (amino acid) structure, the biologic activity per unit weight is remarkably constant for all insulins.

Although the minimum calculated molecular weight of insulin is 5734, it can exist in zinc crystals as hexamers and dimers. When diluted in the circulation, insulin probably exists as the monomer.

The mRNA for preproinsulin has been isolated from islets, the complementary DNA synthesized, and active insulin has been successfully "cloned" in bacteria. Insulin, therefore, is the first high-molecular-weight hormone to be made by the process of genetic engineering.

The secondary and tertiary structures of bovine insulin have been determined by x-ray crystallography. These studies indicate that the A chain portion of the molecule is the more exposed, including the

6–11 disulfide bridge, and possibly involved in hormonal activity (Fig 35–11). The B chain is in the internal portion of the molecule; noncovalent binding between B chains is responsible for the formation of the insulin dimer and higher polymers.

Iodination of tyrosine residues (usually those of the exposed A chain) up to one atom per mol has little effect on the biologic activity of insulin, but increasing iodination causes progressive inactivation. Therefore, in the preparation of radioiodine-tagged insulin (used as a biologic and immunologic tracer), iodination must be restricted to less than one atom per mol.

Sulfated bovine insulin, porcine insulin, and fish insulins are sometimes used in resistant diabetics because of their reduced antigenicity and cross-reactivity with circulating antibody. A highly purified insulin (**monocomponent insulin**) with greatly reduced immunogenicity has been prepared. This insulin currently is proving preferable for routine clinical use.

Other modifications reduce the absorption of insulin from the injected sites, thus prolonging the action of the hormone. These preparations have the occasional disadvantage of being more immunogenic than crystalline insulin. **Protamine zinc insulin** is a combination of insulin with protamine that is absorbed more slowly than ordinary insulin; one injection of protamine zinc insulin may lower the blood glucose for more than 24 hours, whereas 2 or 3 injections of regular (crystalline) insulin might be required for the same effect.

Ultralente insulin is a slow-acting insulin prepared by controlled crystallization in the presence of high concentrations of zinc and acetate in order to produce large crystals which are therefore slowly absorbed. **Lente insulin** is a 7:3 mixture of ultralente and regular insulin that has a duration of effect between the two.

Assay of Insulin

Insulin preparations are standardized in units by measuring their effect on the blood glucose of rabbits. The international standard contains 24 units per mg recrystallized insulin.

Originally, "insulinlike" activity in blood was measured by bioassays utilizing rat diaphragm or epididymal fat pad. Recent evidence suggests that much of the insulinlike activity in blood is the sulfation factor (**somatomedin;** see p 506) released from liver as a result of growth hormone activity. Whatever its role, insulinlike activity is not present in sufficient quantities to prevent ketosis in animals whose insulin supply is removed by pancreatectomy.

Radioimmunochemical assays are more specific and sensitive than the bioassays and permit detection of insulin in concentrations less than 1 μU/mL. The insulin content of serum in the fasting state is reported to be about 25 μU/mL when measured immunochemically. One defect of the radioimmunoassay is the fact that it may measure fragments or precursors of insulin (eg, proinsulin) in plasma. Those substances, while retaining some immunologic activity, have little or no biologic activity.

Biosynthesis of Insulin

In the B cells of the pancreas, insulin is synthesized, as is any other secreted protein, by the ribosomes of the endoplasmic reticulum. Studies in which mRNA from islets is translated in heterologous cell-free systems suggest that the initial, transient product is a peptide of 14–18,000 daltons. However, the ultimate, stable product of ribosomal synthesis is the insulin precursor **proinsulin.**

The structure of porcine proinsulin is shown in Fig 35–11. The molecule consists of a single polypeptide chain that begins with the normal B chain sequence at its amino terminus but contains a linking polypeptide of 33 amino acids that connects the carboxy terminus of the B chain to the amino terminus of the A chain amino acid sequence. The molecular weight of porcine proinsulin is 9082, about 50% greater than that of insulin. The connecting link is about the same size in proinsulins from other species, but it varies greatly in specific amino acid content. The molecule is comparatively inactive biologically, yet it can cross-react with antisera prepared against insulin. Proinsulin, after reduction to its open chain structure, is readily reconverted in high yield to the proper disulfide configuration with mild oxidation. Since the yields are higher than normally obtained with free A or

B chains, the connecting link appears important in providing the **proper alignment of the molecule for correct disulfide synthesis.** The conversion of proinsulin to insulin occurs in Golgi and secretory granules, not in the endoplasmic reticulum where proinsulin is synthesized. The biologic mechanism by which the activation of proinsulin to insulin occurs requires proteolysis but may employ enzymes other than (or in conjunction with) trypsin. During biologic proteolysis, the 2 basic amino acids at either end of the **connecting peptide** (C-peptide) are removed (Arg 31, 32, and Lys 62, Arg 63). The free, biologically inactive C-peptide is retained in the granule and ultimately secreted in equal molar ratio with the mature insulin.

Proinsulin can be measured by specific radioimmunoassay technics or, after separation from insulin, by "molecular sieving" chromatography. Normally, proinsulin represents only a small portion of the insulin stored in the pancreas or found in the plasma. Plasma proinsulin is mildly elevated in human diabetics, but it may be the predominant circulating form in some subjects with tumors of the B islet cells.

After conversion, the insulin inside the vesicle package condenses and forms the typical B granules enclosed by membranous sacs. Current evidence suggests that stored insulin may exist in different "compartments" with the insulin most recently synthesized being the most readily secreted.

Insulin Secretion

Approximately **50 units of insulin per day** are required by the human adult. This is about one-fifth of the amount stored in a human pancreas. During secretion, the insulin-containing granules move to the plasma membrane of the cell where the granule membrane fuses with the cell membrane and the granular contents are liberated into the pericapillary space. This process is called **exocytosis.** Agents that inhibit **microtubule** function (vincristine, colchicine) inhibit insulin secretion, and **microfilaments** have also been implicated in the secretion process.

Secretion of insulin is the resultant of a variety of processes, and thus various agents may influence insulin secretion at different levels. Those agents stimulating release of labile storage forms cause insulin secretion in seconds; those acting on provision of insulin to the secretory system itself may require 15–120 minutes.

Agents such as glucose, acting on more than one process, can produce multiphasic patterns of insulin release (Fig 35–12). Glucose stimulates insulin release within 30–60 seconds. This rapid early phase may be a reflection of a labile storage compartment. In addition, glucose stimulates insulin synthesis, an effect that requires a longer period and probably more chemical energy than that needed for insulin release. Regardless of mechanism, the pancreatic B cell response is to the **rate of change of glucose concentration** as well as to the **static concentration** itself. Experiments with artificial pancreatic devices show that the ability of the pancreas to detect a rising blood sugar and respond

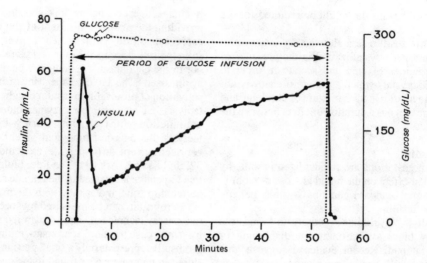

Figure 35–12. Multiphasic response of the in vitro perfused pancreas during constant stimulation with glucose. (Modified from Grodsky GM & others: Further studies on the dynamic aspects of insulin release in vitro with evidence for a 2-compartmental storage system. *Acta Diabetol Lat* 1969;6 [Suppl 1]:554.)

transiently and quickly results in a decrease in the amount of insulin required to maintain proper regulation and minimizes the occurrence of any subsequent hypoglycemia.

In general, sugars that are readily metabolized, eg, glucose, mannose, and to a lesser extent fructose, can stimulate insulin release. The nonmetabolizable sugars, eg, galactose, L-arabinose, 2-deoxyglucose, and xylose, do not stimulate insulin release. Stimulation by glucose is blocked by inhibitors of glucose metabolism such as mannoheptulose and 2-deoxyglucose. Many agents (eg, amino acids, some gastrointestinal products, and fatty acids) can stimulate insulin release but only if glucose is present. Possibly a dual action is required to bring about insulin release— activation of a receptor site and production of a metabolite. Glucose is capable of doing both, whereas other substances having only one of the 2 actions require glucose as a supplementary agent.

It is probable that an intermediate produced in the course of glucose metabolism provides the secretory signal, although the possibility that the glucose molecule itself acts directly on a glucoreceptor in the B cell membrane is not yet excluded. The initial event that stimulates secretion is associated with a K^+-induced depolarization of the membrane. This promotes rapid entry of Ca^{2+} via a voltage-dependent channel. The fusion of the insulin secretory granules with the plasma membrane and thus insulin secretion are **calcium-dependent.**

The second messenger, cAMP, plays a significant role as a potentiator of the effects of glucose and amino acids on insulin secretion. This potentiating effect of cAMP is mediated by its ability to release calcium stored in mitochondria or endoplasmic reticulum. Thus, agents including glucose itself that increase intracellular cAMP concentration enhance in-

sulin secretion. α-Adrenergic stimulation inhibits insulin secretion. Epinephrine, which is both a β- and an α-adrenergic stimulator, acts predominantly as an α-adrenergic stimulator and thus inhibits insulin release. When the α-adrenergic action is blocked by phentolamine, epinephrine increases insulin release. Thus, in vivo release of epinephrine under extreme stress not only provides glucose to the circulation by stimulating glycogenolysis but preferentially preserves it for utilization by the brain since it simultaneously depresses insulin release. As the same time, epinephrine causes the release of fatty acids from adipose tissue to provide the major fuel for muscle contraction in the "fight or flight" response.

Insulin release can also be indirectly influenced by the central nervous system. Lesions of the ventral medial nucleus or stimulation of the vagus increase insulin release. Finally, the sensitivity of pancreas to the above stimuli may vary with the developmental state. For example, the pancreases of fish, amphibians, ruminants, and the mammalian fetus are remarkably insensitive to glucose though they may respond normally to amino acids or other stimulants.

Hypoglycemic Agents

There are several hypoglycemic drugs, effective when taken by mouth, that are useful for control of the hyperglycemia of diabetes. One class of these drugs, the sulfonylureas, may stimulate insulin secretion by a different mechanism from that of glucose, which may explain their effectiveness in maturity-onset diabetes or in patients with islet cell tumors in whom the pancreas does not respond normally to glucose. The sulfonylureas also potentiate the action of glucose on the pancreas. Therefore, their total effect on the pancreas is dependent on the amount of metabolically available glucose in the circulation.

Intestinal Factors

Oral glucose tolerance tests cause greater insulin secretion than a comparable intravenous glucose tolerance test, even though blood glucose levels are usually higher in the latter. Glucose administered orally stimulates the release of intestinal factors that in turn act on the pancreas. Gastrin, pancreozymin, secretin, and a glucagonlike substance are 4 such substances found in the intestine that can stimulate insulin secretion both in vivo and in vitro.

Metabolism of Insulin

Circulating insulin is degraded primarily in liver and kidney by the enzyme **glutathione insulin transhydrogenase.** This enzyme brings about reductive cleavage of the S–S bonds that connect the A and B chains of the insulin molecule (Fig 35–11). After insulin has been reductively cleaved, the A and B chains are further degraded by proteolysis. Insulininactivating systems are rapid-acting; the half-life of circulating insulin is about 7–15 minutes. When insulin is bound to antibody, it is much less sensitive to enzymatic degradation.

Mode of Action of Insulin

Insulin acts in such a variety of ways that it is difficult to establish whether a given effect is a primary or a secondary one. In addition, observations made in vivo can be misleading since a change in the metabolism of one tissue may occur as a result of the ability of insulin to influence the provision of metabolic substrates or inhibitors from a different tissue. Insulin is active in skeletal and heart muscle, adipose tissue, liver, the lens of the eye, and possibly leukocytes. It is comparatively inactive in renal tissue, red blood cells, and the gastrointestinal tract. The major metabolic actions of insulin occur in the muscle, adipose tissue, and liver.

Insulin is firmly bound to a highly **specific receptor** site on the plasma membrane of its target tissues. The amount of membrane-bound insulin parallels its biologic activity in the tissue, and the biologic activities of modified insulins are proportionate to their binding affinities, both suggesting that binding is requisite to hormone activity. The membrane receptor is a glycoprotein. Thus, insulin may carry out most of its functions without actually entering the cell.

Under conditions where insulin levels are high, the number of receptors declines. The target tissues become less sensitive, resulting in "down regulation" or decreased sensitivity to insulin.

When the insulin receptor is occupied by insulin, there seems to be release of a 1000- to 1500-dalton heat-labile factor from target cell membranes. This factor, in turn, activates cellular mechanisms causing calcium translocation in the cell and activation of systems (possibly specific phosphatases) that promote protein dephosphorylation. These protein dephosphorylations may account for many of insulin's actions including activation of transport systems, glycogen synthesis, glycolysis, etc (see below). Thus, although

initial insulin binding to its receptor does not require calcium, expression of insulin action is calcium-dependent.

Muscle & Adipose Tissue

A primary and rapid effect of insulin in muscle and adipose tissue is to facilitate transport of a variety of substances across the plasma membrane. These include **glucose** and related monosaccharides, **amino acids, potassium** ion, **nucleosides,** inorganic **phosphate,** and **calcium** ion. The effects are not secondary to glucose metabolism since they can be demonstrated in in vitro systems when glucose is not present. Insulin will increase transport and facilitate an increase in intracellular concentration of nonmetabolizable sugars such as L-arabinose and xylose, as well as galactose. The hormone promotes the entry into the cells of those sugars possessing the same configuration at carbons 1, 2, and 3 as D-glucose. Fructose does not require insulin for transport into the cells, possibly because of the ketone group at position 2. Intracellular transport of glucose in enhanced by anoxia or uncoupling agents such as dinitrophenol, indicating that exclusion of glucose from muscle or adipose tissue may require energy.

In muscle or adipose tissue, uptake of glucose by the cell is the rate-limiting step for all subsequent intracellular glucose metabolism. The ability of insulin to facilitate transport thus leads to an increase in all pathways of glucose metabolism.

In adipose tissue, insulin increases lipid synthesis by providing acetyl-CoA and NADPH required for fatty acid synthesis, as well as the glycerol moiety (glycerophosphate) for triacylglycerol synthesis. In adipose tissue, insulin sharply depresses the liberation of fatty acids induced by the action of epinephrine or glucagon. Part of this effect of insulin may be its role in glycolysis, which produces glycerophosphate from glucose and thus facilitates the deposition of the fatty acids as triacylglycerol. In part, insulin suppresses lipolysis by suppressing the increased cAMP effected by either epinephrine or glucagon. The effect is still a membrane action of the hormone since adenylate cyclase, the enzyme responsible for the synthesis of cAMP, is membrane-bound. Additionally, insulin can dephosphorylate and thereby inactivate the lipases responsible for lipolysis. The reduction by insulin of fatty acid liberation from adipose tissue is extremely important as circulating fatty acid levels are responsible for many effects on intracellular metabolic events, both in muscle and liver. Release of fatty acids in various states may contribute to inhibition of glucose metabolism by indirectly blocking glycolysis at several steps in the pathway and by stimulating gluconeogenesis. Indeed, many of the effects in liver noted after insulin administration in vivo may be the result of secondary changes induced by reduction in circulating free fatty acids.

Insulin may directly increase protein synthesis by facilitating incorporation of labeled intracellular amino acids into protein. Insulin can act at the ribosomal level to increase the capacity of this organelle to translate information from messenger RNA. In the diabetic animal, the polysomes become disaggregated; insulin, in vivo, restores them to the normal aggregated form. This may not be a direct action of the hormone, since it cannot be demonstrated in vitro. Insulin maintains muscle protein by decreasing protein degradation as well.

Liver

Unlike muscle and adipose tissue, there is **no barrier to glucose in liver cells.** In this organ, extracellular and intracellular concentrations of glucose are approximately equal. However, an action of insulin on the hepatic cell membrane may still be a primary event since specific binding of insulin to hepatic membranes is demonstrable.

In vivo, insulin effects can be explained, in part, as effects secondary to a decrease in the amounts of amino acids, potassium ion, glucose, and fatty acids presented to the liver. The following direct actions of insulin are demonstrable on the isolated perfused liver: decreased glucose output, urea production, protein catabolism, and cAMP; increased potassium and phosphate uptake.

Insulin also indirectly induces synthesis of specific enzymes involved in glycolysis and represses specific gluconeogenic enzymes (Fig 35–13). It is suggested that insulin may act on a genetic locus in the nucleus that coordinates the expression of a group of specific enzymes. Thus, insulin stimulates glycolysis by effecting a simultaneous increase in synthesis of glucokinase, phosphofructokinase, and pyruvate kinase. Simultaneously, insulin represses the enzymes controlling gluconeogenesis: pyruvate carboxylase, phosphoenolpyruvate carboxykinase, fructose-1,6-bisphosphatase, and glucose-6-phosphatase. The relative pattern of the enzyme induction is grossly influenced by diet. Therefore, changes of enzyme activities could arise from the direct actions of the hormone on glucose output, potassium uptake, etc, or from the effect of "signals" in the form of metabolites from peripheral tissues. Glucose itself may not be one of the signals since glycolytic enzyme levels are not increased during the hyperglycemia of diabetes. An increasing number of enzymes are proving to be phosphoenzymes, subject to rapid (minutes) activation or inhibition by phospho- or dephosphorylation (see Chapter 15). A pattern is emerging in which it appears that insulin, by causing calcium translocation, causes conversion of these enzymes to their dephospho form (opposite to the action of cAMP-generating hormones such as glucagon and catecholamines). This action is independent of cAMP and may be at the level of protein kinases or protein phosphatases. Thus, activity of pyruvate kinase (increasing [↑] glycolysis), pyruvate dehydrogenase (↑ tricarboxylic acid pathway), and glycogen synthetase (↑ glycogenesis) are all increased, whereas glucose-1,6-bisphosphatase (↑ gluconeogenesis) is decreased.

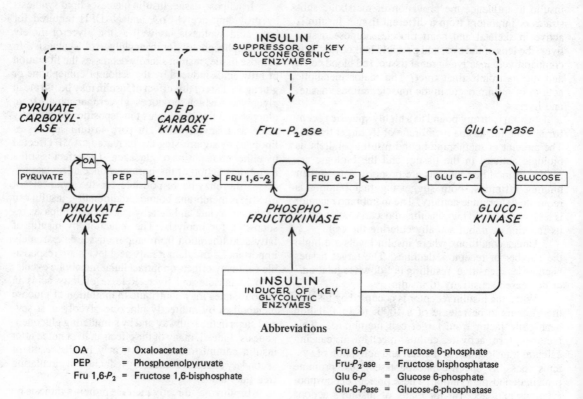

Abbreviations

OA	= Oxaloacetate	Fru 6-P	= Fructose 6-phosphate
PEP	= Phosphoenolpyruvate	Fru-P_2 ase	= Fructose bisphosphatase
Fru 1,6-P_2	= Fructose 1,6-bisphosphate	Glu 6-P	= Glucose 6-phosphate
		Glu-6-Pase	= Glucose-6-phosphatase

Figure 35–13. Repression (--) and induction (–) functions of insulin on key liver enzymes.

The Diabetic States (See Fig 35–14.)

Diabetes mellitus can be characterized as an insufficiency of insulin relative to the requirements of the tissues for this hormone. The juvenile (or "insulin-requiring") diabetic has little detectable circulating insulin, and the pancreas fails to respond to a glucose load. Certain viruses can produce islet cell lesions in experimental animals, similar to those seen in juvenile diabetics. This and other data have led to a current interest in the possibility that some severe forms of this disease may be induced by viral infections. On the other hand, the maturity-onset diabetic

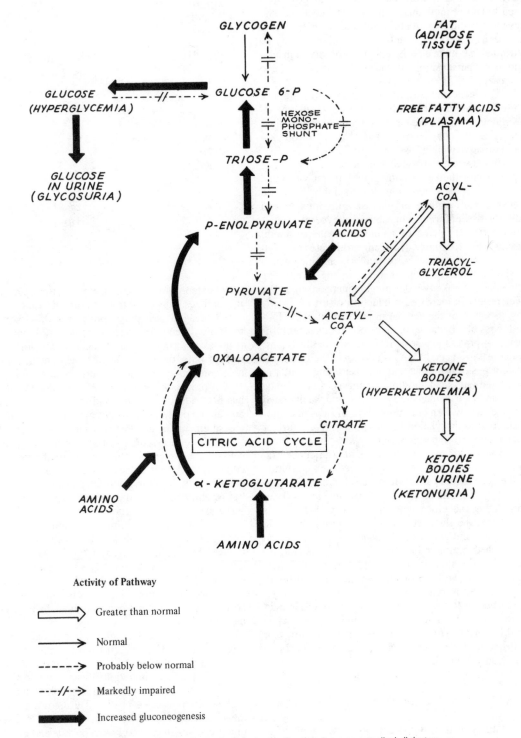

Figure 35–14. Abnormal metabolism in the liver during uncontrolled diabetes.

may show an impaired response to glucose but because of the continued elevated glucose levels may ultimately secrete more insulin for a given glucose load than a normal individual. Usually, however, continued impaired release is indicated since plasma glucose:insulin ratios are much higher than normal in these subjects. Excessive insulin release after a glucose load occurs in obese individuals who are not diabetic or who have only mild abnormalities in glucose tolerance. It has been suggested that this hyperinsulinism may be attributable both to a peripheral insensitivity to insulin and to a hypersensitivity of the pancreatic islet cells to glucose.

The increased peripheral resistance to insulin in obesity is at least partially the result of decreased insulin receptors on the target cell membranes. This is not a genetic characteristic, since receptors quickly increase after weight loss.

In diabetes, hyperglycemia occurs as a result of repression of the key hepatic glycolytic enzymes and derepression of gluconeogenic enzymes. Impaired transport and uptake of glucose into muscle and adipose tissue further contribute to hyperglycemia. Transport and uptake of amino acids in peripheral tissues are also depressed, causing an elevated circulating level of amino acids, particularly alanine, which further enhance gluconeogenesis in the liver. The amino acid breakdown during gluconeogenesis in the liver results in increased production of urea.

Because of the decline in production of ATP—and possibly because of a direct requirement for insulin—protein synthesis is decreased in all tissues. A decrease in acetyl-CoA, ATP, NADPH, and glycerophosphate in muscle and adipose tissue results in decreased fatty acid and lipid synthesis. Stored lipids are hydrolyzed by increased lipolysis, and the liberated fatty acids may then interfere at several steps of carbohydrate phosphorylation in muscle and liver, further contributing to hyperglycemia.

Fatty acids reaching the liver in high concentration inhibit fatty acid synthesis by feedback inhibition at the acetyl-CoA carboxylase step. Increased acetyl-CoA from fatty acids activates pyruvate carboxylase, stimulating the gluconeogenic pathway. Fatty acids also stimulate gluconeogenesis by entering the citric acid cycle and increasing production of citrate, an established inhibitor of glycolysis (at phosphofructokinase). Eventually, the fatty acids inhibit the citric acid cycle at the level of citrate synthetase and both pyruvate and isocitrate dehydrogenases. The **acetyl-CoA that no longer can enter either the citric acid pathway or be used for fatty acid synthesis is shunted to the synthesis of cholesterol or ketones** (or both). The rise in ketone concentration in the body fluids and tissues leads to acidosis.

GLUCAGON

Glucagon is an important hormone involved in the rapid mobilization of hepatic glucose and, to a

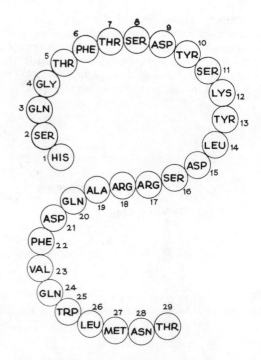

Figure 35–15. Glucagon polypeptide.

lesser extent, of fatty acids from adipose tissue. Thus, it mobilizes substrates from storage depots.

Glucagon is a polypeptide (Fig 35–15) with a molecular weight of 3485. It contains 29 amino acid residues in a single chain. Glucagon contains no cystine, proline, or isoleucine but does contain considerable amounts of methionine and tryptophan.

A precursor (proglucagon) of about 9000 daltons has been identified. This and even larger glucagon-containing peptides can occur in plasma, complicating measurements of glucagon by radioimmunoassay.

Glucagon originates primarily in the A (alpha) cells of the pancreas, although a significant amount comes from A cells in the stomach and other extrapancreatic portions of the gastrointestinal tract. Glucagon has recently been found in mammalian brain and may serve as a neurotransmitter.

In contrast to insulin, secretion of pancreatic glucagon increases with **low blood glucose** whether induced by starvation, insulin, or the sulfonylureas. Glucagon secretion is directly inhibited by glucose in vitro. The A cell may be an insulin-dependent tissue since inhibition of glucagon secretion by glucose in normal pancreas occurs only in the presence of insulin.

Most amino acids, arginine in particular, cause a rapid secretion of glucagon from the pancreas. Fatty acids inhibit glucagon release. Therefore, during mixed, but high-carbohydrate meals, both insulin and glucagon are secreted, but the carbohydrate causes preferential release of insulin. During a high-protein meal, glucagon secretion is favored, and circulating glucose arises from the glycogenolysis and gluconeogenesis stimulated by the glucagon.

The A cells respond positively to β-adrenergic stimulation but may be particularly insensitive to α-adrenergic signals. Thus, epinephrine, which has both α- and β-adrenergic activity, causes beta stimulation of glucagon secretion. (In contrast, insulin secretion is most sensitive to the α-adrenergic activity of epinephrine and is inhibited.) In acute stress, therefore, insulin secretion is inhibited but glucagon secretion is stimulated.

The adenylate cyclase in liver membranes is particularly sensitive to glucagon. Within minutes after the presentation of glucagon to the liver, cAMP levels increase. The cAMP in turn activates the enzyme protein kinase, which causes a "cascade phenomenon," resulting in activation by phosphorylation of dephosphophosphorylase kinase and, thereby, activation of phosphorylase. The activation of phosphorylase results in rapid glycogenolysis and hepatic output of glucose. The same phosphorylation action suppresses glycogen synthetase. Thus, **glucagon increases glycogen breakdown and inhibits synthesis** by the same mechanism. Glucagon, by activating protein kinase, can also activate various phosphoenzymes and, conversely, inhibit dephosphoenzymes. Thus, glucagon can directly stimulate gluconeogenesis by activation of pyruvate carboxylase and probably fructose-1,6-bisphosphatase. At the same time, it inhibits glucose oxidation by inhibiting pyruvate kinase and pyruvate dehydrogenase. The enhanced gluconeogenesis may be mediated by cAMP activation of hepatic and adipose tissue lipase, which produces fatty acid activation of the gluconeogenic process. A rise in glucagon concentration also increases ketogenesis independent of the effects described above.

In adipose tissue, and possibly liver, glucagon increases the breakdown of lipids to fatty acids and glycerol. In general, glucagon and epinephrine act similarly to increase cAMP synthesis and glycogen and lipid breakdown. However, **glucagon is proportionately more active in liver, whereas epinephrine is more active in adipose tissue and skeletal muscle.**

Since the target organ effects of insulin and glucagon are antagonistic and since circulating levels of these hormones change reciprocally in response to glucose and stress, the A and B cells may function as a bihormonal unit; thus, the ratio of insulin to glucagon can determine the quantitative relationship and direction of nutrient flow at the storage depot.

A disturbance of glucagon regulation may contribute to the diabetic state in humans. It is elevated in severe diabetes (with ketoacidosis) and rises to abnormally high levels when milder diabetics are stimulated with arginine. The defect in the diabetic A cell may be an inability to "recognize" and be suppressed by glucose in the absence of insulin. Insulin administration or transplantation of normal islets into insulinopenic animals normalizes glucagon levels. Thus, although elevated glucagon may contribute to the diabetic state, the primary lesion in diabetes is probably at the level of the B cell. Nevertheless,

agents such as somatostatin that inhibit glucagon release and other diabetogenic hormones may have application as an adjunct to insulin treatment for insulin-requiring diabetics.

Although little is known concerning the manner in which glucagon is metabolized, an enzyme capable of degrading glucagon has been identified in beef liver. The action of the enzyme is exerted at the N-terminal position of the glucagon polypeptide (Fig 35–15), where it removes the first 2 amino acids by hydrolysis of the peptide bond between serine and glutamine.

SOMATOSTATIN

The peptide somatostatin (growth hormone release–inhibiting factor) was first isolated from the hypothalamus and was implicated as a regulator of growth hormone secretion (see Chapter 36). It is also the primary peptide secreted from the D cells of the islets of Langerhans. It inhibits both insulin and glucagon secretion and thus may serve as an intra-islet (paracrine) regulator for secretion of these hormones. In addition, somatostatin is secreted into the portal vein blood as a result of glucose or amino acid stimulus, indicating an extra-islet role. Since somatostatin can inhibit a variety of gastrointestinal functions (gastric emptying, gastrointestinal motility), its major function may be to regulate nutritional influx at the level of the gastrointestinal tract. It may also serve as a neurotransmitter substance in the brain.

THE ADRENALS

THE ADRENAL MEDULLA

Function

The adrenal medulla is a derivative of the sympathetic portion of the autonomic nervous system. Despite its diverse physiologic functions, it is not essential to life.

The hormones synthesized by the adrenal medulla are **epinephrine (adrenaline)** and **norepinephrine (noradrenaline)** (Fig 35–16). Epinephrine is primarily synthesized and stored in the adrenal medulla and acts through the circulation on distant organs.

Epinephrine in general duplicates the effect of sympathetic stimulation of an organ. It is necessary to provide a rapid physiologic response to emergencies such as cold, fatigue, shock, etc. In this sense, it mobilizes what has been termed the "fight or flight" mechanism, a cooperative effort of the adrenal medulla and the sympathetic nervous system.

In addition to bringing about effects similar to those which follow stimulation of the sympathetic nervous system, both circulating epinephrine and norepinephrine induce metabolic effects, including glycogenolysis in the liver and skeletal muscle, and an

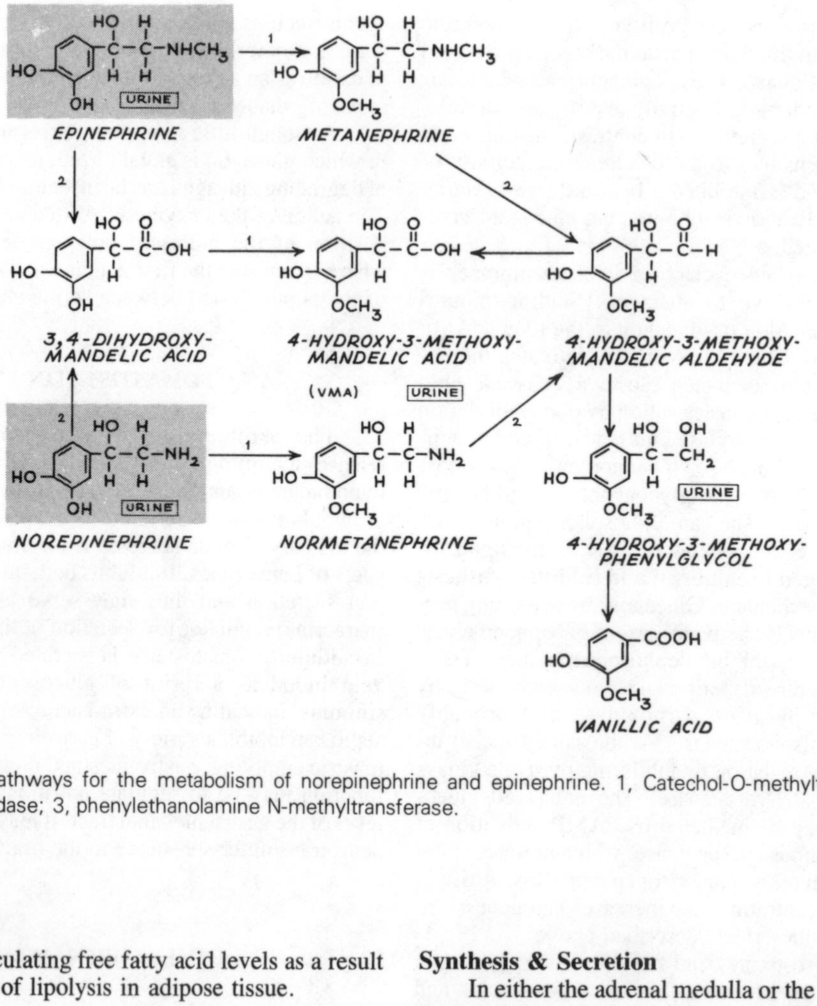

Figure 35–16. Pathways for the metabolism of norepinephrine and epinephrine. 1, Catechol-O-methyltransferase; 2, monoamine oxidase; 3, phenylethanolamine N-methyltransferase.

increase in circulating free fatty acid levels as a result of stimulation of lipolysis in adipose tissue.

Chemistry

The hormones of the adrenal medulla are structurally related to a group of organic compounds designated as **catechols.** Although the adrenal medullary hormones are categorized clinically as catecholamines, this term is not strictly accurate, since the amino group is attached to an aliphatic side chain rather than directly to the aromatic ring as is implied by the term catecholamine.

Eighty percent of the catecholamine hormone activity in the adrenal medulla is attributable to epinephrine, which occurs in the gland at a concentration of 1–3 mg/g of tissue. The chemical structure of **epinephrine** is shown in Fig 35–16. Naturally occurring epinephrine is the L-isomer. The unnatural D-form is only one-fifteenth as active.

Norepinephrine is found principally in the sympathetic nerves, where it acts as a neurotransmitter. This localization is a result of both synthesis in the nervous tissue and uptake by this tissue from the circulation.

As shown in Fig 35–16, epinephrine differs from norephinephrine only in that the former is **methylated** on the primary amino group of the aliphatic side chain.

Synthesis & Secretion

In either the adrenal medulla or the neurons, synthesis of the catecholamines is essentially the same (Fig 23–6). The initial step in conversion of tyrosine to dihydroxyphenylalanine (dopa) occurs in the cytoplasm and requires the enzyme tyrosine hydroxylase. Inhibition of this enzyme (eg, with α-N-methyl-p-tyrosine) is used to block adrenergic activity in pheochromocytoma. The enzyme is also inhibited by the subsequent products, dopamine and norepinephrine. It is activated by cAMP–protein kinase, indicating that it is active in its phosphoenzyme form. Conversion of dopa to dopamine also occurs in the cytoplasm and is catalyzed by a pyridoxal-dependent amino acid decarboxylase. This nonspecific enzyme is present in high concentration and is usually not a significant site of regulation. Dopamine enters vesicles in the adrenal medulla or neuronal cells where conversion to and storage of catecholamines occurs. These vesicles (chromaffin granules) contain dopamine β-hydroxylase for the synthesis of norepinephrine and, particularly in the medulla, phenylethanolamine N-methyltransferase, which specifically converts norepinephrine to epinephrine. S-Adenosylmethionine is the cofactor in this reaction. The hormones are stored in a complex containing ATP (about 4 mol hormone:1 mol ATP) and several incompletely characterized proteins including a specific soluble protein, chromogranin a. The contents of the vesicles, including calcium, are secreted by a calcium-dependent exocytosis in the same proportion as they are stored. As for most exocytotic systems, release is stimulated by β-adrenergic and inhibited by α-adrenergic stimulation. The secreted catecholamines are then metabolized in the target tissue or the liver; or, particularly in the case of norepinephrine, they can be taken up again into the neuronal vesicles by an energy-dependent process. This reuptake into the neuron converts the catecholamines to the inactive storage form and is an important mechanism for quickly terminating hormonal or neurotransmitter activity.

Catecholamines do not penetrate the blood-brain barrier; thus, the norepinephrine in the brain must be synthesized within that tissue. L-Dopa, the precursor for catecholamines, does penetrate the barrier. It is therefore used to increase brain catecholamine synthesis in Parkinson's disease.

When radiotagged epinephrine is injected into animals, only about 5% is excreted in the urine unchanged, most of the hormone being metabolized in the tissues by a series of **methylations** of the phenolic groups or **oxidations** on the amine side chains (Fig 35–16). The main enzymes involved are **monoamine oxidase** for the oxidation reactions and **catechol-O-methyltransferase** (COMT) for catalysis of the methylations. Monoamine oxidase is a mitochondrial enzyme (actually a series of isoenzymes) with a broad specificity capable of catalyzing the oxidation of side chains on a large variety of catechols. Catechol-O-methyltransferase rapidly catalyzes the inactivation of the catecholamines by methylation of the hydroxyl group at the 3 position. This Mg^{2+}-dependent enzyme is located in the cytosol. The enzyme is capable of methoxylating a variety of catecholamine intermediates with utilization of S-adenosylmethionine as the source of the methyl groups. Although monoamine oxidase and catechol-O-methyltransferase are found in most tissues, their activity is particularly high in the liver where most of the degradation of the circulating catecholamines takes place.

The first step in the metabolism of the catecholamines can be either methoxylation or oxidation of the side chain, the preferred step varying with circumstances that have not yet been well established. Since both enzymes usually react with the metabolic products in the liver, the final compounds appearing in the urine are often the same regardless of which of the 2 reactions occurred first.

One of the principal metabolites of epinephrine and of norepinephrine which occurs in the urine is **4-hydroxy-3-methoxymandelic acid.** This substance has also been called **vanilmandelic acid (VMA)** (Fig 35–16). Other metabolites occurring in the urine in significant quantities are 3-methoxyepinephrine (metanephrine) and 4-hydroxy-3-methoxyphenylglycol. The urinary products are excreted mostly as conjugates with sulfate or glucuronide, sulfate being the preferred conjugation moiety in humans.

Regulation

The amount of active catecholamines is controlled at the levels of synthesis, secretion, reuptake, and catabolism. Catecholamines are allosteric inhibitors of their own synthesis at tyrosine hydroxylase. Thus, when the hormones are mobilized rapidly, synthesis is correspondingly reduced. During prolonged stress, feeding, β-adrenergic stimulation, pituitary hyperactivity, and ACTH or corticosteroid administration, all of the enzymes in the synthetic pathway are gradually increased. Glucocorticoids from the adjacent adrenal cortex particularly stimulate phenylethanolamine N-methyltransferase, the final enzyme required for epinephrine synthesis. Exocytotic secretion is highly sensitive to cholinergic control, and acetylcholine is a particularly positive modulator. This cholinergic stimulation, in turn, appears directly regulated by a stress-linked signal at the hypothalamus.

Reserpine and guanethidine are antihypertensive and tranquilizing agents that decrease catecholamines by increasing their destruction, thereby depleting the amounts available in storage form. Cocaine and the antidepressive amphetamines inhibit the fixation and reuptake of the catecholamines by tissues, resulting in increased biologic availability. However, this is probably not the sole action and may not even be the major action of these drugs.

Many agents structurally similar to epinephrine and norepinephrine, though with less biologic activity, can be stored in the tissue sites normally reserved for the active hormones. The agents, known as **"false neurotransmitters,"** prevent either the synthesis or storage of hormones and are released during normal sympathetic stimulation in their place. Thus, these agents or their precursors can be used clinically to reduce release of active hormone and therefore serve as hypotensive agents. "False transmitters" such as β-hydroxytyramine, α-methylnorepinephrine, and metaraminol are produced by administration of tyramine, methyldopa, α-methyltyrosine, or metaraminol itself. Initially, these agents often cause increased circulating hormones by preventing hormone binding in tissues.

Mechanism of Action

Epinephrine can bind to and stimulate both β- and α-adrenergic receptors in many tissues including other endocrine glands (Table 35–1 and Fig 35–17). It now appears that beta effects are those associated with an increase in adenylate cyclase activity and increased cAMP. A rise in cAMP leads in most target tissues to an activation of protein kinases and subsequently increased activation of phosphoenzymes (Fig 35–17). Activation of phosphoenzymes in turn accounts for many of the biochemical effects of epinephrine. In muscle, and to a lesser extent in liver, epinephrine stimulates the breakdown of glycogen, as a result of protein kinase activation leading to phosphorylation and activation of the phosphorylase cascade (Fig 15–8). Conversely, phosphorylation of glycogen synthetase decreases glycogen synthesis. In exercising

Table 35–1. Predominant effects of catecholamines on hormone secretion.*

Endocrine Organ	Hormone	Effect	Receptor	Usual Feedback Loop
Pancreatic cells				
A cells	Glucagon	↑	β_2	Plasma substrate levels
B cells	Insulin	↓	a	Plasma substrate levels
Thyroid				
Follicles	Thyroxine	↑	β_2	TSH
C cells	Calcitonin	↑	β	Plasma ionized calcium
Parathyroid	Parathyroid hormone	↑	β_1	Plasma ionized calcium
Kidney				
Juxtaglomerular apparatus	Renin	↑	β_2	Distal tubular sodium
Not known	Erythropoietin	↑	β_2	Arterial P_{O_2}
Gastric antrum and duodenum; G cells	Gastrin	↑	β	Gastric luminal pH

*Modified and reproduced, with permission, from Young JB, Landsberg L: *Clin Endocrinol Metab* 1977;**6**:657.

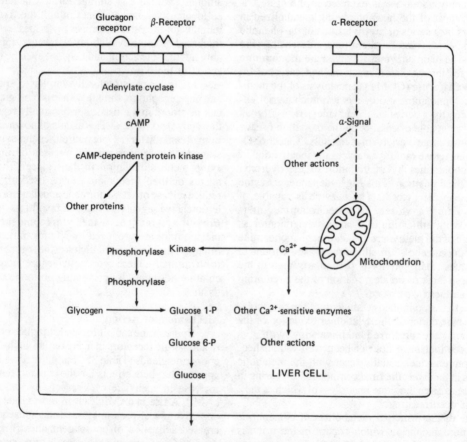

Figure 35–17. Postulated mechanisms by which α-adrenergic and β-adrenergic mechanisms leads to glycogenolysis and other responses in the liver cell. (Slightly modified and reproduced, with permission, from Exton JH: Mechanisms involved in α-adrenergic phenomena: Role of calcium ions in actions of catecholamines in liver and other tissues. *Am J Physiol* 1980;**238**:E3.)

muscle, this can result in increased lactate secretion into the plasma. In heart muscle, epinephrine rapidly increases cardiac output (inotropic effect), which is also related to increased cAMP.

In adipose tissue, epinephrine increases cAMP, which increases the active phospho form of adipose tissue lipase and results in lipolysis and release of fatty acids into the circulation. These fatty acids serve as fuel in muscle and can activate gluconeogenesis in liver.

Epinephrine has a direct inhibitory action on insulin release in the pancreas. It therefore serves as an emergency hormone by (1) rapidly providing fatty acids, which are the primary fuel for muscle action; (2) mobilizing glucose, both by increasing glycogenolysis and gluconeogenesis in the liver and by decreasing glucose uptake in the muscle; and (3) decreasing insulin, thereby preventing the glucose from being taken up by peripheral tissues and preserving it for the central nervous system.

Historically, adrenergic responses have been classified according to the comparative effectiveness of a series of related catechols on vascular, cardiac, and pulmonary physiologic responses. Thus, typical norepinephrine-stimulated responses such as vascular venous constriction were denoted as α-adrenergic. Typical epinephrine effects, such as increased heart rate and contractility, were beta phenomena. Fatty acid mobilization and glycogenolysis are beta-type metabolic reactions since they can be duplicated with β-adrenergic stimulating drugs, eg, isoproterenol. It now appears that beta effects are those associated with an increase in cAMP. Alpha effects are less established. In some cases, they result in less cAMP, producing effects opposite to β-adrenergic action. Epinephrine can stimulate both adrenergic responses; therefore, its effects in a given tissue depend on the relative sensitivities of the alpha and beta receptors.

Norepinephrine in small doses acts primarily, though not exclusively, on alpha receptors. It is becoming increasingly appreciated that many α-adrenergic effects are unrelated to cAMP but act directly at the level of calcium translocation in the cell (Fig 35–17). This can result in activation of cAMP in dependent protein kinases that may lead to metabolic effects parallel to those elicited by β-adrenergic stimulation (eg, glycogen mobilization). Calcium translocation may also explain the less well understood opposing effects of α- and β-adrenergic actions.

Certain tumors of the medullary (chromaffin) cells result in **pheochromocytoma,** characterized by hypertension. The norepinephrine content of adrenal medullary tumors is much higher than that of epinephrine, suggesting that the hypertension produced by these tumors is attributable to norepinephrine.

THE ADRENAL CORTEX

The outer portion of the adrenal gland, the adrenal cortex, is **essential to life.** Its embryologic origin is quite different from that of the adrenal medulla.

The adrenal cortex produces a number of steroid derivatives. As will be noted later, the hormones of the gonads are also steroid hormones not remarkably different from those of the adrenal cortex. The similarity of embryologic origin of the adrenal cortex and of the gonads is of interest in connection with the close relationship of the chemistry of their respective hormones.

General Function

The steroid hormones of the adrenal cortex fall into 3 classes, each with characteristic functions:

(1) The **glucocorticoids,** which primarily affect metabolism of protein, carbohydrate, and lipids, are synthesized in the **zona fasciculata.**

(2) The **mineralocorticoids,** which primarily affect the transport of electrolytes and the distribution of water in tissues, are synthesized in the **zona glomerulosa.**

(3) The **androgens** or **estrogens,** which primarily affect secondary sex characteristics in their specific target organs, are (like the glucocorticoids) synthesized in the **zona fasciculata.**

Individual steroids usually have activities that are predominantly in one of the above categories but may overlap.

General Mechanism of Action

All of the steroids act primarily at the level of the cell nucleus to bring about RNA and protein synthesis. The first step (Fig 34–2) occurs within minutes. It involves the binding of the steroid to receptor proteins in the cytosol. These **receptor proteins** (MW approximately 100,000) are comparatively specific for a given steroid, although some competitive binding can occur. The steroid-receptor complex enters the nucleus, where it binds reversibly to specific sites on the chromatin of the cell nucleus. Binding of the steroid to the receptor "transforms" the receptor and results in a complex with higher affinity to the nuclear binding sites. The nuclear binding sites are possibly closely associated with the DNA itself. By this means, RNA synthesis and, ultimately, cellular protein and enzyme synthesis are modified. It is the enzyme changes that actually produce the effects attributable to the hormone. Since RNA and protein synthesis are initially required, the hormonal effects of steroids usually require 30 minutes to several hours to be apparent; these effects may be prevented by inhibitors of RNA and of protein synthesis.

At high concentrations, steroids may also act directly to alter membranes and enzymatic activity.

General Chemistry

All steroid hormones have a cyclopentanoperhydrophenanthrene ring system as their chemical nucleus. This 4-ring nucleus and its conventional numbering system is illustrated in the structure of cholesterol in Fig 35–18. Most naturally occurring steroids contain alcohol side chains and are therefore usually referred to as sterols.

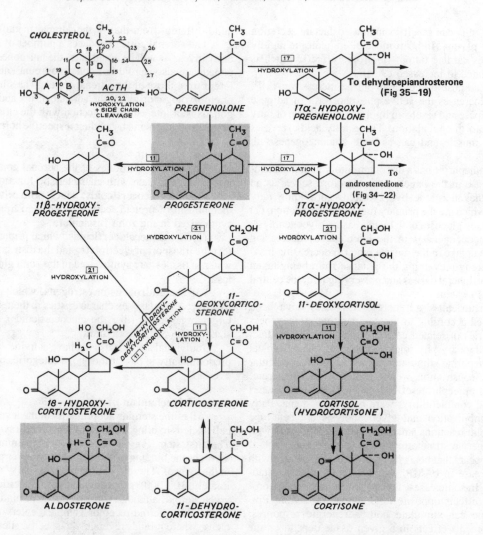

Figure 35–18. Biosynthesis of adrenal corticosteroids. Shaded compounds represent major adrenal steroids.

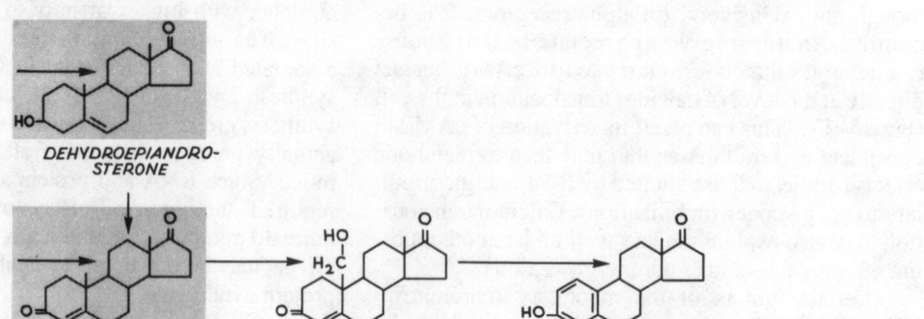

Figure 35–19. Biosynthesis of androgens and estrogens. Shaded compounds represent major adrenal steroids.

Table 35–2. Nomenclature of steroids.

Prefix	Suffix	Chemical Significance
allo-		*Trans* (as opposed to *cis*) configuration of the A and B rings.
epi-		Configuration different from parent compound at a single carbon atom.
	-ane	Saturated carbon atom.
	-ene	A single double bond in ring structure.
hydroxy-, dihydroxy-, etc	-ol, -diol, etc	Alcohols.
oxo-	-one, -dione	Ketones.
dehydro-		Conversion of $-C-OH$ to $-C=O$ by loss of 2 hydrogen atoms.
dihydro-		Addition of 2 hydrogen atoms.
cis-		Arrangement of 2 groups in same plane.
trans-		Arrangement of 2 groups in opposing planes.
α-		A group *trans* to the 19-methyl.
β-		A group *cis* to the 19-methyl.
nor-		One less carbon in a side chain as compared to parent molecules. (*Example:* 19-Nor signifies that the methyl group constituting carbon 19 of a steroid is deleted.)

A variety of stereoisomeric forms of the steroids are possible: (1) The A and B rings may be joined either in a *trans* or *cis* configuration. Estrogens are not capable of this form of isomerism since their A ring is aromatic. (2) Hydrogens or other groups may be attached to the rings with an orientation either above (β-) or below (α-) the plane of the ring. The β-orientation is conventionally assigned to groups in the same plane as the C_{19} methyl group and is diagrammatically represented by solid lines. The opposite α-groups are normally represented by dashed lines. In natural steroids, the chains attached at C_{17} and various substitutions at C_{11} are in the β-configuration. Some general terms of steroid nomenclature are given in Table 35–2.

About 50 steroids have been isolated from the adrenal gland, but only a few of them are known to possess physiologic activity. The most important ones are cortisone, hydrocortisone (cortisol, 17-hydroxycorticosterone), aldosterone, and the 2 androgens androstenedione (androst-4-ene-3,17-dione) and dehydroepiandrosterone (Figs 35–18 and 35–19). Cortisol is the major free circulating adrenocortical hormone in human plasma.

Biosynthesis of Adrenal Hormones

(See Figs 35–18 and 35–19.)

Acetate is the primary precursor for the synthesis of all steroids. The pathway involves the initial synthesis of cholesterol, which, after a series of side chain cleavages and oxidations, is converted to Δ^5-pregnenolone. **Pregnenolone** is the "pivotal" steroid from which all the other steroid hormones are produced. There is evidence that pregnenolone (or progesterone) can be synthesized from acetate by a pathway other than through cholesterol, possibly from 24-dehydrocholesterol. However, in normal tissue this path is relatively minor. The adrenal cortex contains relatively large quantities of cholesterol, mostly as cholesteryl esters that are derived both from synthesis and from extra-adrenal sources.

Pregnenolone is converted in the cytosol to progesterone by a dehydrogenase or to 17-hydroxypregnenolone by a specific 17-hydroxylase. As shown in Figs 35–18 and 35–19, those 2 steroids are converted to a variety of active hormones in the endoplasmic reticulum and the mitochondria by specific oxygenases and dehydrogenases that require molecular oxygen and NADPH. The result of these combined enzymatic reactions is the addition of hydroxyl or keto groups at the C_{11}, C_{17}, or C_{21} positions.

In general, **C-21 hydroxylation is necessary for both glucocorticoid and mineralocorticoid** activities. Those steroids with an additional **–OH at C_{17} have greater glucocorticoid and lesser mineralocorticoid** action. The 2 most important glucocorticoids are **cortisol** and corticosterone. Cortisol predominates in humans and the fish, whereas corticosterone is the most important hormone in rodents.

The most potent mineralocorticoid is **aldosterone.** Its major pathway of synthesis requires a unique 18-hydroxylation (Fig 35–18). Although most hydroxylases involved in adrenal steroid synthesis are found throughout the gland, the **18-hydroxylase activity is restricted to the glomerular layer** below the capsule glomerulosa. Thus, aldosterone synthesis is limited to this area.

Aldosterone has the same structure as corticosterone except that the methyl group at position 18 is replaced by an aldehyde group. Deoxycorticosterone appears to be the precursor in the adrenal of both aldosterone and corticosterone.

11-Deoxycorticosterone is only 4% as potent as aldosterone. However, because it can be prepared synthetically (as the acetate, Doca) and because aldosterone is not yet available for therapeutic use, Doca is important in the treatment of Addison's disease.

The major adrenal androgen, dehydroepiandrosterone, is produced by side chain cleavage of 17-hydroxypregnenolone. The smaller amounts of adrenal estrogens can arise from testosterone produced either from dehydroepiandrosterone or from 17-hydroxyprogesterone. Sulfate conjugates of some of the steroids, most notably of the androgen dehydroepiandrosterone, have been detected in the adrenal gland and in adrenal secretions. Conversion of pregnenolone sulfate to dehydroepiandrosterone sulfate has been reported to occur without the loss of the sulfate. Although sulfate conjugation is generally associated with inactivation mechanisms in the liver for drugs and other hormones, these results indicate that sulfate conjugates are involved in some pathways of biosynthesis of steroid hormones.

Metabolic Functions (See Fig 35–20.)

A. The Glucocorticoids: These steroid hormones (notably cortisol) act, as other steroids, to modify RNA and enzyme synthesis in their many target tissues (see p 487 and Fig 34–2). Though details are unknown, action of the glucocorticoid receptor complex on the nuclear chromatin and DNA leads to highly selective synthesis of specific enzymes. Since one of the mRNAs stimulated is that for RNA polymerase I, a more general increase of protein synthesis may also result from glucocorticoid action. The resulting changes in metabolic processes are summarized in Fig

35–20. (Note that many of the glucocorticoid actions are metabolically antagonistic to insulin.) The glucocorticoids increase circulating glucose, fatty acids, and amino acids.

In the **peripheral tissues (muscle, adipose,** and **lymphoid tissue),** the steroids are **catabolic** and tend to "spare" glucose. Glucose uptake and glycolysis are depressed. Protein synthesis is depressed, whereas protein degradation is increased. In **muscle,** there may be tissue wasting as protein stores are depleted. In **adipose tissue,** glucocorticoids increase lipolysis. The impairment of glucose metabolism in this tissue de-

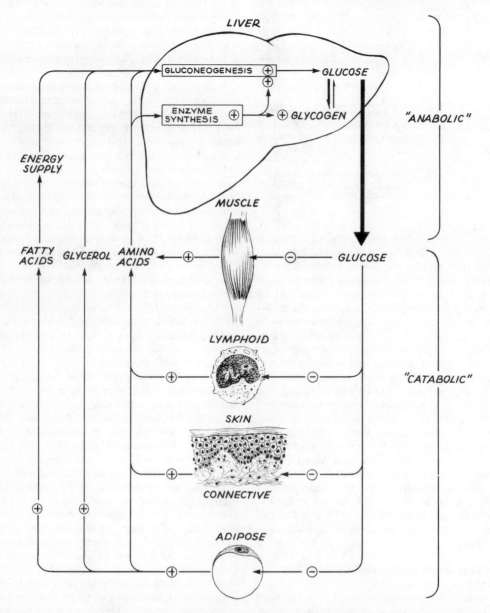

Figure 35–20. Glucocorticoid action on carbohydrate, lipid, and protein metabolism. The arrows indicate the general flow of substrate in response to the catabolic and anabolic actions of glucocorticoids when unopposed by secondary secretions of other hormones. Not shown is increased gluconeogenesis by kidney. The plus or minus signs indicate stimulation or inhibition, respectively. (Redrawn from Baxter JD, Forsham PH: Tissue effects of glucocorticoids. *Am J Med* 1972;**53**:573.)

creases the available glycerol phosphate, thereby impairing fat synthesis. In **Cushing's disease,** centripetal redistribution of fat occurs without change in total body fat, as lipid is mobilized from steroid-sensitive tissue and redeposited elsewhere.

In the livers of animals treated with adrenal steroids, all processes that help remove amino acids are increased. Thus, total protein synthesis, gluconeogenesis, glycogen deposition, amino acid conversion to CO_2, and urea production are all enhanced. Many of the gluconeogenic effects in the liver are caused by glycerol, fatty acids, and amino acids mobilized from peripheral tissues (Fig 35–20).

In particular, the adrenal steroids increase the amount of hepatic enzymes involved in amino acid metabolism such as alanine-α-ketoglutarate and tyrosine transaminases as well as tryptophan pyrrolase. The key enzymes in the regulation of gluconeogenesis (pyruvate carboxylase, phosphoenolpyruvate carboxykinase, fructose-1,6-bisphosphatase, and glucose-6-phosphatase) are also increased. This seems to be a comparatively specialized action of the adrenal steroids since many other hepatic enzymes are not increased. In liver, adrenal steroids not only increase amino acid conversion to glucose but also conversion of CO_2 to glucose, suggesting that they may act on CO_2 fixation, particularly at the level of pyruvate carboxylase, a key enzyme involved in gluconeogenesis (see below). The increase in glucose, glycogen, and protein synthesis observed in the liver indicates an important action of the adrenal steroids on increased metabolic availability of amino acids. However, the adrenal steroids have little effect on the concentration gradient of amino acids across cell membranes. In vivo, the hyperglycemia, particularly during later periods of treatment, is a result of increased gluconeogenesis in the liver and decreased glucose uptake in peripheral tissues. Though the primary source of the glucose moiety in the process of gluconeogenesis is usually considered to be amino acids, the amount of glucose produced cannot be entirely accounted for by amino acid breakdown. It is possible that lactate and glycerol derived from muscle and adipose tissue, respectively (the latter a product of the increased lipolysis), can also serve as sources of carbon for hepatic glucose synthesis.

The glucocorticoids are relatively inactive on heart, brain, and red cells. Other effects of the glucocorticoids can be extremely important:

1. Anti-inflammatory effects–At high concentrations, glucocorticoids decrease cellular protective reactions and in particular retard the migration of leukocytes into traumatized areas. Part of the anti-inflammatory effect may result from cortisol's ability to decrease synthesis and secretion of specific prostaglandins (see p 212). Thus, cortisol is an anti-inflammatory agent.

2. Immunosuppressive effects–Cortisol decreases immune responses associated with infections, allergic states, and anaphylaxis. Indeed, glucocorticoids may be used for the purpose of repressing antibody formation when in organ transplantation procedures an effort to prevent rejection of the transplanted tissue or organ is essential. Most of the steroid effects are at the level of thymus-dependent lymphocytes.

The primary effect of adrenal steroids that depress immune responses is at a nuclear site.

3. Exocrine secretory effects–Chronic treatment with glucocorticoids causes increased secretion of hydrochloric acid and pepsinogen by the stomach and trypsinogen by the pancreas; this can enhance the formation of gastrointestinal ulcers.

4. Effects on bone–Glucocorticoids reduce the osteoid matrix of bone, thus favoring osteoporosis and excessive loss of calcium from the body. Indeed, osteoporosis is a major complication of prolonged adrenal steroid therapy.

5. Cyclic AMP–In some tissues, the glucocorticoids decrease phosphodiesterase activity, thereby increasing cAMP. However, it is unlikely that steroids act primarily to increase cAMP since their action is at the nuclear site. Nevertheless, cAMP and the glucocorticoids have similar effects in almost all tissues (eg, increased protein metabolism, lipolysis, and gluconeogenesis), suggesting that they may have a mechanism of action in common.

6. Stress–The glucocorticoids reverse the decreased blood pressure resulting from emotional or surgical shock. In Addison's disease, exogenous glucocorticoids are required to maintain blood pressure.

B. The Mineralocorticoids: With the exception of the androgens, all of the active corticosteroids increase the absorption of sodium and chloride by the renal tubules and decrease their excretion by the sweat glands, salivary glands, and the gastrointestinal tract. Aldosterone is the most important circulating mineralocorticoid, being about 1000 times as effective as cortisol and about 35 times as effective as 11-deoxycorticosterone (DOC), the second significant mineralocorticoid. Accompanying the retention of sodium by the kidney, there is increased excretion of potassium and magnesium.

Extracellular fluid volume is increased after the administration of mineralocorticoids. There is also an increase in the volume of the circulating blood and in the urinary output, all leading to hypertension.

Aldosterone, like the other adrenal steroids, acts primarily at the nuclear site (Fig 34–2) via a specific cytosolic receptor to increase synthesis of RNA and thus indirectly to influence the synthesis of enzymes or other proteins. The comparatively long period of exposure of tissues, both in vitro and in vivo, that is required before physiologic effects are noted is consistent with this mechanism of action.

C. Sex Hormones (C-19 Corticosteroids): The primary adrenal androgens are dehydroepiandrosterone and androstenedione (Fig 35–19). Testosterone can also be detected in certain adrenal tumors.

The adrenal origin of some sex hormones accounts for the fact that the urine of castrates still contains androgen derivatives. These adrenocorticosteroids of the androgenic type cause retention of nitrogen (a protein anabolic effect), phosphorus, potassium, sodium, and chloride. If present in excessive amounts, they also lead to masculinization in the female.

Analogs of Natural Steroids

Synthetic adrenal hormones are in many instances more potent than the naturally occurring hormones and often more specific in their action (Fig 35–21).

This greater potency probably arises from a greater affinity of the steroid analog for the receptor protein in the cytosol.

The introduction of a halogen (eg, fluorine) at the 9α position of cortisone, cortisol, or corticosterone results in the production of compounds of high potency (Fig 35–21). However, their increased salt-retaining activity is relatively greater than their anti-inflammatory or metabolic activities. Introduction of a double bond between carbon atoms 1 and 2 results in the production of cortisone and cortisol analogs which in therapeutically useful doses are relatively inert as far as salt-retaining properties are concerned, although they retain the anti-inflammatory activity of the natural steroids. The cortisone analog is prednisone; the cortisol analog is prednisolone.

In steroids that have a hydroxy group on position 11 (eg, cortisol, 9α-fluorocortisol, or 11β-hydroxyprogesterone), the addition of the 2-methyl group markedly enhances the sodium-retaining and potassium-losing activity of the hormone.

A synthetic analog of prednisolone, having a similar but more potent anti-inflammatory action, is **dexamethasone** (9α-fluoro-16α-methylprednisolone). It is about 30 times more potent than cortisol.

Many steroids may act as an **antagonist** by competitively binding to the cytosol receptor normally used by another steroid. Although the antagonists may have a greater affinity for the receptor, the resulting receptor-steroid complex is comparatively inactive. Thus, **spironolactone (Aldactone),** useful in treating hyperaldosteronism, acts by forming an inactive complex with the aldosterone receptor. Similarly, progesterone is an antagonist for glucocorticoids in some tissues; this may account for the reduced sensitivity to circulating free cortisol in the later stages of pregnancy.

Regulation of Steroid Secretion (Fig 35–22)

The synthesis and secretion of adrenal steroids of the zona fasciculata (glucocorticoids and sex steroids) is controlled by adrenocorticotropin (ACTH) from the pituitary. The secretion of ACTH, in turn, is regulated by corticotropin-releasing factor that is released from the hypothalamus during stress (see p 512). After stimulation of the gland, there is a rapid decline in the concentration of cholesterol within the adrenal. This and other evidence indicate that ACTH has its effect at some step involving conversion of cholesterol to pregnenolone.

It is still unclear whether the specific action of ACTH is to increase the initial 20-hydroxylation of cholesterol or to activate the "desmolase" step, a series of oxidative cleavages of the cholesterol side chain employing NADPH as cofactor. The ultimate products of these reactions are the C-21 steroids $20\alpha,22\beta$-dihydroxycholesterol and $17\alpha,20\alpha$-dihydroxycholesterol. These compounds are converted directly to pregnenolone or 17α-pregnenolone by loss of an isocaproic aldehyde moiety from their side chains. Since ACTH stimulates synthesis of the substrate for all steroid hormone synthesis in the zona fasciculata, it **does not preferentially stimulate synthesis of a particular class of steroids.**

The role of the large amounts of ascorbic acid found in the adrenal cortex is not known. It may act to provide reducing equivalents for the NADPH-depen-

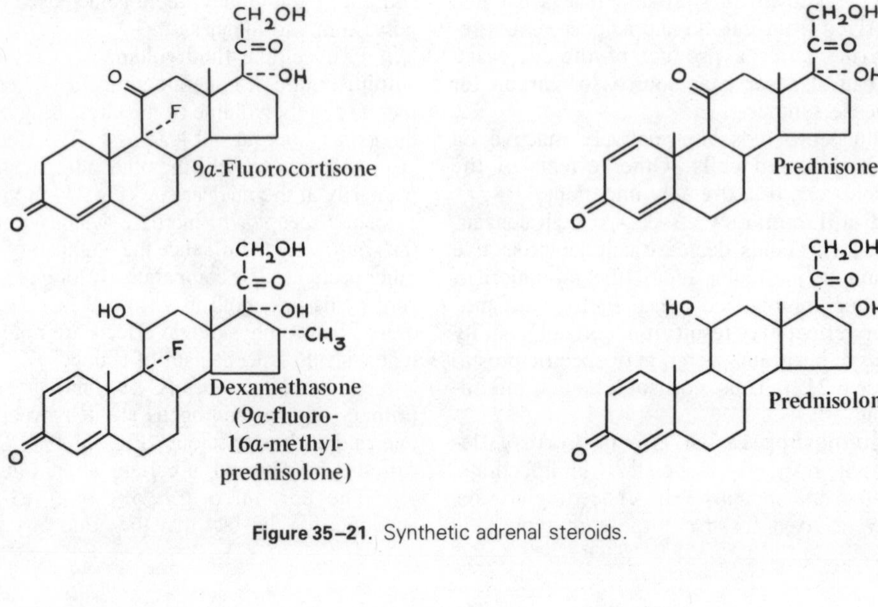

9α-Fluorocortisone

Prednisone

Dexamethasone
(9α-fluoro-
16α-methyl-
prednisolone)

Prednisolone

Figure 35–21. Synthetic adrenal steroids.

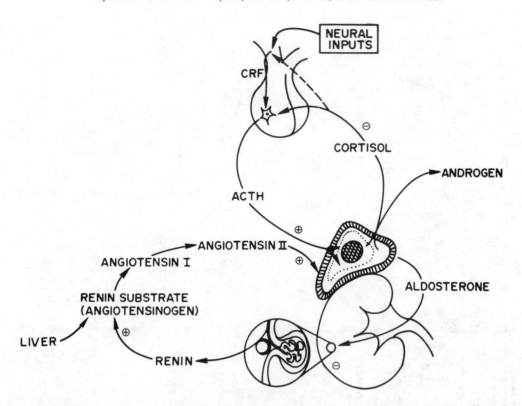

Figure 35–22. Control of adrenal corticosteroid secretion. (1) Hypothalamic corticotropin-releasing factor (CRF) stimulates pituitary adrenocorticotropic hormone (ACTH) secretion. This activates cells in the zona fasciculata and zona reticularis to increase cortisol and androgen secretion. Cortisol feeds back to inhibit ACTH output. (2) Decreased blood pressure in the afferent arteriole of the kidney causes release of renin from the juxtaglomerular cells. Renin acts on its substrate (a serum glycoprotein) to release angiotensin I, which is converted to angiotensin II, and this peptide activates aldosterone secretion from the zona glomerulosa. Aldosterone stimulates sodium retention (and potassium wasting) by the renal tubule, leading to increased blood pressure and diminished renin secretion. (Reproduced, with permission, from Neelon FA: Adrenal physiology and pharmacology. *Urol Clin North Am* 1977;**4**:179.)

dent hydroxylations required for steroid synthesis mentioned below.

Stimulation of steroid synthesis and release by ACTH may be mediated through cAMP since the level of this substance is increased in adrenal slices within minutes by the tropic hormone. cAMP itself can directly simulate ACTH action.

Stimulation of steroid synthesis is usually associated with alterations in structure of the adrenal mitochondrial membrane and is dependent on the presence of calcium ions. The ultimate effect of ACTH and cAMP, therefore, may involve changes in ionic flux across adrenal cell membranes.

The secretion of ACTH is under feedback control by circulating steroids; in humans, **cortisol** is the most important regulator. Glucocorticoids specifically decrease ACTH mRNA synthesis in the pituitary. Since ACTH nonspecifically stimulates all adrenal steroids, a defect in cortisol production will foster overproduction of androgens, resulting in various forms of adrenogenital syndrome. Pregnenolone is a feedback inhibitor of steroidogenesis, possibly by some unspecified "allosteric effect."

Unlike the other corticosteroids, the production of aldosterone by the adrenal is relatively uninfluenced by ACTH. Aldosterone production is increased mainly by deprivation of sodium, by administration of potassium, and by any decline in the normal volume of the extracellular fluid; this latter circumstance is attributed to the presence of what are termed "volume receptors." It follows that activities resulting from an increase in aldosterone production—sodium retention, potassium excretion, and an expansion of extracellular fluid volume—would serve to reduce secretion of the hormone by a type of "feedback regulation." Aldosterone production is also increased by β-adrenergic stimuli—an observation that supports the idea that release of aldosterone is enhanced by cAMP. The kidney, by means of the renin-angiotensin system (renal pressor system) is an important organ controlling aldosterone secretion. Renin is secreted by the **juxtaglomerular cells** of the kidney (Fig 35–22). These cells are located in the walls of the renal afferent arterioles, and it may be that the "volume receptors" are located here. Decreased arterial pressure and renal blood flow resulting from decreased extracellular fluid

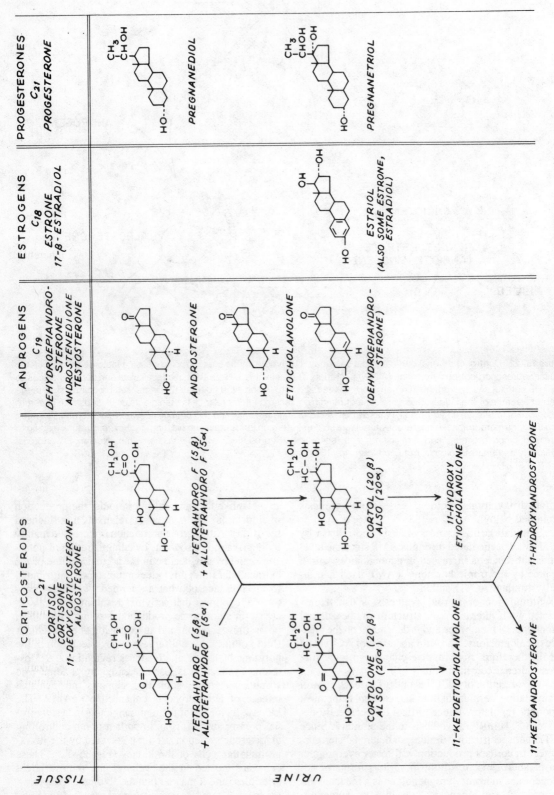

Figure 35–23. Primary excretion products of steroids. (As conjugates with glucuronic acid.)

volume would increase renin secretion. Renin, in turn, converts hypertensinogen to angiotensin I; in lung, angiotensin I is converted to angiotensin II, which acts directly on the aldosterone-producing cells of the zona glomerulosa of the adrenal cortex.

Secretion of aldosterone is increased in several diseases such as cirrhosis, nephrosis, and some types of cardiac failure. The result is enhancement of retention of sodium and water, which further aggravates the edema characteristic of certain of these diseases.

Spironolactone, which blocks the action of aldosterone on sodium retention is used as a diuretic agent in treatment of the edema that occurs in those disease states characterized by excess aldosterone production.

Transport, Metabolism, & Excretion of Adrenal Steroids

About 90% of serum cortisol circulates in the blood bound loosely to a specific alpha globulin (**corticosteroid-binding globulin, CBG, transcortin**). The bound hormone is essentially inactive. Corticosteroid-binding globulin can be increased by estrogens which thereby enhance the total amount of circulating cortisol though the actual amount of free steroid may be normal because of counter regulation. Progesterone, on the other hand, is one of the few steroids with a high affinity for this binding protein and can cause displacement of cortisol to the free, active fraction.

Cortisol has a half-life of about 4 hours. Within 48 hours, 93% of the injected dose disappears from the body: 70% by way of the urine, 20% by the stool, and the remainder presumably through the skin. The steroid nucleus is eliminated in the intact form; no significant breakdown to CO_2 and water occurs.

The corticosteroids are inactivated in the liver by ring reduction catalyzed by NADPH-requiring hydrogenases and by reduction of the 3-ketone group by NADH or NADPH, requiring reversible dehydrogenases (Fig 35–23). The resulting tetrahydro derivatives are in turn conjugated, mainly with glucuronic acid.

Approximately 25–50% of the urinary steroids consist of C-17 or C-21 steroid carboxylic acids (acid steroids). Although it is established that all types of steroids can be converted to their acid derivatives by the liver, the physiologic role of this process remains unknown.

Both free and conjugated corticosteroids are excreted into the intestine by way of the bile and, in part, reabsorbed from the intestine by the enterohepatic circulation, finally to be excreted by the kidney.

Large amounts of aldosterone are produced from androstenedione in the liver. Aldosterone thus produced in the liver may, however, have little peripheral biologic activity since it could be inactivated by reduction and conjugation before leaving the liver. Aldosterone synthesized in the liver would, however, contribute to the conjugates of this hormone measured in the urine.

Most of the androgens are excreted into the urine as 17-ketosteroids (Fig 35–23). Dehydroepiandroster-

one is probably derived mainly from the adrenal. It is found in the urine of both normal men and women, and it is greatly increased in some cases of hyperadrenocorticism, particularly those with excess production of androgens.

Abnormalities

A. Hypoadrenocorticism: In humans, degeneration of the adrenal cortex, often due to a tuberculous process or in association with pernicious anemia as well as with multiple endocrine abnormalities such as diabetes and hypothyroidism, results in **Addison's disease.** The effects of this disease include decreased 17-hydroxycorticoid and aldosterone excretion, excessive loss of sodium chloride in the urine, elevated levels of potassium in the serum, low blood pressure, muscular weakness, gastrointestinal disturbances, low body temperature, hypoglycemia, and a progressive brownish pigmentation which increases over a period of months. The pigmentation is caused by the melanocyte-stimulating hormone activity inherent in the structure of ACTH that is present in increased amounts as a result of the deficiency of cortisol (see Chapter 36).

B. Hyperadrenocorticism: Adrenocortical hyperfunction may be caused by benign or malignant tumors of the cortex or by adrenocortical hyperplasia initiated by increased production of ACTH. **Cushing's disease** has been restricted to those cases that are of pituitary origin. **Cushing's syndrome** denotes adrenocortical hyperfunction directly involving the adrenal gland.

The continuous administration of adrenal steroid hormones or ACTH may also induce signs of hyperadrenocorticism. These include (1) hyperglycemia and glycosuria (diabetogenic effect); (2) retention of sodium and water, followed by edema, increased blood volume, and hypertension; (3) negative nitrogen balance (protein anti-anabolic effect and gluconeogenesis); (4) potassium depletion and hypokalemic alkalosis; (5) hirsutism and acne; and (6) centripetal redistribution of fat.

Congenital hyperplasia as well as certain tumors of the adrenals cause the production of increased amounts of androgenic (C-19) steroids. The resulting disturbance is termed **congenital virilizing hyperplasia** when it is present at birth and **adrenogenital syndrome** when it occurs in the postnatal period. Under the influence of excess androgens, the female assumes male secondary sex characteristics. When it occurs in the male, there is excessive masculinization. Feminizing adrenal tumors may rarely occur in males. In the most common form, the metabolic defect is a virtual absence of C-21 hydroxylase. Consequently, cortisol and cortisone are not produced in normal amounts; aldosterone and other mineralocorticoid production is also impaired.

Other rare adrenogenital syndromes are known in which defects occur in the synthesis of C-11 hydroxylases and Δ^5-isomerase.

In some forms of testicular feminization, pituitary-adrenal balance may be normal; in these instances, the abnormality is attributable to an inability of the target organs to recognize androgens because of reduced specific receptors in the cytosol of target organ cells.

Aldosteronism

"Primary aldosteronism" results from tumors (aldosteronomas) of the adrenals in which the hyperactivity of the adrenal cortex is apparently confined to excess production of aldosterone. The primary metabolic defect may be an inability of the adrenals to perform 17-hydroxylations, thereby shunting progesterone to aldosterone (Fig 35–18). A consistently low level of potassium in the serum is a characteristic finding in primary hyperaldosteronism. The administration of the aldosterone antagonist spironolactone (Aldactone) restores serum potassium to normal levels.

THE ORGANS PRODUCING
SEX HORMONES

The testes and ovaries, in addition to their function of providing spermatozoa or ova, manufacture steroid hormones that control secondary sex characteristics, the reproductive cycle, and the growth and development of the accessory reproductive organs, excluding the ovary and testis themselves. The sex hormones also exert potent protein anabolic effects.

Most of the regulation of hormone production in the testes and ovaries is controlled by tropic hormones from the pituitary that act, in part, by increasing intracellular cAMP.

MALE HORMONES

The principal male hormone, **testosterone,** is synthesized by the interstitial (Leydig) cells of the testes from cholesterol through pregnenolone, progesterone, and hydroxyprogesterone, which is then converted to the C-19 ketosteroid, androstenedione, the immediate precursor of testosterone. Alternatively, the pathway through hydroxypregnenolone and dehydroepiandrosterone can be used to produce androstenedione. A direct conversion of dehydroepiandrosterone to testosterone has been established in which androstenedione is bypassed; dehydroepiandrosterone in this pathway is initially reduced to its 17-hydroxy derivatives, which are then converted to testosterone. These reactions are shown in Figs 35–18 and 35–19, since they are also a part of the biosynthetic pathway in the adrenal that is responsible for the formation of the androgenic (C-19) steroids. It will also be noted that pregnenolone is a common precursor of the adrenocortical hormones and testosterone as well as of progesterone.

Dehydroepiandrosterone (DHA) and 4-androstenedione are relatively weak androgens synthesized and secreted both by the gonads and the adrenal. In both sexes, the quantitatively most important source of dehydroepiandrosterone is the adrenal. In women, it is synthesized in small amounts in the ovaries also, where it can serve as a precursor for estrogen synthesis.

Dehydroepiandrosterone sulfate from the adrenal is usually found in the plasma of young males at levels 400 times that of testosterone. It can be converted in the testes to free dehydroepiandrosterone by a sulfatase and thus provide an additional source of testosterone precursor in this tissue.

The androgens as well as the estrogens are in part transported by binding to specific plasma proteins. These proteins increase in pregnancy or estrogen therapy, which results in a reduction of effective "free" androgenic action. About 99% of the testosterone circulating in the plasma is bound to protein (testosterone-binding globulin, TBG).

Testosterone in some but not all of the target tissues is converted by the enzyme 5α-reductase to the more potent dihydrotestosterone (Fig 35–24), which in adults is the active intracellular androgen. Androsterone-3α,17β-diols are other active androgens that are synthesized in target tissues from dihydrotestosterone or dehydroepiandrosterone.

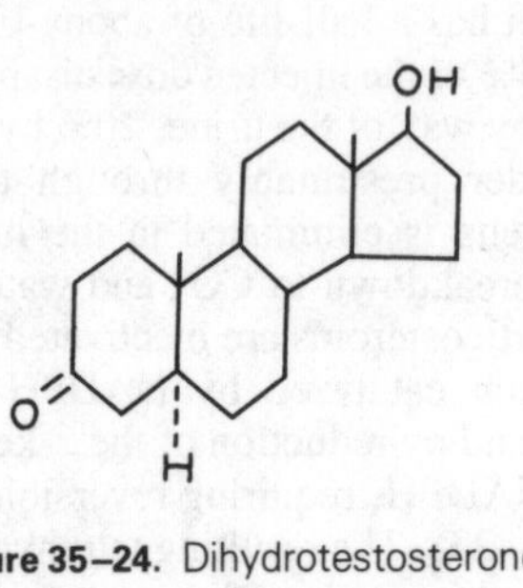

Figure 35–24. Dihydrotestosterone.

In general, the testes and the adrenals have similar qualitative capacities to synthesize androgens. Since the testis lacks 11-hydroxylase activity, however, only the adrenal is capable of synthesizing the glucocorticoids and mineralocorticoids (Figs 35–18 and 35–19).

The small amount of testosterone that is present in female plasma results mainly from peripheral conversion of androstenedione to testosterone by the ovary.

Testicular function is controlled by pituitary FSH, LH, and prolactin, at least partially through activation of adenylate cyclase. FSH also appears capable of inducing LH receptors and thus enhances tissue response to LH. Increased testosterone levels cause feedback inhibition of LH secretion. Total blood testosterone is reduced during surgical or emotional stress.

Testosterone promotes the growth and function of the epididymis, vas deferens, prostate, seminal vesicles, and penis. Its metabolic effect as a protein anabolic steroid exceeds that of any other naturally occurring steroid. It also contributes to the muscular and skeletal growth that accompanies puberty.

As with other steroids, the androgens may initially bind to a specific cytosol receptor protein. The complex in turn is transported to the nucleus where it interacts with chromatin, triggering synthesis of RNA, RNA polymerase, and proteins. Testicular feminization can result from defective conversion of testosterone to dihydrotestosterone or decreased cytosol receptors.

The protein anabolic effect of testosterone (nitrogen-retaining effect) is as important as its androgenic effects. In many clinical situations where promotion of protein anabolism is required, testosterone has proved quite effective, but the accompanying androgenic effects are often undesirable. Consequently, efforts have been directed toward the production of synthetic steroids which, while retaining the protein anabolic action of testosterone, are relatively free of androgenicity. Some synthetic androgens include fluoxymesterone and 2α-methyldehydrotestosterone.

The principal secreted metabolites of testosterone are androsterone and etiocholanolone, the major 17-ketosteroids in the urine (Fig 35–23). In addition, small amounts of dehydroepiandrosterone are excreted as the sulfate. The principal pathway of degradation of testosterone involves oxidation in the liver to androstenedione and subsequent saturation of the double bond in ring A and reduction of the keto groups (Figs 35–19 and 35–23). Some 11-oxy or 11-hydroxy derivatives of androsterone and androstenedione are produced in the liver from adrenal cortisol and cortisone.

Excretion of 17-ketosteroids as their sulfates and glucuronides is in part a reflection of testicular hormone production. The testis contributes about one-third of the urinary neutral 17-ketosteroid, particularly androsterone, etiocholanolone, and epiandrosterone (Fig 35–23).

FEMALE HORMONES

Two main types of female hormones are secreted by the ovary: the follicular or **estrogenic hormones** produced by the cells of the developing graafian follicle and the **progestational hormones** derived from the corpus luteum that is formed in the ovary from the ruptured follicle.

The Estrogenic Hormones

The estrogenic (follicular) hormones are C-18 steroids, differing from androgens in lacking the methyl group at C_{10}. In contrast to all other natural steroids, ring A is **aromatic** (Fig 35–19).

The principal estrogenic hormone in the circulation—and the most important active form of the estrogens—is **estradiol**, which is in metabolic equilibrium with the less active estrone. It is bound to a specific

plasma carrier protein (sex steroid–binding protein), which also transports the androgens.

Estriol (Fig 35–23) is the principal estrogen found in the urine of pregnant women and in the placenta. It is produced by hydroxylation of estrone at C_{16} and reduction of the ketone group at C_{17}.

The androgens, testosterone and androstenedione, are precursors for the synthesis of the estrogens in testes, ovaries, adrenals, and placenta (Fig 35–19). The conversion from testosterone involves 3 enzyme-catalyzed steps that require oxygen and NADPH: (1) 19-hydroxylation to 19-hydroxytestosterone or 19-hydroxyandrostenedione; (2) 19-oxidation to the keto derivatives; and (3) aldehyde lyolysis to remove the C_{19} keto group and cause aromatization of the A ring. **Metyrapone** inhibits estrogen synthesis by blocking 19-hydroxylation. As with the other steroids, estrogens (primarily estriol) can be found in urine either as a conjugate with sulfate or as a glucuronide (Fig 35–23).

Estrogens may also be converted by hydroxylation at the 2 position to nonactive 2-hydroxyestradiol. 2-Hydroxyestradiol (a catechol estrogen) can competitively inhibit the normal methylation (inactivation) of catecholamines by catechol-O-methyltransferase (Fig 35–16). This could explain the increased blood pressure and elevated catecholamines in pregnancy, though an actual quantitative role of 2-hydroxyestradiol in this regard is not established.

Physiologic Effects of Estrogenic Hormones

In the lower animals, the estrogenic hormones induce estrus, a series of changes in the female reproductive system associated with ovulation. These changes may be detected by the histologic appearance of the vaginal smear.

In women, the estrogenic hormones prepare the uterine mucosa for the later action of the progestational hormones. The changes in the uterus include proliferative growth of the endometrium, deepening of uterine glands, and increased vascularity; changes in the epithelium of the uterine (fallopian) tubes and of the vagina also occur. All of these changes begin immediately after menstrual bleeding has ceased.

The estrogens also suppress the production of the pituitary hormone (follicle-stimulating hormone, FSH) that initially started the development of the ovarian follicle. In contrast, they appear to stimulate pituitary LH; peak levels of estrogens precede peak level of LH by 1–2 days. Estrogens are effective in maintenance of female secondary sex characteristics, acting antagonistically to testosterone.

Mechanism of Action

Estradiol is the active estrogen; its metabolites play only a minor role. Estradiol is bound to a specific cytosol receptor protein in its target cells; the resulting complex is then translocated into the nucleus. During this process, the receptor protein is altered structurally ("receptor transformation"), thereby increasing the ability of the complex to bind chromatin and to cause increased RNA synthesis. Binding to the cytosol receptor protein is relatively nonspecific, most of the tissue specificity for estradiol action occurring at the levels of subsequent complex transformation and nuclear binding. Only mRNAs coding for specific proteins are elevated. For example, in chick oviduct the specific synthesis of mRNA coding for ovalbumin has been demonstrated. In addition, estrogens increase RNA polymerase synthesis in target tissue, which can result in a more generalized synthesis of proteins.

Synthetic Estrogens

A number of synthetic estrogens have been produced.

(1) Ethynyl estradiol (Fig 35–25) is a synthetic estrogen which, when given orally, is 50 times as effective as water-soluble estrogenic preparations and 30 times as effective as estradiol benzoate injected intramuscularly.

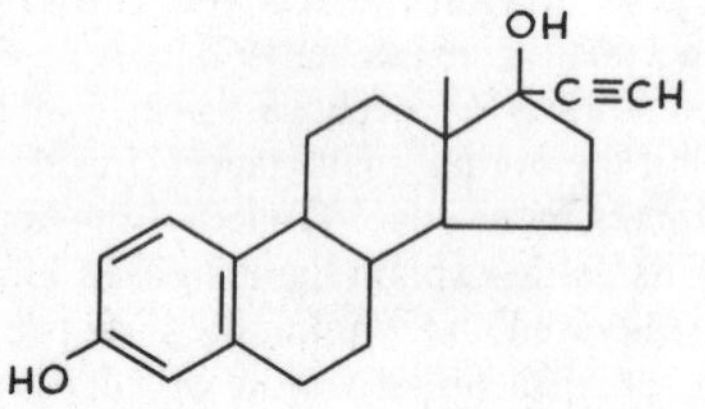

Figure 35–25. Ethynyl estradiol.

(2) Diethylstilbestrol is an example of a group of para-hydroxyphenyl derivatives which, while not steroidal in structure, nonetheless exert potent estrogenic effects. However, as shown in the formula in Fig 35–26, its structure resembles the steroid nucleus.

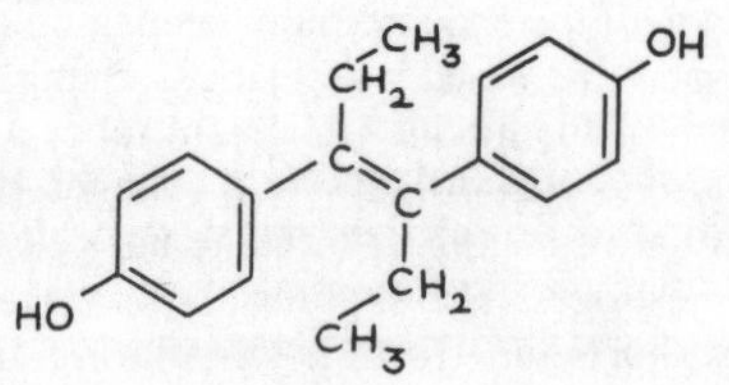

Figure 35–26. Diethylstilbestrol.

The Progestational Hormones (Luteal Hormones)

Progesterone (Fig 35–18) is the hormone of the corpus luteum, the anatomic structure that develops from the ruptured ovarian follicle. It is formed also by the placenta, notably during the latter part of pregnancy. Progesterone is also formed in the adrenal cortex as a precursor of both C-19 and C-21 corticosteroids (Fig 35–18). In all of the above tissues, progesterone is synthesized from its immediate precursor, pregnenolone, by a combined dehydrogenase and isomerase reaction. The steroid analog cyanotrimeth-

ylandrostenolone can inhibit this conversion. In contrast to testosterone and estradiol, progesterone is bound in plasma to the corticosteroid-binding globulin. Intracellularly, it is bound to a specific binding protein in the cytosol. The complex then enters the nucleus and affects RNA synthesis by reacting with the chromatin.

Functions of Progesterone

This hormone appears after ovulation and causes extensive development of the endometrium, preparing the uterus for the reception of the embryo and for its nutrition. The hormone also suppresses estrus, ovulation, and the production of pituitary luteinizing hormone, which originally stimulated corpus luteum formation. Progesterone antagonizes the action of estrogens in various tissues, including the cervical mucus, vaginal epithelium, and uterine tubes. Progesterone also stimulates the mammary glands. When pregnancy occurs, the corpus luteum is maintained and menstruation and ovulation are suspended. The concentration of progesterone decreases near term.

If fertilization does not occur, the follicular and progestational hormones suddenly decrease on about the 26th day of the cycle; the new cycle then begins with menstrual bleeding and sloughing of the uterine wall (Fig 35–27).

The chief excretory product of progesterone is **pregnanediol** (Fig 36–24), which is present as the glucuronide during the latter half of the menstrual cycle. Its presence in the urine signifies that the endometrium is progestational rather than follicular. About 75% of progesterone (or its metabolites) is excreted in the intestine by way of the bile and eliminated in the feces. Large amounts occur in the urine only if the biliary route of excretion is blocked.

Other Progestational Hormones

In addition to progesterone, the corpus luteum may also produce a second hormone that has been termed **relaxin** because of its ability to bring about relaxation of the symphysis pubica of the guinea pig or of the mouse. Relaxin also occurs in the placenta. It is active only when injected into an animal in normal or artificially induced estrus. Relaxin has a molecular weight of 5521 and a 25% amino acid sequence homology with insulin.

Orally Effective Progestational Agents

Progesterone is relatively ineffective when taken by mouth. In recent years, several synthetically produced progestational agents have been devised that are much more effective biologically than progesterone when taken orally. Two such compounds are shown in Figs 35–28 and 35–29. Because, like progesterone, they have the ability to suppress ovulation, they have found application in association with estrogens as oral contraceptives.

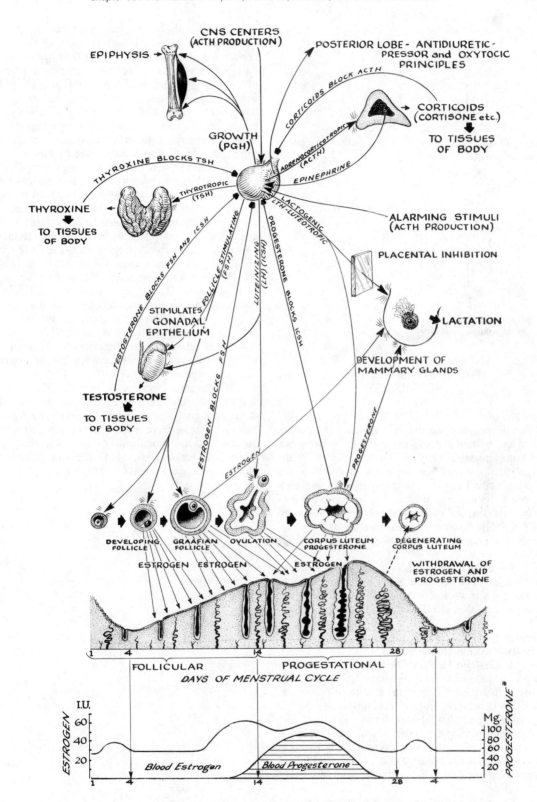

*Progesterone as determined from the urinary pregnanediol.

Figure 35–27. Relationships of the pituitary hormones to the target glands and tissues.

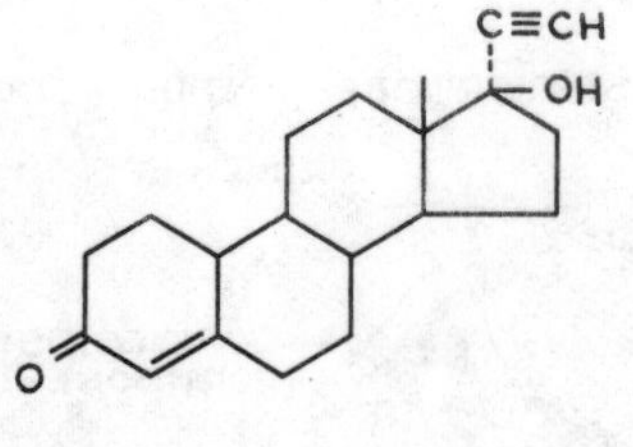

Figure 35–28. Norethindrone (Norlutin; 17α-ethynyl-19-nortestosterone).

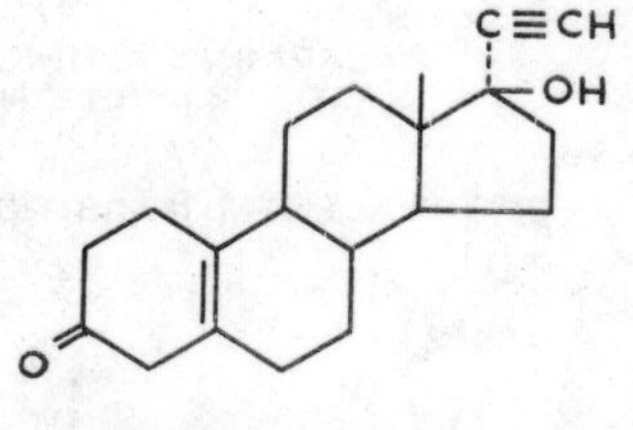

Figure 35–29. Norethynodrel (Enovid; 17α-ethynyl-17-hydroxy-5-[10]-estren-3-one).

THE GASTROINTESTINAL HORMONES

The gastrointestinal hormones are polypeptides produced by mucosal endocrine cells of the stomach and small intestine. They are involved primarily in the regulation of motor and secretory functions of the stomach, small intestine, liver, biliary tract, and pancreas. The 3 major gastrointestinal hormones are **gastrin, secretin,** and **cholecystokinin (pancreozymin) (CCK[PZ]).** A summary of the multiple and overlapping functions of these hormones is given in Table 35–3.

The basic mechanisms of action of the gastrointestinal hormones on their target tissues are unclear; both rapid activation of cAMP synthesis and the slower increases of DNA and RNA synthesis probably occur.

Demonstrable Actions of the Major Gastrointestinal Hormones

A. Gastrin: Two gastrins, I and II, each containing 17 amino acids, have been identified. They differ only in that gastrin II contains a sulfated tyrosine in position 12 whereas gastrin I contains an unmodified tyrosine (Fig 35–30). Most of the physiologic actions of gastrin reside in the carboxy terminal tetrapeptide (number 14–17), which alone is one-sixth as potent as the total molecule. Pentagastrin consisting of the 5 terminal amino acids has been synthesized and is used clinically.

Several larger gastrin polypeptides are found in the circulation and antral mucosa. "Big gastrin," a 34-amino-acid peptide containing a carboxy terminal heptadecapeptide similar to gastrin, is the major component in blood after feeding.

Gastrin is the most effective activator of gastric acid secretion known, though it can also stimulate pepsin and intrinsic factor release from gastric mucosa. To a lesser extent, it can duplicate many actions of the other gastrointestinal hormones (Table 35–3). It stimulates secretin release both directly and by stimulating acid secretion and can also delay delivery of gastric contents into the duodenum by reducing the rate of gastric emptying. Gastric acid secretion resulting from vagal stimulation is augmented by gastrin.

Gastrin release is increased by vagal stimulation (eg, caused by insulin-induced hypoglycemia), by elevated calcium, by acetylcholine, and by food intake, particularly protein or amino acids. Of the amino acids, glycine is the most potent. High levels of gastric acid can cause feedback inhibition of gastrin secretion. **Cholecystokinin** (pancreozymin) has the same carboxy terminal peptide sequence as gastrin and, although less effective, can duplicate many of the actions of gastrin. Gastrin levels increase with age and other conditions where gastric acid secretion is low, including pernicious anemia. Zollinger-Ellison syndrome is characterized by gastrointestinal ulcers, high gastrin, and elevated gastric acid secretion caused by gastrin-producing pancreatic tumors (possibly from D cells in pancreatic islets).

B. Secretin: Historically, secretin (Fig 35–31) was the first substance to be identified as a hormone. It is the most powerful stimulant of **water and bicarbonate secretion** by the pancreas. Secretin is found in the duodenal and jejunal mucosa. It consists of a peptide with 27 amino acids, 14 of which are identical to those found in glucagon; the molecule has no structural

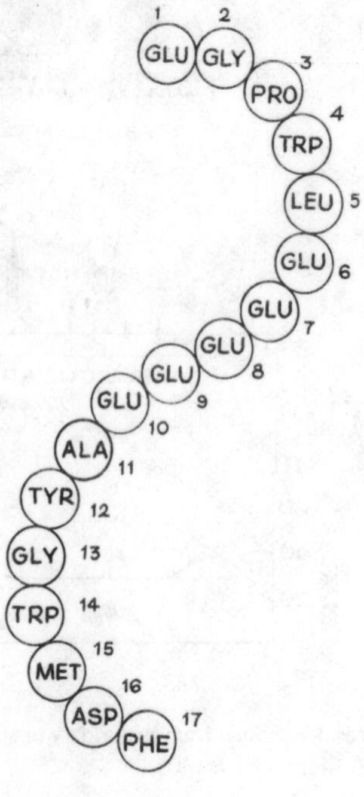

Figure 35–30. Human gastrin.

Table 35–3. Gastrointestinal hormones.*

Activity	Gastrin	Hormone CCK-PZ	Secretin
Water and electrolyte secretion			
Stomach	↑	↑ (1)	↓
Pancreas	↑	↑	↑
Liver	↑	↑	↑
Brunner's glands	↑	↑	↑
Water and electrolyte absorption			
Ileum	↓	↓↑ (2)	↓↑ (2)
Gallbladder	0	0	↓
Enzyme secretion			
Stomach and pancreas	↑	↑	↑
Pancreatic islet secretion			
Insulin	↑	↑	↑
Glucagon	0	↑	↓
Smooth muscle			
Lower esophageal sphincter	↑	↓	↓
Stomach	↑	↑	↓
Pyloric sphincter	↓	↑	↑
Intestine	↑	↑	↓
Ileocecal sphincter	↓	NT	NT
Gallbladder	↑	↑	↑
Sphincter of Oddi	↓	↓	NT
Growth and amino acid uptake			
Gastric mucosa	↑	NT	↓
Pancreas	↑	↑	0
Metabolic			
Lipolysis	0	0	↑
Glycogenolysis	0	0	0
Glucose absorption			
Jejunum	↓	↑	NT

*Reproduced, with permission, from Williams RH (editor): *Textbook of Endocrinology,* 5th ed. Saunders, 1974.
(1) Inhibition of gastrin-mediated water and electrolyte secretion.
(2) Conflicting results.
NT = Not tested; ↑ = increase; ↓ = decrease; 0 = no effect.

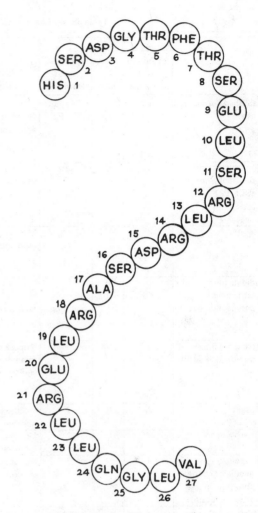

Figure 35–31. Porcine secretin.

homology with gastrin or cholecystokinin (pancreozymin). Though secretin stimulates pepsin secretion in the stomach, it inhibits gastric acid secretion as well as intestinal motor activity. The hormone also shares some of the actions of glucagon, eg, increasing cardiac output and lipolysis. However, its tissue binding sites are not the same as those for glucagon.

Ingestion of food and the resulting increase in acid stimulate secretin release. Secretin administration has been used to assess pancreatic exocrine function, responses being low in subjects with carcinoma of the pancreas.

C. Cholecystokinin (pancreozymin) (CCK [PZ]): Cholecystokinin is an important stimulating agent for pancreatic enzyme secretion and gallbladder contraction. It has been isolated from duodenal-jejunal mucosa. The hormone is a polypeptide containing 33 amino acids, though a possible prohormone containing 6 additional amino acids also occurs. Much of the activity resides in the C-terminal octapeptide.

As noted earlier, the C-terminal pentapeptide is identical to that of gastrin. Besides its activity on pancreatic enzyme synthesis and release, it shares many of the actions of gastrin and secretin on water, bicarbonate, and acid changes (Table 35–3). It is particularly effective in stimulating both insulin and glucagon release from pancreatic islets, which may explain why an oral glucose load is more effective in stimulating insulin release than is a comparable elevation of blood sugar produced by intravenous injection. Possibly, cholecystokinin (pancreozymin) may represent one of the "gut factors" potentiating insulin release during oral administration of insulin secretagogues.

Cholecystokinin is secreted from the mucosa of the small intestine in response to acid, amino acids, fatty acids and a variety of cholinergic influences. Recently, cholecystokinin has been shown to be a neurotransmitter substance.

Table 35–4 summarizes information on the established gastrointestinal polypeptide hormones discussed above as well as a number of additional so-called "candidate" hormones.

Table 35–4. Gastrointestinal polypeptide hormones.*

	Number of Amino Acid Residues	MW	Homologous Hormone	Cellular Location	Stimulus for Release	Actions
Established hormones						
Gastrin	17	2100	CCK-PZ	G cells of antrum and duodenum	Gastric distention and protein in the stomach	Stimulates acid and pepsin secretion; stimulates gastric mucosal growth; possibly stimulates lower esophageal sphincter.
Cholecystokinin-pancreozymin (CCK-PZ)	33	3883	Gastrin	Mucosa of entire small intestine	Fat, protein, and their digestion products in the intestine	Stimulates gallbladder contraction; stimulates pancreatic enzyme secretion; stimulates pancreatic growth; inhibits gastric emptying.
Secretin	27	3056	Glucagon	Mucosa of duodenum and jejunum	Low pH in the duodenum; threshold pH 4.5	Stimulates pancreatic and biliary HCO_3^- secretion; augments action of CCK(PZ) on pancreatic enzyme secretion.
Candidate hormones†						
Gastric inhibitory polypeptide (GIP)	43	5105	Secretin, glucagon	Mucosa of duodenum and jejunum	Glucose or fat in the duodenum	Stimulates release of insulin from pancreas; inhibits gastric H^+ secretion and gastric motility.
Vasoactive intestinal polypeptide (VIP)	28	3100	Secretin	Mucosa of entire small intestine and colon	?	Inhibits gastric H^+ and pepsin secretion; stimulates pancreatic HCO_3^- secretion and secretion from intestinal mucosa; inhibits gastric and gallbladder motility.
Motilin	22	2700	?	Mucosa of duodenum and jejunum	Alkaline pH (8.2) in the duodenum	Stimulates gastric motility.
Enterogastrone	?	?	?	Mucosa of small intestine	Fat in the intestine	Inhibits gastric H^+ secretion.
Entero-oxyntin (mediator of the "intestinal phase" of H^+ secretion)	?	?	?	Mucosa of small intestine	Protein in the intestine	Stimulates gastric H^+ secretion.
Enteroglucagon	?	3500– 7000	Glucagon	Mucosa of small intestine	Glucose or fat in the intestine	Glycogenolysis.
Chymodenin	43	4900	?	Mucosa of small intestine	Fat in the intestine	Specific stimulation of chymotrypsin secretion by the pancreas.
Bulbogastrone	?	?	?	Duodenal bulb	Acid in the duodenal bulb	Inhibits gastric H^+ secretion.

*Slightly modified from Dunphy JE, Way LW (editors): *Current Surgical Diagnosis & Treatment,* 3rd ed. Lange, 1977.
†The candidate hormones are either peptides extracted from the gut which have not yet been proved to have a physiologic role or physiologic actions postulated as being due to as yet unidentified hormones.

• • •

References

Thyroid & Parathyroid

Bernal J, Refetoff S: The action of thyroid hormone. *Clin Endocrinol* 1977;**6:**227.

Deftos LJ: Calcitonin in clinical medicine. *Adv Intern Med* 1978;**34:**159.

DeGroot LJ: Nuclear receptors for thyroid hormone. *Adv Exp Med Biol* 1978;**96:**45.

Goltzman D: Biochemical mode of action of parathyroid hormone. Page 631 in: *Endocrinology.* Vol 2. DeGroot LJ (editor). Grune & Stratton, 1979.

Habener JF, Potts JI: Biosynthesis of parathyroid hormone. (2 parts.) *N Engl J Med* 1978;**299:**580, 635.

Oppenheimer JH & others: Nuclear receptors and the initiation of thyroid hormone action. *Recent Prog Horm Res* 1976;**32:**529.

Schimmel M, Utiger RD: Thyroid and peripheral production of thyroid hormones. *Ann Intern Med* 1977;**87:**760.

Sterling K, Lazarus JH: The thyroid and its control. *Ann Rev Physiol* 1977;**39:**349.

Taurog A: Hormone synthesis. Page 331 in: *Endocrinology.* Vol 1. DeGroot LJ (editor). Grune & Stratton, 1979.

Pancreas (Insulin, Glucagon, Somatostatin)

Cerami A, Koenig RJ: Hemoglobin A_{1c} as a model for the development of the sequelae of diabetes mellitus. *Trends in Biochemical Sciences* (April) 1978;**3:**73.

Chance RE, Ellis RM, Bromer WW: Porcine proinsulin: Characterization and amino acid sequence. *Science* 1968;**161:**165.

Czech MP: Insulin action and the regulation of hexose transport. *Diabetes* 1980;**29:**399.

Figlewicz OP & others: Kinetics of ^{65}zinc uptake and distribution in fractions from cultured rat islets of Langerhans. *Diabetes* 1980;**29:**767.

Freychet P: Interactions of polypeptide hormones with cell membrane specific receptors: Studies with insulin and glucagon. *Diabetologia* 1976;**12:**83.

Gerich JE: Somatostatin, another islet hormone. *Adv Exp Med Biol* 1979;**124:**63.

Grodsky GM & others: Further studies on the dynamic aspects of insulin release in vitro with evidence for a 2-compartmental storage system. *Acta Diabetol Lat* 1969;**6 (Suppl 1):**554.

Hedeskov CJ: Mechanism of glucose-induced insulin secretion. *Physiol Rev* 1980;**60:**442.

Seals JR, Jarett L: Activation of pyruvate dehydrogenase by direct addition of insulin to an isolated plasma membrane/mitochondria mixture: Evidence for generation of insulin's second messenger in a subcellular system. *Proc Natl Acad Sci USA* 1980;**77:**77.

Unger RH, Dobbs RE: Insulin, glucagon, and somatostatin: Secretion in the regulation of metabolism. *Annu Rev Physiol* 1978;**40:**307.

Yip CC, Hew C-L, Hsu H: Translation of messenger ribonucleic acid from isolated pancreatic islets and human insulinomas. *Proc Natl Acad Sci USA* 1975;**72:**4777.

Adrenal Medulla

Exton JH: Mechanisms involved in α-adrenergic phenomena: Role of calcium ions in actions of catecholamines in liver and other tissues. *Am J Physiol* 1980;**238:**E3.

Perlman RL, Chalfie M: Catecholamine release from the adrenal medulla. *Clin Endocrinol Metabol* 1977;**6:**551.

Young JB, Landsberg L: Catecholamines and intermediary metabolism. *Clin Endocrinol Metabol* 1977;**6:**599.

Young JB, Landsberg L: Catecholamines and regulation of hormone secretion. *Clin Endocrinol Metabol* 1977;**6:**657.

Adrenal Cortex (Steroid Hormones)

Baxter JD, Forsham PH: Tissue effects of glucocorticoids. *Am J Med* 1972;**53:**573.

Bischoll F, Bryson G: Pharmacodynamics and toxicology of steroids and related compounds. *Adv Lipid Res* 1977;**15:**61.

Chatterjee M, Munro HH: Structure and biosynthesis of human placental peptide hormones. *Vitam Horm* 1977;**35:**149.

Craddock CG: Corticosteroid-induced lymphopenia, immunosuppression, and body defense. *Ann Intern Med* 1978;**88:**564.

Drucker WD: Biologic activity and metabolism of androgenic hormone: The role of the adrenal androgens. *Bull NY Acad Med* 1977;**53:**347.

Duax WL, Weeks CM, Rohrer DC: Crystal structure of steroids: Molecular conformation and biologic function. *Recent Prog Horm Res* 1976;**32:**81.

Edelman IS: Mechanism of action of steroid hormones. *J Steroid Biochem* 1975;**6:**147.

Gelbke HP, Ball P, Knuppen R: 2-Hydroxy-estrogens. *Adv Steroid Biochem Pharmacol* 1977;**6:**81.

Givens JR: Normal and abnormal androgen metabolism. *Clin Obstet Gynecol* 1978;**21:**115.

Mainwaring WI: The mechanism of action of androgens. *Monogr Endocrinol* 1977;**10:**1.

Monder C, Bradlow L: Carboxylic acid metabolites of steroids. *J Steroid Biochem* 1977;**8:**897.

Neelon FA: Adrenal physiology and pharmacology. *Urol Clin North Am* 1977;**4:**179.

Gastrointestinal Hormones

Barrington EWJ, Dockray GT: Gastrointestinal hormones. *J Endocrinol* 1976;**69:**299.

Chen WY, Gutierrez JG: The endocrine control of gastrointestinal function. *Adv Intern Med* 1978;**23:**61.

Dunphy JE, Way LW: *Current Surgical Diagnosis & Treatment,* 4th ed. Lange, 1979.

Straus E: The explosion of gastrointestinal hormones. *Med Clin North Am* 1978;**62:**21.

Williams RH (editor): *Textbook of Endocrinology,* 5th ed. Saunders, 1974.

Chemistry & Functions of the Hormones: II. Pituitary & Hypothalamus

Gerold M. Grodsky, PhD

The human pituitary is a 0.5- to 0.7-g reddish-gray oval structure located in the brain just behind the optic chiasm as an extension from the floor of the hypothalamus. The pituitary gland is composed of tissue embryologically derived from 2 sources: a neural component and a buccal component. The terms **adenohypophysis** and **neurohypophysis** are used to differentiate the buccal and neural components, respectively.

The adenohypophysis includes the anterior lobe (anterior pituitary) and the intermediate or middle lobe of the developed endocrine organ. The neurohypophysis includes the posterior lobe of the gland (posterior pituitary) and the infundibular or neural stalk that attaches the gland to the floor of the brain at the hypothalamus (Fig 36–1).

The pituitary secretes a variety of hormones that either regulate other endocrine glands (**trophic hor-** mones) or directly influence the metabolism of nonendocrine target tissues. Thus, removal of the pituitary is followed by atrophy of the sex glands and organs, involution of the thyroid, parathyroids, and adrenal cortex, and a depression of their functions. In addition, there are direct alterations in protein, fat, carbohydrate, and salt and water metabolism.

Control of hormone secretion from the pituitary is in part modulated by regulating factors or hormones from the hypothalamus, that region of the brain immediately proximal to the pituitary (Fig 36–1). The median eminence of the hypothalamus is connected directly to the pituitary by the pituitary stalk. Within this stalk is a portal system of blood vessels required to maintain normal secretory activity of the pituitary gland. The regulating factors originating from endings of the hypothalamic nerve fibers are transported via the capillaries of the median eminence that empty with the portal vessels leading to the pituitary gland.

At present, 10 discrete regulating factors have been described that may affect the synthesis as well as the secretion of specific pituitary hormones (Table 36–1). In 3 instances (growth hormone, melanocyte-

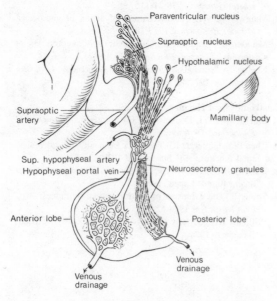

Figure 36–1. Simplified schematic reconstruction of the hypothalamus and the pituitary. (After Hansel; courtesy *International Journal of Fertility.* Redrawn and reproduced, with permission, from Schally & others: *Science* 1973;**179**:341. Copyright © 1973 by The American Association for the Advancement of Science.)

Table 36–1. Hypothalamic hormones known to control the release of pituitary hormones.*

Hypothalamic Hormone (or Factor)	Abbreviation
Corticotropin (ACTH)-releasing hormone	CRH or CRF
Thyrotropin (TSH)-releasing† hormone	TRH or TRF
Luteinizing hormone (LH)-releasing† hormone	LH-RH or LH-RF
Follicle-stimulating hormone (FSH) releasing† hormone	FSH-RH or FSH-RF
Growth hormone (GH)-releasing† hormone	GH-RH or GH-RF
Growth hormone (GH) release-inhibiting hormone	GH-RIH or GIF
Prolactin release-inhibiting hormone	PRIH or PIF
Prolactin-releasing hormone	PRH or PRF
Melanocyte-stimulating hormone (MSH) release-inhibiting hormone	MRIH or MIF
Melanocyte-stimulating hormone (MSH) releasing hormone	MRH or MRF

*Reproduced, with permission, from Schally & others: *Science* 1973;**179**:341. Copyright © 1973 by The American Association for the Advancement of Science.
†Or regulating hormone.

stimulating hormone, and prolactin), both stimulating and inhibiting regulators are known. This "on-off" regulation may be particularly useful for rapid control of pituitary secretion.

Both the releasing and inhibitory factors can be found in other portions of the central nervous system and in other tissues (eg, somatotropin release–inhibiting hormone, somatostatin [SRIF, GH-RIH] is produced in the D cells of the islets of Langerhans), where they may act as intra-organ "synaptic transmitters" or neuromodulators. Thus, the role of the regulating factors is much broader than the regulation of pituitary function. In turn, secretion and production of these regulators are controlled by various neurotransmitters, including dopamine, epinephrine, norepinephrine, serotonin, histamine, acetylcholine, and γ-aminobutyric acid. At least some of these neuromodulators also act directly at the pituitary level. This complex feedback regulation may be responsible for the pulsatile nature of most pituitary hormone secretions, characterized by on-off release at intervals of minutes. Therefore, the regulatory factors arising from hypothalamic or neuroendocrine centers provide one explanation for the ability of neurologic and psychic (eg, stress) stimulation to evoke endocrine and metabolic responses.

THE ANTERIOR PITUITARY GLAND

The anterior lobe is the largest and most essential portion of the pituitary. In humans, this lobe comprises about 70% of the total weight of the gland.

HORMONES
OF THE ANTERIOR PITUITARY

Growth Hormone (Somatotropin)

A. Chemistry: Growth hormone is found in high concentration in the pituitary, 5–15 mg/g, which is much higher than the μg/g quantities of other pituitary hormones. Growth hormone from all mammalian species consists of a single polypeptide with a molecular weight of about 21,500. The structure of human growth hormone consisting of 191 amino acids is shown in Fig 36–2. Although there is a high degree of similarity in the amino acid sequences of human, bovine, and porcine growth hormones, only human growth hormone or that of other primates is active in humans.

Growth hormone can bring about some of the actions of lactogenic hormone (prolactin) and of human placental lactogen. Although all of these hormones are separate entities in the various species that have been studied, there is considerable similarity in their structures and, consequently, a significant degree

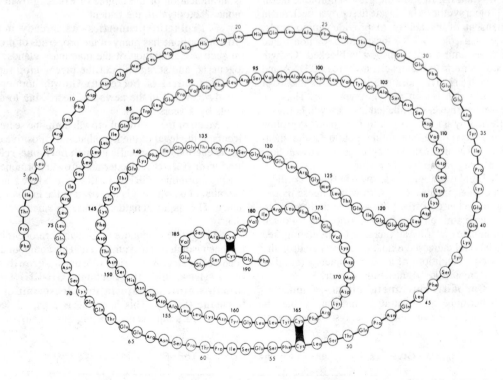

Figure 36–2. Proposed structure of human growth hormone. The numbers identify the amino acid residues, starting from the N terminal. (Courtesy of CH Li.)

of immunologic and biologic cross-reactivity.

B. Function: Growth hormone binds directly to specific receptors in target tissues. It stimulates production of **somatomedins (sulfation factors)** from liver and possibly kidney, which can produce many of the anabolic effects of growth hormone. Somatomedin is similar to **serum insulin-like activity** described earlier (see p 477). Although both can bind to insulin receptors at high concentration, each has its own specific receptor and differs structurally from insulin.

Growth hormone has a variety of effects on different tissues, including muscle, adipose tissue, and liver. Its actions can be demonstrated in vitro. In vivo, it increases total growth and can cause gigantism in children. Dwarfism may also occur as a result of growth hormone deficiency or tissue insensitivity to normal amounts of growth hormone. As with steroids, part of the action of growth hormone is to spare circulating glucose. The hormone acts slowly, requiring from 1–2 hours to several days before its biologic effects are detectable.

1. Protein synthesis–Growth hormone stimulates overall protein synthesis in the intact animal, resulting in a pronounced increase in nitrogen retention with an associated retention (actually increased renal tubular reabsorption) of phosphorus. Blood amino acids and urea are decreased. Thus, growth hormone in this regard acts synergistically with insulin. In muscle, growth hormone can stimulate protein synthesis by increasing the transport of amino acids into the cells, an action that is not mediated by a direct action on protein synthesis. In addition, growth hormone facilitates protein synthesis in muscle tissue by a mechanism independent of its ability to provide amino acids. Thus, increased protein synthesis can be demonstrated even when amino acid transport is blocked. Growth hormone administration results in increased DNA and RNA synthesis. The hormone increases synthesis of collagen, which is rich in hydroxyproline. Thus, an increase in turnover of collagen after growth hormone is reflected by an increase in urinary hydroxyproline and hydroxyproline-containing peptides, the measurement of which can be used to assess growth hormone activity in the intact animal.

2. Lipid metabolism–Growth hormone is mildly lipolytic when incubated in vitro with adipose tissue, promoting release of free fatty acids and glycerol. In vivo, administration of growth hormone is followed 30–60 minutes later by an increase in circulating free fatty acids and increased oxidation of fatty acids in the liver. Under conditions of insulin deficiency (eg, diabetes), increased ketogenesis may occur.

3. Carbohydrate metabolism–In muscle, growth hormone administration antagonizes the effects of insulin. Impairment of glycolysis may occur at several steps, as well as inhibition of transport of glucose. Whether this latter effect is a direct effect on transport or a result of the inhibition of glycolysis has not yet been established. The mobilization of fatty acids from triacylglycerol stores may also contribute to the inhibition of glycolysis in the muscle. In liver there is an increase in liver glycogen, probably arising from activation of gluconeogenesis from amino acids. Hyperglycemia after growth hormone administration is a combined result of decreased peripheral utilization of glucose and increased hepatic production via gluconeogenesis. Prolonged administration of growth hormone results in an enhanced release of insulin from the pancreas during glucose stimulation. This effect may be secondary to the peripheral diabetogenic action of growth hormone, to increased circulating pancreatic stimulants such as glucose, fatty acids, and ketones, or it may be caused by a direct but slow action on the pancreas.

4. Ion or mineral metabolism–Growth hormone increases intestinal absorption of calcium as well as its excretion. Since growth hormone stimulates the growth of the long bones at the epiphyses as well as the growth of soft tissue, increased calcium retention results for the most part from the increased metabolic activity of the bone. The hormone, by increasing somatomedin from the liver, thereby fosters sulfate incorporation into cartilage. In addition to calcium, sodium, potassium, magnesium, phosphate, and chloride are also retained. Serum phosphate levels are usually elevated in acromegaly and are often measured as an indication of the degree of excess growth hormone "activity" in the patient.

5. Prolactin properties–As already noted, growth hormone has many of the properties of prolactin such as stimulation of the mammary glands, lactogenesis, and stimulation of the pigeon crop sac.

C. Control of Secretion: Growth hormone is usually elevated in the newborn, decreasing to adult levels by 4 years of age.

Much of the control of growth hormone secretion occurs at the level of the hypothalamus. Positive control is exerted by a specific **growth hormone-releasing factor (GHRF),** also termed growth hormone-releasing hormone (GRH). GHRF is produced in the hypothalamus where it is localized in the median eminence. The chemical nature of this substance is not yet clear.

A negative modulator of growth hormone release has been isolated and synthesized. This compound has been designated by a variety of names—**growth hormone release-inhibiting hormone (GH-RIH, GIH), somatostatin, somatostatin release-inhibiting hormone (SRIF).** This hormone is a peptide composed of 14 amino acids (see Fig 36–3 below). It is

H—Ala—Gly—Cys—Lys—Asn—Phe—Phe—Trp—Lys—Thr—Phe—Thr—Ser—Cys—OH

Figure 36–3. Structure of growth hormone release-inhibiting hormone (GIH; somatostatin).

active when injected either in its linear or cyclic form.

Injected growth hormone release-inhibiting hormone also inhibits release of insulin, glucagon, thyrotropin, and follicle-stimulating hormone (FSH). However, it does not appear to affect secretion of prolactin. Because of its ability to inhibit secretion of growth hormone and of glucagon, growth hormone release-inhibiting hormone (**somatostatin**) may have therapeutic application as an adjunct to insulin in the management of insulin-requiring diabetic patients. Somatostatin has now been found in the D cells of pancreatic islets and in the stomach, suggesting that the "hypothalamic" releasing hormones may actually be more widely distributed and in fact may be secreted into the circulation. Part of the inhibitory effect of somatostatin on its target cells may be related to its ability to affect cellular calcium uptake and efflux.

Control of these regulating factors is in turn regulated by signals from the ventromedial nucleus, which can be excited and bring about secretion of growth hormone by α-adrenergic and dopaminergic stimulation, or by serotonin, the opiate polypeptides, glucagon, or arginine. The inhibition by glucose of release of growth hormone may also occur at this level. The effects of these agents are at the level of the hypothalamus to influence GHRF and possibly somatostatin release. In addition, some (eg, dopaminergic agents) may act directly at the pituitary level where dopamine receptors have been detected.

Release of growth hormone, as for many of the pituitary hormones, is episodic or pulsatile, changing in rate in minutes.

The plasma growth hormone level in the adult is not stable; depending on the nature of a stimulus, it may change as much as 10-fold within a few minutes. Plasma growth hormone concentration is increased following stress (pain, apprehension, cold, surgical stress, severe insulin hypoglycemia) and exercise, the response to exercise being greater in females than in males. In females, the generally higher circulating growth hormone levels are related to the fact that estrogens positively modulate growth hormone released by various stimuli. Progesterone, in contrast, is inhibitory. The rapid rise after exercise necessitates careful control to ensure that the subject is resting before blood samples are taken for growth hormone measurements. The increased growth hormone after stress may be caused by increases in catecholamines acting at the hypothalamic level. Factors decreasing glucose availability to the hypothalamic regulating centers also stimulate release. This can be accomplished (1) by fasting, (2) by hypoglycemia associated with an insulin tolerance test, or (3) by administration of an agent such as 2-deoxyglucose, which inhibits the normal glycolysis of glucose, making it unavailable to the regulating centers even though circulating blood sugar becomes elevated. Since 2-deoxyglucose causes the prompt release of growth hormone while at the same time producing an elevated blood sugar, it is apparent that regulation in the hypothalamus is dependent on the normal metabolism of glucose, not on the circulating level of glucose as such.

Stimulation is also increased by protein meals and by amino acids, particularly arginine. This provides a regulatory system whereby increases in amino acids result in secretion of growth hormone which itself facilitates uptake of amino acids into protein. It will be recalled that arginine also facilitates the secretion of insulin, which, like growth hormone, is required for protein synthesis. Curiously, growth hormone is elevated in malnutrition with **kwashiorkor**. This may be due to abnormal glucose metabolism and decreased glucose availability at the control sites.

In the **acromegalic** patient, normal control mechanisms for growth hormone release are lost. This is reflected in an inability to suppress plasma growth hormone values by administration of glucose or to respond to arginine stimulation. Conversely, growth hormone deficiency may be documented by demonstration of inadequate responses to insulin-induced hypoglycemia or arginine infusion.

Peptides of variable metabolic activity that are not necessarily detectable by immunoassay have been prepared from growth hormone. Whether these peptides are released from the pituitary or indeed play any physiologic role is not yet established.

The Pituitary Tropins

The most characteristic function of the anterior pituitary is the elaboration of hormones that influence the activities of other endocrine glands, principally those involving reproduction or stress. Such hormones are called **tropic hormones.** They are carried by the blood to other (target) glands and aid both in maintaining these glands and in stimulating production of their respective hormones. For this reason, atrophy and decline in the function of many endocrine glands occur in pituitary hypofunction or after hypophysectomy.

The pituitary tropic hormones are under the positive and negative control of peptide factors from the hypothalamus (**releasing** and **inhibiting factors** or **hypothalamic neurohormones**) (Table 36–1). The production and release of the neurohormones, in turn, are sensitive to neural and metabolic stimuli and can be inhibited by their respective tropic hormones ("short loop feedback") (Fig 34–1).

In addition, the tropic hormones are usually subject to feedback inhibition at the pituitary or hypothalamic level by the hormone product of the final target gland. Thus, hydrocortisone, sex steroids, and thyroxine inhibit the release of their respective tropic hormones.

A. Prolactin (PL) (Lactogenic Hormone, Mammotropin, Luteotropic Hormone, LTH): Pituitary prolactin is a protein with a molecular weight of approximately 23,000 which, like growth hormone, is produced by the pituitary **acidophil cells.** Its complete structure is shown in Fig 36–4. As has been noted, prolactin and growth hormone share some common structures and indeed cross-react immunologically. Prolactin and growth hormone are distinct pituitary

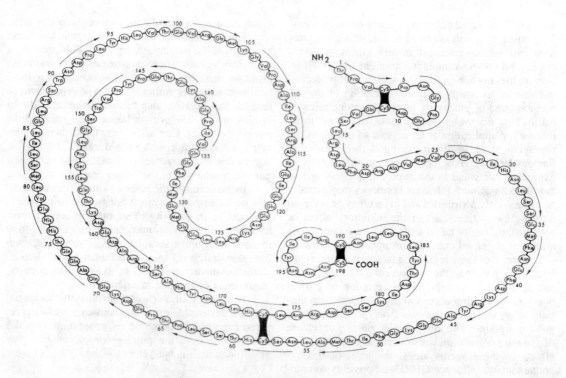

Figure 36–4. Ovine prolactin. (Courtesy of CH Li.)

hormones in humans and other species but probably evolved from a common ancestor.

In animals, prolactin activates the corpus luteum and causes progesterone production to be maintained by the developed corpus luteum. Prolactin increases during pregnancy and may stimulate mammary development and growth hormone–like metabolic changes. It also stimulates enlargement of crop gland and formation of "crop milk" in pigeons.

Prolactin secretion is under direct negative control by the tuberinfundibular dopaminergic system. This may be a direct inhibitory effect on the pituitary since dopamine receptors have been detected on pituitary cells, and L-dopa inhibits pituitary secretion of prolactin in vitro. Prolactin can also be inhibited by a hypothalamic factor, **prolactin-inhibiting factor (PIF),** and possibly may be stimulated by a less well established releasing factor and by thyrotropin-releasing hormone (TRF). Both estrogens and the act of suckling stimulate prolactin secretion. The estrogens can act to decrease dopaminergic receptors at the pituitary, which can lead to increased prolactin levels during pregnancy.

B. The Gonadotropins: Follicle-stimulating hormone (FSH) and luteinizing hormone (LH) are tropic substances that influence the function and maturation of the testis and ovary. They are glycoproteins with molecular weights of about 25,000 (FSH) and 40,000 (LH).

FSH and LH—as well as thyrotropin and human chorionic gonadotropin—consist of 2 nonidentical, noncovalently linked subunits, the α and β chains: The β chains vary in length from 110 to 120 amino acids,

have partial homology only, and confer the specific biologic activity. The somewhat shorter α chains, if from the same species, are identical for all 3 hormones. The role of this common subunit is not established. However, it is necessary to maintain activity since the separated chains have little biologic action. The carbohydrate content of the gonadotropins consists of sialic acid, hexose, and hexosamine.

The secretions of luteinizing hormone and of follicle-stimulating hormone are regulated by a single hypothalamic releasing factor, **luteinizing hormone/ follicle-stimulating hormone–releasing hormone (LH/FSH-RH)** (Fig 36–5). Luteinizing hormone/ follicle-stimulating hormone–releasing hormone is a decapeptide whose N-terminal amino acid is a derivative of glutamic acid, the cyclic compound **(pyroglutamic acid, pyroglu)** formed by removal of water to cause cyclization. LH/FSH-RH release is stimulated by dopamine, the α-adrenergic system, and some prostaglandins. As a result, inhibition of prostaglandin synthesis results in decreased ovulation. LH/FSH-RH acts directly on the pituitary to increase cAMP and gonadotropin release. It has been used to increase fertility in patients with hypothalamic amenorrhea. Although this single releasing factor probably mediates the hypothalamic control of gonadotropins, levels of follicle-stimulating hormone and luteinizing hormone do not always rise and fall together. Apparently much of the specific regulation of these gonadotropins can occur by end-organ steroids (estrogens, testosterone) at the pituitary and hypothalamic level (Fig 34–1).

1. Follicle-stimulating hormone (FSH)–FSH

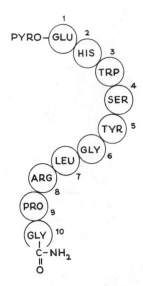

Figure 36–5. Structural formula of LH/FSH-releasing hormone.

binds to specific receptors on the plasma membranes of its target cells, resulting in an increase in adenylate cyclase and cAMP. It promotes follicular growth, prepares the follicle for the action of luteinizing hormone (LH), and enhances the release of estrogen induced by luteinizing hormone. In the male, it stimulates seminal tubule and testicular growth and plays an important role in the early stages of spermatogenesis. Plasma follicle-stimulating hormone concentrations increase through puberty from the low levels of infancy. In the female, there is marked cycling of levels, with peaks of the order of 10-fold or more over basal levels being reached at or slightly before the time of ovulation, Follicle-stimulating hormone secretion is inhibited at the pituitary and possibly the hypothalamic level by the administration of testosterone, progesterone, and possibly follicle-stimulating hormone itself. Estrogens usually stimulate FSH secretion but may inhibit depending on the circumstances.

2. Luteinizing hormone (LH) in the female stimulates final maturation of the graafian follicle, ovulation, and the development of the corpora lutea. Both estrogen and progesterone secretion are stimulated.

In the ovary, luteinizing hormone can stimulate the nongerminal elements, which contain the interstitial cells, to produce the androgens androstenedione, dehydroepiandrosterone, and testosterone. In subjects with polycystic ovaries (Stein-Leventhal disease), part of the observed masculinization (hirsutism) may result from overactivity of the ovarian stroma to produce these androgens.

In the male, luteinizing hormone stimulates testosterone production by the testis, which in turn maintains spermatogenesis and provides for the development of accessory sex organs such as the vas deferens, prostate, and seminal vesicles.

Luteinizing hormone binds to relatively specific membrane plasma receptors in luteal and interstitial cells, which are not affected by FSH. This results ultimately in conversion of acetate to squalene (the precursor for cholesterol synthesis). Additionally, there is also acceleration of the conversion of cholesterol to 20α-hydroxycholesterol, a necessary intermediate in the synthesis of progesterone or testosterone (Fig 35–19).

The signal initiated by LH binding involves cAMP; this nucleotide is increased after addition of luteinizing hormone to incubating corpora lutea. Furthermore, added cAMP duplicates the stimulatory action of luteinizing hormone on progesterone synthesis both at the site of acetate incorporation into cholesterol and at the site of cholesterol incorporation into pregnenolone (Fig 35–19). The effects of cAMP and luteinizing hormone may be associated with protein synthesis, but the rapid rise in cAMP after hormone administration indicates that rapid effects also occur.

The plasma concentration and pituitary content of luteinizing hormone increase through puberty. In women, there is cycling of plasma luteinizing hormone levels, with midcycle (ovulatory) peaks many times the basal level. The sequential relationship between blood levels of gonadotropins, estrogens, and progesterone to the events during cycling in females is still obscure.

Androgens inhibit LH secretion predominantly at the pituitary gland.

Both LH and FSH may sensitize cells by increasing the number of specific receptors to which the sex steroids bind and thereby affect androgenic and estrogenic action.

C. Thyrotropic Hormone; Thyroid-Stimulating Hormone (TSH): Thyrotropin is a glycoprotein of approximately 30,000 molecular weight. As is the case with the gonadotropins, this tropin consists of α and β subunits. The α subunits of thyrotropin, luteinizing hormone, HCG, and follicle-stimulating hormone are nearly identical; the biologic specificity of thyrotropin must therefore reside in the β subunit.

Thyrotropin binds to specific membrane receptors and activates thyroidal adenylate cyclase, resulting in increased cellular cAMP. Injection of thyrotropin will bring about all of the symptoms of hyperthyroidism (see p 473). It increases thyroid growth and general metabolic activity, including glucose oxidation, oxygen consumption, and synthesis of phospholipids and RNA. Within minutes, thyrotropin rapidly increases each phase of thyroxine metabolism, including iodine uptake, organification, and, finally, the breakdown of thyroglobulin with the concomitant release of thyroid hormone.

Control of thyrotropin release. As was described for other pituitary tropins, the release of thyrotropin is also controlled by a releasing factor originating in the hypothalamus. This factor has been designated **hypothalamic, hypophysiotropic thyrotropic releasing hormone (TRH).** This releasing hormone is a neutral tripeptide, ie, it has no terminal ionized

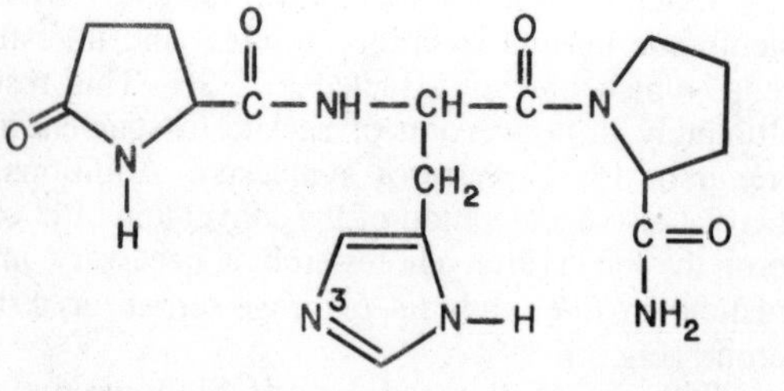

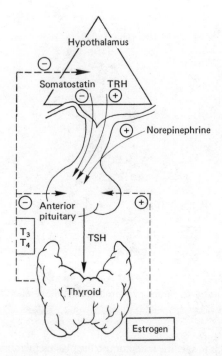

Figure 36–6. Molecular structure of thyrotropin-releasing hormone (TRH): L-2 pyrrolidone-5-carboxyl-L-histidyl-L-proline.

groups. The tripeptide consists of pyroglutamic acid, histidine, and prolinamide as shown in Fig 36–6. Activity is increased 8-fold by methylation at the 3 position of the histidine residue.

Thyrotropic-releasing hormone from the pig and from the sheep are identical. The synthetic tripeptide does not appear to be species-specific.

Inhibitors of protein synthesis have no effect on synthesis of thyrotropic-releasing hormone in the hypothalamus, indicating that the process is non-ribosomal. The factor is also abundant in the pineal gland and frog skin.

TRH causes an increase in cAMP and thyrotropin release within 1 minute; thus, it acts on a cAMP-dependent secretion process independently of an additional established action on thyrotropin synthesis. As with most secretagogues, thyrotropic-releasing hormone action is calcium-dependent (Fig 34–5). TRH is specific, acting primarily on the thyrotropin-secreting cells. TRH, however, also stimulates prolactin secretion.

Excess chronic production of this releasing factor results in a decrease in its receptor sites in the pituitary and ''down regulation.'' Administration of thyrotropic-releasing hormone is now used to test the thyrotropin-secreting capacity of the pituitary as well as to distinguish between hypothalamic and pituitary lesions. TRH retains much of its activity when given by mouth. This regulating hormone is rapidly destroyed in liver and kidney and has a half-time of disappearance from the blood of 4 minutes.

Thyroid hormone is a feedback inhibitor at the levels of both TSH secretion and pituitary sensitivity to TRH. A direct effect on TRH production in the hypothalamus is not established (Fig 36–7).

Estrogens act to increase sensitivity of the pituitary to TRH and thus TSH secretion. TSH secretion is also increased by α-adrenergic stimulation. It is probable that increased TSH and the subsequent thyroid hormone production caused by cold-induced stress is mediated by norepinephrine through this α-adrenergic system. The opiate polypeptides (eg, endorphins) inhibit TSH production; however, the physiologic significance of this regulation is unknown.

D. Adrenocorticotropic Hormone (ACTH, Corticotropin): Adrenal function is regulated by the pituitary tropic hormone ACTH. ACTH is a single

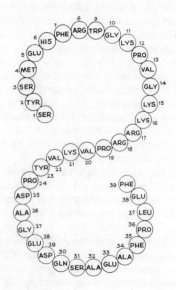

Figure 36–7. The regulation of TSH secretion mediated by 17β-estradiol, norepinephrine, and T_3-T_4 at the level of the anterior pituitary and at the hypothalamus. The latter is likely by way of an effect on TRH release.

Figure 36–8. Structure of human ACTH.

chain polypeptide with a molecular weight of 4500 containing 39 amino acids (Fig 36–8). Only the first 23 amino acids (from the N-terminal end of the chain) are required for activity. The sequence of these 23 amino acids in the peptide chain is the same in all species examined including humans, whereas the sequence of

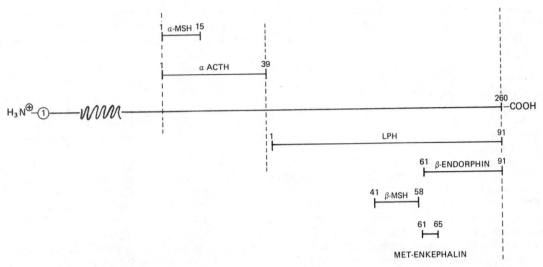

Figure 36–9. Structural relationships of ACTH, MSH, LPH, and endorphins on the precursor molecule. ACTH terminates within 5 amino acids of the initial amino acid of LPH.

the remaining biologically inactive 16 amino acids varies according to the animal source. A synthetic 24 amino acid analog is now used clinically.

ACTH is synthesized as part of a larger precursor peptide of MW 31,000 (260 amino acids) that exists briefly in the endoplasmic reticulum of the anterior lobe (Fig 36–9). It is of great interest that LPH, MSH, and the endorphins are also synthesized as part of the same molecule. This explains why synthesis of all of these hormones is stimulated or inhibited coordinately.

1. Biologic effects–ACTH not only increases the synthesis of corticosteroids by the adrenal but also stimulates their release from the gland. It increases total protein synthesis as indicated by increased incorporation of ^{14}C-labeled acetate into adrenal tissue proteins and increased adrenal RNA. Thus, ACTH produces both a tropic effect on steroid production and a trophic effect on adrenal tissue. Adrenal target organ specificity is apparent since other hormones such as thyrotropin, growth hormone, and gonadotropins are inactive.

ACTH affects steroid hormone synthesis in the adrenal at an early stage in the conversion of cholesterol to pregnenolone, the primary precursor for the synthesis of all adrenal steroids (Figs 35–18 and 35–19). Thus, ACTH stimulation results in an increase in mineralocorticoids, glucocorticoids, and androgens. As already noted, ACTH has only a mild effect on the output of aldosterone. The administration of ACTH to normal human beings, therefore, causes the following effects: (1) increased excretion of nitrogen, potassium, and phosphorus; (2) retention of sodium, chloride, and secondary retention of water; (3) elevation of fasting blood sugar and a diabetic glucose tolerance curve; (4) increase in circulating free fatty acids; (5) increased excretion of uric acid; (6) increased androgenicity (in extreme cases); and (7) decline in circulating eosinophils and lymphocytes and elevation of polymorphonuclear leukocytes.

Like most polypeptide hormones, ACTH acts at the cell membrane. ACTH action requires calcium; the hormone causes calcium uptake and redistribution in the adrenal.

Another action of ACTH may involve cAMP, since this compound is increased within seconds in the adrenal gland by ACTH and, if added directly, will in itself stimulate steroidogenesis. The effect of ACTH on the adrenal can be inhibited by blocking protein synthesis with puromycin, whereas the blocking of RNA synthesis by dactinomycin has little inhibitory effect. Perhaps because of its ability to activate adenylate cyclase and increase intracellular levels of cAMP, ACTH can increase lipolysis in adipose tissue and stimulate insulin secretion from the pancreas. However, these extra-adrenal effects are small, require large concentrations of the hormone, and are comparatively unimportant under normal physiologic conditions.

Endorphins and enkephalins. A group of peptides (endorphins and enkephalins) have been isolated from the pituitary. These peptides have higher analgesic potencies (18–30 times on a molar basis) than morphine. They bind directly to the same central nervous system receptors as do the morphine opiates and probably play an important role in endogenous control of pain perception. It is now apparent that these peptides arise from the same precursor molecule that contains the structure of ACTH and MSH (Fig 36–9). β-Lipotropin, consisting of 91 amino acids toward the carboxyl terminal end of the precursor, causes lipolysis and fatty acid mobilization. Its contribution as an active hormone is unknown; it may serve as the precursor of the analgesic peptides, since the latter are contained in its structure. Thus, β-endorphin consists of the terminal 31 amino acids of β-lipotropin, and α-endorphin comprises the first 17 of these amino acids. Met-enkephalin is an opiate pentapeptide at amino acids 61–65 of lipotropin. Lipotropin, ACTH, and MSH have no analgesic activity.

Prostaglandins may also play a role in ACTH action: ACTH mobilizes some prostaglandins in the adrenal, and prostaglandin E_2 can duplicate ACTH action to increase steroidogenesis.

2. Control of ACTH secretion–As with most of the other tropic hormones, ACTH is controlled by a specific corticotropin-releasing hormone (CRH), found in the hypothalamus, and to a lesser extent by CRH-like agents (tissue CRH) in other tissues. Three hormones have been designated α_1-, α_2-, and β-corticotropin-releasing hormones. β-Corticotropin-releasing hormone may be vasopressin, vasotocin, or a peptide similar in structure. The structures of α_1- and α_2-corticotropin-releasing hormones are similar to that of α-melanocyte-stimulating hormone (see p 513). Activation of the hypothalamic centers occurs via neurotransmitters in the central nervous system (eg, acetylcholine and serotonin). Thus, stresses such as cold, pyrogens, insulin hypoglycemia, epinephrine, estrogens, surgical trauma, or psychic stimuli result in increased production of ACTH, leading to increased adrenal cortical activity and protective compensation against the stress. High levels of ACTH may affect synthesis by a "short loop" inhibition of corticotropin-releasing hormone production in the hypothalamus (Fig 34–1).

A reciprocal relationship between corticosteroid production and ACTH secretion is well established; exogenous cortisol causes feedback inhibition of ACTH release at the pituitary level. Androgens and progesterone may be less inhibitory at the same site.

As with most protein hormones, secretion is calcium-dependent and increased by K^+-induced depolarization. Secretion is episodic or pulsatile, consisting of short bursts lasting only a few minutes. The half-time of disappearance of injected ACTH from serum is 3–4 minutes.

Abnormalities of Pituitary Function
A. Hyperpituitarism:
1. Excess production of growth hormone (eosinophilic adenoma)–Gigantism results from hyperactivity of the gland during childhood or adolescence, ie, before closure of the epiphyses. The long bones increase in length so that the patient reaches an unusual height. There are also associated metabolic changes attributed to a generalized pituitary hyperfunction.

Acromegaly results from hyperactivity that begins after epiphyseal closure has been completed and growth has ceased. Characteristics include facial changes (growth and protrusion of the jaw, enlargement of the nose), growth and enlargement of the hands, feet, and viscera, and thickening of the skin.

2. Excess production of ACTH (basophilic adenoma) produces Cushing's disease.

B. Hypopituitarism: Hypopituitarism may occur as a result of certain types of pituitary tumors, or after hemorrhage (especially postpartum), infarct, or atrophy of the gland. It can produce **dwarfism** if the abnormality is at the level of the growth hormone–producing cells. **Pituitary myxedema** will occur if the defect results in diminished thyrotropin production.

Panhypopituitarism refers to deficiency of function of the hypophysis that involves all of the hormonal functions of the gland.

Pituitarylike Hormones From the Placenta
Gonadotropic hormones of placental origin are also found.

A. Human Chorionic Gonadotropin (hCG) or Human Chorionic Somatomammotropin (hCS): This is a protein with immunologic and biologic properties similar to those of pituitary LH. As with the pituitary gonadotropins, the structure of human chorionic gonadotropin consists of α and β subunits. It has a high structural homology with LH, the α subunits in the 2 hormones being almost identical. Human chorionic gonadotropin is derived from the syncytiotrophoblast. It is elevated in the plasma and urine of pregnant females. Measurement of hCG in urine is the basis of most pregnancy tests. Because of its long half-life, human chorionic gonadotropin may remain in the circulation several days after parturition.

B. Human Placental Lactogen, Chorionic Growth Hormone Prolactin: This hormone has many physicochemical and immunologic similarities to human growth hormone. The complete structure has been determined, and a high degree of homology with growth hormone and to a lesser degree with pituitary prolactin was found. Human placental lactogen has lactogenic and luteotropic activity. It also has some metabolic effects which are qualitatively similar to those of growth hormone, including inhibition of glucose uptake, stimulation of free fatty acid and glycerol release, enhancement of nitrogen and calcium retention (despite increased urinary calcium excretion), reduction in the urinary excretion of phosphorus and potassium, and an increase in the turnover of hydroxyproline, as reflected by increased urinary excretion of that amino acid.

C. Thyrotropin: Recent evidence indicates that the placenta may also be a source of a thyrotropinlike substance.

THE MIDDLE LOBE OF THE PITUITARY

The middle lobe of the pituitary secretes a hormone, **intermedin,** which was first detected by its effect on the pigment cells in the skin of lower vertebrates. This hormone also increases the deposition of melanin by the melanocytes of the human skin and is thus referred to as **melanocyte-stimulating hormone (MSH).** Both hydrocortisone and cortisone inhibit the secretion of melanocyte-stimulating hormone; this is similar to their action on ACTH. Epinephrine and, even more strongly, norepinephrine inhibit the action of melanocyte-stimulating hormone. When production of the corticosteroids is inadequate, as in Addison's disease, melanocyte-stimulating hormone is secreted in excess, the synthesis of melanin is increased, and there is an accompanying brown pigmentation of the skin. In patients suffering from panhypopituitarism (see above), in which case there is lack of melanocyte-stimulating hormone as well as corticosteroids, pigmentation does not occur.

Chemistry

Two peptides (α-MSH and β-MSH) have been isolated from the pituitaries of various species. In the human, there is about 50 times more β- than α-melanocyte-stimulating hormone. The structure of β-MSH is shown in Fig 36–10. α-MSH is smaller, containing only 13 amino acids. Both MSH peptides have considerable structural homology with ACTH. α-MSH is identical to the first 13 amino acids of ACTH (Fig 36–9), except that the N-terminal amino acid of α-MSH, serine, is acetylated and the C-terminal, valine, is in amide form. Amino acids 11–17 of β-MSH are common to both α-MSH and ACTH. This is of interest in view of the fact that ACTH has small but definite melanocyte-stimulating activity (about 1% that of MSH). Although α-MSH has some corticotropic activity, this is not the case with β-MSH.

Regulation

The secretion of melanocyte-stimulating hormone is regulated at the hypothalamic level by **melanocyte-stimulating hormone release-inhibiting hormone.** A tripeptide and 2 pentapeptides have been isolated from the hypothalamus with melanocyte-inhibiting hormone activity, though the

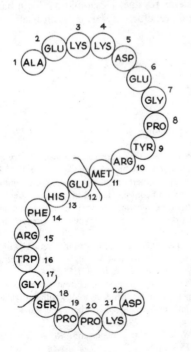

Figure 36–10. Amino acid sequence of human β-MSH.

tripeptide appears to be the predominant and most important form. A **melanocyte-releasing hormone,** a pentapeptide, has also been described. All of these regulatory hormones have structures identical to fragments of oxytocin (Fig 36–11), suggesting that oxytocin may serve as their prohormone.

THE POSTERIOR LOBE OF THE PITUITARY

Extracts of the posterior pituitary contain at least 2 active substances: a pressor-antidiuretic principle, **vasopressin (Pitressin);** and an oxytocic principle, **oxytocin (Pitocin).** Both are produced primarily, however, in the neurosecretory neurons—specifically, the neurons of supraoptic and paraventricular nuclei of the hypothalamus. Thus, they may act as pituitary-releasing hormones. The hormones are stored in the pituitary in association with 2 proteins, **neurophysin I and II,** with molecular weights of 19,000 and 21,000, respectively. Each neurophysin is specific for its hormone. It is probable that neurophysin was originally a part of the same prohormone that contains the respective hormone. The half-life in plasma is extremely short, varying from 3 to 5 minutes depending on the chemical structure of the hormone and the particular species. Part of the vasopressin concentrated by the kidney is excreted in the urine, but most is degraded. Arginine vasotocin, a combination of the structure of vasopressin and oxytocin, is also found in the pineal gland.

Function

A. Vasopressin: In high concentration, this substance raises blood pressure by its vasopressor effect on the peripheral blood vessels. Vasopressin has been used in surgical shock as an adjuvant in elevating blood pressure. It may also be used in the management of delayed postpartum hemorrhage.

Vasopressin primarily acts on the kidney, where it exerts an antidiuretic effect as the so-called posterior pituitary **antidiuretic hormone (ADH).** The hormone affects the renal tubules and provides for the facultative reabsorption of water. It binds firmly to renal tissue, an action that can be inhibited by sulfhydryl group (SH) blocking agents. Such observations have led to the suggestion that the action of vasopressin involves the opening of the disulfide (S–S) bridge (Fig 36–11), which is followed by a combination of the now available SH groups with other SH groups on membranes. Although such a binding can occur, there is as yet little support for the view that this is a required step in the action of the hormone. cAMP can duplicate many of the actions of vasopressin in kidney tissue, indicating that the hormone may act to increase levels of this substance. Vasopressin is an effective inhibitor of the gonadotropins, particularly LH.

Antidiuretic hormone may be increased by a variety of stimulators of neural activity. Emotional and physical stress, electrical stimulation, acetylcholine, nicotine, and morphine increase antidiuretic hormone secretion, as does dehydration or increased blood osmolality experimentally induced by injection of hypertonic saline or mannitol. Indeed, most of the stress-induced effects may be indirect reflections of the more direct signals, blood osmolality and volume. In general, these effects appear to increase synthesis of the hormones since their action does not cause a depletion of stored hormone. Furthermore, these stimulations are usually associated with an increase in RNA synthesis in the neuron, indicating an increased protein synthetic activity. Epinephrine and factors increasing blood volume are effective inhibitors of antidiuretic hormone secretion. Alcohol also inhibits antidiuretic hormone secretion.

In the absence of antidiuretic hormone, **diabetes insipidus** occurs. This is characterized by extreme diuresis—up to 30 L of urine per day. The disease may be controlled by nasal administration of synthetic vasopressin or its derivatives. There is an additional form of diabetes insipidus (nephrogenic) where posterior pituitary production of antidiuretic hormone is normal but the target tissues are unresponsive to the hormone.

B. Oxytocin: (Fig 36–11.) This substance is increased during labor. It causes uterine contraction and is employed in obstetrics when induction of uterine contraction is desired. It also causes contraction of the smooth muscles in the mammary gland, resulting in milk excretion. Both uterine and mammary gland tissue contain membrane receptors for oxytocin. The number of these receptors is increased by estrogens and decreased by progesterone. Thus, the concomitant rise in estrogens and fall in progesterone that occurs before parturition can precipitate increased sensitivity to oxytocin and resulting labor.

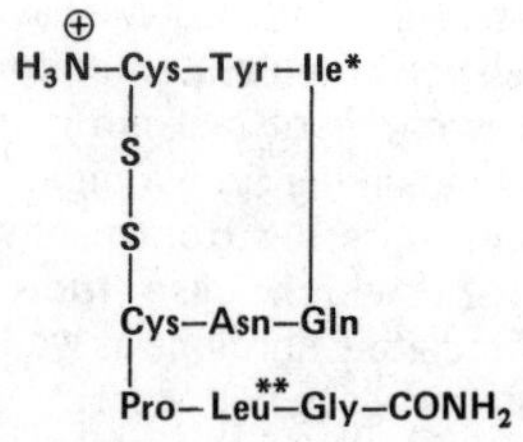

Figure 36–11. Structure of oxytocin. *Phe in vasopressin. **Arg in bovine, sheep, and primate vasopressin but Lys in porcine vasopressin.

Chemistry

The structure of oxytocin is shown in Fig 36–11. It is a cyclic polypeptide containing 8 amino acids and has a molecular weight of about 1000.

The structure of vasopressin is quite similar to that of oxytocin. The differences are in 2 amino acids: (1) isoleucine of oxytocin is replaced in vasopressin by phenylalanine; and (2) leucine of oxytocin is replaced in vasopressin obtained from hog pituitary by lysine (**lysine vasopressin**) and in that from beef as well as many other animals by arginine (**arginine vasopressin**).

The functional chemical groups in oxytocin include the primary amino group of cystine; the phenolic hydroxyl group of tyrosine; the 3 carboxamide groups of asparagine, glutamine, and glycinamide; and the disulfide (S–S) linkage. By removal of certain of these groups, analogs of oxytocin have been produced. Examples are deoxy oxytocin, which lacks the phenolic group of tyrosine; and desamino oxytocin, which lacks the free primary amino group of the terminal cysteine residue. Desamino oxytocin has 5 times the antidiuretic activity of oxytocin itself.

• • •

References

Anterior Pituitary

Beaumont A: Biology of opioid peptides. *Annu Rev Pharmacol Toxicol* 1979;**19**:245.

Bewley TA, Li CH: The chemistry of human pituitary growth hormone. *Adv Enzymol* 1975;**42**:73.

Brown-Grant K: Physiological aspects of the steroid hormones–gonadotropin interrelationship. *Reproductive Physiol II* 1977;**13**:57.

Catt KJ & others: Basic concepts of the mechanism of action of peptide hormones. *Biol Reprod* 1976;**14**:1.

Delofsen W: The chemistry of the adrenocorticotropins and of the melanotropins. *Pharmacol Ther* [B] 1975;**1**:459.

Frantz AG: Prolactin. *N Engl J Med* 1978;**298**:201.

Jungmann RG, Hunzicker-Dunn M: Mechanisms of action of gonadotropins and the regulation of gene expression. Pages 1–39 in: *Structure and Function of the Gonadotropins.* McKerns KW (editor). Plenum Press, 1978.

Li CH: β-Endorphin: A pituitary peptide with potent morphine-like activity. *Arch Biochem Biophys* 1977; **183**:592.

Liu WK, Ward DN: Purification and chemistry of pituitary glycoprotein hormones. *Adv Clin Chem* 1975;**1**:545.

Roberts JL, Herbert E: Characterization of a common precursor to corticotropin and β-lipoprotein: Identification of β-lipotropin peptides and their arrangement relative to corticotropin in the precursor synthesized in a cell-free system. *Proc Natl Acad Sci* 1977;**74**:5300.

Ryan RJ & others: Gonadotropin interactions with the gonad as assessed by receptor binding and adenyl cyclase activity. *Reproductive Physiol II* 1977;**13**:85.

Scanlon MF & others: Some current aspects of clinical and experimental neuroendocrinology with particular reference to growth hormone, thyrotropin and prolactin. *J Endocrinol Invest* 1979;**2**:307.

Vale W & others: Somatostatin. *Recent Prog Horm Res* 1975;**31**:365.

Van Wyk JJ & others: Explorations of the insulin-like and growth-promoting properties of somatomedin by membrane receptor assays. *Adv Metab Disord* 1975;**8**:127.

Placental Hormones

Bahl OP: Human chorionic gonadotropin, its receptor and mechanism of action. *Fed Proc* 1977;**36**:2119.

Chatterjee M, Munro HN: Structure and biosynthesis of human placental peptide anomers. *Vitam Horm* 1977;**35**:149.

Pituitary-Releasing Factors of the Hypothalamus

Brodish A, Lymangraver JR: The hypothalamic-pituitary-adrenocortical system. *Endocr Physiol* 1977;**16**:93.

Krulich L: Central neurotransmitters and the secretion of prolactin, GH, LH and TSH. *Annu Rev Physiol* 1979;**41**:603.

Labrie F & others: Mechanism of action of hypothalamic hormones in the adenohypophysis. *Annu Rev Physiol* 1979;**41**:555.

Schally AV, Arimura A, Kastin AJ: Hypothalamic regulatory hormones. *Science* 1973;**179**:341.

Smyth GA: Role of serotonin and dopamine in hypothalamic-pituitary function. *Clin Endocrinol* 1977;**7**:325.

Terry LC, Martin JB: Hypothalamic hormones: Subcellular distribution and mechanism of release. *Annu Rev Pharmacol Toxicol* 1978;**18**:111.

Middle & Posterior Pituitary

Chord IT: The posterior pituitary gland. *Clin Endocrinol* 1975;**4**:89.

Robertson GL: Regulation of vasopressin function in health and disease. *Recent Prog Horm Res* 1977;**33**:333.

Sawyer WH, Manning M: Synthetic analogs of oxytocin and the vasopressins. *Annu Rev Pharmacol* 1973;**13**:1.

Soloff MS: Minireview: Regulation of oxytocin action at the receptor level. *Life Sci* 1979;**25**:1453.

37 | The Chemistry of Respiration

David W. Martin, Jr., MD

The term respiration is here applied to the interchange of 2 gases, oxygen and carbon dioxide (CO_2), between the body and its environment. Respiration may be divided into 4 major processes: (1) pulmonary ventilation, ie, the inflow and outflow of air between the atmosphere and the alveoli; (2) the diffusion of oxygen and CO_2 between the alveoli and the blood; (3) the transport of oxygen and CO_2 to and from the cells of the organism via the blood; and (4) the regulation of ventilation.

The process of pulmonary ventilation per se will not be discussed in this text, although it is necessary to note that during the introduction of atmospheric air into the alveoli of the lungs, the air is warmed to body temperature and maximally humidified.

CHEMICAL & PHYSIOLOGIC EVENTS AFFECTING DIFFUSION OF OXYGEN & CARBON DIOXIDE

To understand the processes of gas diffusion and gas transport, it is necessary to comprehend the **physics of ideal gases.** If the temperature and mass (molar quantity) of a gas in a chamber remain constant but the volume of the chamber is increased or decreased, the pressure of the gas within that chamber will vary inversely with the volume, ie,

$$\text{Pressure} = \text{Constant} \div \text{Volume}$$
(or, rearranged)
$$\text{Pressure} \times \text{Volume} = \text{Constant}$$

at a fixed mass and temperature of an ideal gas.

For example, at 0 C and 1 atm of pressure (760 mm Hg), one gram-mole of gas occupies 22.4 L; if the volume of the gas is reduced by one-half, ie, 11.2 L, then the pressure would increase to 2 atm, or 1520 mm Hg. Conversely, if the volume of the gas is expanded to 44.8 L, the pressure would be reduced to 0.5 atm, or 380 mm Hg. This relationship is known as **Boyle's law.**

Given a fixed mass of gas at a constant pressure, when the temperature changes, the volume of the gas also changes proportionately to the increase or decrease in temperature (expressed in absolute or Kelvin [K] degrees of temperature):

$$\text{Volume} = \text{Constant} \times \text{Temperature (}^\circ\text{K)}$$

As an example, 1 gram-mole of an ideal gas at 273 K (0 C) occupies a volume of 22.4 L; if the temperature of the gas is increased to 37 C (310 K), it would occupy a volume of 25.4 L. This relationship is referred to as **Gay-Lussac's law.**

The combination of Gay-Lussac's law and Boyle's law generates the relationship

$$PV = nRT$$

where P = pressure,
V = volume,
n = the mass quantity of the gas,
R is a constant, and
T = temperature in absolute or Kelvin degrees.

The above expression is called the **ideal gas law.** When P is expressed in mm Hg, V in liters, n in gram-moles, and T in absolute degrees, the value of the **gas constant** = 62.36.

On a clear, cool day, atmospheric air contains 78.62% nitrogen, 20.84% oxygen, 0.04% carbon dioxide, and 0.5% water. In a mixture of gases in air, each gas exerts its own partial pressure. For example, the partial pressure of oxygen at sea level would be 20.84% of the total pressure of 760 mm Hg, or 159 mm Hg. However, when atmospheric air is inhaled, by the time it has reached the alveoli it has been saturated with water in the gas phase. Since the water vapor has mass, it occupies space, and yet the pressure in the lungs at the end of inspiration will not exceed that of the atmosphere (760 mm Hg). It follows that the partial pressures of the other components of the inspired air must be appropriately reduced. **At 37 C, the water vapor pressure is 47 mm Hg,** an important number to remember. Therefore, the sum of the partial pressures of the other components of air must contribute $760 - 47$, or 713 mm Hg. In Table 37–1 are shown the partial pressures of the respiratory gases in atmospheric air and in humidified air at 37 C.

At a liquid-gas interface, the number of mole-

Table 37—1. Partial pressures of respiratory gases in air. (Values in parentheses are percentage concentrations.)

	mm Hg (%)				
	N_2	O_2	CO_2	H_2O	Total
Atmospheric air	597.0 (78.62)	159.0 (20.84)	0.3 (0.04)	3.7 (0.50)	760.0 (100)
Humidified air	563.4 (74.09)	149.3 (19.67)	0.3 (0.04)	47.0 (6.2)	760.0 (100)
Alveolar air	569.0 (74.9)	104.0 (13.6)	40.0 (5.3)	47.0 (6.2)	760.0 (100)
Expired air	566.0 (74.5)	120.0 (15.7)	27.0 (3.6)	47.0 (6.2)	760.0 (100)

cules of gas entering the liquid phase will eventually equal the number of dissolved gas molecules leaving the liquid phase and entering the gaseous phase, a condition referred to as a **steady state equilibrium.** At equilibrium, the quantity of gas dissolved in a liquid phase will be determined by 2 factors: (1) the partial pressure of the gas surrounding the water, and (2) the solubility of the gas in the liquid at the given temperature. More specifically, **at equilibrium, the volume of dissolved gas equals the product of the partial pressure of that gas and its solubility coefficient (α) in that particular liquid.** The solubilities of the respiratory gases in water at 37 C and 1 atm of pressure are shown in Table 37–2.

Table 37—2. Solubility coefficients (α values) of respiratory gases at 37 C and 1 atm of pressure.

Oxygen	0.024
Carbon dioxide	0.57
Carbon monoxide	0.018
Nitrogen	0.012
Helium	0.008

At equilibrium, the force exerted by the gas attempting to enter the liquid will equal the force exerted by the same gas attempting to leave the liquid. The **pressure exerted by the gas attempting to escape from the liquid is referred to as its tension.** This is expressed as P_{O_2}, P_{CO_2}, P_{N_2}, etc. Thus it can be said that at equilibrium, **the partial pressure of a gas equals the tension** of that gas in the liquid. It should be evident that a gas which is highly soluble in a given liquid will be present at much higher **concentrations** in the liquid before it would exert a **tension** equal to its partial pressure in the gas phase. As is true for any solute dissolved in a liquid, the ability of each gas to dissolve in a liquid is independent of the presence of any other gas. As an important example, the quantity of CO_2 dissolved in a body fluid does not significantly affect the quantity of oxygen that can be dissolved in the same fluid (in the absence of any competition for a common carrier molecule).

When a gas is introduced into a chamber containing a liquid such as water, the gas molecules will collide with the liquid phase in an attempt to enter and to establish a condition of equilibrium such that the tension of the gas within the liquid will be equal to its partial pressure in the gaseous phase. The collision and

entrance of the gas molecules into the liquid occur by a process known as **diffusion.**

The rate at which the diffusion process occurs will be influenced by several factors in addition to the difference between the partial pressure of the gas above the liquid and its tension within it. The greater the cross-sectional **area** of the gas-liquid interphase, the greater will be the diffusion rate. The greater **distance** the molecules must diffuse, the longer it will take to achieve equilibrium. The greater the **solubility** of the gas in the liquid, the greater will be the number of molecules available for diffusion at any given pressure difference. Finally, the greater the velocity or **kinetic movement** of the molecules (a property that is dependent upon the molecular weight of the gas and its temperature), the greater will be the rate of diffusion.

All of the above factors influencing the diffusion rate (DR) can be expressed in a single equation:

$$DR \propto \frac{PD \times A \times S}{D \sqrt{MW}}$$

where PD = the pressure difference of the gas between the 2 phases,
 A = the cross-sectional area of the interfaces,
 S = the solubility of the gas in a particular liquid,
 D = the distance through which the gas must diffuse, and
 MW = the molecular weight of the gas.

It will be noted that the diffusion rate for any given gas in a given liquid will be proportionate to $S \div \sqrt{MW}$, a property that is termed its **diffusion coefficient.** Relative to oxygen, the diffusion coefficients for other respiratory gases in the aqueous body fluids are as follows:

Carbon dioxide, 20.3
Carbon monoxide, 0.81
Nitrogen, 0.53

These gases of respiratory importance are highly soluble in lipids and thus also highly soluble in cell membranes. Therefore, the major control on the movement of gases in body tissues is the rate at which gases can diffuse through the tissue fluids, which for practical purposes can be considered as water.

As seen from Table 37–1, the partial pressures and percentage concentrations of the respiratory gases are different in alveolar air than in humidified air. These differences are due to the following factors:

(1) The constant absorption of oxygen from the alveolar air.

(2) The constant diffusion of CO_2 from the pulmonary blood into the alveoli.

(3) The relatively slow replacement of alveolar air during normal ventilation.

In the total of both lungs of a normal human, there are approximately 300 million alveoli where gas exchange occurs. Each alveolus has extremely thin alveolar walls in a near-solid network of interconnecting capillaries such that the alveolar gases are in extraordinarily close proximity to the blood in the pulmonary capillaries. The **total surface area** of the functional respiratory membranes approximates 70 m^2, an area equivalent to a flat surface 10 m long by 7 m wide. The amount of blood present in the capillaries of the lungs at any given moment is approximately 100 mL, an amount that is effectively spread over the entire 70 m^2 surface area. As described above for the diffusion of a gas into water in a chamber, the diffusion of the respiratory gases into the blood in the pulmonary capillaries will be dependent upon (1) the functional alveolar surface area and (2) the distance through which the gases must diffuse, the so-called **respiratory membrane.** Obviously, pathologic states that decrease the effective surface area for gas exchange (such as emphysema) or thicken the effective functional respiratory membrane (such as increased interstitial fluid) will severely impair gas exchange and thus the process of respiration.

The overall ability of the total respiratory membrane to bring about the exchange of gases between the alveoli and pulmonary blood can be expressed as the **diffusing capacity,** ie, the volume of a gas that diffuses through the respiratory membrane in 1 minute at a pressure difference of 1 mm Hg. The diffusing capacity for oxygen is approximately 21 mL/min in an average young adult male under resting conditions. The normal difference in mean oxygen pressure across the respiratory membrane is approximately 11 mm Hg. Thus, the oxygen diffusing through the respiratory membrane each minute would equal 11 × 21, or 231 mL of oxygen. Importantly, during strenuous exercise, the diffusing capacity for oxygen can increase to a maximum of about 65 mL/min in young male adults. This 3-fold increase in diffusing capacity is due to an increased surface area of the blood perfusing the lungs as a result of the opening of previously dormant capillaries and dilatation of previously patent capillaries. In addition, the stretching of the alveolar membranes increases their surface area and decreases thickness.

As described above, the diffusion coefficient of CO_2 in water is 20 times higher than that of oxygen. In fact, the diffusing capacity of CO_2 is so great that it is immeasurable. This high diffusing capacity of CO_2 allows for virtually instantaneous equilibration of the pulmonary blood P_{CO_2} with the alveolar CO_2. Thus, the difference between plasma and alveolar CO_2 is normally less than 1 mm Hg. The diffusing capacity for CO_2 can be reduced to a degree where it causes significant clinical symptoms only when lung damage

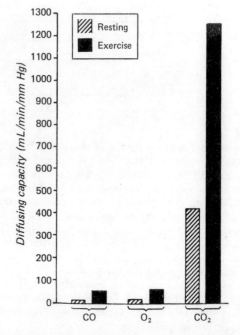

Figure 37–1. Diffusing capacities of carbon monoxide, oxygen, and carbon dioxide in the normal lungs. (Redrawn and reproduced, with permission, from Guyton AC: *Textbook of Medical Physiology,* 5th ed. Saunders, 1976.)

is so severe that it would ordinarily lead to death. This may occur when a patient's life is being maintained by intensive oxygen therapy necessary to overcome an equally severe, although more significant, reduction in oxygen-diffusing capacity.

In Fig 37–1 are depicted the diffusing capacities of carbon monoxide, oxygen, and CO_2 in normal lungs at rest and during exercise.

Exchange of Oxygen & CO_2 During Respiration

As can be seen in Table 37–3, the P_{O_2} of the blood as it enters the pulmonary capillary is 40 mm Hg, whereas the P_{O_2} in the alveolus is 104 mm Hg. Because of the large surface area of the respiratory membrane and the fact that the membrane is extremely thin, the uptake of oxygen from the alveolus into the pulmonary capillary blood occurs so rapidly that the P_{O_2} values are equal in the pulmonary capillary and alveolus even before the blood has reached the midpoint of the capillary (Fig 37–2). The time-integrated aver-

Table 37–3. Partial pressures and tensions (in mm Hg) of oxygen, CO_2, and water in the pulmonary system.

	Pulmonary Artery	Alveolus	Pulmonary Vein
Oxygen	40	104	104
Carbon dioxide	45	40	40
Water	47	47	47

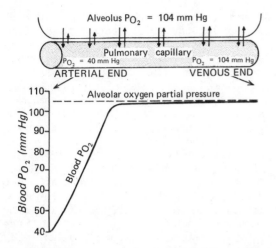

Figure 37–2. Uptake of oxygen by the pulmonary capillary blood. (The curve in this figure was constructed from data in Milhorn and Pulley: *J Biophys* 1968;**8**:337.) (Reproduced, with permission, from Guyton AC: *Textbook of Medical Physiology,* 5th ed. Saunders, 1976.)

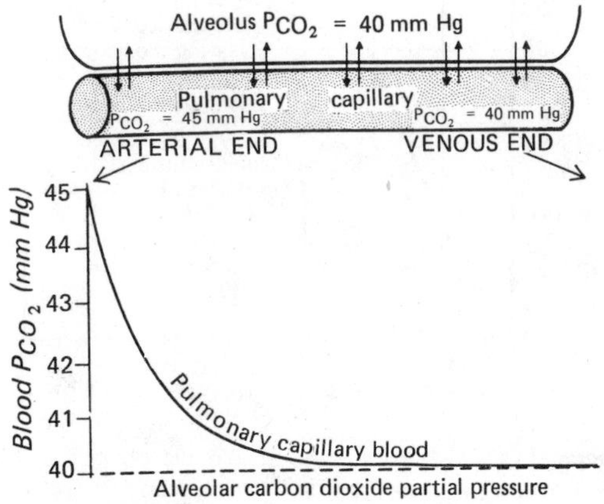

Figure 37–3. Diffusion of carbon dioxide from the pulmonary blood into the alveolus. (This curve was constructed from data in Milhorn and Pulley: *J Biophys* 1968;**8**:337.) (Reproduced, with permission, from Guyton AC: *Textbook of Medical Physiology,* 5th ed. Saunders, 1976.)

age pressure difference during normal respiration is about 11 mm Hg. During exercise, the increased cardiac output greatly reduces the time blood remains in the pulmonary capillary bed. However, this reserve transit distance within the capillary bed still permits almost complete saturation of the blood with oxygen by the time it leaves the pulmonary capillaries. In addition, as shown in Fig 37–1, the diffusing capacity for oxygen increases with exercise, providing a further safety margin to allow the rapid diffusion of oxygen through the respiratory membrane.

In the periphery, as the oxygenated blood passes through the tissue capillaries, the process occurs in reverse. The high P_{O_2} in arterial blood (about 95 mm Hg) diffuses by this gradient into the interstitial fluids, where the P_{O_2} averages about 40 mm Hg. By the time the blood has passed the tissue capillaries, its P_{O_2} has approached the 40 mm Hg oxygen tension of the interstitial fluid.

Arterial blood entering the tissue capillaries contains CO_2 at a tension of 40 mm Hg. Because of the high diffusion coefficient for CO_2, the relatively low gradient of CO_2 tension between interstitial fluid and the capillary blood is still sufficient to assure rapid equilibration of the P_{CO_2}. As a result, the P_{CO_2} of the venous blood is also about 45 mm Hg.

As the blood arrives in the pulmonary capillaries, the P_{CO_2} is approximately 45 mm Hg (Table 37–3), whereas the P_{CO_2} in the alveolar air is 40 mm Hg. Thus, the gradient of P_{CO_2} is far less than that of oxygen as between the alveolar gas and pulmonary artery (also, of course, it is in the opposite direction). Again, because of the 20-fold greater diffusion coefficient of CO_2 than that of oxygen, the CO_2 in the blood is rapidly equilibrated with that in the alveoli; furthermore, it occurs during less than the first half of the transit time of the blood through the pulmonary capillary (Fig 37–3).

TRANSPORT OF OXYGEN IN BLOOD

From the partial pressures of the respiratory gases shown in Table 37–3 and their solubilities as shown in Table 37–2, the expected content of these dissolved gases in blood can be calculated. A comparison of this **calculated** content with the **actual** content (Table 37–4) reveals that there is a marked difference. Thus, it must be evident that substantial quantities of oxygen as well as CO_2 are carried in the blood in other than simple solution.

Hemoglobin is the principal molecule responsible for transport in the blood of both oxygen and CO_2 (see Chapter 5). It is the hemoglobin contained within the erythrocytes that accounts for all of the "extra" oxygen content of the blood and a significant portion of the "extra" CO_2.

Normally, about 97–98% of the oxygen transported from the lungs to the tissues is carried in reversible combination with the hemoglobin molecule. This may be represented in simplistic terms by the equation

$$Hb + O_2 \rightleftarrows HbO_2$$

where Hb = deoxygenated hemoglobin and
HbO_2 = oxyhemoglobin.

The combination of hemoglobin and oxygen is not that of a compound or of a chemical combination such as an oxide. The nature of the oxygen hemoglobin affinity was, in fact, not understood until the

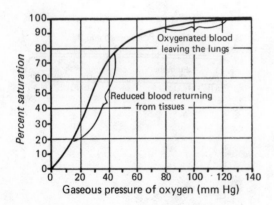

Figure 37–4. The oxygen-hemoglobin dissociation curve. (Reproduced, with permission, from Guyton AC: *Textbook of Medical Physiology,* 5th ed. Saunders, 1976.)

discoveries of the molecular events of the hemoglobin-oxyhemoglobin interchange were made by Perutz. This is discussed in detail in Chapter 5.

The degree of combination of oxygen with hemoglobin or of its reversal, ie, dissociation of oxyhemoglobin to release oxygen or association of oxygen with hemoglobin, is determined by the tension (P_{O_2}) of the oxygen in the medium surrounding the hemoglobin. At the tension of oxygen in the blood as it is leaving the pulmonary capillaries (104 mm Hg), hemoglobin is approximately 97% saturated (Fig 37–4). However, when the blood that has perfused peripheral tissues has returned to the lungs and enters the pulmonary capillary, it has a P_{O_2} of 40 mm Hg; at this tension, hemoglobin is about 70% saturated (Fig 37–4). The relationship between the percentage saturation of the hemoglobin in blood and the oxygen tension of the blood shown in Fig 37–4 depicts the **oxygen dissociation curve of hemoglobin.** The oxygen-dissociation curves of hemoglobin are somewhat dependent upon the P_{CO_2} in the blood, as discussed below.

When fully saturated, each gram of hemoglobin combines with approximately 1.34 mL of oxygen. Assuming a hemoglobin concentration of 14.5 g/dL of blood, the total oxygen that could be carried as oxyhemoglobin would be

$$14.5 \times 1.34 = 19.4 \text{ mL/dL blood}$$

This amount, when added to the amount of oxygen physically dissolved in the blood (0.33 mL/dL), yields the **total oxygen capacity** of blood, which is approximately 20 mL/dL. It is evident that the oxygen-carrying capacity of the blood is almost entirely a function of the blood **hemoglobin concentration.**

As can be perceived from Fig 37–4, the shape of the oxygen-hemoglobin dissociation curve is **sigmoid.** This property of the hemoglobin-oxygen interaction results from 2 properties important to the transport of oxygen. First, the relatively flat portion of the dissociation curve above an oxygen tension of 70–80 mm Hg results in minimal loss of oxygen from hemoglobin

despite rather significant changes in P_{O_2} above 70–80 mm Hg. Second, the precipitous change of the dissociation curve below a P_{O_2} of 40 mm Hg ensures that a disproportionately greater release of oxygen from hemoglobin will occur at any given decline in P_{O_2}. These 2 characteristics of hemoglobin-oxygen dissociation minimize the effects of small changes in pulmonary P_{O_2} on the oxygen content of the blood and maximize the delivery of oxygen to the oxygen-depleted peripheral tissues.

Under normal conditions (when the P_{O_2} of arterial blood is approximately 100 mm Hg and that of venous blood returning to the heart is 40 mm Hg), 5–6 mL of oxygen are delivered to the peripheral tissues by each 100 mL of blood. During strenuous exercise, the P_{O_2} in peripheral tissues may fall to as low as 15 mm Hg, which allows delivery of approximately 15 mL of oxygen per 100 mL of blood.

The hemoglobin-oxygen dissociation curve depicted in Fig 37–4 is that of normal, average blood, pH 7.4 and P_{CO_2} 40 mm Hg, at sea level. However, several factors can shift the hemoglobin-oxygen dissociation curve to the right or to the left. A **shift of the dissociation curve to the right** results in greater release of oxygen from the oxyhemoglobin at a given oxygen tension. In other words, **a shift to the right decreases the affinity** of hemoglobin for oxygen. Conversely, **a shift to the left increases the affinity** of hemoglobin for oxygen; accordingly, it results in a decreased release of oxygen from the hemoglobin at a given oxygen tension.

There are 4 major factors that bring about **a rightward shift** of hemoglobin-oxygen dissociation: (1) increased hydrogen ion or acidity (decreased blood pH), (2) increased CO_2 tension, (3) increased temperature, and (4) increased erythrocyte concentration of 2,3-diphosphoglycerate (DPG, also called 2,3-bisphosphoglycerate). All of the first 3 of these circumstances occur in situations where there are increased demands for oxygen by the tissue. The result is to bring about enhancement of delivery of oxygen. As discussed below, increased erythrocyte DPG concentrations occur under stressful situations such as a decreased atmospheric pressure; as is the case with increased CO_2 tension, the effect of DPG on oxygen affinity is also advantageous to the organism.

As shown in Fig 37–5, decreasing blood pH causes a small but significant rightward shift of the curve.

Shift of the hemoglobin-oxygen dissociation curve to the right by increasing CO_2 tension is termed the **Bohr effect.** It is due chiefly to the increased hydrogen ion concentration resulting from increased carbonic acid generation, as discussed below.

2,3-Diphosphoglycerate (DPG) is a metabolic intermediate in the Embden-Meyerhof pathway of glycolysis (see also Chapter 5). In the erythrocyte, 1 molecule of DPG binds noncovalently to the α-amino groups of the N-terminal valine residues of the 2 β-chains of deoxyhemoglobin, but not to those of oxygenated hemoglobin (see Chapter 5). Thus, in ef-

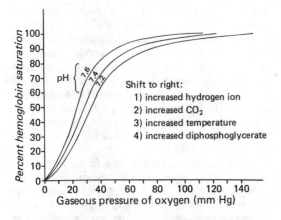

Figure 37–5. Shift of the oxygen-hemoglobin dissociation curve to the right by increases in (1) hydrogen ions, (2) CO_2, (3) temperature, or (4) diphosphoglycerate. (Reproduced, with permission, from Guyton AC: *Textbook of Medical Physiology,* 5th ed. Saunders, 1976.)

fect, DPG pulls the equilibrium between oxyhemoglobin and deoxyhemoglobin plus oxygen to the right, favoring the deoxygenated state of hemoglobin:

$$HbO_2 \xrightleftharpoons[\quad]{DPG} Hb \cdot DPG + O_2$$

The higher the DPG, the more favored will be the deoxyhemoglobin state and thus the farther to the right will be the shift of the hemoglobin-oxygen dissociation curve. In fact, the normal DPG concentration in erythrocytes shifts the dissociation curve somewhat to the right at all times.

Erythrocyte DPG levels are increased by chronic hypoxia, such as that occurring at altitudes above 2500–2750 m, in anemia, and in some disorders in which inherited abnormalities of hemoglobin alter the interaction of hemoglobin with oxygen and thereby diminish oxygen transport. It is not clear, however, whether the increased DPG concentrations are important in the adaptation to hypoxic conditions, because the presence of excess DPG diminishes also the affinity of hemoglobin for oxygen in the lungs.

One cause of a shift of the hemoglobin-oxygen dissociation curve to the left is an increased content of fetal hemoglobin (hemoglobin F) in the erythrocytes. An increased affinity for oxygen is characteristic of erythrocyte hemoglobin F. Obviously, this property is advantageous to the fetus, which normally is exposed to the diminished oxygen tension of the placental blood. It was once thought that this increased affinity of hemoglobin F for oxygen was an intrinsic property of the fetal hemoglobin molecule; however, an alteration in its oxygen affinity has not been demonstrable in vitro in purified preparations of hemoglobin F. It is now recognized that while hemoglobin F does not differ in its affinity for oxygen, when compared to

hemoglobin A, hemoglobin F has a significantly reduced affinity for DPG. It is this fact that results in an *apparent* increased affinity for oxygen in the presence of normal concentrations of DPG.

The rate of transport of oxygen to tissues depends on the oxygen utilization per unit volume, ie, the oxygen utilization coefficient, as well as the cardiac output. The normal utilization of oxygen, as mentioned above, is approximately 5 mL/dL blood; the oxygen content is normally 20 mL/dL blood. Thus, the utilization coefficient normally is 25%, but it can be increased another 3-fold—as, for instance, during strenuous exercise. In addition, the cardiac output can be increased 5-fold during exercise, resulting in nearly a 15-fold increase in the rate of oxygen transport to peripheral tissues.

In peripheral tissues, the utilization of oxygen is controlled not merely by its availability but more importantly by the intracellular concentration of ADP available for the process of oxidative phosphorylation. Whenever the oxygen tension in peripheral tissues is greater than 4 mm Hg, the cellular chemical reactions can proceed without regard to the availability of oxygen.

TRANSPORT OF CO_2 IN BLOOD

From the data in Table 37–4, it should be apparent that the content of CO_2 in blood, like that of oxygen, depends on factors other than simply its solution in the aqueous component of whole blood. In fact, only about 6% of the CO_2 present in blood is in the form of dissolved CO_2. According to the following equation,

$$CO_2 + H_2O \rightleftarrows H_2CO_3$$

CO_2 reacts with water in the blood to form carbonic acid (H_2CO_3), although the reaction is very slow in the absence of catalytic activity. It is the enzyme carbonic anhydrase present in erythrocytes that catalyzes the rapid equilibration of the above reaction. Carbonic acid rapidly and spontaneously dissociates into hydrogen ion and bicarbonate ion and, because it goes to about 99.9% completion, only 0.1% of the carbonic acid remains in the undissociated form. Since an increase in hydrogen ion concentration is severely detri-

Table 37–4. Comparison of calculated content with actual content (in mL/dL) of oxygen, CO_2, and nitrogen in the blood.

	Oxygen	Carbon Dioxide	Nitrogen
Calculated content	0.33	3.0	0.9
Actually present			
Arterial blood	20.0	50.0	1.7
Venous blood	14.0	56.0	1.7

mental to an organism, a buffer must be available to remove the free proton.

Hemoglobin is the major buffer in blood that removes the free hydrogen ion from blood to form a protonated hemoglobin, ''freeing'' an equimolar quantity of bicarbonate ion, as depicted in the reaction,

$$H^+ + HCO_3^- + KHb \rightleftharpoons HHb + K^+ + HCO_3^-$$

This reaction, of course, occurs only within the red cell, which is highly impermeable to potassium ion but readily permeable to bicarbonate anion. As the bicarbonate anion diffuses out of the erythrocyte into the plasma, another ion must enter the erythrocyte in equimolar quantities in order to maintain electrical neutrality across the erythrocyte membrane. This is chloride ion, so that the exchange between bicarbonate and chloride ions across the erythrocyte membrane is designated the **chloride shift** (Fig 37–6). It accounts for the greater chloride content in venous erythrocytes than in arterial erythrocytes, where the CO_2 tension is less. The conversion of CO_2 (via carbonic acid) to bicarbonate ion accounts for about 70% of the CO_2 transport. When carbonic anhydrase activity is inhibited, such as by acetazolamide, CO_2 transport from the tissues is inhibited. As a result, the CO_2 tension may rise to 70 or 80 mm Hg.

In addition to being transported in simple solution and as bicarbonate ion, CO_2 can combine (carbamino binding) in a rather loose covalent structure with the α-amino groups of the N-terminal valine residues of all 4 chains of the hemoglobin molecule. Since DPG binds to 2 of the amino termini of hemoglobin, clearly there is antagonism between the binding of CO_2 and that of diphosphoglycerate to the hemoglobin molecule. However, even though hemoglobin is the principal molecule for CO_2 transport, its role is minor when compared to the transport of CO_2 in the form of bicarbonate.

The carbamino-hemoglobin formed by the interaction of CO_2 with the amino termini of the hemoglobin molecule is independent of P_{CO_2} once that tension is greater than 15 mm Hg; but it is significantly influenced by the degree of oxygen saturation of the hemoglobin. The binding of oxygen to hemoglobin displaces CO_2, a phenomenon referred to as the **Haldane effect.**

The Haldane effect has a quantitatively greater importance in promoting CO_2 transport than the Bohr effect has in promoting oxygen transport. The Haldane effect results from the fact that oxyhemoglobin is a stronger acid than is deoxyhemoglobin, because the oxygenation of hemoglobin promotes the release of protons (hydrogen ions) from the hemoglobin molecule. The displacement of CO_2 from blood following the oxygenation of hemoglobin results from

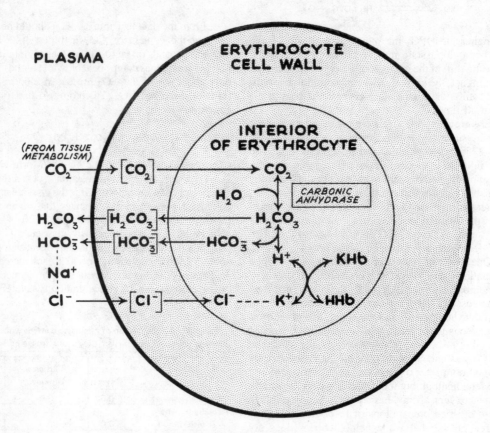

Figure 37–6. The chloride shift.

this increased availability of protons to combine with bicarbonate ions to form carbonic acid. Carbonic acid in the presence of carbonic anhydrase can be released as CO_2. The more acidic oxyhemoglobin also has a lesser tendency to form carbamino-hemoglobin from CO_2 and accounts for what has been referred to as the "oxylabile" carbamate.

The contribution of the carbamino-CO_2 to transport of CO_2 in an adult at rest is only about 10%. The Haldane effect nearly doubles the quantity of CO_2 that is released from the blood upon its oxygenation in the lungs, and upon the deoxygenation of hemoglobin in the peripheral tissues, the Haldane effect nearly doubles the uptake of CO_2.

The **respiratory exchange (RE) ratio** is the ratio of CO_2 released in the lungs divided by the rate of oxygen uptake in the lungs,

$$\frac{CO_2 \text{ release}}{O_2 \text{ uptake}} = RE \text{ ratio}$$

The respiratory exchange ratio changes under different metabolic conditions. In tissues utilizing carbohydrate as an energy source, there exists a 1:1 relationship between CO_2 production and oxygen consumption. However, the CO_2 production is diminished for each oxygen molecule consumed during the oxidation of fats as an energy source. For persons consuming a diet average in the quantities of carbohydrates, fats, and proteins, the respiratory exchange ratio (formerly termed respiratory quotient, RQ) is approximately 0.825.

Regulation of Respiration

Although the regulation of the hemoglobin affinity for oxygen, ie, the relative position of the hemoglobin-oxygen dissociation curve, is brought about by changes in blood pH and not by CO_2 tension, the regulation of respiration through a central nervous system mechanism is mediated predominantly by the **CO_2 tension of the blood.** An increase in P_{CO_2} as it exceeds 40 mm Hg causes an almost linear increase in the alveolar ventilation. The **oxygen tension alters ventilatory rate only when the CO_2 tension is abnormally low or exceedingly high.**

RESPIRATORY REGULATION OF ACID–BASE BALANCE

As described in Chapter 2, the buffering power of a buffer system is greatest at a pH equal to its pK_a. The pH of extracellular body fluids is 7.4, while the pK_a of the bicarbonate-CO_2 buffer system is 6.1. From the Henderson-Hasselbalch equation, it can be seen that at pH 7.4, the concentration of bicarbonate ion is 20 times greater than that of dissolved CO_2, a state which a priori would not provide significant buffering power. This can be seen by the following calculation, applying the Henderson-Hasselbalch equation to conditions in the blood.

$7.4 = $ pH of blood

$6.1 = pK_a$ of H_2CO_3

$$pH = pK_a + \log \frac{(salt)}{(acid)}$$

$$7.4 = 6.1 + \log \frac{(HCO_3^-)}{(H_2CO_3)}$$

$$1.3 = \log \frac{(HCO_3^-)}{(H_2CO_3)}$$

antilog $1.3 = 20$

$$\frac{(HCO_3^-)}{(H_2CO_3)} = \frac{20}{1}$$

However, because the concentration of each of these 2 components of the bicarbonate–carbonic acid system can be physiologically regulated, it provides a very powerful buffering system for the organism, as described below.

The CO_2 tension can be increased in blood by either increased production from the peripheral tissues or decreased removal by ventilation. From the Henderson-Hasselbalch equation, it should also be apparent that increased CO_2 tension will lead to a lower pH and acidosis. Acidosis due to the retention of excessive CO_2 results from ventilation that is inadequate for the rate of CO_2 production. For example, reducing ventilation at rest to one-fourth of normal rates *increases* the CO_2 tension and drops the pH from 7.4 to about 7.0. On the other hand, increasing the rate of alveolar ventilation (hyperventilation) 2-fold will *diminish* the CO_2 tension and lead to an increase of blood pH to about 7.6. Since alveolar ventilation can be reduced to nil or increased to about 15 times normal, it is readily understandable how changes in ventilation can severely affect the pH of extracellular fluid, which verifies the important role of the bicarbonate-CO_2 buffering system.

An acidosis due to *decreased* ventilation and the consequential *increase* in CO_2 tension is referred to as **respiratory acidosis.** An alkalosis due to hyperventilation and reduction of CO_2 tension in blood is referred to as **respiratory alkalosis.** However, because of the rapidity with which the respiratory system can change the blood pH, this system is frequently called upon to make rapid adjustments to pH changes that are generated by metabolic rather than by respiratory causes. The **respiratory-mediated readjustments of pH are rapid but incomplete.** On the other hand, **renal mechanisms can completely readjust the pH but are slow to act.**

Disturbances in acid-base balance which are due to alterations in the content of bicarbonate in the blood are said to be metabolic in origin. A deficit of bicarbonate without any change in H_2CO_3 will produce a **metabolic acidosis;** an excess of bicarbonate, a **metabolic alkalosis. Compensation** will occur by adjustments of the carbonic acid concentrations, in the first instance by elimination of more CO_2 (hyperventilation) and in the latter instance by retention of CO_2 (hypoventilation). The CO_2 content of the plasma will obviously be lower than normal in metabolic acidosis and higher than normal in metabolic alkalosis.

Causes of Disturbances in Acid-Base Balance

A. Metabolic Acidosis: Metabolic acidosis is caused by a decrease in the bicarbonate fraction, with either no change or a relatively smaller change in the carbonic acid fraction. This is the most common, classic type of acidosis. It occurs in uncontrolled diabetes with ketosis, in renal insufficiency, in poisoning by an acid salt, and in excessive loss of intestinal fluids (particularly from the lower small intestine and colon, as in diarrhea or colitis). Increased respirations (hyperpnea) may be an important sign of an uncompensated acidosis and is an attempt to reestablish the 20:1 ratio of HCO_3^-:H_2CO_3 by appropriately reducing the CO_2 tension of blood.

B. Respiratory Acidosis: Respiratory acidosis is caused by an increase in carbonic acid relative to bicarbonate. This may occur in any disease that impairs respiration, such as pneumonia, emphysema, congestive failure, asthma, or in depression of the respiratory center (as by morphine poisoning). A poorly functioning respirator may also contribute to respiratory acidosis.

C. Metabolic Alkalosis: Metabolic alkalosis occurs when there is an increase in the bicarbonate fraction, with either no change or a relatively smaller change in the carbonic acid fraction. A simple alkali excess leading to alkalosis is produced by the ingestion of large quantities of alkali, such as might occur in patients under treatment for peptic ulcer. But this type of alkalosis occurs much more commonly as a consequence of high intestinal obstruction (as in pyloric stenosis), after prolonged vomiting of acidic stomach contents, or after the excessive removal of gastric secretions containing hydrochloric acid (as in gastric suction). The common denominator in this form of alkalosis is a chloride deficit caused by the removal of gastric secretions that are low in sodium but high in chloride (ie, as hydrochloric acid). The chloride ions which are lost are then replaced by bicarbonate. This type of metabolic alkalosis is aptly termed "hypochloremic" alkalosis. Potassium deficiency is frequently associated with the development of hypochloremic alkalosis due to the unavailability of H^+ for the exchange with Na^+ from the lumen of the renal tubule.

In all types of uncompensated alkalosis, the respirations are slow and shallow; the urine may be alkaline, but usually, because of a concomitant deficit of sodium and potassium, will give an acid reaction even though the blood bicarbonate is elevated. This paradox is attributable in part to the fact that the excretion of the excess bicarbonate by the kidney will require an accompanying loss of sodium which under the conditions described (low sodium) cannot be spared. Thus, the kidney defers to the necessity of maintaining sodium concentrations in the extracellular fluid at the expense

of acid-base balance. However, an equal—if not, in the usual situations, a more important—cause of the excretion of an acid urine in the presence of an elevated plasma bicarbonate is the effect mentioned above of a potassium deficit on the excretion of hydrogen ions by the kidney. Metabolic alkalosis as encountered clinically is almost always associated with a concomitant deficiency of potassium.

D. Respiratory Alkalosis: Respiratory alkalosis occurs when there is a decrease in the carbonic acid fraction with no corresponding change in bicarbonate. This is brought about by hyperventilation, either voluntary or forced. Examples are hysterical hyperventilation, central nervous system disease affecting the respiratory system, the early stages of salicylate poisoning (see below), or injudicious use of respirators. Respiratory alkalosis may also occur in patients in hepatic coma.

Measurement of Acid-Base Balance; pH of Blood

The existence of uncompensated acidosis or alkalosis is most accurately determined by measurement of the pH of the blood. However, determination of the pH of the blood may not be feasible in some clinical circumstances. Furthermore, it is necessary to know in what manner the electrolyte pattern of the blood is disturbed in order to prescribe the proper corrective therapy. For these reasons, a determination of the CO_2 derived from a sample of blood plasma after treatment with acid (CO_2 capacity or CO_2 combining power) is also used. This measures essentially the total quantity of H_2CO_3 and of bicarbonate in the plasma but gives no information as to the ratio of distribution of the 2 components of the bicarbonate buffer system. Because of the properties of the Henderson-Hasselbalch equation, knowing any 2 out of the 3 variables—P_{CO_2}, bicarbonate concentration, and pH—or even knowing only the pH and the total CO_2 content permits determination of the remaining unknown variable (Fig 37-7). Accordingly, knowing 2 of the 3 variables also permits diagnosis of the nature of the acid-base disturbance by utilizing diagrams such as that shown in Fig 37-8.

For example, in **acute respiratory failure,** the retention of CO_2 would produce an **uncompensated respiratory acidosis.** The conditions of the blood might be transformed from the normal at point A to point B (Fig 37-8) with a P_{CO_2} of 60 mm Hg. The pH would be 7.3, and, because of the requirement that the Henderson-Hasselbalch relationship be satisfied, the bicarbonate must rise minimally to 28 mEq/L. If the respiratory failure is prolonged, the kidneys may well compensate for the acidosis, at least partially, by retaining bicarbonate. The condition of the blood might then move to point C, which would return the blood pH to the normal 7.4. This would accomplish what is termed a **compensated respiratory acidosis.**

Were hyperventilation to be induced, the P_{CO_2} might fall to 20 mm Hg—point D—with an ensuing **uncompensated respiratory alkalosis.** Again, owing to the requirement that the Henderson-Hasselbalch

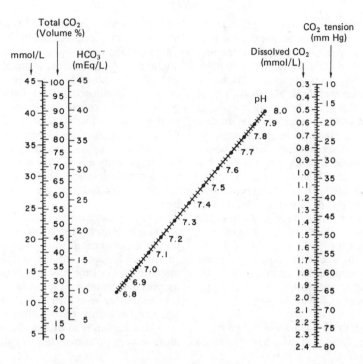

Figure 37–7. Nomogram of relationships between components of HCO_3^--CO_2 buffering system in the blood. (Reproduced, with permission, from Davenport HW: *The ABC of Acid-Base Chemistry,* 6th ed. University of Chicago Press, 1974.)

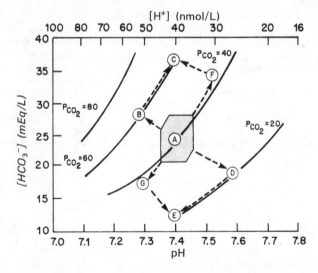

Figure 37–8. Diagram of relationships between HCO_3^-, P_{CO_2}, H^+, and pH of blood under normal conditions (shaded area, A) and in the presence of uncompensated and compensated acidosis and alkalosis. See text for details.

equation be satisfied, the bicarbonate concentration must accordingly fall to about 20 mEq/L. The kidney, by excreting excess bicarbonate, might bring about a change in the status of the blood to point E, which is nearly that of a normal pH of 7.4. This would then result in a **compensated respiratory alkalosis.** As mentioned above, these renal-mediated compensations for respiratory acidosis or respiratory alkalosis

occur slowly and thus would be seen only in chronic respiratory abnormalities.

In an **acute metabolic alkalosis** such as that due to an infusion of sodium bicarbonate, the condition of the blood might change from normal point A to point F, with a bicarbonate concentration of 34 mEq/L and a P_{CO_2} of slightly greater than 40 mm Hg. This mild elevation of the P_{CO_2} is due to the requirement that the conditions of the Henderson-Hasselbalch equation be satisfied at any given pH. Thus, at point F, with a plasma pH of 7.5, decreased respiration (retaining CO_2) could change the condition from point F to point C by increasing the P_{CO_2} to 60 mm Hg. This would result in a **compensated metabolic alkalosis,** but the previous state of the blood must be known in order to determine whether the condition at point C was due to a compensated metabolic alkalosis or a compensated respiratory acidosis, as described immediately above.

An **acute metabolic acidosis** might result in a situation wherein the blood is transformed from normal point A to point G, with a pH of 7.3. Hyperventilation would reduce the P_{CO_2} to 20 mm Hg and thereby compensate for the metabolic acidosis by changing the condition of the blood to condition E. Once again it should be emphasized that finding the blood in the condition at point E still would not allow a distinction to be made between **compensated metabolic acidosis** and compensated respiratory alkalosis unless the previous condition of the blood were known.

The Role of the Kidney in Acid-Base Balance

In addition to carbonic acid, which is eliminated by the respiratory organs as CO_2, other acids, which are not volatile, are produced by metabolic processes. These include lactic and pyruvic acids and the more important inorganic acids, hydrochloric, phosphoric, and sulfuric. About 50–150 mEq of these inorganic acids are eliminated by the kidneys in a 24-hour period. It is of course necessary that these acids be partially buffered with cation, largely sodium; but in the distal tubules of the kidney some of this cation is reabsorbed (actually exchanged for hydrogen ion), and the pH of the urine is allowed to fall. This acidification of the urine in the distal tubule is a valuable function of the kidney in conserving the reserves of cation in the body.

Another device used by the kidney to buffer acids and thus to conserve fixed base (cation) is the production of ammonia from amino acids. The ammonia is substituted for alkali cations, and the amounts of ammonia mobilized for this purpose may be markedly increased when the production of acid within the body is excessive (eg, as in metabolic acidosis occurring as a result of the ketosis of uncontrolled diabetes).

When alkali is in excess, the kidney excretes an alkaline urine to correct this imbalance.

•   •   •

References

Anderson OS: The acid-base status of the blood. *Scand J Clin Lab Invest* 1963;**15 (Suppl 70):**1.

Astrup P: A new approach to acid-base metabolism. *Clin Chem* 1961;**7:**1.

Best CH, Taylor NB: *The Physiological Basis of Medical Practice,* 9th ed. Williams & Wilkins, 1973.

Christensen HN: *Body Fluids and the Acid-Base Balance.* Saunders, 1964.

Davenport HW: *The ABC of Acid-Base Chemistry,* 6th ed. Univ of Chicago Press, 1974.

Filley GF: *Acid-Base and Gas Regulation.* Lea & Febiger, 1971.

Goldberger E: *A Primer of Water, Electrolyte, and Acid-Base Syndromes,* 5th ed. Lea & Febiger, 1975.

Hills AG: *Acid-Base Balance: Chemistry, Physiology, Pathophysiology.* Williams & Wilkins, 1973.

Michel CC: The transport of oxygen and carbon dioxide by the blood. Page 67 in: *Physiology,* Series One. Guyton AC (editor). University Park Press, 1974.

Robinson JR: *Fundamentals of Acid-Base Regulation,* 5th ed. Blackwell, 1975.

Digestion/Absorption in the Gastrointestinal Tract | 38

Peter A. Mayes, PhD, DSc

Most foodstuffs are ingested in forms that are unavailable to the organism, since they cannot be absorbed from the digestive tract until they have been broken down into smaller molecules. This disintegration of the naturally occurring foodstuffs into assimilable forms constitutes the process of digestion.

The chemical changes incident to digestion are accomplished with the aid of hydrolase enzymes of the digestive tract, which catalyze the hydrolysis of native proteins to amino acids, of starches to monosaccharides, and of triacylglycerols to monoacylglycerols, glycerol, and fatty acids. In the course of these digestive reactions, the minerals and vitamins of the foodstuffs are also made more assimilable. For example, the lipid-soluble vitamins are not absorbed efficiently unless fat digestion is proceeding normally.

A systematic account of the nature and functions of the gastrointestinal hormones is given in Chapter 35.

DIGESTION IN THE ORAL CAVITY

Constituents of the Saliva

The oral cavity contains saliva secreted by 3 pairs of salivary glands: parotid, submaxillary, and sublingual. The saliva consists of about 99.5% water, although the content varies with the nature of the factors exciting its secretion. It acts as a lubricant for mastication in the oral cavity and for swallowing. Adding water to dry food provides a medium in which food molecules can dissolve and in which hydrolases can initiate digestion. Mastication subdivides the food, increasing its solubility and surface area for enzyme attack. The saliva is also a vehicle for the excretion of certain drugs (eg, ethanol and morphine), of inorganic ions such as K^+, Ca^{2+}, HCO_3^-, thiocyanate (SCN^-), and iodine, and of immunoglobulins (IgA).

The pH of the saliva is usually slightly on the acid side, about 6.8, although it may vary on either side of neutrality.

Salivary Digestion

Saliva contains a starch-splitting enzyme, **salivary amylase (ptyalin)**. Although saliva is capable of bringing about the hydrolysis of starch and glycogen to maltose, this is of little significance in the body because of the short time it can act on the food. Salivary amylase is readily inactivated at pH 4.0 or less, so that digestive action on food in the mouth will soon cease in the acid environment of the stomach. Furthermore, pancreatic amylase, which has a similar enzymatic action and specificity, is capable of accomplishing complete starch digestion. In many animals, a salivary amylase is entirely absent.

DIGESTION IN THE STOMACH

Gastric Constituents & Gastric Digestion

In the mucosa of the stomach wall, 2 types of secretory glands are found: those exhibiting a single layer of secreting cells (the chief cells) and those with cells arranged in layers (the parietal cells) which secrete directly into the gastric glands. The mixed secretion is known as **gastric juice.** It is normally a clear, pale yellow fluid of high acidity, 0.2–0.5% HCl, with a pH of about 1.0. The gastric juice is 97–99% water. The remainder consists of mucin and inorganic salts, the digestive enzymes (pepsin and rennin), and a lipase.

A. Hydrochloric Acid: The parietal cells are the sole source of gastric hydrochloric acid. HCl originates according to the reactions shown in Fig 38–1.

The process is similar to that of the "chloride shift" described for the red blood cell on p 522. There is also a resemblance to the renal tubular mechanisms for secretion of H^+, wherein the source of H^+ is also the **carbonic anhydrase**-catalyzed formation of H_2CO_3 from H_2O and CO_2. An alkaline urine often follows the ingestion of a meal ("alkaline tide"), as a result of the formation of bicarbonate in the process of hydrochloric acid secretion by the stomach in accordance with the reaction shown in Fig 38–1.

As a result of contact with gastric HCl, proteins are denatured, ie, the tertiary protein structure is lost as a result of the destruction of hydrogen bonds. This allows the polypeptide chain to unfold, making it more accessible to the actions of proteolytic enzymes (proteases). The low pH also has the effect of destroying most microorganisms entering the gastrointestinal tract.

B. Pepsin: The chief digestive function of the stomach is the initiation of protein digestion. Pepsin is

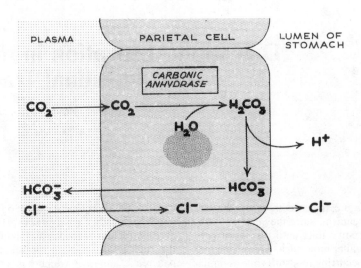

Figure 38–1. Production of gastric hydrochloric acid.

produced in the chief cells as the inactive zymogen, **pepsinogen.** This is activated to pepsin, first, by the proteolytic attack of another pepsinogen molecule at acid pH that splits off a polypeptide to expose active pepsin; and second, by pepsin, which rapidly activates further molecules of pepsinogen (**autocatalysis**). Pepsin transforms denatured protein into proteoses and then peptones, which are large polypeptide derivatives. Pepsin is an **endopeptidase,** since it hydrolyses peptide bonds within the main polypeptide structure rather than adjacent to N- or C-terminal residues, which is characteristic of **exopeptidases.** It is specific for peptide bonds formed by aromatic or dicarboxylic amino acids.

C. Rennin (Chymosin, Rennet): The enzyme causes the coagulation of milk. This is important in the digestive processes of infants because it prevents the rapid passage of milk from the stomach. In the presence of calcium, rennin changes irreversibly the casein of milk to a paracasein which is then acted on by pepsin. Rennin is said to be absent from the stomach of adults. It is used in the making of cheese.

D. Lipase: Although it does contain a lipase capable of hydrolyzing triacylglycerols of short and medium chain length, the lipolytic action of gastric juice is not important.

PANCREATIC & INTESTINAL DIGESTION

The stomach contents, or **chyme,** which are of a thick creamy consistency, are intermittently introduced during digestion into the duodenum through the pyloric valve. The pancreatic and bile ducts open into the duodenum at a point very close to the pylorus. The alkaline content of pancreatic and biliary secretions neutralizes the acid of the chyme and changes the pH of this material to the alkaline side; this shift of pH is necessary for the activity of the enzymes contained in

pancreatic and intestinal juice, but it inhibits further action of pepsin.

THE BILE

In addition to many functions in intermediary metabolism, the liver, by producing bile, plays an important role in digestion. The gallbladder, a saccular organ attached to the hepatic duct, stores a certain amount of the bile produced by the liver between meals. In humans, the gallbladder is a dispensable organ. During digestion, the gallbladder contracts and supplies bile rapidly to the small intestine by way of the common bile duct. The pancreatic secretions mix with the bile, since they empty into the common duct shortly before its entry into the duodenum.

Composition of Bile

The composition of hepatic bile differs from that of gallbladder bile. As shown in Table 38–1, the latter is more concentrated.

Table 38–1. The composition of hepatic and of gallbladder bile.

	Hepatic Bile (as secreted)		Bladder Bile
	Percent of Total Bile	Percent of Total Solids	Percent of Total Bile
Water	97.00	. . .	85.92
Solids	2.52	. . .	14.08
Bile acids	1.93	36.9	9.14
Mucin and pigments	0.53	21.3	2.98
Cholesterol	0.06	2.4	0.26
Esterified and nonesteri- fied fatty acids	0.14	5.6	0.32
Inorganic salts	0.84	33.3	0.65
Specific gravity	1.01	. . .	1.04
pH	7.1–7.3	. . .	6.9–7.7

Bile Acids

The primary bile acids are synthesized in the liver from cholesterol by several intermediate steps. **Cholic acid** is the bile acid found in the largest amount in the bile itself. Both cholic acid and **chenodeoxycholic acid** are formed from a common precursor, itself derived from cholesterol (Fig 38–2).

The 7α-hydroxylation of cholesterol is the first committed step in the biosynthesis of bile acids, and it is probably this reaction that is rate-limiting in the pathway for synthesis of the acids. The α-hydroxylation reaction is catalyzed by a microsomal system; it requires oxygen and NADPH, and it is partially inhibited by carbon monoxide. This system appears similar to that for the mono-oxygenases previously described

in connection with hydroxylation of steroids and of certain drugs (see p 128). It appears that cytochrome P-450 is a component of the system, as it is for the 12α- and 26-hydroxylation steps. Vitamin C deficiency interferes with bile acid formation at the 7α-hydroxylation step and leads to cholesterol accumulation, hypercholesterolemia, and increased atherosclerosis in guinea pigs.

Under normal circumstances in humans, bile acids are synthesized by the liver at the relatively low rate of 200–500 mg/d. This rate is regulated to just replace the daily loss of bile acids in the feces. The bile acids are the end products of cholesterol catabolism in the body. Because the tissues cannot break down the steroid nucleus, these compounds, together with

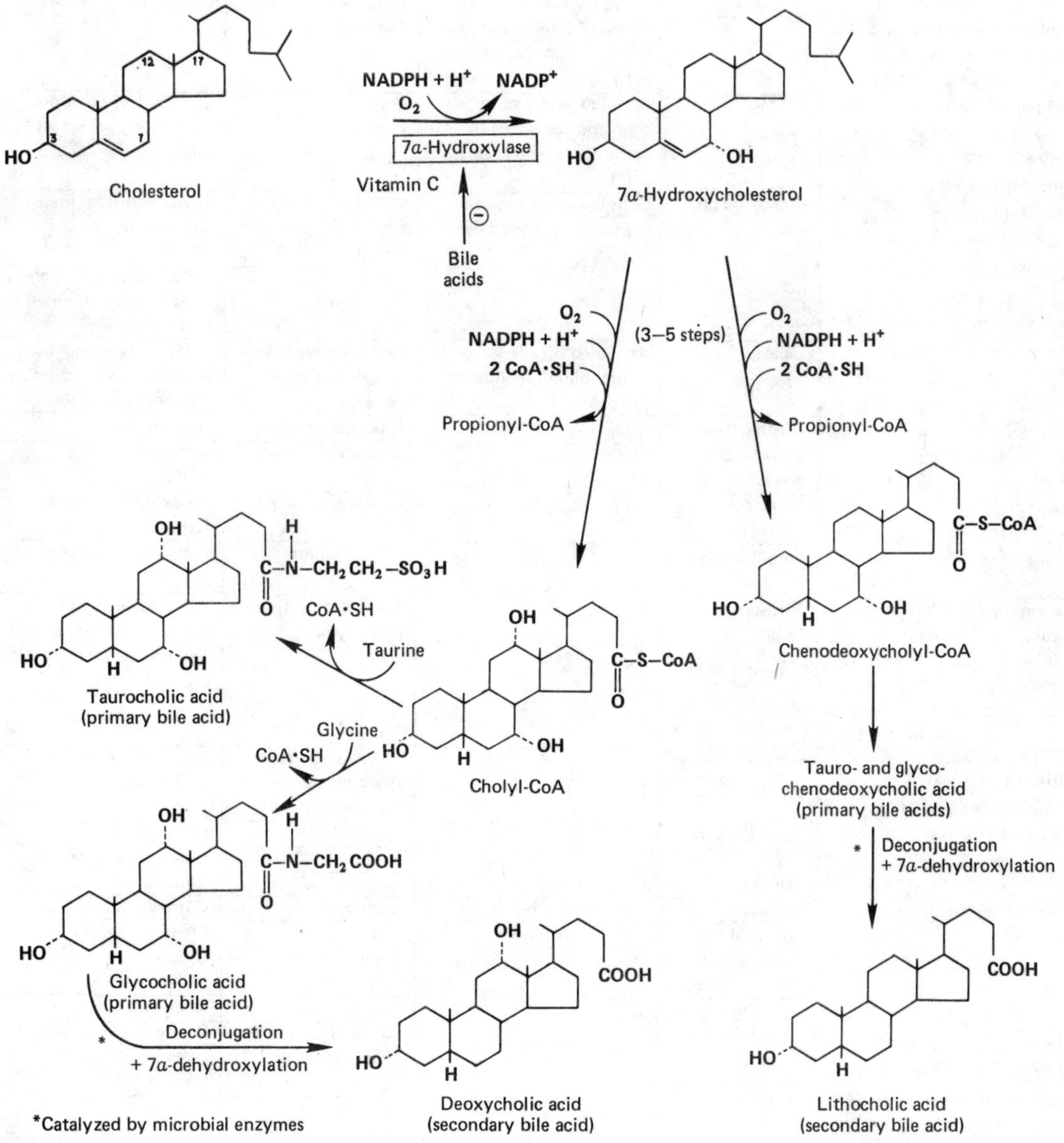

Figure 38–2. Biosynthesis and degradation of bile acids.

Table 38—2. Summary of digestive processes.

Source of Secretion and Stimulus for Secretion	Enzyme	Method of Activation and Optimal Conditions for Activity	Substrate	End Products or Action
Salivary glands of mouth: Secrete saliva in reflex response to presence of food in mouth.	Salivary amylase	Chloride ion necessary. pH 6.6–6.8.	Starch Glycogen	Maltose plus 1:6 glucosides (oligosaccharides) plus maltotriose
Stomach glands: Chief cells and parietal cells secrete gastric juice in response to reflex stimulation and chemical action of gastrin.	Pepsin	Pepsinogen converted to active pepsin by HCl. pH 1.0–2.0.	Protein	Proteoses Peptones
	Rennin	Calcium necessary for activity. pH 4.0.	Casein of milk	Coagulates milk
Pancreas: Presence of acid chyme from the stomach activates duodenum to produce (1) secretin, which hormonally stimulates flow of pancreatic juice; (2) cholecystokinin, which stimulates the production of enzymes.	Trypsin	Trypsinogen converted to active trypsin by enterokinase of intestine at pH 5.2–6.0. Autocatalytic at pH 7.9.	Protein Proteoses Peptones	Polypeptides Dipeptides
	Chymotrypsin	Secreted as chymotrypsinogen and converted to active form by trypsin. pH 8.0.	Protein Proteoses Peptones	Same as trypsin. More coagulating power for milk.
	Carboxypeptidase	Secreted as procarboxypeptidase, activated by trypsin.	Polypeptides at the free carboxyl end of the chain	Lower peptides. Free amino acids.
	Pancreatic amylase	pH 7.1	Starch Glycogen	Maltose plus 1:6 glucosides (oligosaccharides) plus maltotriose
	Lipase	Activated by bile salts, phospholipids, colipase. pH 8.0.	Primary ester linkages of triacylglycerol	Fatty acids, monoacylglycerols, diacylglycerols, glycerol
	Ribonuclease		Ribonucleic acid	Nucleotides
	Deoxyribonuclease		Deoxyribonucleic acids	Nucleotides
	Cholesteryl ester hydrolase	Activated by bile salts.	Cholesteryl esters	Free cholesterol plus fatty acids
	Phospholipase A_2		Phospholipids	Fatty acids, lysophospholipids
Liver and gallbladder: Cholecystokinin, a hormone from the intestinal mucosa—and possibly also gastrin and secretin—stimulate the gallbladder and secretion of bile by the liver.	(Bile salts and alkali)		Fats—also neutralize acid chyme	Fatty acid-bile salt conjugates and finely emulsified neutral fat—bile salt micelles
Small intestine: Secretions of Brunner's glands of the duodenum and glands of Lieberkühn.	Aminopeptidase		Polypeptides at the free amino end of the chain	Lower peptides. Free amino acids.
	Dipeptidases		Dipeptides	Amino acids
	Sucrase	pH 5.0–7.0	Sucrose	Fructose, glucose
	Maltase	pH 5.8–6.2	Maltose	Glucose
	Lactase	pH 5.4–6.0	Lactose	Glucose, galactose
	Phosphatase	pH 8.6	Organic phosphates	Free phosphate
	Isomaltase or 1:6 glucosidase		1:6 glucosides	Glucose
	Polynucleotidase		Nucleic acid	Nucleotides
	Nucleosidases (nucleoside phosphorylases)		Purine or pyrimidine nucleosides	Purine or pyrimidine bases, pentose phosphate

cholesterol itself, which is also present in the bile, represent the only significant route for **elimination of cholesterol from the body.** Measurement of the output of bile acids is therefore the most accurate way to estimate the amount of cholesterol lost from the body.

The bile acids normally enter the bile as glycine or taurine conjugates. The newly synthesized primary bile acids are considered to exist within the liver cell as esters of CoA, ie, cholyl- or chenodeoxycholyl-CoA (Fig 38–2). The CoA derivatives are formed with the aid of an activating enzyme occurring in the microsomes of the liver. A second enzyme catalyzes conjugation of the activated bile acids (the CoA derivatives) with glycine or taurine to form glycocholic or glycochenodeoxycholic and taurocholic or taurochenodeoxycholic acids. These are the **primary bile acids.** In humans, the ratio of the glycine to the taurine conjugates is normally 3:1.

Since bile contains significant quantities of sodium and potassium and the pH is alkaline, it is assumed that the bile acids and their conjugates are actually in a salt form—hence the term **"bile salts."**

The Enterohepatic Circulation

A portion of the primary bile acids in the intestine may be subjected to some further changes by the activity of the intestinal bacteria. These include deconjugation and 7α-dehydroxylation, which produces the **secondary bile acids,** deoxycholic acid from cholic acid, and lithocholic acid from chenodeoxycholic acid (Fig 38–2). Although fat digestion products are normally absorbed in the first 100 cm of small intestine, the primary and secondary bile acids are absorbed almost exclusively in the ileum, to return almost quantitatively to the liver by way of the portal circulation about 9% of the bile acids secreted into the intestine. This is known as the **enterohepatic circulation** (Fig 38–3). However, lithocholic acid, because of its

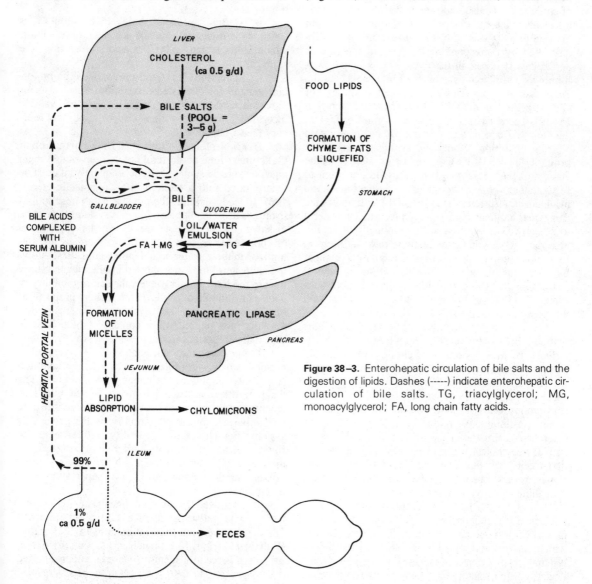

Figure 38–3. Enterohepatic circulation of bile salts and the digestion of lipids. Dashes (-----) indicate enterohepatic circulation of bile salts. TG, triacylglycerol; MG, monoacylglycerol; FA, long chain fatty acids.

insolubility, is not reabsorbed to any significant extent.

A small fraction of the bile salts—perhaps only as little as 500 mg/d—escapes absorption and is therefore eliminated in the feces. Even though this is a very small amount, it nonetheless represents a major pathway for the elimination of cholesterol. The enterohepatic circulation of the bile salts is so efficient that each day the relatively small pool of bile acids (about 3–5 g) can be cycled through the intestine 6–10 times with only a small amount lost in the feces, ie, only approximately 1% per pass through the enterohepatic circulation. However, **each day, an amount of bile acid equivalent to that lost in the feces is produced from cholesterol** by the liver, so that a pool of bile acids of constant size is maintained. This is accomplished by a system of feedback control.

Hepatic synthesis of cholesterol, in addition to being subject to feedback regulation by dietary intake of cholesterol, is also under regulatory control by the bile acids in the enterohepatic circulation. Changes in the rate of synthesis of bile acids are nearly always paralleled by corresponding changes in the rate of cholesterol synthesis in the liver. The principal rate-limiting step in the biosynthesis of bile acids is at the **7α-hydroxylase reaction,** and in the biosynthesis of cholesterol it is at the HMG-CoA reductase step (Fig 18–12). The activities of these 2 enzymes change in parallel, and consequently it is difficult to ascertain whether inhibition of bile acid synthesis takes place primarily at the HMG-CoA reductase step or at the 7α-hydroxylase reaction. Bile acids do not seem to regulate these enzyme activities by a direct allosteric mechanism. A differential effect on the activities of the 2 enzymes has been reported upon feeding cholesterol to rats. HMG-CoA reductase is inhibited but 7α-hydroxylase activity increases with increase in bile acid formation. Humans do not respond in a similar manner but rather may increase the excretion of neutral steroids in the feces and may suppress cholesterol synthesis. However, the ability to do this varies with different human subjects.

There is lower excretion of bile acids in patients with familial hypercholesterolemia (see p 243) that is reflected by lower synthesis of cholic acid. A similar pattern is observed in hepatic cirrhosis and cholestasis where cholic and deoxycholic acid formation and presence in bile is reduced, whereas chenodeoxycholic acid production is normal. Recently it has been reported (Halloran, 1978) that in humans, when the enterohepatic circulation has been interrupted by a bile fistula, free cholesterol in plasma HDL (high-density lipoprotein) was the preferred source of both biliary cholesterol and chenodeoxycholic acid.

Clinically, hypercholesterolemia may be treated by attempts to interrupt the enterohepatic circulation of bile acids. It is reported that significant reductions of plasma cholesterol can be effected by this procedure, which can be accomplished by the use of cholestyramine resin (Cuemid, Questran) or surgically by the ileal exclusion operations. Both procedures cause a block in the reabsorption of bile acids. Then, because of release from feedback regulation normally exerted by bile acids, the conversion of cholesterol to bile acids is greatly enhanced in an effort to maintain the pool of bile acids.

Functions of Bile

A. Emulsification: The bile salts have considerable ability to lower surface tension. This enables them to emulsify fats in the intestine and to dissolve fatty acids and water-insoluble soaps. The presence of bile in the intestine is an important adjunct to accomplish the digestion and absorption of fats as well as the absorption of the fat-soluble vitamins A, D, E, and K. When fat digestion is impaired, other foodstuffs are also poorly digested, since the fat covers the food particles and prevents enzymes from attacking them. Under these conditions, the activity of the intestinal bacteria causes considerable putrefaction and production of gas.

B. Neutralization of Acid: In addition to its functions in digestion, the bile is a reservoir of alkali, which helps to neutralize the acid chyme from the stomach.

C. Excretion: As stated above, bile is an important vehicle for cholesterol excretion, but it also removes many drugs, toxins, bile pigments, and various inorganic substances such as copper, zinc, and mercury (see Chapter 40).

D. Cholesterol Solubility in Bile; Formation of Gallstones: Free cholesterol is totally insoluble in an aqueous vehicle such as bile; consequently, it must be incorporated into a lecithin–bile salt micelle (see p 196). Indeed, lecithin, the predominant phospholipid in bile, is itself insoluble in aqueous systems but can be dissolved by bile salts in micelles. The large quantities of cholesterol present in the bile of humans are solubilized in these water-soluble mixed micelles, allowing cholesterol to be transported in bile via the biliary tract to the intestine. However, the actual solubility of cholesterol in bile depends on the relative proportions of bile salt, lecithin, and cholesterol. The solubility also depends on the water content of bile. This is especially important in dilute hepatic bile.

Using triangular coordinates (Fig 38–4), Redinger and Small were able to determine the maximum solubility of cholesterol in human gallbladder bile. The diagram was constructed from studies of bile salt, lecithin, and cholesterol mixtures in water to illustrate the limits of cholesterol solubility in this quaternary system. For cholesterol solubility, reference to the figure indicates that any triangular point falling above the line ABC would represent a bile whose composition is such that cholesterol is either supersaturated or precipitated.

It is believed that at some time during the life of a patient with gallstones there is formed an abnormal bile that has become supersaturated with cholesterol. With time, various factors such as infection, for example, serve as seeding agents to cause the supersaturated bile to precipitate the excess cholesterol as crystals.

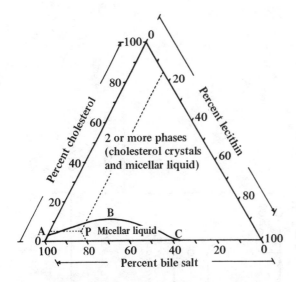

Figure 38–4. Method for presenting 3 major components of bile (bile salts, lecithin, and cholesterol) on triangular coordinates. Each component is expressed as a percentage mole of total bile salt, lecithin, and cholesterol. Line ABC represents maximum solubility of cholesterol in varying mixtures of bile salt and lecithin. Point P represents normal bile composition, containing 5% cholesterol, 15% lecithin, and 80% bile salt, and falls within the zone of a single phase of micellar liquid. Bile having a composition falling above the line would contain excess cholesterol in either supersaturated or precipitated form (crystals or liquid crystals). (Reproduced, with permission, from Redinger RN, Small DM: Bile composition, bile salt metabolism, and gallstones. *Arch Intern Med* 1972;**130**:620. Copyright © 1972. American Medical Association.)

Unless the newly formed crystals are promptly excreted into the intestine with the bile, the crystals will grow to form stones.

Utilizing the information concerning cholesterol solubility described above, attempts have been made to dissolve gallstones or to prevent their further formation. Chenodeoxycholic acid appears to offer specific medical treatment of asymptomatic radiolucent gallstones in functioning gallbladders because of its specific inhibition of HMG-CoA reductase in the liver, with consequent reduction in cholesterol synthesis.

E. Bile Pigment Metabolism: The origin of the bile pigments from hemoglobin is discussed on p 317.

Constituents of Pancreatic Secretion

Pancreatic secretion is a nonviscid watery fluid that is similar to saliva in its content of water and contains some protein and other organic and inorganic compounds, mainly Na^+, K^+, HCO_3^-, and Cl^-. Ca^{2+}, Zn^{2+}, HPO_4^{2-}, and SO_4^{2-} are present in small amounts. The pH of pancreatic secretion is distinctly alkaline, 7.5–8.0 or higher.

Many enzymes are found in pancreatic secretion; some are secreted as zymogens.

A. Trypsin and Chymotrypsin: The proteolytic action of pancreatic secretion is due to the 2 endopeptidases trypsin and chymotrypsin, which attack protein, proteoses, and peptones from the stomach to produce polypeptides. Trypsin is specific for peptide bonds of basic amino acids whereas chymotrypsin is specific for peptides containing uncharged amino acid residues such as aromatic amino acids. Both enzymes are secreted as zymogens. Activation of **trypsinogen** is due to another proteolytic enzyme, **enterokinase,** secreted by the intestinal mucosa. Once trypsin is formed, it will attack the other zymogens in the pancreatic secretion, **chymotrypsinogen** and **procarboxypeptidase,** liberating chymotrypsin and **carboxypeptidase,** respectively.

B. Carboxypeptidase: The further attack on the polypeptides produced by the action of endopeptidases is carried on by the exopeptidase carboxypeptidase, which attacks the carboxyl terminal peptide bond, liberating single amino acids.

C. Amylase: The starch-splitting action of pancreatic secretion is due to a pancreatic α-amylase. It is similar in action to salivary amylase, hydrolyzing starch and glycogen to maltose, maltotriose, and a mixture of branched (1:6) oligosaccharides (α-limit dextrins) and some glucose.

D. Lipase: The pancreatic lipase acts at the oil-water interface of the finely emulsified lipid droplets formed by mechanical agitation in the gut in the presence of the bile salts, colipase (a protein present in pancreatic secretion), phospholipids, and **phospholipase A$_2$** (also present in the pancreatic secretion). A limited hydrolysis of the ester bond in the 2 position of the phospholipid by phospholipase A$_2$ (see Fig 17–19) results in the binding of lipase to the substrate interface and a rapid rate of hydrolysis of triacylglycerol. The complete hydrolysis of triacylglycerols produces glycerol and fatty acids. However, the second and third fatty acids are hydrolyzed from the triacylglycerols with increasing difficulty. Pancreatic lipase is virtually specific for the hydrolysis of primary ester linkages, ie, at positions 1 and 3 of triacylglycerols.

Because of the difficulty of hydrolysis of the secondary ester linkage in the triacylglycerol, it is probable that the digestion of triacylglycerol proceeds by removal of the terminal fatty acids to produce 2-monoacylglycerol. Since this last fatty acid is linked by a secondary ester bond, its removal requires isomerization to a primary ester linkage. This is a relatively slow process; as a result, 2-monoacylglycerols are the major end products of triacylglycerol digestion, and less than one-fourth of the ingested triacylglycerol is completely broken down to glycerol and fatty acids (Fig 38–5).

E. Cholesteryl Ester Hydrolase (Cholesterol Esterase): This enzyme may either catalyze the esterification of free cholesterol with fatty acids or, depending upon the conditions of equilibrium, it may catalyze the opposite reaction, ie, hydrolysis of cholesteryl esters. According to Goodman, under the conditions existing within the lumen of the intestine, the

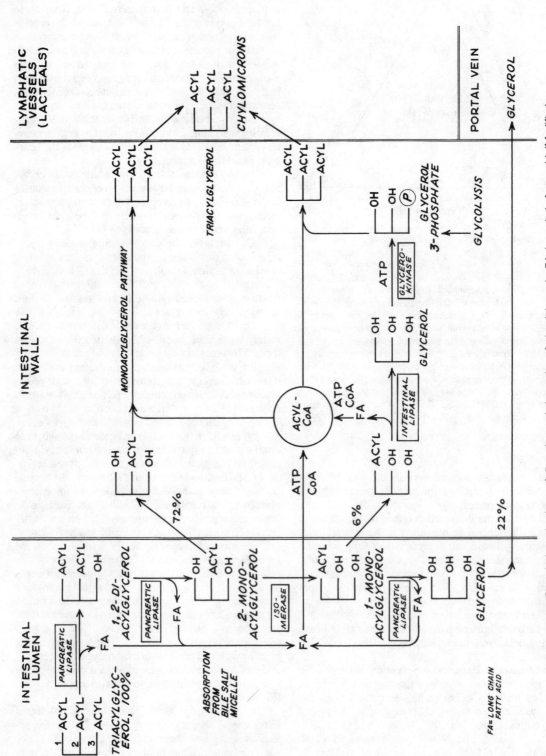

Figure 38-5. Chemical mechanisms of digestion and absorption of triacylglycerols. FA, long chain fatty acid. (Modified from Mattson & Volpenheim: *J Biol Chem* 1964;239:2772.)

enzyme catalyzes the hydrolysis of cholesteryl esters, which are thus absorbed from the intestine in a nonesterified, free form.

F. Ribonuclease (RNase) and **Deoxyribonuclease (DNase)** have been prepared from pancreatic tissue (see Chapter 28).

G. Phospholipase A₂: Phospholipase A_2 hydrolyzes the ester bond in the 2 position of glycerophospholipids of both biliary and dietary origins to lysophospholipids.

Constituents of Intestinal Secretion

The intestinal juice secreted by the glands of Brunner and of Lieberkühn also contains digestive enzymes, including the following:

(1) **Aminopeptidase,** which is an exopeptidase attacking peptide bonds next to N-terminal amino acids of polypeptides and oligopeptides, and **dipeptidases** of various specificity, some of which may be within the intestinal epithelium. The latter complete digestion of dipeptides to free amino acids.

(2) Specific **disaccharidases** and **oligosaccharidases,** ie, α-**glucosidase (maltase),** which removes single glucose residues from $\alpha(1-4)$ linked oligosaccharides and disaccharides, α-**dextrinase,** which hydrolyzes $1\rightarrow6$ bonds in α-limit dextrins, β-**galactosidase** (lactase) for removing galactose from lactose, and **sucrase** for hydrolyzing sucrose.

(3) A **phosphatase,** which removes phosphate from certain organic phosphates such as hexosephosphates, glycerophosphate, and the nucleotides derived from the diet and the digestion of nucleic acids by nucleases.

(4) **Polynucleotidases,** which split nucleic acids into nucleotides.

(5) **Nucleosidases** (nucleoside phosphorylases), one of which attacks only guanine- and hypoxanthine-containing nucleosides. The pyrimidine nucleosides (uridine, cytidine, and thymidine) are broken down by another enzyme that differs from the purine nucleoside phosphorylase.

(6) The intestinal secretion is also said to contain a **phospholipase** that attacks phospholipids to produce glycerol, fatty acids, phosphoric acid, and bases such as choline.

The Major Products of Digestion

The final result of the action of the digestive enzymes described is to reduce the foodstuffs of the diet to forms that can be absorbed and assimilated. These end products of digestion are, for carbohydrates, the monosaccharides (principally glucose); for proteins, the amino acids; for triacylglycerol, the fatty acids, glycerol, and monoacylglycerols; and for nucleic acids, the nucleobases, nucleosides, and pentoses.

ABSORPTION FROM THE GASTROINTESTINAL TRACT

There is little absorption from the stomach, even of smaller molecules like glucose that can be absorbed directly from the intestine. Although water is not absorbed to any extent from the stomach, considerable gastric absorption of ethanol is possible.

The small intestine is the main digestive and absorptive organ. About 90% of the ingested foodstuffs is absorbed in the course of passage through the small intestine, and water is absorbed at the same time. Considerably more water is absorbed after the foodstuffs pass into the large intestine, so that the contents, which were fluid in the small intestine, gradually become more solid in the colon.

There are 2 pathways for the transport of materials absorbed by the intestine: the **hepatic portal system,** which leads directly to the liver; and the **lymphatic vessels,** which lead to the blood by way of the thoracic duct.

Absorption of Carbohydrates

The products of carbohydrate digestion are absorbed from the jejunum into the blood of the portal venous system in the form of monosaccharides, chiefly the hexoses (glucose, fructose, mannose, and galactose), although the pentose sugars, if present in the food ingested, will also be absorbed. The oligosaccharides (compounds derived from starches that yield 3–10 monosaccharide units upon hydrolysis) and the disaccharides are hydrolyzed by appropriate enzymes derived from the mucosal surfaces of the small intestine, which may include pancreatic amylase adsorbed onto the mucosa. There is little free disaccharidase activity in the intestinal lumen. Most of the activity is associated with small "knobs" on the brush border of the intestinal epithelial cell.

Two mechanisms are responsible for the absorption of monosaccharides: active transport against a concentration gradient and simple diffusion. However, the absorption of some sugars does not fit clearly into one or the other of these mechanisms. The molecular configurations that seem necessary for active transport, both of which are present in glucose and galactose, are the following: the OH on carbon 2 should have the same configuration as in glucose, a pyranose ring should be present, and a methyl or substituted methyl group should be present on carbon 5. Fructose is absorbed more slowly than glucose and galactose. Its absorption appears to proceed by diffusion with the concentration gradient, which is different from the energy-dependent active transport mechanism for glucose, which is against a concentration gradient.

To explain the active absorption of glucose, a carrier has been postulated which binds both glucose and Na^+ at separate sites and which transports them both through the plasma membrane of the intestinal cell. It is envisaged that both glucose and Na^+ are released into the cytosol, allowing the carrier to take up more "cargo." The Na^+ is transported down its con-

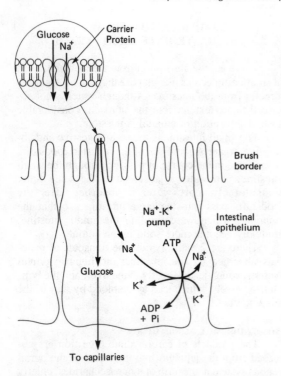

Figure 38-6. Transport of glucose across the intestinal epithelium (Crane). Active glucose transport is coupled to the Na^+-K^+ pump.

centration gradient and at the same time causes the carrier to transport glucose against its concentration gradient. The free energy required for this active transport is obtained from the hydrolysis of ATP linked to a sodium pump that expels Na^+ from the cell in exchange for K^+ (Fig 38-6). The active transport of glucose is inhibited by ouabain (cardiac glycoside), an inhibitor of the sodium pump, and by phlorhizin, a known inhibitor of glucose reabsorption in the kidney tubule. Phlorhizin, a plant glycoside, probably displaces Na^+ from its binding site on the glucose carrier.

Hydrolysis of polysaccharides, oligosaccharides, and disaccharides is a rapid process; therefore, the absorptive mechanisms for glucose and fructose are quickly saturated. A conspicuous exception is the hydrolysis of lactose, which proceeds at only half the rate for sucrose, accounting for the fact that digestion of lactose does not lead to saturation of the transport mechanisms for glucose and galactose.

Defects in Digestion & Absorption of Carbohydrates

A. Lactase Deficiency: Intolerance to lactose, the sugar of milk, may be attributable to a deficiency of lactase. The syndrome should not be confused with intolerance to milk resulting from a sensitivity to milk proteins, usually to the β-lactoglobulin. The signs and symptoms of lactose intolerance are the same regardless of the cause. These include abdominal cramps,

diarrhea, and flatulence. They are attributed to accumulation of lactose, which is osmotically active, so that it holds water, and to the fermentative action on the sugar of the intestinal bacteria which produce gases and other products that serve as intestinal irritants.

There are 3 types of lactase deficiency:

1. Inherited lactase deficiency–In this syndrome, which is relatively rare, symptoms of intolerance to milk such as diarrhea and wasting, incident to fluid and electrolyte disturbances as well as inadequate nutrition, all develop very **soon after birth.** The feeding of a lactose-free diet results in disappearance of the symptoms. Occasionally, infants who appear to be able to digest and absorb lactose nonetheless develop severe symptoms after ingestion of milk or lactose. The occurrence of lactose in the urine is a prominent feature of this syndrome, which appears to be attributable to an effect of lactose on the intestine.

2. Secondary low lactase activity–Because digestion of lactose is limited even in normal humans, intolerance to milk is not uncommon as a consequence of intestinal diseases. These include many gastrointestinal conditions prevalent in tropical as well as nontropical countries. Examples are tropical and nontropical (celiac) sprue, kwashiorkor, colitis, and gastroenteritis. The disorder may be noted also after surgery for peptic ulcer.

3. Primary low lactase activity–This is a relatively common syndrome, particularly among nonwhite populations in the USA as well as other parts of the world. Since intolerance to lactose was not a feature of the early life of adults with this disorder, it is presumed to represent a gradual decline in activity of lactase in susceptible individuals.

B. Sucrase Deficiency: There are a number of reports of an inherited deficiency of the disaccharidases sucrase and isomaltase. Symptoms occur in early childhood following ingestion of the sugars in question. The symptoms are the same as those described in lactase deficiency.

C. Disacchariduria: An increase in the excretion of disaccharides may be observed in some patients with disaccharidase deficiencies. As much as 300 mg or more of disaccharide may be excreted in the urine of these people and in patients with intestinal damage (eg, sprue).

D. Monosaccharide Malabsorption: There is a congenital condition in which glucose and galactose are absorbed only slowly due to a defect in the carrier mechanism. Because fructose is not absorbed via the carrier, its absorption is normal.

Absorption of Lipids

The 2-monoacylglycerols, fatty acids, and small amounts of 1-monoacylglycerols leave the oil phase of the lipid emulsion and diffuse into the mixed micelles consisting of bile salts, lecithin, and cholesterol, furnished by the bile (Fig 38-3). Because the micelles are soluble, they allow the products of digestion to be transported through the aqueous environment of the intestinal lumen to the brush border of the mucosal cells where they are absorbed into the intestinal epithelium. The bile salts pass on to the ileum, where most are absorbed into the enterohepatic circulation (Fig 38–3). Phospholipids of dietary and biliary origin (eg, lecithin) are hydrolyzed by phospholipase A_2 of the pancreatic secretion to fatty acids and lysophospholipids, which are also absorbed from the micelles. Cholesteryl esters are hydrolyzed by cholesteryl ester hydrolase of the pancreatic juice, and the free cholesterol, together with most of the biliary cholesterol, is absorbed through the brush border after transportation in the micelles.

Within the intestinal wall, 1-monoacylglycerols are further hydrolyzed to produce free glycerol and fatty acids by a lipase, which is distinct from pancreatic lipase, whereas 2-monoacylglycerols may be reconverted to triacylglycerols via the **monoacylglycerol pathway** (Fig 38–5). The utilization of fatty acids for resynthesis of triacylglycerols requires first their "activation." This is accomplished by formation of a coenzyme A (acyl) derivative of the fatty acid (see p 105). The reaction (which also requires ATP) is catalyzed by the enzyme **thiokinase.**

$$CoA \cdot SH$$
$$R-COOH \xrightarrow[\underset{Mg^{2+}}{}]{\boxed{THIOKINASE}} R-\overset{O}{\overset{\|}{C}}\!\sim\!S-CoA$$
$$ATP \quad AMP + PP_i$$

It is likely that the synthesis of triacylglycerols proceeds in the intestinal mucosa in a manner similar to that which takes place in other tissues, as described on p 215. The absorbed lysophospholipids, together with much of the absorbed cholesterol, are also reacylated with acyl-CoA to regenerate phospholipids and cholesteryl esters.

The free glycerol released in the intestinal lumen (from approximately 22% of the total amount of triacylglycerol originally present) is not reutilized but passes directly to the portal vein. However, the glycerol released within the intestinal cells can be reutilized for triacylglycerol synthesis by activation by ATP to glycerol 3-phosphate. Thus, all long chain fatty acids absorbed in intestinal wall mucosal cells are ultimately utilized in the re-formation of triacylglycerols.

Triacylglycerols, having been synthesized in the intestinal mucosa, are not transported to any extent in the portal venous blood. Instead, the great majority of absorbed lipids, including phospholipids and cholesteryl esters, appear in the form of **chylomicrons** that pass to the lymphatic vessels of the abdominal region and later to the systemic blood (see also Fig 18–4).

The majority of absorbed fatty acids of more than 10 carbon atoms in length, irrespective of the form in which they are absorbed, are found as esterified fatty acids in the lymph of the thoracic duct. Fatty acids with carbon chains **shorter than 10–12 carbons** are transported in the portal venous blood as unesterified (free) fatty acids.

Of the plant sterols (phytosterols), none are absorbed from the intestine except activated ergosterol (provitamin D).

Chyluria is an abnormality in which the patient excretes milky urine because of the presence of an abnormal connection between the urinary tract and the lymphatic drainage system of the intestine, a so-called "chylous fistula." In a similar abnormality, **chylothorax,** there is an abnormal connection between the pleural space and the lymphatic drainage of the small intestine that results in the accumulation of milky pleural fluid. Feeding triacylglycerols in which the fatty acids are of medium-chain length (less than 12 carbons) in place of dietary fat results in a disappearance of chyluria. In chylothorax, the use of triacylglycerol with short-chain fatty acids results in the appearance of clear pleural fluid.

Absorption of Amino Acids & Protein

Under normal circumstances the dietary proteins are almost completely digested to their constituent amino acids and these end products of protein digestion are then rapidly absorbed from the intestine into the portal blood. It is possible that some hydrolysis, eg, of dipeptides, is completed in the intestinal wall. Animals may be successfully maintained with respect to protein nutrition when a complete amino acid mixture is fed to them. This indicates that intact protein is not necessary.

There is a difference in the rate of absorption from the intestine of the 2 isomers of an amino acid. The natural (L) isomer is actively transported across the intestine from the mucosa to the serosa; vitamin B_6 (pyridoxal phosphate) may be involved in this transfer. The D-isomers, on the other hand, are transported only by free diffusion. This active transport of the L-amino acids is energy-dependent, as evidenced by the fact that, in studies of small pieces of segmented intestine, 2,4-dinitrophenol, the uncoupler of oxidative phosphorylation (see p 134), inhibits the concentration of L-amino acids.

A valuable tool for the study of amino acid transport is the synthetic amino acid α-aminoisobutyric acid. This compound is transported across cell membranes as are the natural amino acids; but once within the cells it cannot be metabolized, so that it remains for identification and analysis. Another amino acid model is 1-aminocyclopentane-1-carboxylic acid.

When groups of amino acids are fed, there is some evidence that one amino acid fed in excess can retard the absorption of another. These observations are similar to those made with respect to reabsorption of amino acids by the renal tubules.

A puzzling feature of protein absorption is that in some individuals sensitivity to protein (in the immunologic sense) results when they eat certain proteins. It is known that a protein is antigenic, ie, able to stimulate an immunologic response, only if it is in the form of a relatively large molecule; the digestion of a protein even to the polypeptide stage destroys its antigenicity. Those individuals in whom an immunologic

Table 38—3. Site of absorption of nutrients.

Site	Nutrient
Jejunum	Glucose and other monosaccharides; some disaccharides
	Monoacylglycerols, fatty acids, glycerol, cholesterol
	Amino acids, peptides
	Vitamins, folate
	Electrolytes, iron, calcium, water
Ileum	Bile acids
	Vitamin B_{12}
	Electrolytes
	Water

Table 38—4. Summary of disturbances due to malabsorption.

Sign or Symptom	Substance Malabsorbed
Anemia	Iron, vitamin B_{12}, folate
Edema	Products of protein digestion
Tetany	Calcium, magnesium, vitamin D
Osteoporosis	Calcium, products of protein digestion, vitamin D
Milk intolerance	Lactose
Bleeding, bruising	Vitamin K

response to ingested protein occurs must therefore be able to absorb some unhydrolyzed protein. This is not entirely undocumented, since the antibodies of the colostrum are known to be available to the infant.

There is increasing support for the hypothesis that the basic defect in **nontropical sprue** is located within the mucosal cells of the intestine and permits the polypeptides resulting from the peptic and tryptic digestion of gluten, the principal protein of wheat, not only to exert a local harmful effect within the intestine but also to be absorbed into the circulation and thus to elicit the production of antibodies. It has been definitely established that circulating antibodies to wheat gluten or its fractions are frequently present in patients with nontropical sprue. The harmful entity is a polypeptide composed of 6 or 7 amino acids of which glutamine and proline must be present to ensure the harmful properties of the peptide.

These observations on a disease entity that is undoubtedly the adult analog of celiac disease in children advance the possibility that protein fragments of larger molecular size than amino acids are absorbed from the intestine under certain conditions.

Tables 38–3 and 38–4 summarize the sites of intestinal absorption of some common nutrients and some disorders resulting from malabsorption, respectively.

INTESTINAL PUTREFACTION & FERMENTATION

Most ingested food is absorbed from the small intestine. The residue passes into the large intestine.

Here considerable absorption of water takes place, and the semiliquid intestinal contents gradually become more solid. During this period, considerable bacterial activity occurs. By fermentation and putrefaction, the bacteria produce various gases, such as CO_2, methane, hydrogen, nitrogen, and hydrogen sulfide, as well as acetic, lactic, and butyric acids. The bacterial decomposition of lecithin may produce choline and related toxic amines such as neurine.

Choline   Neurine

Fate of Amino Acids

Many amino acids undergo decarboxylation as a result of the action of intestinal bacteria to produce toxic amines (ptomaines).

A ptomaine

Such decarboxylation reactions produce cadaverine from lysine; agmatine from arginine; tyramine from tyrosine; putrescine from ornithine; and histamine from histidine. Many of these amines are powerful vasopressor substances.

The amino acid tryptophan undergoes a series of reactions to form indole methylindole (skatole), the substances particularly responsible for the odor of feces.

Indole   Skatole

The sulfur-containing amino acid cysteine undergoes a series of transformations to form mercaptans such as ethyl and methyl mercaptan as well as H_2S.

Ethyl mercaptan   Methyl mercaptan

$$CH_3SH \xrightarrow{[2H]} CH_4 + H_2S$$

Methyl   Methane and
mercaptan   hydrogen sulfide

The large intestine is a source of considerable quantities of ammonia, presumably as a product of the putrefactive activity on nitrogenous substrates by the intestinal bacteria. This ammonia is absorbed into the portal circulation, but under normal conditions it is rapidly removed from the blood by the liver. In liver disease this function of the liver may be impaired, in which case the concentration of ammonia in the peripheral blood will rise to toxic levels. It is believed that ammonia intoxication may play a role in the genesis of hepatic coma in some patients. In dogs on whom an Eck fistula has been performed (complete diversion of the portal blood to the vena cava), the feeding of large quantities of raw meat will induce symptoms of ammonia intoxication (meat intoxication) accompanied by elevated levels of ammonia in the blood. The oral administration of neomycin has been shown to reduce the quantity of ammonia delivered from the intestine to the blood, due undoubtedly to the antibacterial action of the drug. The feeding of high-protein diets to patients suffering from advanced liver disease, or the occurrence of gastrointestinal hemorrhage in such patients, may contribute to the development of ammonia intoxication. Neomycin is also beneficial under these circumstances.

Intestinal Bacteria

The intestinal flora may comprise as much as 25% of the dry weight of the feces. In herbivora, whose diet consists largely of cellulose, the intestinal or ruminal bacteria are essential to digestion, since they decompose the polysaccharide and make it available for absorption. In addition, these symbiotic bacteria accomplish the synthesis of essential amino acids and vitamins. In humans, although the intestinal flora is not as important as in the herbivora, nevertheless some nutritional benefit is derived from bacterial activity in the synthesis of certain vitamins, particularly vitamins K and B_{12}, and possibly other members of the B complex, which are made available to the body. Information gained from experiments with animals raised under strictly aseptic conditions should help to define further the precise role of the intestinal bacteria.

● ● ●

References

Digestion & Absorption

Borgström B: Importance of phospholipids, pancreatic phospholipase A_2, and fatty acid for the digestion of dietary fat. *Gastroenterology* 1980;**78**:954.

Johnston JM: Intestinal absorption of fats. In: *Comprehensive Biochemistry*. Vol 18. Florkin M, Stotz EH (editors). Elsevier, 1970.

Larson B, Nilsson A: *Scand J Gastroenterol* 1978;**13**:273.

Masoro EJ: Lipids and lipid metabolism. *Annu Rev Physiol* 1977;**39**:301.

Reiser R, Williams MC: *J Biol Chem* 1953;**202**:815.

Scow RO, Stein Y, Stein O: *J Biol Chem* 1967;**242**:4919.

Senior JR: *J Lipid Res* 1964;**5**:495.

Shreeve WW: *Physiological Chemistry of Carbohydrates in Mammals*. Saunders, 1974.

Smyth DH (editor): *Intestinal Absorption*. Plenum Press, 1974.

Bile

Danielsson H, Sjövall J: Bile acid metabolism. *Annu Rev Biochem* 1975;**44**:233.

Dietschy JM (editor): Symposium on bile acids. *Arch Intern Med* 1972;**130**:473.

Forker EL: Mechanisms of hepatic bile formation. *Annu Rev Physiol* 1977;**39**:323.

Ginter E: Marginal vitamin C deficiency, lipid metabolism, and atherosclerosis. *Adv Lipid Res* 1978;**16**:167.

Halloran LG & others: *Surgery* 1978;**84**:1.

Nair PP, Kritchevsky D (editors): *The Bile Acids*. 2 vols. Plenum Press, 1971–1973.

39 | Blood Plasma & Clotting

David W. Martin, Jr., MD

BLOOD PLASMA

Blood is a tissue that circulates in what is virtually a closed system of blood vessels. It consists of solid elements—the red and white blood cells and the platelets—suspended in a liquid medium, the **plasma.**

Once the blood has clotted (coagulated), as discussed below, the remaining liquid phase is called **serum.** Serum lacks the clotting factors (including fibrinogen) that are normally present in plasma but have been consumed during the process of coagulation. Serum does contain some degradation products of clotting factors—products that have been generated during the coagulation process and thus are *not* normally present in plasma.

The Functions of the Blood

The functions of blood—all except specific cellular ones such as oxygen transport and cell-mediated immunologic defense—are carried out by plasma and its constituents. They are as follows: (1) respiration—transport of oxygen from the lungs to the tissues and of CO_2 from the tissues to the lungs; (2) nutrition—transport of absorbed food materials; (3) excretion—transport of metabolic wastes to the kidneys, lungs, skin, and intestines for removal; (4) maintenance of normal acid-base balance in the body; (5) regulation of water balance through the effects of blood on the exchange of water between the circulating fluid and the tissue fluid; (6) regulation of body temperature by the distribution of body heat; (7) defense against infection in the white cells and the circulating antibodies; (8) transport of hormones; regulation of metabolism; (9) transport of metabolites.

Plasma consists of water, electrolytes, metabolites, nutrients, proteins, and hormones. Some of the plasma components are listed in Table 39–1. The water and electrolyte composition of plasma is practically the same as that of all extracellular fluids (see Chapter 40).

THE PLASMA PROTEINS

The total protein of the plasma is about 7–7.5 g/dL. Thus, the plasma proteins comprise the major part of the solids of the plasma. The proteins of the plasma are actually a very complex mixture that includes not only simple proteins but also mixed or conjugated proteins such as glycoproteins and various types of lipoproteins.

The separation of individual proteins from a complex mixture is frequently accomplished by the use of various solvents or electrolytes (or both) to remove different protein fractions in accordance with their solubility characteristics. This is the basis of the so-called "salting-out" methods commonly utilized in the determination of protein fractions in the clinical laboratory. Thus, it is customary to separate the pro-

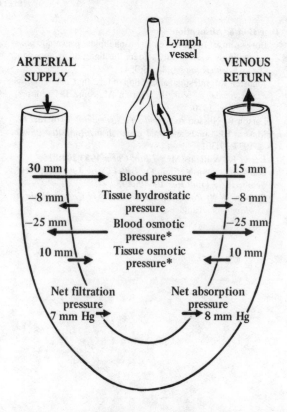

Figure 39–1. Capillary filtration and reabsorption ("Starling hypothesis"). The starred osmotic pressures are actually due only to the protein content of the respective fluids. They do not represent the total osmotic pressure.

teins of the plasma into 3 major groups—fibrinogen, albumin, and globulin—by the use of varying concentrations of sodium or ammonium sulfate.

Blood plasma is by definition an intravascular fluid. On the arterial side of the circulation, the intravascular hydrostatic pressure generated by the heart and large vessels is 20–25 mm Hg greater than the hydrostatic pressure in the tissue spaces (Fig 39–1). In order to prevent too much intravascular fluid from being forced into the extravascular tissue spaces, the hydrostatic pressure is opposed by an **intravascular colloid osmotic pressure** generated by the plasma proteins (Fig 39–1).

Albumin

Of the 3 major plasma proteins, albumin is present in the highest mass concentration (Table 39–1). Albumin also has the lowest molecular weight of the major protein molecules in plasma (Fig 39–2); thus, **albumin is the largest contributor to the intravascular colloid osmotic pressure.** Albumin is synthesized in the liver and consists of a single chain of 610 amino acids. In addition to contributing to the colloid osmotic pressure, albumin also acts as a **carrier molecule** for fatty acids, trace elements, and many drugs. Some of its ligand binding sites are highly specific and saturable, while others are much less so. The major effect of low serum albumin concentration (hypoalbuminemia), which occurs frequently in liver and kidney disease, is soft tissue edema due to the diminished intravascular colloid osmotic pressure.

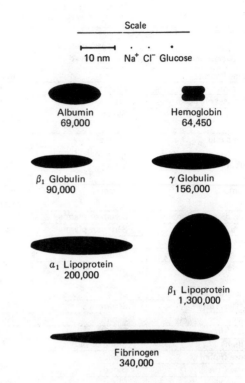

Figure 39–2. Relative dimensions and molecular weights of protein molecules in the blood (Oncley).

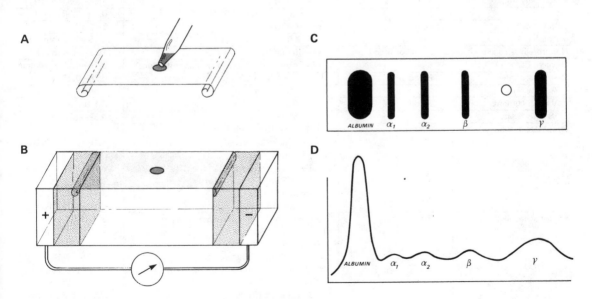

Figure 39–3. Technic of cellulose acetate zone electrophoresis. *A:* Small amount of serum or other fluid is applied to cellulose acetate strip. *B:* Electrophoresis of sample in electrolyte buffer is performed. *C:* Separated protein bands are visualized in characteristic position after being stained. *D:* Densitometer scanning from cellulose acetate strip converts bands to characteristic peaks of albumin, α_1-globulin, α_2-globulin, β-globulin, and γ-globulin. (Reproduced, with permission, from Fudenberg HH & others [editors]: *Basic & Clinical Immunology,* 3rd ed. Lange, 1980.)

Table 39–1. Blood, plasma, or serum values.

Determination	Material Analyzed	Normal Values (Values vary with procedure used)	SI Units
Acetone bodies	Plasma	0.3–2 mg/dL	3–20 mg/L
Aldosterone	Plasma	0.003–0.01 µg/dL	0.03–0.1 µg/L
Amino acid nitrogen	Plasma	3–5.5 mg/dL	2.1–3.9 mmol/L
Ammonia	Blood	40–70 µg/dL	22.16–38.78 µmol/L
Amylase	Serum	80–180 Somogyi units/dL; 0.8–3.2 IU/L	2.48–5.58 µkat/L
Ascorbic acid	Plasma	0.4–1.5 mg/dL (fasting)	23–85 µmol/L
	White cells (blood)	25-40 mg/dL	1420–2272 µmol/L
Bilirubin	Serum	Direct: 0.1–0.4 mg/dL	1.71–6.84 µmol/L
		Indirect: 0.2–0.7 mg/dL	3.42–11.97 µmol/L
Calcium	Serum	9–10.6 mg/dL; 4.5–5.3 mEq/L (varies with protein concentration)	2.25–2.65 mmol/L
Carbon dioxide: Content	Serum or plasma	24–29 mEq/L; 55–65 vol %	24–29 mmol/L
Combining power	Serum or plasma	55–75 vol %	
Carotenoids	Serum	50–300 µg/dL	
Vitamin A	Serum	24–60 IU/dL; 24–60 µg/dL	0.84–2.10 µmol/L
Chloride	Serum	100–106 mEq/L; 350–375 mg/dL (as chloride)	100–106 mmol/L
Cholesterol	Serum	150–280 mg/dL	3.9–7.3 mmol/L
Cholesteryl esters	Serum	50–65% of total cholesterol	
Copper	Serum	100–200 µg/dL	16–31 µmol/L
Cortisol (free)	Plasma	4–18 µg/dL	110–497 nmol/L
Creatinine	Blood or serum	0.7–1.5 mg/dL	60–130 µmol/L
Glucose (Folin)	Blood	80–120 mg/dL (fasting)	4.4–6.6 mmol/L
Glucose (true)	Blood	60–100 mg/dL	3.3–5.5 mmol/L
Hemoglobin	Blood	Women: 12–16 g/dL	1.86–2.48 mmol/L
		Men: 14–18 g/dL	2.17–2.79 mmol/L
Iodine (BEI)	Serum	3–6.5 µg/dL	0.24–0.51 µmol/L
Iodine, protein-bound	Serum	4–8 µg/dL	0.32–0.63 µmol/L
Iron	Serum	65–175 µg/dL	11.6–31.3 µmol/L
Iron-binding capacity	Serum	250–410 µg/dL	44.8–73.3 µmol/L
Lactic acid	Blood (in iodoacetate)	0.44–1.8 mmol/L; 4–16 mg/dL	0.44–1.28 µmol/L
Lactic dehydrogenase	Serum	90–200 IU/L	1.50–3.34 µkat/L
Lipase	Serum	0.2–1.5 units (mL of 0.1N NaOH)	0.93–6.96 µkat/L
Lipids, total	Serum	500–600 mg/dL	5–6 g/L
Magnesium	Serum	1.5–2.5 mEq/L; 1–3 mg/dL	0.75–1.25 mmol/L
Nonprotein nitrogen	Serum or blood	15–35 mg/dL	10.7–25 mmol/L
Oxygen: Capacity	Blood	16–24 vol % (varies with Hb concentration)	0.16–0.24 of volume
Arterial content	Blood	15–23 vol % (varies with Hb content)	0.15–0.23 of volume
Arterial % sat.		94–100% of capacity	0.94–1.00 of total
Venous content	Blood	10–16 vol %	0.1–0.16 of total
Venous % sat.		60–85% of capacity	0.6–0.85 of total
Phosphatase, acid	Plasma	1–5 units (King-Armstrong); 0.5–2 units (Bodansky); 0.5–2 units (Gutman); 0.1–1 unit (Shinowara); 0.1–0.63 unit (Bessey-Lowry) Women: 0.2–9.5 IU/L Men: 0.5–11 IU/L	4.48–17.94 µkat/L 0.90–8.97 µkat/L 27.5–175.14 µkat/L 3.34–158.65 nkat/L 8.35–183.7 nkat/L
Phosphatase, alkaline	Plasma	5–13 units (King-Armstrong); 2–4.5 units (Bodansky); 3–10 units (Gutman); 2.2–8.6 units (Shinowara); Children: 0.1–0.63 unit (Bessey-Lowry) Adults: 30–85 IU/L; 0.8–2.3 units (Bessey-Lowry)	59–153.4 µkat/L 17.94–40.37 µkat/L 19.73–77.14 µkat/L 27.8–175.14 µkat/L 501–1419 nkat/L 222.4–639.4 µkat/L
Phospholipid	Serum	145–200 mg/dL	1.87–2.58 mmol/L
Phosphorus, inorganic	Serum	3–4.5 mg/dL (children, 4–7 mg)	1–1.5 mmol/L
Potassium	Serum	2.5–5 mEq/L; 14–20 mg/dL	2.5–5.0 mmol/L

Table 39–1 (cont'd). Blood, plasma, or serum values.

Determination	Material Analyzed	Normal Values (Values vary with procedure used)	SI Units
Protein: Total	Serum	5–8 g/dL	60–80 g/L
Albumin*	Serum	3.5–5.5 g/dL	0.54–0.847 mmol/L
Globulin*	Serum	1.5–3 g/dL	15–30 g/L
Fibrinogen	Plasma	0.2–0.6 g/dL	5.8–6.8 μmol/L
Pyruvic acid	Blood	0.07–0.2 mmol/L; 0.7–2 mg/dL	79.8–228 μmmol/L
Sodium	Serum	136–145 mEq/L; 310–340 mg/dL	136–145 mmol/L
Sulfate	Plasma or serum	0.5–1.5 mEq/L	50–150 μmol/L
Transaminases: Glutamic-oxaloacetic (SGOT)	Serum	5–40 units 6–25 IU/L	40.1–320.8 nkat/L
Glutamic-pyruvic (SGPT)	Serum	5–35 units 3–26 IU/L	40.1–280.7 nkat/L
Triglycerides	Serum	<165 mg/dL	<18 mmol/L
Urea nitrogen	Serum or blood	8–20 mg/dL	2.86–7.14 mmol/L
Uric acid	Serum	3–7.5 mg/dL	0.18–0.29 mmol/L

*Albumin and globulin values obtained by use of 22% sodium sulfate; not in agreement with electrophoretic data.

Globulins

As described in Chapter 4, globulins are protein molecules that are insoluble in plain water but soluble in salt water. The serum globulins are a heterogeneous, complex mixture of protein molecules that are frequently designated as α-, β-, or γ-globulins, sometimes with number designations as well, all based on their electrophoretic mobility (Fig 39–3). A more rational classification is based on their structure or function.

The **glycoproteins** contain covalently bound oligosaccharide moieties (see Chapter 32) and are found principally in the α_1- and α_2-globulin fractions. Among the glycoproteins are many specific molecules with specific functions, some understood and others not.

Lipoproteins contain lipids, usually noncovalently bound to the protein molecule (see Chapter 18). The lipoproteins migrate with the α-globulins or the β-globulins. The higher the fat content and the lower the protein content of a lipoprotein, the lower its specific gravity. The lipoproteins act as **carrier molecules** for many different types of lipids and lipid-soluble molecules that are not soluble in the plasma water.

Some **metal-binding proteins** such as transferrin have the properties of globulins and act as carriers for trace elements (see Chapter 40).

Plasma normally contains a number of specific **enzyme molecules** such as phosphatases, lipases, lactate dehydrogenase, amylase, and ferroxidase (ceruloplasmin). In addition, as tissues break down or their membranes leak, intracellular enzymes can be released into the intravascular space, and their catalytic activities may serve as qualitative or quantitative indexes of tissue damage. Determinations of serum transaminases, creatine kinases, and acid phosphatases are particularly useful in clinical medicine.

Polypeptide **hormones** circulate in plasma. Hormones such as the steroids and 1,25-dihydroxyvitamin D_3 circulate in plasma bound to specific receptor molecules.

Fibrinogen, the precursor of fibrin that forms blood clots, and **immunoglobulins,** which constitute the effector arm of the humoral immunity system, are important plasma proteins discussed in detail below.

The plasma lipoproteins are described in Chapter 18.

Immunoglobulins

Immunoglobulins, or **antibodies,** are synthesized in B lymphocytes or their derivatives, plasma cells, and with remarkable specificity **bind to antigenic sites** on other molecules.

All immunoglobulin molecules consist of 2 identical light (L) chains (MW 23,000) and 2 identical heavy (H) chains (MW 53,000–75,000) held together as a tetramer (L_2H_2) by disulfide bonds (Fig 39–4). Each chain can be divided conceptually into specific **domains** or regions that have structural and functional significance. The half of the **light** (L) chain toward the carboxy terminal is referred to as the **constant region** (C_L), while the amino-terminal half is the **variable region** of the light chain (V_L). Approximately one-quarter of the heavy chain at the amino terminal is referred to as its variable region (V_H), and the other three-quarters of the heavy chain are referred to as the constant regions (C_H1, C_H2, C_H3) of that H chain. The portion of the immunoglobulin molecule that **binds the specific antigen** is formed by the amino-terminal portions (variable regions) of both the H and L chains—ie, the V_H and V_L **domains.** The domains of the protein chains do not simply exist as linear sequences of amino acids but form globular regions with secondary and tertiary structure.

As depicted in Fig 39–4, digestion of an immunoglobulin by the enzyme papain produces 2 antigen-binding fragments (**Fab**) and one crystallizable frag-

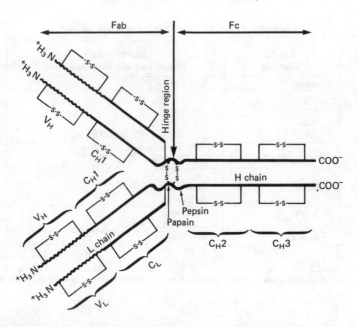

Figure 39–4. A simplified model for an IgG human antibody molecule showing the 4-chain basic structure and domains. V indicates variable region; C, the constant region; and the vertical arrow, the hinge region. Thick lines represent H and L chains; thin lines represent disulfide bonds. (Modified and reproduced, with permission, from Fudenberg HH & others [editors]: *Basic & Clinical Immunology,* 3rd ed. Lange, 1980.)

ment **(Fc).** The area in which papain cleaves the immunoglobulin molecule—ie, the region between the C_H1 and C_H2 domains—is referred to as the **hinge region.**

There are 2 general types of light chains, kappa (κ) and lambda (λ), which can be distinguished on the basis of structural differences in their C_L regions (Table 39–2). A given immunoglobulin molecule always contains two κ or two λ light chains, **never a mixture of κ and λ.** In humans, the κ chains are more frequent than λ chains in immunoglobulin molecules.

Five classes of H chains have been found in humans, and these classes can be distinguished by differences in their C_H regions (Table 39–2). The 5 classes of H chains are designated γ, α, μ, δ, and ϵ and vary in molecular weight from 50,000 to 70,000 (Table 39–2). The μ and ϵ chains each have four C_H domains rather than the usual 3. The type of H chain determines the class of immunoglobulin, and thus there are 5 immunoglobulin classes: **IgG, IgA, IgM, IgD,** and **IgE.** As shown in Table 39–2, many of the H chain classes can be further divided into subclasses on the basis of subtle structural differences in the C_H regions.

The variable regions of immunoglobulin molecules consist of the V_L and V_H domains and are quite heterogeneous. In fact, no 2 variable regions

Table 39–2. Properties of human immunoglobulin chains.*

Designation	H Chains					L Chains		Secretory Component	J Chain
	γ	α	μ	δ	ϵ	κ	λ	SC	J
Classes in which chains occur	IgG	IgA	IgM	IgD	IgE	All classes	All classes	IgA	IgA, IgM
Subclasses or subtypes	1,2,3,4	1,2	1,2	...	...	...	1,2,3,4	...	...
Allotypic variants	Gm(1)–(25)	A2m(1), (2)	...	...	...	Km(1)–(3)†	...	...	...
Molecular weight (approximate)	50,000‡	55,000	70,000	62,000	70,000	23,000	23,000	70,000	15,000
V region subgroups	V_HI –V_HIV					V_κI –V_κIV	V_λI –V_λVI		
Carbohydrate (average percentage)	4	10	15	18	18	0	0	16	8
Number of oligosaccharides	1	2 or 3	5	?	5	0	0	?	1

*Reproduced, with permission, from Fudenberg HH & others (editors): *Basic & Clinical Immunology,* 3rd ed. Lange, 1980.
†Formerly Inv(1)–(3).
‡60,000 for γ3.

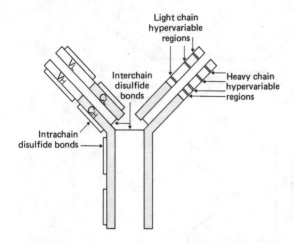

Light chain hypervariable regions

Interchain disulfide bonds

Heavy chain hypervariable regions

Intrachain disulfide bonds

Figure 39–5. Schematic model of an IgG molecule showing approximate positions of the hypervariable regions in heavy and light chains. (Modified and reproduced, with permission, from Fudenberg HH & others: *Basic & Clinical Immunology,* 3rd ed. Lange, 1980.)

from different humans have been found to have identical amino acid sequences. However, there are discernible patterns between the regions from different individuals, and these shared patterns have been divided into 3 main groups based on the degree of amino acid sequence homology. There is a V_κ group for kappa L chains, a V_λ group for lambda L chains, and a V_H group for the H chains. At higher resolution, there are even subgroups within each of these 3 groups.

Thus, within the variable regions there are some positions that are relatively invariable to account for the groups and subgroups. Upon comparing variable regions from different light chains of the same group or subgroup or different heavy chains from the same group or subgroup, it is apparent that there are **hypervariable regions** interspersed between the relatively invariable (subgroup-determining) positions (Fig 39–5). L chains have 3 hypervariable regions (in V_L), and H chains have 4 (in V_H).

The constant regions of the immunoglobulin molecules, particularly the C_H2 and C_H3 (and C_H4 of IgM and IgE), which constitute the Fc fragment, are responsible for the class-specific functions of the different immunoglobulin molecules (Table 39–3). Some immunoglobulins such as immune IgG exist only in the basic tetrameric structure, while others such as IgA and IgM can exist as higher order polymers of 2, 3 (IgA) or 5 (IgM) tetrameric units (Fig 39–6).

The L chains and H chains are synthesized as separate molecules and are subsequently assembled within the B cell or plasma cell into the mature immunoglobulin molecule, all of which are **glycoproteins** (Table 39–2).

Each immunoglobulin light chain is the product of at least 3 separate structural genes: a variable region (V_L) gene, a joining region (J) gene (bearing no relationship to the J chain of IgA or IgM), and a constant region (C_L) gene. Each heavy chain is the product of at least 4 different genes: a variable region (V_H) gene, a joining region (J) gene, a diversity region (D) gene, and a constant region (C_H) gene. Thus, the "one gene, one protein" concept is invalid. The molecular mechanisms responsible for the generation of the single immunoglobulin chains from multiple structural genes are discussed in Chapters 28 and 30.

Each person is capable of generating antibodies directed against perhaps 1 million different antigens. The generation of such immense antibody diversity

Table 39–3. Properties of human immunoglobulins.*

	IgG	IgA	IgM	IgD	IgE
H chain class	γ	α	μ	δ	ϵ
H chain subclass	$\gamma1, \gamma2, \gamma3, \gamma4$	$\alpha1, \alpha2$	$\mu1, \mu2$		
L chain type	κ and λ	κ and λ	κ and λ	κ and λ	κ and λ
Molecular formula	$\gamma_2 L_2$	$\alpha_2 L_2$† or $(\alpha_2 L_2)_2 SC\S J$‡	$(\alpha_2 L_2)_5 J$‡	$\delta_2 L_2$	$\epsilon_2 L_2$
Sedimentation coefficient (S)	6–7	7	19	7–8	8
Molecular weight (approximate)	150,000	160,000† 400,000**	900,000	180,000	190,000
Electrophoretic mobility (average)	γ	Fast γ to β	Fast γ to β	Fast γ	Fast γ
Complement fixation (classica)	+	0	++++	0	0
Serum concentration (approximate; mg/dL)	1000	200	120	3	0.05
Placental transfer	+	0	0	0	0
Reaginic activity	?	0	0	0	++++
Antibacterial lysis	+	+	+++	?	?
Antiviral activity	+	+++	+	?	?

*Reproduced, with permission, from Fudenberg HH & others (editors): *Basic & Clinical Immunology,* 3rd ed. Lange, 1980.
†For monomeric serum IgA.
‡J chain.
§Secretory component.
**For secretory IgA.

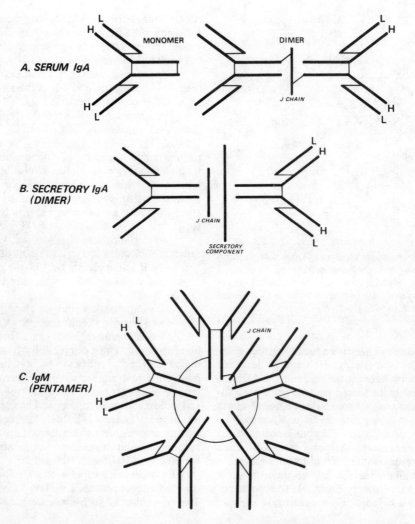

Figure 39–6. Highly schematic illustration of polymeric human immunoglobulins. Polypeptide chains are represented by thick lines; disulfide bonds linking different polypeptide chains are represented by thin lines. (Reproduced, with permission, from Fudenberg HH & others: *Basic & Clinical Immunology,* 3rd ed. Lange, 1980.)

appears to depend upon the combinations of the various structural genes contributing to the formation of each immunoglobulin chain.

In most humoral immune responses, antibodies with identical specificity but of different classes are generated in a specific chronologic order in response to the immunogen (immunizing antigen). A single type of immunoglobulin light chain can combine with an antigen-specific μ chain to generate a specific IgM molecule. Subsequently, the same antigen-specific light chain combines with an α chain with an identical V_H region to generate an IgA molecule with antigen specificity identical to that of the original IgM molecule. Subsequently, the same light chain can combine with a γ heavy chain, again containing the identical V_H region, to form an IgG molecule with identical antigen specificity. These 3 classes (IgM, IgA, and IgG) of immunoglobulin molecules against the same antigen have identical variable domains of

both their light chains and heavy chains and are said to share an **idiotype.** The different class **isotypes** are determined by the C_H regions combined with the same antigen-specific V_H region. One aspect of the genetic regulatory mechanisms responsible for the switching of the C_H region gene is discussed in Chapter 30.

Disorders of immunoglobulins include increased production of specific classes of immunoglobulins or even specific immunoglobulin molecules, the latter by clonal tumors of plasma cells called **myelomas. Hypogammaglobulinemia** may be restricted to a single class of immunoglobulin molecules (eg, IgA or IgG) or may involve underproduction of all classes of immunoglobulins (IgA, IgD, IgE, IgG, and IgM). The disorders of immunoglobulin levels are almost without exception due to disordered rates of immunoglobulin production or secretion, for which there can be many causes.

BLOOD CLOTTING

Hemostasis is the cessation of bleeding that follows traumatic interruption of vascular integrity. There are 4 phases to hemostasis. The **first phase** is **constriction** of the injured vessel to diminish blood flow distal to the injury. The **second phase** consists of formation of a loose **platelet plug,** or white thrombus, at the site of injury. **Collagen** exposed at the site of injury acts as a binding site for platelets, which, in response to binding collagen, undergo disruption of their internal structure and release thromboxane and **ADP.** These induce other platelets to adhere to those bound to collagen, forming the loose and temporary platelet plug. This phase of hemostasis is measured by determining the **bleeding time.** The **third phase** is the formation of the red thrombus (blood clot). The **fourth phase** is the partial or complete **dissolution** of the clot.

There are 3 types of thrombi or clots. The white thrombus is composed of platelets and fibrin and is relatively poor in erythrocytes. It forms at the site of an injury or abnormal vessel wall, particularly in areas of rapid blood flow (arteries). A second type of thrombus is a disseminated fibrin deposit in small vessels (capillaries).

The **red thrombus** is the third type of clot and consists of red cells and fibrin. The red thrombus morphologically resembles the clot formed in a test tube. It can form in vivo in areas of **retarded blood flow** without any abnormal vascular wall, or it may form at the site of the **injury** or **abnormal vessel wall** in conjunction with the initiating platelet plug. Initiation of the clot formation in response to tissue injury is carried out by the **extrinsic pathway.** The initiation of the pure red thrombus in an area of restricted blood flow or in response to an abnormal vessel wall without tissue injury is carried out by the **intrinsic pathway.** The intrinsic and extrinsic pathways converge in a **final common pathway**—the activation of prothrombin to thrombin and the thrombin-catalyzed conversion of fibrinogen to the fibrin clot.

Table 39–4. Numerical system for nomenclature of blood clotting factors. The numbers have no relationship to the order in which the factors act.

Factor	Name
I	Fibrinogen
II	Prothrombin
IV	Calcium
V	Labile factor, proaccelerin, accelerator (Ac-) globulin
VII	Proconvertin, serum prothrombin conversion accelerator (SPCA), cothromboplastin, autoprothrombin I
VIII	Antihemophilic factor, antihemophilic globulin (AHG)
IX	Plasma thromboplastin component (PTC) (Christmas factor)
X	Stuart-Prower factor
XI	Plasma thromboplastin antecedent (PTA)
XII	Hageman factor
XIII	Laki-Lorand factor (LLF)

The Conversion of Fibrinogen to Fibrin by Thrombin

Fibrinogen* (factor I; see Fig 39–2 and Table 39–4) is a soluble plasma protein, 46 nm in length, with a molecular weight of 340,000, which consists of 6 polypeptide chains. The 6 chains are two Aα chains, two Bβ chains, and two γ chains, making the structure Aα_2 Bβ_2 γ_2. The ends of the fiber-shaped fibrinogen molecule are **highly negatively charged,** the negative charges being contributed by a large number of aspartate and glutamate residues in the A portion of the Aα chains and the B portions of the Bβ chains (Fig 39–7). In addition, the B portion of the Bβ chains contains the unusual negatively charged tyrosine O-sulfate residue. These negatively charged termini of the fibrinogen molecules not only contribute to its water solubility but also repulse the termini of other fibrinogen molecules, thereby preventing aggregation.

Thrombin is a 34,000-MW serine **protease** that

---

*Except for fibrinogen and prothrombin (and their activated products) and Ca^{2+}, all clotting factors will be referred to by their designated roman numerals (Table 39–4).

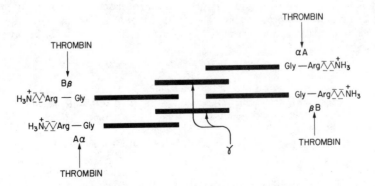

Figure 39–7. Diagrammatic representation of fibrinogen, its (Aα Bβ γ)$_2$ structure, charged termini, and the sites of thrombin cleavage (arrows) of four Arg-Gly peptide bonds.

consists of 2 polypeptide chains and hydrolyzes four Arg-Gly peptide bonds in fibrinogen (Fig 39–7). These 4 peptide bonds are the 2 between the A and α portions of the 2 Aα chains and the 2 between the B and β portions of the Bβ chains. Removal of the A and B portions of the fibrinogen molecule releases these negatively charged **fibrinopeptides** and generates the **fibrin monomer,** which has the subunit structure ($\alpha\beta\gamma)_2$. These long insoluble fibrin monomers spontaneously associate in a regularly staggered array to form the insoluble **fibrin polymer clot.** The A and B fibrinopeptides consist of only 18 amino acid residues; thus, the fibrin monomer retains 97% of the amino acid residues of fibrinogen. It is the formation of this fibrin polymer that traps red cells, platelets, and other components to form the red thrombus or the white thrombus (platelet plug). The initial fibrin clot is a rather weak one, held together only by the noncovalent staggered array of insoluble fibrin monomers.

Thrombin, in addition to converting fibrinogen to fibrin, also converts factor XIII to active factor XIII (XIII$_a$). Factor XIII$_a$ is a **transglutaminase.** The transglutaminase covalently **cross-links** fibrin monomers by forming a specific peptide bond between the γ-carboxyl group of glutamine and the ϵ-amino group of Lys (Fig 39–8). This strengthening of the initial fibrin clot contributes to retraction of the clot that can be observed in the test tube. Individuals with an inherited deficiency of factor XIII have a bleeding tendency because they cannot form a stable fibrin clot.

The activity of thrombin must be carefully controlled in order to avoid the formation of uncalled for, potentially catastrophic blood clots. This control is exerted by 2 mechanisms. One is the existence of a thrombin antagonist called antithrombin III (see below). The second mechanism involves the synthesis and circulation of a catalytically **inactive thrombin zymogen, prothrombin.** Prothrombin, or factor II, is synthesized in the liver and contains the vitamin K-dependent Gla residues (see Chapter 11). Prothrombin is a 72,000-MW single-chain glycoprotein; its primary and secondary structure is represented in Fig 39–9. The amino-terminal region of prothrombin, indicated by 1 in Fig 39–9, contains up to fourteen Gla residues. The dotted line represents a disulfide bridge between region A and region B of prothrombin. The serine-dependent active protease site is indicated by the arrow.

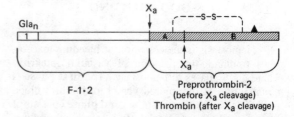

Figure 39–9. Diagrammatic representation of prothrombin. The amino terminus is to the left; region 1 contains all the Gla residues. The sites of cleavage by factor X$_a$ are shown and the products named. The site of the catalytically active serine residue is indicated by ▲. The A and B chains of active thrombin (shaded) are held together by the disulfide bridge.

The **activation of prothrombin occurs on the platelet** and requires platelet anionic phospholipid, Ca^2, factor V$_a$, and factor X$_a$. The phospholipids on the internal side of the platelet plasma membrane must be exposed as a result of the collagen-induced platelet disruption and degranulation. These phospholipids bind Ca^{2+} and prothrombin, the latter at the Gla-containing N-terminal region. The platelets also contain factor V, which, when activated as factor V$_a$, binds to specific receptors in the platelet membrane (Fig 39–10). Factor V$_a$ acts as a receptor for factor X$_a$, which in turn binds prothrombin in the F-1.2 region (Fig 39–9). Factor X$_a$ is a serine protease also and cleaves the catalytically inactive prothrombin at the sites indicated in Fig 39–9, and the amino portion of prothrombin is released. The disulfide bridge holds together the thrombin A and B polypeptides that have been generated by the X$_a$ cleavages.

The bridging of the phospholipid via Ca^{2+} to the Gla residues of prothrombin accelerates the activation of prothrombin 50- to 100-fold, apparently as a result of providing a high local concentration of the prothrombin and factor X$_a$ (Fig 39–10). Factor V$_a$ adds about a 350-fold acceleration, also as the result of locally concentrating factor X$_a$.

Factor V$_a$, which is generated by thrombin, is also subsequently **inactivated by thrombin,** thereby providing a means of limiting the activation of prothrombin to thrombin.

Prothrombin can also be activated by staphylocoagulase as a result of a simple conformational alteration not involving cleavage of the molecule.

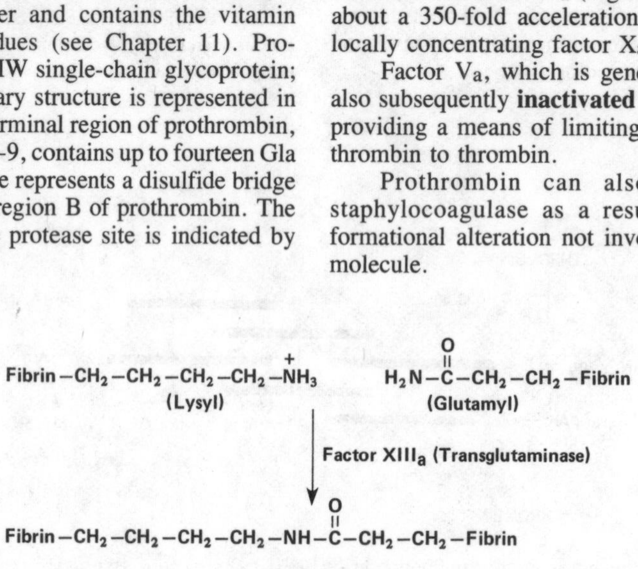

$$\underset{\text{(Lysyl)}}{\text{Fibrin}-CH_2-CH_2-CH_2-CH_2-\overset{+}{N}H_3} \qquad \underset{\text{(Glutamyl)}}{H_2N-\overset{\overset{\text{O}}{\|}}{C}-CH_2-CH_2-\text{Fibrin}}$$

Factor XIII$_a$ (Transglutaminase)

$$\text{Fibrin}-CH_2-CH_2-CH_2-CH_2-NH-\overset{\overset{\text{O}}{\|}}{C}-CH_2-CH_2-\text{Fibrin}$$

Figure 39–8. Cross-linking of fibrin monomers by activated factor XIII.

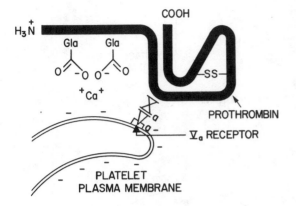

Figure 39–10. Diagrammatic representation of the binding of factors V_a, X_a, Ca^{2+}, and prothrombin to the platelet plasma membrane.

Activation of Factor X_a

Activation of factor X_a occurs at the site at which the intrinsic and extrinsic pathways join to form **the final common pathway** (Fig 39–11). Factor X is a zymogen (MW 55,000) of a serine protease and contains Gla residues. As in prothrombin, the Gla residues of factor X are responsible for the calcium-mediated binding of factor X to the acidic phospholipids of platelet membranes. In order to convert factor X to factor X_a, an Arg-Ile bond must be cleaved by still another serine protease. There are 2 serine proteases capable of cleaving the specific Arg-Ile bond of factor X.

The Extrinsic Pathway for Generating Factor X_a

Factor VII_a operates exclusively in the extrinsic pathway in conjunction with tissue factor to cleave this Arg-Ile bond and generate X_a. This extrinsic pathway is very **rapid in response to tissue injury.** The precursor of factor VII_a is factor VII, another

Gla-containing glycoprotein synthesized in the liver. Factor VII can be cleaved by thrombin or factor X_a. Factor VII is a zymogen but has rather high endogenous activity. The **tissue factor** necessary to accelerate the attack of factor VII or VII_a on factor X is abundant in **placenta, lung,** and **brain.**

While there is approximately 3 mg of fibrinogen in 1 mL of plasma, there is only 0.01 mg of factor X per milliliter of plasma. What this means is that the clotting system must provide the amplification. Conversion of factor X to X_a is an autocatalytic process and therefore an **amplification system.** In this group of reactions, it is difficult to know which came first, the chicken or the egg—II_a (thrombin) or X_a (Fig 39–11).

The Intrinsic Pathway for Generating Factor X_a

The intrinsic pathway for the generation of X_a commences with the exposure of **prekallikrein, high-molecular-weight kininogen, factor XII,** and **factor XI** to an activating surface, perhaps collagen in vivo (Fig 39–12). Glass or kaolin will provide an activating surface for in vitro tests of the intrinsic pathway. Exposure to the activating surface makes factor XII more labile to proteolysis by kallikrein. Factor XII_a is generated by kallikrein and attacks prekallikrein to generate more kallikrein, setting up a reciprocal activation. Factor XII_a releases bradykinin from high-molecular-weight kininogen and activates factor XI to XI_a. Factor IX, a Gla-containing zymogen, is activated in a 2-step reaction by factor XI_a. Factor IX_a, in the presence of calcium and acid phospholipids, slowly **activates factor X by cleaving the same Arg-Ile bond** that factor VII_a of the extrinsic system hydrolyzes. The factor IX_a–catalyzed activation of factor X is accelerated about 500-fold by the presence of **factor VIII** or VIII_a. Factor VIII probably requires activation by minute quantities of thrombin to form factor VIII_a. **Factor VIII is not a protease** but probably serves as a receptor for factor IX_a as it cleaves the Arg-Ile bond of factor X. The **intrinsic pathway is**

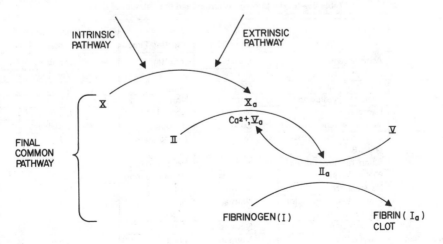

Figure 39–11. Relationship between the intrinsic, extrinsic, and final common pathways of blood clotting.

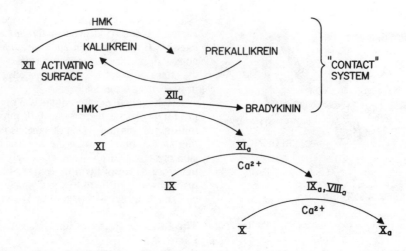

Figure 39–12. The intrinsic pathway for activating factor X to X_a. HMK is high-molecular-weight kininogen.

slow, because it involves many factors operating in a **cascade mechanism** to generate factor X_a (Fig 39–12).

Table 39–5 lists many of the inherited deficiencies of the clotting system in humans. The most common deficiency is that of factor VIII, which produces a disease known as **hemophilia A.** The X chromosome–linked deficiency of factor VIII has played a major role in the history of the royal families of Europe.

Factor VIII seems to have a second function in hemostasis. Individuals with **von Willebrand's disease** have an autosomal dominant defect in **platelet adherence** and a deficiency of factor VIII clotting activity (and antigenic material). Individuals with hemophilia A lack only factor VIII clotting activity and have normal platelet adherence. The platelet adherence factor (von Willebrand factor) is part of or tightly associates with the factor VIII molecule and may con-

tribute an oligosaccharide component to that glycoprotein. Von Willebrand's disease may be an inherited defect of a specific **oligosaccharide** moiety. The latter probably contributes to the antigenicity of factor VIII as well as to the platelet adherence function. Hemophilia A is a factor VIII **protein** defect that interrupts its clotting function but not its oligosaccharide or platelet adherence function.

Clotting Tests

The **bleeding time** determination mentioned above reflects the effectiveness of the initial platelet plug formation at the site of vascular injury. The **Rumpel-Leede** tourniquet test determines capillary fragility and initial platelet plug formation.

All in vitro clotting tests depend upon the formation of a **visible fibrin clot as the end point.** In order to form a visible fibrin clot, only about 10% of the fibrinogen normally present in plasma must be con-

Table 39–5. Hemorrhagic disorders and their abnormalities.

Factor	Disorder	Bleeding Time	Clotting Time	Activated Partial Thromboplastin Time	Prothrombin Time
I	Afibrinogenemia	Variable	Infinite	Infinite	Infinite
II	Hypoprothrombinemia	Normal	Normal to long	Variable	Long
V	Parahemophilia	Normal	Long	Long	Long
VII	Factor VII deficiency	Normal	Normal	Normal	Long
VIII	Hemophilia A	Normal	Normal to long	Long	Normal
VIII	Von Willebrand's disease	Long	Variable	Variable	Normal
IX	Christmas disease, hemophilia B	Normal	Normal to long	Long	Normal
X	Stuart factor deficiency	Normal	Normal to long	Long	Long
XI	PTA deficiency	Variable	Normal to long	Long	Normal
XII	Hageman trait	Normal	Long	Long	Normal
XIII	Fibrin-stabilizing factor deficiency	Normal	Normal	Normal	Normal
Prekallikrein	Fletcher trait	Normal	Long	Long	Normal
High-molecular-weight kininogen	Fitzgerald trait	Normal	Long	Long	Normal

verted to fibrin; thus, all of the clotting tests are insensitive to all but the most severe reductions in fibrinogen concentration. In the cascade system of blood coagulation, the clotting factors function as both enzymes and substrates for other enzymes, and in the latter role the factor concentrations may be relatively high or relatively low. Variations in the concentrations of a given factor therefore may or may not have major effects on the overall rate of fibrin clot formation. The effect will depend upon whether the factor is functioning as an enzyme or as a substrate and—if a substrate—upon whether its concentration is high or low relative to the K_m of the enzyme acting upon it. The design and use of the various clotting tests depends upon whether one wishes to determine the concentration of a factor or factors that participate in the intrinsic system, the extrinsic system, or the final common pathway of fibrin clot formation.

The **one-stage prothrombin time** is a test of the **extrinsic pathway** and the **final common pathway** of clotting. It is performed by adding a tissue factor to the unknown plasma and determining the time necessary for formation of the visible fibrin clot, ie, coagulation. The tissue factor, along with factor VII, activates factor X to X_a in the presence of factor V_a, Ca^{2+}, and platelet phospholipids. This complex on the platelet membrane converts prothrombin to thrombin, which in turn catalyzes the formation of fibrin from fibrinogen. Thus, a deficiency of factor II, V, VII, or X or a severe deficiency of fibrinogen will prolong the prothrombin time. Normal **serum** contains factors VII and X; therefore, if normal serum corrects the prothrombin time, the defect must be due to a deficiency of one of those 2 factors.

The **clotting time** is determined by introducing freshly drawn whole blood into small glass test tubes. Care must be taken not to introduce any tissue factor from the site of venipuncture. In effect, the blood is gently agitated at regular intervals to determine the time required for coagulation. In this test, the **intrinsic pathway** is activated by exposure of whole blood to the glass surface of the tube. It therefore assays the **intrinsic pathway** and the **final common pathway.** Thus, the clotting time is dependent upon all clotting factors except factors VII and XIII. Although the clotting time is widely used in clinical medicine, it is not sensitive to mild deficiencies of factors VIII, IX, or XI.

The **activated partial thromboplastin time** involves the addition of acid phospholipids and kaolin (an activating surface) to plasma to make certain that platelets are not rate-limiting and that factors XI and XII are fully activated. Therefore, the normal response

time of 35–45 seconds requires a nearly normal concentration of **all of the factors in the intrinsic pathway.** Accordingly, it is more useful than the bedside clotting time determination.

The **thromboplastin generation test** activates the intrinsic system to form a prothrombinase, or "plasma thromboplastin." The generated prothrombinase is then assayed on normal plasma, which contains prothrombin. The generated prothrombinase itself will not, of course, clot the fibrinogen; it is only capable of activating prothrombin to thrombin, which in turn will catalyze the formation of the fibrin clot from fibrinogen. Factor VII does not participate in this test, nor does the patient's prothrombin. The test involves mixing the patient's plasma after adsorption (containing factors I, V, VIII, XI, XII) with the patient's serum (containing factors VII, IX, X, XI, XII) and normal platelets (or a platelet substitute) and Ca^{2+}. Thus, everything except prothrombin should have been provided, and the prothrombinase generated is assayed on normal plasma containing prothrombin. If no clot forms and the addition of normal serum or normal plasma corrects the defect, one can narrow down the missing factor or factors (Table 39–6). If only normal serum corrects the defect, factor IX or X must be defective in the patient's serum. If only normal plasma corrects the defect, factor V or VIII must be defective in the patient's plasma. If plasma alone and serum alone both correct the defect, factor XI or XII must be missing from both the patient's serum and plasma. Further studies using plasma or serum from individuals known to be defective in specific single factors will allow one to determine which specific factor is defective. Antisera specific to the various factors are also available for determining which specific component of the clotting system is missing or defective. Table 39–5 lists the inherited deficiencies of different clotting factors and the response of blood from those patients to the various in vivo and in vitro tests.

Anticoagulants

Three naturally occurring antithrombin activities exist in normal plasma. Alpha$_1$-antitrypsin contributes only a minor antithrombin activity, but a specific α_2 globulin is responsible for about 25% of the antithrombin activity present in plasma. The α_2 globulin forms an irreversible complex with thrombin but does not interfere with the polymerization of preformed fibrin monomer. The α_2 globulin is referred to as α_2 plasmin inhibitor because it also inactivates plasmin, another serine protease with fibrinolytic activity discussed below.

Table 39–6. Blood clotting factors normally present in plasma, adsorbed plasma, and serum.

Fluid	I	II	V	VII	VIII	IX	X	XI	XII
Plasma	+	+	+		+			+	+
Adsorbed plasma	+		+		+			+	+
Serum				+		+	+	+	+

The major antithrombin activity is contributed by antithrombin III. **Antithrombin III** has some endogenous activity but is greatly **activated** by the presence of **heparin,** a strongly anionic proteoglycan (see Chapter 32). Heparin probably binds to a specific cationic site of antithrombin III, inducing a conformational change that promotes the binding of antithrombin III to **all serine proteases,** including trypsin, chymotrypsin, and plasmin. In the clotting system, antithrombin III will **inhibit the activity of thrombin, IX$_a$, X$_a$, XI$_a$,** and **XII$_a$.** Heparin appears to dissociate from antithrombin III as the latter binds to the serine proteases. Individuals with inherited deficiencies of antithrombin III are prone to develop frequent and severe widespread clots, providing evidence that antithrombin III has physiologic functions and that the **clotting system in humans is normally very dynamic.**

Heparin is frequently used in clinical medicine to inhibit clotting. Its major anticoagulant action depends upon its activation of antithrombin III, which in turn inhibits the serine proteases described above. Heparin therapy can be monitored by the whole blood clotting time and by the activated partial thromboplastin time, both of which are dependent upon the intrinsic and final common pathways for clot formation. The prothrombin time may also be prolonged by high-dose intermittent heparin therapy but usually is not prolonged by continuous intravenous administration of heparin. In addition, heparin in low doses appears to coat the endothelial lining of vessels and perhaps thereby reduces the activation of the intrinsic pathway. The anticoagulant effects of heparin can be antagonized by the use of strongly cationic polypeptides such as protamine to compete with the antithrombin III cationic region for the binding of the polyanionic heparin.

The **coumarin** drugs, as described in Chapter 11, inhibit the vitamin K-dependent carboxylation of Glu to Gla residues at the amino-terminal regions of factors II, VII, IX, and X. These factors, all of which are synthesized in the liver, are dependent upon the Gla residues for maturation and thus normal function in the intrinsic, extrinsic, and final common pathways.

Thus, coumarin therapy can be monitored by the one-stage prothrombin time. The coumarin drugs seem to inhibit reduction of the quinone derivatives of vitamin K to the active hydroquinone forms. Thus, the administration of vitamin K will bypass the coumarin-induced block and allow maturation of the Gla-dependent clotting factors in the liver to occur. Reversal of coumarin effects by vitamin K takes place over 12–24 hours, whereas reversal of the anticoagulant effects of heparin by protamine is practically instantaneous, because of the nature of the antagonistic mechanisms.

Fibrinolysis

As described above, there is ample evidence that the blood clotting system is normally in a dynamic steady state in which fibrin clots are constantly being laid down and subsequently dissolved. **Plasmin** is a serine protease capable of digesting both fibrinogen and fibrin as well as factor V, VIII, complement, and various polypeptide hormones. Plasmin exists normally in plasma in a proenzyme or inactive form, **plasminogen.** Plasminogen activators of various types are found in most body tissues. The urine contains the proteolytic enzyme **urokinase,** which is also a serine protease and can cleave plasminogen at 2 sites, activating the protease activity of plasmin.

Plasminogen normally coprecipitates with fibrin and thus is **incorporated into fibrin deposits.** When activated, the plasmin in clots digests the fibrin to soluble fragments, dissolving the clot. Cross-linked fibrin clots are less sensitive to dissolution by plasmin.

There are a number of disorders, including cancers and shock, in which the concentrations of plasminogen activators increase. In addition, the antiplasmin activities contributed by alpha$_1$-antitrypsin and alpha$_2$ plasmin inhibitor may be impaired in diseases such as cirrhosis of the liver. Some bacterial products are capable of activating plasminogen without cleavage and may be responsible for the diffuse hemorrhage sometimes observed in patients with disseminated bacterial infections.

• • •

References

Deykin D: Thrombogenesis. *N Engl J Med* 1967;**276**:622.

Fudenberg HH & others (editors): *Basic & Clinical Immunology,* 3rd ed. Lange, 1980.

Genton E & others: Platelet-inhibiting drugs in the prevention of clinical thrombotic disease. (2 parts.) *N Engl J Med* 1975;**293**:1236, 1296.

Heimark RL & others: Surface activation of blood coagulation, fibrinolysis and kinin formation. *Nature* 1980;**286**:456.

Jackson CM, Nemerson Y: Blood coagulation. *Annu Rev Biochem* 1980;**49**:767.

Kane WH & others: Factor V$_a$–dependent binding of factor X$_a$ to human platelets. *J Biol Chem* 1980;**255**:1170.

Ratinoff OD: Hereditary disorders of hemostasis. In: *The Metabolic Basis of Inherited Disease,* 4th ed. Stanbury JB, Wyngaarden JB, Fredrickson DS (editors). McGraw-Hill, 1978.

Stenflo J, Suttie JW: Vitamin K-dependent formation of gamma-carboxyglutamic acid. *Annu Rev Biochem* 1977;**46**:157.

Weiss HJ: Platelet physiology and abnormalities of platelet function. (2 parts.) *N Engl J Med* 1975;**293**:531, 580.

Water & Minerals | 40

David W. Martin, Jr., MD

WATER

The mass of the human body consists mostly of water. Water forms an essential part of all body cells and fluids; it enters into biochemical reactions, acts as a solvent for many ions and molecules, provides a medium of transport for intra- and extracellular processes, and serves as a lubricant. It also regulates body temperature by means of evaporation from lungs and skin.

The total amount of body water ranges from just over 50% to nearly 90% of body weight in direct proportion to body surface area. The proportion of weight as water declines with age and with increased body fat content; it is higher in athletes than in nonathletes.

BODY WATER

Body water is distributed between 2 main compartments: **intracellular** and **extracellular.** Intracellular water comprises 50–60% of the total body water of normal healthy adults. Extracellular water includes that present in plasma, lymph, interstitial fluid, connective tissue, cartilage, skin, bone, and secretory fluids. Because most cells of the body are freely permeable to water, the distinction between intracellular and extracellular water is somewhat arbitrary.

The electrolyte composition of blood plasma and intracellular fluid is shown in Fig 40–1. Blood plasma differs only slightly from interstitial fluid. Because plasma proteins are largely retained within blood vessels, the interstitial fluid utilizes as anion Cl^- rather than plasma proteins. Thus, the composition of plasma can be taken to represent that of extracellular fluid in general. Fig 40–1 reveals 3 major differences in composition between intracellular and extracellular fluids: (1) **Potassium is the principal cation within cells,** whereas sodium predominates in extracellular fluid. (2) Because of the many phosphorylated organic compounds present within cells, **phosphate is the primary intracellular anion;** chloride replaces it in extracellular fluids. (3) Finally, the intracellular protein concentration is higher than that of blood plasma.

WATER BALANCE

In a normal healthy person, total body water volume remains remarkably constant, fluctuating less than 1% of body weight per day, and this constancy is maintained in spite of large variations in water intake.

Typical water balance data for normal human adults are presented in Table 40–1. The average daily intake and output of water in this study was 2750 mL. There is wide individual variation in total intake and output and in day-to-day water balance.

WATER LOSSES

Water is required to replace fluid lost through the skin, lungs, and gastrointestinal tract and to accompany renal excretion of urea, salts, and other osmotically active solutes. The amounts of these **obligatory losses** vary significantly with climate, activity level, state of health, and diet. Hot temperatures, dry climates, vigorous physical activity, and fever all increase water losses from the skin and lungs. These factors can also increase sweat losses to as much as 2.5 L/h. Water secreted into the gastrointestinal tract is usually reabsorbed, but diarrhea and other intestinal disease can result in very large water losses.

Total urine volume generally depends on water intake, but a minimum amount of water—an obligatory volume—is required to accompany the excretion of osmotically active solutes, especially urea and

Table 40–1. Average daily intake and output of water in a normal adult human.*

Water Intake (mL)			Water Output (mL)		
Source	Obligatory	Facultative	Source	Obligatory	Facultative
Drink	650	1000	Urine	700	1000
Preformed	750	....	Skin	500	....
Oxidative	350	....	Lungs	400	....
			Feces	150	....
Subtotals	1750	1000	Subtotals	1750	1000
Total	2750	....	Total	2750	....

*Slightly modified and reproduced, with permission, from Wolf AV: *Thirst.* Thomas, 1958.

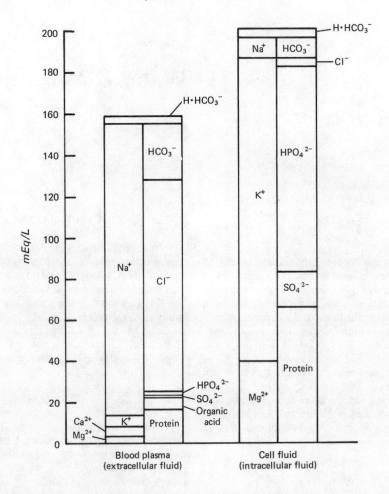

Figure 40–1. Electrolyte composition of blood plasma and intracellular fluid. Blood plasma is typical of extracellular fluid except that its protein content is higher than that of interstitial fluid. (Modified from Gamble.)

sodium chloride. The amount of these substances excreted depends in turn on dietary intake of protein and salt.

The effect of diet on obligatory urine production can be estimated by assuming that each gram of dietary protein contributes 5 milliosmoles (mOsm), and each gram of salt yields 34 mOsm (1 mOsm = mmol solute × n, where n = the number of particles produced by dissociation). These numbers are derived from the following calculations: Protein is approximately 16% nitrogen; thus, 1 g of protein yields 0.16 g N. This nitrogen is excreted as urea (MW = 60); N comprises 28/60 of urea. Thus, each gram of protein yields 0.3 g (300 mg) of urea, and 300/60, or 5 mOsm. One gram of NaCl yields 34 mOsm, because 1 g/58.5 MW = 17 mmol × 2 particles (Na$^+$ and Cl$^-$). A typical diet may contain 100 g of protein and 10 g salt per day; it produces (100 × 5) + (10 × 34) = 840 mOsm. As the adult kidney can concentrate urine to about 1400 mOsm/L, an obligatory volume of 700 mL (840/1400) of water is required to excrete these solutes.

WATER INTAKE

To maintain fluid balance, all water losses must be replaced. Most water intake derives from drinking water or other beverages or from the preformed water content of food (see Table 40–4). Water is also formed as a product of molecular oxidation reactions. The oxidation of 1 g each of starch, protein, and fat yields 0.6, 0.41, and 1.07 g of water, respectively, but the total amount of metabolic water is quite small relative to that ingested in food or drink.

Because variable factors such as climate and activity are important in determination of water intake, no minimum daily water requirement has been established. For persons in moderate climates, 1 mL/kcal for adults and 1.5 mL/kcal for infants seems adequate, but these amounts must be adjusted to account for the increased fluid needs of exceptionally active people and those in hot climates; of patients with fever, vomiting, diarrhea, or excessive urine losses; and of persons taking diuretics or high-protein diets.

Because variations in water balance of only 1–2% lead to illness or even death, water intake must precisely balance water losses. This balance is achieved by a regulatory system located in the hypothalamus (see Chapter 36).

MINERALS

Of the large number of chemical elements found in the human body, only a few have demonstrable biochemical or physiologic functions. These elements can be considered in 5 groups. The first includes carbon, hydrogen, oxygen, nitrogen, and sulfur, the **major components of body molecules.** These elements are obtained through intake of water and food fats, carbohydrates, and proteins. The second group includes the nutritionally important **minerals** — calcium, phosphorus, magnesium, sodium, potassium, and chloride—that are required in the diet in amounts greater than 100 mg/d. The **trace elements**—chromium, cobalt, copper, iodine, iron, manganese, molybdenum, selenium, and zinc—are required in the human diet in much smaller amounts. Fluorine, which is essential for certain animal species but is not known to be required in the human diet, is usually considered to be part of this group, because fluorides have a well-defined role in the prevention of tooth decay. A fourth group contains additional elements required for animal nutrition but having no known essential functions in humans: arsenic, cadmium, nickel, silicon, tin, and vanadium. The final group contains elements such as lead and mercury that are clearly toxic.

The nutritionally important minerals and trace elements are discussed in this chapter. Most of these elements share many common metabolic characteristics.

Absorption of Minerals

Most minerals (sodium and potassium are notable exceptions) form salts and other compounds that are relatively insoluble; they are not readily absorbed, and most ingested minerals are excreted in feces. Mineral absorption often requires specific carrier proteins; the

Table 40–2. Transport of trace elements in blood.

	Transferrin	Albumin	Amino Acids	Transco-balamin II	Globulins
Co				++	
Cr	+				
Cu		+	+		
Fe	++			(+)*	
Mn	+				++
Mo	(Not known)				
Se	(Not known)				
Zn	+	+			

*(+) = small amount.

Table 40–3. Normal routes of trace element excretion.

	Bile	Urine	Pancreatic Juice	Sweat	Mucosal Cell Sloughing
Co		++			
Cr	+	++			
Cu	++				
Fe					+
Mn	++				
Mo		+			
Se	(Not known)				
Zn	+	+	++	++	+

synthesis of these proteins serves as an important mechanism for control of mineral levels in the body. **Transport** and storage also require specific binding to carrier proteins. The transport molecules for trace metals in blood are shown in Table 40–2. **Excretion** of most minerals is accomplished by the kidneys, but many minerals are also secreted into the digestive juices and bile and lost in feces. The routes of excretion of the trace elements are summarized in Table 40–3.

Disorders Due to Mineral Excess or Deficiency

Deficient intake of all of the essential minerals eventually leads to defined clinical syndromes. Because body mineral concentrations are regulated at the level of absorption or excretion, circulating levels do not necessarily reflect intake. Instead, they represent an equilibrium between the amounts absorbed, utilized, stored, and excreted. Laboratory tests of serum or urine mineral levels are not always accurate indicators of intake. Mineral deficiency syndromes are rare among persons whose diet includes a sufficient variety of foods. When deficiency does occur, it is usually secondary to malabsorption, excess bleeding (iron), renal disease (calcium), or other clinical problems.

Excess intake of almost all of the minerals produces toxic symptoms. For minerals regulated by absorption, toxicity occurs more commonly when control of absorption fails in some way.

Sources & Daily Requirements of Minerals

The essential minerals and trace elements are found in most foods, especially whole grain cereals, fruits and vegetables, dairy foods, and meats and fish, but they generally occur in these foods only in trace amounts. Thus, it is necessary to consume a sufficient quantity and variety of foods to meet nutritional requirements. The nutritional aspects of mineral metabolism are summarized in Chapter 41.

CALCIUM

Functions

The human body contains more calcium than any of the other essential minerals—as much as 1200 g in a

70-kg adult. At least 99% of the total is in bones and teeth. Most skeletal calcium is deposited as a form of hydroxyapatite, $Ca_{10}(PO_4)_6(OH)_2$, but bone also contains considerable amounts of noncrystalline calcium phosphates and carbonates as well as small amounts of other salts. These minerals comprise about 50% of the total skeletal mass; the remaining mass consists of an organic matrix of proteins, glycoproteins, and proteoglycans on which the calcium salts are deposited. Because **bone is constantly being remodeled,** its mineral levels reflect the equilibrium between daily deposits and withdrawals. As much as 700 mg of calcium may enter and leave the bones each day.

The immediate source of new bone calcium is that present in body fluids and cells. Although this amount is extremely small (< 10 g) relative to that in the skeletons, it is critically important to the regulation of a surprisingly large number of vital cellular activities: nerve and muscle function, hormonal actions, blood clotting, cellular motility, and many others. Because calcium is involved in the control of so many processes, it has been described as a "second messenger" that mediates cellular responses to a wide range of stimuli in a manner analogous to the regulatory actions of cyclic nucleotides. The action of calcium appears to be mediated by an intracellular receptor protein, **calmodulin,** that binds calcium ions when their concentration increases in response to a stimulus. Calmodulin has been found to be present in every nucleated cell type examined. When Ca^{2+} is bound to calmodulin, it modulates the activities of a great variety of enzymes, including those involved in cyclic nucleotide metabolism, protein phosphorylation, secretory function, muscle contraction, microtubule assembly, glycogen metabolism, and calcium flux.

The importance of Ca^{2+} in these activities is reflected in the precision with which plasma Ca^{2+} levels are regulated. Normal plasma contains the equivalent of 9–11 mg calcium per deciliter; the daily variation is rarely more than $\pm 3\%$. These narrow limits are maintained by the complex regulatory actions of vitamin D, parathyroid hormone, calcitonin, and other hormones (see Chapters 11 and 35).

Metabolism

Calcium is absorbed in the duodenum and proximal jejunum by means of a calcium-binding protein synthesized in response to the action of 1,25-dihydroxycholecalciferol (1,25-dihydroxyvitamin D_3). Absorption is inhibited by compounds that form insoluble calcium salts (oxalates, phytates, phosphates) and by undigested fat through formation of insoluble calcium soaps. A large part of ingested calcium is not absorbed and is excreted in feces.

Once absorbed, calcium is excreted through several routes. The kidney excretes calcium when the blood calcium level exceeds 7 mg/dL. A large amount of calcium is secreted into the intestinal lumen and mostly lost in feces; small amounts of calcium are also excreted in sweat. For any one individual, urine calcium remains relatively constant while fecal calcium varies widely in response to diet, suggesting that **calcium levels are well controlled at the level of absorption.** High-protein diets have been reported to cause significant increases in calcium excretion.

Deficiency

The symptoms of calcium deficiency include tetany and related muscle and neurologic disorders. These symptoms occur most commonly as a result of vitamin D deficiency, hypoparathyroidism, or renal insufficiency, but calcium deprivation is also a cause. When plasma levels fall below normal, bone calcium is mobilized, thus increasing circulating Ca^{2+}, and new bone formation is hindered. The net negative Ca^{2+} balance leads to **rickets** in children or **osteomalacia** in adults.

An additional factor that bears on bone mineral loss is the ratio of calcium to phosphorus (Ca:P) in the diet. In animals, a Ca:P ratio of 2:1 leads to maximal calcium absorption and minimal bone mineral losses, whereas high phosphate intakes enhance bone loss. In humans, high phosphorus intake leads to large fecal calcium losses. The ideal Ca:P ratio in humans is not known, but recent trends in food consumption patterns in the USA include significant increases in phosphorus consumption as a result of the increased use of phosphate food additives in processed foods and soft drinks. The Ca:P ratio in the current United States diet approaches 1:1.2 to 1:1.5. Whether this ratio is responsible for excess bone loss found in postmenopausal osteoporotic women is not yet clear.

Toxicity

Hypercalcemia does not seem to occur in normal persons as a result of high dietary intake, because excess calcium is simply not absorbed. Excessive intakes, however, may contribute to the high serum Ca^{2+} levels that accompany clinical disorders such as hyperparathyroidism, vitamin D intoxication, sarcoidosis, and cancer.

PHOSPHORUS

Phosphorus as **phosphate** plays a major role in the structure and function of all living cells. Hence, phosphorus depletion from simple dietary deficiency does not occur. Phosphate exists in cells as a free ion at a concentration of a few milliequivalents per liter and is also an integral component of nucleic acids, nucleotides, phospholipids, and some proteins. In the extracellular space, phosphate circulates as free ion and is present as hydroxyapatite, a major component of bone. All cells possess enzymes that can attach phosphates in **ester or acid anhydride linkages** to other molecules. Enzymes also exist both inside and outside of the cells for the removal of phosphates from phosphate-containing molecules. Included in the latter group of enzymes are several phosphatases that have important roles in the intestinal digestion of foodstuffs.

Free phosphate is absorbed in the mid jejunum

and enters the bloodstream by way of the portal circulation. The regulation of phosphate absorption is mediated by 1α,25-dihydroxycholecalciferol (1,25-dihydroxyvitamin D_3), discussed in Chapter 11. Phosphate participates in a regulatory loop with this active derivative of vitamin D_3. When the serum phosphate level is abnormally low, the formation of 1,25-dihydroxyvitamin D_3 in the renal tubule is stimulated, causing enhanced phosphate absorption from the intestine (see Fig 11–7).

The deposition of phosphate as hydroxyapatite in bone is regulated by parathyroid hormone levels. The 1,25-dihydroxyvitamin D_3 plays a permissive role in the parathyroid hormone–mediated mobilization of calcium and phosphate from bone.

Excretion of phosphate occurs primarily in the kidney and is under complex regulation. Eighty-five to 90% of plasma phosphate is filtered at the renal glomeruli, and the amount of phosphate excreted in urine represents the difference between the quantity filtered and that reabsorbed by the proximal and distal tubules of the kidney. 1,25-Dihydroxyvitamin D_3 stimulates reabsorption of phosphate along with calcium in the proximal tubule. However, parathyroid hormone diminishes the renal tubular reabsorption of phosphate and thereby overrides the effect of 1,25-dihydroxyvitamin D_3 on phosphate excretion. In the absence of a strong effect of parathyroid hormone, the kidney is able to respond to 1,25-dihydroxyvitamin D_3 by complete conservation of filtered phosphate.

The depletion of phosphate occurs as a result of diminished absorption from the intestine or excessive wasting through the kidney. The hypophosphatemic state affects most cell types. The effects on the skeleton and the hematologic systems have been most thoroughly studied. **Rickets** in children and **osteomalacia** in adults are the result of abnormal calcium and phosphate metabolism. In addition, there are abnormalities in the erythrocytes, leukocytes, and platelets and in the liver.

Phosphate toxicity is rare except when acute or chronic kidney failure prevents normal phosphate excretion. The presence of hyperphosphatemia is associated with renal disease, and the serum calcium level is usually depressed as a consequence of the regulatory effect phosphate has on the production of 1,25-dihydroxyvitamin D_3. **The absorption of dietary phosphates can be prevented by the use of antacids to bind phosphates in the intestinal lumen.** This will eventually result in return of the concentrations of serum phosphates toward normal and concomitant increase in 1,25-dihydroxyvitamin D_3. The latter will then promote calcium absorption from the intestine as discussed above.

MAGNESIUM

Magnesium ions are present in all cells. In essentially all reactions for which ATP is a substrate, the true substrate is Mg^{2+}-ATP. As such, Mg^{2+} is chelated between the beta and gamma phosphates and diminishes the dense anionic character of ATP, so that it can approach and bind reversibly to specific protein sites. Thus, the synthesis of all proteins, nucleic acids, nucleotides, lipids, and carbohydrates and the activation of muscle contraction require magnesium.

Although magnesium is widely available in natural foodstuffs, much Mg^{2+} and Ca^{2+} are lost during refining and processing of food. The absorption of Mg^{2+} occurs throughout the small intestine and apparently depends upon the load presented rather than any single factor, such as vitamin D. On a low-magnesium diet, more than three-fourths of dietary Mg^{2+} can be absorbed, whereas absorption may decrease to one-fourth on a high-magnesium diet. The absorption of Mg^{2+} is not an active process, and there is no common mechanism of transport of calcium and magnesium across the intestinal wall. In the plasma, most of the Mg^{2+} exists in a form that can be filtered by the kidney glomerulus. However, the kidney has an extraordinary ability to conserve Mg^{2+}, so that the daily loss on a low-magnesium diet is only about 1 mEq/d. On an average diet, the amount excreted in the urine is 35–45% of the daily intake. Magnesium deficiency is not uncommon. High levels of calcium, protein, and phosphate in the diet will diminish Mg^{2+} absorption from the intestine. Malabsorption in chronic diarrhea from any cause, protein-calorie malnutrition, and adult starvation in the form of alcoholism can all result in magnesium deficiency. The sudden termination of starvation by feeding protein and carbohydrate without cofactors such as thiamin and Mg^{2+} can lead to serious metabolic and neurologic disturbances. In the presence of chronic renal failure, magnesium requirements decline, but in renal tubular acidosis or diabetes mellitus, magnesium wasting by the kidneys increases the dietary requirement of Mg^{2+}. A number of drugs, including the diuretics, promote magnesium wastage. During lactation, magnesium requirements are increased.

Magnesium toxicity is rare in the presence of normal renal function. In patients in renal failure, hypermagnesemia can be an important medical problem. The depressant effects of magnesium on the nervous system usually dominate the toxicity of hypermagnesemia.

SODIUM

Sodium is the major cation (Na^+) of the **extracellular fluid** and is largely associated with chloride and bicarbonate in the regulation of acid-base equilibrium. Na^+ is also important in the maintenance of osmotic pressure of body fluids and thus in protection against excessive fluid loss. Although Na^+ is widely distributed in foodstuffs, the main dietary source is table salt (NaCl) used in cooking and seasoning. In general, meats contain more Na^+ than do vegetable foodstuffs, but some processed foods contain added NaCl.

The dietary consumption of NaCl depends greatly

upon cultural and individual eating habits. In the USA, 5–15 g of NaCl may be consumed daily by adults, but 90–95% of this intake is excreted in the urine. Na^+ is readily absorbed in the ileum, and little is present in feces. By mechanisms described in Chapter 36, the kidney is capable of conserving Na^+ at the expense of K^+ or H^+. Accordingly, the daily adult requirement for sodium is only a few milliequivalents. Most of this requirement is due to the nonurinary loss of sodium. The average daily intake of sodium is quite high in relation to the minimal requirement. In **susceptible individuals,** there is a clear relationship between Na^+ intake and diastolic **blood pressure.** Thus, the excessive and wasteful intake of sodium as NaCl may lead to or aggravate preexisting hypertension.

However, whenever a water intake of more than 4 L/d is required to replace sweat loss, extra NaCl should be provided. With prolonged exposure to high temperatures and excessive sweating, the Na^+ loss in sweat will be minimized by an adaptive process involving aldosterone.

Although extravascular Na^+ is in equilibrium with intravascular (plasma) Na^+, the concentration of the latter may not reflect total body stores of sodium. Accordingly, a patient with low serum Na^+ (hyponatremia) may not be depleted of body Na^+ but may have instead an excess of intravascular (and perhaps extravascular) water. Similarly, increased serum Na^+ (hypernatremia) can occur in the face of low or normal body Na^+ content if water depletion (dehydration) is present. In renal disease, the ability to conserve Na^+ is frequently lost, and severe disorders of sodium, chloride, potassium, and water balance can result.

POTASSIUM

Potassium is the principal cation (K^+) of the intracellular fluid. Accordingly, the major sources of dietary K^+ are the cellular materials we consume as foodstuffs; a dietary deficiency is extraordinarily rare except in severe protein-calorie malnutrition. Table 40–4 provides values for the K^+ contents of some common foodstuffs.

K^+ is readily absorbed in the small intestine in proportion to the presented load and circulates in the plasma. Potassium in extracellular fluid invades all tissues in the body and can have profound effects on the function of some organs, particularly depolarization and contraction of the heart.

The kidney cannot conserve K^+ nearly so effectively as it can Na^+. As mentioned above, the conservation of sodium is at the expense of potassium, an effect mediated by aldosterone. Thus, there is an obligatory potassium loss in normal renal function, and this obligatory loss amounts to approximately 40 mEq (equivalent to 160 mg) per day. When K^+ intake falls below this minimal requirement, the serum K^+ concentration drops, the intracellular K^+ begins to fall, and both the renal tubules and other cells of the body begin to utilize protons (H^+) in place of K^+. Thus, the

Table 40–4. Values for K^+ contents of some common foodstuffs.

	mEq K^+		mEq K^+
Almonds, 9–10	1.8	Egg (chicken)	1.8
Apple (½), raw, with skin	1.7	Fish, albacore, 3½ oz	7.5
		Frankfurter	3
Asparagus, raw, 5–6 spears	7	Ginger ale, 1 cup	0.03
		Grapes, Thompson seedless, ½ cup	2.8
Avocado (½)	15		
Banana (½), raw	9.6	Lamb, shoulder blade chop, 3½ oz	11
Beans, lima, 4 tsp	17		
Beef patty, ¼ lb	10	Milk, whole, 1 cup	9
Beer, 1 cup	1	Orange, 1 small	5.1
Bread, whole wheat, 1 slice	1.6	Orange juice, 1 cup	13
		Parsley, raw, 3½ oz	19
Butter, salted, 1 tsp	0.08	Peanut butter, 1 tsp	4.2
Cabbage, raw, 1 cup shredded	6	Pork, loin chop, 3½ oz	15
		Postum, instant, 2 tsp	3
Celery, raw, 1 large stalk	4	Potato, sweet, 1 small	6.2
Cheese, cheddar, ¾ inch cube	0.4	Potatoes, white raw, 2½ inch diameter	10
Chicken, broiler, 3½ oz	8	Prune juice, 1 cup	14
		Tomato juice, 1 cup	14
Cider, sweet, 1 cup	6	Turkey, roasted, 1 slice (3 X 2½ X ¼ inch)	4
Dates, raw, 10 medium	17		

intracellular H^+ concentration increases, producing an intracellular acidosis. The obligatory K^+ loss incurred by the renal tubules becomes an obligatory H^+ loss, as the renal tubules conserve Na^+ at the expense of H^+ rather than at the expense of K^+. This leads to an **extracellular alkalosis** and **intracellular acidosis.**

In renal failure, the obligatory K^+ loss may be much greater than normal. Similarly, the use of diuretic drugs increases the renal wasting of Na^+ and K^+. The deficiency of K^+ occurs frequently in the setting of inappropriate K^+ replacement during administration of intravenous fluids to replace gastrointestinal fluid losses.

Toxicity of K^+ (hyperkalemia) occurs frequently in renal failure, when the kidney is not capable of excreting excessive K^+. Hyperkalemia produces characteristic electrocardiographic changes reflecting the **profound and life-threatening effect of excess K^+ on the heart.**

The electrical effects of hyperkalemia can be antagonized by increased serum calcium concentration. As described in Chapter 31, the sodium-potassium pump in membranes is sensitive to inhibition by the digitalis preparation ouabain. In the presence of hypokalemia, the heart is sensitized to ouabain, and ouabain toxicity may occur. The toxicity of ouabain can be antagonized by increasing serum potassium concentration.

TRACE ELEMENTS

1. COBALT

The only known function of cobalt in animals is its role as a component of cobalamin, vitamin B_{12} (see Chapter 10). Cobalt must be provided to mammals in the form of vitamin B_{12}, although theoretically elemental cobalt in the diet could be converted to cobalamin by the intestinal bacteria.

Elemental cobalt is well absorbed in the intestine and seems to share a transport mechanism with iron as discussed below. Cobalt absorption, like that of iron, is significantly increased in patients with liver disease, iron overload, and idiopathic hemochromatosis. Cobalt is excreted primarily in the urine and has a low order of toxicity in all species studied.

2. COPPER

The adult human body contains approximately 100 mg of copper; the highest concentrations are in liver, brain, kidney, and heart. The average diet in North America provides 2–4 mg of copper per day in the form of meat, shellfish, nuts, raisins, legumes, and cereals.

The absorption of copper in the gastrointestinal tract requires a specific mechanism, because of the highly insoluble nature of cupric ions (Cu^{2+}). An unidentified low-molecular-weight substance from human saliva and gastric juice complexes with Cu^{2+} to keep it soluble at the pH of intestinal fluid. In the intestinal mucosal cell, copper is probably associated with a low-molecular-weight metal-binding protein called **metallothionein.** Copper enters the plasma, where it is bound to amino acids, particularly histidine, and to serum albumin at a single strong binding site. In less than an hour, the recently absorbed copper is removed from the circulation by the liver.

The liver processes copper through 2 routes. Copper is excreted in bile into the gastrointestinal tract, from which it is not reabsorbed. In fact, **copper homeostasis is maintained almost exclusively by biliary excretion;** the higher the dose of copper, the more is excreted in feces. Normally, human urine contains only traces of copper.

The second route of copper metabolism in the liver is its incorporation as an integral part of **ceruloplasmin,** a glycoprotein synthesized exclusively in the liver. Ceruloplasmin is a copper-dependent **ferroxidase.** It accounts for 95% of the total copper in human plasma. **Ceruloplasmin is not a Cu^{2+} transport protein,** since ceruloplasmin copper is not exchanged with copper ion or copper bound to other molecules. Ceruloplasmin contains 6–8 atoms of copper, half as cuprous (Cu^+) and half as cupric (Cu^{2+}) ions.

As a dispensable component of the gastrointestinal iron absorption mechanism, ceruloplasmin oxidizes Fe^{2+} to Fe^{3+}. Other copper metalloproteins include cytochrome oxidase, tyrosinase, monoamine oxidase, superoxide dismutase, and lysyl oxidase.

Manifestations of copper toxicity include blue-green diarrheal stools and saliva, acute hemolysis, and abnormalities of kidney function.

Menkes' disease (kinky or steely hair syndrome) is an X-linked disorder of intestinal copper absorption. The first phase of copper absorption, its uptake into the mucosal cell, and the second phase, its intracellular transport within the mucosal cell, are both normal in patients with Menkes' disease. The third phase, transport across the serosal aspect of the mucosal cell membrane, is defective. Intravenously administered copper is handled normally by these children, but unless therapy is commenced promptly at birth, many of the severe signs of this disease (mental retardation, temperature instability, abnormal bone formation, and susceptibility to infection) are not prevented.

Wilson's disease is an autosomal, recessively inherited defect in the incorporation of copper into newly synthesized apoceruloplasmin to form ceruloplasmin. It is not clear whether the genetic defect is in the structural gene for ceruloplasmin or in the process of incorporating the Cu^{2+} into ceruloplasmin. In addition, patients with Wilson's disease have an **impaired ability of the liver to excrete copper into the bile.** The total body retention of copper is increased, particularly in the liver, brain, kidney, and cornea. Dementia and liver failure occur. Because the ceruloplasmin in the patient's plasma contains no Cu^{2+}, the **serum copper level is low.** Urinary excretion of copper is markedly increased in these patients. They do not exhibit any abnormality of iron absorption, in spite of the fact that the ceruloplasmin without copper cannot function as a ferroxidase. Chelation of the excess copper can reverse some of the organ damage.

3. IRON

Iron is one of the most abundant elements in the earth's crust, but the body of a normal adult weighing 70 kg contains only 3–4 g of iron. Table 40–5 sets forth the distribution and functions of iron compounds in humans. As described in Chapter 5, the major use of iron is for **oxygen transport** by hemoglobin. Both ferrous (Fe^{2+}) and ferric (Fe^{3+}) iron are highly insoluble at neutral pH, and special systems are therefore required to transport iron and to insert these ions into their functional sites.

Organ meats, legumes, molasses, shellfish, and parsley are rich sources of iron. Food iron is predominantly in the ferric state, tightly bound to organic molecules. In the stomach, where the pH is less than 4, Fe^{3+} can dissociate and react with low-molecular-weight compounds such as fructose, ascorbic acid, citric acid, and amino acids to form complexes that will allow Fe^{3+} to remain soluble at the neutral pH of intestinal fluid. Iron is not lost from heme in the stomach but is delivered as such to the intestine.

Normally, the loss of iron from the body of a man

Table 40–5. Distribution and functions of the iron compounds in normal humans.*

	Compound	Nature of Compound	Function	Molecular Weight	Amount (Grams)	Amount of Iron (Grams)
5% 1%	Transferrin	Nonheme	Iron transport	76,000	14.0	0.007
10%	Cytochrome c	Heme enzyme	Oxidation	13,200	0.8	0.004
9%	Cytochromes a, a₃, b	Heme enzyme	Oxidation	?	?	?
10%	Peroxidase	Heme enzyme	Oxidation	44,100	?	?
	Catalase	Heme enzyme	H₂O₂ decomposition	225,000	5.0	0.004
	Iron-sulfur	Nonheme enzymes	Flavoproteins, oxidases, hydroxylases		?	?
	Unknown					0.20
65%	Myoglobin	Heme	O₂ storage	17,000	120	0.40
	Hemosiderin	Nonheme	Iron storage	Variable	1.2	0.36
	Ferritin	Nonheme apoferritin	Iron storage	444,000	2.0	0.40
	Hemoglobin	Heme	O₂ transport	66,700	750	2.60

Percent of normal body iron (left axis label)

Total iron (70-kg man) .... 4 grams

*Slightly modified and reproduced, with permission, from Stanbury JB, Wyngaarden JB, Fredrickson DS: *The Metabolic Basis of Inherited Disease,* 4th ed. McGraw-Hill, 1978.

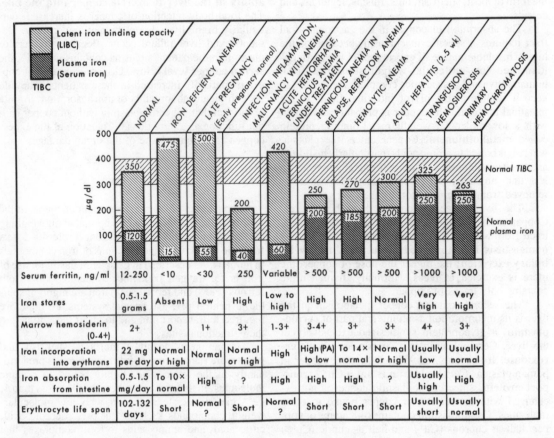

Figure 40–2. Iron metabolism in human beings under various conditions. (Reproduced, with permission, from Stanbury JB, Wyngaarden JB, Fredrickson DS: *The Metabolic Basis of Inherited Disease,* 4th ed. McGraw-Hill, 1978.)

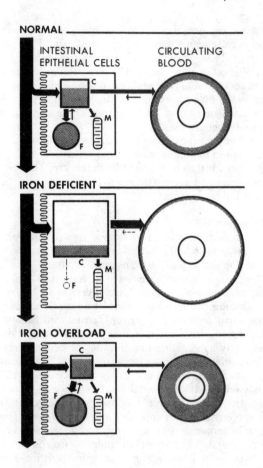

NORMAL

INTESTINAL
EPITHELIAL CELLS

CIRCULATING
BLOOD

IRON DEFICIENT

IRON OVERLOAD

Figure 40–3. Model of distribution and transfer of iron in the intestinal epithelial cell. The rate of iron transfer is proportionate to the square of the width of the arrow. The amounts of intracellular iron carrier (square C) and intracellular ferritin (circle F) and the concentration of transferrin in circulating blood (annulus) are proportionate to the corresponding areas. The fractional saturation of the iron-binding compounds (intracellular carrier and transferrin) is indicated by the fraction of the compartmental area that is crosshatched. M designates mitochondria. In this cybernetic model, the amount of intracellular iron carrier is inversely proportionate to the amount of plasma iron entering and conditioning the cell during development. Normal saturation of intracellular carrier is associated with iron absorption of 1 mg/d of the 3 mg/d incorporated into the mucosal cells from the 15 mg/d entering the lumen. Ferritin deposition and mitochondrial uptake for synthesis of iron enzymes are shown, corresponding to 1.7 mg/d and 0.3 mg/d, respectively. (Reproduced, with permission, from Stanbury JB, Wyngaarden JB, Fredrickson DS: *The Metabolic Basis of Inherited Disease,* 4th ed. McGraw-Hill, 1978.)

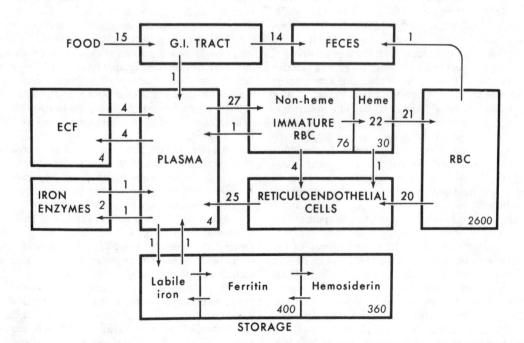

Figure 40–4. Normal iron kinetics: pools and transfer rates. (Reproduced, with permission, from Stanbury JB, Wyngaarden JB, Fredrickson DS: *The Metabolic Basis of Inherited Disease,* 4th ed. McGraw-Hill, 1978.)

is limited to 1 mg/d as a result of the sloughing of intestinal and other iron-containing cells. Menstruating women lose iron with menstrual blood. Accordingly, the **only mechanism by which total body stores of iron can be regulated is at the level of iron absorption,** a unique and precarious arrangement. In the ordinary diet, 10–20 mg of iron are taken in each day, but less than 10% of this is absorbed. Thus, under normal conditions, very little dietary iron is absorbed, the amounts excreted in urine are minimal, and a high proportion of total body iron is continuously redistributed throughout the body in several metabolic circuits. The greatest need for iron occurs in **infancy and adolescence;** children in these stages of development absorb a higher percentage of iron from foods than do adults. Iron deficiency in infants, adolescents, and menstruating women can be attributed to dietary inadequacy. Iron deficiency in adult men can usually be attributed to substantial bleeding.

Absorption

Heme iron is absorbed by the intestinal mucosal cell intact, and the heme is subsequently broken down and iron released within the cell. Nonheme iron is **absorbed in the ferrous state.** The Fe^{2+} is absorbed into the mucosal cell of the duodenum and proximal jejunum and promptly oxidized to Fe^{3+}. Ferric ion is bound by an **intracellular carrier molecule.** Within the cell, the carrier molecule delivers Fe^{3+} to mitochondria and then, depending upon the state of iron metabolism of the individual, distributes the Fe^{3+} in specific proportions to apoferritin or to apotransferrin.

Apoferritin is a molecule of approximately 500,000 MW, composed of 24 identical 18,000-MW subunits. Apoferritin assimilates up to **4300 iron atoms** into a single molecule to form **ferritin,** the primary and most available **iron storage protein.**

Apotransferrin is a 90,000-MW protein that can bind **2 atoms of iron** to form transferrin. **Transferrin is the true carrier of iron** that exists in plasma as a β-globulin. The iron-binding capacity of transferrin is normally **20–33% saturated** with iron (Fig 40–2).

Under **normal conditions** in the adult, when approximately **1 mg of iron is absorbed daily,** the intracellular iron carrier of the mucosal cell is nearly saturated (Fig 40–3). It transfers significant quantities of iron to apoferritin to form ferritin and transfers the usual quantity of iron to mitochondria. The remainder is transported across the serosal surface to apotransferrin.

In the **iron-deficient state,** the capacity of the intracellular iron carrier is expanded, and more iron will be absorbed if available in the diet (Fig 40–3). Although the mitochondria receive their usual supply of iron, ferritin is not formed in the cell, and the majority of iron is transferred to the expanded apotransferrin compartment in the plasma.

In the case of **iron overload,** the intracellular iron carrier is simply diminished in capacity and saturated (Fig 40–4). A significant quantity of ferritin is formed

within the mucosal cell, and less iron is transferred to the already nearly saturated apotransferrin. The iron trapped in the mucosal cell ferritin can be lost by exfoliation of those cells. The intracellular mucosal transfer of iron can be regulated to some extent. Erythropoiesis, by a mechanism not understood, promotes the rapid transfer of mucosal iron to the transferrin compartment in plasma.

The transfer of iron from the storage ferritin (as Fe^{3+}) form to plasma involves the **reduction to Fe^{2+} in order for it to be released from ferritin.** The Fe^{2+} is subsequently again oxidized to Fe^{3+} so that it can be bound to transferrin.

Transport

Iron is transported to storage sites in the bone marrow and to some extent to the liver **in the Fe^{3+} state, bound to plasma transferrin.** At those storage sites, Fe^{3+} is again transferred to apoferritin as a stable but exchangeable storage form. **Ferritin in the reticuloendothelial system provides an available storage form for iron.** However, ferritin can become denatured, losing apoferritin subunits and subsequently aggregating into micelles of hemosiderin. **Hemosiderin** contains a larger fraction of its mass as iron than does ferritin and exists as **microscopically visible iron-staining particles.** Hemosiderin is usually seen in states of iron overload, when the synthesis of apoferritin and its uptake of iron are maximal. The **iron in hemosiderin is available** for the formation of hemoglobin, but the mobilization of iron is much slower from hemosiderin than from ferritin. The plasma transferrin iron pool is in equilibrium with the iron in storage forms in the gastrointestinal tract and reticuloendothelial system (Fig 40–4).

Although ferritin is not found in plasma, apoferritin is and seems to reflect the size of the pools of stored iron in the reticuloendothelial system. The formation of ferritin from apoferritin involves first the binding of Fe^{2+} to the inner surface of the apoferritin shell. Apoferritin then acts as a ferroxidase and oxidizes Fe^{2+} to Fe^{3+}, which is then tightly bound to ferritin. In order to be released from ferritin, iron must be reduced from Fe^{3+} to Fe^{2+}.

An inherited defect in regulation of mucosal absorption of iron leads to the iron overload syndrome known as **hemochromatosis.** In this multisystem disease, 2 or 3 mg rather than the normal 1 mg of iron are absorbed daily from the gastrointestinal tract. Over a period of 20–30 years in males, this will lead to an accumulation of perhaps 20–30 g of total body iron rather than the normal 3–4 g. The accumulated iron is stored in **hemosiderin deposits in liver, pancreas, skin, and joints,** leading to the disease.

When total body iron stores are increased and hemosiderin deposits are widespread, **hemosiderosis** is said to exist. This might result from increased dietary intake of iron or from increased lysis of red cells and the increased iron absorption that accompanies erythropoiesis, in this case a compensatory mechanism. When the hemosiderin deposits begin to **disrupt**

normal cellular and organ function, the disorder is called **hemochromatosis.**

4. MOLYBDENUM

Although the human requirements for molybdenum are unknown, this metal is clearly required for the function of the metalloenzymes **xanthine oxidase, aldehyde oxidase,** and **sulfite oxidase.** Molybdenum deficiency has not been observed in humans or any other species under natural conditions. Essentially nothing is known about its metabolism except that the hexavalent water-soluble forms are absorbed well across the intestine. The urine is the major route of molybdenum excretion. The food content of molybdenum is highly dependent upon the soil type in which the foodstuffs are grown.

There is some evidence that molybdenum can interfere with copper metabolism by diminishing the efficiency of copper utilization and perhaps even copper mobilization from tissues.

5. SELENIUM

Selenium is an integral component of **glutathione peroxidase,** an enzyme with an intracellular **antioxidant** role closely similar to the related function of vitamin E or α-tocopherol. The vitamin E–sparing effects of selenium (and the converse) are discussed in Chapter 11. Selenium intake is highly dependent upon the soil in which the foodstuffs are grown. There has been no reported case of selenium deficiency in humans, but such does exist in other animals such as livestock. Selenium toxicity does occur in humans and other animals, although its mechanism is not understood. An early hallmark of selenium toxicity is a garlicky breath caused by exhalation of dimethyl selenide. The most likely cause of selenium toxicity is occupational exposure in the electronics, glass, and paint industries.

6. MANGANESE

Manganese is widely distributed in nuts, whole grain cereals, and vegetables but is present in low concentrations in meat, fish, and dairy products. Tea is exceptionally rich in Mn^{2+}. Manganese is present in high concentrations in mitochondria and functions as a necessary factor for activation of glycosyltransferases responsible for the synthesis of oligosaccharides, glycoproteins, and proteoglycans (see Chapter 32). Manganese is well absorbed throughout the small intestine by a mechanism similar to that described above for iron, involving transfer across the mucosal cells into the portal blood. In fact, Mn^{2+} absorption is increased in iron deficiency and can be inhibited by iron. The presence of ethanol in the intestine can significantly increase Mn^{2+} absorption. The Mn^{2+} ions are delivered to the liver from the portal circulation and there rapidly equilibrate with liver mitochondrial Mn^{2+}. Deficiency of Mn^{2+} seems to profoundly reduce oligosaccharide synthesis and formation of glycoproteins and proteoglycans. In addition, several Mn^{2+} metalloenzymes such as hydrolases, kinases, decarboxylases, and transferases are affected.

Manganese toxicity is extremely rare, but it does occur among miners following occupational exposure to Mn^{2+} ores.

7. ZINC

There are perhaps 2 dozen known zinc metalloenzymes, including carbonic anhydrase, lactate dehydrogenase, glutamate dehydrogenase, alkaline phosphatase, superoxide dismutase, and thymidine kinase. Thus, it is not surprising that a deficiency of zinc is accompanied by multisystem dysfunction. Animal protein is an important source; processed foods, citrus fruits, and nonleafy vegetables are poor in zinc.

In the intestinal lumen there exists a zinc-binding factor that seems to be secreted by the pancreas and promotes zinc absorption. Zinc, like iron, can be sequestered in the mucosal cell by zinc-binding proteins. It is subsequently transferred to the **albumin** molecule on the serosal side of the mucosal cell membrane. Copper can interfere with zinc absorption by competing for the binding sites on the albumin molecule in the intravascular space. High phosphate and calcium both aggravate zinc deficiency. Zinc is secreted in **pancreatic juice** and to a small extent in bile, and feces is thus the major route of excretion. However, significant quantities of zinc can be lost in **sweat,** particularly in the tropics. Zinc, like copper, can be bound by liver metallothionein when zinc intake increases.

Zinc deficiency can occur as a primary disorder of zinc absorption in **acrodermatitis enteropathica,** a rare autosomal recessive disease characterized by dermatologic, ophthalmologic, gastrointestinal, and neuropsychiatric signs, along with growth retardation and hypogonadism. Secondary Zn deficiency can occur from malabsorption due to any cause or from increased excretion in urine. The latter appears to account for the relatively frequent finding of Zn deficiency in patients with sickle cell disease. Dietary Zn may be bound in the intestinal lumen by phytates (inositol hexaphosphate), which are abundant in unleavened bread. The phytate-zinc complex is not absorbed and can result in an isolated zinc deficiency as a syndrome of growth retardation, hypogonadism, alopecia, and poor appetite. Acute ingestion of alcohol appears to increase urinary zinc excretion.

In patients with zinc deficiencies, serum ribonuclease activity appears to be high, whereas erythrocyte carbonic anhydrase activity is low. There is also evidence of abnormalities of nucleic acid metabolism, particularly diminished RNA synthesis in zinc deficiency. Individuals with zinc deficiency exhibit poor wound healing.

8. CHROMIUM

Chromium is thought to play some functional role in the regulation of glucose metabolism, perhaps as a component of the "glucose tolerance factor" (GTF). The trivalent form of chromium (Cr^{3+}) can improve the glucose tolerance of individuals suffering from protein-calorie malnutrition. Brewer's yeast is rich in chromium, and most grain and cereal products contain significant quantities. There have been suggestions that chromium is important in the metabolism of proteins and lipids, particularly cholesterol. Chromium is absorbed in the small intestine by a pathway it appears to share with zinc. It is transported to tissues bound to transferrin and appears in liver mitochondria, microsomes, and the cytosol. Chromium is excreted chiefly in the urine.

Hexavalent chromium is much more toxic than the trivalent chromium. Chronic occupational exposure to chromate dust seems to carry an increased risk of lung cancer. Significant chromium is contributed to the diet by cooking in stainless steel cookware.

•   •   •

References

Aisen P, Listowsky I: Iron transport and storage proteins. *Annu Rev Biochem* 1980;**49**:357.

Fitzgerald F: Trace elements. *West J Med* 1978;**128**:223.

Flink EB: Nutritional aspects of magnesium metabolism. *West J Med* 1980;**133**:304.

Klee CB, Crouch TH, Richman PG: Calmodulin. *Annu Rev Biochem* 1980;**49**:489.

Paterson CR: Calcium requirements in man: A critical review. *Postgrad Med J* 1978;**54**:244.

Prasad AS: *Trace Elements and Iron in Human Metabolism.* Plenum Press, 1978.

Smith LH Jr: Hemochromatosis. *West J Med* 1978;**128**:133.

Underwood EJ: *Trace Elements in Human and Animal Nutrition,* 4th ed. Academic Press, 1977.

Weitzman RE, Kleeman CR: The clinical physiology of water metabolism. *West J Med* 1979;**131**:373.

Nutrition | 41

Marion Nestle, PhD

Humans have evolved to depend on a continuous supply of exogenous substances for growth, development, and maintenance of life. These heterogeneous substances include sources of energy and of carbon, nitrogen, and other inorganic elements, as well as more than 20 complex organic molecules—fatty acids, amino acids, and vitamins—whose biosynthetic pathways have been lost during evolution. All of these nutrients are required in the diet, and all are normally obtained from food.

The goals of nutritional science are to define for each individual the complete set of nutrients required in the diet, the optimal amount of each nutrient, and the combination of foods that best meets these requirements; to determine how these requirements vary throughout the normal life cycle; and to understand how nutritional factors affect and are affected by injury, illness, and treatment. None of these goals have been entirely achieved as yet. Information currently available on human nutritional requirements is reviewed in this chapter.

NUTRITIONAL REQUIREMENTS IN HUMANS

A nutrient is considered essential if its deficiency results in recognizable clinical symptoms that are relieved by its addition to the diet. Because research studies of human nutritional requirements are notoriously difficult to conduct and interpret, it has often proved difficult to demonstrate specific biochemical or physiologic lesions resulting from a deficiency of any one nutrient. The results of animal studies can only be applied to humans with extreme caution. As a result, much information on human nutritional requirements remains incomplete.

A current summary of the substances required in the human diet is given in Table 41–1. In addition to sources of energy, more than 40 organic compounds or inorganic elements are considered to be essential to human nutrition. For most of them, dietary deficiency results in symptoms of illness in children or adults.

Table 41–1. Human nutritional requirements.

	Essential for Human Nutrition; Requirement Established	Essential for Certain Animal Species; Human Requirement Not Established
Amino acids	Isoleucine, leucine, lysine, methionine, phenylalanine, threonine, tryptophan, valine, histidine[1]	Arginine
Fatty acids	Linoleic acid	Linolenic acid
Vitamins		
Water-soluble	Ascorbic acid, biotin,[2] cobalamine (B_{12}) folic acid, niacin, pantothenic acid, pyridoxine (B_6), riboflavin, thiamin (B_1)	Choline, myo-inositol
Fat-soluble	Vitamin A, vitamin D, vitamin E,[3] vitamin K[2]	
Minerals		
Minerals (> 100 mg/d)	Calcium, chlorine, magnesium, phosphorus, potassium, sodium	
Trace elements (< 100 mg/d)	Chromium, cobalt (as vitamin B_{12}), copper, iodine, iron, manganese, molybdenum, selenium, zinc	Arsenic, cadmium, fluorine,[4] nickel, silicon, tin, vanadium
Fiber[4]		
Water[5]		
Energy[6]	Carbohydrate, fat, protein	

[1] Essential for infant nutrition; adult requirement uncertain.
[2] Synthesized by intestinal microorganisms; dietary requirement uncertain.
[3] Human deficiency syndrome undefined; efficacious in treating certain hemolytic disorders of infants and adults.
[4] Functions in human physiology, but no requirement has been determined.
[5] Nutritional aspects of water consumption and utilization are discussed in Chapter 35.
[6] Specific energy sources are not required except as necessary to provide essential amino acids (protein), or fatty acids (fat) or to prevent ketosis (carbohydrate).

Table 41–2. Recommended daily dietary allowances.[1] (Revised 1980.) Designed for the maintenance of good nutrition of practically all healthy people in the USA.

	Age (years)	Weight (kg)	Weight (lb)	Height (cm)	Height (in)	Protein (g)	Fat-Soluble Vitamins			Water-Soluble Vitamins							Minerals					
							Vitamin A (μg RE)[2]	Vitamin D (μg)[3]	Vitamin E (mg α-TE)[4]	Vitamin C (mg)	Thiamin (mg)	Riboflavin (mg)	Niacin (mg NE)[5]	Vitamin B_6 (mg)	Folacin[6] (μg)	Vitamin B_{12} (μg)	Calcium (mg)	Phosphorus (mg)	Magnesium (mg)	Iron (mg)	Zinc (mg)	Iodine (μg)
Infants	0.0–0.5	6	13	60	24	kg × 2.2	420	10	3	35	0.3	0.4	6	0.3	30	0.5[7]	360	240	50	10	3	40
	0.5–1.0	9	20	71	28	kg × 2.0	400	10	4	35	0.5	0.6	8	0.6	45	1.5	540	360	70	15	5	50
Children	1–3	13	29	90	35	23	400	10	5	45	0.7	0.8	9	0.9	100	2.0	800	800	150	15	10	70
	4–6	20	44	112	44	30	500	10	6	45	0.9	1.0	11	1.3	200	2.5	800	800	200	10	10	90
	7–10	28	62	132	52	34	700	10	7	45	1.2	1.4	16	1.6	300	3.0	800	800	250	10	10	120
Males	11–14	45	99	157	62	45.	1000	10	8	50	1.4	1.6	18	1.8	400	3.0	1200	1200	350	18	15	150
	15–18	66	145	176	69	56	1000	10	10	60	1.4	1.7	18	2.0	400	3.0	1200	1200	400	18	15	150
	19–22	70	154	177	70	56	1000	7.5	10	60	1.5	1.7	19	2.2	400	3.0	800	800	350	10	15	150
	23–50	70	154	178	70	56	1000	5	10	60	1.4	1.6	18	2.2	400	3.0	800	800	350	10	15	150
	51+	70	154	178	70	56	1000	5	10	60	1.2	1.4	16	2.2	400	3.0	800	800	350	10	15	150
Females	11–14	46	101	157	62	46	800	10	8	50	1.1	1.3	15	1.8	400	3.0	1200	1200	300	18	15	150
	15–18	55	120	163	64	46	800	10	8	60	1.1	1.3	14	2.0	400	3.0	1200	1200	300	18	15	150
	19–22	55	120	163	64	44	800	7.5	8	60	1.1	1.3	14	2.0	400	3.0	800	800	300	18	15	150
	23–50	55	120	163	64	44	800	5	8	60	1.0	1.2	13	2.0	400	3.0	800	800	300	18	15	150
	51+	55	120	163	64	44	800	5	8	60	1.0	1.2	13	2.0	400	3.0	800	800	300	10	15	150
Pregnant						+30	+200	+5	+2	+20	+0.4	+0.3	+2	+0.6	+400	+1.0	+400	+400	+150	[8]	+5	+25
Lactating						+20	+400	+5	+3	+40	+0.5	+0.5	+5	+0.5	+100	+1.0	+400	+400	+150	[8]	+10	+50

Reference: *Recommended Dietary Allowances*, 9th ed. Food and Nutrition Board, National Research Council–National Academy of Sciences, 1980.

[1] The allowances are intended to provide for individual variations among most normal persons as they live in the United States under usual environmental stresses. Diets should be based on a variety of common foods in order to provide other nutrients for which human requirements have been less well defined.

[2] Retinol equivalents. 1 retinol equivalent = 1 μg retinol or 6 μg β-carotene.

[3] As cholecalciferol. 10 μg cholecalciferol = 400 IU of vitamin D.

[4] α-Tocopherol equivalents. 1 mg α-tocopherol = 1 α-TE.

[5] 1 NE (niacin equivalent) is equal to 1 mg of niacin or 60 mg of dietary tryptophan.

[6] The folacin allowances refer to dietary sources as determined by *Lactobacillus casei* assay after treatment with enzymes (conjugases) to make polyglutamyl forms of the vitamin available to the test organism.

[7] The recommended dietary allowance for vitamin B_{12} in infants is based on average concentration of the vitamin in human milk. The allowances after weaning are based on energy intake (as recommended by the American Academy of Pediatrics) and consideration of other factors, such as intestinal absorption.

[8] The increased requirement during pregnancy cannot be met by the iron content of habitual American diets or by the existing iron stores of many women; therefore the use of 30–60 mg of supplemental iron is recommended. Iron needs during lactation are not substantially different from those of nonpregnant women, but continued supplementation of the mother for 2–3 months after parturition is advisable in order to replenish stores depleted by pregnancy.

Other nutrients are more difficult to classify as essential in humans but can be assumed to be essential because of the observed effects of deficiency on animals (eg, vitamin E) or because clinical symptoms have been produced by specific antagonists (eg, biotin, vitamin K).

The importance to human nutrition of a number of nutrients known to be required by certain animal species—tin, vanadium, and linolenic acid, for instance—is simply not known. Fluoride is the nutrient among this group most likely to be a required substance; it contributes to the hardness of bones and the resistance of teeth to caries, but its role in human growth has not been established. The status of fiber is also undefined; it has beneficial effects on gastrointestinal function but does not seem to be required for normal growth and development. An important goal of recent research has been to clarify the role of these substances in human nutrition.

Quantitative Aspects of Nutrient Requirements

The minimum quantity of each nutrient necessary to maintain normal function and health has long been the subject of active investigation. An ideal research study would determine the average requirement for each nutrient among a large (statistically significant) group of healthy people of varying ages and would assess the statistical variability of requirements within each age group. It would then be possible to calculate the amount by which the average requirements should be increased to meet the needs of nearly all healthy individuals within the various age groups. In practice, very few studies of nutrient requirements meet these criteria; human nutrition research is too difficult and costly when more than a few adult subjects are used. For many nutrients, data are so limited that it has not been possible to define a precise set of minimum requirements for any one individual. Instead, established nutrient requirements are generous overestimations that attempt to include the needs of most individuals within a given population.

Recommended Dietary Allowances

The most thorough review of data on daily needs for essential nutrients is published by the Food and Nutrition Board of the National Academy of Sciences-National Research Council as *Recommended Dietary Allowances* (RDA) (Table 41–2). In establishing its recommendations, the Board considered a variety of factors that may affect the specific requirements of individuals—height, weight, sex, developmental stage, physical activity level, and climate. Some of these factors are considered in the table. In general, the allowances increase gradually from infancy to early adulthood. The lower recommendations for adults reflect cessation of growth. Significant increases in nutrient intake are recommended for pregnant or lactating women. For most nutrients, recommendations are higher for males, who generally have a larger lean body mass, than for females. Iron is a notable exception; premenopausal adult women must replace iron losses incurred during menstruation.

Recommended Dietary Allowances includes specific recommendations for protein, 10 vitamins, and 6 minerals. For the remaining essential nutrients, too little information is available to establish a meaningful allowance. Instead, the Board has established ranges of intake of these nutrients that appear to be safe and adequate. These estimates are presented in Table 41–3 according to age group.

Because *Recommended Dietary Allowances* is used to establish standards for individual dietary intake, food labeling, and food supplementation programs, it is important to recognize its limitations. An individual whose dietary intake falls below the allowance for a specific nutrient may have an *average* requirement for that nutrient and, therefore, an entirely adequate intake. Conversely, a person with a very high nutrient requirement may fail to achieve an adequate intake by simply following the recommendations in Table 41–2.

Even more important, the Food and Nutrition Board bases its recommendations on the needs of healthy people; very little information is available on the requirements of people who are ill or stressed. Recent studies of patients with bone fractures, infected surgical wounds, or severe burns reveal that nitrogen losses and energy expenditures are greatly increased by such conditions (Table 41–11). Requirements for energy and protein, as well as for other nutrients, apparently increase during injury and illness, but not nearly enough is known at present to establish specific allowances that compensate for pathologic disorders.

Finally, *Recommended Dietary Allowances* does not address directly the question of nutrient toxicity. Excessive intake of fat-soluble vitamins (vitamins A, D, E, and K) and many—if not all—of the minerals produces toxic symptoms. Excessive consumption of carbohydrate, fat, or protein may also be harmful. Overweight results from excess energy intake, whereas high-protein diets produce symptoms of uric acid excess (from the accompanying nucleic acids) and calcium losses in susceptible individuals. For these nutrients, intakes below minimum requirements result in deficiency disorders, but toxic symptoms develop when safe levels are surpassed. Maximum health benefits seem to accrue from a moderate range of intake of essential nutrients.

COMPOSITION OF FOODS

The selection of foods that must be consumed to ensure an adequate intake of required nutrients depends on cultural and economic factors as well as on biologic necessity, and societies have developed many different ways of meeting their nutritional needs.

Foods contain a great many nutrient and nonnutrient substances, but most analyses of their composition are incomplete. Standard food tables provide data for only a limited number of essential nutrients.

Typical food composition data are presented in

Table 41—3. Estimated safe and adequate daily dietary intakes of selected vitamins and minerals.*

	Vitamins			Trace Elements						Electrolytes		
Age (years)	Vitamin K (µg)	Biotin (µg)	Pantothenic Acid (mg)	Copper (mg)	Manganese (mg)	Fluoride (mg)	Chromium (mg)	Selenium (mg)	Molybdenum (mg)	Sodium (mg)	Potassium (mg)	Chloride (mg)
Infants												
0–0.5	12	35	2	0.5–0.7	0.5–0.7	0.1–0.5	0.01–0.04	0.01–0.04	0.03–0.06	115–350	350–925	275–700
0.5–1	10–20	50	3	0.7–1.0	0.7–1.0	0.2–1.0	0.02–0.06	0.02–0.06	0.04–0.08	250–750	425–1275	400–1200
Children												
and ado-												
lescents												
1–3	15–30	65	3	1.0–1.5	1.0–1.5	0.5–1.5	0.02–0.08	0.02–0.08	0.05–0.1	325–975	550–1650	500–1500
4–6	20–40	85	3–4	1.5–2.0	1.5–2.0	1.0–2.5	0.03–0.12	0.03–0.12	0.06–0.15	450–1350	775–2325	700–2100
7–10	30–60	120	4–5	2.0–2.5	2.0–3.0	1.5–2.5	0.05–0.2	0.05–0.2	0.10–0.3	600–1800	1000–3000	925–2775
11+	50–100	100–200	4–7	2.0–3.0	2.5–5.0	1.5–2.5	0.05–0.2	0.05–0.2	0.15–0.5	900–2700	1525–4575	1400–4200
Adults	70–140	100–200	4–7	2.0–3.0	2.5–5.0	1.5–4.0	0.05–0.2	0.05–0.2	0.15–0.5	1100–3300	1875–5625	1700–5100

*From: Recommended Dietary Allowances, 9th ed. Food and Nutrition Board, National Research Council—National Academy of Sciences, 1980.

Table 41—4. Composition of foods: 100 g, edible portion.*

				Fat				Carbohydrate		Minerals						Vitamins				
	Water (%)	Food Energy (kcal)	Protein (g)	Total Fat (g)	Saturated Fatty Acids (g)	Linoleic Acid (g)	Cholesterol (g)	Total (g)	Crude Fiber (g)	Calcium (mg)	Phosphorus (mg)	Iron (mg)	Sodium (mg)	Potassium (mg)	Magnesium (mg)	Vitamin A (IU†)	Thiamin (mg)	Riboflavin (mg)	Niacin (mg)	Ascorbic Acid (mg)
Beverages																				
Beer (4.5% by volume)	92.1	42	0.3	...	...	...	...	3.8	...	5	30	Trace	7	25	...	...	Trace	0.03	0.6	...
Gin, rum, vodka, whiskey (80 proof)	66.6	231	...	...	...	...	...	Trace	...	...	...	...	1	2	...	...	...	...	...	...
Wine (12.2% by volume)	85.6	85	0.1	...	...	...	...	4.2	...	9	10	0.4	5	92	...	...	Trace	0.01	0.1	...
Club soda	100	...	...	...	...	...	...	...	...	...	...	...	...	...	...	...	...	...	...	...
Cola	90	39	...	...	...	...	...	10	...	...	...	...	...	...	...	...	...	...	...	...
Milk: Whole	87.4	65	3.5	3.5	2	Trace	11	4.9	...	118	93	Trace	50	144	13	140	0.03	0.17	0.1	1
Skim	90.5	36	3.6	0.1	1	Trace	3	5.1	...	121	95	Trace	52	145	14	Trace	0.04	0.18	0.1	1
Bread: Whole wheat	36.4	243	10.5	3.0	...	...	...	47.7	1.6	99	238	2.3	527	273	78	Trace	0.26	0.12	2.8	Trace
White, enriched‡	35.8	269	8.7	3.2	...	...	...	50.4	0.2	70	87	2.4‡	507	85	22	Trace	0.25‡	0.17‡	2.3‡	Trace
Broccoli: Raw	89.1	32	3.6	0.3	...	...	...	5.9	1.5	103	78	1.1	15	382	24	2500	0.1	0.23	0.9	113
Cooked, boiled, drained	91.3	26	3.1	0.3	...	...	...	4.5	1.5	88	62	0.8	10	267	21	2500	0.09	0.2	0.8	90
Frozen	90.6	29	3.2	0.3	...	...	...	5.2	1.1	58	59	0.7	17	241	21	2600	0.07	0.13	0.6	70
Frozen, cooked, drained	91.6	26	2.9	0.3	...	...	...	4.6	1.1	54	56	0.7	15	212	...	2600	0.06	0.12	0.5	57
Carrots, raw	88.2	42	1.1	0.2	...	...	...	9.7	1.0	37	36	0.7	47	341	23	11000	0.06	0.05	0.6	8
Chicken, cooked	75.4	120	19.9	3.9	2	1	60	...	...	11	211	1.3	...	...	23	130	0.05	0.16	6.7	...
Eggs, hard cooked	73.7	163	12.9	11.5	4	1	550	0.9	...	54	205	2.3	122	129	...	1180	0.09	0.28	0.1	...
Hamburger, lean, cooked	60	219	27.4	11.3	5	4	70	...	...	12	230	3.5	48	558	25	20	0.09	0.23	6	...
Oil, cooking	...	884	...	100	23	7	...	...	...	...	...	...	...	...	...	...	...	...	...	...
Oranges, peeled	86	49	1	0.2	...	...	...	12.2	0.5	41	20	0.4	1	200	11	200	0.1	0.04	0.4	50
Sugar: Brown	2.1	373	...	...	...	...	...	96.4	...	85	19	3.4	30	344	...	...	0.01	0.03	0.2	...
White	0.5	385	...	...	...	...	...	99.5	...	...	...	0.1	1	3	...	...	...	...	...	...

*Data from Watt BK, Merrill AL: *Composition of Food: Raw, Processed, Prepared.* Agriculture Handbook No. 8, US Department of Agriculture, 1963. If no figure is given, either none of the nutrient is present or it was not measured.

†One IU (international unit) of vitamin A is approximately equivalent to 0.2 μg retinol equivalents.

‡These nutrients are added to enrich white flour to the levels found in whole wheat.

Table 41–4. The values presented are derived from small samples of each food and represent average approximations for each nutrient reported. The actual nutrient content of a food depends on several variables: genetic strain, growing location, soil nutrient content, handling and storage, and cooking and processing. Even without this information, Table 41–4 reveals that individual foods vary greatly in their nutrient composition. No single food contains adequate amounts of all essential nutrients. Each plant and animal food contributes a unique complement of nutrients. Thus, the human diet must include sufficient quantities of a wide variety of foods in order to provide the full range of nutritional requirements.

In assessing the nutritional value of any food, it is important to consider its content of essential nutrients relative to its energy value. When 2 foods with equivalent energy values are compared, the one with the higher nutrient content has the higher **nutrient concentration,** or **nutrient density.** Equivalent energy portions of eggs and oranges, for example, differ in nutrient concentration depending on which nutrient is being considered; eggs have more protein and vitamin A but oranges more ascorbic acid and fiber. In practice, these terms do not make such fine distinctions but are used to classify foods into 2 general groups—those of relatively high and those of relatively low nutrient concentration. The first group includes foods that contain significant amounts of essential nutrients or fiber along with their energy. Foods of low nutrient concentration, however, always contain relatively large amounts of fat, which is high in energy, or sugar and alcohol, which have few nutrients. Food processing and storage, illustrated by the data for broccoli in Table 41–4, generally lowers nutrient concentration by destroying or inactivating vitamins.

FOOD ENERGY

Food energy is contained in molecules of carbohydrate, fat, protein, and alcohol. The metabolic oxidation of these molecules releases energy in the form of ATP and other high-energy compounds that are used to maintain concentration gradients of ions, to carry out biosynthetic reactions, to transport and secrete molecules across cell membranes, and to provide power for cell movement and muscle activity. The transduction of food energy to mechanical work occurs at a maximal efficiency of about 25%. The remainder is lost as heat, some of which functions to maintain body temperature.

In the USA, energy intake and expenditure are measured in kilocalories (kcal), or Calories (Cal); 1 kcal or Cal is the amount of heat needed to raise the temperature of 1 L of water from 14.5 C to 15.5 C. The international unit of energy measurement is the kilojoule (kJ), defined as the energy required to lift 1 kilogram up 1 meter. One megajoule (MJ) = 1000 kJ. The conversion factor for the 2 systems of units is 1 kcal = 4.2 kJ.

Table 41–5. Heats of combustion and energy available from the major food sources.*

	Energy kcal/g (kJ/g)		
	Heat of Combustion (Bomb Calorimeter)	Human Oxidation	Standard Conversion Factors†
Protein	5.4 (22.6)	4.1 (17.2)‡	4 (17)
Fat	9.3 (38.9)	9.3 (38.9)	9 (38)
Carbohydrate	4.1 (17.2)	4.1 (17.2)	4 (17)
Ethanol	7.1 (29.7)	7.1 (29.7)	7 (29)

*Adapted from Davidson S & others: *Human Nutrition and Dietetics,* 7th ed. Churchill Livingstone, 1979.
†Conversion factors are obtained by rounding off heats of combustion and correcting for estimates of absorption efficiency.
‡Protein oxidation corrected for loss of amino groups excreted in urine.

The amount of energy available in food can be measured by taking advantage of the fact that biologic oxidation reactions are thermodynamically equivalent to chemical oxidation reactions outside the body. When food molecules are heated to high temperature in the presence of oxygen in a closed chamber (a bomb calorimeter), they undergo complete oxidation. In the body, fat and carbohydrate are oxidized completely to carbon dioxide and water, and the heat they release in the calorimeter is equivalent to their available biochemical energy.

Calorimeter heats of combustion for the major food molecules are presented in Table 41–5.

The biologic oxidation of protein, however, is not complete; its amino groups are converted to urea or creatinine, 2 compounds that are eventually excreted in urine. In order to determine the usable amount of energy that can be obtained from food, calorimeter values must be corrected to account for the loss of protein amino groups and for incomplete absorption of food molecules. Finally, the figures are rounded off to standard conversion factors for each of the major energy sources. These factors are used routinely to estimate the energy content of foods with known weights of carbohydrate, fat, and protein. Note that the energy content per unit mass for fat is twice that for either carbohydrate or protein and that alcohol also has a relatively high energy content.

Energy Expenditure

Food must supply enough energy to maintain body functions, muscle activity, and growth. The amount of energy required for these processes has been calculated by both direct and indirect methods. Human energy expenditure was measured directly in classic turn-of-the-century studies of young men who rested or worked in a sealed, insulated chamber while the energy value of their food, excretory products, and heat loss was measured. These experiments were difficult, time-consuming, and expensive, but they produced 2 important results. They confirmed that the total energy of this system was conserved and that energy expended—heat, work, and excreted products—was equivalent to the energy value of the food consumed. With the subject at rest, nearly all ingested energy could be accounted for by heat loss.

The studies also demonstrated that energy expenditure was almost directly proportionate to the consumption of oxygen. For every liter of oxygen consumed, 4.83 kcal (20 kJ) are expended. This useful result made it possible to calculate the energy expenditure indirectly by measuring the amount of oxygen consumed by individuals engaged in a great variety of activities. Such measurements have demonstrated that for any individual, energy output depends on 3 factors: the basal metabolic rate, the thermogenic effects of food, and the level of physical activity.

The **basal metabolic rate** (BMR) is an approximate measure of the energy cost of maintaining body housekeeping activities at rest—heartbeat, respiration, kidney function, osmotic balance, brain activity, and body temperature. It compares measured oxygen consumption with predicted standard values and is expressed as a percentage of the prediction, with the normal variation considered to be ± 10–15%. The BMR is measured under a defined set of standard conditions; the subject must be awake, resting supine in a warm room, at least 12 hours after eating. Thus, it closely approximates energy expenditure during sleep. Among patients in the hospital, however, it is sometimes impossible to maintain standard conditions during oxygen uptake measurements. Under these circumstances, energy requirements are expressed as the **resting metabolic expenditure** (RME). Long and his colleagues have calculated that the BMR and RME differ by no more than about 3%. For all practical purposes, they may be considered to be equivalent.

Measurements of resting metabolic expenditures are shown in Table 41–6. Resting expenditures are proportionate to body surface area and to the percentage of body fat. The BMR is somewhat higher than these values in men and in young children, in cold climates, and in various disease states; it is generally depressed during starvation.

The BMR must be measured 12 hours after eating because of the immediate postabsorptive **thermogenic effect** ("specific dynamic action") of food. Within a

Table 41–7. Energy expended in physical activity.*

	kcal/min (kJ/min)	
Very light work Card playing, eating, ironing, lying down, knitting, writing, typing	< 2.5	(< 10.5)
Light work Carpentry, cleaning house, cooking, dancing (ballroom), food shopping, table tennis, walking	2.5–4.9	(10.5–20.5)
Moderate work Cycling (9½ mph), gardening, golf, scrubbing floors, shoveling, tennis	5–7.4	(20.9–31)
Heavy work Basketball, field hockey, football, swimming (slow crawl)	7.5–9.9	(31.4–41.4)
Very heavy work Cycling (racing), chopping trees, judo, marathon running, skiing uphill, snowshoeing, squash	> 10	(> 41.8)

*Data from Katch FI, McArdle WD: *Nutrition, Weight Control, and Exercise.* Houghton Mifflin, 1977.

few minutes after eating, the BMR may rise as much as 30% over resting values. The cause of this effect is uncertain; it has been attributed to gastric secretion, protein synthesis, and protein turnover. It appears that over a 24-hour period, the thermogenic effect amounts to no more than 5–10% of metabolic expenditure and that its effect on overall energy balance is minimal.

Muscle activity, however, is a highly significant factor affecting oxygen consumption. The energy costs of many activities have been measured and are summarized in Table 41–7. These figures indicate that the amount of energy expended is proportionate to the intensity of muscle contraction. For an individual, energy expenditure at any intensity level depends on body weight, as shown in Table 41–8.

Energy Requirement

Body weight is determined by the balance between energy consumed and energy expended; if more energy is consumed than expended, body weight increases. One pound (0.45 kg) of body fat contains a potential energy of approximately 3500 kcal or 14.7 MJ. This figure is based on the assumption that adipose tissue is 85% fat: 454 g/lb × 9 kcal/g × 0.85 = 3500 kcal/lb, and it implies that a 1-lb per week weight loss requires a daily energy deficit of 500 kcal (2.1 MJ).

Desirable weight ranges for men and women of various heights are given in Table 41–9. These figures are derived from data reported to life insurance companies and therefore represent the average weights of insured persons. Recommended energy intake ranges are summarized in Table 41–10. At least 5 variables affect energy intake: activity levels, body size and composition, age, climate, and state of health. The values given in Table 41–10 assume light activity

Table 41–6. Normal values for the resting metabolic expenditure of adults.*

Percent Body Fat	Weight (kg)			
	50	60	70	80
	kcal/min (kJ/min)			
5	0.98 (4.1)	1.12 (4.7)	1.27 (5.3)	1.39 (5.8)
10	0.93 (3.9)	1.08 (4.5)	1.22 (5.1)	1.34 (5.6)
15	0.88 (3.7)	1.03 (4.3)	1.17 (4.9)	1.29 (5.4)
20	0.83 (3.5)	0.98 (4.1)	1.12 (4.7)	1.24 (5.2)
25	0.79 (3.3)	0.93 (3.9)	1.08 (4.5)	1.20 (5.0)
30	...	0.88 (3.7)	1.03 (4.3)	1.15 (4.8)

*Data from Davidson S & others: *Human Nutrition and Dietetics,* 7th ed. Churchill Livingstone, 1979.

Table 41—8. Energy expenditure in kcal (kJ) while running depends on body weight and speed.*

Speed Per Mile	Body Weight, lb (kg)				
	110 (50)	130 (59)	150 (68)	170 (77)	190 (86)
11½ min	6.8 (28.5)	8 (33.5)	9.2 (38.5)	10.5 (43.9)	11.7 (49)
9 min	9.7 (40.6)	11.4 (47.7)	13.1 (54.8)	14.9 (62.3)	16.6 (69.5)
8 min	10.8 (45.2)	12.5 (52.3)	14.2 (59.4)	16 (66.9)	17.7 (74.1)
7 min	12.2 (51)	13.9 (58.2)	15.6 (65.3)	17.4 (72.8)	19.1 (79.8)
6 min	13.9 (58.2)	15.6 (65.3)	17.3 (72.4)	19.1 (79.9)	20.8 (87)
5½ min	14.5 (60.7)	17.1 (71.5)	19.7 (82.4)	22.3 (93.2)	24.9 (104.2)

*Data from tables in Katch FI, McArdle WD: *Nutrition, Weight Control, and Exercise.* Houghton Mifflin, 1977.

Table 41—9. Suggested desirable weights for heights and ranges for adult males and females.*

Height[1]		Weight[2]			
		Men		Women	
in.	cm	lb	kg	lb	kg
58	147	—	—	102 (92—119)	46 (42—54)
60	152	—	—	107 (96—125)	49 (44—57)
62	158	123 (112—141)	56 (51—64)	113 (102—131)	51 (46—59)
64	163	130 (118—148)	59 (54—67)	120 (108—138)	55 (49—63)
66	168	136 (124—156)	62 (56—71)	128 (114—146)	58 (52—66)
68	173	145 (132—166)	66 (60—75)	136 (122—154)	62 (55—70)
70	178	154 (140—174)	70 (64—79)	144 (130—163)	65 (59—74)
72	183	162 (148—184)	74 (67—84)	152 (138—173)	69 (63—79)
74	188	171 (156—194)	78 (71—88)	—	—
76	193	181 (164—204)	82 (74—93)	—	—

*From: *Recommended Dietary Allowances,* 9th ed. Food and Nutrition Board, National Research Council—National Academy of Sciences, 1980.
[1] Without shoes.
[2] Without clothes. Average weight ranges in parentheses.

Table 41—10. Mean heights and weights and recommended energy intake.*

Category	Age (years)	Weight (kg)	Weight (lb)	Height (cm)	Height (in.)	Energy Needs (With Range) (kcal)		(MJ)
Infants	0.0—0.5	6	13	60	24	kg × 115	(95—145)	kg × 0.48
	0.5—1.0	9	20	71	28	kg × 105	(80—135)	kg × 0.44
Children	1—3	13	29	90	35	1300	(900—1800)	5.5
	4—6	20	44	112	44	1700	(1300—2300)	7.1
	7—10	28	62	132	52	2400	(1650—3300)	10.1
Males	11—14	45	99	157	62	2700	(2000—3700)	11.3
	15—18	66	145	176	69	2800	(2100—3900)	11.8
	19—22	70	154	177	70	2900	(2500—3300)	12.2
	23—50	70	154	178	70	2700	(2300—3100)	11.3
	51—75	70	154	178	70	2400	(2000—2800)	10.1
	76+	70	154	178	70	2050	(1650—2450)	8.6
Females	11—14	46	101	157	62	2200	(1500—3000)	9.2
	15—18	55	120	163	64	2100	(1200—3000)	8.8
	19—22	55	120	163	64	2100	(1700—2500)	8.8
	23—50	55	120	163	64	2000	(1600—2400)	8.4
	51—75	55	120	163	64	1800	(1400—2200)	7.6
	76+	55	120	163	64	1600	(1200—2000)	6.7
Pregnancy						+300		
Lactation						+500		

*From: *Recommended Dietary Allowances,* 9th ed. Food and Nutrition Board, National Research Council—National Academy of Sciences, 1980.

Table 41-11. Increases in energy expenditure and protein catabolism following injury and illness.*

	Percentage Increase Above Resting Metabolic Expenditure	Loss of Urinary Nitrogen (g/kg/d)
Elective surgery	23.9	0.214
Skeletal trauma	32.2	0.317
Blunt trauma	36.6	0.322
Trauma requiring concurrent glucocorticoid therapy	60.8	0.338
Sepsis	79.2	0.366
Burns	131.7	0.369

Severe illness and injury result in large increases in basal oxygen consumption and in urinary nitrogen losses over values found among normal individuals consuming equivalent amounts of energy and protein. Nitrogen losses occur primarily as urea derived from the catabolism of skeletal muscle protein.

*Data from Long CL & others: Metabolic response to injury and illness: Estimation of energy and protein needs from indirect calorimetry and nitrogen balance. *J Parent Ent Nutr* 1979;3:452.

levels, and they must be increased for additional work and exercise, for larger or leaner (see Table 41-6) bodies, and to meet the requirements of body growth in infancy, childhood, and adolescence. Pregnancy and lactation increase requirements by an additional 300–500 kcal per day. Basal metabolism decreases after early adulthood by about 2% per decade. Thus, with age, energy intake must be reduced proportionately to maintain constant body weight.

Recent studies of hospitalized patients reveal that injury and illness have a major effect on energy requirements and nitrogen balance. As shown in Table 41-11, the resting energy expenditure can increase by more than 100% during severe catabolic stress. Food greatly in excess of amounts normally needed to maintain body weight and nitrogen balance must be provided to compensate for the increased requirements of very sick patients.

SOURCES OF ENERGY

The 3 major sources of food energy are carbohydrates, fats, and proteins; alcohol also contributes variable amounts of energy.

Based on US Department of Agriculture statistics, the present diet in the USA contains 46% of total energy intake as carbohydrate, 42% as fat, and 12% as protein (Fig 41-3). The proportions of energy from fat and carbohydrate have changed significantly during this century. Figure 41-1 displays these changes. Since 1909–1913, the proportion of calories from fat has increased while that from carbohydrate has decreased. The overall increase in fat calories derives mainly from a large increase in the use of vegetable oils, shortenings, and margarine. Fat intake from meat consumption has increased only slightly, and the use of butter has declined. The overall decrease in calories

derived from carbohydrate is due to a large reduction in intake of complex carbohydrate (starches), especially flour and cereals; in contrast, sugar intake has increased considerably. Consumption of food energy and of dietary protein has remained relatively constant throughout this period.

These trends also include significant increases in consumption of frozen and processed foods, food additives, alcohol, and foods prepared and eaten outside the home. Taken together, they point toward a general decrease in the proportion of essential nutrients to energy among foods consumed in the USA, and they raise disturbing questions about the adequacy of the average American diet.

Carbohydrate

Food carbohydrates include starches (complex carbohydrate), sugars, and fiber. Because some amino acids and the glycerol portion of triglyceride can be converted into glucose, dietary carbohydrate would not seem to be essential. In the absence of carbohydrate, however, ketosis occurs, along with excessive breakdown of muscle protein and significant salt and water losses. To prevent these effects, the Food and Nutrition Board recommends a minimum daily carbohydrate intake of 50–100 g.

Although it takes only a small amount of carbohydrate to prevent ketosis, it has recently been recommended that more than half the total energy intake be derived from **complex carbohydrates** such as wheat, rice, legumes, and potatoes. These foods provide large amounts of vitamins and minerals and are relatively low in energy content.

Unfortunately, many of the nutrients in complex carbohydrate foods may be removed or destroyed during food processing. When whole wheat is converted to white flour, for example, the outer bran layers and embryo (wheat germ) are removed. This process leaves about 70% of the original seed but far less of the essential nutrients. The percentage of several nutrients that remains in white flour is illustrated in Table

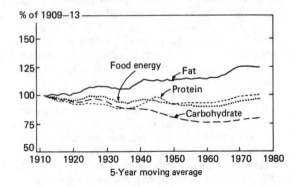

Figure 41-1. Trends in food energy, protein, fat, and carbohydrate consumption per capita in the USA. (Adapted from Friend B: *Changes in Nutrients in the US Diet Caused by Alterations in Food Intake Patterns.* Agricultural Research Service. US Department of Agriculture.)

Table 41–12. Percentage of nutrients in whole wheat flour remaining in white flour (72% extraction) per 100 g.*

Energy	100	Riboflavin	38†
Protein	85	Niacin	13†
Fat	60	Pyridoxine	30
Fiber	31	Folic acid	54
Calcium	43	Vitamin E	Trace
Phosphorus	38	Iron	38†
Thiamin	22†	Zinc	30

*Data from Davidson S & others: *Human Nutrition and Dietetics,* 7th ed. Churchill Livingstone, 1979.
†Fortified to original levels in the USA.

41–12. In the USA, 3 vitamins—niacin, riboflavin, thiamin—and iron are restored to their original levels through enrichment of white flour, but the concentration of the remaining nutrients remains greatly reduced.

Food carbohydrates also include the **sugars** such as glucose and fructose that are found in fruits and honey, lactose from milk, and maltose from beer. By far the most important sugar, however, is sucrose, or common table sugar, which comes from beets and cane. The increased consumption of sucrose and other sugars during this century is of concern because these foods generally lack essential nutrients and they contribute "empty calories" to the diet. While sucrose is certainly one of the major etiologic factors in dental caries, it has not yet been implicated as a cause of diabetes, heart disease, or obesity. Populations with a high incidence of these diseases tend to consume large amounts of sucrose, but other dietary and environmental factors may be far more important.

The third important component of food carbohydrate is **dietary fiber,** a collective term that includes all indigestible plant cell wall components: celluloses, hemicelluloses, lignins, gums, pectins, and pentosans. Dietary fiber must be distinguished from the **crude fiber** listed in food composition data such as that presented in Table 41–4. Crude fiber includes only those components that remain after chemical extraction with solvents, hot acid, and hot alkali, and it comprises only a small fraction (10–50%) of dietary fiber. The indigestible dietary fiber carbohydrates add bulk to the diet and absorb water in the intestinal lumen, thus aiding in the elimination of larger, softer feces. Within this century, decrease in fiber consumption in industrialized countries has been associated with a high incidence of diverticulosis, colon cancer, cardiovascular disease, and diabetes. Large amounts of dietary fiber have been reported to decrease bowel transit time, alter the composition of intestinal bacteria, reduce enterohepatic circulation of cholesterol, delay intestinal sugar absorption, and reduce the absorption of certain minerals. Until more is known about the effects of intake of large amounts of fiber, the Food and Nutrition Board recommends eating fruits, vegetables, and whole grain cereals to achieve moderate increases in fiber consumption.

Fat

Fats have several important food functions. They increase the palatability of foods by absorbing and retaining flavors. As they tend to be digested slowly, they produce a feeling of satiety. With more than twice the energy value of either protein or carbohydrate, fats provide a concentrated source of food energy. Most cells of the body (erythrocytes and the central nervous system are notable exceptions) can utilize fatty acids directly as sources of energy. During starvation, the brain adapts and is able to use ketones derived from fatty acid breakdown as fuel.

In addition, dietary fat has 2 functions that are essential to human nutrition: It acts as a solvent for the absorption of fat-soluble vitamins, and it provides the essential fatty acid **linoleic acid** (ω-6, C18:2). Humans lack the capacity to introduce an additional unsaturated bond between the ω-carbon and the existing double bond (ω-9) of oleic acid and thus cannot synthesize linoleic acid (see Chapter 17). Linoleic acid is required for the synthesis of arachidonic acid (ω-6, C20:4), which is the major precursor for the biosynthesis of prostaglandins (Figs 17–11 to 17–14).

Essential fatty acid (EFA) deficiency is exceedingly rare in humans, although it has been reported in infants restricted to a skim milk diet and in children and adults fed a lipid-free diet intravenously. The major symptoms of essential fatty acid deficiency are a scaly dermatitis, hair loss, and poor wound healing. Laboratory studies reveal depressed serum levels of polyunsaturated fatty acids and unusual elevations of serum 5,8,11-eicosatrienoic (ω-9, C20:3) acid. When linoleic acid (and, therefore, arachidonic acid) is deficient in serum, the body attempts to compensate by increased synthesis of oleic acid (ω-9, C18:1) and its products (Fig 41–2). One of these products, 5,8,11-eicosatrienoic acid (triene), is usually present in serum in very small amounts; its elevation relative to arachidonic acid (tetraene) is diagnostic of essential fatty acid deficiency, and the triene/tetraene ratio can be used to monitor the effectiveness of linoleic acid in patients with essential fatty acid deficiency.

Linoleic acid is widely distributed in the lipid portion of both plant and animal foods; vegetable seed oils are especially rich sources (see Table 18–2). No recommended allowance has been established for essential fatty acids, but 1–2% of the total dietary energy consumed as linoleic acid prevents clinical signs of deficiency. For a diet containing 2000–3000 kcal/d (8.4–12.6 MJ/d), 5 g of linoleic acid meets the requirements; this amount is well below the quantity (23 g/d) estimated to be available in the food supply in the USA. The wide availability of linoleic acid in the food supply is consistent with the absence of essential fatty acid deficiency in the general population.

Table 18–2 demonstrates that linoleic acid is more prevalent in vegetable than in animal fats. (In premature infants, linoleic acid can be effectively administered by applying vegetable seed oil to the skin.) Fats of animal origin differ from vegetable fats in 2 significant ways: Animal foods generally contain a

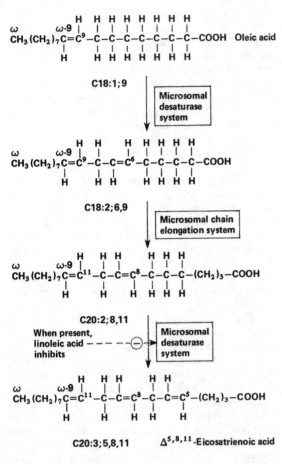

Figure 41–2. Synthesis of $\Delta^{5,8,11}$-eicosatrienoic acid from oleic acid. Eicosatrienoate accumulates in plasma in linoleate deficiency.

higher proportion of saturated fatty acids than vegetable foods, and cholesterol is found only in foods of animal origin (Table 41–4).

These differences may have important implications for health. In societies where fat forms a major proportion of total energy intake, the population tends to develop a high incidence of coronary heart disease, obesity, and cancers of the bowel and breast. The high energy value of fat accounts for its relationship to obesity. The association between fat intake and certain cancers, however, is still unexplained.

A large number of studies point toward a relationship between dietary fat and coronary heart disease. Along with smoking and hypertension, the level of cholesterol in serum is a major risk factor for the development of atherosclerosis. It is now well established that blood cholesterol levels can be reduced significantly by changing the diet to one that contains less saturated fat or cholesterol. The effect of these changes on the clinical course of heart disease is currently under investigation. While aspects of these relationships remain controversial, it seems prudent to advise at least a moderate reduction in fat intake from levels typical of the average diet consumed in the USA. Thus, most current dietary recommendations suggest a reduction in cholesterol, saturated fat, and overall fat intake and an increase in the ratio of polyunsaturated to saturated fatty acids within the remaining fat allowance. As discussed in Chapter 17, the effects of consuming large amounts of partially hydrogenated vegetable oils and margarine containing *trans*-unsaturated fatty acids are as yet unknown. Because they may be hazardous, *Recommended Dietary Allowances* advises an upper limit of 10% of dietary energy as polyunsaturated fatty acids. This recommendation is consistent with the dietary goals set forth in Fig 41–3.

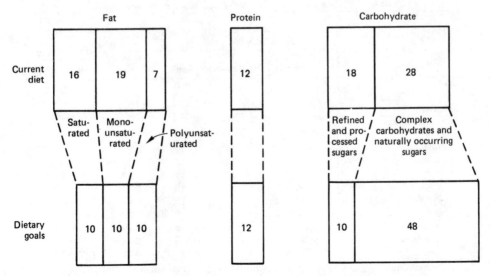

Figure 41–3. Dietary goals for the USA. Current and recommended intakes of carbohydrate, fat, and protein as percent of total energy consumption. (Reproduced from Senate Select Committee on Nutrition and Human Needs, US Senate: *Dietary Goals for the United States,* 2nd ed. US Government Printing Office, 1977.)

Protein

Protein is required in the diet as a source of essential amino acids and of the **nitrogen** needed for de novo synthesis of nonessential amino acids and other nitrogen-containing compounds. Nitrogen in plant food proteins (and, therefore, in animal proteins) derives from the reduction (or "fixation") of the inert N_2 of air. Certain bacterial species that inhabit the root nodules of legumes (peas and beans) and a few blue-green algae are responsible for all biologic **nitrogen fixation.** Nitrogen fixation is also accomplished by lightning and by industrial methods (eg, nitrogenous fertilizer production). All methods for fixing nitrogen gas require large amounts of energy, making nitrogen fixation a rate-limiting and expensive process. Thus, the **availability of fixed nitrogen** is almost always the limiting factor in the production of plant food crops.

The synthesis of protein can occur only when all 20 amino acids are readily available for polypeptide formation. The immediate source of amino acids for protein synthesis is the body pool formed from amino acids released by the normal breakdown of body proteins (protein turnover), those provided by digestion of food proteins, and those newly synthesized by the biochemical pathways described in Chapter 20.

At least 8 (possibly 9) amino acids must be supplied by the diet. These are listed in Table 41–13 along with estimations of the amounts of each required by infants, children, and adults. Histidine has been shown to be essential in the diet of infants, but an adult requirement has not been established. Arginine is no longer considered to be required for growth of the normal human infant, although its synthesis may be inadequate under certain conditions.

The protein content of the diet must be sufficient to replace the essential amino acids and nitrogen lost through normal protein turnover, excreted in feces, sweat, and saliva, or lost through sloughed skin, hair, and nails. Normal protein turnover amounts to 1–2% of total body protein per day. On a protein-free diet, daily nitrogen losses from all sources have been estimated to be 54 mg/kg body weight, or 3.8 g/d for a 70-kg person. Assuming that protein contains approximately 16% nitrogen, this figure is equivalent to about 24 g of protein ($3.8 \div 0.16$). Increasing this amount by 2 standard deviations to include the requirements of most healthy individuals brings the 70-kg adult requirement to the 56 g of protein per day listed in Table 41–13.

For most individuals, this amount of protein is sufficient to maintain **nitrogen balance**—the equilibrium between nitrogen incorporated into protein and other nitrogen-containing compounds and the amount excreted in urine or lost in skin and sweat. Regardless of their source, amino acids that are not immediately incorporated into new protein are rapidly degraded. Their carbon skeletons are either converted to fatty acids or glucose or oxidized as an energy source; their amino groups are excreted as urea and other nitrogenous compounds.

The utilization of dietary protein, as reflected in nitrogen balance, depends not only upon the quantity of protein available but also upon 2 additional factors: protein quality and the ratio of energy to nitrogen in the diet. **Protein quality** refers to the concentration of essential amino acids in a food relative to their concentrations in protein molecules being synthesized, ie, the human requirement for them (as estimated in Table 41–13). In general, animal food proteins are closer in amino acid composition to human proteins than are those from vegetable foods. (From a strictly biochemical aspect, the best source of food protein for humans would be healthy humans!)

Table 41–13. Estimated protein and amino acid requirements and intakes.*

	Requirement (mg/kg Body Weight/d)			Intake (g/d)	
	Infant (4–6 months)	Child (10–12 years)	Adult	Adult (70 kg) Allowance*	Estimated US Adult Intake†
Protein	2000	1400	800	56	101
Animal	...	...	...	...	71
Vegetable	...	...	...	...	30
Essential amino acids					
Histidine	33	?	?	?	?
Isoleucine	83	28	12	0.84	5.3
Leucine	135	42	16	1.12	8.2
Lysine	99	44	12	0.84	6.7
Methionine (and cysteine)	49	22	10	0.70	2.1
Phenylalanine (and tyrosine)	141	22	16	1.12	4.7
Threonine	68	28	8	0.56	4.1
Tryptophan	21	4	3	0.21	1.2
Valine	92	25	14	0.98	5.7

*Data from *Recommended Dietary Allowances,* 9th ed. Food and Nutrition Board, National Research Council–National Academy of Sciences, 1980.

†Data from Munro HN, Crim M: The proteins and amino acids. In: Goodhart RS, Shils ME: *Modern Nutrition in Health and Disease,* 6th ed. Lea & Febiger, 1980.

Because egg and milk proteins are utilized efficiently in balance studies performed on growing laboratory animals, they are used as standards for comparison of protein quality. The major vegetable food crops serve less well in such studies because they are especially deficient in one or another essential amino acid.

The most deficient amino acid in a protein relative to the composition of standard egg or milk proteins is said to be the **limiting amino acid.** Fortunately, the limiting amino acids of the major food crops differ; corn is low in tryptophan, wheat is low in lysine, and certain beans are low in methionine. The consumption of 2 low-quality proteins can be synergistic and can yield an entirely adequate amino acid intake if the proteins are complementary in amino acid composition. Complementary vegetable proteins form the basis of vegetarian diets and many traditional vegetable food combinations such as succotash (lima beans and corn) or tortillas and beans.

The second factor affecting protein utilization is the **ratio of energy to protein in the diet.** Nitrogen balance requires an adequate intake of both protein and energy. Dietary deficiency of either one results in negative nitrogen balance, and more nitrogen is excreted than is retained. The higher the energy intake, the less protein is required to achieve nitrogen balance, because there is less need to break down amino acids to produce energy. The relationship between energy and protein is a continuous one in which nitrogen balance has been found to change by about 0.2–0.3 g of nitrogen (equivalent to 1–2 g of protein) for every increase or decrease of 100 kcal (420 kJ) in the diet. In severe illnesses such as those resulting from trauma or infection, energy intakes of 150 kcal per gram of protein or even higher may be necessary to compensate for protein catabolism and to restore nitrogen balance.

Even for healthy individuals, an energy intake equivalent to 1½ times the basal metabolic expenditure seems to be necessary to maintain nitrogen balance. At least some of this energy should be supplied as carbohydrate in order to spare protein from being used in gluconeogenesis. Finally, physical activity has been shown to increase nitrogen retention and is important in determining nitrogen equilibrium.

Protein allowances must be increased to meet the biosynthetic demands of growth, pregnancy, and lactation; to compensate for higher physical activity levels at work or during exercise; to maintain nitrogen balance in the elderly; and to replace excessive nitrogen losses during injury-induced protein catabolism. As summarized in Table 41–13, the average protein intake in the USA is well above the amounts listed in *Recommended Dietary Allowances;* it usually accounts for 12–20% of the total daily energy. This average amount should be more than sufficient to maintain nitrogen balance for most individuals. High-protein diets appear to confer no special advantage; they may, in fact, be disadvantageous. Diets with very large amounts of protein have produced toxic effects in premature infants, and they seem to be associated with excessive calcium losses in adults. At

present, a diet that contains 12–15% of energy as protein appears to be both adequate and safe. There is no reason to recommend higher protein intakes.

Various human societies routinely subsist on diets with daily protein intakes ranging from less than 50 g to more than 200 g. At the lowest end of this range are vast numbers of people in developing countries in Asia, Africa, and South America whose intakes of energy and essential amino acids are not adequate to sustain optimal biosynthetic activity. The effects of the resulting **protein-energy malnutrition** are especially severe in growing children and constitute the single most important nutritional problem in the world today. The lack of food, coupled with chronic infections, leads to a wide range of clinical symptoms of starvation.

When edema is present in children consuming a diet that is apparently **adequate in energy but limited in protein,** the condition is known as **kwashiorkor.** The generalized loss of body tissue that occurs with **deficient intake of both energy and protein** is called **marasmus.** Both conditions lead to enormous waste of human life; they result from poverty and ignorance and require social and economic intervention in order to increase the quantity and quality of the food supply.

Typical protein-energy malnutrition also occurs in developed countries among adults as a consequence of malabsorption, gastrointestinal surgery, or severe illness. Recent surveys of medical and surgical wards of several major urban hospitals suggest that as many as 30–50% of patients hospitalized for more than 2 weeks met World Health Organization standard criteria for protein-energy malnutrition. Many of these patients require nutritional support for recovery.

VITAMINS

Vitamins are organic molecules in food that are required in small amounts for normal metabolism but cannot be synthesized in adequate amounts by the human body. A dietary or physiologic deficiency of any one of them leads to a specific set of disease symptoms that can be corrected by administration of that vitamin alone.

Vitamins were given alphabetic designations in the order of their discovery. As they were isolated individually and their chemical structures identified, they were given names. Nine compounds or groups of closely related compounds are considered to be vitamins for human nutrition. Although they are exceedingly heterogeneous in chemical structure and biochemical function, they can be grouped conveniently into 2 classes that share common characteristics: water-soluble vitamins and fat-soluble vitamins. The chemistry, metabolism, and physiologic functions of the vitamins are discussed in detail in Chapters 10 and 11. Their most important characteristics are summarized in Tables 41–14 and 41–15.

The **water-soluble vitamins** include the B complex group and ascorbic acid (vitamin C). Because

Table 41–14. Essential water-soluble vitamins: Summary of major characteristics.*

Vitamin	Coenzymes	Biochemical or Physio-logic Function[1]	Deficiency Syndrome or Symptoms[2] (and Associated Diet)	Sources[3]	Stability[4]
Niacin (nicotinic acid, nicotin-amide)	Nicotinamide adenine dinucleotide (NAD); nicotinamide adenine dinucleotide phosphate (NADP).	Electron (hydrogen) transfer reactions carried out by de-hydrogenase enzymes, eg, pyruvate dehydrogenase, glyceraldehyde-3-phosphate dehydrogenase.	Pellagra (milled corn).	Protein foods containing tryptophan, in addition to niacin sources in note.[3]	Stable.
Thiamin (vitamin B_1)	Thiamin pyrophosphate (TPP).	Oxidative decarboxylation of α-ketoacids (pyruvate and α-ketoglutarate dehydrogenases) and 2-ketosugars (transketolases).	Beriberi (milled rice); Wernicke-Korsakoff syndrome (alcohol). Antagonized by thiaminase in raw fish.		Stable in acid solution.
Riboflavin (vitamin B_2)	Flavin adenine dinucleotide (FAD); flavin mononucleotide (FMN).	Electron (hydrogen) transfer reactions (eg, pyruvate dehydrogenase, acyl-CoA dehydrogenase).	Cheilosis.		Stable in acid solution. Light-sensitive.
Pantothenic acid	CoA.	Acyl transfer reactions (citrate synthase, choline acetylase, etc).			Stable in neutral solution.
Vitamin B_6, pyridoxine, pyridoxal, pyridoxamine	Pyridoxal phosphate (PLP).	Transamination and decarboxylation via Schiff's base (many aminotransferase and decarboxylase enzymes).	Low serum levels are associated with pregnancy and oral contraceptive agents. Antagonized by isoniazid, penicillamine, and other drugs.		Stable in acid solution. Light-sensitive.
Biotin	N-Carboxybiotinyl lysine.	CO_2 transfer reactions of carboxylase coenzymes (pyruvate carboxylase, acetyl-CoA carboxylase).	Induced by avidin, a protein in raw egg white. Antibiotic therapy can induce deficiency.	Synthesized by intestinal microorganisms.	
Vitamin B_{12} (cobalamin)	Methylcobalamin; 5'-deoxyadenosyl cobalamin.	Methylation of homocysteine to methionine; conversion of methylmalonyl-CoA to succinyl-CoA.	Megaloblastic anemia, methylmalonic aciduria, peripheral neuropathy (strict vegetarian diet). Pernicious anemia induced by lack of intrinsic factor.		Stable in neutral solutions.
Folic acid (folacin)	Derivatives of tetrahydrofolic acid.	One-carbon transfer reactions, eg, purine nucleotide and thymidylate synthesis.	Megaloblastic anemia.		
Ascorbic acid (vitamin C)	Unknown.	Antioxidant; collagen biosynthesis; tyrosine catabolism (?).	Scurvy (lack of fresh fruits and vegetables).	Fresh fruits (especially citrus) and vegetables.	Unstable to heat. Easily oxidized in the presence of copper or iron.

*Consult Chapter 10 for detailed information.

[1] The metabolism of most water-soluble vitamins is similar. They are absorbed in the intestine, stored bound to enzymes and transport proteins, and excreted in urine when plasma levels exceed kidney thresholds. The one notable exception is vitamin B_{12}, which requires intrinsic factor (synthesized by gastric parietal cells) for absorption in the distal ileum, is stored in milligram amounts in the liver, and is excreted in bile (and reabsorbed via the enterohepatic circulation) as well as in urine.

[2] Excess intake of water-soluble vitamins is not usually toxic. Exceptions: Excess nicotinic acid—but not nicotinamide—causes vascular dilatation of skin ("flushing"); megadose intake of ascorbic acid has been reported to produce diarrhea, oxalate kidney stones, and a variety of other toxic symptoms. Deficiency of these vitamins affects actively metabolizing tissues; symptoms usually include disorders of the digestive and nervous systems, skin, and blood cells.

[3] Unless otherwise stated, a varied intake of adequate amounts of foods from the following groups will meet nutritional requirements for water-soluble vitamins: whole grain cereals, legumes, leafy green vegetables, meat, and dairy products.

[4] Stability refers to survival of vitamin activity during normal food preparation, cooking, and storage. Unless noted to the contrary, water-soluble vitamins are unstable to heat, strong acid or alkali solutions, and prolonged storage. These vitamins all dissolve in cooking water.

Table 41–15. Vitamin-responsive syndromes. Examples of specific defects in vitamin cofactor metabolism that can be corrected by vitamin therapy, usually requiring very large doses.*

Vitamin	Disease	Biochemical Defect
Biotin	Propionic acidemia	Propionyl-CoA carboxylase
Vitamin B_{12}	Methylmalonic aciduria	Formation of cobamide coenzyme
Folic acid	Folate malabsorption	Folic acid transport
Niacin	Hartnup's disease	Tryptophan transport
Pyridoxine (vitamin B_6)	Infantile convulsions	Glutamic acid decarboxylase (?)
	Cystathioninuria	Cystathioninase
	Homocystinuria	Cystathionine synthase
Thiamin	Hyperalaninemia	Pyruvate decarboxylase
	Thiamin-responsive lactic acidosis	Hepatic pyruvate carboxylase

*From: Herman RH, Stifel FB, Greene HL: Vitamin-deficient states and other related diseases. In: *Disorders of the Gastrointestinal Tract; Disorders of the Liver; Nutritional Disorders.* Dietschy JM (editor). Grune & Stratton, 1976.

they are soluble in water, they are generally associated with the fluid compartment of the body. They are excreted in urine when their serum levels exceed tissue saturation (which, in turn, reflects the binding of vitamin cofactors to enzymes and transport proteins). Thus, the water-soluble vitamins must be supplied continually in the diet even though tissue saturation levels may not be depleted for months (ascorbic acid) or even years (vitamin B_{12}). Because water-soluble vitamins taken in excess are usually excreted, they are generally nontoxic, although symptoms have been reported in some individuals ingesting megadose quantities of niacin or ascorbic acid.

Water-soluble vitamins are found together in the same foods. Whole grain cereals, legumes, leafy green vegetables, meat, and dairy products are good sources of all of them except ascorbic acid and vitamin B_{12}. Ascorbic acid is found in fresh fruits and vegetables, especially citrus fruits. Vitamin B_{12} is synthesized by microorganisms; it is incorporated into animal tissues and is present only in meat and dairy foods. Thus, strict vegetarians may be at risk for vitamin B_{12} deficiency.

As described in Chapter 10, most of the vitamins present in food must be metabolized to active coenzyme forms. Inborn errors in these pathways that result in failure to activate coenzymes or in coenzyme binding defects can lead to symptoms of vitamin deficiency even when the diet is adequate. In some cases, deficiency symptoms can be corrected by administration of large amounts of the missing vitamin. Examples of these **vitamin-responsive syndromes** are listed in Table 41–15.

The biochemical roles of water-soluble vitamin cofactors are reasonably well defined (Chapter 10); among this group, only ascorbic acid lacks a known coenzyme function. The roles of these vitamins are closely interrelated, and several of them may function

in the same pathway or even in the same enzyme complex. For example, both biotin and vitamin B_{12} are required for the metabolism of propionyl-CoA to succinyl-CoA (Fig 15–14); the pyruvate dehydrogenase complex includes cofactors of 4 vitamins: thiamin, pantothenic acid, riboflavin, and niacin (Fig 15–5). Thus, a dietary deficiency of any one vitamin may adversely affect the utilization or metabolism of another.

Because water-soluble vitamins occur in the same foods and in interrelated biochemical pathways, deficiency diseases caused by the lack of a single vitamin are rare; their symptoms reflect the lack of the most limiting vitamin in the diet. Only 5 of the water-soluble vitamins are associated with major syndromes, and each of these disorders can be attributed to consumption of a diet highly restricted in food choices. This information is summarized in Table 41–14. In general, the lack of water-soluble vitamins affects tissues that are growing or metabolizing rapidly: skin, blood, the digestive tract, and the nervous system. Correspondingly, deficiency symptoms nearly always consist of dermatitis, anemia, digestive difficulties, and neurologic disorders.

As a group, water-soluble vitamins are somewhat unstable to heat, light, and strong acid or alkali solutions; they dissolve in cooking water, which should therefore be kept to a minimum to prevent vitamin losses. The effect of food preparation on vitamin content is illustrated for broccoli in Table 41–4. Ascorbic acid is especially labile to heat, and large losses occur during cooking of vegetables. Because of nutrient removal during cereal refinement, 3 of the B vitamins (riboflavin, niacin, and thiamin) are used in the USA to enrich white flour and corn meal to the original level of these nutrients (Table 41–12).

The **fat-soluble vitamins** (vitamins A, D, E, and K) differ from the water-soluble group in significant ways. They are present in food fats: fatty meats, liver, dairy fats, egg yolks, vegetable seed oils, and leafy green vegetables. Fortification of milk with vitamin D and margarine with vitamin A makes these foods major dietary sources of vitamins A and D in the USA.

The most important characteristics of the fat-soluble vitamins are discussed in Chapter 11 and summarized in Table 41–16. In general, these vitamins are metabolized along with fat in the body. They are digested with fat, require fat for absorption, are transported with fat in chylomicrons and lipoproteins, and are stored in the liver or in adipose tissue. They are not excreted in urine and can therefore accumulate in storage tissues to toxic levels. Well-defined toxicity syndromes have been described for vitamins A and D. Megadose intakes of vitamin E have been reported to produce symptoms of toxicity, and cases of vitamin K toxicity have occurred among patients undergoing therapy with water-dispersible preparations of this vitamin. Fat-soluble hypervitaminoses occasionally result from acute poisoning, but they can also occur with chronic administration of amounts 50–100 times higher than the recommended dietary allowance for

Table 41–16. Essential fat-soluble vitamins: Summary of major characteristics.*

Vitamin/Provitamin[1]	Metabolism[2]	Active Metabolite: Physiologic Function	Deficiency Syndrome or Symptoms	Toxicity Syndrome or Symptoms	Sources[3]
Vitamin A Provitamin: β-carotene Vitamin: retinol	Transported in lymph as retinyl esters in blood bound to retinol-binding protein and prealbumin.	11-*Cis* retinal: constituent of rhodopsin and other light-receptor pigments. Unknown metabolite(s) (retinoic acid?): required for growth and differentiation of epithelial, nervous, and bone tissues.	Children: poor dark adaptation, xerosis, keratomalacia, growth failure, death. Adults: night blindness, xeroderma.	Hypervitaminosis A: headache, dizziness, nausea, skin sloughing, bone pain.	Yellow vegetables, fortified margarine.
Vitamin D Provitamins: ergosterol (plants, yeast) and 7-dehydrocholesterol (skin) Vitamins D_2 (ergocalciferol) and D_3 (cholecalciferol)	Provitamins converted to vitamins by ultraviolet irradiation. Vitamins hydroxylated in liver to 25-hydroxyvitamin D and in kidney to 1,25-dihydroxy-vitamin D and other metabolites.	1,25-Dihydroxy-vitamin D_3 is major hormonal regulator of bone mineral (calcium and phosphorus) metabolism.	Children: rickets. Adults: osteomalacia.	Hypervitaminosis D: hypercalcemia, hypercalciuria, nephrocalcinosis.	Fortified milk; sunlight on skin.
Vitamin E tocopherols	Generally unknown.	Active metabolite unknown. Functions as an antioxidant.	Children: anemia in premature infants. Adults: no known syndrome.	Undefined. Megadose intake reported to induce blurred vision, headaches.	Vegetable seed oils are major source.
Vitamin K K_1 (phylloquinone), K_2 (menaquinone), others	Generally undefined.	Active metabolite unknown but probably hydroquinone derivative. Activates blood clotting factors II, VII, IX, and X by γ-carboxylating glutamic acid residues; also carboxylates bone and kidney proteins.	Infants: hemorrhagic disease of newborn. Adults: defective blood clotting. Deficiency symptoms can be produced by coumarin anticoagulants and by antibiotic therapy.	Can be induced by water-dispersible analogs: hemolytic anemia, liver damage.	Synthesized by intestinal bacteria.

*For more detailed information, consult Chapter 11.
[1] The fat-soluble vitamins are insoluble in water but dissolve in fats and oils. They are relatively stable to normal cooking temperatures but are slowly inactivated by ultraviolet light and by oxidation.
[2] Absorption of fat-soluble vitamins requires dietary fat and bile; malabsorption or biliary obstruction leads to deficiency. Transport is via lipoproteins or specific transport proteins. Storage is mainly in liver, some in adipose tissue. These vitamins are excreted in bile and either reabsorbed via the enterohepatic circulation or excreted in feces. Some metabolites may be excreted in urine.
[3] Food sources of all fat-soluble vitamins include leafy green vegetables, vegetable seed oils, and fat-containing meat and dairy products, in addition to the specific sources listed here.

long periods. Except as indicated therapeutically, megadose administration of fat-soluble vitamins is potentially dangerous and should be avoided.

Deficiencies of fat-soluble vitamins occur primarily in young children who lack adequate body stores. Deficiencies are rare in adults; when they do occur, they are almost always secondary to malabsorption, biliary obstruction, or other conditions that affect fat metabolism.

MINERALS

Body composition studies demonstrate that nearly all of the known chemical elements can be found in the human body. Elements known to have defined physiologic functions (essential nutrients) are listed in Table 41–1. Elements for which requirements are greater than 100 mg/d are referred to as **minerals.** The so-called **trace elements** are needed in much smaller amounts. Present knowledge of the function of many of these elements is limited; additional minerals are known to be required for certain animal species, and others are found in the body but have no known function. Some of these elements eventually may prove to be required for human nutrition.

Minerals are described in Chapter 40; this information is summarized in Table 41–17. The metabolism of most minerals is incompletely understood. Certain generalizations, however, apply to nearly all of them. **Absorption** of minerals in the intestine is usually inefficient, and greater quantities of them are excreted in the feces than are absorbed. Specific proteins are required for their absorption, and the synthesis of these specific proteins is a necessary part of mineral metabolism. Absorption of minerals can be affected by chelating agents (phytates, oxalates), protein, fat, other minerals, and fiber in the diet, but the results of studies of such interactions do not lead to any consistent pattern. Iron, for example, is absorbed better from meat than from vegetable foods, but high-protein diets increase zinc and calcium requirements. Vitamin C improves the absorption of iron but decreases copper absorption. Diets high in fiber inhibit the absorption of calcium and magnesium but not of iron or phosphorus. These interactions clearly need further study before dietary changes to alter mineral intake can be recommended.

Once absorbed, minerals are transported in blood by albumin or specific carrier proteins. They may be stored in liver and other tissues in association with special proteins. Nearly all essential minerals can accumulate to toxic concentrations. Because mineral intake is usually controlled at the level of absorption, toxicity generally occurs secondary to some malfunction in the regulation of absorption.

The mineral nutrients are widely distributed in whole grain cereals, fruits and vegetables, dairy products, meats, and seafood, but they are usually present in these foods in very small quantities. A sufficient quantity and variety of food must be consumed to meet daily requirements. Food processing removes significant amounts of minerals (Table 41–12). In the USA, iron is the only mineral replaced by fortification. People whose energy intake is low as a result of dieting, aging, or sedentary life-style or whose diet contains a large proportion of foods with a low nutrient content may not have a sufficient mineral intake. Deficient mineral intake results in the deficiency syndromes outlined in Table 41–17. In addition, marginal mineral deficiencies have been associated with a wide variety of diseases of multifactorial causation. Coronary heart disease, for example, has been attributed to trace element deficiencies, but this association is only one of many factors that might be responsible. Until more is known about trace mineral metabolism, these associations must be considered suggestive but unproved. In the absence of contrary evidence, optimum mineral nutrition depends on the consumption of a wide variety of foods of relatively high nutrient concentration.

WATER

Sufficient water must be consumed to meet physiologic requirements (covered in detail in Chapter 40). A significant fraction of these requirements can be met by the water present in food. The first column of Table 41–4 gives the range of water content of some typical foods. Hydrophobic energy sources such as cooking oil or concentrated ones such as sugar contain almost no water, whereas fruits and vegetables contain most of their weight as water.

NUTRITIONAL SUPPLEMENTS

The diet that best meets human nutritional requirements is one that contains many different foods with a nutrient content that is high in relation to energy value. Persons whose overall energy intake is low, those whose diet consists largely of processed foods of low nutritional content, and those who have increased nutritional needs as a result of pregnancy, drug therapy, or illness may not be able to meet their nutrient requirements from food. For such people, pharmacies and health food stores make available a great variety of nutritional supplements. These products include dietary supplements (liquid protein formulas), whole food extracts (alfalfa, bone meal, kelp, etc), nutrients that function in the body but are not known to be essential in the human diet (choline, *p*-aminobenzoic acid, bioflavonoids), and essential nutrients (vitamins, minerals, amino acids). Many other people, however, take diet supplements in the belief that they will prevent or cure specific illnesses. The questions that arise concerning these products are whether they are safe and whether they are effective. For most nutritional supplements, insufficient evidence exists at present to answer either question with confidence.

As an approach to dealing with these questions, it is useful to keep in mind that neither the exact number of required nutrients nor the amounts required are completely defined. As many as 40–50 nutrients are essential in the diet, and the absence of any one of them leads to disease. Because the biochemical functions of nutrients are interrelated, supplying one in the absence of the others can never meet nutritional requirements.

The safety of most nutritional products has never been tested. Among the products that have been studied, however, are several whose safety is questionable. The incidence of deaths among users of the liquid protein diet (Lantigua & others, 1980) and the discovery of the mutagenic potential of pangamic acid ("vitamin B_{15}") are 2 recent examples. Ingestion of supplemental minerals and fat-soluble vitamins greatly in excess of the amounts required produces well-defined toxic syndromes. While megadose intakes of water-soluble vitamins appear to be generally nontoxic, there are 2 exceptions: Large doses of niacin induce vasodilatation and have been reported to cause abnormal liver function, and ingestion of large quantities (several grams) of ascorbic acid induces diarrhea

Table 41–17. Essential minerals and trace elements: Summary of major characteristics.*

Elements	Functions	Metabolism[1]	Deficiency Disease or Symptoms	Toxicity Disease or Symptoms[2]	Sources[3]
Minerals: required intake > 100 mg/d					
Calcium	Constituent of bones, teeth; regulation of nerve, muscle function.	Absorption requires calcium-binding protein. Regulated by vitamin D, parathyroid hormone, calcitonin, etc.	Children: rickets. Adults: osteomalacia. May contribute to osteoporosis.	Occurs with excess absorption due to hypervitaminosis D or hypercalcemia due to hyperparathyroidism, or idiopathic hypercalcemia.	
Phosphorus	Constituent of bones, teeth, ATP, phosphorylated metabolic intermediates. Nucleic acids.	Control of absorption unknown (vitamin D?). Serum levels regulated by kidney reabsorption.	Children: rickets. Adults: osteomalacia.	Low serum Ca^{2+}/P_i ratio stimulates secondary hyperthyroidism; may lead to bone loss.	Phosphate food additives.
Sodium	Principal cation in extracellular fluid. Regulates plasma volume, acid-base balance, nerve and muscle function, Na^+, K^+-ATPase.	Regulated by aldosterone.	Unknown on normal diet; secondary to injury or illness.	Hypertension (in susceptible individuals).	Table salt; salt added to prepared food.
Potassium	Principal cation in intracellular fluid; nerve and muscle function, Na^+, K^+-ATPase.	Also regulated by aldosterone.	Occurs secondary to illness, injury, or diuretic therapy; muscular weakness, paralysis, mental confusion. Low Na^+/K^+ ratio may predispose to hypertension.	Cardiac arrest, small bowel ulcers.	
Chlorine	Fluid and electrolyte balance; gastric fluid.		Infants fed salt-free formula. Secondary to vomiting, diuretic therapy, renal disease.		Table salt.
Magnesium	Constituent of bones, teeth; enzyme cofactor (kinases, etc.).		Secondary to malabsorption or diarrhea, alcoholism.	Depressed deep tendon reflexes and respiration.	Leafy green vegetables (containing chlorophyll).
Trace elements: required intake < 100 mg/d					
Chromium	Trivalent chromium, a constituent of "glucose tolerance factor."	Undefined.	Impaired glucose intolerance; secondary to parenteral nutrition.		
Cobalt	Constituent of vitamin B_{12}.	As for vitamin B_{12}.	Vitamin B_{12} deficiency.		Foods of animal origin.
Copper	Oxidase enzymes: cytochrome C oxidase, tyrosinase, ferroxidase, etc.	Transported by albumin; bound to ceruloplasmin.	Anemia (hypochromic, microcytic); secondary to malnutrition, Menke's syndrome.	Rare; secondary to Wilson's disease.	
Iodine	Thyroxine, triiodothyronine.	Stored in thyroid as thyroglobulin.	Children: cretinism. Adults: goiter and hypothyroidism, myxedema.	Thyrotoxicosis, goiter.	Iodized salt, seafood.
Iron	Heme enzymes (hemoglobin, cytochromes, etc).	Transported as transferrin; stored as ferritin or hemosiderin; excreted in sloughed cells, bleeding.	Anemia (hypochromic microcytic).	Siderosis; hereditary hemochromatosis.	Iron cookware.
Manganese	Hydrolase, decarboxylase, and transferase enzymes. Glycoprotein and proteoglycan synthesis.		Unknown in humans.	Inhalation poisoning produces psychotic symptoms and parkinsonism.	
Molybdenum	Oxidase enzymes (xanthine oxidase).		Unknown in humans.		
Selenium	Glutathione peroxidase.	Synergistic antioxidant with vitamin E.	Marginal deficiency when soil content is low; secondary to parenteral nutrition, protein-energy malnutrition.	Observed in experimental animals and livestock.	

Table 41–17 (cont'd). Essential minerals and trace elements: Summary of major characteristics.*

Elements	Functions	Metabolism[1]	Deficiency Disease or Symptoms	Toxicity Disease or Symptoms[2]	Sources[3]
Trace elements: required intake < 100 mg/d (cont'd)					
Zinc	Cofactor of many enzymes: lactic dehydrogenase, alkaline phosphatase, carbonic anhydrase, etc.		Hypogonadism, growth failure, impaired wound healing, decreased taste and smell acuity; secondary to acrodermatitis enteropathica.	Gastrointestinal irritation, vomiting.	
Fluorine[4]	Increases hardness of bones and teeth.		Dental caries; osteoporosis (?).	Dental fluorosis.	Drinking water.

*For detailed information, see Chapter 40.

[1] In general, minerals require carrier proteins for absorption. Absorption is rarely complete; it is affected by other nutrients and compounds in the diet (eg, oxalates and phytates that chelate divalent cations). Transport and storage also require special proteins. Excretion occurs in feces (unabsorbed minerals) and in urine, sweat, and bile.

[2] Excess mineral intake produces toxic symptoms. Unless otherwise specified, symptoms include nonspecific nausea, diarrhea, and irritability.

[3] Mineral requirements are met by a varied intake of adequate amounts of whole grain cereals, legumes, leafy green vegetables, meat, and dairy products.

[4] Fluorine is essential for rat growth. While not proved to be strictly essential for human nutrition, fluorides have a well-defined role in prevention and treatment of dental caries.

(and other symptoms reported but controversial).

The effects of nutritional supplements in prevention and treatment of diseases other than those known to be caused by nutrient deficiency have been shown, in most cases, to be indistinguishable from the effects of placebo. Exceptions include therapy of vitamin-responsive syndromes (Table 41–15), choline treatment of tardive dyskinesia and other acetylcholine deficiency disorders, and the use of vitamin E to improve red cell stability in patients with glucose-6-phosphate dehydrogenase deficiency.

FOOD TOXINS & ADDITIVES

Foods contain a large number of potentially harmful compounds. Some occur naturally; they include harmful substances such as the neurotoxins from shellfish or mushrooms, goitrogens from plants of the cabbage family, bean compounds that interfere with collagen formation, and the carcinogenic aflatoxin from peanut mold. Pesticides and packaging materials may be added to food through inadvertent contamination. Many thousands of compounds are added to foods in order to preserve them or to add color, flavor, or texture. Most additives have never been tested; some may be harmful. Since most foods have not been analyzed for their content of natural or added toxins, prudent advice would be to avoid substances known to be toxic, to eat moderate amounts of a wide variety of foods, and to emphasize consumption of fresh, unprocessed foods in order to minimize intake of natural toxins and additives whose biologic effects are as yet unknown.

NUTRITION & HEALTH

Nutritional deficiency syndromes are rare among people whose income is adequate. They are found chiefly among the poor, the elderly, individuals with unusually high nutrient requirements (growing children, pregnant and lactating women), those who are seriously ill, and alcoholics or other people whose diets are restricted out of choice or necessity to one food as the primary energy source.

In contrast, diseases associated with nutrient excess—obesity, for example—are common in developed societies. Of the 10 leading causes of death in the USA, 6 have been associated with excess intake of certain foods: coronary heart disease, cancers of the bowel and breast, cerebrovascular disease, diabetes, arteriosclerosis, and cirrhosis of the liver.

Studies have demonstrated that populations with a high salt intake exhibit a greater frequency of hypertension than occurs among groups whose salt intake is low. Populations of pigs or rats who had salt added to their food have higher blood pressures than animals raised on salt-free diets. Do these results imply that dietary salt causes hypertension in humans? Clinical trials that might answer this question—and similar questions regarding nutrition as a factor in the etiology of heart disease, cancer, or diabetes—are exceedingly difficult to design and carry out. The studies are expensive and must often be conducted on samples too small to be statistically significant; they are subject to investigator and subject bias (placebo effects); they reveal considerable genetic variation among individuals; and they depend on the presence of well-designed control populations. These difficulties lead to great variation in the results of human nutritional research and make the results very difficult to interpret. Dietary advice must take these problems into consideration.

DIETARY RECOMMENDATIONS

An approach to diet and health has been recommended in at least 2 major US Government publications. In the more specific of these reports, *Dietary Goals for the United States,* the US Senate Select Committee on Nutrition and Human Needs reviewed the proportion of energy derived from protein, fat, and carbohydrate in the current US diet and developed specific recommendations for changing these proportions to achieve a healthier food intake. Figure 41–3 summarizes these recommendations. To achieve the goals set forth in Fig 41–3, the Committee suggested specific changes in food selection and preparation: increased consumption of fruits, vegetables, and whole grain cereals; decreased consumption of foods containing large amounts of sugars, fats (especially saturated fat and cholesterol), and salt; partial replacement of saturated fats with unsaturated fats; and substitution of low-fat for high-fat dairy products (except in young children). The net result of following these goals is to increase the proportion of nutrients in the diet relative to energy intake.

The dietary goals were designed to improve the food intake of healthy people, but they are very similar to the recommendations proposed for several years by organizations such as the American Heart Association, whose main nutritional concern has been to reduce the atherogenic potential of the American diet. These recommendations are now supported by the American Diabetes Association, which since 1979 has suggested that patients with diabetes mellitus eat a diet high in complex carbohydrate and low in fat, in proportions almost identical to those presented in *Dietary Goals.*

Dietary Goals, therefore, represents a working hypothesis for both normal and therapeutic diets. Whether such recommendations are appropriate for everyone or, instead, should be restricted to individuals especially susceptible to diseases of overconsumption cannot be established until effective methods are developed for identifying susceptible individuals before they become ill. Until then, the goals appear likely to be safe and effective; they are also capable of being assessed, evaluated, and modified as needed, consistent with the results of future nutritional research studies.

• • •

References

Ahrens EH, Connor WE (Cochairmen): Symposium report of the task force on the evidence relating 6 dietary factors to the nation's health. *Am J Clin Nutr* (Dec) 1979;**32 (12 Suppl);** 2627.

Amos HE, Drake JJ-P: Problems posed by food additives. *J Hum Nutr* 1976;**30:**165.

Bistrian BR & others: Prevalence of malnutrition in general medical patients. *JAMA* 1976;**235:**1567.

Bistrian BR & others: Protein status of general surgical patients. *JAMA* 1974;**230:**858.

Brewster L, Jacobson MF: The changing American diet. Center for Science in the Public Interest, 1978.

Committee on Dietary Allowances, Food and Nutrition Board, National Research Council: *Recommended Dietary Allowances,* 9th ed. National Academy of Sciences, 1980.

Corash L & others: Reduced chronic hemolysis during high-dose vitamin E administration in Mediterranean-type glucose-6-phosphate dehydrogenase deficiency. *N Engl J Med* 1980; **303:**416.

Davidson S & others: *Human Nutrition and Dietetics,* 7th ed. Churchill Livingstone, 1979.

Goodhart RS, Shils ME: *Modern Nutrition in Health and Disease,* 6th ed. Lea & Febiger, 1980.

Growdon JH, Cohen EL, Wurtman RJ: Treatment of brain disease with dietary precursors of neurotransmitters. *Ann Intern Med* 1977;**86:**337.

Herbert V, Gardner A, Colman N: Mutagenicity of dichloroacetate, an ingredient of some formulations of pangamic acid (trade-named "vitamin B_{15}"). *Am J Clin Nutr* 1980;**33:**1179.

Herman RH, Stifel FB, Greene HL: Vitamin-deficient states and other related diseases. In: *Disorders of the Gastrointestinal Tract; Disorders of the Liver; Nutritional Disorders.* Dietschy JM (editor). Grune & Stratton, 1976.

Katch FI, McArdle WD: *Nutrition, Weight Control, and Exercise.* Houghton Mifflin, 1977.

Lantigua & others: Cardiac arrhythmias associated with a liquid protein diet for the treatment of obesity. *N Engl J Med* 1980; **303:**735.

Long CL & others: Metabolic response to injury and illness: Estimation of energy and protein needs from indirect calorimetry and nitrogen balance. *J Parent Ent Nutr* 1979;**3:**452.

Michiel RR & others: Sudden death in a patient on a liquid protein diet. *N Engl J Med* 1978;**298:**1005.

Rodricks JV: Food hazards of natural origin. *Fed Proc* 1978; **37:**2587.

Select Committee on Nutrition and Human Needs, United States Senate: *Dietary Goals for the United States,* 2nd ed. US Government Printing Office, 1977.

Watt BK, Merrill AL: *Composition of Foods: Raw, Processed, Prepared.* Agriculture Handbook No. 8, US Department of Agriculture, 1963.

Wilmore DW: *The Metabolic Management of the Critically Ill.* Plenum, 1977.

ABBREVIATIONS ENCOUNTERED IN BIOCHEMISTRY

A (Å)	Angstrom unit(s) (10^{-10}m, 0.1 nm)
AA	Amino acid
α-AA	α-Amino acid
ACTH	Adrenocorticotropic hormone, adrenocorticotropin, corticotropin
Acyl-CoA	An acyl derivative of CoA (eg, butyryl-CoA)
ADH	Alcohol dehydrogenase
ADH	Antidiuretic hormone
AHG	Antihemophilic globulin
Ala	Alanine
ALA	Aminolevulinic acid
AmLev	Aminolevulinic acid
AMP	Adenosine monophosphate
Arg	Arginine
Asn	Asparagine
Asp	Aspartic acid
ATP	Adenosine triphosphate
BAL	Dimercaprol (British anti-lewisite)
Cal	Calorie (ie, kilocalorie, kcal)
CBG	Corticosteroid-binding globulin
CBZ	Carbobenzoxy
CCCP	m-Chlorocarbonyl cyanide phenylhydrazone
CCK-PZ	Cholecystokinin-pancreozymin
CDP	Cytidine diphosphocholine
Cer	Ceramide
CI	Chain-initiating
CK	Creatine phosphokinase (see also CPK)
CMP	Cytidine monophosphate; 5'-phosphoribosyl cytosine
CoA·SH	Free (uncombined) coenzyme A. A pantothenic acid–containing nucleotide which functions in the metabolism of fatty acids, ketone bodies, acetate, and amino acids

$$\overset{O}{\overset{\|}{CoA \cdot S \cdot C \cdot CH_3}}$$ Acetyl-CoA, "activated acetate." The form in which acetate is "activated" by combination with coenzyme A for participation in various reactions

CPK	Creatine phosphokinase (see also CK)
CRF	Corticotropin-releasing factor
CRH	Corticotropin-releasing hormone
CRP	C-reactive protein
CTP	Cytidine triphosphate
Cys	Cysteine
D-	Dextrorotatory
D_2 (vitamin)	Ergocalciferol
D_3 (vitamin)	Cholecalciferol
1,25-$(OH)_2$-D_3	1,25-Dihydroxycholecalciferol
dA	Deoxyadenosine
dC	Deoxycytosine
dG	Deoxyguanosine
DNA	Deoxyribonucleic acid
DNP	Dinitrophenol
dopa	3,4-Dihydroxyphenylalanine
DPN	Diphosphopyridine nucleotide (now replaced by NAD)
dT	Deoxythymidine
dUMP	Deoxyribose uridine-5'-phosphate

E	Enzyme (also Enz)
E.C.	Enzyme code number (IUB system)
EDTA	Ethylenediaminetetraacetic acid. A reagent used to chelate divalent metals
Enz	Enzyme (also E)
Eq	Equivalent
eu	Enzyme unit
FAD	Flavin adenine dinucleotide (oxidized form)
$FADH_2$	Flavin adenine dinucleotide (reduced form)
FDA	Food & Drug Administration
FFA	Free fatty acids
figlu	Formiminoglutamic acid
FMN	Flavin mononucleotide
FP	Flavoprotein
FSF	Fibrin stabilizing factor
FSH	Follicle-stimulating hormone
FSHRF	Follicle-stimulating hormone–releasing factor
FSHRH	Follicle-stimulating hormone–releasing hormone
g	Gram(s)
g	Gravity
Gal	Galactose
GalNAc	N-Acetylgalactose
GDP	Guanosine diphosphate
GFR	Glomerular filtration rate
GH	Growth hormone
GHRF	Growth hormone–releasing factor
GHRH	Growth hormone–releasing hormone
GH-RIF	Growth hormone release–inhibiting factor
GHRIH	Growth hormone release–inhibiting hormone
GIH	Growth hormone release–inhibiting hormone
GLC	Gas-liquid chromatography
Glc	Glucose
GlcUA	Glucuronic acid
Gln	Glutamine
Glu	Glutamic acid
Gly	Glycine
GMP	Guanosine monophosphate
GRH	Growth hormone–releasing hormone
Hb	Hemoglobin
HCG	Human chorionic gonadotropin
HDL	High-density lipoproteins
H_2folate	Dihydrofolate
H_4folate	Tetrahydrofolate
His	Histidine
HMG-CoA	β-Hydroxy-β-methylglutaryl coenzyme A
Hyl	Hydroxylysine
Hyp	4-Hydroxyproline
ICD	Isocitric dehydrogenase
IDL	Intermediate-density lipoproteins
IDP	Inosine diphosphate
IF	Initiation factor (for protein synthesis)
Ile	Isoleucine
IMP	Inosine monophosphate; hypoxanthine ribonucleotide
INH	Isonicotinic acid hydrazide (isoniazid)

ITP	Inosine triphosphate	PRF	Prolactin release–inhibiting factor
ITyr	Monoiodotyrosine	PRH	Prolactin release–inhibiting hormone
I_2Tyr	Diiodotyrosine	PRIH	Prolactin release–inhibiting hormone
IU	International unit(s)	Pro	Proline
IUB	International Union of Biochemistry	PRPP	5-Phosphoribosyl 1-pyrophosphate
α-KA	α-Keto acid	PTA	Plasma thromboplastin antecedent
kcal	Kilocalorie	PTC	Plasma thromboplastin component
α-KG	α-Ketoglutarate	RBC	Red blood cell
kJ	Kilojoule	RDA	Recommended daily allowance
K_m	Substrate concentration producing half-maximal velocity (Michaelis constant)	RE	Retinol equivalents
		RNA	Ribonucleic acid
		RQ	Respiratory quotient
L-	Levorotatory	S (Sf) units	Svedberg units of flotation
LCAT	Lecithin:cholesterol acyltransferase	SDA	Specific dynamic action
LD	Lactate dehydrogenase (see also LDH)	SDS	Sodium dodecyl sulfate
LDH	Lactic dehydrogenase	Ser	Serine
LDL	Low-density lipoproteins	SGOT	Serum glutamic oxaloacetic transaminase
Leu	Leucine		
LH	Luteinizing hormone	SGPT	Serum glutamic pyruvic transaminase
LHRF	Luteinizing hormone–releasing factor	SH	Sulfhydryl
LHRH	Luteinizing hormone–releasing hormone	SLR	*Streptococcus lactis* R
		SPCA	Serum prothrombin conversion accelerator
LLF	Laki-Lorand factor		
LTH	Luteotropic hormone	sRNA	Soluble RNA (same as tRNA, which term is preferred)
Lys	Lysine		
M	Molar	STP	Standard temperature and pressure (273° absolute, 760 mm Hg)
MAO	Monoamine oxidase		
MCH	Mean corpuscular hemoglobin	T_3	Triiodothyronine
MCHC	Mean corpuscular hemoglobin concentration	T_4	Tetraiodothyronine
		TBG	Testosterone-binding globulin
MCV	Mean corpuscular volume	TG	Triacylglycerols (formerly called triglycerides)
Met	Methionine		
MIF	Melanocyte inhibiting factor	Thr	Threonine
mol	Mole	TLC	Thin layer chromatography
MRF	Melanocyte releasing factor	TmCa	Tubular maximum for calcium
MRH	Melanocyte releasing hormone	TmG	Tubular maximum for glucose
MRIH	Melanocyte release–inhibiting hormone	dTMP	Thymidine monophosphate (5'-phosphoribosyl-thymine)
mRNA	Messenger RNA		
MSH	Melanocyte-stimulating hormone	TPN	Triphosphopyridine nucleotide (now replaced by NADP)
MW	Molecular weight		
NAD	Nicotinamide adenine dinucleotide (oxidized)	TRF	Thyrotropin-releasing factor
		TRH	Thyrotropin-releasing hormone
NADH	Nicotinamide adenine dinucleotide (reduced)	Tris	Tris(hydroxymethyl)aminomethane, a buffer (tromethamine)
NADP	Nicotinamide adenine dinucleotide phosphate (oxidized)	tRNA	Transfer RNA (see also sRNA)
		Trp	Tryptophan
NADPH	Nicotinamide adenine dinucleotide phosphate (reduced)	TSH	Thyroid-stimulating hormone; thyrotropin
NANA	N-Acetylneuraminic acid	Tyr	Tyrosine
NDP	Any nucleoside diphosphate	UDP	Uridine diphosphate
NTP	Any nucleoside triphosphate	UDPG	Uridine diphosphoglucose
OA	Oxaloacetic acid	UDPGal	Uridine diphosphogalactose
OD	Optical density	UDPGlcUA	Uridine diphosphoglucuronic acid
P	Phosphate (radical)	UDPGluc	Uridine diphosphoglucuronic acid
PCV	Packed cell volume	UMP	Uridine monophosphate; uridine-5'-phosphate; uridylic acid
PGH	Plasma growth hormone		
Phe	Phenylalanine	UTP	Uridine triphosphate
P_i	Inorganic phosphate (orthophosphate)	Val	Valine
PIF	Prolactin release–inhibiting factor	VLDL	Very low density lipoproteins
PL	Prolactin	VMA	Vanilmandelic acid
PL	Pyridoxal	V_{max}	Maximal velocity
PLP	Pyridoxal phosphate	vol%	Volumes percent
PP_i	Pyrophosphate		

Index